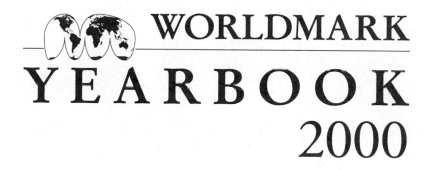

WORLDMARK
YEARBOOK
2000

ISSN 1527-6503

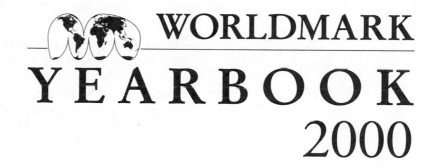

WORLDMARK
YEARBOOK
2000

Volume 1
A–H

Mary Rose Bonk, Editor

 GALE GROUP

Detroit
New York
San Francisco
London
Boston
Woodbridge, CT

Editor: Mary Rose Bonk
Associate Editors: Nancy Matuszak, Matthew May, John F. McCoy, Michael Reade
Assistant Editors: R. David Riddle, Chris Romig, Christy Wood
Permissions Manager: Maria Franklin
Permissions Specialist: Margaret Chamberlain
Permissions Associate: Shalice Shah-Caldwell
Image Cataloger: Mary Grimes

Composition Manager: Mary Beth Trimper
Assistant Production Manager: Evi Seoud
Manufacturing Manager: Dorothy Maki
Senior Buyer: Wendy Blurton
Product Design Manager: Cynthia Baldwin
Senior Art Director: Michelle DiMercurio
Graphic Specialist: Christine O'Bryan
Indexing Specialists: Susan Kelsch, Amy Suchowski, Cindy Tsiang

British Library Cataloguing in Publication Data. A Catalogue record of this book is available from the British Library.
ISBN 0–7876–4931–7 (2-Volume set)
ISBN 0–7876–4932–5 (Volume 1)
ISBN 0–7876–4933–3 (Volume 2)
ISBN 0–7876–5088–9 (Volume 3)
ISSN 1527–6503

Printed in the United States of America

10 9 8 7 6 5 4 3 2 1

CONTENTS

Contents

FOREWORD

A NEW, YEARLY REFERENCE FOR A NEW ERA

As a new addition to the Worldmark family, *Worldmark Yearbook* presents to users a comprehensive profile of 229 of the world's nations and territories and their current events. Information often scattered throughout books, articles, and various agencies is compiled here in an easy to use reference. It complements other Worldmark publications by presenting the most current information on countries around the world. The Worldmark line already provides you with an in-depth historical account for these countries in *Worldmark Encyclopedia of the Nations*. With the introduction of the *Worldmark Yearbook*, you can be kept up-to-date with the latest developments.

The Year in Review

Worldmark Yearbook begins with a look at the year in review. From Tokyo to Berlin, and from Moscow to Auckland and Pretoria, major events from the past year are highlighted and placed in an international perspective. The main focus of the *Yearbook* is on national events, so the Year in Review provides a broader look at how national issues can affect regional neighbors and the world.

Where in the World?

Each country is accompanied by a map that places it within its area of the world and which details major cities and landmarks. Geography often plays an important role in a nation's politics and economy. The expansive maps can help *Yearbook* users better understand how geography may affect what goes on within a nation. In addition, in a world increasingly referred to as a "global village," national events often spill over into neighboring states. To easily identify neighbors, six color regional maps are on hand for reference.

National Symbols

An added feature of the *Worldmark Yearbook* is the color illustration of national symbols, including flags and official insignia. Each country's offi-cial flag is represented and a brief description is included in each entry. A country's official insignia, such as an emblem or seal, is also represented.

Profiles

A national profile highlights basic information for each country. The national capital, monetary unit, anthem, and climate are a few examples of the data available at the beginning of each entry.

Background Check

A yearbook of current events would be of little use without a context in which to put those events. *Worldmark Yearbook*'s introductory survey provides users with this context. Recent history from the mid-twentieth century onward is outlined to provide background in and support for the events of the past year. But history itself does not present a comprehensive picture of how a nation operates. Do you want to know how a country's government is set up? Who can participate in it? How the economy operates? What are the major industrial and economic developments of the past few years? The answers to these questions, and more, can be found in the introductory survey.

Analyzing the Year's Events

A timeline is included in each entry and lists chronologically the events of the past year. Selecting the most significant of these events, an analysis explains them in greater depth and pulls together the threads of politics, economy, and culture to create a cohesive picture of a distinct nation. Economic struggles, cultural revivals, political triumphs: the analysis paints a more personal picture of each country, which can not be as easily portrayed through the simple listing of facts or statistics.

Who's Who?

Who's been running the country while these events have taken place? To find out, users can reference the *Yearbook*'s directory, which, when possible, includes information on how to contact an individual or group. Main government func-tionaries, including the heads and ministers of state, are listed, as are political organizations active within the country and its major judicial courts. In this "global village," knowing one's neighbors is important, and maintaining official contact with them is a vital part of government operations. In this light, users will find a comprehensive listing of diplomatic representation for each country.

Just the Facts

If hard data is what you're looking for, you can find it in the statistical survey. Population size and growth, economic output and development, major industrial production, and more can be located in the statistical survey. Statistics complement the analysis by explaining numerically much of what's going on in a country's society and economy. It creates a numerative picture that can be easily compared with that of other nations.

Want More?

Check out the Further Reading section for sources of additional information on statistics, current events, and historical background. You can also refer to the International Organizations listing. It provides contact information and a brief description of over 1,800 international organizations that are involved in a variety of global concerns.

At Your Fingertips

Are you looking for something specific? A glance at the *Yearbook*'s comprehensive index will help you find your way. The user-friendly index covers personal names, subjects, and geographies and can refer you quickly to the information you need.

A COMPREHENSIVE TOOL TO TODAY'S WORLD

The *Worldmark Yearbook* pulls together the many components that make up a government and a society to give users a well-balanced, comprehensive, and illustrative source of information on the world's nations. Its many headers make quick reference points to easily locate information. *Worldmark Yearbook* is a proud new edition to the Worldmark line and will enhance the libraries of all reference users. This is just the beginning.

We encourage you to contact us with comments or suggestions. Tell us what you want to see in the *Yearbook* and how we can better meet your needs. Comments and suggestions can be sent to: The Editors, *Worldmark Yearbook*, The Gale Group, 27500 Drake Road, Farmington Hills, MI 48331. Or, call toll free at 1-800-877-4253.

ACKNOWLEDGEMENTS

For editorial and technical assistance that helped keep this project on track and on time, the editors are extremely grateful to the following Gale Group contributors:

Richard Antonowicz, programmer/analyst, Pamela A. Dear, associate editor, Shelly Dickey, senior editor, Kathy Droste, editor, Anthony Gerring, technical support, Bernard Grunow, editor, Amanda Moran, senior market analyst, Rita Runchock, managing editor, and Phyllis Spinelli, associate editor.

For editorial and textual contributions to the *Worldmark Yearbook*, the editors are indebted to the following:

Advanced Information Consultants, Canton, Michigan, Kimberly Burton, Ann Arbor, Michigan, Michael Dawson, Carlsbad, California, Eastword Publications Development, Cleveland, Ohio, Editorial Code and Data, Inc. (ECDI), Southfield, Michigan, GGS Information Services, York, Pennsylvania, Richard Clay Hanes, Eugene, Oregon, Margery Heffron, Exeter, New Hampshire, Paul Kobel, Charlotte, North Carolina, John Macaulay, Miami, Florida, and Vocabula Communications Company, Lexington, Massachusetts.

For permission to take material from personal or published sources, use of images, and for other courtesies extended during the preparation of this edition, the editors are grateful to the following sources:

Eastword Publications Development, The Flag Institute, International Monetary Fund, Publications Services Unit, Maryland Cartographics, UNESCO (United Nations Education, Scientific and Cultural Organization), UNIDO (United Nations Industrial Development Organization), United Nations Publications, author of original material, Oxford University Press, Inc., Pascal Vagnat, and the World Bank.

KEY TO
ABBREVIATIONS

ABEDA: Arab Bank for Economic Development in Africa

ACC: Arab Cooperation Council

ACCT: Agence de Cooperation Culturelle et Technique; see Agency for Cultural and Technical Cooperation

ACP: African, Caribbean, and Pacific Countries

AfDB: African Development Bank

AFESD: Arab Fund for Economic and Social Development

AG: Andean Group

AL: Arab League

ALADI: Asociacion Latinamericana de Intergracion; see Latin American Integration Association (LAIA)

AMF: Arab Monetary Fund

AMU: Arab Maghreb Fund

ANZUS: Australia-New Zealand-United States Security Trust

APEC: Asia Pacific Economic Cooperation

AsDB: Asian Development Bank

ASEAN: Association of Southeast Asian Nations

BAD: Banque Africaine de Developpement; see African Development Bank (AfDB)

BADEA: Banque Arabe de Developpement Economique en Afrique; see Arab Bank for Economic Development in Africa (ABEDA)

BCIE: Banco Centroamericano de Integracion Economico; see Central American Bank for Economic Integration (BCIE)

BDEAC: Banque de Development des Etats de l'Afrique Centrale; see Central African States Development Bank

Benelux: Benelux Economic Union

BID: Banco Interamericano de Desarrollo; see Inter-American Development Bank (IADB)

BIS: Bank for International Settlements

BOAD: Banque Ouest-Africaine de Developpement; see West African Development Bank (WADB)

BSEC: Black Sea Economic Coorperation Zone

C: Commonwealth

CACM: Central American Common Market

CAEU: Council of Arab Economic Unity

CARICOM: Caribbean Community and Common Market

CBSS: Council of Baltic Sea States

CCC: Customs Cooperation Council

CDB: Caribbean Development Bank

CE: Council of Europe

CEAO: Communaute Economique de l'Afrique de l'Ouest; see West African Economic Community (CEAO)

CEEAC: Communaute Economique des Etats de l' Afrique Centrale; see Economic Community of Central African States (CEEAC)

CEI: Central European Initiative

CEMA: Council for Mutual Economic Assistance; also known as CMEA or Comecon

CEPGL: Communaute Economique de Pays des Grands Lacs; see Economic Community of the Great Lakes Countries (CEPGL)

CERN: Conseil European pour la Recherche Nucleaire; see European Organization for Nuclear Research (CERN)

CG: Contadora Group

CIS: Commonwealth of Independent States

CMEA: Council for Mutual Economic Assistance (CEMA); also known as Comeecon

COCOM: Coordinating Committee on Export Controls

Comecon: Council for Mutual Economic Assistance (CEMA); also known as CMEA

CP: Colombo Plan

CSCE: Conference on Security and Cooperation in Europe

DC: Developed country

EADB: East African Development Bank

EBRD: European Bank for Reconstruction and Development

EC: European Community; see European Union (EU)

ECA: Economic Commission for Africa

ECAFE: Economic Commission for Asia and the Far East; see Economic and Social Commission for Asia and the Pacific (ESCAP)

ECE: Economic Commission for Europe

ECLA: Economic Commission for Latin America; see Economic Commission for Latin America and the Caribbean (ECLAC)

ECLAC: Economic Commission for Latin America and the Caribbean

ECO: Economic Cooperation Organization

ECOSOC: Economic and Social Council

ECOWAS: Economic Community of West African States

ECSC: European Coal and Steel Community

ECWA: Economic Commission for Western Asia; see Economic and Social Council for Western Asia (ESCWA)

EEC: European Economic Community

EFTA: European Free Trade Association

EIB: European Investment Bank

Entente: Council of the Entente

ESA: European Space Agency

ESCAP: Economic and Social Commission for Asia and the Pacific

ESCWA: Economic and Social Commission for Western Asia

EU: European Union

Euratom: European Atomic Energy Community

FAO: Food and Agriculture Organization

FLS: Front Line States

FZ: Franc Zone

G-2: Group of 2

G-3: Group of 3

G-5: Group of 5

G-6: Group of 6

G-7: Group of 7

G-8: Group of 8

G-9: Group of 9

G-10: Group of 10

G-11: Group of 11

G-15: Group of 15

G-19: Group of 19

G-24: Group of 24

G-30: Group or 30

G-33: Group of 33

G-77: Group of 77

GATT: General Agreement on Tariff and Trade

Habitat: Commission on Human Settlements

IADB: Inter-American Development Bank

IAEA: International Atomic Energy Agency

IBEC: International Bank for Economic Cooperation

IBRD: International Bank for Reconstruction and Development

ICAO: International Civil Aviation Organization

ICC: International Chamber of Commerce

ICEM: Intergovernmental Committee for European Migration; see International Organization for Migration (IOM)

ICFTU: International Confederation of Free Trade Unions

ICJ: International Court of Justice

ICM: Intergovernmental Committee for Migration; see International Organization for Migration (IOM)

ICRC: International Committee of the Red Cross

ICRM: International Red Cross and Red Crescent Movement

IDA: International Development Association

IDB: Islamic Development Bank

IEA: International Energy Agency

IFAD: International Fund for Agriculture Development

IFC: International Finance Corporation

IFCTU: International Federation of Christian Trade Unions

IFRCS: International Federation of Red Cross and Red Crescent Societies

IGADD: Inter-Governmental Authority on Drought and Development

IIB: International Investment Bank

ILO: International Labor Organization

IMCO: Intergovernmental Maritime Consultative Organization; see International Maritime Organization (IMO)

IMF: International Monetary Fund

IMO: International Maritime Fund

INMARSAT: International Maritime Satelite Organization

INTELSAT: International Telecommunications Satellite Organization

INTERPOL: International Criminal Police Organization

IOC: International Olympic Committee

IOM: International Organization for Migration

ISO: International Organization for Standardization

ITU: International Telecommunications Union

LAES: Latin American Economic System

LAIA: Latin American Integration Association

LAS: League of Arab States; see Arab League (AL)

LDC: Less developed country

LLDC: Least developed country

LORCS: League of Red Cross and Red Crescent Societies

MERCOSUR: Mercado Commun del Cono Sur; see Southern Cone Common Market

MINURSO: United Nations Mission for the Referendum in Western Sahara

MTCR: Missile Technology Control Regime

NACC: North Atlantic Cooperation Council

NAM: Nonaligned Movement

NATO: North Atlantic Treaty Organization

NC: Nordic Council

NEA: Nuclear Energy Agency

NIB: Nordic Investment Bank

NIC: Newly industrializing country; see newly industrializing economy (NIE)

NIE: Newly industrializing economy

NSG: Nuclear Suppliers Group

OAPEC: Organization of Arab Petroleum Exporting Countries

OAS: Organization of American States

OAU: Organization of African Unity

OECD: Organization for Economic Cooperation and Development

OECS: Organization of Eastern Caribbean States

OIC: Organization of the Islamic Conference

ONUSAL: United Nations Observer Mission in El Salvador

OPANAL: Organismo para la Proscripcion de las Armas Nuclearea en la America Latina y el Caribe; see Agency for the Prohibition of Nuclear Weapons in Latin America and the Caribbean

OPEC: Organization of Petroleum Exporting Countries

OSCE: Organization on Security and Cooperation in Europe

PCA: Permanent Court of Arbitration

PPP: Partnership for Peace

RG: Rio Group

SAARC: South Asian Association for Regional Cooperation

SACU: South African Customs Union

SADC: South African Development Community

SADCC: South African Development Coordination Conference

SELA: Sistema Economico Latinamericana; see Latin American Economic System (LAES)

SPARTECA: South Pacific Regional Trade and Economic Cooperation Agreement

SPC: South Pacific Commission

SPF: South Pacific Forum

UDEAC: Union Douaniere et Economique de l'Afrique Centrale; see Central African Customs and Economic Union (UDEAC)

UN: United Nations

UNAVEM II: United Nations Angola Verification Mission

UNAMIR: United Nations Assistance Mission for Rwands

UNCTAD: United Nations Conference on Trade and Development

UNDOF: United Nations Disengagement Observer Force

UNDP: United Nations Development Program

UNEP: United Nations Environment Program

UNESCO: United Nations Educational, Scientific, and Cultural Organization

UNFICYP: United Nations Forces in Cyprus

UNFPA: United Nations Fund for Population Activities; see UN Population Fund (UNFPA)

UNHCR: United Nations Office of the High Commissioner for Refugees

UNICEF: United Nations Children's Fund

UNIDO: United Nations Industrial Development Organization

UNIFIL: United Nations Interim Force in Lebanon

UNIKOM: United Nations Iraq-Kuwait Observation Mission

UNITAR: United Nations Institute for Training and Research

UNMIH: United Nations Mission in Haiti

UNMOGIP: United Nations Military Observer Group in India and Pakistan

UNOMIG: United Nations Observer Mission in Georgia

UNOMIL: United Nations Observer Mission in Liberia

UNOMOZ: United Nations Operation in Mozambique

UNOMUR: United Nations Observer Mission Uganda-Rwanda

UNOSOM: United Nations Operation in Somalia

UNPROFOR: United Nations Protection Force

UNRISD: United Nations Research Institute for Social Development

UNRWA: United Nations Relief and Works Agency for Palestine Refugees in the Near East

UNTAC: United Nations Transitional Authority in Cambodia

UNTSO: United Nations Truce Supervision Organization

UNU: United Nations University

UPU: Universal Postal Union

USSR/EE: USSR/Eastern Europe

WADB: West African Development Bank

WCL: World Confederation of Labor

WEU: Western European Union

WFC: World Food Council

WFP: World Food Program

WFTU: World Federation of Trade Unions

WHO: World Health Organization

WIPO: World Intellectual Property Organization

WMO: World Meteorological Organization

WP: Warsaw Pact

WTO: World Trade Organization

WtoO: World Tourism Organization

ZC: Zangger Committee

IMPERIAL/METRIC CONVERSION KEY

WHEN YOU KNOW	MULTIPLY BY	TO FIND	WHEN YOU KNOW	MULTIPLY BY	TO FIND
Length			**Length**		
Millimeters (mm)	0.04	inches (in)	inches (in)	25.4	millimeters
Centimeters (cm)	0.4	inches (in)	inches (in)	2.54	centimeters (cm)
Meters (m)	3.3	feet (ft)	feet (ft)	30.5	centimeters (cm)
Meters (m)	1.1	yards (yd)	yards (yd)	0.9	meters (m)
Kilometers (km)	0.6	miles (mi)	miles (m)	1.1	kilometers (km)
Area			**Area**		
sq. centimeters (cm^2)	0.155	sq. inches (in^2)	sq. inches (in^2)	6.45	sq. centimeters (cm^2)
sq. meters (m^2)	10.76	sq. feet (ft^2)	sq. feet (ft^2)	0.09	sq. meters (m^2)
sq. meters (m^2)	1.2	sq. yards (yd^2)	sq. yards (yd^2)	0.84	sq. meters (m^2)
sq. kilometers (km^2)	0.4	sq. miles (mi^2)	sq. miles (mi^2)	0.4	sq. kilometers (km^2)
hectares (ha)	2.5	acres	acres	0.4	hectares (ha)
Weight			**Weight**		
grams (g)	0.035	ounces (oz)	ounces (oz)	28.0	grams (g)
kilograms (km)	2.2	pounds (lbs)	pounds (lbs)	0.45	kilograms (kg)
metric tons (t)	1.1	short tons (2,000 lbs)	short tons (2,000 lbs)	0.9	metric tons (t)
Volume			**Volume**		
milliliters (ml)	0.03	fluid ounces (fl oz)	fluid ounces (fl oz)	30.0	milliliters (ml)
liters (L)	2.1	pints (pt)	pints (pt)	0.47	liters (L)
liters (L)	1.06	quarts (qt)	quarts (qt)	.95	liters (L)
liters (L)	0.26	gallons (gal)	gallons (gal)	3.8	liters (L)
cubic meters (m^3)	35.0	cubic feet (ft^3)	cubic feet (ft^4)	0.03	cubic meters (m^3)
cubic meters (m^3)	1.3	cubic yards (yd^3)	cubic yards (yd^3)	0.76	cubic meters (m^3)
Temperature			**Temperature**		
Celsius (°C)	9/5 + 32	Fahrenheit (°F)	Fahrenheit (°F)	5/9 − 32	Celsius (°C)

STATUS OF NATIONS

COUNTRY NAME: SYSTEM OF GOVERNMENT

Afghanistan: transitional government

Albania: emerging democracy

Algeria: republic

American Samoa: unincorporated territory of the United States

Andorra: parliamentary democracy

Angola: transitional government, nominally a multiparty democracy with a strong presidential system

Anguilla: British crown colony

Antigua and Barbuda: parliamentary democracy

Argentina: republic

Armenia: republic

Aruba: parliamentary

Australia: democratic, federal-state system recognizing the British monarch as sovereign

Austria: federal republic

Azerbaijan: republic

Bahamas, The: commonwealth

Bahrain: traditional monarchy

Bangladesh: republic

Barbados: parliamentary democracy

Belarus: republic

Belgium: federal parliamentary democracy under a constitutional monarch

Belize: parliamentary democracy

Benin: republic under multiparty democratic rule

Bermuda: British crown colony

Bhutan: monarchy

Bolivia: republic

Bosnia and Herzegovina: emerging democracy

Botswana: parliamentary republic

Brazil: federal republic

British Virgin Islands: British crown colony

Brunei: constitutional sultanate

Bulgaria: republic

Burkina Faso: parliamentary

Burundi: republic

Cambodia: multiparty liberal democracy under a constitutional monarchy

Cameroon: unitary republic; multiparty presidential regime (opposition parties legalized in 1990)

Canada: federation with parliamentary democracy

Cape Verde: republic

Cayman Islands: British crown colony

Central African Republic: republic

Chad: republic

Chile: republic

China: Communist state

Christmas Island: territory of Australia

Colombia: republic; executive branch dominates government structure

Comoros: independent republic

Congo, Democratic Republic of: dictatorship; presumably undergoing a transition to representative government

Congo, Republic of: republic

Cook Islands: self-governing parliamentary democracy

Costa Rica: democratic republic

Cote d'Ivoire: republic

Croatia: presidential/parliamentary democracy

Cuba: Communist state

Cyprus: republic

Czech Republic: parliamentary democracy

Denmark: constitutional monarchy

Djibouti: republic

Dominica: parliamentary democracy

Dominican Republic: republic

Ecuador: republic

Egypt: republic

El Salvador: republic

Equatorial Guinea: republic in transition to multiparty democracy

Eritrea: transitional government

Estonia: parliamentary democracy

Ethiopia: federal republic

Falkland Islands: British crown colony

Faroe Islands: part of the Kingdom of Denmark; self-governing overseas administrative division of Denmark since 1948

Fiji: republic

Finland: republic

France: republic

French Guiana: French overseas department

French Polynesia: territory of France

Gabon: republic; multiparty presidential regime

Gambia, The: republic under multiparty democratic rule

Georgia: republic

Germany: federal republic

Ghana: constitutional democracy

Gibraltar: British crown colony

Greece: parliamentary republic

Greenland: part of the Kingdom of Denmark; self-governing overseas administrative division of Denmark since 1979

Grenada: parliamentary democracy

Guadeloupe: overseas department and administrative region of France

Guam: unincorporated territory of the United States

Guatemala: republic

Guernsey: dependency of the British crown

Guinea: republic

Guinea-Bissau: republic

Guyana: republic

Haiti: republic

Honduras: republic

Hungary: republic

Iceland: constitutional republic

India: federal republic

Indonesia: republic

Iran: theocratic republic

Iraq: republic

Ireland: republic

Israel: republic

Italy: republic

Jamaica: parliamentary democracy

Japan: constitutional monarchy

Jersey: dependency of the British crown

Jordan: constitutional monarchy

Kazakstan: republic

Kenya: republic

Kiribati: republic

Korea, North: Communist state; one-man dictatorship

Korea, South: republic

Kuwait: nominal constitutional monarchy

Kyrgyzstan: republic

Laos: Communist state

Latvia: parliamentary democracy

Lebanon: republic

Lesotho: parliamentary constitutional monarchy

Liberia: republic

Libya: Jamahiriya (a state of the masses) in theory, governed by the populace through local councils; in fact, a military dictatorship

Liechtenstein: hereditary constitutional monarchy

Lithuania: parliamentary democracy

Luxembourg: constitutional monarchy

Macau: Chinese province

Macedonia: emerging democracy

Madagascar: republic

Malawi: multiparty democracy

Malaysia: constitutional monarchy

Maldives: republic

Mali: republic

Malta: parliamentary democracy

Man, Isle of: British crown dependency

Marshall Islands: constitutional government in free association with the US

Martinique: overseas department and administrative region of France

Mauritania: republic

Mauritius: parliamentary democracy

Mayotte: territory of France

Mexico: federal republic operating under a centralized government

Micronesia, Federated States of: constitutional government in free association with the US

Midway Islands: territory of the United States

Moldova: republic

Monaco: constitutional monarchy

Mongolia: republic

Montenegro: republic

Montserrat: British crown colony

Morocco: constitutional monarchy

Mozambique: republic

Myanmar: military regime

Namibia: republic

Nauru: republic

Nepal: parliamentary democracy

Netherlands: constitutional monarchy

Netherlands Antilles: parliamentary

New Caledonia: territory of France

New Zealand: parliamentary democracy

Nicaragua: republic

Niger: republic

Nigeria: republic transitioning from military to civilian rule

Niue: self-governing parliamentary democracy

Norfolk Island: territory of Australia

Northern Mariana Islands: commonwealth

Norway: constitutional monarchy

Oman: monarchy

Pakistan: federal republic

Palau: constitutional government in free association with the US

Panama: constitutional republic

Papua New Guinea: parliamentary democracy

Paraguay: republic

Peru: republic

Philippines: republic

Poland: democratic state

Portugal: parliamentary democracy

Puerto Rico: commonwealth

Qatar: traditional monarchy

Reunion: overseas department of France

Romania: republic

Russia: republic

Rwanda: republic

Saint Helena: British dependency

Saint Kitts and Nevis: constitutional monarchy

Saint Lucia: constitutional monarchy

Saint Pierre and Miquelon: French territorial collectivity

Saint Vincent and the Grenadines: constitutional monarchy

Samoa: constitutional monarchy under native chief

San Marino: republic

Sao Tome and Principe: republic

Saudi Arabia: monarchy

Senegal: republic under multiparty democratic rule

Serbia: republic

Seychelles: republic

Sierra Leone: constitutional democracy

Singapore: republic within Commonwealth

Slovakia: parliamentary democracy

Slovenia: parliamentary democratic republic

Solomon Islands: parliamentary democracy

Somalia: none

South Africa: republic

Spain: parliamentary monarchy

Sri Lanka: republic

Sudan: transitional

Suriname: republic

Swaziland: monarchy

Sweden: constitutional monarchy

Switzerland: federal republic

Syria: republic under military regime since March 1963

Taiwan: multiparty democratic regime headed by popularly elected president

Tajikistan: republic

Tanzania: republic

Thailand: constitutional monarchy

Togo: republic under transition to multiparty democratic rule

Tonga: hereditary constitutional monarchy

Trinidad and Tobago: parliamentary democracy

Tunisia: republic

Turkey: republican parliamentary democracy

Turkmenistan: republic

Turks and Caicos: British dependency

Tuvalu: constitutional monarchy with a parliamentary democracy

Uganda: republic

Ukraine: republic

United Arab Emirates: federation with specified powers delegated to the UAE federal government and other powers reserved to member emirates

United Kingdom: constitutional monarchy

United States: federal republic; strong democratic tradition

Uruguay: republic

Uzbekistan: republic; effectively authoritarian presidential rule, with little power outside the executive branch; executive power concentrated in the presidency

Vanuatu: republic

Vatican City: monarchical-sacerdotal state

Venezuela: republic

Vietnam: Communist state

Virgin Islands: territory of the United States

Wallis and Futuna: French overseas territory

Yemen: republic

Zambia: republic

Zimbabwe: parliamentary democracy

SOURCES OF STATISTICS

GEOGRAPHY—1

SOURCE. U.S. Central Intelligence Agency (CIA) 1998, *The World Factbook 1998* [Online]. Available: http://www.cia.gov/cia/publications/factbook/index.html [October 1999].

NOTES.

Comparative area—Based on total area equivalents. Most entities are compared with the entire United States or one of the 50 states. The smaller entities are compared with Washington, D.C. (178 square km, 69 square miles), or the Mall in Washington, D.C. (0.59 square km, 0.23 square miles, 146 acres).

km—Kilometers.

Land area—Aggregate of all surfaces delimited by international boundaries and/or coastlines, excluding inland water bodies (lakes, reservoirs, rivers).

Land use—Human use of the land surface is categorized as *arable land*—land cultivated for crops that are replanted after each harvest (wheat, maize, rice); *permanent crops*—land cultivated for crops that are not replanted after each harvest (citrus, coffee, rubber); *meadows and pastures*—land permanently used for herbaceous forage crops; *forest and woodland*—land under dense or open stands of trees; and *other*—any land type not specifically mentioned above (urban areas, roads, deserts).

mi—Miles.

NA—Data are not available.

Total area—Sum of all land and water area delimited by international boundaries and/or coastlines.

DEMOGRAPHICS—2A

SOURCE. U.S. Bureau of the Census (1998). *International Database 1998* [Online]. Available: http://www.census.gov:80/ipc/www/wp98.html [October 1999].

NOTES.

NA—Data are not available.

DEMOGRAPHICS—2B

SOURCE. U.S. Central Intelligence Agency (CIA) 1998, *The World Factbook 1998* [Online]. Available: http://www.cia.gov/cia/publications/factbook/index.html [October 1999].

NOTES.

NA—Data are not available.

HEALTH PERSONNEL—3

SOURCE. The World Bank, *World Development Indicators 1999* (March 1999), pages 90–92. Reprinted with permission.

United Nations Development Program (UNDP) and Oxford University Press, *Human Development Report 1999*, pages 172–175. Reprinted with permission.

NOTES.

Public Health Expenditure—This category consists of recurrent and capital spending from government (central and local) budgets, external borrowings and grants (including donations from international agencies and nongovernmental organizations), and social (or compulsory) health insurance funds.

Private Health Expenditure—This category includes direct household (out-of-pocket) spending, private insurance, charitable donations, and direct service payments by private corporations.

FOOTNOTES.

a—Data are for the most recent year available.

b—Data may not sum to totals because of rounding.

c—Data refer to 1993 or a year around 1993.

HEALTH CARE INDICATORS—4

SOURCE. The World Bank, *World Development Indicators 1999* (March 1999), pages 94–112. Reprinted with permission.

United Nations Development Program (UNDP) and Oxford University Press, *Human Development Report 1999*, pages 211–214. Reprinted with permission.

NOTES.

Percentage of Population with Access to Safe Water.—This is the share of the population with reasonable access to an adequate amount of safe water (including treated surface water and untreated but uncontaminated water, such as from springs, sanitary wells, and protected boreholes). In urban areas the source may be a public fountain or standpipe located not more than 200 meters away. In rural areas the definition implies that members of a household do not have to spend a disproportionate part of the day fetching water. An adequate amount of safe water is that needed to satisfy metabolic, hygienic, and domestic requirements—usually about 20 liters a person a day. The definition of safe water has changed over time.

Percentage of Population with Access to Sanitation.—This is the share of the population with at least adequate excreta disposal facilities that can effectively prevent human, animal, and insect contact with excreta. Suitable facilities range from simple but protected pit latrines to flush toilets with sewerage. To be effective, all facilities must be correctly constructed and properly maintained.

Adult HIV Prevalence—This is the percentage of people aged 15-49 who are infected with human immunodeficiency virus (HIV).

FOOTNOTES.

...—Data are not available.

a—Data are for most recent year available.

b—Official estimate.

c—UNICEF-WHO estimate based on statistical modeling.

d—Indirect estimate based on a sample survey.

e—Based on a survey covering 30 provinces.

f—Based on a sample survey.

INFANTS & MALNUTRITION—5

SOURCE. United Nations Children's Fund (UNICEF), *The State of the World's Children 1999*, pages 94–105.

The World Bank and Oxford University Press, *Entering the 21st Century: World Development Report 1999/2000* (August 1999), pages 232 and 233. Reprinted with permission.

The World Bank, *World Development Indicators 1999* (March 1999), pages 98–101. Reprinted with permission.

NOTES.

Under-five mortality rate—Probability of dying between birth and exactly five years of age expressed per 1,000 live births.

Low birthweight—Weights at birth that are less than 2,500 grams.

TB—Tuberculosis

DPT—Diphtheria, pertussis (whooping cough) and tetanus.

Prevalence of child malnutrition—Expressed in percentage of children under age 5.

FOOTNOTES.

NA—Data are not available.

x—Indicates data that refer to years other than those specified, differ from the standard definitions, or refer to only part of a country.

a—Data are for the most recent year available within the range listed.

b—Data are for the most recent year available within the range.

ETHNIC DIVISION—6

SOURCE. U.S. Central Intelligence Agency (CIA) 1998, *The World Factbook 1998* [Online]. Available: http://www.cia.gov/cia/publications/factbook/index.html [October 1999].

NOTES.

Tables show the major ethnic divisions of peoples in the given country for the most recent year available. When available, the distribution is shown in percent.

NA—Data are not available.

RELIGION—7

SOURCE. U.S. Central Intelligence Agency (CIA) 1998, *The World Factbook 1998* [Online]. Available: http://www.cia.gov/cia/publications/factbook/index.html [October 1999].

NOTES.

Tables show major religious denominations of the peoples of the given country for the most recent year available. When available, the distribution is shown in percent.

NA—Data are not available.

MAJOR LANGUAGES—8

SOURCE. U.S. Central Intelligence Agency (CIA) 1998, *The World Factbook 1998* [Online]. Available: http://www.cia.gov/cia/publications/factbook/index.html [October 1999].

NOTES.

Tables show major language(s) spoken by inhabitants of the given country for the most recent year available. When available, the distribution is shown in percent.

NA—Data are not available.

PUBLIC EDUCATION EXPENDITURES—9

SOURCE. The World Bank, *World Development Indicators 1999* (March 1999), pages 74–77. Reprinted with permission.

NOTES.

The data on education spending refer solely to public spending—that is, government spending on public education plus subsidies for private education. The data generally exclude foreign aid for education.

They also may exclude religious schools, which play a significant role in many developing countries.

The percentage of GNP devoted to education can be interpreted as reflecting a country's effort in education. Often it bears a weak relationship to measures of output of the education system, as reflected in educational attainment. The pattern suggests wide variations across countries in the efficiency with which the government's resources are translated into education outcomes.

Public Expenditures of Education.—This is the percentage of GNP accounted for by public spending on public education plus subsidies to private education at the primary, secondary, and tertiary levels.

Expenditure of Teaching Materials.—The public spending on teaching materials (textbooks, books, and other scholastic supplies) as a percentage of total public spending on primary or secondary education.

FOOTNOTES.

1—Data are for years or periods other than those specified.

EDUCATION ATTAINMENT—10

SOURCE. United Nations Education, Scientific, and Cultural Organization and Bernan Press, *UNESCO 1999 Statistical Yearbook*, pages 51–64. Reprinted with permission.

NOTES.

The percentage distribution of the population aged 25 years and over according to the highest level of education attained reflects both the outcomes of participation in education in the past and the educational composition of the population. These data have been collected mainly during national population censuses and sample surveys. The six levels of educational attainment presented here are based on the International Standard Classification of Education (ISCED) and are defined as follows:

No schooling—Refers to persons who have completed less than one year of primary education.

Primary education incomplete—Includes all persons who have completed at least one grade of primary education but who did not complete the final grade of this level of education.

Primary education completed—Refers to all persons who have completed the final grade of primary education but did not enter secondary education.

Attended lower secondary education—Comprises all persons who have attended lower secondary education but not (upper) secondary education.

Attended (upper) secondary education—Includes all persons who have attended (upper) secondary education but not post-secondary education.

Post-secondary education—Refers to all persons who have completed secondary education and attended post-secondary education.

FOOTNOTES.

1—Not including persons with no schooling or less than one year of primary education.

2—The category "No Schooling" comprises illiterates.

3—"Completed primary education" refers to the last two years of primary education.

4—Persons who can read and write have been counted with "incomplete primary."

5—Not including population attending and never attended school.

6—Data refer only to persons who have attended school but left school.

7—Based on a sample survey of 35,502 persons.

8—Not including persons still in school.

9—Based on a sample survey of 51,372 persons.

10—Post-secondary education refers to universities only.

11—Not including transients and residents of former canal zone.

12—The category "No schooling" refers to those who have attended less than one grade of primary education.

13—Not including armed forces stationed in the area.

14—Lower secondary education refers to "intermedio" level of education. (Upper) secondary education refers to "Media," "Tecnica" and "Normal" education.

15—Not including rural population of Northern Brazil.

16—Not including persons whose level of education is unknown.

17—Not including Jammu and Kashmir.

18—Not including persons still attending school for whom the level is unknown.

19—Household survey results based on a sample of 6,393 households. The category of "No schooling" includes illiterates.

20—(Upper) secondary education includes 'polytechnic'; post-secondary education refers to universities only.

21—Data are based on a sample of 8,619 households (5,563 urban and 3,056 rural) from the 1993 Demographic and Health Survey.

22—"Incomplete primary education" refers to grades 1 to 4 and "Complete primary education" refers to grades 5 to 8.

23—Not including expatriate workers and their families.

24—The category "No schooling" includes persons who are still in school.

25—The category "No schooling" comprises persons who did not state their level of education.

26—Based on a 20% sample of census returns.

LITERACY RATES—11A

SOURCE. United Nations Education and Culture Organization (UNESCO), *Compendium of Statistics on Illiteracy* (1995 Edition), pages 40–49. Reprinted with permission.

NOTES.

Literacy statistics are concerned with the stock of persons who have successfully acquired the basic reading, writing and numerical skills essential for personal growth and cohesion within contemporary societies. Levels of literacy within a population constitute on the one hand a reflection of the level of development and accomplishments of the education systems, and on the other hand a pointer on the potential for human input into further economic, social and cultural development. Literacy rate has therefore been widely used as a key common indicator for monitoring and assessing progress in the current world thrusts of Education for All and Human Resources Development, and has been regularly incorporated into various reports and publications.

As the national statistics on literacy made available to UNESCO are collected during population censuses that usually take place once every ten years, estimations and projections are carried out to fill the data gaps for the years between two censuses, as well as to provide projections showing likely progress in literacy for the future.

Literacy continues to progress in the world. Adult literacy rate, or the percentage of literates within the adult population aged 15 years and over, has been steadily growing in all countries. Entering the 1990s, over three-quarters (75.3 percent) of the world's adult population have become literate—increasing from 69.5 percent in 1980. Based on the past trends, it is estimated that the overall literacy rate in the world has further improved to 77.4 percent in 1995, and is projected to reach 80 percent at the beginning of the 21st century.

The literate adult population in the world has undergone phenomenal expansion during the past fifteen years from 1980 to 1995, and is projected to further increase in the future. In absolute numbers, the adult literate population in the world rose from 2 billion in 1980 to an estimated 3 billion in 1995, i.e. by 1 billion persons. If the current rate of progress can be maintained, the number of adult literates in the world may reach 3.4 billions in the year 2000, and 4.2 billion in 2010.

Despite these signs of positive progress in both literacy rates and number of literates, one may notice that there remains a large illiterate population in the world of today—numbering some 885 million adults aged 15 years and over—and that this illiterate population increased from an estimated 877 million in 1980. The expansion of the world's illiterate population seems to have reached its turning point during the first half of the 1990s. The projections show that if the past trend were to continue, this world total would gradually decrease to some 881 million by the year 2000. But the huge mass of more than 880 million illiterates shall continue to constitute major challenges to education in the future.

Literate—A person is literate who can with understanding both read and write a short simple statement on his everyday life.

Illiterate—A person is illiterate who cannot with understanding both read and write a short simple statement on his everyday life.

Adult—Refers to persons aged 15 years or older.

LITERACY RATES—11B

SOURCE. United Nations Children's Fund (UNICEF), *The State of the World's Children 1999*, pages 106–109.

NOTES.

Adult Literacy Rate—Percentage of persons aged 15 years and over who can read and write.

-—Data not available.

X—Indicates data that refer to years or periods other than those specified, differ from the standard definitions, or refer to only part of a country.

POLITICAL PARTIES—12

SOURCE. U.S. Central Intelligence Agency (CIA) 1998, *The World Factbook 1998* [Online]. Available: http://www.cia.gov/cia/publications/factbook/index.html [October 1999].

NOTES.

When available, political party representation is shown for the lower house of the legislative branch of government. The lower house was chosen in order to present, in most cases, a picture of the electoral results of voting by the general public. The name of this legislative body is shown in the legend of the given table.

When available, election results are shown as a percent distribution of votes in the most recent election. Otherwise, percent distribution of seats, or number of seats, by political party is shown. If there are no political parties or there is one-party rule, this information is provided in place of tabular data.

Wherever possible, political party names have been presented in English translation.

NA—Data are not available.

GOVERNMENT BUDGETS—13A

SOURCE. International Monetary Fund (IMF), *Government Finance Statistics Yearbook 1998*, pages 18–421.

FOOTNOTES.

f—Forecast.

p—Preliminary / provisional.

....—Data not available.

——Zero or less than half a significant digit.

GOVERNMENT BUDGET—13B

SOURCE. U.S. Central Intelligence Agency (CIA) 1998, *The World Factbook 1998* [Online]. Available: http://www.cia.gov/cia/publications/factbook/index.html [October 1999].

NOTES.

IMF data were obtained primarily by means of a detailed questionnaire distribution to government finance statistics correspondents, who are usually located in each country's respective ministry of finance or central bank. Three of the six categories of central government expenditure shown in the IMF tables are comprised of subcategories, whose subtotals have been summed. Below is a list of these subcategories.

Education/Health—Also includes *Welfare* and *Social security.*

Industry—Includes *Fuel and energy; Agriculture, forestry, fishing, and hunting; Mining, manufacturing, and construction; Transportation and communication;* and *Other economic affairs and services.*

Other—Includes *Recreational, cultural, and religious affairs and other expenditures.*

Some of the subcategory data are incomplete for Guatemala, India, and Nepal, and consequently have been calculated as zero (0).

Minor differences between published totals and the sum of components are attributable to rounding.

Following are definitions of acronyms and terms pertinent to these tables.

Central government—All units representing the territorial jurisdiction of the central authority throughout a country.

CY—Calendar year: 12-month year beginning January 1 and ending the following December 31.

A dash (-)—Data are nil or negligible.

est.—Estimate.

Expenditure—All nonrepayable payments by government, including both capital and current expenditures and regardless of whether goods or services were received for such expenditures.

FY—Fiscal Year: presented within the calendar year containing the greatest number of months for that fiscal year. Fiscal years ending June 30 are presented within the same calendar year. For example, the fiscal year July 1, 1995–June 30, 1996 is shown within the calendar year 1996.

Government—All units that implement public policy by providing nonmarket services and transferring income; these units are financed mainly by compulsory levies on other sectors.

NA—Data are not available.

Revenue—All nonrepayable government receipts other than grants.

MILITARY AFFAIRS—14A

SOURCE. U.S. Central Intelligence Agency (CIA) 1998, *The World Factbook 1998* [Online]. Available: http://www.cia.gov/cia/publications/factbook/index.html [October 1999].

FOOTNOTES.

e—Estimate based on partial or uncertain data.

NA—Data not available.

0—Nil or negligible.

MILITARY AFFAIRS—14B

SOURCE. U.S. Arms Control and Disarmament Agency, *World Military Expenditures and Arms Transfers 1996* (WMEAT), (July 1997), pages 57 99 and 108–150.

NOTES.

Military Expenditures

For NATO countries, military expenditures are from NATO publications and are based on the NATO definition. In this definition, (a) civilian-type expenditures of the defense ministry are excluded and military-type expenditures of other ministries are included; (b) grant military assistance is included in the expenditures of the donor country; and (c) purchases of military equipment for credit are included at the time the debt is incurred, not at the time of payment.

For other non-communist countries, data are generally the expenditures of the ministry of defense. When these are known to include the costs of internal security, an attempt is made to remove these expenditures. A wide variety of data sources is used for these countries, including the publications and data resources of other U.S. government agencies, standardized reporting to the United Nations by country, and other international sources.

It should be recognized by users of the statistical tables that the military expenditure data are of uneven accuracy and completeness. For example, there are indications or reasons to believe that the military expenditures reported by some countries consist mainly or entirely of recurring or operating expenditures and omit all or most capital expenditures, including arms purchases.

In some cases it is believed that a better estimate of total military expenditures is obtained by adding to nominal military expenditures the value of arms imports. It must be cautioned, however, that this method may over- or underestimate the actual expenditures in a given year due to the fact that payment for arms may not coincide in time with deliveries. Also, arms acquisitions in some cases may be financed by, or consist of grants from, other countries.

For countries that have major clandestine nuclear or other military weapons development programs, such as Iraq, estimation of military expenditures is extremely difficult and especially subject to errors of underestimation.

Further information in the quality of the military expenditure data presented for countries throughout the world will be difficult to achieve without better reporting by the countries themselves. As has been noted elsewhere, ''There is growing evidence that important amounts of security expenditures may not enter the accounts or the national budgets of many developing countries.'' Among the mechanisms commonly used to obscure such expenditures are: double-bookkeeping budget categories, military assistance, and manipulation or foreign exchange.

Particular problems arise in estimating the military expenditures of communist countries due to the exceptional scarcity and ambiguity of released information. As in past editions of this publication, data on the military expenditures of the Soviet Union are based on Central Intelligence Agency (CIA) estimates. For most of the series, these are estimates of what it would cost in the United States in dollars to develop, procure, staff, and operate a military force similar to that of the Soviet Union. Estimates of this type—that is, those based entirely on one country's price pattern—generally overstate the relative size of the second country's expenditures in intercountry comparisons. Also, such estimates are not consistent with the methods used here for converting other countries' expenditures into dollars.

Nevertheless, the basic CIA estimates are the best available for present purposes; in fact, there are no alternative estimates that can inspire confidence and have the capability to detect relatively small changes over time, such as the slowdown and decline in Soviet military spending that the CIA estimates have indicated.

For Russia, estimated military spending trends in rubles are used in conjunction with dollar estimates for earlier years to make rough estimates of spending in dollars.

For former Warsaw Pact countries other than the Soviet Union, the estimates of military expenditures through 1989 are from Thad P. Alton et al. These estimates cover the officially announced state budget expenditures on national defense and thus understate total military expenditures to the extent of possible defense outlays by non-defense agencies of the central government, local governments, and economic enterprises. Possible subsidization of military procurement may also cause understatement. The dollar estimates were derived by calculating pay and allowances at the current full U.S. average rates for officers and for lower ranks. After subtraction of pay and allowances, the remainder of the official defense budgets in national currencies was converted into dollars at overall rates based on comparisons of the various countries' GNPs expressed in dollars and in national currencies. The

rates are based in part on the purchasing power parites (PPPs) estimated by the International Comparison Project of the United Nations, including there latest (Phase V) versions.

Estimates for these countries in 1990 and 1991 are based on total military spending in national currency as reported by the respective governments to the UN (in most cases) or the IMF. These expenditures in toto are converted to dollars at the Alton GNP conversion rates for 1989 as adjusted to 1991 by the respective U.S. and national GNP deflators (per the World Bank), without estimating personnel compensation separately at U.S. dollar rates, as was done for earlier years. The resulting military conversion rates (in national currency per dollar) are substantially lower than the 1991 market rate, and approximately the same as the implied rate for GNP.

Estimates for the newly independent states of the former Soviet Union, Yugoslavia, and Czechoslovakia and other former Warsaw Pact countries present difficulties due to scarcity of reliable data in national currencies and to problems in converting to dollars. The basic method employed for most of these countries was to establish the ratio of military expenditures to GNP in national currency and then to multiply this ratio by the World Bank's estimate of GNP in dollars as converted to international dollars by estimate PPPs and reported in the *World Bank Atlas 1997*. This method implicitly converts military spending at the GNP-wide PPP, which, as with conversion by exchange rates, preserves the same ME/GNP ratio in dollars as obtains in national currency.

Data for China are based on U.S. Government estimates of the yuan costs of Chinese forces, weapons, programs, and activities. Costs in yuan are here converted to dollars using the same estimated conversion rate as used for GNP. Due to the exceptional difficulties in both estimating yuan costs and converting them to dollars, comparisons of Chinese military spending with other data should be treated as having a wide margin of error.

Other published sources used include the *Government Finance Statistics Yearbook,* issued by the International Monetary Fund; *The World Factbook,* produced annually the Central Intelligence Agency; *The Military Balance,* issued by the International Institute for Strategic Studies (London); and the *SIPRI Yearbook: World Armaments and Disarmament,* issued by the Stockholm International Peach Research Institute.

Gross National Product (GNP)

GNP represents the total output of goods and services produced by residents of a country, valued at market prices. The source of GNP data for most noncommunist countries is the International Bank for Reconstruction and Development (World Bank).

For a number of countries whose GNP is dominated by oil exports (Bahrain, Kuwait, Libya, Oman, Qatar, Saudi Arabia, and the United Arab Emirates), the World Bank's estimate of deflated (or constant price) GNP in domestic currency tends to understate increases in the monetary value of oil exports, and thus of GNP, resulting from oil price increases. These World Bank estimates are designed to measure real (or physical) product. An alternative estimate of constant-price GNP was therefore obtained using the implicit price deflator for U.S. GNP (for lack of a better national deflator). This considered appropriate because a large share of the GNP of these countries is realized in U.S. dollars.

GNP estimates of the Soviet Union are by the CIA, as published in its *Handbook of Economic Statistics 1990* and updated. GNP estimates for other Warsaw Pact countries through 1989 are from "East European Military Expenditures, 1965–1978," by Thad P. Alton and others, *op. cit.,* as updated and substantially revised by the authors. These estimates through 1989 have been extended to 1990 and 1991 on the basis of estimates for those years in the CIA's *Handbook of Economic Statistics, 1992.*

Estimates of GNP in 1992–1994 for successor states to the Soviet Union, Yugoslavia, and Czechoslovakia are based on World Bank estimates of GNP per capita employing PPPs and population, as published in the *World Bank Atlas 1997.*

GNP data for China are based on World Bank estimates in yuan. These are in line with estimates of GDP in Western accounting terms made by Chinese authorities. Converting estimates in yuan to dollars is highly problematic, however, due to the inappropriateness of the official exchange rate and lack of sufficient yuan price information by which to reliably estimate PPPs. (The ratio of the highest to the lowest estimates by various sources of China's GNP is on the order of 6 or 7 to 1, which would make the world rank of China's GNP vary between about third or fourth and twelfth). The conversion rate used here is based on a PPP estimated for 1981 and moved by respective U.S. and China implicit GNP deflators to 1994.

GNP estimates for a few non-communist countries are from the CIA's *Handbook of Economic Statistics* cited above. Estimates for the other communist countries are rough approximations.

Military Expenditures-to-GNP Ratio

It should be noted that the meaning of the ratio of military expenditures to GNP differs somewhat between most communist (or previously communist) and other countries. For non-communist countries, both military expenditures and GNP are converted from the national currency unit to dollars at the same exchange rate; consequently, the ratio of military expenditures to GNP is the same in dollars as in the national currency and reflects national relative prices. For communist countries, however, military expenditures and GNP are converted differently. Soviet military expenditures, as already noted, are estimated in a way designed to show the cost of the Soviet armed forces in U.S. prices, as if purchased in this country. On the other hand, the Soviet GNP estimates used here are designed to

show average relative size when both U.S. and Soviet GNP are valued and compared at both dollar and ruble prices. The Soviet ratio of military expenditures to GNP in ruble terms, the preferred method of comparison, is estimated to have been 15-18% in that country's latest years.

The estimated ratio for Russia derived here in dollars is probably somewhat overstated since military spending in dollars is relative to earlier estimates for the Soviet Union, while GNP estimates (at PPPs) are by the World Bank. Russia's burden ratio in ruble term is preferably estimated to be under 10%.

For Eastern European countries before 1992, the ratios of military expenditures to GNP in dollars were about twice the ratios that would obtain in domestic currencies. However, since official military budgets in these countries probably substantially understated their actual military expenditures, the larger ratios on dollar estimates are believed to be the better approximations of the actual ratios.

Central Government Expenditures (CGE)

These expenditures include current and capital (developmental) expenditures plus net lending to the government enterprises by central (or federal) governments. A major source is the International Monetary Fund's *Government Finance Statistics Yearbook.* The category used here is "Total Expenditures and Lending minus Repayment, Consolidated Central Government."

Other sources for these data are the International Monetary Fund, *International Financial Statistics* (monthly); OECD, *Economics Surveys;* and CIA, *The World Factbook* (annual). Data for Warsaw Pact countries are from national publications and are supplied by Thad P. Alton and others. For all Warsaw Pact countries and China, conversion to dollars is at the implicit rates used for calculating dollar estimates of GNP.

For all countries, with the same exceptions as noted above for the military expenditures-to-GNP ratio, military expenditures and central government expenditures are converted to dollars at the same rate; the ratio of the two variables is thus the same in dollars as in national currency.

It should be noted that for the Soviet Union, China, Iran, Jordan, and possibly others, the ratio of military expenditures to central government expenditures may be overstated, inasmuch as the estimate for military expenditures is obtained at least in part independently of nominal budget or government expenditure data, and it is possible that not all estimated military expenditures pass through the nominal central government budget.

Population

Population estimates are for midyear and are made available to ACDA by the U.S. Bureau of the Census.

Armed Forces

Armed forces refer to active-duty military personnel, including paramilitary forces if those forces resemble regular units in their organization, equipment, training, or mission. Reserve forces are not included unless specifically noted.

Figures for the United States and all other North American Treaty Organization (NATO) countries are as reported by NATO. Estimates of the number of personnel under arms for other countries are provided by U.S. Government sources. The armed forces series for the Soviet Union includes all special forces judged to have national security missions (e.g., KGB border guards) and excludes uniformed forces primarily performing noncombatant services (construction, railroad, civil defense, and internal security troops).

Arms Transfers

Arms transfers (arms imports and exports) represent the international transfer (under terms of grant, credit, barter, or cash) of military equipment, usually referred to as "conventional," including weapons of war, parts thereof, ammunition, support equipment, and other commodities designed for military use. Among the items included are tactical guided missiles use. Among the items included are tactical guided missiles and rockets, military aircraft, naval vessels, armored and nonarmored military vehicles, communications and electronic equipment, artillery, infantry weapons, small arms, ammunition, other ordinance, parachutes, and uniforms. Dual use equipment, which can have application in both military and civilian sectors, is included when its primary mission is identified as military. The building of defense production facilities and licensing fees paid as royalties for the production of military equipment are included when they are contained in military transfer agreements. There have been no international transfers of purely strategic weaponry. Military services such as training, supply operations, equipment repair, technical assistance, and construction are included where data are available. Excluded are foodstuffs, medical equipment, petroleum products and other supplies.

Redefinition of U.S. Arms Exports. The scope of U.S. arms exports data was modified in the *WMEAT 1995* edition. These exports include both government-to-government transfers under the Foreign Military Sales (FMS), Military Assistance Program (MAP), and other programs administered by the Department of Defense, and commercial (enterprise-to-government) transfers licensed by the Department of State under International Traffic in Arms Regulations. Under the previous practice, the material component (arms, equipment, and "hardware" items) of FMS and MAP sales was included, while the military services component was excluded (although the magnitude and general destination of the omitted services was reported in these Statistical Notes).

Beginning with the previous edition, both the material and the military services components of FMS and other government-to-government sales (such as the International Military Education and Training Program—IMET) are included in total U.S. arms exports as reported here. The commercial sales category, covering both material and military services, was included in its entirety.

The omission of FMS and other military services prior to the previous edition had been intended to improve comparability with available estimates of the arms exports of other countries, which tended to contain a much smaller services component and/or were subject to significant underestimation (services being less easily observed). The increasing importance of these services and the desire to present a full picture of U.S. arms exports consistent with other sources prompted the change to inclusion. Users should be aware, however, of both the lower true share of services in other countries' arms exports and the tendency to underestimate them. It should also be noted that a portion of the IMET program is devoted to programs that promote improved civil-military relations.

The change in scope of U.S. arms exports increased their overall volume by amounts ranging over the last decade from $2.3 billion (current dollars) to $3.7 billion for deliveries and $2.3 billion to $7.3 billion for agreements.

The statistics contained herein are estimates of the value of goods actually delivered during the reference year, in contrast both to payments and the value of programs, agreements, contracts, or orders concluded during the period, which are expected to result in future deliveries.

U.S. Arms Imports. U.S. arms import data in this and the previous four editions of WMEAT are revised upward substantially from earlier editions. The present series consist of data obtained from the Department of Commerce, Bureau of Economic Analysis (BEA), including (a) imports of military-type (formerly "special category") goods, as compiled by the Bureau of the Census, and (b) Department of Defense direct expenditures abroad for major equipment, as compiled from DOD data by BEA. The goods in (a) include: complete military aircraft, all types; engines and turbines for military (naval) ships and boats; tanks, artillery, missiles, guns, and ammunition; military apparel and footwear; and other military goods, equipment, and parts.

Data on countries other than the United States are estimates by U.S. Government sources. Arms transfer data for the Soviet Union and other former communist countries are approximations based on limited information.

It should be noted that the arms transfer estimates for the most recent year, and to a lesser extent for several preceding years, tend to a lesser extent for several preceding years, tend to be understated. This applies to both foreign and U.S. arms exports. In former case, information on transfers comes from a variety of sources and is sometimes acquired and processed with a considerable time lag. In the U.S. case, commercial arms transfer licenses are now valued for three years, causing a delay in the reporting of deliveries made on them to statistical agencies.

Close comparisons between the estimated values shown for arms transfers and for GNP and military expenditures are not warranted. Frequently, weapons prices do not reflect true production costs. Furthermore, much of the international arms trade involves offset or barter arrangements, multiyear loans, discounted prices, third party payments, and partial debt forgiveness. Acquisitions of armaments thus may not [necessarily] impose the burden on an economy, whether in the same or in other years, that is implied by the estimated equivalent U.S. dollar value of the shipment. Therefore, the value of arms imports should be compared to other categories of data with care.

Total Imports and Exports

The values for imports and exports cover merchandise transactions and come mainly from International Financial Statistics published by the IMF. The trade figures for presently and formerly communist countries and from the CIA's *Handbook of Economic Statistics, 1996* edition.

FOOTNOTES.

e—Estimate based on partial or uncertain data.

NA—Data not available.

p—Estimate based on purchasing power parities.

r—Rough estimate.

0—Nil or negligible.

1—Estimated by adding arms imports to data on military expenditures, which are believed to exclude arms purchases. However, it should be noted that the value of arms deliveries in a given year may differ significantly from actual expenditures on arms imports in that year.

2—This ratio is calculated from the dollar values shown in previous columns. In most cases it also is equal to the ratio that could be calculated from national currency values, since both numerator and denominator are usually converted into dollars by the same exchange rate or other conversion factor. In the case of this country, however, the two variables are converted at different rates, yielding a different ratio than would obtain in national currency. The ratio for Russia in rubles terms, for example, is believed to be less than 10 percent in 1995.

3—This series or entry is believed to omit a major share of total military expenditures, probably including most expenditures on arms procurement.

4—Germany, (The Federal Republic of), was known as West Germany through 1990. Thereafter, Germany refers to the unified Germany.

5—In order to reduce distortions in the trend for worked, region, and organization totals caused by

data gaps for individual countries and years, rough approximations for all gaps are included in the totals.

6—To avoid the appearance of excessive accuracy, arms transfer data by country are rounded, with greater severity for larger amounts. All country group totals for arms exports and arms imports shown here are the sums of rounded country data. Consequently, world totals for arms imports and arms exports will not be equal.

7—Total imports and exports usually are as reported by individual countries and the extent to which arms transfers are included is often uncertain. Imports are reported "cif" (including cost of shipping, insurance, and freight) and exports are reported "fob" (excluding these costs). For these reasons and because of divergent sources, world totals for imports and exports are not equal.

8—Because some countries exclude arms imports or exports from their trade statistics and their "total" imports and exports are therefore understated, and because arms transfers may be estimated independently for trade data, the resulting ratios of arms to total imports or exports may be overstated and may even exceed 100 percent.

9—Some part of estimated total military expenditures may not be included in announced central budget expenditures. The ratio of ME to CGE therefore may be overstated.

10—Included major equipment purchased by the U.S. Army Corps of Engineers for use in military construction projects in Saudi Arabia, recorded in U.S. accounts as U.S. imports.

11—U.S. arms imports data shown here is revised upward substantially form reports before 1993.

12—Little data are available because of an ongoing civil war.

CRIME—15

SOURCE. Crime Prevention and Criminal Justice Division, United Nations Criminal Justice Information Network (UNCJIN), *The Fifth United Nations Survey of Crime Trends and Operations of Criminal Justice Systems* [Online], Available: http://www.uncjin.org/stats/wcs.html [October 1999]. Reprinted with permission.

NOTES.

The major goal of the Fifth United Nations Survey is to collect data on the incidence of reported crime and the operations of criminal justice systems with a view to improving the dissemination of that information globally. To that end, the Survey should facilitate an overview of trends and interrelationships between various parts of the criminal justice system so as to promote informed decision making in its administration, nationally and cross-nationally.

As with data collected for the Fourth United Nations Survey, these data demonstrate the difficulty of comparing crime internationally. One difficulty is that the vast majority of incidents that become known to the police come from reports by victims. Thus, credibility becomes a statistical determinant. Another difficulty is that comparison is severely undermined by differences in legal definitions and by administrative procedures regarding counting, classification, and disclosure. The researcher should be aware of these shortcomings when using these data.

NA—Data are not available.

TOTAL LABOR FORCE—16

SOURCE. U.S. Central Intelligence Agency (CIA) 1998, *The World Factbook 1998* [Online]. Available: http://www.cia.gov/cia/publications/factbook/index.html [October 1999].

NOTES.

Data show the number of persons in the labor force for the most recent year available.

NA—Data are not available.

UNEMPLOYMENT RATE—17

SOURCE. U.S. Central Intelligence Agency (CIA) 1998, *The World Factbook 1998* [Online]. Available: http://www.cia.gov/cia/publications/factbook/index.html [October 1999].

NOTES.

Data show the rate of unemployment in percent for the most recent year available.

NA—Data are not available.

ENERGY PRODUCTION—18

SOURCE. U.S. Central Intelligence Agency (CIA) 1998, *The World Factbook 1998* [Online]. Available: http://www.cia.gov/cia/publications/factbook/index.html [October 1999].

NOTES.

Btu—British thermal units.

TRANSPORTATION—19

SOURCE. U.S. Central Intelligence Agency (CIA) 1998, *The World Factbook 1998* [Online]. Available: http://www.cia.gov/cia/publications/factbook/index.html [October 1999].

NOTES.

Following are CIA definitions of terms used in these tables.

Airports—Only airports with usable runways are included in this listing. Not all airports have facilities for refueling, maintenance, or air traffic control. Paved runways have concrete or asphalt surfaces; unpaved runways have grass, dirt, sand, or gravel surfaces.

DWT—Deadweight tons.

GRT—Gross register tons.

km—Kilometers.

m—Meters.

Merchant marine—All ships engaged in the carriage of goods. All commercial vessels (as opposed to all nonmilitary ships), which excludes tugs, fishing vessels, offshore oil rigs, etc. Also, a grouping of merchant ships by nationality or register.

NA—Data are not available.

TOP AGRICULTURAL PRODUCTS—20

SOURCE. U.S. Central Intelligence Agency (CIA) 1998, *The World Factbook 1998* [Online]. Available: http://www.cia.gov/cia/publications/factbook/index.html [October 1999].

NOTES.

GDP—Gross Domestic Product: the value of all goods and services produced within a nation in a given year.

GDP & MANUFACTURING SUMMARY—21

SOURCE. United Nations Industrial Development Organization (UNIDO), *Industrial Development Global Report 1996*, pages 129—254. Reprinted with permission.

NOTES.

Gross domestic product (GDP)—All economic activity in a given country, including activity engaged in by foreign nationals. For example, assets of a General Motors plant in Mexico would contribute to Mexico's GDP. *Real GDP* measures economic activity in constant prices, that is, after adjustments for inflation.

Manufacturing value added (MVA)—The value of output minus the cost of raw materials and other inputs.

FOOTNOTES.

1—Value originating from the National Accounts Statistics.

2—In 1990 constant prices.

3—The data presented here are for activities in the former Federal Republic of Germany and do not include those of the former Democratic Republic of Germany, even after unification in 1990.

Numbers in *italics*—Estimated by UNIDO, Research and Publication Division, Research and Studies Branch.

NA—No value available.

——Value is less than half a unit.

ECONOMIC INDICATORS—22

SOURCE. U.S. Central Intelligence Agency (CIA) 1998, *The World Factbook 1998* [Online]. Available: http://www.cia.gov/cia/publications/factbook/index.html [October 1999].

NOTES.

Following are CIA definitions of acronyms and terms used in these tables.

est.—Estimate.

External debt—The amount of debt owed to foreign entities by the given country.

GDP—Gross domestic product: the value of all goods and services produced within a nation in a given year. Methodology: GDP dollar estimates for all countries are derived from purchasing power parity (PPP) calculations rather than from conversions at official currency exchange rates. The PPP method involves the use of international dollar price weights, which are applied to the quantities of goods and services produced in a given economy. The data derived from the PPP method provide a better comparison of economic well-being between countries. The division of a GDP estimate in domestic currency by the corresponding PPP estimate in dollars gives the PPP conversion rate. When priced in PPPs, $1,000 will buy the same market basket of goods in any country. Whereas PPP estimates for OECD countries are quite reliable, PPP estimates for developing countries are often rough approximations. Most of the GDP estimates are based on extrapolation of numbers published by the UN International Comparison Program and by Professors Robert Summers and Alan Heston of the University of Pennsylvania and their colleagues. Note: the numbers for GDP and other economic data can not be chained together from successive volumes of the *Factbook* because of changes in the U.S. dollar measuring rod, revisions of data by statistical agencies, use of new or different sources of information, and changes in national statistical methods and practices.

Inflation rate—An increase in prices unrelated to value.

NA—Data are not available.

National product—The total output of goods and services in a given country. (See gross domestic product).

BALANCE OF PAYMENTS SUMMARY—23

SOURCE. United Nations Conference on Trade and Development, *Handbook of International Trade and Development Statistics*, pages 214–241.

NOTES.

The following explanatory notes are intended to provide a brief description of the balance of payments categories presented. In actual practice, there are many exceptions to the definitions of categories, and for these the reader should refer to the country notes in the *Balance of Payments Yearbook*.

Exports of goods (fob)—The export figure here differs from that reported in the trade returns because of adjustments for coverage, valuation, timing, inland freight, etc. Such adjustments to the reported export and import figures are necessary in order to make the trade statistics compatible with the concepts employed in the balance of payments. In particular, valuation adjustments are required in those cases in which the market price at which goods have been sold differs from the price used for customs' purposes. This problem in valuation is probably more important for imports than for exports and is likely to be a factor whenever there is a long delay between the date of sale and the date at which an import duty becomes payable.

The coverage of goods in Balance of Payments Manual, 5th edition, has been expanded to include (a) the value of goods (on a gross basis) received/sent for processing and their subsequent export/import in the form of processed goods; (b) the value of repairs on goods; and (c) the value of goods procured in ports by carriers. In Balance of Payments Manual, 4th edition, the net value between goods imported for processing and subsequently re-exported was included in processing services; repairs of goods and goods procured in ports by carriers were also included under services.

Imports of goods (fob)—Adjustments for coverage, valuation, timing, etc., are made to imports reported in trade returns, as described in the notes above. In addition, an adjustment is made to convert imports from a cif to an fob basis for those countries reporting imports cif. The import figures reported here include imports of non-monetary gold.

Balance of goods—Measured on a fob/fob basis and including transactions in monetary gold.

Services and income-debit (total)—Total payments for services and income.

The Balance of Payments Manual, 5th edition, classifies income and services separately; in Balance of Payments Manual, 4th edition, income was a subcomponent of services. Balance of Payments Manual, 5th edition, also reclassifies certain income and services transactions. In Balance of Payments Manual, 4th edition, labor income included non-resident workers' expenditures as well as workers' earnings; in Balance of Payments Manual, 5th edition, workers' earnings are classified under compensation of employees in the income category, and their expenditures appear under travel services. In Balance of Payments Manual, 4th edition, compensation of resident staff of foreign embassies and military bases and of international organizations was included under government services; this compensation is classified as a credit item of compensation of employees in Balance of Payments Manual, 5th edition. Balance of Payments Manual, 4th edition, treated payments for the use of patents, copyrights, and similar non-financial intangible assets as property income; these are regarded as subcomponents of other services in Balance of Payments Manual, 5th edition. In general, the Balance of Payments Manual, 5th edition, concept of income covers investment income plus all forms of compensation of employees; whereas, in Balance of Payments Manual, 4th edition, the concept included investment income, most forms of labor income (including workers' expenditures abroad), and property income.

Services and income-credit (total)—Counterpart to service and income-debit (total).

Current transfers: government-net—Current transfers are classified, according to the sector of the compiling economy, into two main categories: general government and other sectors. General government transfers comprise current international cooperation, which covers current transfers—in cash or in kind—between governments of different economies or between governments and international organizations.

Current transfers: other sectors-net—Current transfers between other sectors of an economy and non-residents comprise those occurring between individuals, between non-governmental institutions or organizations (or between the two groups), or between non-resident governmental institutions and individuals or non-governmental institutions. The same basic items (described in paragraphs 298 to 300 of the IMF Manual) for the government sector are generally applicable to other sectors, although there are some differences within components. In addition, there is the category of workers' remittances.

Balance of current account—Covered in the current account are all transactions (other than those in financial items) that involve economic values and occur between resident and non-resident entities. Also covered are offsets to current economic values provided or acquired without a quid pro quo. Specifically, the major classifications are goods and services, income, and current transfers.

FOOTNOTES.

f.o.b—Free On Board, i.e., the value of goods does not include insurance and freight charges.

..—Data are not available.

———Data are nil or negligible.

EXCHANGE RATES—24

SOURCE. U.S. Central Intelligence Agency (CIA) 1998, *The World Factbook 1998* [Online]. Available: http://www.cia.gov/cia/publications/factbook/index.html [October 1999].

NOTES.

Following are CIA definitions of acronyms and terms used in these tables.

Exchange rate—The official value of a nation's monetary unit, at a given date or over a given period of time, as expressed in units of local currency per U.S. dollar and as determined by international market forces or official fiat. These often have little relation to domestic output. In developing countries with weak currencies, the exchange rate estimate in GDP (gross domestic product) in dollars is typically one-fourth to one-half the PPP (purchasing power parity) estimate. Although exchange rates may suddenly go up or down by 10% or more, real output

may have remained unchanged. On January 12, 1994, for example, the 14 countries of the African Financial Community (whose currencies are tied to the French franc) devalued their currencies by 50%. This move, of course, did not cut the real output of their countries by half.

BMR—Black Market rate.

NA—Data are not available.

SOURCE. U.S. Central Intelligence Agency (CIA) 1998, *The World Factbook 1998* [Online]. Available: http://www.cia.gov/cia/publications/factbook/index.html [October 1999].

NOTES.

Top import origins are distributed in percent when data are available.

Following are CIA definitions of the acronyms and terms used here.

BLEU—Belgium-Luxembourg Economic Union.

Caricom—Caribbean Community and Common Market.

CEMA—Council for Mutual Economic Assistance; also known as CMEA or Comecon.

c.i.f.—Cost, insurance, freight.

CIS—Commonwealth of Independent States.

CMEA—Council for Mutual Economic Assistance; also known as CEMA or Comecon.

ECOWAS—Economic Community of West African States.

EFTA—European Free Trade Association.

est.—Estimate.

EU—European Union.

f.o.b.—Free on board.

FSU—Former Soviet Union.

NA—Data are not available.

OECD—Organization for Economic Cooperation and Development.

OECS—Organization of Eastern Caribbean States.

OPEC—Organization of Petroleum Exporting Countries.

SACU—South African Customs Union.

UAE—United Arab Emirates.

UK—United Kingdom.

U.S.—United States.

U.S.S.R.—Union of Soviet Socialist Republics (Soviet Union).

TOP EXPORT—26

SOURCE. U.S. Central Intelligence Agency (CIA) 1998, *The World Factbook 1998* [Online]. Available: http://www.cia.gov/cia/publications/factbook/index.html [October 1999].

NOTES.

Top export destinations are distributed in percent when data are available.

Following are CIA definitions of the acronyms and terms used in these tables.

BLEU—Belgium-Luxembourg Economic Union.

Caricom—Caribbean Community and Common Market.

CEMA—Council for Mutual Economic Assistance; also known as *CEMA* or *Comecon*.

c.i.f.—Cost, insurance, freight.

CIS—Commonwealth of Independent States.

CMEA—Council for Mutual Economic Assistance; also known as *CEMA* or *Comecon*.

ECOWAS—Economic Community of West African States.

EFTA—European Free Trade Association.

est.—Estimate.

EU—European Union.

f.o.b.—Free on board.

FSU—Former Soviet Union.

NA—Data are not available.

OECD—Organization for Economic Cooperation and Development.

OECS—Organization of Eastern Caribbean States.

OPEC—Organization of Petroleum Exporting Countries.

SACU—South African Customs Union.

UAE—United Arab Emirates.

UK—United Kingdom.

U.S.—United States.

U.S.S.R.—Union of Soviet Socialist Republics (Soviet Union).

FOOTNOTES.

f.o.b—Free on board, i.e., the value of goods does not include insurance and freight charges.

..—Data are not available.

———Data are nil or negligible.

FOREIGN AID—27

SOURCE. U.S. Central Intelligence Agency (CIA) 1998, *The World Factbook 1998* [Online]. Available: http://www.cia.gov/cia/publications/factbook/index.html [October 1999].

NOTES.

Following are CIA definitions of terms used in these tables.

Donor—Country that pledges official economic aid to another country.

NA—Data are not available.

ODA—Official development assistance. ODA refers to financial assistance which is concessional in characters, has the main objective of promoting economic development and welfare in less developed countries (LDCs), and contains a grant element of at least 25 percent.

OOF—Other official flows. OOF also refers to official government assistance, but with a main objective other than development and with a grant element less than 25 percent. Transactions include official export credits (such as Export-Import Bank credits), official equity and portfolio investment, and debt reorganization by the official sector that does not meet concessional terms. Aid is considered to have been committed when the parties involved initial agreements constituting a formal declaration of intent.

Recipient—Country that receives official economic aid from another country.

IMPORT AND EXPORT COMMODITIES—28

SOURCE. U.S. Central Intelligence Agency (CIA) 1998, *The World Factbook 1998* [Online]. Available: http://www.cia.gov/cia/publications/factbook/index.html [October 1999].

NOTES.

Category 39: *Top Import Origins* and Category 40: *Top Export Destinations* provide corresponding year of commodity imports/exports respectively.

When available, commodities are distributed in percent.

1999 YEAR IN REVIEW

The last year of the twentieth century, 1999 was a year to reflect on the events of the decade and of the century. It offered significant anxiety resulting from Y2K technology issues and the economic dislocations produced in previous years. During 1999 much of Asia continued on the path to economic recovery in the aftermath of the Asian Financial Crisis. Some countries recovered much more quickly than others, but the vast majority of Asian nations experienced significant economic growth. For eastern Europe, Latin America, and Africa the economic picture was filled with more uncertainty as they faced recession, reform, and unemployment woes. Latin American economies fell into a recession early in 1999, but many began a slow turnaround to growth by the fourth quarter. The nations of eastern Europe that had successfully adopted liberal economic reform throughout the 1990s performed admirably in comparison to Russia and other reform laggards. In Russia the economic situation deteriorated during most of the year, but was assisted by an infusion of Western funds in the second half of the year.

In the political realm, the strong forces of nationalism and ethnic identity clashed with the centralizing forces of globalization. As politics enters the twenty-first century the definition of what makes a nation-state and the constraints imposed by the process of globalization will continue to create new forms of political conflict and exacerbate old conflicts, such as the ethnic strife which afflicted Rwanda and states of the former Yugoslavia in the 1990s. The demarcation between domestic and international politics will continue to blur, as the events in 1999 attest.

Economic and social issues have significant impacts on the politics of a country. The outflow of capital from developing nations had a worsening effect on many countries around the world. Political instability was acute in parts of Latin America, including Peru, Ecuador, and Brazil. In Asia, Indonesia's government experienced successive crises of legitimacy before launching a new democracy. On the African continent, Nigeria, long a military state, returned to civilian rule, and South Africa consolidated its democratic foundation with its second all-race elections. The western nations of Europe, moving towards further economic integration under the European Union, faced a powerful backlash from labor unions while continuing to tout the benefits of unionization to a concerned and dubious public. NATO was reinvigorated by the addition of new members, but experienced division over the alliance's new direction of collective action in Kosovo. Ending the year with surprise, the first democratically elected president of Russia, Boris Yeltsin, resigned on December 31, 1999, signaling a changing-of-the-guard in Russian politics.

Most societies spent 1999 recovering from various crises related to emerging markets. Asian nations moved firmly toward economic recovery in the early part of the year, while Latin America and eastern Europe in particular faced continued social instability brought on by economic uncertainty. Countries in western Europe, in particular the United Kingdom and Germany, faced increased unemployment. Though its economy remained stable, Japan's society distressed over alarming statistics about increased depression, suicide, and violence. The United States, experiencing an unprecedented economic high, faced social lows with a concerning increase in school violence and the perceived threat of terrorism from abroad, which heightened considerably as 1999 drew to a close.

Nature brought its own woes to the world in a series of natural disasters, including flooding and mud slides throughout many Latin American countries, in particular Venezuela; powerful and damaging wind storms sweeping across Europe; and serious earthquakes in Taiwan, Turkey, and Greece. These natural disasters did succeed in bringing about significantly increased international cooperation and at times even reopened previously closed venues of communication and negotiation, as in the case of Turkey and Greece. As the twentieth century and, for some, the millenium, drew to a close most countries overlooked economic, political, and social problems for a day and engaged in elaborate celebrations on New Year's Eve, ushering in a new era.

As we step into the twenty-first century the forces of globalization, including the communication revolution spearheaded by the Internet; mergers, acquisitions, and privatization fueled by capital flows; and an emerging global production system are clearly affecting the world's nations, both economically and politically.

POLITICS AND GOVERNMENT

Major themes of politics and government throughout the world in 1999 included global economic harmonization, democratic transitions and consolidations, and the negative economic and social effects of globalization. At the dawn of the twenty-first century the record of governance among nation-states remained one of stark dichotomies. While advanced post-industrial nations such as Great Britain, Germany, France, the United States, Canada, Australia, and Japan managed to find solutions to pressing political problems, much of the developing world suffered with governments unable to create the necessary responses to economic and political crises. Some nations, including Sierra Leone and Zaire, suffered from state collapse, while others such as Indonesia, Malaysia, and Ecuador saw governmental legitimacy plummet.

Europe

Throughout 1999 the pressures of economic harmonization affected politics. With much of Europe in an early stage of a recession during the first half of 1999, many governments faced economic, political, and social difficulties. Western European governments sought to conform with European Union (EU) requirements of low budget deficits and stringent fiscal and monetary policies highlighted by the introduction of the single European monetary unit, the euro. As currency analysts suggested that many policy coordination difficulties continued to plague the EU the euro declined in value throughout the year and slipped below par with the U.S. dollar.

In Germany, Oscar LaFontaine, the Social Democratic Party (SPD) leader and Finance Minister under Gerhard Schröder, resigned. In June Germany hosted the G-7 meeting, which followed an

meeting of the European Union promising an infusion of cash into eastern Europe. Given the continuing costs of re-integrating eastern Germany into the republic and the overall sluggishness of the nation's economy, however, it remained unlikely that Germany would be able to provide the significant capital necessary for further economic reconstruction in eastern Europe.

While it continues to struggle with a lagging economy and putting a once divided nation back together again, German leadership has seen its approval ratings decline. In July, Johannes Rau became the first SPD president of Germany in three decades. Within the SPD and Green coalition government, Chancellor Schröder and Foreign Minister Joschka Fischer opposed each other on the issue of NATO attacks in Kosovo and Serbia, contributing to the diminishing popularity of the current government, and the Greens lost its majority in the Bundesrat (upper house). In April, Germany moved its parliament from Bonn to the pre-World War II capital of Berlin, beginning a new era in a united Germany.

Germany was not alone in experiencing declining governmental legitimacy. In Greece the government of Prime Minister Costas Simitis was reshuffled in March amidst a wave of strikes in opposition to EU fiscal conformity measures. Simitis' Panhellenic Socialist Movement (PASOK) cut social spending, and his legitimacy subsequently declined. Furthermore, Greek public opinion overwhelmingly opposed the government's support of the NATO campaign in Kosovo. Similarly, the war in Kosovo also caused political turmoil in France as Philippe Seguin of the Rally for the Republic (Gaullists) resigned in reaction to the new government coalition with the Socialist Party (PS), led by Prime Minister Lionel Jospin.

In eastern Europe, countries that had pursued a pro-Western policy since the end of the Cold War and implemented liberal economic reforms performed better than those that sought to maintain the vestiges of communism. Russia and less social and economically integrated nations such as Belarus and Serbia experienced acute political and economic instability, while Poland, the Baltic Republics, and Slovenia continued to become more integrated with western Europe.

NATO expansion is seen by many former communist bloc nations as a symbol of security and achievement in the post-Cold War world. NATO expanded its membership in 1999 to include Hungary, the Czech Republic, and Poland. In order to enter NATO Hungary beefed up its military spending to professionalize its defense forces and reduced its troop strength from 160,000 to 60,000. Preliminary plans were made for the eventual acceptance of Romania.

Focusing on economic rather than military goals, the European Union's expansion is likely to rival that of NATO's over the next three to five years, as many European nations prepare their governments, economies, and peoples for more complete integration within the organization.

Meanwhile, the virtual collapse of the Russian economy created increased political instability for many former Soviet republics. In October gunmen stormed the parliament of Armenia, killing eight political leaders, including Prime Minister Sarkisian and parliamentary speaker Karen Demirchyan. The Republic of Georgia, frustrated with the inadequacies of the Commonwealth of Independent States (CIS), suggested an end to cooperation. Georgia also faced the attempted assassination of President Eduard Shevardnadze and a series of major explosions including a powerful bomb in Sukhuni, the capital of Abkhazia, a renegade region of the country. In Croatia, President Tudjman, who had sought the country's entry into the EU, died and Croatia entered into successful democratic elections.

Russia, long a powerful force in the region, contended with successionist movements, economic difficulty, and criminal activity throughout 1999, which weakened the legitimacy of the state. As Russia gradually recovered from the worst of the 1998 economic crisis, it remained hampered by President Boris Yeltsin's declining health and the renewal of war in the Russian province of Chechnya. Continued economic stagnation and a series of apartment bombings in Moscow and several other Russian cities demoralized the public, which suffered from high unemployment and inflation. In addition, it was revealed that substantial sums of monies obtained through international aid agencies were being diverted to banks outside of Russia, hindering rather than helping the struggling economy.

In a surprise move, Boris Yeltsin resigned from the presidency on December 31 and Prime Minister Vladimir Putin was appointed acting-president until elections could be held in March. Putin, who was appointed prime minister in the latter half of 1999, quickly rose to prominence and popular-

ity. In early 2000 he was the strongest candidate for the March elections.

Despite its change in leadership, the Russian government maintains many of the same policies and continues to support the Serbian regime of Slobodan Milosevic. Russia was vehemently opposed to the NATO led attacks on Serbia, which began on March 24, 1999, in support of the Kosovar rebels. On June 12 the bombings halted as Milosevic ceded to NATO demands, leading to the deployment of NATO's KFOR into Kosovo to maintain order and establish governance for the province. Meanwhile, the United Nations in Bosnia and Herzegovina (UNIBH) continued to maintain order in what remained an ethnically polarized environment in 1999.

Americas

In the United States, political division became a permanent feature of 1999 with the impeachment of President Bill Clinton. Clinton was impeached by the House of Representatives after the alternatives of censure, request for resignation, and other punitive measures failed to muster the necessary majority. As expected, however, the Senate acquitted the president on House charges of obstruction of justice and grand jury perjury. Split along party lines, with a few Republican defections against impeachment, the vote was split 50 to 55 on each count, far short of the necessary two-thirds majority required for a president's removal from office. A politically crippled president and a cantankerous Congress failed to pass any major initiatives in 1999, including a tax cut touted by Republicans.

Preparing for what is already a highly scrutinized senate campaign, the Clintons purchased a home in New York in anticipation of First Lady Hillary Rodham Clinton's run for the Senate seat of Patrick Moynihan. Meanwhile, the presidential campaign season picked up steam as the Republican field narrowed to two primary candidates, George Bush, Jr., and Arizona Senator John McCain. Frontrunners for the Democratic Party were Vice President Al Gore and former congressman Bill Bradley.

Comforted by an unprecedented balanced budget for 1999 and a rapidly growing economy and stock market, America's attention seemed focused away from domestic politics. On the international scene, the United States successfully orchestrated a NATO supported and coordinated attack on Serbia and reopened peace talks between Israel and Syria.

The governments and politics of both Canada and Mexico benefited from the continued economic growth in the United States. Of major importance to Canadian politics in 1999 was the creation of a new province, Nunvat, in northern Canada, while the predominantly French province of Québec continued to make rumblings for independence. Mexico and Latin America remained engaged in the "War on Drugs," with significant political fallout. Colombia, a large recipient of U.S. aid, continued to fight rebels who controlled much of the drug-producing regions of the country. In the U.S. Congress, aid to Colombia was debated, pointing to the dubious reputation of the nation's military and the ever-tenuous political situation in the country.

In an effort to resolve the country's political turmoil Colombian president Pastrana opened talks with the Revolutionary Armed Forces of Columbia (FARC) to end an ongoing thirty-five year civil war which has seen atrocities committed on both sides. Despite political debate, the United States pledged $1 billion in emergency assistance to the country in July to curb drug trafficking and bolster the government's effort to stabilize the country's economy and politics.

Aid to Latin American countries is often linked to a nation's cooperation with the U.S. "War on Drugs." Despite opposition from members of Congress, President Clinton decided not to penalize Mexico for its questionable degree of co-operation with U.S. drug policies and opened the way for a continued influx of economic and foreign aid to the country. In February Mexico announced a spending plan for $500 million to combat illegal drug trafficking, while in March President Ernesto Zedillo marked the 70th anniversary of the ruling political party, PRI, with an announcement that the party would conduct national primaries to select presidential candidates.

In Brazil, continuing economic problems weakened the government despite the Brazilian *real* becoming pegged to the U.S. dollar. President Cardoso's popularity, as evidenced in his 1998 election, vanished as the International Monetary Fund (IMF) was forced to rescue the Brazilian currency as the economy spiraled downward. Socially, significant public attention in Brazil focused on the Landless Peasants movement, an attempt to seek land reform and alleviate the continuing high levels of poverty and unemployment.

Adverse economic conditions also affected Argentina and Chile, whose political legitimacy was weakened by economic problems. Chile, in recession, experienced its first budget deficit in thirteen years in 1999, and Argentine president Carlos Menem's popularity hit an all-time low during the year as the country's economy continued to flounder.

Asia and Middle East

Politics and government in Asia and the Middle East demonstrated both continuance and major changes. There were numerous positive signs regarding democracy in Asia during 1999, but declining social and economic conditions in many countries led to concerns about globalization. Sudden leadership changes in the region sometimes overshadowed these concerns, as did renewed conflicts between India and Pakistan and between China and Taiwan. Indonesia experienced internal political and economic turmoil coupled with leadership change and the arrival of an Australian-led UN force in the de facto independent region of East Timor.

Two potential pariah nations, North Korea and Iraq, continued to face censure from world leaders and organizations. As the result of international sanctions and poor economic management North Korea suffered from famine and economic collapse, but still managed to launch missiles across the Sea of Japan in 1998, and threatened to do so again in 1999.

The United States and NATO continued to maintain "no fly zones" in southern and northern Iraq, effectively maintaining the boundaries established at the end of the Gulf War until Iraqi leader Saddam Hussein complies with all points of the UN Security Council's resolution obligations. The embargo on Iraq continued to damage the country's economy, despite calls from Saudi Arabia, among others, for its end.

Also in the Middle East, Israel experienced a major change in political leadership which led to the resumption of discussions with Syria over the issue of "peace for land" in December. In Jordan, King Hussein, a major partner in promoting peace and stability in the Middle East, died in February and was replaced by his son, Prince Abdullah.

In Asia, human rights violations in China, Myanmar, Vietnam, Afghanistan, and Malaysia drew international attention. Riots took place in Beijing and cities across China when NATO forces accidentally bombed the Chinese embassy in Serbia in the latter half of 1999. Riots also occurred in

Malaysia when former deputy prime minister Anwar Ibrahim was sentenced to six years in prison.

Japan's government continued to be at a loss in dealing with a lingering recession despite repeated official pronouncements that recovery was forthcoming. Despite the low approval ratings and a humiliating local elections defeat in April for the ruling Liberal Democratic Party, the LDP leadership, including Obuchi Keizo, remained in firm control over the Diet, Japan's national assembly. In January, the LDP invited the opposition Liberal Party, headed by Ozawa Ichiro, to join the coalition. Subsequently, in June Ozawa and Obuchi approached the Clean Government Party (CGP), also known as New Komieto, to participate in a grand coalition. Under this new coalition the Japanese Diet passed legislation in August to make Japan's flag and national anthem official, despite lingering concern by neighboring states about the lack appropriate remorse and admission of guilt by Japan's leadership for World War II atrocities. Concerns about Japan's role in the world, however, did not affect its decision to become a more active player in international and regional affairs.

China also indicated a willingness for greater involvement with the world, but it also desires to maintain tight control over its domestic affairs. When 10,000 people gathered around Zhongnanhai, the headquarters of the religious sect Falun Gong, the Chinese government summarily arrested its leaders and declared the cult illegal. This action garnered much international attention and disapproval for the government's human rights violations.

The People's Republic of China (PRC) celebrated its 50th anniversary in September and raised the level of nationalist fervor in the country following Taiwan's desire to seek relations with China on a state-to-state basis. Taiwan is considered by the PRC to be a rogue province rather than the independent state Taiwan claims itself to be. The proposal for state-to-state relations aggravated relations between the mainland and the island.

Though China's economy remained relatively firm against the onslaught of the 1997–98 Asian Financial Crisis, both South Korea and Indonesia felt its effects. But unlike Indonesia, South Korea was able to reform its economy and begin to pay back its external debt. Turmoil entered South Korea's National Assembly when President Kim Dae-Jung's ruling National Congress for New Politics locked horns with the opposition, the United Liberal Democrats, and resorted to passing legislation unilaterally. As a result, opposition leaders charged that democracy was being weakened.

In Indonesia, separatist movements in Aceh, Irian Jaya, and East Timor and violent protests in Jakarta by students and workers destabilized the fragile regime of B. J. Habibie. In June elections, the ruling party—Golkar—was defeated by Megawati Sukarnoputri's Indonesian Democratic Party. Habibie lost the support of the military and his party and left office in October after a legislative vote of no confidence. Abdurrahman Wahid, a cleric, and Megawati were elected president and vice-president respectively. Meanwhile, the referendum for independence in East Timor led to chaos in the country as the Indonesian military backed militia in the region embarked on a campaign of terror and destruction, resulting in a serious refugee situation. On September 20, 1999, almost a month after the Timorese decided overwhelmingly for independence, UN troops consisting mostly of an Australian contingent entered East Timor to stabilize the region.

One of the most troubling political events in Asia was the renewed conflict between India and Pakistan. Despite discussions between India's Prime Minister Vajpayee and Pakistan's Nawaz Sharif in February regarding the disputed territory of Kashmir, tensions flared in May when India accused Pakistan of sending infiltrators into Indian controlled territory. As elections neared for Vajpayee, who had by then become head of a minority government, the Indian leader stirred nationalist sentiments by criticizing Pakistan. The BJP (Hindu Nationalist Party)-led National Democratic Alliance soundly defeated the Congress Party in fall elections, and Vajpayee was sworn in as prime minister on October 13. Vajpayee's counterpart Nawaz Sharif did not fare as well. Blaming Sharif for increased corruption, failure in Kashmir, and nepotism in government contracts, the military launched a successful coup. General Pervez Musharaff, who was previously relieved as army chief, became the new leader and summarily placed Sharif under arrest.

Africa

The major political stories in Africa consisted of the continued consolidation of democracy in South Africa and the long awaited democratic transition in Nigeria. Given the potential of these two nations to become the economic superpowers of Africa and their leadership capacity, these events reflect positive changes for a continent neglected throughout the decade. Despite these positive trends several countries existed as "collapsed states." Somalia, Sudan, Liberia, Sierra Leone, Rwanda, and the Democratic Republic of Congo possess either no genuinely established governments or barely functioning ones. In Angola, rebel leader Jonas Savimbi continued to resist calls by the government to lay down arms.

In addition, Algeria's political stability remained tenuous, with intermittent violence and riots continuing even under the leadership of Abdelaziz Boutiflika, the first civilian to lead the country in thirty years. Egypt's President Hosni Mubarak easily won reelection in a presidential referendum, signaling support for his statesmanship since the assassination of Anwar Sadat in 1981. Opposition parties charged that the elections were not free or fair.

In Sierra Leone, ECOMOG (West African Peace Monitoring Group) was accused of human rights abuses, primarily perpetrated by unpaid Nigerian troops. Despite these problems, in late October ECOMOG forces withdrew from Liberia as the political situation there stabilized. Economic Community of West African States (ECOWAS), which is the parent organization of ECOMOG, has become an African success story as it continues to provide assistance to African nations. In April Guinea-Bissau's leadership asked ECOMOG to supervise and operate multiparty elections in that country.

Perhaps most surprising was the noticeable improvement of relations between Libya and the western world after Muammar Gaddafi allowed two men accused of the 1988 bombing of Pan Am flight 103 over Lockerbie, Scotland, to be tried by a Scottish court in the Netherlands. Immediately afterwards, flights in and out of Tripoli resumed with normalcy and discussions began for the end to the sanctions which have plagued Libya. In August, U.S. president Bill Clinton decided to drop Libya from its list of terrorist nations, while human rights groups urged the Libyan government to improve its record.

South Africa held its second all-race democratic elections in June, which resulted in the expected victory of Thabo Mbeki and the African National Congress (ANC). While the ANC fell short of a two-thirds majority, its strength in the National Assembly increased. In many provincial legislatures the ANC maintained solid majorities.

With the exception of Western Cape and KwaZulu-Natal provinces the ANC emerged as the dominant party in South African politics.

Nelson Mandela graduated to an unofficial senior statesman, and the enigmatic Mbeki began to govern an increasingly disunited ANC. The most surprising aspect of the elections consisted of white and coloreds abandoning the New National Party (NNP), with the NNP placing fourth overall. Meanwhile, the Democratic Party (DP) of Tony Leon emerged as the largest opposition party. In order to shore up a core constituency Leon pointed to the mismanagement of the government on national unity and accused the NNP of wavering in the face of increasing crime and other social problems. In doing so, he alienated a large sector of the population.

Nigeria also held elections in 1999, following years of military rule and misrule. In January the results of local elections showed that the People's Democratic Party had won control over most municipal governments, upsetting the supporters of former dictator Sani Abacha. In February Obasanjo Olusegun received 62 percent of the vote and became president, defeating Olu Falae. Despite some irregularities, international observers gave the elections their seal of approval. Upon election Obasanjo reformed the civil service by instituting a compulsory retirement program and began an anti-corruption drive.

BUSINESS AND ECONOMICS

During 1999 the dominant themes in the world of business and economics were mergers and acquisitions in Europe, internet commerce in the United States, Asia, and western Europe, and economic recession followed by fourth quarter recovery in the emerging markets. Asian stock markets in particular recovered from 1998s lows, and South Korean and Japanese markets performed particularly well. Latin America, eastern Europe, and Russia experienced major economic dislocations throughout the year.

Europe

The year 1999 saw the debut of the much heralded euro, a single monetary unit to be used throughout the European Union's (EU) member nations. The process of European integration, which began with the creation of European Steel and Coal Community (ESCC) in 1952 and the creation of the European Economic Community (EEC) was expanded by the Maastricht Treaty in

1992. The treaty sought to create a politically and socially unified Europe to parallel economic integration. Despite economic slowdown in Germany, the euro managed to hold its value at about par to the U.S. dollar.

Movement toward expanding European Union membership gained steam with an EU summit in Berlin, which allocated $70 billion in aid to east and central Europe. A group of twelve nations, including Hungary, the Czech Republic, and the Baltic republics, is slated to enter the EU by 2003. Unemployment continues to plague western Europe, and the harmonization of central and eastern European nations' economies with EU standards is likely to increase unemployment in those countries while decreasing social spending.

European integration was tested over agricultural issues and privatization in 1999. In the United Kingdom, a dispute over "mad cow" disease prevented the sale of British beef in continental Europe, and a Belgian dioxin scare plunged that country's agricultural industry into a deep recession, with losses of over $1 billion. In addition, concern over the loss of national economic control prompted Denmark to drop its participation in the euro. In the United Kingdom privatization issues continued, with a need for a more coordinated public-private partnership in railway management and the health system of mixed providers. A need for greater cost control and a crisis induced by a lack of funding and staff affected Britain's National Health Service.

Global firms in Europe did well in 1999. Finland's Nokia was just one of the many companies announcing large profits for the year. Mergers and acquisitions flurry also hit Europe in 1999. With the integration of the European economies, many companies sought to improve their competitive edge by expanding and partnering with host country corporations. In Sweden, Ford Motor Company acquired Volvo's car division, and Volvo purchased rival truck manufacturer Scania for $7.4 billion. In Denmark, insurance firms Unianmark and Tryg-Baltica merged, as did two dairy firms, MD Foods and Klover. In France, Banque Nationale Paris took control over Paribas, an event that seemed to symbolize the merger flurry as many formerly government-owned firms across different sectors of the economy merged in preparation for euro exclusivity. And in Germany, shopping on Sundays, previously not allowed, became part of the economic way of life.

In eastern Europe and Russia the economic picture was more unstable than that of the West. Central and eastern European nations seeking entry into the EU experienced monetary and fiscal stress, while reform laggard economies suffered, as seen in the Russian economy, which continued to sputter. The worsening economic picture in Russia resulted in an IMF emergency loan after the government stated it would be unable to make payments. Significant amounts of hard currency were smuggled out of the country beginning in 1994, and despite government investigations funds continued to leave Russia, further injuring its fragile economy. The government also defaulted on hard currency bonds during the year. Russia's capital loss in 1999 was estimated at $2 billion a month. In addition, the opening of a pipeline from Azerbaijan to Georgia, bypassing Russia, reduced that country's monopoly over oil transport to the Black Sea. In less dire straits, the Czech Republic, under Prime Minister Milos Zemin, embarked on a privatization plan and cut interest rates. The measures, however, failed to address the budget deficit as hoped.

Americas

While Europe and many emerging markets throughout the world started the year under pressure, the U.S. equities market benefited from the benign policies of Federal Reserve Chairman Alan Greenspan, who refrained from immediately increasing interest rates in fear of recession. As the U.S. economy continued its rapid expansion, however, the Federal Reserve tightened the money supply and warned investors about the overvalued stock market. Despite those concerns, both the Dow Industrial and NASDAQ indicators put the stock market at an all time high by the end of the year. The U.S. government also experienced a budgetary surplus for the first time since Lyndon Johnson's administration, and Congress debated about whether to shore up the Social Security program or provide a tax cut. Meanwhile, with significant amount of capital flowing into the United States and inflating equity prices, consumers went on a spending spree and the U.S. trade deficit soared.

In Latin America, a recessionary climate lasted until the fourth quarter of 1999. The strength of the U.S. economy helped pull many Latin American countries out of recession. Chile, for example, had its first budget deficit in thirteen years and unemployment reached 11 percent in June. The government, led by Eduardo Frei, passed a $90 million fiscal stimulus package and privatized water utilities and state-owned ports. Ecuador defaulted on its foreign debt in September and required an IMF bailout, while the pillar of the South American economy, Brazil, continued to experience instability. The *real* was devalued, and in August it reached its lowest point ever. Mexico also experienced economic difficulty, for which the IMF approved a $4.12 billion package. Argentina's unemployment rate reached 14.5 percent, and landless peasants staged numerous strikes. In a novel attempt to stabilize the economy, Argentine policymakers suggested adopting the U.S. dollar as the national currency. They soon realized, however, that fiscal and monetary autonomy would then be severely compromised.

Asia and Middle East

In East and Southeast Asia governments experienced renewed public faith as the economic recession caused by the 1997–98 Asian Financial Crisis ended in all but Indonesia. As a sign of recovery, Malaysia began to lift currency and financial restrictions imposed in the wake of the crisis. Some aftershocks of the crisis, however, could still be felt throughout Asia in the form of accumulated bad debt. During the summer of 1999 Daewoo, South Korea's second largest *chaebol* declared bankruptcy, highlighting the need for continued corporate reform. Earlier in the year Korea First Bank, which had become insolvent in 1998, was purchased by an American firm. In Thailand the government estimated that 46 percent of all bank loans consisted of bad debt, and in China the government launched a plan to restructure debt-saddled banks and allowed Guangdong International Trust to collapse. Throughout 1999, Asian governments continued to manage these and other aftereffects of the crisis.

Perhaps the strongest area of Asian growth came from the computer and information based industries, which exploded onto the scene throughout the region. In November, Hong Kong launched a Growth Enterprise Market consisting of the stocks of small over-the-counter firms. At the same time, Cyberport—a $1.6 billion industrial park for high-tech firms—was created. In Malaysia the government announced the opening of Cyberjava, Southeast Asia's Silicon Valley. South Korea and Singapore, both seeking to diversify into the banking and finance sectors, established Internet banking. In Australia the government enacted a series of laws governing e-commerce privacy, copyright, and online content, and in New Zealand, despite

fallout from the Asian economic crisis, the government continued to refrain from intervening in ongoing mergers and foreign acquisitions, much to the delight of transnational corporations. For instance, Fletcher Challenge Canada Ltd. became the Pacific Rim's largest producer of ground-wood products with the September acquisition of numerous New Zealand paper mills, and Coca-Cola Co. purchased the bottling rights for Cadbury Schweppes brands in New Zealand.

The Japanese stock market saw initial public offerings of Internet stocks soar. Stock values were boosted by a merger frenzy in the financial realm, including the mega-merger of Fuji Bank, Dai-Ichi Kangyo Bank, and the Industrial Bank of Japan, as well as another merger involving Sakura and Sumitomo banks. After the announcement of the latest economic stimulus package, Japan finally appeared to be pulling out of its recession. A half percent increase in 2000's GDP was predicted.

While many South Korean *chaebols* were forced to restructure their financials and operations in 1999, the government continued to plough money into the weak banking system. As a result of economic restructuring, the unemployment rate jumped to 9 percent and numerous strikes broke out.

Taiwan's strong economy experienced dislocations due to a major earthquake which struck the Taipei area. It was, however, expected that rebuilding would actually add to the country's economy over the next few years.

The financial straits of oil producing states in the Middle East improved under OPEC agreements to cut production and the Iraqi refusal to sell more oil for food and necessities. And in Israel, significant oil reserves were located, creating a possible scenario for that country's self-sufficiency in energy.

Africa

Throughout sub-Saharan Africa, governments struggled to contain the AIDS epidemic, which siphoned off precious economic resources. In particular, Zambia, South Africa, Zimbabwe, and Malawi experienced an explosion of AIDS-related social and economic costs. With collapsed states in Sierra Leone, Somalia, and Zaire, the economic performance of most African countries was abysmal. Even the economic giants of Africa faced virtually impossible odds in resurrecting strong growth.

Zimbabwe's fiscal and monetary outlook deteriorated as President Mugabe's government became embroiled in the conflicts of neighboring Democratic Republic of Congo. Once considered the most promising economy north of South Africa, Zimbabwe struggled through 1999 as inflation and devaluation both reached close to 50 percent. In July the IMF provided $200 million to assist the government in balancing its budget and the African Development Bank provided a loan of $130 million.

Nigeria's economy inherited major debt after fifteen years of military misrule. As oil prices increased, however, Nigeria—like Gabon and Libya—benefited from increased revenue later in the year. The Nigerian government began a privatization program for many industries, including telecommunications. Corruption, however, is likely to play a major role in hampering the beleaguered country's return to economic growth.

In South Africa, foreign investment slowed, largely due to increased concern over crime, especially car jackings, murders, and rapes. Crime statistics suggest that South Africa has the world's highest murder rate among all industrialized nations. One of the major factors which accounted for the country's economic woes was the drop in the price of gold, facilitated in part by increased production and the decision by many central governments to unload gold onto the international market.

CULTURE AND SOCIETY
Europe

As if to symbolize the fear of American-style globalization, José Bove, leader of the French farm workers union, was arrested for trashing a McDonald's construction site in protest of American cultural imperialism. Though M. Bove protested U.S. economic policy, 1999 also saw numerous anti-American political protests in Greece, France, Russia, and Serbia resulting from U.S. actions in Kosovo.

The trend toward social, political, and economic integration was further confirmed by the Eurobarometer Survey released in March 1999. According to that survey, 52 percent of respondents stated that they expected the EU to play a greater role in their lives in the coming century, and the overwhelming majority of citizens believed that the EU should play a major role in dealing with transnational issues such as foreign policy, drug trafficking, and the maintenance of peace and security in Europe.

Throughout Europe the issue of gay and minority rights assumed prominence. In the United Kingdom a bomb exploded in a gay bar in London, killing three people and wounding seventy, and a report on institutionalized racism in the aftermath of the murder of Stephen Lawrence resulted in the implementation of an ethnic quota hiring system. Furthermore, the European Court of Human Rights declared that Britain's ban on homosexual military service violates the right to privacy. Across the channel in France, a crowd of 200,000 protested the court's decision to legalize gay marriages.

While social protests and divisions rose to prominence, steps towards resolution were also made on significant matter. After the severe earthquake in Turkey in August 1999, the Greek government provided humanitarian assistance to Turkey, with whom it has had a long-standing fued. When Greece suffered a severe earthquake in September, Turkey reciprocated by providing assistance through personnel and equipment. This mutual assistance opened the door for renewed hopes of reconciliation between the two countries.

Americas

In both the United States and Canada economic prosperity led to an overall decrease in crime and an increase in citizens' satisfaction with their lives. A United Nations report based on the human development index claimed that Canada was the best place in the world to live. And in Québec, for a time, secessionist fervor took a backstage to prosperity.

Canadian hockey icon Wayne Gretzky announced his retirement after a twenty-year career. A few months later in August representatives of the Canadian Ice Hockey Association held a three-day conference on improving the image and attractiveness of Canada's national sport.

The Canadian message for the year was increased social inclusiveness. The Aboriginal Peoples Television Network marked a long road toward the reconciliation between native peoples and the Canadian government. The cultural decentralization of Canada promised to lead to even greater cultural expression throughout the provinces, but may also lead to future conflict as each respective culture attempts to assert its distinctiveness.

Across the border in the United States a rash of high school violence involving teenage gunmen became a national crisis, especially after the massacre at Columbine high school in Colorado. Media coverage, including television, radio, newspapers, and news magazines, discussed the need for greater gun control and intervention for troubled youth. Despite these problems Americans continued to enjoy unprecedented economic prosperity, as evidenced by high levels of holiday spending.

A political first came from the world of American sports when the Baltimore Orioles played baseball against the Cuba's national team in April and May. The games marked the first time in forty years that an American professional baseball team played against Cuba. The games were held in still-communist Cuba, with whom the United States still refuses to normalize relations.

In contrast to the United States and Canada, Latin America experienced economic and social instability. Mexico, for instance, experienced increased crime and the effectiveness of its police force was criticized. Not only was the crime wave situation in Mexico City becoming worse, but human rights groups also reported that police brutality in the country had reached crisis proportions. In Argentina, a primarily Catholic nation, South America's largest mosque was constructed amidst some controversy. Also noteworthy was Nicaragua's destruction of 10,000 land mines and the official return of the Panama Canal to Panama at the end of 1999. While the return of the canal increased nationalism in Panama, American leaders largely ignored the event, much to Panamanian dismay. Neither President Bill Clinton, Vice President Al Gore, nor Secretary of State Madeline Albright attended the ceremonies.

Asia and Middle East

For years an explosion in the West, the Internet became an increasingly important tool for business and social communications throughout Asian society, despite attempts to control information by several Asian states such as Singapore, Malaysia, and China. The government's desire to control the flow of information can be evidenced in Malaysia, where the government forbade subscriptions to any magazine critical of the country's political leaders or system. In China the government cracked down on a religious sect, the Falun Gong, which used the Internet for much of its recruitment. These countries sought to create a filtered Internet system to limit the free flow of information.

Citizens benefited from an economic recovery sweeping through Asia, and the level of satisfaction with society increased markedly over 1998. At the same time, the lingering effects of the crisis could be seen in the record levels of unemployment in both Japan and South Korea. In Indonesia the economic picture improved only slightly, and ethnic violence made the nation unstable and daily food staples remained scarce for the poor and middle class.

Despite economic and social unrest in many countries, there were also numerous points of progress throughout Asia. Asia's largest concert hall opened at South Korea's Kyung Hee University, and three South Korean films were invited to compete at the 35th Chicago International Film Festival.

In a nuclear scare, Japan's experienced a nuclear accident in September, alarming the nation. The 300,000 residents of Tokaimura, where the accident occurred, were ordered to stay indoors. Long-term effects are thought to be minimal, though three people died from radiation exposure. The accident sparked debate over the need for nuclear facilities.

In Thailand, a country ravaged by the AIDS virus, a team of researchers commenced Phase III testing of a vaccine. The government reported that over one million people are infected with HIV. In a medical controversy, a Thai hospital was accused of trading human organs and harvesting them without the consent of patients.

Like many parts of Asia, governments in the Middle East struggled with similar problems related to the globalization of commerce and information. The United Arab Emirates (UAE) created Internet City, but remained concerned about the impact of information and globalization on the stability and social fabric of the nation. In Jordan the government promoted greater cultural openness by lifting a ban on literature thought to be offensive to Islam and Arabs. In Iran the Khatami government struggled to relax censorship of the press and certain cultural and social restrictions against opposition. In the patriarchal Saudi Arabia, women are now allowed to attend meetings of the consultative council and have access to the Internet.

Africa

Many countries in Africa experienced a rebirth through democracy and a greater openness toward social equality and human rights. A workshop held early in the year in Dakar, Senegal, sought to amend the African Human Rights Charter with a greater emphasis on equality between men and women. In Senegal, Tamaro Toure became the first woman to head the executive committee of the African region of International Planned Parenthood. The country also became the first in Africa to ban excision (female genitalia mutilation) despite objections from some legislators and religious leaders.

Contributing to social and human rights progress, Seychelles became the first country to ratify the International Labor Organization's treaty on standards for child labor, and increased political roles for women could be seen throughout sub-Saharan Africa.

Three famous sites in South Africa, including Robben Island, were designated as World Heritage Sites by UNESCO. Affirmative action continued to create discomfort among the white South African population, and few benefits resulted for the country's poor blacks. A new elite consisting of blacks and coloreds, however, emerged in the bureaucracy, businesses, and the military and became increasingly visible during 1999.

AFGHANISTAN

Islamic State of Afghanistan
Dowlat-e Eslami-ye Afghanestan

INTRODUCTORY SURVEY

RECENT HISTORY

Following World War II, King Mohammed Zahir Shah aligned his government with the Soviet Union and accepted extensive economic assistance. He was overthrown in 1973 by his cousin Mohammed Daoud, who in turn was overthrown in 1978 by Noor Taraki. Taraki and Babrak Karmal moved to Marxism. Islamic fundamentalists, however, opposed every move of each of these governments. Fearing collapse, Karmal requested Soviet troops and in December 1979, Moscow invaded the country to maintain communist control.

Pledging a jihad, or holy war, Islamic guerrillas fiercely fought the Soviet army occupation. The United States supported the resistance, funneling weapons through Pakistan, and the Soviet Union experience became very similar to the United States experience in Vietnam. In April, 1988, the Soviet Union, United States, Afghanistan, and Pakistan signed accords ending outside aid to the warring factions. The Soviet Union withdrew its troops in February of 1989.

In April of 1992, Islamic rebels ousted the Soviet backed government, but immediate infighting among the rebels delayed real control of the government. A faction called the Taliban seized control of the capital in September, 1996, imposing harsh Islamic law. The Taliban had control of about 90% of the country by late 1998. However, the remaining area is controlled by former president Burhanuddin Rabbani, whose government is still recognized by the United Nations as the legitimate

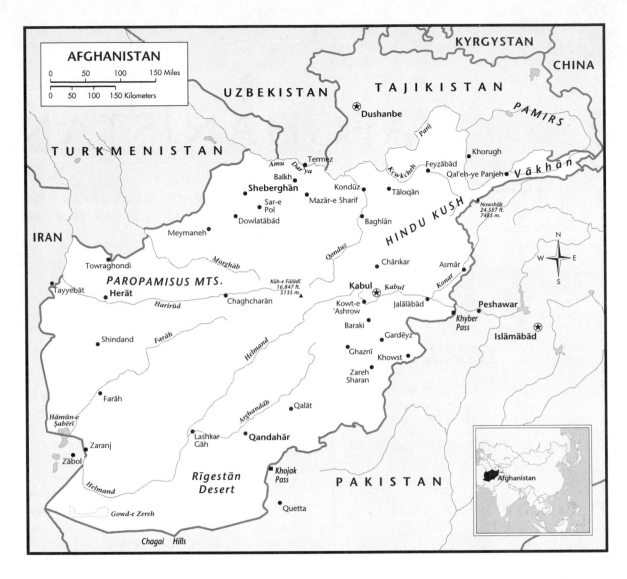

government of Afghanistan. Fighting among rebel factons and Rabbani continued into 1999.

The United States struck a terrorist training camp in Afghanistan with cruise missiles on August 20, 1998. The camp was believed to be financed and controlled by Osama bin Laden, an Islamic radical accused of the bombing of U.S. embassies. The Taliban protect bin Laden, and the attack did not result in his capture. Through 1999, the Taliban have concentrated on consolidating their control of the country. Only three countries have recognized its government as legitimate.

GOVERNMENT

No new constitution has been drafted since the end of the Najibullah government in 1997. The Taliban controlled all but the northernmost provinces of Afghanistan in early 1998. Mullah Mohammed Omar is the leader of the Taliban, which consists of a six-member ruling council in Kabul that rules by proclamation. Ultimate authority for the Taliban rests in Mullah Omar and the inner *Shura* (Assembly), located in Qandahar.

Judiciary

As of mid-1997 there was no rule of law. In areas under Taliban control, justice is based on the interpretation of Islamic law. In non-Taliban controlled areas, many municipal and provincial authorities rely on some form of Islamic law and traditional codes of justice. The administration and carrying out of justice varies from area to area and depends on the whims of local authorities.

Political Parties

There are no traditional political parties in Afghanistan. The Pashtun-dominated fundamentalist

Islamic Taliban movement controls Kabul. The Shia Hazara community, led by Abdul Karim Khalili, retains control over a small portion of central Afghanistan.

DEFENSE

There is currently no reliable estimate of Afghanistan's military weapons and expenditures, or the size and composition of any armed forces.

ECONOMIC AFFAIRS

Afghanistan's economy has been ruined by almost 20 years of war. Fully two thirds of the labor force is engaged in agriculture. Crops include wheat, fruit, nuts, karakul pelts, wool, and mutton. Small industries manufacture textiles, soap, furniture, shoes, fertilizer, cement, and handwoven carpets. Exploitable natural resources include natural gas, oil, coal, and copper.

Public Finance

Government budget breakdowns have not been available since 1979/80, when revenues totaled Af15,788 million and expenditures Af16,782 million.

Income

Gross Domestic Product (GDP) was estimated in 1997 at $19.3 billion, with a per capita estimate of just $800. Agriculture accounts for 65% of GDP, industry 15%, and services 20%.

Industry

The main modern industry is cotton textile production. There are small woolen and rayon textile industries. Carpet making is the most important handicraft industry. Other handicrafts include feltmaking and the weaving of cotton, wool, and silk cloth. Other industries are wheat flour processing, cement, raisin cleaning and fruit preservation, leather tanning, preparation of casings, sugar refining, and vegetable oil extraction.

Banking and Finance

The government central bank, the Bank of Afghanistan, founded in 1939 and with 65 branches throughout the country in 1996, issues bank notes, administers government loans, grants loans to municipalities and to other banks, and provides short-term loans. All banks in Afghanistan were nationalized in 1975. Foreign banks are not permitted in Afghanistan. Afghans may not own foreign securities. There is no organized domestic securities market.

Economic Development

Common to communist governments, five year plans were used to plan and control economic development in the post World War II era. The 1990/91 Action Plan was interrupted by civil war. The Taliban government has been consolidating its position and economic development has been postponed.

SOCIAL WELFARE

Social welfare in Afghanistan has traditionally relied on family and tribal organization. In 1996, the Taliban reversed a trend towards liberalization. Women are now only allowed to go out in public if they wear a long black garment with a veil covering the face. The Taliban have also banned girls from attending school, and have prohibited women from working outside the home. The Taliban also apply harsh measures against crime. Theft is punishable by amputation and public executions are used for more serious crimes.

Healthcare

Even before the war disrupted medical services, health conditions in Afghanistan were inadequate by western standards. Since 1980, volunteer medical programs from France, Sweden, the United States, and other countries have provided medical services to war-ravaged areas of Afghanistan. In 1992, only 29% of the population had access to health services. In 1992, estimated life expectancy was 45 years—one of the lowest in the world.

Housing

The war has severely damaged or destroyed countless houses. According to an official report, there were 200,000 dwellings in Kabul in the mid-1980s. The latest available figures for 1980–88 show a total housing stock of 3.5 million with 4.4 people per dwelling.

EDUCATION

Adult illiteracy in 1995 was estimated at 52.8% for men and 85% for women. Education is free at all levels. Officially, primary education is compulsory and lasts for eight years, while secondary education lasts for a further four years. In 1995, 1.3 million pupils were enrolled in primary schools. Most girls' schools have been closed in Taliban-controlled areas.

By 1988 a total of five universities were established in Afghanistan, besides eight vocational colleges and fifteen technical colleges. Teacher-training institutes have been established in the provinces of Balkh and Qandahar.

1999 KEY EVENTS TIMELINE

February

- The Taliban says Saudi terrorist Osama bin Laden is no longer in the territory it controls.

March

- Taliban and opposition forces agree to form a coalition government following UN-brokered peace talks.

July

- A new round of peace talks between the Taliban and the opposition breaks down without reaching a power-sharing agreement.

- The Taliban launches a major new offensive against opposition forces.

- Following the imposition of U.S. sanctions the Taliban admits that it is still harboring terrorist Osama bin Laden.

August

- A Taliban military offensive drives opposition forces from the Shomali plains outside of Kabul.

- The Taliban and the United States hold talks regarding terrorist Osama bin Laden, accused of masterminding the bombing of U.S. embassies in Africa.

- The UN Secretary-General condemns the displacement of civilians by latest Taliban military initiative.

September

- The Taliban's Islamic militia launches the second phase of a military offensive aimed at gaining control of the entire country.

- The Taliban protests a UN refusal to recognize its government.

October

- The Taliban warns of reprisals against Tajikistan for supplying arms to Afghan opposition forces.

- The International Olympic Committee suspends Afghanistan's Taliban-appointed national Olympic committee.

December

- The United States lifts a ban on shipments to Afghanistan to allow the international organization Doctors Without Borders to send medicine to the country.

- The ruling Taliban is praised for assisting in ending the eight-day crisis involving a Indian airliner, hijacked during a flight between Katmandu, Nepal and New Delhi, India on December 24 and flown to Afghanistan. The Taliban gave the five hijackers and three Muslim militants who were freed to end the crisis ten hours to leave the country.

ANALYSIS OF EVENTS: 1999

BUSINESS AND THE ECONOMY

Events of 1999 brought little relief for the endemic poverty caused by two decades of civil war in Afghanistan. Although the Taliban had brought a repressive order to the 90 percent of the country under its rule, it remained unable to attract foreign investment as long as it failed to gain international recognition or bring lasting peace to the country. Hyperinflation had increased the number of Afghanis (the country's currency) needed to equal one U.S. dollar from 50 in the early 1990s to a virtually worthless 42,000.

Unfortunately, the one industry that thrived in 1999 was opium production, in which Afghanistan continued to lead the world. Encouraged by good weather and high prices, producers had increased the area under cultivation by 43 percent and harvested a bumper crop—a record 4,600 tons, compared with 2,100 tons the year before. As a further factor in the country's large output of opium, which is used to manufacture heroin that is sold in the West, UN spokesmen noted the Taliban government's lack of cooperation in international efforts to divert agricultural production from illegal drugs to other crops.

GOVERNMENT AND POLITICS

The year began on an optimistic note as leaders of Afghanistan's three-year-old Taliban government, which controls 90 percent of the country, met with opposition leaders in UN-sponsored peace talks, at which both sides agreed to form a coalition government, raising hopes that the country's 20-year civil war would finally have a permanent resolution. Peace in Afghanistan would also help ease tensions among Afghanistan's neighbors, who had taken sides in the conflict: Pakistan supported the Taliban, while Russia and Iran supported the alliance of opposition forces led by Ahmad Shah Masoud, a longtime guerrilla fighter who had been the military leader of the government deposed by the Taliban in 1996.

However, hopes for peace were dashed when a second round of talks in July ended in stalemate. A week later, the Taliban launched a new offensive aimed at gaining full control of the country. By the end of September, Masoud's forces had been driven from the Shomali plains outside Kabul, and Taliban forces launched a second offensive. At this point, international agencies including the United Nations voiced concern over the plight of tens of thousands of Afghans who had been displaced from their homes since August and declared the possibility of a major humanitarian crisis in the area.

Meanwhile, the Taliban was protesting the refusal of the UN to recognize its regime as the official government of Afghanistan. Since the formation of an Islamic state in the country in 1996, only three other nations—Pakistan, Saudi Arabia, and the United Arab Emirates—had recognized its government, and Afghanistan's UN seat was still held by representatives of the ousted government of former president Burhanuddin Rabbani.

The Taliban's relations with the U.S. were further complicated by charges that it was harboring Saudi terrorist Osama bin Laden, suspected of arranging the bombing of two U.S. embassies in East Africa in 1998. After earlier denying the presence of bin Laden within its territories, Taliban leaders admitted that he was still under special guard within the country after U.S. president Bill Clinton imposed sanctions on Afghanistan in July. In August, representatives of both countries met in New York to hold talks on bin Laden.

CULTURE AND SOCIETY

In 1999 the Afghan population suffered not only poverty and the repressive policies of the Taliban government but also the effects of renewed warfare as the Taliban launched new military initiatives against opposition forces. Tens of thousands of refugees were driven from the Shomali valley by fighting in August, including many whose villages

were reportedly torched in a "scorched-earth" attempt to decimate the opposition's base of support in the region. About 40,000 fled to the capital city of Kabul, where they stayed in public buildings or with relatives, while some 100,000 took refuge in the Panjsher valley opposition stronghold in the northeast. Most refugees fled with little more than the clothes on their backs, and international observers warned of a major humanitarian crisis with the approach of winter, especially in the Panjsher valley, where the displaced were living in mosques or open-air encampments without adequate food, shelter, or medical aid.

In September a UN human rights investigator reported systematic discrimination against women in the part of Afghanistan under Taliban control. Women were forbidden to work, which forced increasing numbers to beg or become prostitutes. Women were frequently the victims of physical violence, including public beatings. Prosecution in cases of rape was all but impossible under Taliban restrictions, and adultery was punishable by death. The Taliban was also accused of persecuting the country's Shi'ite Muslim minority in a United States report on religious freedom worldwide.

In October the International Olympic Committee suspended the national Olympic committee of Afghanistan because it had been appointed by the Taliban, which did not have international recognition as the country's legitimate government.

DIRECTORY

On 27 September 1996 the ruling members of the Afghan government, including President Burhanuddin Rabbani, were displaced by members of the Islamic Taliban movement. Afghanistan has no official functioning government at this time, and it remains divided among fighting factions. The Taliban, however, has established a de facto regime led by Mullah Mohammad Omar and exerts its authority from the capital of Kabul. The following are members of this regime.

CENTRAL GOVERNMENT
Head of State

Leader
Mullah Mohammad Omar

Ministers

Head of Kabul Council
Mullah Mohammad Rabbani, Office of the Head of Kabul Council

Foreign Minister
Mullah Sher Mohammad Stanakzai, Office of the Foreign Ministry

Information Minister
Mullah Amir Khan Muttaqi, Ministry of Information

Head of Security
Mullah Fazel Ahmad Akhond, Ministry of Security

Minister of Planning
Qari Din Mohammad, Ministry of Planning

Minister of Refugee Repatriation
Mullah Abdul Raqib, Ministry of Refugee Repatriation

Acting Deputy of Labor and Social Affairs
Mullah Abdul Salaam, Ministry of Labor and Social Affairs

Acting Minister of Martyrs and the Disabled
Mullah Abdul Bakh, Ministry of Martyrs and the Disabled

Acting Minister of Urban Reconstruction
Mullah Mohammad Rustan, Ministry of Urban Reconstruction

POLITICAL ORGANIZATIONS
Taliban
NAME: Mohammad Omar

United Islamic Front for the Salvation of Afghanistan comprised of Jumbesh-I-Melli Islami (National Islamic Movement)
Jamiat-I-Islami (Islamic Society)
NAME: Burhanuddin Rabbani

Hizbi Wahdat-Khalili faction (Islamic Unity Party)
NAME: Abdul Karim Khalili

DIPLOMATIC REPRESENTATION
Embassies in Afghanistan

India
Malalai Wat, Shahre-Nau, Kabul, Afghanistan
PHONE: +93 30556; 30557

Russia
Dar-UI-Aman Wat, Kabul, Afghanistan
PHONE: +93 41541; 21261

United Kingdom
Karte Parwan, Kabul, Afghanistan

JUDICIAL SYSTEM
Islamic law

FURTHER READING
Articles

"Afghanistan's Poppy Politics." *The Economist* (September 18, 1999): 46.

"Back to War in Afghanistan." *The Economist* (July 31, 1999): 33.

"Living with the Taliban." *The Economist* (July 24, 1999): 39.

Books

Edwards, David B. *Heroes of the Age: Moral Fault Lines on the Afghan Frontier.* Berkeley: University of California Press, 1996.

Giustozzi, Antonio. *War, Politics and Society in Afghanistan, 1978–1992.* Washington, DC: Georgetown University Press, 1999.

Maley, William, ed. *Fundamentalism Reborn? Afghanistan and the Taliban.* New York: New York University Press, 1998.

AFGHANISTAN: STATISTICAL DATA

For sources and notes see "Sources of Statistics" in the front of each volume.

GEOGRAPHY

Geography (1)

Area:

Total: 647,500 sq km.

Land: 647,500 sq km.

Water: 0 sq km.

Area—comparative: slightly smaller than Texas.

Land boundaries:

Total: 5,529 km.

Border countries: China 76 km, Iran 936 km, Pakistan 2,430 km, Tajikistan 1,206 km, Turkmenistan 744 km, Uzbekistan 137 km.

Coastline: 0 km (landlocked).

Climate: arid to semiarid; cold winters and hot summers.

Terrain: mostly rugged mountains; plains in north and southwest.

Natural resources: natural gas, petroleum, coal, copper, talc, barites, sulfur, lead, zinc, iron ore, salt, precious and semiprecious stones.

Land use:

Arable land: 12%

Permanent crops: 0%

Permanent pastures: 46%

Forests and woodland: 3%

Other: 39% (1993 est.).

HUMAN FACTORS

Demographics (2A)

	1990	1995	1998	2000	2010	2020	2030	2040	2050
Population	14,767.0	21,571.4	24,792.4	26,668.3	34,098.1	43,049.7	53,333.5	64,564.4	76,230.6
Net migration rate (per 1,000 population)	NA	NA	NA	NA	NA	NA	NA	NA	NA
Births	NA	NA	NA	NA	NA	NA	NA	NA	NA
Deaths	NA	NA	NA	NA	NA	NA	NA	NA	NA
Life expectancy - males	43.8	46.0	47.4	48.3	53.1	57.8	62.4	66.4	69.8
Life expectancy - females	42.2	44.7	46.3	47.4	53.1	59.0	64.7	69.8	74.1
Birth rate (per 1,000)	44.7	43.3	42.4	41.6	37.1	32.5	28.3	24.7	21.5
Death rate (per 1,000)	20.4	18.5	17.4	16.6	13.0	10.1	8.1	6.8	6.1
Women of reproductive age (15-49 yrs.)	3,323.3	4,899.7	5,656.9	6,102.4	7,969.4	10,382.9	13,278.4	16,473.3	19,671.6
of which are currently married	NA	NA	NA	NA	NA	NA	NA	NA	NA
Fertility rate	6.5	6.2	6.0	5.9	5.1	4.3	3.6	3.1	2.7

Except as noted, values for vital statistics are in thousands; life expectancy is in years.

Infants and Malnutrition (5)

Under-5 mortality rate (1997) 257

% of infants with low birthweight (1990-97) 20

Births attended by skilled health staff % of total[a] . . .NA

% fully immunized (1995-97)

TB 66

DPT 45

Polio 45

Measles 58

Prevalence of child malnutrition under age 5
(1992-97)[b] . . . . .NA

Ethnic Division (6)

Pashtun 38%

Tajik 25%

Uzbek 6%

Hazara 19%

Population includes minor ethnic groups (Aimaks, Turkmen, Baloch, and others).

Religions (7)

Sunni Muslim 84%

Shi'a Muslim 15%

Other 1%

Languages (8)

Pashtu 35%, Afghan Persian (Dari) 50%, Turkic languages (primarily Uzbek and Turkmen) 11%, 30 minor languages (primarily Balochi and Pashai) 4%, much bilingualism.

EDUCATION

Educational Attainment (10)

Age group (1979) . . . . .25+

Total population 4,891,473

Highest level attained (%)

No schooling 89.0

First level

Not completed 6.5

Completed 0.3

Entered second level

S-1 . . . . .1.1

S-2 . . . . .NA

Postsecondary 3.0

Literacy Rates (11A)

In thousands and percent[1]	1990	1995	2000	2010
Illiterate population (15+ yrs.)	6,173	8,169	10,191	10,780
Literacy rate - total adult pop. (%)	27.1	31.5	35.9	45.4
Literacy rate - males (%)	42.1	47.2	51.9	60.6
Literacy rate - females (%)	11.2	15.0	19.2	29.6

GOVERNMENT & LAW

Political Parties (12)

There is no functioning legislative branch in Afghanistan.

Government Budget (13B)

Revenues . . . . .NA

Expenditures . . . . .NA

Capital expenditures . . . . .NA

NA stands for not available.

LABOR FORCE

Labor Force (16)

Total (million) 7.1

Agriculture and animal husbandry 67.8%

Industry 10.2%

Construction 6.3%

Commerce 5.0%

Services and other 10.7%

Data for 1980 est.

Unemployment Rate (17)

8% (1995 est.)

PRODUCTION SECTOR

Electric Energy (18)

Capacity . . . . .494,000 kW (1995)

Production . . . . .655 million kWh (1995)

Consumption per capita . . . . .37 kWh (1995)

Transportation (19)

Highways:

total: 21,000 km

paved: 2,793 km

unpaved: 18,207 km (1996 est.)

Waterways: 1,200 km; chiefly Amu Darya, which handles vessels up to about 500 DWT

Pipelines: petroleum products—Uzbekistan to Bagram and Turkmenistan to Shindand; natural gas 180 km

Airports: 44 (1997 est.)

Airports—with paved runways:

total: 11

over 3,047 m: 3

2,438 to 3,047 m: 4

1,524 to 2,437 m: 2

under 914 m: 2 (1997 est.)

Airports—with unpaved runways:

total: 33

2,438 to 3,047 m: 5

1,524 to 2,437 m: 14

914 to 1,523 m: 4

under 914 m: 10 (1997 est.)

Top Agricultural Products (20)

Wheat, fruits, nuts, karakul pelts; wool, mutton.

FINANCE, ECONOMICS, & TRADE

Exchange Rates (24)

Exchange rates:

Afghanis (Af) per US$1

December 1996	17,000
January 1995	7,000
January 1994	1,900
March 1993	1,019
1991	850

These rates reflect the free market exchange rates rather than the official exchange rate, which was fixed at 50.600 afghanis to the dollar until 1996, when it rose to 2,262.65 per dollar, and finally became fixed again at 3,000.00 per dollar on April 1996.

MANUFACTURING SECTOR

GDP & Manufacturing Summary (21)

	1980	1985	1990	1992	1993	1994
Gross Domestic Product						
Millions of 1990 dollars	1,255	1,402	1,070	1,174	*1,186*	*1,198*
Growth rate in percent	-3.72	0.27	-3.12	2.00	*1.00*	*1.00*
Per capita (in 1990 dollars)	78.2	96.5	71.1	70.6	*67.0*	*63.4*
Manufacturing Value Added						
Millions of 1975 dollars	272	299	198	206	*217*	*221*
Growth rate in percent	-6.06	3.32	-10.34	3.74	*5.25*	*1.99*
Manufacturing share in percent of current prices	NA	NA	NA	NA	NA	NA

FINANCE, ECONOMICS, & TRADE

Balance of Payments (23)

	1985	1986	1987	1988	1989
Exports of goods (f.o.b.)	628.2	497.0	538.7	453.8	252.3
Imports of goods (f.o.b.)	-921.6	-1,138.8	-904.5	-731.8	-623.5
Trade balance	-293.4	-641.8	-365.8	-278.0	-371.2
Services - debits	-162.7	-215.9	-167.6	-131.5	-111.3
Services - credits	69.2	53.1	54.8	92.9	28.3
Private transfers (net)	NA	NA	NA	NA	-1.2
Government transfers (net)	143.7	267.4	311.7	342.8	312.1
Overall balance	26.0	-18.7	10.8	-25.8	-20.1

Economic Indicators (22)

National product: GDP—purchasing power parity—$19.3 billion (1997 est.)

National product real growth rate: NA%

National product per capita: $800 (1997 est.)

Inflation rate—consumer price index: 240% (1996 est.)

Top Import Origins (25)

$150 million (1996 est.)

Origins	%
FSU	NA
Pakistan	NA
Iran	NA
Japan	NA
Singapore	NA
India	NA
South Korea	NA
Germany	NA

NA stands for not available.

GOVERNMENT & LAW

Military Affairs (14B)

	1990	1991	1992	1993	1994	1995
Military expenditures						
Current dollars (mil.)	310[e]	NA	NA	NA	NA	NA
1995 constant dollars (mil.)	356[e]	NA	NA	NA	NA	NA
Armed forces (000)	58	45	45	45	45	20
Gross national product (GNP)						
Current dollars (mil.)	NA	NA	NA	NA	NA	12,800[r]
1995 constant dollars (mil.)	NA	NA	NA	NA	NA	12,800[r]
Central government expenditures (CGE)						
1995 constant dollars (mil.)	NA	NA	NA	NA	NA	NA
People (mil.)	14.8	15.0	16.6	18.9	20.4	21.6
Military expenditure as % of GNP	NA	NA	NA	NA	NA	NA
Military expenditure as % of CGE	NA	NA	NA	NA	NA	NA
Military expenditure per capita (1995 $)	24	NA	NA	NA	NA	NA
Armed forces per 1,000 people (soldiers)	3.9	3.0	2.7	2.4	2.2	0.9
GNP per capita (1995 $)	NA	NA	NA	NA	NA	593
Arms imports[6]						
Current dollars (mil.)	3,500	1,900	0	5	20	20
1995 constant dollars (mil.)	4,022	2,100	0	5	21	20
Arms exports[6]						
Current dollars (mil.)	0	0	0	0	20	0
1995 constant dollars (mil.)	0	0	0	0	21	0
Total imports[7]						
Current dollars (mil.)	936	616	NA	NA	NA	NA
1995 constant dollars (mil.)	1,076	681	NA	NA	NA	NA
Total exports[7]						
Current dollars (mil.)	235	188	NA	NA	NA	NA
1995 constant dollars (mil.)	270	208	NA	NA	NA	NA
Arms as percent of total imports[8]	373.8	308.4	NA	NA	NA	NA
Arms as percent of total exports[8]	0	0	NA	NA	NA	NA

FINANCE, ECONOMICS, & TRADE

Top Export Destinations (26)

$80 million (1996 est.).

Destinations	%
FSU	NA
Pakistan	NA
Iran	NA
Germany	NA
India	NA
United Kingdom	NA
Belgium	NA
Luxembourg	NA
Czechoslovakia	NA

NA stands for not available.

Economic Aid (27)

Recipient: ODA; about $45 million in UN aid plus additional bilateral aid and aid in kind (1997). Note: US provided $450 million in bilateral assistance (1985-93); US continues to contribute to multilateral assistance through the UN programs of food aid, immunization, land mine removal, and a wide range of aid to refugees and displaced persons.

Import Export Commodities (28)

Import Commodities	Export Commodities
Food and petroleum products; most consumer goods	Fruits and nuts
	Handwoven carpets
	Wool
	Cotton
	Hides and pelts
	Precious and semi-precious gems

ALBANIA

Republic of Albania
Republika é Shqipërisë

INTRODUCTORY SURVEY

RECENT HISTORY

Italy annexed Albania early in World War II. Communist guerrillas seized power in 1944. Their leader, Enver Hoxha, was a Stalinist who adopted the Russian's repressive tactics and killed or imprisoned all who disagreed with him. Hoxha aligned Albania with the Communist Chinese in 1961 after a falling out with Soviet leader Nikita Khrushchev. When Mao died in 1978, Albania went its own way and turned to isolationism.

Following a March 1991 victory by the Albanian Communist Party, a general strike and street demonstrations ensued. The all-Communist cabinet resigned. In June of 1991, the Communist Party renamed itself the Socialist Party and renounced communism. The Democratic Party won the 1992 elections by a landslide and the country moved towards a free-market economy. This move to free markets was interrupted in 1997, when Albania's nation-wide system of individual investment plans, in fact "pyramid" schemes, collapsed and Albanian citizens lost $1.2 billion of their savings. Amidst rumors of government involvement in the schemes, rioting ensued, the government and the fragile economy collapsed, and gangsters and rebels took control. More than 1,500 died. A multinational protection force was required to restore order and supervise elections.

Albanians north of the country, in the Serbian province of Kosovo, have long fought the Serbian government, and Albania became increasingly involved. In the spring of 1999, with Kosovoan Alba-

ALBANIA

overwhelming defeat of a draft constitution in December 1994 continues to cloud Albania's future.

Albania is divided into 26 districts *(rrethe),* subdivided into 65 cities and towns and 438 united villages.

Judiciary

The judicial system includes district courts, a court of appeals, and a Court of Cassation. The district courts are trial level courts from which appeal can be taken to the court of appeals and then to the Court of Cassation. There is also a Constitutional Court that has authority over how the constitution is interpreted.

Political Parties

In the elections held in 1997, some 18 parties participated: leading parties were the Democratic Party; the Socialist Party (the new name of the Communist Party); the Social Democratic Party; the Unity for Human Rights (Greek Minority) Party; and the Republican Party.

DEFENSE

As of 1996, the estimated strength of the Albanian armed forces was 54,000. This number includes 45,000 in the army, 2,500 in the navy, and 6,500 in the air force.

ECONOMIC AFFAIRS

With the end of communist rule in 1992, farmland was returned to private ownership. But despite significant progress, living standards in Albania are among the lowest in Europe. When socialist-style central planning was abandoned, there was no alternate system to take its place. After falling 45% during 1990–92, Albania's gross domestic product (GDP) increased by 5% in 1995.

Albania is one of the poorest of the European nations. Its agricultural based economy produces vegetables, fruit, and tobacco for export along with asphalt, metals and metallic ores, electricity, and crude oil.

Public Finance

After launching ambitious reforms in 1991, Albania became a member of the World Bank, IMF, and EBRD, enabling it to receive multilevel financial assistance to jump-start its economy. The EBRD in particular will provide technical assistance to develop telecommunications and tourism infrastructures, as well as assist in banking reform and privatization.

nians fleeing the Serbian military, Albania took in about 440,000 Kosovar refugees. Albania also served as a staging ground for NATO troops who entered Kosovo to restore order and protect the civilian populace.

GOVERNMENT

Albania is in the process of drafting a new constitution. Albania's government is still based on the 29 April 1991 Law on Constitutional Provisions, enacted to provide a transition from a communist form of government to a democratic one. Delays in drafting a new constitution caused a severe political crisis in the summer of 1993. The

In 1996, government revenues totaled approximately $490 million and expenditures $550 million, including capital expenditures of $124 million. External debt totaled $977 million, approximately 32% of which was financed abroad.

Income

Albania's gross domestic product (GDP) was estimated at $4.5 billion in 1997, with a per capita estimate of $1,237. Real growth rates in 1997 were a negative 8%; inflation ran at 40%.

Industry

Production of major items in 1995 included cement, residual fuel oil, gasoline, kerosene, phosphate fertilizers, and cigarettes. Industrial production fell 44% in 1992 and 10% in 1993, but by 1995 was growing at a rate of 6%. The return of business to private ownership is proceeding slowly.

Banking and Finance

The Communist regime nationalized all banking and financial institutions in 1945 and established the Bank of the Albanian State, which is the bank of issue. The bank also controlled foreign transactions, helped prepare financial plans for the economy, accepted savings deposits, financed economic activities, and performed other banking functions. An agricultural bank was created in 1970 to provide credit facilities for agricultural cooperatives.

The privatization of the three state-owned commercial banks has long been advocated by the International Monetary Fund and the World Bank, which have persuaded the government to bring forward the first privatization of the Rural Commercial Bank (RCB) to the end of 1997. The government planed to privatize the National Commercial Bank (NCB) before the end of 1998, and the National Savings Bank (NSB) at a later date.

Economic Development

Albania formerly had a state-controlled, centrally-planned economy, with emphasis on industrial development and socialized agriculture. Under Workers Party directives, short-term and long-range plans were formulated by the Economic Planning Commission, a government agency. By the mid-1980s, the economy was virtually under complete state control; enterprises were either directly owned by the state or managed through cooperatives.

A sweeping economic reform program was announced in 1992. It called for widespread private ownership of farmland, state-owned companies and housing, and the removal of trade restrictions and price controls. Albania's chief foreign aid donor, the EU, had issued grants worth $2.4 billion by early 1994. Albania received $335.3 million in economic aid during 1991.

SOCIAL WELFARE

The Act on State Social Insurance provided benefits for disability, old age, survivors, and retirement. An old age pension is granted when the insured reaches a certain age, depending upon class of work and length of service.

Albania's constitution prohibits discrimination based on sex, and women make up roughly half the labor force.

Healthcare

About 92% of the population has access to health care. Average life expectancy is estimated at 72 years, compared to 38 years at the end of World War II.

Housing

At the time of the 1986 census, 72% of Albania's housing units had a water supply, 67% had a bath or shower, 40% had central heating, and 60% had toilet facilities. The total housing stock in 1991 numbered 756,000 units.

EDUCATION

Compulsory school extends for eight years (ages 7 to 15). Institutions of higher learning include the Institute of Sciences, Enver Hoxha University of Tiranë (formerly Tiranë State University), and the University of Shkodër. Estimates put the literacy rate at 72%.

1999 KEY EVENTS TIMELINE

March

- Italians deliver equipment for a ''tent city'' which is to house 20,000 Kosovar refugees.

- Estimates of the number of Kosovar refugees in Albania range from 65,000 to 80,000 and many more are expected.

April

- Albania shows a willingness to be a staging area for the NATO bombing campaign against the Serbs.

- International organizations promise economic aid to help Albania cope with refugee crisis.

May

- The United States announces a financial aid plan to assist Albanian families who house Kosovar refugees.

- Fighting spreads into Albanian villages as two are killed.

June

- NATO forces mistakenly bomb an Albanian town that is serving as a refuge for fleeing Kosovars.

- A British transport plane crashes near refugee camps in Albania.

- Albanian universities welcome ethnic-Albanian students and faculty.

July

- U.S. Defense Secretary William S. Cohen cancels a planned trip to Albania for security reasons.

October

- Prime Minister Pandeli Majko resigns after losing leadership of the Socialist Party. President Mejdani appoints Ilir Meta in his place.

December

- The death penalty is abolished when the Constitutional Court in Tirana rules that it violates the country's constitution. Abolishing the death penalty was a requirement for Albania to apply for membership in the Council of Europe. Twenty convicts on Albania's death row will now serve life in prison.

- President Rexhep Meidani begins an official visit to China. Presidents of the two nations meet to discuss economic cooperation between their two countries.

ANALYSIS OF EVENTS: 1999

BUSINESS AND THE ECONOMY

Albania is the poorest country in Europe. It entered the twentieth century after 400 years of Turkish rule. Occupied by Italy and Germany during World War II, its post-war communist leadership had led the resistance against the Axis powers, aided by the neighboring Yugoslav anti-fascist resistance movement. The break-up of the Soviet Union and its eastern European client states in the late 1980s subverted the power of the Albanian Communist Party. It was banned in 1992, but Albanian politics continued to reflect a much longer tradition of autocratic, arbitrary, and bloody rule.

In 1997 the country teetered on the edge of anarchy when an extensive network of ''pyramid'' individual investment schemes fell apart. During this scandal, unscrupulous promoters had unleashed a variety of speculative schemes on an unsuspecting Albanian population as the formerly socialist economy groped its way through the transition to free market principles. Many families were stripped of their savings. Total money lost amounted to almost 50 percent of Albania's Gross Domestic Product. The resulting social chaos brought violent street demonstrations and extensive property damage, government repression causing the violent death of an estimated 1,500 people, and an 8 percent drop in the Gross Domestic Product.

GOVERNMENT AND POLITICS

It was into this volatile and exasperated atmosphere in 1999 that the Kosovar refugee crisis imposed additional economic burdens on Albania. Albania's neighboring Serbian province of Kosovo, which contained an ethnic Albanian majority, suffered a protracted reign of terror at the hands of the Serb military seeking to crush Albanian separatist aspirations of the Kosovars. In March 1999, after Serbian head of state Slobodan Milosevic refused to sign an agreement allowing the stationing of UN peacekeeping forces in the area, the NATO forces launched air attacks on Serbia. These strikes were intended to disrupt Serbian attacks on ethnic Albanians in Kosovo.

Serbian bombing, looting, and torching of ethnic Albanian villages inside Kosovo created a growing refugee crisis in the early months of 1999, and Albania, which shares a border with the troubled province, was drawn into the turmoil as thousands of refugees fleeing Kosovo entered the country. By the end of March, estimates of Kosovar refugees in Albania ranged from 65,000 to 80,000. The number grew to over 300,000 in April and some observers thought it might reach nearly a million by the end of the summer.

In addition to the refugee crisis, the military operations directed by the U.S. and its allies also spilled into Albania. In May an American pilot was killed on a training mission inside Albania and two Albanians died when Serbian forces shelled four villages across the border. In June Albania also became the unintended target of NATO attacks when NATO forces accidentally bombed an Albanian border town serving as a main crossing point for fleeing refugees. Later the same month a British military transport plane narrowly missed a refugee camp when it crashed in northern Albania.

Albania, many of whose families relied on money sent back from relatives working abroad, had absorbed roughly half a million refugees by the end of May, 1999—the equivalent of about 14 percent of its own population. The Albanian people hosted roughly 90 percent of the refugees in private quarters with Albanian families. In July 1997 new elections brought a reform government to power. Supported by the International Monetary Fund's "Post-Conflict Emergency Assistance Policy," the new Albanian government put an end to pyramid promotions, reformed the banking system, and funded a social safety net.

By April the Albanian government had launched a plea for international financial aid to help cope with the influx of refugees, and international organizations responded. As NATO's major regional ally in its war against the Serbs and the site of a high-profile humanitarian crisis, Albania commanded high levels of international attention. The World Bank pledged $30 million; the European Union offered 100 million euros. Aid also included relief services, such as the staff members from a rape crisis center in Dublin who were dispatched to Albania to counsel Kosovar refugees and train Kosovars themselves in counseling techniques.

At the end of May, Albanian president Rexhep Meidani stated that expenditures could total nearly $1 billion if the refugees stayed until the end of the year. In June the European Union pledged additional amounts of aid to pay for rebuilding wartime damage and updating the country's crumbling infrastructure. Sources at the International Monetary Fund estimated that the financial cost of the fighting in Serbia to the six neighboring countries most affected by it—including Albania—could total as much as $2 billion.

Although Albania's economic growth was expected to slacken somewhat from the previous year, inflation during 1999 was falling and the national currency—the lek—was stable. In addition, the presence of UN peacekeeping forces and agency personnel was expected to supply an economic boost in some areas, such as transport, telecommunications, and service industries. Locations including Tirana and the port of Durres were targeted as sites for new construction, including NATO military installations and refugee camps, and the outdated Rinas airport in Tirana underwent improvements to accommodate as many as 60 flights per day of war material and relief supplies. Upgrades included new navigation equipment and lighting, runway repairs, and a security perimeter.

CULTURE AND SOCIETY

In spite of the fact that the refugee crisis shook the foundations of Albanian society, there were many instances in which Albanian people rose to the challenge as they provided their ethnic brethren a sanctuary from the violence of Serbian depredations. In the academic world, for instance, ethnic Albanian refugees found a temporary home, either as faculty members or students at Albania's universities. The Polytechnic University in Tirana accepted 30 new faculty members from among the Kosovars and admitted a number of students, allowing them to resume their academic careers in exile.

DIRECTORY

CENTRAL GOVERNMENT

Head of State

President
Rexhep Meidani, Office of the President, Boulevard Zeshmoret E. Komvit, Tirana, Albania
E-MAIL: presec@presec.tirana.al.

Prime Minister
Ilir Meta, Office of the Council of Ministers, Boulevard Zeshmoret E. Komvit, Tirana, Albania

Ministers

Minister of Agriculture
Lufter Xhuveli, Ministry of Agriculture

Minister of Culture, Youth, and Sports
Edi Rama, Ministry of Culture, Youth, and Sports

Minister of Defense
Luan Hajdaraga, Ministry of Defense

Minister of Economic Cooperation and Trade
Ermelinda Meksi, Ministry of Economic Cooperation and Trade

Minister of Education
Et'hem Ruka, Ministry of Education

Minister of Finance
Anastas Angjeli, Ministry of Finance

Minister of Foreign Affairs
Paskal Milo, Ministry of Foreign Affairs

Minister of Governmental Coordination
Ilir Meta, Ministry of Governmental Coordination

Minister of Health
Leonard Solis, Ministry of Health

Minister of Information
Musa Ulqini, Ministry of Information
PHONE: +355 4256266
E-MAIL: mininf@albnet.net

Minister of Justice
Thimio Kondi, Ministry of Justice

Minister of Labor and Social Affairs
Kadir Rrapi, Ministry of Labor and Social Affairs

Minister of Local Government
Arben Demeti, Ministry of Local Government

Minister of Public Order
Petro Koci, Ministry of Public Order

Minister of Public Sector Economy and Privatization
Ylli Bufi, Ministry of Public Sector Economy and Privatization

Minister of Public Works and Transport
Shuli Ingrid, Ministry of Public Works and Transport

Minister of State for Legislative Reform and Relations with the Parliament
Arben Imami, Ministry of State for Legislative Reform and Relations with the Parliament

State Secretary for European Integration
Maqo Lakrori

POLITICAL ORGANIZATIONS

Partia Demokratike Shqiptare (Democratic Party of Albania)
E-MAIL: PDChairman@albaniaonline.net
TITLE: Chairman
NAME: Sali Berisha

Partia Aliancë Demokratika ë Shqipërisë (Democratic Alliance Party)
TITLE: Chairman
NAME: Neritan Ceka

Partia Lëvizja e Legalitetit (Movement of Legality Party)
NAME: Guri Durollari

Balli Kombetar (National Front)
NAME: Hysen Selfo

Partia Social Demokraike ë Shqipërisë (Social Democratic Party of Albania)
NAME: Skender Gjinushi

Partia Socialiste ë Shqipërisë (Socialist Party of Albania)
TITLE: Chairman
NAME: Fatos Nano

Partia për Mbrojten e te Drejtave te Njeriut (Unity for Human Rights Party)
TITLE: Chairman
NAME: Vasil Melo

Partia Agrar Shqiptare (Albanian Agrarian Party)

Partia Republika ë Shqipërisë (Republican Party of Albania)

DIPLOMATIC REPRESENTATION

Embassies in Albania

Austria
Rruga: "Skenderbeu," Tirana, Albania
PHONE: +355 33157
FAX: +355 33140
TITLE: Ambassador Extraordinary and Plenipotentiary
NAME: Georg Calice

Bosnia and Herzegovina
Rruga: "Themistokli Germenji," 5 Tirana, Albania
PHONE: +355 30454

FAX: +355 34848
TITLE: Charge d'Affairs
NAME: Muharrem Zejnullahu

Bulgaria
Rruga: ''Skenderbeu,'' Tirana, Albania
PHONE: +355 33155
TITLE: Ambassador Extraordinary and
Plenipotentiary
NAME: Stefan Naumov

China
Rruga: ''Skenderbeu,'' Tirana, Albania
PHONE: +355 28303
FAX: +355 33159
TITLE: Ambassador Extraordinary and
Plenipotentiary
NAME: Ma Veimao

Croatia
Rruga: ''Abdyl Frasheri,'' Tirana, Albania
PHONE: +355 28390
FAX: +355 30577
TITLE: Ambassador Extraordinary and
Plenipotentiary
NAME: Mlladen Juricic

Czech Republic
Rruga: ''Skenderbeu,'' Tirana, Albania
PHONE: +355 34004
FAX: +355 32159
TITLE: Charge d'Affairs a.i.
NAME: Imrich Sedlak

Egypt
Rruga: ''Skenderbeu,'' Tirana, Albania
PHONE: +355 33022
FAX: +355 32295
TITLE: Ambassador Extraordinary and
Plenipotentiary
NAME: Attia Qaram Attia

France
Rruga: ''Skenderbeu,'' Tirana, Albania
PHONE: +355 34054
FAX: 34442
TITLE: Ambassador Extraordinary and
Plenipotentiary
NAME: Patrick Chrismant

Germany
Rruga: ''Skenderbeu,'' Tirana, Albania
PHONE: +355 32050
FAX: +355 33497
TITLE: Ambassador Extraordinary and
Plenipotentiary
NAME: Hannspeter Disdorn

Greece
Rruga: ''Skenderbeu,'' Tirana, Albania

PHONE: +355 34290; 34291
FAX: +355 32168
TITLE: Ambassador Extraordinary and
Plenipotentiary
NAME: Constandin Provedourakis

Hungary
Rruga: ''Skenderbeu,'' Tirana, Albania
PHONE: +355 32253
FAX: +355 32211
TITLE: Ambassador Extraordinary and
Plenipotentiary
NAME: Istvan Bognar

Iran
Rruga: ''Skenderbeu,'' No. 21, Tirana, Albania
PHONE: +355 27869
FAX: +355 30409
TITLE: Charge d'Affairs a.i.
NAME: Vahid Farmand

Italy
Rruga: ''Deshmoret e 4 Shkurtit,'' Tirana,
Albania
PHONE: +355 34343
FAX: +355 32507
TITLE: Ambassador Extraordinary and
Plenipotentiary
NAME: Paolo Foresti

Libya
Rruga: ''Sulejman Pasha,'' No. 58, Tirana,
Albania
PHONE: +355 28101
TITLE: Chief of the Bureau of the Charge
d'Affairs
NAME: Youssef Omar Sagar

Macedonia
Rruga: ''Skenderbeu,'' Tirana, Albania
PHONE: +355 33036
FAX: +355 34559
TITLE: Ambassador Extraordinary and
Plenipotentiary
NAME: Nikola Todorcevski

Malta
Bulevardi ''Deshmoret e Kombit,'' Near Hotel
''Rogner-Europark,'' Tirana, Albania
PHONE: +355 23636
TITLE: Ambassador Extraordinary and
Plenipotentiary
NAME: Guenther A. Granser

Palestinian Authority
Rruga: ''Skenderbeu,'' No. 45, Tirana, Albania
PHONE: +355 34300
FAX: +355 32092
TITLE: Ambassador Extraordinary and
Plenipotentiary

NAME: Ali Kurdi

Poland
Rruga: "Durresit," Tirana, Albania
PHONE: +355 34190
FAX: +355 33364
TITLE: Ambassador Extraordinary and
Plenipotentiary
NAME: Miroslaw Palasz

Romania
Rruga: "Asim Zeneli," Tirana, Albania
PHONE: +355 32287
FAX: +355 32317
TITLE: Ambassador Extraordinary and
Plenipotentiary
NAME: Gheorghe Micu

Russia
Rruga: "Asim Zeneli," Tirana, Albania
PHONE: +355 32253
TITLE: Ambassador Extraordinary and
Plenipotentiary
NAME: Viktor Nreubajllo

Serbia
Rruga: "Durresit," Tirana, Albania
PHONE: +355 23042
FAX: +355 32089
TITLE: Charge d'Affairs a.i.
NAME: Stanimir Vukicevic

Switzerland
Rruga: "Elbasanit," No. 81, Tirana, Albania
PHONE: +355 34890
FAX: +355 34889
TITLE: Ambassador Extraordinary and
Plenipotentiary
NAME: Thomas Feller

Turkey
Rruga: "Kavajes," Tirana, Albania
PHONE: +355 33399
FAX: +355 32405
TITLE: Ambassador Extraordinary and
Plenipotentiary
NAME: Ahmet Rifat Okcun

United Kingdom
Rruga: "Skenderbeu," No.14, Tirana, Albania
PHONE: +355 34973
FAX: +355 30869
TITLE: Ambassador Extraordinary and
Plenipotentiary
NAME: Andrew Tesoriere

United States
Rruga: "Elbasanit," No. 103, Tirana, Albania

PHONE: +355 32875
TITLE: Ambassador Extraordinary and
Plenipotentiary
NAME: Marisa R. Lino

JUDICIAL SYSTEM
Constitutional Court
Court of Cassation
Court of Appeals
District Courts

FURTHER READING
Government Publications
Zickel, Raymond E., and Walter R. Iwaskiw.
Albania, A Country Study. Federal Research
Division, Library of Congress. 2nd ed.
Washington, D.C.: U.S. Government Printing
Office, 1994.

Articles
"Albania Braces for Renewed Rush of
Refugees, Straining a Country Already
Deeply Burdened." *The Wall Street Journal*,
(March 31, 1999): C14.

"Albania is Willing. It Just Isn't Able." *U.S.
News and World Report*, (April 26, 1999): 27.

Bollag, Burton. "Albanian University Opens Its
Doors to Scholars and Students Driven from
Kosovo." *Chronicle of Higher Education*
(June 4, 1999): A5.

"Shelter for the Refugees." *Newsweek
International* (May 31, 1999): 72.

"West Scrambles to Lend Aid to Albania." *The
Wall Street Journal* (April 19, 1999): A14.

Books
Carver, Robert. *The Accursed Mountains:
Journeys in Albania.* London: John Murray,
1998.

Jacques, Edwin E. *The Albanians: An Ethnic
History from Prehistoric Times to the Present.
Jefferson.* New York: McFarland and Co.,
1995.

Sherer, Stan. *Long Life to Your Children!: A
Portrait of High Albania.* Sherer, Stan, and
Marjorie Senechal. Amherst: University of
Massachusetts Press, 1997.

ALBANIA: STATISTICAL DATA

For sources and notes see "Sources of Statistics" in the front of each volume.

GEOGRAPHY

Geography (1)

Area:

Total: 28,750 sq km.

Land: 27,400 sq km.

Water: 1,350 sq km.

Area—comparative: slightly smaller than Maryland.

Land boundaries:

Total: 720 km.

Border countries: Greece 282 km, The Former Yugoslav Republic of Macedonia 151 km, Serbia and Montenegro 287 km (114 km with Serbia, 173 km with Montenegro).

Coastline: 362 km.

Climate: mild temperate; cool, cloudy, wet winters; hot, clear, dry summers; interior is cooler and wetter.

Terrain: mostly mountains and hills; small plains along coast.

Natural resources: petroleum, natural gas, coal, chromium, copper, timber, nickel.

Land use:

Arable land: 21%

Permanent crops: 5%

Permanent pastures: 15%

Forests and woodland: 38%

Other: 21% (1993 est.).

HUMAN FACTORS

Demographics (2A)

	1990	1995	1998	2000	2010	2020	2030	2040	2050
Population	3,272.9	3,218.7	3,330.8	3,401.1	3,784.0	4,154.8	4,425.6	4,575.8	4,609.1
Net migration rate (per 1,000 population)	NA	NA	NA	NA	NA	NA	NA	NA	NA
Births	NA	NA	NA	NA	NA	NA	NA	NA	NA
Deaths	NA	NA	NA	NA	NA	NA	NA	NA	NA
Life expectancy - males	66.0	64.6	65.6	66.3	70.0	73.1	75.5	77.3	78.6
Life expectancy - females	72.6	70.8	71.9	72.7	76.4	79.4	81.7	83.4	84.7
Birth rate (per 1,000)	25.6	23.3	21.4	20.1	17.6	14.7	11.7	10.1	8.6
Death rate (per 1,000)	7.3	7.8	7.4	7.3	6.5	6.5	7.0	8.0	9.3
Women of reproductive age (15-49 yrs.)	828.4	856.1	902.9	935.7	1,063.7	1,109.9	1,134.9	1,084.6	995.9
of which are currently married	NA	NA	NA	NA	NA	NA	NA	NA	NA
Fertility rate	3.0	2.8	2.6	2.4	2.1	1.8	1.6	1.5	1.4

Except as noted, values for vital statistics are in thousands; life expectancy is in years.

Health Personnel (3)

Total health expenditure as a percentage of GDP, 1990-1997[a]

Public sector 2.5

Private sector . . . . .NA

Total[b] . . . . .NA

Health expenditure per capita in U.S. dollars, 1990-1997[a]

Purchasing power parity . . . . .NA

Total . . . . .NA

Availability of health care facilities per 100,000 people

Hospital beds 1990-1997[a] 320

Doctors 1993[c] 141

Nurses 1993[c] 423

Health Indicators (4)

Life expectancy at birth

1980 69

1997 72

Daily per capita supply of calories (1996) 2,523

Total fertility rate births per woman (1997) 2.5

Maternal mortality ratio per 100,000 live births (1990-97) . . . . .28[b]

Safe water % of population with access (1995) 76

Sanitation % of population with access (1995) 58

Consumption of iodized salt % of households (1992-98)[a] . . . .

Smoking prevalence

Male % of adults (1985-95)[a] 50

Female % of adults (1985-95)[a] 8

Tuberculosis incidence per 100,000 people (1997) 28

Adult HIV prevalence % of population ages 15-49 (1997) 0.01

Infants and Malnutrition (5)

Under-5 mortality rate (1997) 40

% of infants with low birthweight (1990-97) 7

Births attended by skilled health staff % of total[a] . . .91

% fully immunized (1995-97)

TB 94

DPT 99

Polio 99

Measles 95

Prevalence of child malnutrition under age 5 (1992-97)[b] . . . . .NA

Ethnic Division (6)

Albanian 95%

Greeks 3%

Other 2%

Note: In 1989, other estimates of the Greek population ranged from 1% (official Albanian statistics) to 12% (from a Greek organization). Other is made up of Vlachs, Gypsies, Serbs, and Bulgarians. Data for 1989 est.

Religions (7)

Muslim 70%

Albanian Orthodox 20%

Roman Catholic 10%

All mosques and churches were closed in 1967 and religious observances prohibited; in November 1990 Albania began allowing private religious practice.

Languages (8)

Albanian (Tosk is the official dialect), Greek.

EDUCATION

Public Education Expenditures (9)

Public expenditure on education (% of GNP)

1980 . . . .

1996 . . . . .3.1[1]

Expenditure per student

Primary % of GNP per capita

1980 . . . .

1996 . . . . .9.5[1]

Secondary % of GNP per capita

1980 . . . .

1996 . . . .

Tertiary % of GNP per capita

1980 . . . .

1996 . . . .

Expenditure on teaching materials

Primary % of total for level (1996) . . . .

Secondary % of total for level (1996) . . . . .5.5[1]

Primary pupil-teacher ratio per teacher (1996) . . . . .18[1]

Duration of primary education years (1995) 8

GOVERNMENT & LAW

Political Parties (12)

People's Assembly	% of seats
Albanian Socialist Party (PS)	.53.36
Democratic Party (PD)	.25.33
Social Democratic Party (PSD)	.2.5

Unity for Human Rights Party (PBDNJ) 2.78

National Front (PBK) 2.36

Democratic Alliance (PAD) 2.85

Albanian Republican Party (PR) 2.25

Movement of Legality Party (PLL) 3.09

Christian Democratic Party (PDK) 1.00

Government Budget (13A)

Year: 1995

Total Expenditures: 69,687 Millions of Leks

Expenditures as a percentage of the total by function:

General public services and public order 13.80

Defense 7.09

Education 2.30

Health 5.61

Social Security and Welfare 21.70

Housing and community amenities 3.47

Recreational, cultural, and religious affairs 1.68

Fuel and energy 49

Agriculture, forestry, fishing, and hunting 3.87

Mining, manufacturing, and construction 2.07

Transportation and communication 4.70

Other economic affairs and services 1.69

Military Affairs (14B)

	1990	1991	1992	1993	1994	1995
Military expenditures						
Current dollars (mil.)	NA	NA	NA	NA	NA	45
1995 constant dollars (mil.)	NA	NA	NA	NA	NA	45
Armed forces (000)	NA	NA	65[e]	65[e]	75	52
Gross national product (GNP)						
Current dollars (mil.)	4,100[e]	2,700[e]	2,500[e]	3,300[e]	3,800[e]	4,100[e]
1995 constant dollars (mil.)	4,712[e]	2,984[e]	2,689[e]	3,460[e]	3,895[e]	4,100[e]
Central government expenditures (CGE)						
1995 constant dollars (mil.)	NA	1,547[e]	NA	NA	1,435[e]	1,413[e]
People (mil.)	3.3	3.3	3.2	3.1	3.2	3.2
Military expenditure as % of GNP	NA	NA	NA	NA	NA	1.1
Military expenditure as % of CGE	NA	NA	NA	NA	NA	3.2
Military expenditure per capita (1995 $)	NA	NA	NA	NA	NA	14
Armed forces per 1,000 people (soldiers)	NA	NA	20.4	20.6	23.7	16.2
GNP per capita (1995 $)	1,440	916	844	1,099	1,229	1,278
Arms imports[6]						
Current dollars (mil.)	0	0	0	0	0	0
1995 constant dollars (mil.)	0	0	0	0	0	0
Arms exports[6]						
Current dollars (mil.)	0	0	0	0	0	0
1995 constant dollars (mil.)	0	0	0	0	0	0
Total imports[7]						
Current dollars (mil.)	444[e]	467[e]	541[e]	602[e]	601[e]	680[e]
1995 constant dollars (mil.)	510[e]	516[e]	581[e]	631[e]	616[e]	680[e]
Total exports[7]						
Current dollars (mil.)	222[e]	168[e]	174[e]	117[e]	141[e]	205[e]
1995 constant dollars (mil.)	255[e]	186[e]	187[e]	123[e]	145[e]	205[e]
Arms as percent of total imports[8]	0	0	0	0	0	0
Arms as percent of total exports[8]	0	0	0	0	0	0

Crime (15)

Crime rate (for 1997)

Crimes reported 6,400

Total persons convicted 224,000

Crimes per 100,000 population 200

Persons responsible for offenses

Total number of suspects 3,400

Total number of female suspects . . . . .NA

Total number of juvenile suspects 14,600

LABOR FORCE

Labor Force (16)

Total (million) 1.692

Agriculture (nearly all private) 49.5%

Private sector 22.2%

State (nonfarm) sector .28.3%

Data for 1994 est. Total includes 352,000 emigrant workers and 261,000 domestically unemployed. State sector includes state- owned industry 7.8%). Distribution data show only those domestically employed.

Unemployment Rate (17)

14% (October 1997) officially, but likely to be as high as 28%.

PRODUCTION SECTOR

Electric Energy (18)

Capacity . . . . .1.892 million kW (1995)

Production . . . . .4.435 billion kWh (1995)

Consumption per capita . . . . .1,314 kWh (1995)

Transportation (19)

Highways:

total: 18,000 km

paved: 5,400 km

unpaved: 12,600 km (1996 est.)

Waterways: 43 km plus Albanian sections of Lake Scutari, Lake Ohrid, and Lake Prespa (1990)

Pipelines: crude oil 145 km; petroleum products 55 km; natural gas 64 km (1991)

Merchant marine:

total: 8 cargo ships (1,000 GRT or over) totaling 36,582 GRT/54,832 DWT (1997 est.)

Airports: 9 (1997 est.)

Airports—with paved runways:

total: 5

2,438 to 3,047 m: 3

914 to 1,523 m: 2 (1997 est.)

Airports—with unpaved runways:

total: 4

over 3,047 m: 1

1,524 to 2,437 m: 1

914 to 1,523 m: 2 (1997 est.)

Top Agricultural Products (20)

Wide range of temperate-zone crops and livestock.

MANUFACTURING SECTOR

GDP & Manufacturing Summary (21)

Detailed value added figures are listed by both International Standard Industry Code (ISIC) and product title.

	1980	1985	1990	1994
GDP ($-1990 mil.)[1]	992	1,098	1,121	945
Per capita ($-1990)[1]	371	371	341	277
Manufacturing share (%) (current prices)[1]	29.9	28.0	26.3	NA
Manufacturing				
Value added ($-1990 mil.)[1]	245	298	295	*123*
Industrial production index	NA	NA	NA	NA
Value added ($ mil.)	580	675	300	*364*
Gross output ($ mil.)	NA	NA	NA	NA
Employment (000)	*165*	*204*	*252*	63
Profitability (% of gross output)				
Intermediate input (%)	NA	NA	NA	NA
Wages and salaries inc. supplements (%)	NA	NA	NA	NA
Gross operating surplus	NA	NA	NA	NA
Productivity ($)				
Gross output per worker	NA	NA	NA	NA
Value added per worker	3,463	3,307	1,190	5,817
Average wage (inc. supplements)	829	858	424	521
Value added ($ mil.)				
311/2 Food products	*151*	*147*	*60*	*40*
313 Beverages	*20*	*29*	*8*	*4*
314 Tobacco products	*5*	*6*	*3*	*1*
321 Textiles	*68*	*106*	*55*	*81*
322 Wearing apparel	*28*	*57*	*28*	*42*
323 Leather and fur products	*9*	*8*	*6*	*8*

	1980	1985	1990	1994
324 Footwear	13	16	9	13
331 Wood and wood products	25	19	8	8
332 Furniture and fixtures	23	16	8	8
341 Paper and paper products	3	7	4	5
342 Printing and publishing	7	7	3	5
351 Industrial chemicals	22	19	9	12
352 Other chemical products	10	7	4	5
353 Petroleum refineries	14	13	5	7
354 Miscellaneous petroleum and coal products	4	4	2	3
355 Rubber products	7	6	2	3
356 Plastic products	2	2	1	2
361 Pottery, china and earthenware	-	1	1	1
362 Glass and glass products	2	2	1	3
369 Other non-metal mineral products	21	23	13	18
371 Iron and steel	22	16	5	4
372 Non-ferrous metals	10	9	3	4
381 Metal products	8	10	4	5
382 Non-electrical machinery	35	59	25	35
383 Electrical machinery	27	31	15	22
384 Transport equipment	20	31	12	15
385 Professional and scientific equipment	4	5	2	4
390 Other manufacturing industries	19	16	4	6

FINANCE, ECONOMICS, & TRADE

Economic Indicators (22)

National product: GDP—purchasing power parity—$4.5 billion (1997 est.)

National product real growth rate: -8% (1997 est.)

National product per capita: $1,370 (1997 est.)

Inflation rate—consumer price index: 40% (1997 est.)

Exchange Rates (24)

Exchange rates:

Leke (L) per US$1

January 1998	152.28
1997	148.93
1996	104.50
1995	92.70
1994	94.62
1993	102.06

Top Import Origins (25)

$879 million (f.o.b., 1996 est.)

Origins	%
Italy	NA
Greece	NA
Bulgaria	NA
Turkey	NA
The Former Yugoslav Republic of Macedonia	NA

NA stands for not available.

Balance of Payments (23)

	1990	1992	1994	1995	1996
Exports of goods (f.o.b.)	322	70	141	205	244
Imports of goods (f.o.b.)	-456	-540	-601	-680	-922
Trade balance	-134	-470	-460	-475	-678
Services - debits	-31	-127	-174	-185	-201
Services - credits	32	23	134	171	213
Private transfers (net)	15	150	261	349	476
Government transfers (net)	NA	374	81	129	83
Overall balance	-32	-51	-157	-11	-107

Top Export Destinations (26)

$228 million (f.o.b., 1996 est.).

Destinations	%
Italy	NA
Greece	NA
Germany	NA
Belgium	NA
United States	NA

NA stands for not available.

Economic Aid (27)

Recipient: $630 million pledged 1997.

Import Export Commodities (28)

Import Commodities	Export Commodities
Machinery	Asphalt
Consumer goods	Metals and metallic ores
Grains	Electricity
	Crude oil
	Vegetables
	Fruits
	Tobacco

ALGERIA

Democratic and Popular Republic of Algeria
Al-Jumhuriyah al-Jaza'iriyah ad-Dimuqratiyah ash-Shaʿbiyah

INTRODUCTORY SURVEY

RECENT HISTORY

Algeria gained its independence from France in 1962. Its first president, Ahmed Ben Bella, was elected in 1963, and he took the country in a socialist direction. Foreign holdings were nationalized, but he was overthrown in a military coup on June 19, 1965.

The first parliamentary elections were held in December of 1991, but when a fundamentalist Islamic party received the largest number of votes, the military again voided the election. A bloody civil war ensued, and an estimated 100,000 persons were massacred. The civil war escalated in 1997–98 when Islamic extremists targeted defenseless villagers. Algeria has kept its borders sealed, and little real information is known.

The government authorized elections for April 1999 and seven candidates were to participate. However, the day before voters cast their ballots, six of the seven candidates withdrew claiming that the government had rigged the results. The sole candidate to remain in the race was former foreign minister Abdelaziz Bouteflika, who retained the support of the military. Although Bouteflika won an overwhelming majority, many supporters of his opponents took to the streets in protest.

Bouteflika's election was with nearly 74% of the votes. His September 1999 referendum of a peace plan passed with 98% of the vote.

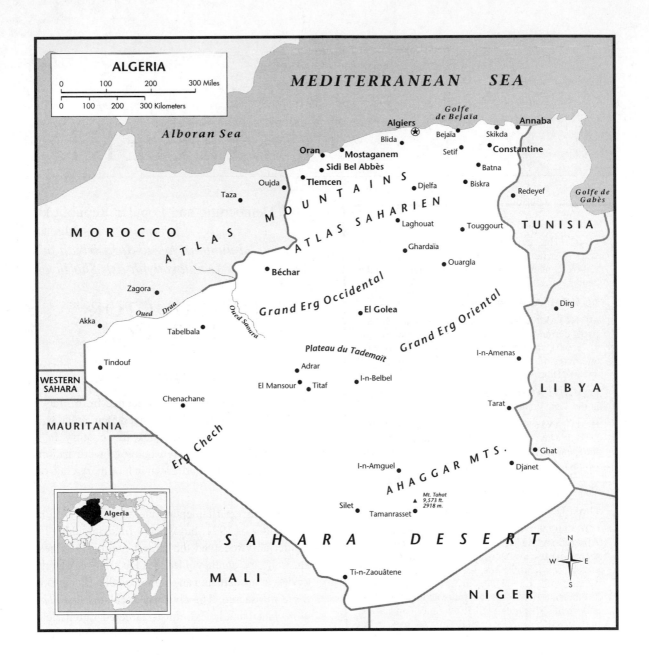

GOVERNMENT

Algerian voters approved a new constitution in 1996 that strengthened the already dominant role of the president. Under the new constitution, a second legislative body called the Council of the Nation would join the National Assembly. One-third of the council is appointed by the president, and the rest are elected by local and regional governments. The council must approve any legislation from the National Assembly with a three-fourths majority. The 380 deputies of the National Assembly are elected to five-year terms.

Since the 1991 constitution was suspended, the military has been the ultimate power in Algeria. In 1994, a retired general, Liamine Zeroual, was appointed to the presidency.

Judiciary

The judicial system now includes civil and military courts. Within each *wilayat* (district) is a court for civil and some criminal cases. At the head of the system is the Supreme Court. The Special Court of State Security was abolished in 1995. Algeria's present legal codes, adopted in 1963, are based on the laws of Islam and of other Northern African and Socialist states, as well as on French laws.

Political Parties

In September 1989 the government approved a multiparty system. By December 1990, over 30 legal political parties existed, including Islamic Salvation Front (FIS), National Liberation Front (FLN), and Socialist Forces Front (FFS).

With the annulment of the 1991 elections, several parties (including FIS) were outlawed. The main parties that took part in the June 1997 elections included the official government party known as the National Democratic Rally (RND); the Movement for a Peaceful Society (formerly Hamas); Ennahda (a moderate Islamic party); two ethnic Berber parties, the FFS and the Rally for Culture and Democracy; and the FLN, which now operates outside the government.

DEFENSE

Six months' military service is compulsory for males. Algeria's armed forces in 1996 totaled 121,500 members. The army had 105,000 officers and men, plus reserves of up to 150,000. The navy had 6,500 men. Vessels included 2 submarines, 3 frigates, 3 corvettes (frigates and corvettes are types of warships), and 11 missile patrol craft. The air force had 10,000 men, about 242 combat aircraft, and 60 combat helicopters.

ECONOMIC AFFAIRS

Agriculture produced less than 10% of the country's Gross Domestic Product (GDP) in 1995. Saharan oil and natural gas have been important export items since 1959, and they now dominate Algeria's economy, accounting for over 95% of total export value and over 25% of gross domestic product. Debt restructuring in 1994 and 1995 restored economic growth to 3% per year.

Public Finance

Because of the rise in petroleum revenues, government expenditures have increased rapidly since 1973. In 1996, revenues were $14.3 billion and expenditures were $17.9 billion. About 60% of total government revenue came from the petroleum and natural gas industries.

Income

In 1997, Algeria's Gross Domestic Product (GDP) was estimated at $120.4 billion at current prices, or a per capita of $4,000. Real growth rate was at 2.5%; inflation at 7%.

Industry

Industries, which are concentrated around Algiers and Oran, include carpet mills, cement factories, chemical plants, automobile assembly plants, food-processing plants, oil refineries, soap factories, and textile plants. Other major industries produce bricks and tiles, rolled steel, farm machinery, electrical supplies, machine tools, phosphates, sulfuric acid, paper and cartons, matches, and tobacco products.

In 1995, industrial production (in tons) included cement, 6.2 million; pig iron, 940,000; crude steel, 827,000; and refined lead, 8,000. Liquid petroleum gas (LPG) production totaled 9.5 million barrels in 1995.

Banking and Finance

The Central Bank of Algeria, created in December 1962, is the sole bank of issue. The Algerian Development Fund was established in 1963 to provide financial assistance for economic development. Following the separation of the French and Algerian treasuries in late 1962, the Directorate of Treasury and Credit was established as the government's fiscal agent. The state has also established cooperative banks. Private companies were permitted to set up money-changing shops following a directive issued in December 1996 by the Central Bank.

Foreign banks ceased operations after the nationalization of banks in 1963 and were absorbed by three government-owned banks including the Foreign Bank of Algeria, the National Bank of Algeria, and the People's Credit of Algeria. There are also four government banks for financing economic development and a savings institution that offers housing loans. These include the Algerian Development Bank, the Agriculture and Rural Development Bank, and the Maghreb Bank for Investment and Commerce. Foreign banks in Algeria include the Banque Nationale de Paris, Beogrossska Banka, Credit Lyonnais and Societe Generale. There are securities exchanges in Algeria.

Economic Development

Following independence in 1962, Algeria adopted an economic policy favoring a socialist organization of society.

The Boumedienne regime, while reaffirming Algeria's commitment to socialism, followed a gradual national development policy with deliberate economic planning and an emphasis on financial stability. The government's desire to create an atmosphere of confidence in Algeria's economy was reflected in the cautious pace of agrarian reform and the introduction of a new investment code in September 1966.

By OPEC standards, Algeria has a relatively high population and low per capita income; hence, it has concentrated on its own development requirements rather than on aid to other countries. Algeria's debt burden has increased since the mid-1980s due to lower oil prices and dollar weakness. At the end of 1996, the external debt totaled $34 billion.

SOCIAL WELFARE

Since the early 1960s, the government has repeatedly proposed a family code, based on Islamic principles, that would treat any woman as a legal minor for life, under the authority of her father, husband, or other male head of the family. In part because of opposition by the National Union of Algerian Women, the proposed code was withdrawn by the Council of Ministers after it had been submitted to the National Assembly in early 1982. A compromise code was passed in 1984 that did not fully address the objections of women's groups.

Ethnic tensions exist between Arabs and Berbers, who were Algeria's original inhabitants. In 1995, the government created the High Commission for Berber Affairs to protect and promote Berber language and culture.

Healthcare

The principal health problems have been tuberculosis, malaria, trachoma, and malnutrition. By 1990, the incidence of tuberculosis was 53 in 100,000. In 1995, the average life expectancy was 70 years, with a death rate of 7 per 1,000 people. Infant mortality in 1995 was 34 per 1,000 live births, with 775,000 births that same year. Medical care provided by the government was introduced in 1974 under a Social Security system, which reimburses 80% of private consultations and prescription drugs.

Housing

The need for adequate housing is a serious problem in Algeria. The average number of persons per dwelling was 6.9 in 1987, compared to 5.9 in 1966.

EDUCATION

Education is officially compulsory for children between the ages of 6 and 15. Adult literacy stood at 57%. In 1994–95 there were a total of 166,771

teachers and 4.5 million students in primary schools. There are 10 universities along with 5 centers, 7 colleges, and 5 institutes for higher learning. The University of Algiers (founded in 1909) and other regional universities enrolled 257,379 students in 1992.

1999 KEY EVENTS TIMELINE

January

- Since President Liamine Zeroual's September 1998 surprise decision to cut his own term short, the only official declared candidate is Abdelaziz Bouteflika. Bouteflika is a former foreign minister who has remained detached from the political scene for 18 years. He has the support of the National Liberation Front (FLN). Expectations are that he will emerge as the military's candidate.

March

- Suspicions are raised over the government's role in the country's violence. Estimates are that over 80,000 Algerians have been killed in terrorist attacks since 1992 in Algeria's civil war. The battle wages between Islamic fundamentalists, mainly the Armed Islamic Group (GIA), and nationalist and secular government security forces.

- Meetings in Saudi Arabia of the Gulf Cooperation Council (GCC) propose a cut by OPEC and non-OPEC oil producers of 2.3 million barrels per day (bpd). In order to revive depressed oil prices OPEC members Saudi Arabia, Venezuela, Algeria and Iran, and non-OPEC Mexico meet to discuss the GCC proposed cuts. An OPEC deal sets oil prices at $15 per barrel.

- The seven candidates for the election begin their formal campaigns on March 25.

- A natural gas line linking Beni Mansour with Algiers is sabotaged on March 27 by an unidentified group.

April

- Algeria and Kuwait sign an agreement for a $600 million fertilizer plant at Ennaba, Algeria, northeast of Algiers.

- Six presidential candidates pull out of the race on the evening before elections are to take place. The six accuse the *pouvoir* (the Algerian power elite made up of senior politicians and generals) of fixing the election.

- The presidential elections goes forward on April 15 with only one real candidate, although the names of the six candidates who pulled out of the election remain on the ballot. Former Foreign Minister Abdelaziz Bouteflika is declared elected.

- Riot police in Algiers attack several hundred protesters yelling anti-Bouteflika slogans. Many voters state that they voted out of fear that by having the wrong stamp on their registration cards, local government officials may deny them services in the future.

- Bouteflika is formally named the winner of the presidential election and he takes office April 20.

June

- The Islamic Salvation Army (AIS), the armed faction of the Islamic Salvation Front (FIS), ends its struggle against the government. Bouteflika agrees to grant amnesty to Muslim rebels who reject violence.

- Twenty-one Islamic guerrillas are reported killed by government security forces.

- Official Algerian radio reports that the conflict between Muslim guerrillas and government forces have resulted in 100,000 deaths and over 1,000,000 victims during the seven years of rebellion.

- Fourteen are killed in an attack by an armed group on a village south of Algiers, a region of Islamic insurgency.

July

- French President Chirac and Algerian President Bouteflika meet briefly at the funeral of Morocco's King Hassan. France decides to reopen its consulates and cultural centers in Algeria which have been closed since late 1993 due to violence in Algeria, but Air France has yet to resume flights to Algeria.

- The Algiers stock exchange officially opens on July 28.

- Seven pro-government militia are killed on July 31 when suspected Muslim rebels bomb a military convoy 300 kilometers south of Algiers.

August

- In a strong stance against corruption, twenty-two of Algeria's forty-seven provincial governors are dismissed by Bouteflika.

- By decree on August 1, Bouteflika sets a national referendum for his peace initiatives for September 16.

- With bombs and machine guns, Muslim rebels kill nineteen in an attack on August 7.

- Algeria announces on August 11 that it will open its land border with Morocco in an effort to normalize relations between the two countries.

- Thirty Algerians are massacred by Muslim guerrillas in an August 15 attack on Beni Ounif, a town on the border with Morocco. The next day, a fake roadblock is used to stop cars near Bouaich village, where twenty-five rebels massacre twenty-nine people with shotguns and meat cleavers.

- Burlington Resources Inc. successfully stikes oil and gas in the Berkins basin of Algeria.

September

- French oil company Elf Aquitaine announces on September 15 that it will return to Algeria after a thirty-year absence.

- Algeria announces it will permit Amnesty International to visit.

- A national referendum is held September 16 on Bouteflika's peace initiatives. Eighty-five percent of 17.5 million voters cast ballots, and almost ninety-nine percent approve the referendum, and Bouteflika gets his mandate.

- Youssef Yousfi, Algeria's Energy and Mining Minister and current president of OPEC (Organization of Petroleum-Exporting Countries), withdraws his candidacy for OPEC secretary-general.

- French Prime Minister Lionel Jospin and President Bouteflika announce September 21 that relations between France and Algeria are returning to normal.

- The Armed Islamic Group (GIA) stops two cars at a fake roadblock set up on September 29. Forcing the seven occupants out of their cars, the rebels slash their throats.

October

- Algeria has trade surplus of $1.19 billion in the first nine months of 1999.

- President Bouteflika is attacked for speaking French publicly. Arabic is the only official language of Algeria and officials are banned from speaking publicly in any other language.

- On October 23, more rebels surrender under President Bouteflika's amnesty provisions, bringing the total number of surrenders under the amnesty program since July 13, 1999 to 1,130.

- During October 24 and 25, rebels kill a militiaman and three children gathering firewood in two separate attacks. Government troops retaliate by killing thirteen GIA rebels.

- To further his campaign against corruption, Bouteflika dismisses eight deputy governors and 73 council chiefs on October 28. Another twelve deputy governors and 235 council chiefs are transferred to other provinces and councils. Fifteen new deputies and 87 new council heads are appointed.

November

- In spite of living under constant police surveillance, respected Islamist leader Abdelkader Hachani is assassinated by a lone gunman in his dentist's waiting room in Algiers; the killer escapes.

December

- President Abdelaziz Bouteflika names Ahmed Benbitour to be the new prime minister.

ANALYSIS OF EVENTS: 1999

BUSINESS AND THE ECONOMY

Algeria's debt service obligation is at its peak. This debt has already been restructured twice before in the last five years. Restructuring a third time would limit the ability to attract foreign investment to create new jobs. Estimates are that debt service in 1999 would require half the annual income, or about $6 billion.

The hydrocarbon sector is the backbone of the economy. Algeria has been severely affected by the collapse of oil prices. Algeria's export income is based on oil and natural gas accounting for 96 percent of exports. Total exports dropped by over $3,000 million in 1998 and foreign exchange reserves declined prior to January 1999. A budget deficit of five percent of Gross Domestic Product (GDP) occurred in 1998 and the five percent deficit of GDP was projected in 1999. The oil price also affects earnings from natural gas as the formulas for gas pricing are related to the oil pricing. Algeria has the world's fifth-largest natural gas reserve and is the second largest natural gas exporter. Its oil reserves are the 14th largest in the world. In September oil ministers of Algeria, Iran, Iraq, Saudi Arabia agreed that cuts in oil production agreed upon in March 1999 should be kept in place until March 2000.

Welfare and education budgets were cut as these revenues decreased. About 40 percent of the oil revenues financed the civil war. Power consumption is expected to grow by eight percent this year.

Algeria's reforms backed by the International Monetary Fund (IMF) are aimed at its making a transition from a state-controlled economy to an economy dominated by the private sector. These reforms include privatization of agriculture and of the financial system. An infrastructure issue related to agriculture is that less than 10 percent of Algeria's agricultural land is irrigated. Algeria imports wheat mainly from the United States, but in April, Algeria bought French wheat for the first time in two years. The purchase was for 150,000 tons, followed by another purchase of 275,000 tons before June. Total exports from France to Algeria in the first half of 1999 were valued at $1 billion.

These unpopular economic reform programs under outgoing President Zeroual have resulted in the loss of 400,000 public sector jobs. In 1997 the IMF placed Algeria's unemployment rate at a staggering 26.4 percent. More current estimates place it at about 30 percent. There is little chance of large-scale new jobs to alleviate this chronic unemployment. Even with large foreign firms like Coca Cola and Saidal pharmaceuticals investing in Algeria, these are typically capital intensive industries with limited job creation potential.

GOVERNMENT AND POLITICS

The army maintains 120,000 front line troops; 80 percent of these are conscripted. The army is under increasing attack by Islamic militants. The rebels ambush military convoys and when soldiers are killed their weapons are seized. Removing troops from critical areas to defend the polling places leaves other civilians unprotected.

A presidential election, which had raised hopes, turned into a disappointing process. When six of the seven candidates dropped out over voting irregularities on the eve of the election, the outcome became a foregone conclusion. The sole candidate, Abdelaziz Bouteflika, was backed by the military. A supposed "candidate of consensus," this image was shattered as he stood alone. Voters were skeptical and disillusioned. The election was considered a sideshow, a distraction, a "no hope" situation. Two out of three voters were under 30 with little feeling for old-guard politics and politicians. Algeria's two main international allies, France and the U.S., considered the election a disappointing sign of movement away from freedom and democracy.

President Bouteflika made extensive efforts to mend ties internally and externally. He renewed contacts with his neighbors—Israel, France, and Morocco—and Western countries. He also alienated Morocco again by blaming the August massacre at Beni Ounif on guerrillas who crossed the border from Morocco and accused Morocco of being and "international provider of narcotics." In a United Nations address to the General Assembly Bouteflika raised issues surrounding the concept of "humanitarian interference." He warned the rich north against interference in the internal affairs of the poorer southern countries of the world.

CULTURE AND SOCIETY

In July 1999 the Algerian population was estimated to be 31,133,486. Infant mortality was high at 43.82 deaths per 1,000 live births. Only three percent of the land is arable. The quality of life is further compromised by environmental degradation—soil erosion from overgrazing and poor farming practices, dumping of raw sewage, and petroleum refining wastes. Waterways and the Mediterranean Sea are becoming polluted from oil wastes, soil erosion, and fertilizer runoff, and there are inadequate supplies of potable water.

As the economic duress increases, the health, welfare, and education of Algerians has suffered with budget cuts. Seventy percent of Algerians are under 30 years of age. Communications are improving with over 1.3 million telephones in service and 5,200 cellular subscribers.

DIRECTORY

CENTRAL GOVERNMENT

Head of State

President
Abdelaziz Bouteflika, El Mouradia, Algiers, Algeria
PHONE: +213(2) 600366
FAX: +213 (2) 609618

Prime Minister
Ahmed Benbitour, El Mouradia, Algiers, Algeria
PHONE: +213 (2) 600366
FAX: +213 (2) 609618

Ministers

Minister of Agriculture and Fisheries
Boulahouadjeb Benalia, Ministry of Agriculture and Fisheries, 4, rue des Quatre Canons, Algiers, Algeria
PHONE: +213 (2) 711712
FAX: +213 (2) 612542

Minister of Commerce
Bakhti Belaïb, Ministry of Commerce, Palais du Gouvernement Algiers, Algiers, Algeria
PHONE: +213 (2) 732340
FAX: +213 (2) 733091

Minister of Communication, Culture and Government Spokesman
Abdelaziz Rahabi, Ministry of Communication, Culture and Government Spokesman

Minister of Energy and Mines
Youcef Yousfi, Ministry of Energy and Mines

Minister of Equipment and Urban and Rural Development
Abderrahmane Belayat, Ministry of Equipment and Urban and Rural Development, Ex-Grand Seminaire Kouba, Algiers, Algeria
PHONE: +213 (2) 689503
FAX: +213 (2) 747543

Minister of Finance
Abdelkrim Harchaoui, Ministry of Finance, Palais du Gouvernement, Algiers, Algeria
PHONE: +213 (2) 732340
FAX: +213 (2) 735472

Minister of Foreign Affairs
Ahmed Attaf, Ministry of Foreign Affairs

Minister of Health and Population
Yahia Guidoum, Ministry of Health and Population

Minister of Higher Education and Scientific Research
Amar Tou, Ministry of Higher Education and Scientific Research

Minister of Housing
Abdelkader Bounekraf, Ministry of Housing

Minister of Industry and Restructuring
Abdelmadjid Menasra, Ministry of Industry and Restructuring, Immeuble Le Colisee, Algiers, Algeria
PHONE: +213 (2) 592440
FAX: +213 (2) 604584

Minister of Interior, Local Communities and Environment
Abdelmalek Sellal, Ministry of Interior, Local Communities and Environment
FAX: +213 (2) 2606106

Minister of Justice
Ghaouti Mekamcha, Ministry of Justice

Minister of Labor, Social Protection and Vocational Training
Hacene Laskri, Ministry of Labor, Social Protection and Vocational Training

Minister of National Education
Boubakeur Benbouzid, Ministry of National Education

Minister of National Solidarity and Family
Rabea Mechernene, Ministry of National Solidarity and Family

Minister of Posts and Telecommunications
Mohamed Salah Youyou, Ministry of Posts and Telecommunications, 4, bd Krim Belkacem, Algiers, Algeria
PHONE: +213 (2) 711220
FAX: +213 (2) 711771

Minister of Religious Affairs
Bouabdallah Ghoulemallah, Ministry of Religious Affairs

Minister of Small and Medium-Sized Enterprises
Bougerra Soltani, Ministry of Small and Medium-Sized Enterprises, Immeuble Le Colisee, Algiers, Algeria
PHONE: +213 (2) 592232
FAX: +213 (2) 592658

Minister of Tourism and Handicrafts
Abdelkader Bengrina, Ministry of Tourism and Handicrafts

Minister of Transportation
Sid Ahmed Boulil, Ministry of Transportation, 119, rue Didouche Mourad, Algiers, Algeria
PHONE: +213 (2) 747506
FAX: +213 (2) 646637

Minister of Veterans Affairs
Said Abadou, Ministry of Veterans Affairs

Minister of Youth and Sports
Mohamed Aziz Derouaz, Ministry of Youth and Sports

Minister in Charge of Relations with Parliament
Mohamed Kachoud, Ministry in Charge of Relations with Parliament

POLITICAL ORGANIZATIONS

Islamic Salvation Front (FIS, outlawed April 1992)
TITLE: Secretary General
NAME: Ali Benhadj

National Liberation Front (FLN)
TITLE: Secretary General
NAME: Boualem Benhamouda

Socialist Forces Front (FFS)
TITLE: Secretary General
NAME: Hocine Ait Ahmed (self-exile in Switzerland)

Movement of a Peaceful Society (MSP or Hamas)
TITLE: Chairman
NAME: Mahfoud Nahnah

Rally for Culture and Democracy (RCD)
TITLE: Secretary General
NAME: Said Saadi

Algerian Renewal Party (PRA)
TITLE: Chairman
NAME: Noureddine Boukrouh

Al Nahda (Nada Movement)
TITLE: President
NAME: Abdallah Djaballah

Democratic National Rally (RND)
TITLE: Chairman
NAME: Ahmed Ben Bella

Worker's Party (PT)

TITLE: Chairman
NAME: Louisa Hanoun

Republican Progressive Party

TITLE: Chairman
NAME: Khadir Driss

Union for Democracy and Freedoms

TITLE: Chairman
NAME: Mouley Boukhalafa

Liberal Social Party

TITLE: Chairman
NAME: Ahmed Khelil

Democratic National Rally (RND)

TITLE: Chairman
NAME: Abdelkader Bensalah

Movement for Democracy in Algeria (MDA)

NAME: Ahmed Ben Bella

DIPLOMATIC REPRESENTATION

Embassies in Algeria

Albania
19/S, rue Abd el-Karim, Lagoune el-Mouradia, Algiers, Algeria
PHONE: +213 (2) 662890

Angola
14, rue Curie el-Biar, Algiers, Algeria
PHONE: +213 (2) 925441
FAX: +213 (2) 797441

Argentina
26, rue Finaltieri el-Biar, Algiers, Algeria

Australia
12, Emile Marquis Djenane el-Malik Hydra, Algiers, Algeria
PHONE: +213 (2) 602846

Austria
Les Vergers, rue 2, Villa 9 Bir Khadem, Algiers, Algeria
PHONE: +213 (2) 562699
FAX: +213 (2) 567352

Bangladesh
140, avenue des Maouradie Frères Oughlis, Le Golf, Algiers, Algeria
PHONE: +213 (2) 603629

FAX: +213 (2) 594616

Belgium
22, chemin Youcef Tayebi el-Blair, Le Golf, Algiers, Algeria
PHONE: +213 (2) 602446
FAX: +213 (2) 925036

Benin
36, Lot du Stade Birkhadem, B.P. 156, el-Harrach, Algeria
PHONE: +213 (2) 566271

Brazil
10, chemin Laroussi Messaoud Les Glycines, B.P. 186, Algiers, Algeria
PHONE: +213 (2) 749575
FAX: +213 (2) 749687

Bulgaria
13, boulevard Colonel M'Hamed Bougara el-Biar, Algiers, Algeria
PHONE: +213 (2) 691514
FAX: +213 (2) 691787

Burkina Faso
10, rue du Vercors El-Hammadia, Algiers, Algeria
PHONE: +213 (2) 942677
FAX: +213 (2) 942535

Cameroon
34, rue Yahia Mazouni, Bougara 16011 el-Biar, Algiers, Algeria
PHONE: +213 (2) 921124
FAX: +213 (2) 921125

Canada
27 bis, rue Ali Messaoudi, B.P. 225, Gare 16000, Algiers, Algeria
PHONE: +213 (2) 606611
FAX: +213 (2) 605920; 693920

Chad
6, rue Sylvain Fourastier, Cité DNC Villa No. 18, Hydra, Algeria
PHONE: +213 (2) 692662
FAX: +213 (2) 692663

People's Republic of China
4, boulevard des Martyrs, Algiers, Algeria
PHONE: +213 (2) 602724
FAX: +213 (2) 592962; 692962

Colombia
7, avenue Malika Gaid el-Biar, Algiers, Algeria
PHONE: +213 (2) 922090
FAX: +213 (2) 923817

Democratic Republic of Congo
5, rue St. Georges Kouba, Algiers, Algeria
PHONE: +213 (2) 591227

Republic of Congo
111, Parc Ben Omar Kouba, Algiers, Algeria
PHONE: +213 (2) 586800

Côte d'Ivoire
Immeuble Le Bosquet Parc 6 Le Paradou,
Hydra, Algiers, Algeria
PHONE: +213 (2) 602378; 692378
FAX: +213 (2) 693683

Croatia
5, rue des Crêtes Hydra, Algiers, Algeria
PHONE: +213 (2) 961835
FAX: +213 (2) 691781

Cuba
22, avenue Larbi Alik Hydra, Algiers, Algeria
PHONE: +213 (2) 692148
FAX: +213 (2) 693281

Czech Republic
Villa Malika 7, chemin Ziryab, B.P. 999,
Algiers, Algeria
PHONE: +213 (2) 600525; 692274
FAX: +213 (2) 693031

Denmark
12, Émile Marquis Lot, Djenane el-Malik,
Hydra, Algiers 16035, Algeria
PHONE: +213 (2) 692234
FAX: +213 (2) 692846

Egypt
8, chemin Adb el-Kader, Gadouche, B.P. 297,
Hydra, Algiers 16300, Algeria
PHONE: +213 (2) 601673
FAX: +213 (2) 602952

Finland
4, boulevard Mohammed V, B.P. 256, Hydra,
Algiers 16035, Algeria
PHONE: +213 (2) 691292
FAX: +213 (2) 691637

France
chemin Abd el-Kader Gadouche, Hydra, Algiers,
Algeria
PHONE: +213 (2) 692488
FAX: +213 (2) 691369

Gabon
21, rue Hadj Mohammed, Hydra, Algiers,
Algeria
PHONE: +213 (2) 692400
FAX: +213 (2) 602546

Germany
165, chemin Sfindja, B.P. 664, Algiers, Algeria
PHONE: +213 (2) 741956
FAX: +213 (2) 740521

Ghana
62, rue Frères Benali Abdellah, Hydra, Algiers,
Algeria
PHONE: +213 (2) 606444
FAX: +213 (2) 692856

Greece
60, boulevard Col. Bougara, Hydra, Algiers,
Algeria
PHONE: +213 (2) 600855
FAX: +213 (2) 691655

Guinea
43, boulevard Centrel Said Hamdine, Hydra,
Algiers, Algeria
PHONE: +213 (2) 600611
FAX: +213 (2) 600468

Guinea-Bissau
17, rue Ahmed Kara, Hydra, Algiers, Algeria
PHONE: +213 (2) 609725

Hungary
18, avenue des Frères Oughlis, B.P. 68, el-
Mouradia, Algeria
PHONE: +213 (2) 697975
FAX: +213 (2) 693431

India
119, rue Didouche Mourad, Algiers, Algeria
PHONE: +213 (2) 747135
FAX: +213 (2) 748513

Indonesia
16, chemin Abd el-Kader Gadouchee, el-
Mouradia, Algiers 16070, Algeria
PHONE: +213 (2) 632011
FAX: +213 (2) 693931

Iran
84 bis, rue des Trois Frères Djillali, Algiers,
Algeria
PHONE: +213 (2) 566614

Iraq
4, rue Arezki Abri, Hydra, Algiers, Algeria
PHONE: +213 (2) 691097

Italy
18, rue Mohammed Ouidir Amellel el-Biar,
Algiers, Algeria
PHONE: +213 (2) 922330
FAX: +213 (2) 793766

Japan
1, chemin el-Bakri el-Biar, Algiers, Algeria
PHONE: +213 (2) 912004; 921255
FAX: +213 (2) 912046; 924293

Jordan
6, rue du Chenoua, Hydra, Algiers, Algeria
PHONE: +213 (2) 602031

Democratic People's Republic of Korea (North Korea)
49, rue Abd el-Rezak Hamia Bologhine, Algiers, Algeria
PHONE: +213 (2) 602031

Republic of Korea (South Korea)
21, rue Abd el-Kader Stambouli, el-Mouradia, Algiers, Algeria
PHONE: +213 (2) 692060
FAX: +213 (2) 693014

Kuwait
chemin Abd el-Kader Gadouche, Hydra, Algiers, Algeria
PHONE: +213 (2) 593157

Lebanon
9, rue Kaid Ahmed el-Biar, Hydra, Algiers, Algeria
PHONE: +213 (2) 782094

Libya
15, chemin Bachir el-Ibrahimi el-Biar, Algiers, Algeria
PHONE: +213 (2) 921502
FAX: +213 (2) 924687

Madagascar
22, rue Abd el-Kadar Aouis Bologhine, Algiers, Algeria
PHONE: +213 (2) 623196
FAX: +213 (2) 577169

Mali
Cité DNC, Villa No. 15, chemin Ahmed Kara, Hydra, Algiers, Algeria
PHONE: +213 (2) 691351
FAX: +213 (2) 692082

Malta
24, Niveau C Hotel Aurassi 2, avenue Frantz Fanon, Algiers, Algeria
PHONE: +213 (2) 631974

Mauritania
107, Lot Baranès el-Hamadya Bouzaréah, Algiers, Algeria

Mexico
21, rue du Commandant Amar Azzouz el-Biar, B.P. 329, Algiers, Algeria
PHONE: +213 (2) 924023
FAX: +213 (2) 923451

Morocco
8, rue des Cé, B.P. 329, Algiers, Algeria
PHONE: +213 (2) 607408; 607737
FAX: +213 (2) 605900

The Netherlands
23, chemin Cheikh Bashir el-Ibrahimi el-Biar, B.P. 72, Algiers, Algeria
PHONE: +213 (2) 782829; 922828
FAX: +213 (2) 780770

Niger
54, rue Vercois Rostamia, el-Hamadya Bouzareah, Algiers, Algeria
PHONE: +213 (2) 788921
FAX: +213 (2) 789713

Nigeria
27 bis, rue Blaise Pascal, B.P. 629, Algiers, Algeria
PHONE: +213 (2) 691849
FAX: +213 (2) 691175

Oman
53, rue Djamel Eddine, el-Afghani, Bouzareah, Algiers, Algeria
PHONE: +213 (2) 941310
FAX: +213 (2) 941375

Pakistan
14, avenue Souidani Boudjemaa, B.P. 1023, Algiers, Algeria
PHONE: +213 (2) 693781
FAX: +213 (2) 692212

Poland
37, avenue Mustapha Ali, Khodja el-Biar, Algiers, Algeria
PHONE: +213 (2) 922553
FAX: +213 (2) 921435

Portugal
12, Lot el-Feth el-Biar, Algiers, Algeria
PHONE: +213 (2) 925313
FAX: +213 (2) 745313

Qatar
7, chemin Doudou Mokhtar, B.P. 118, Algiers, Algeria
PHONE: +213 (2) 922856
FAX: +213 (2) 922415

Romania
24, rue Abri Arezki, Hydra, Algiers, Algeria

PHONE: +213 (2) 600871
FAX: +213 (2) 693642

Russia
7, chemin du Prince d'Annam el-Bair, Algiers, Algeria
PHONE: +213 (2) 923139
FAX: +213 (2) 782882

Serbia
7, rue des Frères Benhafid, B.P. 209, Hydra, Algiers, Algeria
PHONE: +213 (2) 6691218
FAX: +213 (2) 693472

Saudi Arabia
62, rue Med. Drafini, Hydra, Algiers, Algeria
PHONE: +213 (2) 603518

Senegal
B.P. 379, Alger-Gare, Algiers, Algeria
PHONE: +213 (2) 691627
FAX: +213 (2) 692684

Slovakia
7, chemin du Zirajab Didouche, Mourad 16006, Algiers, Algeria
PHONE: +213 (2) 693525
FAX: +213 (2) 692197

Spain
10, rue Med. Chabane el-Biar, Algiers, Algeria
PHONE: +213 (2) 922713
FAX: +213 (2) 922719

Sudan
45, rue des Jardins Djnane el-Malik, Hydra, Algiers, Algeria
PHONE: +213 (2) 608048
FAX: +213 (2) 607019

Sweden
rue Olof Palme Paradou, Hydra, Algiers, Algeria
PHONE: +213 (2) 692300

Switzerland
27, boulevard Zighout Youcef, Algiers, Alger-Gare DZ-16000, Algeria
PHONE: +213 (2) 737310
FAX: +213 (2) 738158

Syria
11, Domaine Tamzali Chemin A. Gadouche, Hydra, Algiers, Algeria
PHONE: +213 (2) 912026
FAX: +213 (2) 912030

Tunisia
11, rue du Bois de Boulogne, Hydra, Algiers, Algeria

PHONE: +213 (2) 601388
FAX: +213 (2) 692316

Turkey
Dar el-Ouard, chemin de la Rochelle Bd. Colonel Bougara, Algiers, Algeria
PHONE: +213 (2) 691257
FAX: +213 (2) 693161

United Arab Emirates
19, rue Frères Benhafid, Hydra, B.P. 454, Algiers,, Algeria
PHONE: +213 (2) 692574
FAX: +213 (2) 593770

United Kingdom
Residence Cassiopé, e 7, chemin des Glycines, B.P. 43, Alger-Gare DZ-16000, Algeria
PHONE: +213 (2) 692411
FAX: +213 (2) 692410

United States
chemin Cheikh Bachir el-Ibrahimi, B.P. 549, Alger-Gare DZ-16000, Algeria
PHONE: +213 (2) 60 11 86
FAX: +213 (2) 603979

Uruguay
chemin Poitton el-Biar, Algiers, Algeria
PHONE: +213 (2) 789420

Vatican City
rue Nourredine Mekiri Bologhine, Algiers 16090, Algeria
PHONE: +213 (2) 623430
FAX: +213 (2) 572375

Venezuela
rue Impasse Ahmed kara el-Mouradia, B.P. 813, Algiers, Algeria
PHONE: +213 (2) 693846
FAX: +213 (2) 693555

Vietnam
30, rue de Chenoua, Hydra, Algiers, Algeria
PHONE: +213 (2) 600752

Yemen
Villa 19, Citè DNC, rue Ahmed Kara, Hydra, Algiers, Algeria
PHONE: +213 (2) 693085
FAX: +213 (2) 691758

Zimbabwe
5, chemin des Vieillards Bouzaréah, B.P. 69, Algiers, Algeria
PHONE: +213 (2) 798250

JUDICIAL SYSTEM
Supreme Court

FURTHER READING
Books

Andersson, Christian. *Peasant of Proletarian? Wage Labour and Peasant Economy During Industrialization: The Algerian Experience.* Sweden: Almqvist and Wiksell International, 1985.

Bennoune, Mahfoud. *The Making of Contemporary Algeria, 1830-1987: Colonial Upheavals and Post-Independence Development.* Cambridge: Cambridge University Press, 1988.

Boissier, Gaston. *Roman Africa: Archaeological Walks in Algeria and Tunis.* New York: G. P. Putnam's Sons, 1999.

Christelow, Allan. *Muslim Law Courts and the French Colonial State in Algeria.* Princeton, N.J.: Princeton University Press, 1985.

Kaye, Jacqueline, and Abdelhamid Zoubir. *The Ambiguous Compromise: Language, Literature, and National Identity in Algeria and Morocco.* London: Routledge, 1990.

Lorcin, Patricia M. E. *Imperial Identities: Stereotyping, Prejudice and Race in Colonial Algeria.* London: I. B. Tauris Publishers, 1995.

Lustick, Ian S. *Unsettled States, Disputed Lands: Britain and Ireland, France and Algeria, Israel and the West Bank-Gaza.* Ithaca, N.Y.: Cornell University Press, 1993.

MacMaster, Neil. *Colonial Migrants and Racism: Algerians in France, 1900–62.* New York: St. Martin's Press Inc., 1997.

Metz, Helen Chapin. *Algeria, A Country Study.* Area Handbook Studies. Washington, D.C.: Federal Research Division, Library of Congress. U.S. Government, Department of the Army, 1994.

Potter, T. W. *Towns in Late Antiquity.* Ian Sanders Memorial Fund, Occasional Publications. Oxford: Oxbow Books, 1995.

Sumruld, William A. *Augustine and the Arians: The Bishop of Hippo's Encounters with Ulfilan Arianism.* London: Associated University Presses, 1994.

Internet

Algeria Info. Available Online @ http://www.algeriainfo.com. (Accessed November 2, 1999).

People's Democratic Republic of Algeria, London Website. Available Online @ http://www.consalglond.u-net.com. (Accessed November 2, 1999).

World Algerian Action Coalition. Available Online @ http://www.waac.org. (Accessed November 2, 1999).

ALGERIA: STATISTICAL DATA

For sources and notes see "Sources of Statistics" in the front of each volume.

GEOGRAPHY

Geography (1)

Area:

Total: 2,381,740 sq km.

Land: 2,381,740 sq km.

Water: 0 sq km.

Area—comparative: slightly less than 3.5 times the size of Texas.

Land boundaries:

Total: 6,343 km.

Border countries: Libya 982 km, Mali 1,376 km, Mauritania 463 km, Morocco 1,559 km, Niger 956 km, Tunisia 965 km, Western Sahara 42 km.

Coastline: 998 km.

Climate: arid to semiarid; mild, wet winters with hot, dry summers along coast; drier with cold winters and hot summers on high plateau; sirocco is a hot, dust/sand-laden wind especially common in summer.

Terrain: mostly high plateau and desert; some mountains; narrow, discontinuous coastal plain.

Natural resources: petroleum, natural gas, iron ore, phosphates, uranium, lead, zinc.

Land use:

Arable land: 3%

Permanent crops: 0%

Permanent pastures: 13%

Forests and woodland: 2%

Other: 82% (1993 est.).

HUMAN FACTORS

Demographics (2A)

	1990	1995	1998	2000	2010	2020	2030	2040	2050
Population	25,351.8	28,539.3	30,480.8	31,787.6	38,478.6	44,783.3	50,408.6	55,240.9	58,879.8
Net migration rate (per 1,000 population)	NA	NA	NA	NA	NA	NA	NA	NA	NA
Births	NA	NA	NA	NA	NA	NA	NA	NA	NA
Deaths	NA	NA	NA	NA	NA	NA	NA	NA	NA
Life expectancy - males	65.4	66.9	67.8	68.4	70.9	73.0	74.7	76.1	77.2
Life expectancy - females	67.4	69.1	70.1	70.8	73.8	76.4	78.6	80.4	81.8
Birth rate (per 1,000)	32.2	29.0	27.5	26.5	22.3	18.2	16.1	14.5	13.2
Death rate (per 1,000)	7.0	6.1	5.6	5.4	4.8	4.7	5.4	6.6	8.0
Women of reproductive age (15-49 yrs.)	5,739.7	6,900.4	7,701.1	8,267.9	10,480.7	12,211.0	13,322.1	13,515.3	13,629.1
of which are currently married	NA	NA	NA	NA	NA	NA	NA	NA	NA
Fertility rate	4.4	3.7	3.4	3.2	2.5	2.2	2.1	2.0	2.0

Except as noted, values for vital statistics are in thousands; life expectancy is in years.

Health Personnel (3)

Total health expenditure as a percentage of GDP, 1990-1997[a]

Public sector 3.3

Private sector 1.3

Total[b] 4.6

Health expenditure per capita in U.S. dollars, 1990-1997[a]

Purchasing power parity 210

Total 85

Availability of health care facilities per 100,000 people

Hospital beds 1990-1997[a] 210

Doctors 1993[c] 83

Nurses 1993[c] . . . . .NA

Health Indicators (4)

Life expectancy at birth

1980 59

1997 70

Daily per capita supply of calories (1996) 3,020

Total fertility rate births per woman (1997) 3.6

Maternal mortality ratio per 100,000 live births (1990-97) . . . . .140[b]

Safe water % of population with access (1995) . . . .

Sanitation % of population with access (1995) . . . .

Consumption of iodized salt % of households (1992-98)[a] 92

Smoking prevalence

Male % of adults (1985-95)[a] 53

Female % of adults (1985-95)[a] 10

Tuberculosis incidence per 100,000 people (1997) 44

Adult HIV prevalence % of population ages 15-49 (1997) 0.07

Infants and Malnutrition (5)

Under-5 mortality rate (1997) 39

% of infants with low birthweight (1990-97) 9

Births attended by skilled health staff % of total[a] . . .77

% fully immunized (1995-97)

TB 94

DPT 79

Polio 79

Measles 74

Prevalence of child malnutrition under age 5 (1992-97)[b] 13

Ethnic Division (6)

Arab-Berber 99%

European . . . .<1%

Religions (7)

Sunni Muslim (state religion) 99%

Christian and Jewish 1%

Languages (8)

Arabic (official), French, Berber dialects.

EDUCATION

Public Education Expenditures (9)

Public expenditure on education (% of GNP)

1980 . . . . .7.8

1996 . . . . .5.1

Expenditure per student

Primary % of GNP per capita

1980 . . . .

1996 . . . . .26.4

Secondary % of GNP per capita

1980 . . . . .23.9

1996 . . . .

Tertiary % of GNP per capita

1980 . . . .

1996 . . . .

Expenditure on teaching materials

Primary % of total for level (1996) . . . .

Secondary % of total for level (1996) . . . .

Primary pupil-teacher ratio per teacher (1996) 27

Duration of primary education years (1995) 6

Literacy Rates (11A)

In thousands and percent[1]	1990	1995	2000	2010
Illiterate population (15+ yrs.)	6,570	6,582	6,484	5,916
Literacy rate - total adult pop. (%)	54.6	61.6	67.7	77.2
Literacy rate - males (%)	68.2	73.9	78.7	85.8
Literacy rate - females (%)	40.8	49.0	56.6	68.5

GOVERNMENT & LAW

Political Parties (12)

National People's Assembly	No. of seats
Democratic National Rally (RND)	156
Movement of a Peaceful Society (MSP)	69
National Liberation Front (FLN)	62
Nahda Movement	34
Socialist Forces Front (FFS)	20
Rally for Culture and Democracy (RCD)	19
Workers Party (PT)	4
Republican Progressive Party	3
Union for Democracy and Freedoms	1
Liberal Social Party	1
Independents	11

Government Budget (13B)

Revenues	$13.7 billion
Expenditures	$13.1 billion
Capital expenditures	$5.1 million

Data for 1996 est.

Military Affairs (14B)

	1990	1991	1992	1993	1994	1995
Military expenditures						
Current dollars (mil.)[1]	697	582	689	1,040	1,226	1,238
1995 constant dollars (mil.)[1]	801	643	741	1,091	1,257	1,238
Armed forces (000)	126	126	139	139	126	120
Gross national product (GNP)						
Current dollars (mil.)	34,060	34,630	36,260	36,720	36,950	38,940
1995 constant dollars (mil.)	39,150	38,270	39,000	38,500	37,880	38,940
Central government expenditures (CGE)						
1995 constant dollars (mil.)	10,430	NA	12,460[e]	NA	16,860[e]	17,900[e]
People (mil.)	25.4	26.0	26.6	27.3	27.9	28.5
Military expenditure as % of GNP	2.0	1.7	1.9	2.8	3.3	3.2
Military expenditure as % of CGE	7.7	NA	5.9	NA	7.5	6.9
Military expenditure per capita (1995 $)	32	25	28	50	45	43
Armed forces per 1,000 people (soldiers)	5.0	4.8	5.2	5.1	4.5	4.2
GNP per capita (1995 $)	1,544	1,473	1,465	1,413	1,358	1,365
Arms imports[6]						
Current dollars (mil.)	310	130	5	20	140	230
1995 constant dollars (mil.)	356	144	5	21	144	230
Arms exports[6]						
Current dollars (mil.)	0	0	0	0	0	0
1995 constant dollars (mil.)	0	0	0	0	0	0
Total imports[7]						
Current dollars (mil.)	9,715	7,538	8,573	7,770	9,370	10,250
1995 constant dollars (mil.)	11,160	8,330	9,221	8,146	9,605	10,250
Total exports[7]						
Current dollars (mil.)	12,930	12,570	11,130	10,230	8,880	10,240
1995 constant dollars (mil.)	14,860	13,890	11,970	10,720	9,103	10,240
Arms as percent of total imports[8]	3.2	1.7	.1	.3	1.5	2.2

LABOR FORCE

Labor Force (16)

Total (million) 7.8

Government 29.5%

Agriculture 22%

Construction and public works 16.2%

Industry 13.6%

Commerce and services 13.5%

Transportation and communication 5.2%

Data for 1996 est. Percent distribution for 1989.

Unemployment Rate (17)

28% (1997 est.)

PRODUCTION SECTOR

Electric Energy (18)

Capacity . . . . .6.007 million kW (1995)

Production . . . . .19.1 billion kWh (1995)

Consumption per capita . . . . .630 kWh (1995)

Transportation (19)

Highways:

total: 102,424 km

paved: 70,570 km (including 608 km of expressways)

unpaved: 31,854 km (1995 est.)

Pipelines: crude oil 6,612 km; petroleum products 298 km; natural gas 2,948 km

Merchant marine:

total: 78 ships (1,000 GRT or over) totaling 928,965 GRT/1,094,104 DWT ships by type: bulk 9, cargo 27, chemical tanker 7, liquefied gas tanker 11, oil tanker 5, roll-on/roll-off cargo 13, short-sea passenger 5, specialized tanker 1 (1997 est.)

Airports: 136 (1997 est.)

Airports—with paved runways:

total: 50

over 3,047 m: 8

2,438 to 3,047 m: 24

1,524 to 2,437 m: 13

914 to 1,523 m: 4

under 914 m: 1 (1997 est.)

Airports—with unpaved runways:

total: 86

2,438 to 3,047 m: 3

1,524 to 2,437 m: 24

914 to 1,523 m: 40

under 914 m: 19 (1997 est.)

Top Agricultural Products (20)

Wheat, barley, oats, grapes, olives, citrus, fruits; sheep, cattle.

MANUFACTURING SECTOR

GDP & Manufacturing Summary (21)

Detailed value added figures are listed by both International Standard Industry Code (ISIC) and product title.

	1980	1985	1990	1994
GDP ($-1990 mil.)[1]	43,416	55,328	59,902	61,504
Per capita ($-1990)[1]	2,317	2,528	2,402	2,251
Manufacturing share (%) (current prices)[1]	12.3	12.1	10.5	*11.8*
Manufacturing				
Value added ($-1990 mil.)[1]	3,333	5,101	5,783	5,092
Industrial production index	100	162	174	139
Value added ($ mil.)	3,644	6,515	5,556	*4,084*
Gross output ($ mil.)	9,023	14,579	12,773	*9,147*
Employment (000)	312	420	435	*419*
Profitability (% of gross output)				
Intermediate input (%)	60	55	56	*55*
Wages and salaries inc. supplements (%)	22	24	19	*16*
Gross operating surplus	18	21	24	29
Productivity ($)				
Gross output per worker	28,928	34,739	29,371	*21,831*
Value added per worker	11,682	15,525	12,776	*9,819*
Average wage (inc. supplements)	6,380	8,175	5,581	*3,503*
Value added ($ mil.)				
311/2 Food products	655	811	481	*686*
313 Beverages	135	167	99	*141*
314 Tobacco products	176	218	129	*184*
321 Textiles	282	529	414	*132*
322 Wearing apparel	227	426	333	*109*
323 Leather and fur products	57	71	71	*15*
324 Footwear	100	123	124	*27*
331 Wood and wood products	109	171	159	*79*
332 Furniture and fixtures	51	80	*75*	*37*

	1980	1985	1990	1994
341 Paper and paper products	129	199	186	92
342 Printing and publishing	14	25	23	11
351 Industrial chemicals	14	28	32	13
352 Other chemical products	93	184	216	89
353 Petroleum refineries	83	165	194	146
354 Miscellaneous petroleum and coal products	4	8	9	7
355 Rubber products	17	33	39	16
356 Plastic products	34	67	79	32
361 Pottery, china and earthenware	10	17	17	10
362 Glass and glass products	36	61	62	37
369 Other non-metal mineral products	355	595	602	358
371 Iron and steel	323	777	698	594
372 Non-ferrous metals	19	45	41	34
381 Metal products	265	639	574	489
382 Non-electrical machinery	46	112	100	83
383 Electrical machinery	123	297	267	227
384 Transport equipment	181	435	390	333
385 Professional and scientific equipment	30	71	64	55
390 Other manufacturing industries	76	164	79	47

FINANCE, ECONOMICS, & TRADE

Economic Indicators (22)

National product: GDP—purchasing power parity—$120.4 billion (1997 est.)

National product real growth rate: 2.5% (1997 est.)

National product per capita: $4,000 (1997 est.)

Inflation rate—consumer price index: 7% (1997 est.)

Exchange Rates (24)

Exchange rates:

Algerian dinars (DA) per US$1

January 1998	58.969
1997	57.707
1996	54.749
1995	47.663
1994	35.059
1993	23.345

Top Import Origins (25)

$10 billion (f.o.b., 1997 est.) Data are for 1995 est.

Origins	%
France	.29
Spain	10.5
Italy	8.2
United States	8
Germany	5.6

Balance of Payments (23)

	1987	1988	1989	1990	1991
Exports of goods (f.o.b.)	9,029	7,620	9,534	12,965	12,330
Imports of goods (f.o.b.)	−6,616	−6,675	−8,372	−8,786	−6,862
Trade balance	2,413	945	1,162	4,179	5,468
Services - debits	−3,464	−3,917	−3,390	−3,662	−3,781
Services - credits	675	542	607	570	463
Private transfers (net)	522	385	535	345	239
Government transfers (net)	−5	5	6	−12	−23
Overall balance	−351	−959	−773	1,420	2,366

Top Export Destinations (26)

$13.1 billion (f.o.b., 1997 est.) Data are for 1995 est.

Destinations	%
Italy	18.8
United States	14.8
France	11.8
Spain	8
Germany	7.9

Economic Aid (27)

Recipient: ODA, $420 million (1996).

Import Export Commodities (28)

Import Commodities	Export Commodities
Capital goods	Petroleum and natural gas 97%
Food and beverages	
Consumer goods	

AMERICAN SAMOA

Territory of American Samoa

CAPITAL: Pago Pago.

FLAG: Blue, with a white triangle edged in red that is based on the outer side and extends to the hoist side; a brown and white American bald eagle flying toward the hoist side is carrying two traditional Samoan symbols of authority, a staff, and a war club.

ANTHEM: *Star Spangled Banner*

MONETARY UNIT: 1 U.S. dollar (U.S.$) = 100 cents.

WEIGHTS AND MEASURES: Customary System.

HOLIDAYS: Territorial Flag Day, 17 April (1900)

TIME: 1 AM = noon GMT.

LOCATION AND SIZE: American Samoa is located in Oceania in the South Pacific Ocean, about one-half of the way between Hawaii to New Zealand. It is slightly larger in size than Washington, D.C. Composed of 119 square km of land, including Rose Island and Swains Island, this American territory has 116 km of coastline.

CLIMATE: The climate in American Samoa is tropical marine. It is moderated by southeast trade winds. Annual rainfall in the area averages 124 inches. The rainy season holds from November to April, and the dry season is from May to October. There is little variation in temperature from season to season.

INTRODUCTORY SURVEY

RECENT HISTORY

American Samoa is a group of islands populated centuries ago by proto-polynesians. They have been a territory of the United States since 1900, when the High Chiefs of Tutuila signed deeds of cession to the U.S. The United States maintained a coaling station and naval station on Pago Pago until World War II and the islands were administered by the U.S. Navy. During the war, the islands were used as a staging area for operations against the Japanese.

American Samoa ratified a territiorial constitution in 1960 and has a modern, self governing political system. The people of American Samoa are U.S. nationals, not U.S. citizens, but many become naturalized. Financial aid from the United States is important to the island's economy.

GOVERNMENT

The basic law of American Samoa is a constitution established in 1966. The executive branch of the government is headed by a governor who, along with the lieutenant governor, is elected by popular vote. Before 1977, the two posts were appointed by the U.S. government. Village, county, and district councils have full authority to regulate local affairs. The territory sends one delegate to the U.S. House of Representatives.

The legislature (Fono) is composed of the House of Representatives and the Senate. The 15 counties elect 18 matais (chiefs) to four-year terms in the senate, while 20 house members are elected for two-year terms by popular vote within the counties.

The secretary for Samoan Affairs, who heads the Department of Local Government, is appointed by the governor. Under his administration are three district governors, the country chiefs, village mayors, and police officials.

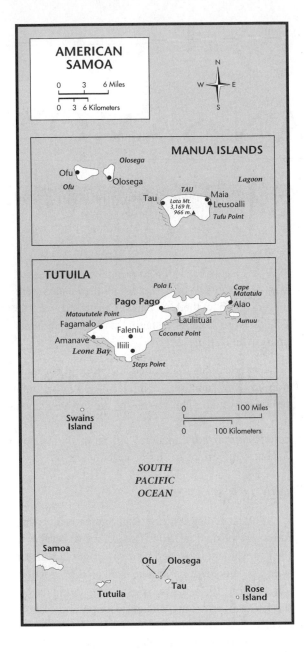

AMERICAN SAMOA

0   3   6 Miles

0   3   6 Kilometers

MANUA ISLANDS

Olosega

Ofu

Ofu   Olosega

Lagoon

TAU

Tau   Lata Mt.   Maia
3,169 ft.   Leusoalli
966 m.
Tufu Point

TUTUILA

Pola I.
Cape
Matatula

Pago Pago   Alao

Mataututele Point

Fagamalo   Lauliituai   Aunuu

Faleniu   Coconut Point

Amanave   Iliili

Leone Bay

Steps Point

Swains   0   100 Miles
Island
0   100 Kilometers

*SOUTH
PACIFIC
OCEAN*

Samoa

Ofu   Olosega

Tau

Tutuila   Rose
Island

Judiciary

The judiciary of the islands is an independent branch of the government, and functions through the high court and five district courts.

DEFENSE

Defense of the islands is the responsibility of the United States government. There is a small police force on the islands.

ECONOMIC AFFAIRS

The economy is primarily agricultural. Small plantations occupy about one-third of the land area;

70% of the land is communally owned. The principal crops are bananas, breadfruit, taro, papayas, pineapples, sweet potatoes, tapioca, coffee, cocoa, and yams. Hogs and poultry are the principal livestock raised; dairy cattle are few. The principal cash crop is copra.

More than half of the total labor force is employed by the federal and territorial government. The largest employers in the private sector, with more than 15% of the labor force, are two modern tuna canneries supplied with fish caught by Japanese, U.S., and Taiwanese fishing fleets. Between 80% and 90% of foreign trade is conducted with the U.S.

Public Finance

Exports in 1992 were $318 million and imports were $418 million. The United States provided $21 million in operational funds and $1.2 million in construction funds from the U.S. Department of Interior in 1991.

Income

In 1995, estimated Gross Domestic Product (GDP) for American Samoa was $150 million, with a per capita estimate of $2m600. Economic growth rate and inflation are not measured. Unemployment was estimated in 1991 at 12%.

Industry

Island industries are agriculture, fishing, and fish product processing. Canned tuna and copra are the principal export items.

Banking and Finance

United States banking and banking principles apply to American Samoa. The currency is the U.S. dollar.

Economic Development

Economic development activities center on the fishing canneries and some tourism.

SOCIAL WELFARE

Samoans are entitled to free medical care and education.

Healthcare

Samoans are entitled to free medical treatment, including hospital care. Besides district dispensaries, the government maintains a central hospital, a tuberculosis unit, and a leprosarium. U.S. trained physicians work with Samoan medical practitioners and nurses. The 170 bed LBJ Tropical Medical Center opened in 1986.

EDUCATION

Education is a joint undertaking between the territorial government and the villages. School attendance is compulsory for all children between the ages of 6 and 18. About 99% of the population over 10 years of age is literate. The villages furnish the elementary-school buildings and living quarters for the teachers; the territorial government pays teachers' salaries and provides buildings and supplies for all schools other than the primary schools.

Since 1964, educational television has served as the basic teaching tool in the school system. In 1995, total enrollment in elementary and secondary schools was 14,406. American Samoa Community College enrolled 1,249 in 1994/95.

1999 KEY EVENTS TIMELINE

January

- President Bill Clinton announces $29 million plan to strengthen protections at 12 marine sanctuaries, including one in American Samoa.

March

- The territory's government investigates allegations that Vietnamese workers at garment factory are being treated improperly.

June

- The American Samoa Coral Reef Task Force announces that the territory's coral reefs are over-fished and calls for an immediate plan to restore the fish stocks.

July

- Salainaoloa "Mafa" Luafalemana, 1994 Mrs. American Samoa, dies in a Honolulu hospital. She was 59. Mafa was well known in American Samoa, where she spent most of her life working for the government.

August

- Lisa Misipeka wins a bronze medal in the Track and Field World Championships in Seville. She is the first American Samoan to win any medal in world competition. In 1998, she wins the U.S. collegiate title in the event.

- American Samoa legislators closely monitor legislation concerning the "Made in USA" label before U.S. Congress. It could affect the garment industry in the territory. A bill that would require separate elections for the posts of Governor and Lieutenant Governor passes the Senate by a 11–2 vote.

September

- American Samoa's government considers a plan to legalize gambling to raise revenues.

- American Samoa is one of many islands around the world that expresses concern about the climate, and tourism that is hurting pristine environments. Scientists predict sea levels will rise by about a foot to 3.3 feet in the next century.

- A Chinese couple that worked 15–16 hours a day, 7 days a week, for 16 months receives a $64,000 court-ordered judgment from their former employer.

October

- Residents in American Samoa cheer for neighboring Samoa's rugby team's victory over Wales in World Cup play.

- The U.S. Postal Service announces that new stamp to be released in 2000 will recall the centennial of U.S. sovereignty over American Samoa.

- More than 15 inmates escape as rioting prisoners burn the Territorial Correctional Facility's four cellblock buildings to the ground. Prisoners were protesting new children visitation policy.

ANALYSIS OF EVENTS: 1999

BUSINESS AND THE ECONOMY

American Samoa is located in Oceana, a cluster of islands in the Pacific Ocean halfway between New Zealand and Hawaii. An unincorporated and unorganized territory of the U.S., it is an artifact of the U.S. attempt in the late nineteenth and early twentieth centuries to build an empire in the Pacific Ocean. It is a traditional Polynesian society in which 90 percent of the land is communally owned. Its economy is heavily dependent on tuna fishing. Canned tuna fish accounted for 90 percent of the exports as of 1996.

The heavily indebted territory considered gambling as one way to improve the economy in 1999. The legislature considered a bill that would allow up to 1,500 slot machines, and other electronic gaming machines by the San Francisco-based Faala Group.

The government, which has a budget deficit of $30 million, would receive 20 percent of the casino's net revenues. The legislation would require American Samoan ownership and control of the gaming operation, with 80 percent of jobs going to American Samoans. A vote was expected in January 2000.

GOVERNMENT AND POLITICS

In February, the Senate considered asking the federal government to pay for the salaries of the Governor, Lieutenant Governor, and members of the legislative branch. The pay issue came up as the Senate voted on a bill increasing the salaries of the Governor from $50,000 to $85,000, and Lieutenant Governor, from $45,000 to $80,000 annually. The Chief Justice and Associate Justice are appointed and paid by the United States government.

The discovery of a dead turtle in July underscored government agencies' urgent need to help protect wildlife. The Department of Marine and Wildlife Resources proposed education programs in the territory to protect turtles and other wildlife. The warnings followed the findings of a scientific panel that concluded American Samoa's coral reefs were over-fished, and an immediate recovery plan was needed.

The American Samoa Coral Reef Task Force, a panel of local agency representatives, and scientists who met in the territory in May, said they collected more than enough evidence to support their conclusion. They said that along with scientific data collected on the territory, they also interviewed 100 local fishermen and elders in 50 villages. The panel said the giant clam and parrotfish have been over-fished, and there is growing pressure on surgeonfish. They found fewer numbers of sea turtles, atule, and snappers.

The panel said scuba gear used by spear fishermen should be prohibited. They also recommended a network of marine protected areas to allow fish to recover, and a community-based fisheries management plan.

CULTURE AND SOCIETY

In October, the U.S. Postal Service announced that a new stamp to be released in 2000 will recall the centennial of U.S. sovereignty over American Samoa. The news was well received in the territory, where residents lobbied to make it happen.

In February, American Samoans persuaded the Secretary of the U.S. Department of Interior, Bruce Babbitt, to sign a petition in support of a centennial stamp. His signature came after the Postal Commission refused the territory's request in 1998 for a stamp. The commission then said postal stamps were not issued for U.S. territories. But that information was incorrect. The territory collected more than 9,000 signatures at schools, government agencies, and throughout the community, including signatures from tourists, during a petition drive that started in August 1998. Petitioners also collected signatures in Hawaii and mainland U.S.A. The Postal Service did not release details on what would go on the stamp.

American Samoans celebrated Lisa Misipeka's hammer bronze medal in the Track and Field World Championships in Seville in August. It was the first international medal of any kind for American Samoa. Misipeka said news of her victory would travel slowly around the territory. ''I'll call my father in California, in turn he'll call my uncle in the family village of Fagatogo. From there, the news will travel slowly around the island,'' she told Reuters news service. But Misipeka said she was unlikely to travel to the territory to celebrate her victory with fellow Samoans. She had no money. In other sports developments, American Samoans adopted neighboring Samoa's rugby team, which participated in the Rugby World Cup in October, and they celebrated the team's 38–31 victory over Wales.

DIRECTORY

CENTRAL GOVERNMENT
Head of State

President
Bill Clinton, Office of the President, 1600 Pennsylvania Ave., Washington, D.C. 20500, United States
PHONE: +(202) 4561414
FAX: +(202) 4562461
E-MAIL: president@whitehouse.gov

Vice President
Albert Gore, Jr., Office of the Vice President, 1600 Pennsylvania Ave., Washington, D.C. 20500, United States

PHONE: +(202) 4561414
FAX: +(202) 4562461
E-MAIL: vice.president@whitehouse.gov

Governor

Tauese P. Sunia, Office of the Governor,
American Samoa Government, Pago Pago,
American Samoa 96799
PHONE: +684 6334116
FAX: +684 6332269
E-MAIL: sili.sataua@samoatelco.com

Ministers

Director of Administrative Services

Department of Administrative Services,
American Samoa Government, Pago Pago,
American Samoa 96799
PHONE: +684 6334156
FAX: +684 6331841

Director of Agriculture

Department of Agriculture, American Samoa
Government, Pago Pago, American Samoa
96799
PHONE: +684 6339272
FAX: +684 6992567

Director of Communications

Department of Communications, American
Samoa Government, Pago Pago, American
Samoa 96799
PHONE: +684 6331121

Director of Development Planning

Department of Development Planning, American
Samoa Government, Pago Pago, American
Samoa 96799
PHONE: +684 6335237
FAX: +684 6334195

Director of Education

Department of Education, American Samoa
Government, Pago Pago, American Samoa
96799
PHONE: +684 6335237

Director of Marine Wildlife Resources

Department of Marine Wildlife Resources,
American Samoa Government, Pago Pago,
American Samoa 96799
PHONE: +684 6334456
FAX: +684 5335944
E-MAIL: Dmwr@samoatelco.com

Director of Medical Services

Department of Medical Services, American
Samoa Government, L. B. J. Tropical Medical
Center, Turner Drive, Pago Pago, American
Samoa 96799
PHONE: +684 6334590; 6335743
FAX: +684 6331869
E-MAIL: Tia@samoatelco.com

Director of Parks and Recreation

Department of Parks and Recreation, American
Samoa Government, Pago Pago, American
Samoa 96799
PHONE: +684 6999545

Director of Port Administration

Department of Port Administration, American
Samoa Government, Pago Pago, American
Samoa 96799
PHONE: +684 6334251

Director of Program Budget and Planning

Department of Program Budget and Planning,
American Samoa Government, Pago Pago,
American Samoa 96799
PHONE: +684 6334021
FAX: +684 6331148

Director of Public Defender

Department of Public Defender, American
Samoa Government, Pago Pago, American
Samoa 96799
PHONE: +684 6331286; 6331287

Director of Public Information

Department of Public Information, American
Samoa Government, KVZK-TV Building and
Studios, Pago Pago, American Samoa 96799
PHONE: +684 6334191

Commissioner of Public Safety

Department of Public Safety, American Samoa
Government, Fagatogo Police Station, Pago
Pago, American Samoa 96799
PHONE: +684 6331111
FAX: +684 6337296
E-MAIL: m.sala@samoatelco.co

Director of Public Works

Department of Public Works, American Samoa
Government, Fagatogo Police Station, Pago
Pago, American Samoa 96799
PHONE: +684 6334141; 6334142; 6334143
FAX: +684 6335958

Director of the Territorial Administration on Aging

Department of Territorial Administration on
Aging, American Samoa Government, Pago
Pago, American Samoa 96799
PHONE: +684 6331251; 6331252; 6331253

Director of Territorial Audit
Department of Territorial Audit, American Samoa Government, Pago Pago, American Samoa 96799
PHONE: +684 6335191

Director of the Territorial Energy Office
Territorial Energy Office, American Samoa Government, Pago Pago, American Samoa 96799
PHONE: +684 6991325

Director of Tourism
Department of Tourism, Department of Commerce, American Samoa Government, PO Box 1147, Pago Pago, American Samoa 96799
PHONE: +684 6331092; 6331093
FAX: +684 6331094
E-MAIL: samoa@samoatelco.com

Treasurer
Department of Treasury, American Samoa Government, Pago Pago, American Samoa 96799
PHONE: +684 6334155
FAX: +684 6334100

Director of Criminal Justice Planning Agency
Criminal Justice Planning Agency, American Samoa Government, Pago Pago, American Samoa 96799
PHONE: +684 6335221

POLITICAL ORGANIZATIONS

Democratic Party

Republican Party

JUDICIAL SYSTEM
High Court
American Samoa Government, Pago Pago, American Samoa 96799
PHONE: +684 6331262
FAX: +684 6335127
E-MAIL: Hcourt@samoatelco.com

FURTHER READING
Articles
"Children Visitation Policy Sparks Prison Riot." Associated Press, October 10, 1999.

"Clinton Seeks $183 Million for the Ocean." *CNN Online*, January 14, 1999.

"Flood of Stamps Planned for 2000." Associated Press, October 14, 1999.

"Romanian Becomes First World Hammer Throw Women's Champion." The Associated Press, August 24, 1999.

"Small Islands Express Climate, Tourism Fear at UN." Reuters, September 27, 1999.

Books
1990 Census of Population and Housing. Social, economic, and Housing Characteristics: American Samoa. Washington, DC: U.S. Government Printing Office, 1992.

Talbot, Dorinda. *Samoa.* 3rd ed. Hawthorn, Vic., Australia: Lonely Planet, 1998.

Internet
The World Factbook 1999. Central Intelligence Agency. Available Online @ http://wwwodci.gov/cia/publications/factbook/aq.html (Accessed November 6, 1999).

AMERICAN SAMOA: STATISTICAL DATA

For sources and notes see "Sources of Statistics" in the front of each volume.

GEOGRAPHY

Geography (1)

Area:

Total: 199 sq km.

Land: 199 sq km.

Water: 0 sq km.

Note: includes Rose Island and Swains Island.

Area—comparative: slightly larger than Washington, DC.

Land boundaries: 0 km.

Coastline: 116 km.

Climate: tropical marine, moderated by southeast trade winds; annual rainfall averages 124 inches; rainy season from November to April, dry season from May to October; little seasonal temperature variation.

Terrain: five volcanic islands with rugged peaks and limited coastal plains, two coral atolls (Rose Island, Swains Island).

Natural resources: pumice, pumicite.

Land use:

Arable land: 5%

Permanent crops: 10%

Permanent pastures: 0%

Forests and woodland: 70%

Other: 15% (1993 est.).

HUMAN FACTORS

Demographics (2A)

	1990	1995	1998	2000	2010	2020	2030	2040	2050
Population	47.2	56.9	62.1	65.5	81.0	96.3	110.2	121.1	130.4
Net migration rate (per 1,000 population)	NA	NA	NA	NA	NA	NA	NA	NA	NA
Births	NA	NA	NA	NA	NA	NA	NA	NA	NA
Deaths	NA	NA	NA	NA	NA	NA	NA	NA	NA
Life expectancy - males	65.7	70.1	71.0	71.5	74.8	77.0	78.5	79.4	80.0
Life expectancy - females	76.2	79.3	79.8	80.1	82.2	83.8	84.8	85.5	86.0
Birth rate (per 1,000)	39.3	30.1	27.3	25.8	20.5	19.7	16.2	14.3	13.7
Death rate (per 1,000)	5.1	4.0	4.0	4.1	4.4	5.0	5.7	6.5	7.2
Women of reproductive age (15-49 yrs.)	11.9	13.8	14.9	15.7	21.0	24.9	28.5	30.8	30.3
of which are currently married	NA	NA	NA	NA	NA	NA	NA	NA	NA
Fertility rate	4.6	3.9	3.7	3.6	2.7	2.3	2.1	2.0	2.0

Except as noted, values for vital statistics are in thousands; life expectancy is in years.

Ethnic Division (6)

Samoan (Polynesian) 89%

Caucasian 2%

Tongan 4%

Other 5%

Religions (7)

Christian Congregationalist 50%

Roman Catholic 20%

Protestant denominations and other 30%

Languages (8)

Samoan (closely related to Hawaiian and other Polynesian languages), English. Most people are bilingual.

EDUCATION

Educational Attainment (10)

Age group (1990)[13] . . . . .25+

Total population 19,570

Highest level attained (%)

No schooling[2] 1.9

First level

  Not completed 16.8

  Completed . . . . .NA

Entered second level

  S-1 . . . . .58.7

  S-2 . . . . .NA

Postsecondary 22.6

GOVERNMENT & LAW

Political Parties (12)

Legislative branch is the bicameral Fono or Legislative Assembly. It consists of the House of Representatives (21 seats—20 of which are elected by popular vote and 1 is an appointed, nonvoting delegate from Swains Island; members serve two-year terms) and the Senate (18 seats members are elected from local chiefs who serve four-year terms).

Government Budget (13B)

Revenues $97 million. Of this, $43 million in local revenue and $54 million in grant revenue.

Military Affairs (14A)

Defense is the responsibility of the US.

LABOR FORCE

Labor Force (16)

Total 14,400

Government 33%

Tuna canneries 34%

Other 33%

Data for 1990. Percent distribution for 1990.

Unemployment Rate (17)

12% (1991)

PRODUCTION SECTOR

Electric Energy (18)

Capacity .33,000 kW (1995)

Production . . . . .105 million kWh (1995)

Consumption per capita . . . . .1,830 kWh (1995)

Transportation (19)

Highways:

total: 350 km

paved: 150 km

unpaved: 200 km

Merchant marine: none

Airports: 4 (1997 est.)

Airports—with paved runways:

total: 2

2,438 to 3,047 m: 1

under 914 m: 1 (1997 est.)

Airports—with unpaved runways:

total: 2

under 914 m: 2 (1997 est.)

Top Agricultural Products (20)

Bananas, coconuts, vegetables, taro, breadfruit, yams, copra, pineapples, papayas; dairy farming.

FINANCE, ECONOMICS, & TRADE

Economic Indicators (22)

National product: GDP—purchasing power parity—$150 million (1995 est.)

National product real growth rate: NA%

National product per capita: $2,600 (1995 est.)

Inflation rate—consumer price index: NA %

Exchange Rates (24)

Exchange rates: U.S. currency is used.

Top Import Origins (25)

$418 million (c.i.f., 1992)

Origins	%
United States	.62
Japan	.9
NZ	.7
Australia	.11
Fiji	.4
other	.7

Top Export Destinations (26)

$318 million (f.o.b., 1992).

Destinations	%
United States	.99.6

Economic Aid (27)

Recipient: ODA, $NA. Note: important financial support from the US. NA stands for not available.

Import Export Commodities (28)

Import Commodities	Export Commodities
Materials for canneries 56%	Canned tuna 93%
Food 8%	
Petroleum products 7%	
Machinery and parts 6%	

ANDORRA

Principat d'Andorra

INTRODUCTORY SURVEY

RECENT HISTORY

Although Andorra is said to have gained its independence from Charlemagne in AD 803, that independence has taken several forms over the last 1200 years. Recent history has Andorra establishing a parliamentary democracy in just 1993 with the adoption of a formal constitution. Isolated and outside the mainstream of European history, Andorra has for centuries relied exclusively on its only two neighbors, France and Spain, for international affairs, security, and trade.

Andorra has been forced by the circumstances of post World War II Europe to shed its feudal system of government and adjust to modern realities. A constitution was ratified in 1993 and the country joined the United Nations in the same year. The advent of the European Union with its open borders and liberal tax and tariff policies has also affected Andorra's economy and society.

GOVERNMENT

The government of Andorra has the traditional western democracy's three branches of government: separate executive, legislative, and judicial branches. This government, established by the constitution of 1993, retains elements and influence from Andorra's history as a feudal region. The head of state remains the dual principality that was established in the 13th century to represent both Spain and France. The rights to the Spanish prince reside in the Bishop of Urgel, and the French rights rest with the President of France. Each prince is

represented by a Permanent Delegate to Andorra, who is granted ex officio citizenship. Andorra continues to pay a nominal annual tribute to its princes.

The head of government is the Executive Council President, who is appointed by the co-princes. The cabinet is the Executive Council, a subset of the General Council. Elections are held every four years, and suffrage is granted to eligible residents over the age of 18. However, the majority of the country's 65,000 (estimated, 1999) residents are resident aliens from France and Spain. The 1997 elections drew 8,842 voters, 81.6% of those eligible.

The legislative branch consists of the twenty-eight member General Council. Each of seven parishes of Andorra are represented by four councilors who are elected at the same time to four year terms. Half of the councilors are elected nationally and the other half specifically in the parish. A quorum for the General Council includes a minimum of one representative present from each parish. The General Council is led by a president, or syndic, and a subsyndic who are appointed to three year terms and can be reappointed once.

Each of the seven parishes or districts, which are Canillo, Ordino, Encamp, La Massana, Sant Julia de Loria, Andorra la Vella, and Les Escaldes, has a parish council, elected on a four year rotation coinciding with the General Council. Each Council elects a senior and junior consul to lead it. Villages are governed by quarts, who function as a municipality and administer communal property.

Judiciary

The judicial branch of government is independent. A Superior Council of Justice of five members oversees and administers the judicial system. One member is appointed by each of the co-princes, the head of government, the president of the parliament, and the members of the lower courts. Each member of the judiciary is appointed for a six year term. Customary laws, supplemented by Roman law and customary Catalan law form the basis for the system.

Civil cases are heard by four judges; appeals are heard in the Court of Appeals. Final appeals may be brought to the Ecclesiastical Court of the Bishop of Seu d'Urgell in Spain or the Supreme Court of Andorra at Perpignan, France. Criminal cases are heard in the capital city of Andorra la Vella by the Tribunal des Cortes. Few criminal cases are heard, but convicted criminals are given the choice of French or Spanish jails.

Political Parties

Political parties are new to Andorra with the 1993 constitution. Formed in 1979 while parties were illegal, the Democratic Party of Andorra was tolerated until the new government was formed in the general elections of December 1993. The 1997 General Council election included successful candidates from five political parties. They are the Liberal Union, the National Andorran Coalition, the Andorran National Democracy, the New Democracy, and the National Democratic Initiative.

DEFENSE

Andorra has no formal defense forces. Adult males are required to serve some time in the army, which is a ceremonial force. Defense expenditures are limited to purchases of ammunition used in flag salutes. France and Spain nominally provide all the defense security Andorra requires. There is a small police force.

ECONOMIC AFFAIRS

Andorra has a Gross Domestic Product of over $1 billion. Tourism is the principal element of the economy, and the country has approximately 340 hotels and nearly 400 restaurants. Prior to the advent of the European Union's liberal tariff policies, Andorra was an established duty-free zone that drew many visitors from France and Spain. Some duty-free quotas survived Andorra's joining of the European Union, although there are limits on certain items. A side effect of duty-free status, however, is a significant smuggling component to the economy. Retail shops, handicrafts, and tourist attractions such as skiing are significant income generators.

With only 2% of the land arable, agriculture cannot sustain the country's economy. Most foods are imported. Sheep and cattle are raised; timber is available and harvested. Tobacco is a lucrative crop, and cigars and cigarettes are manufactured. About 40% of the country's electricity is produced at the Les Escaldes hydroelectric plant, with the rest imported from Spain.

Public Finance

Government income in 1993 was reported at $138 million with government expenditures at $177 million.

Income

Gross Domestic Product in Andorra was estimated in 1995 at $1.2 billion. Andorra enjoys a relatively high per capita income, with per capita purchasing power estimated in 1995 at $18,000.

Industry

Andorra is not an industrial nation, with tourism and agriculture the leading elements of the economy. Manufacturing is limited to tobacco products (cigars and cigarettes) and furniture, which comprise the bulk of all exports.

Banking and Finance

Known to a degree as a tax haven and capitalizing on its duty-free status, Andorra's banking community is profitable. In 1997, there were six private banking firms. There is no stock exchange. There are a number of local insurance companies.

Andorra has no domestic currency. The French franc and Spanish peseta are the currencies used.

Economic Development

Tourism is the principal growth element in the Andorran economy. While the economy of the country has suffered some recession due to the change in duty-free quotas and sales associated with the country's entry into the European Union, the country's tourism remains strong and is promoted.

SOCIAL WELFARE

Andorra instituted a form of social welfare in 1966 and it was expanded shortly afterwards to cover the entire population. However, poorer laborers with only temporary work permits lack access to social benefits. Labor unions have been permitted since 1993, but immediate dismissal from a job without notice is permitted and this discourages union activism. Those dismissed, though, are immediately granted one month of social security and health benefits. There are government mandated health and safety standards.

Healthcare

Health care is available. Infant mortality rates were estimated for 1999 at 4.08/1000 live births. The average life expectancy for the total population was also estimated at 83.5 years.

Housing

Most Andorrans live in homes made of stone. Since flat land is at a premium in the country, most houses are backed up against mountain sides. Many families involved in agriculture or sheep raising maintain temporary dwellings in the high pasture areas.

EDUCATION

Schooling is required by law up until the age of 16, and virtually all adults are literate. Schools are divided into French, Spanish, and Andorran, but the curriculum generally follows those of Spanish schools and diplomas are recognized by Spain. There are no institutions of higher education and those wishing to continue their education do so in either Spain for France.

1999 KEY EVENTS TIMELINE

August

- Andorra passes new laws making cigarette smuggling a crime.

- The European Union reports that cigarette smuggling through Andorra has been significantly reduced in 1998 and 1999 due to government's increased enforcement of laws and customs regulations.

September

- The national holiday, Festival of Meritxell, is celebrated.

October

- The 7th International Narciso Yepes Festival is sponsored by the Ordino Festival Association (Ordino-Andorra).

November

- The 4th Andorran Environmental Forum is held from November 17–19 to consider environmental issues in Andorra, where tourism focusing on outdoor activities forms an significant part of the economy.

- On November 18, Andorrans celebrate All Saint's Day, with compulsory closing of all businesses.

December

- Andorrans celebrate the Roman Catholic Feast of the Immaculate Conception on December 8 with closing of businesses required by law.

ANALYSIS OF EVENTS: 1999

BUSINESS AND THE ECONOMY

International criminal organizations are believed to be behind the network of cigarette smugglers that had been expanding their operation through Andorra during the 1990s. Tobacco firms, like the manufacturer of Silk Cut and Benson and Hedges in the UK, had been shipping cigarettes to Andorra with the knowledge that they would be smuggled back into the UK. Beginning in 1998, Andorran authorities initiated efforts to stem the illegal flow of cigarettes across the country's borders; legal and administrative actions were taken by the Andorran government, including stricter enforcement of customs regulations. In addition, the penal code of Andorra was amended to make smuggling specifically illegal. Pressure from the European Union (EU), which estimated that EU member countries were losing about 400 million euros ($428 million) in revenue annually as a result of the illegal cigarette smuggling, helped to bring about the crackdown.

CULTURE AND SOCIETY

The people of Andorra celebrate a number of festivals during the year. The most significant celebration falls on September 8, when the festival of Meritxell, patron saint of Andorra is celebrated. The Sanctuary of Notre Dame de Meritxell, is the site of the beginning the festival. People from Andorra, as well as neighboring Spain and France, travel to the sanctuary to participate in a religious service. The celebration continues with folk dancing and music for hours in the area surrounding the sanctuary.

DIRECTORY

CENTRAL GOVERNMENT
Head of State

Co-Prince
Joan Marti Alanis, Bishop of Urgel

Co-Prince
Jacques Chirac, President of France

President
Marc Forné Molné, Office of the President, C. Prat de la Creu, 62-64, Andorra la Vella, Andorra
PHONE: +376 829345
FAX: +376 822882

Ministers

Minister of Culture
Pere Canturri Montanya, Ministry of Culture
E-MAIL: turisme@andorra.ad

Minister of the Economy
Enric Casadevall Medrano, Ministry of the Economy

Minister of Education, Youth and Sports
Carme Sala Sansa, Ministry of Education, Youth and Sports

Minister of the Environment and Tourism
Enric Pujal Areny, Ministry of the Environment and Tourism

Minister of Finance
Susagna Aransanz Serra, Ministry of Finance

Minister of Foreign Affairs
Albert Pintat Santolària, Ministry of Foreign Affairs

Minister of Health and Welfare
Josep Marie Goicoechea Utrillo, Ministry of Health and Welfare

Minister of the Interior
Luis Montanya Tarrés, Ministry of the Interior

Minister of Planning
Josep Garrallá Rossell, Ministry of Planning

Minister for the Presidency
Estanislaus Sangrá Cardona, Ministry for the Presidency

POLITICAL ORGANIZATIONS

Agrupament Nacional Democràtic-AND (National Democratic Group)

E-MAIL: and@mypic.ad
NAME: Oscar Ribas Reig

Uniò Liberal-UL (Liberal Union)

NAME: Francesc Cerqueda

Nova Democracia-ND (New Democracy)

NAME: Jaume Bartomeu Cassany

Andorran National Coalition

NAME: Antoni Cerqueda Gispert

Initiatíva Democratica Nacional-IDN (National Democratic Initiative)

NAME: Vincenc Mateu Zamora

Partit Liberal d'Andorra-PLA (Liberal Party of Andorra)

NAME: Marc Forne

Unio Parroquial d'Ordino

Unio del Poble d'Ordino-UPO (Union of the People of Ordino)

DIPLOMATIC REPRESENTATION

Embassies in Andorra

France
38140 Carrer-les-Canals, BP 155, Andorra La Vella, Andorra
PHONE: +33 820809; 820239; 820556
FAX: +33 860132

JUDICIAL SYSTEM

Supreme Court

Ecclesiastical Court of the Bishop of Seo de Urgel

Tribunal of the Courts

FURTHER READING
Books

Background Notes, Andorra. Washington, DC: Government Printing Office, 1995.

Duursma, Jorri. *Self-Determination, Statehood, and International Relations of Micro-states: the Cases of Liechtenstein, San Marino, Monaco, Andorra, and the Vatican City*. New York: Cambridge University Press, 1996.

Articles

''Andorra Takes Steps to Prevent Cigarette Smuggling.'' Xinhua News Agency, 5 August 1999.

Internet

Andorra Central. Available Online @ http://www.turisme.ad/angles/angles.htm (November 15, 1999).

Andorra Online. Available Online @ http://www.andorraonline.net/aolang/index.htm (November 15, 1999).

Government of Andorra. Available Online @ http://www.andorra.ad/govern/governuk.html (November 15, 1999).

Principality of Andorra. Available Online @ http://www.andorra.ad/cniauk.html (November 15, 1999).

ANDORRA: STATISTICAL DATA

For sources and notes see "Sources of Statistics" in the front of each volume.

GEOGRAPHY

Geography (1)

Area:

Total: 450 sq km.

Land: 450 sq km.

Water: 0 sq km.

Area—comparative: 2.5 times the size of Washington, DC.

Land boundaries:

Total: 125 km.

Border countries: France 60 km, Spain 65 km.

Coastline: 0 km (landlocked).

Climate: temperate; snowy, cold winters and warm, dry summers.

Terrain: rugged mountains dissected by narrow valleys.

Natural resources: hydropower, mineral water, timber, iron ore, lead.

Land use:

Arable land: 2%

Permanent crops: 0%

Permanent pastures: 56%

Forests and woodland: 22%

Other: 20% (1993 est.).

HUMAN FACTORS

Demographics (2A)

	1990	1995	1998	2000	2010	2020	2030	2040	2050
Population	52.8	64.1	64.7	67.7	82.9	88.8	86.0	78.9	69.3
Net migration rate (per 1,000 population)	NA	NA	NA	NA	NA	NA	NA	NA	NA
Births	NA	NA	NA	NA	NA	NA	NA	NA	NA
Deaths	NA	NA	NA	NA	NA	NA	NA	NA	NA
Life expectancy - males	74.8	80.5	80.5	80.6	80.7	80.7	80.8	80.9	81.0
Life expectancy - females	80.8	86.5	86.5	86.6	86.6	86.7	86.8	86.9	87.0
Birth rate (per 1,000)	14.6	10.9	10.5	10.1	7.8	6.7	6.0	5.3	5.2
Death rate (per 1,000)	6.4	4.9	5.3	5.6	7.2	9.2	12.2	16.2	20.0
Women of reproductive age (15-49 yrs.)	14.4	17.8	17.5	18.0	19.7	17.8	15.2	12.6	10.6
of which are currently married	NA	NA	NA	NA	NA	NA	NA	NA	NA
Fertility rate	1.7	1.2	1.2	1.3	1.3	1.3	1.3	1.3	1.3

Except as noted, values for vital statistics are in thousands; life expectancy is in years.

Infants and Malnutrition (5)

Under-5 mortality rate (1997) 6

% of infants with low birthweight (1990-97) . . . . . .NA

Births attended by skilled health staff % of total[a] . . .NA

% fully immunized (1995-97)

TB . . . . .NA

DPT 90

Polio 90

Measles 90

Prevalence of child malnutrition under age 5
(1992-97)[b] . . . . .NA

Ethnic Division (6)

Spanish 61%

Andorran 30%

French 6%

Other 3%

Religions (7)

Roman Catholic (predominant).

Languages (8)

Catalan (official), French, Castilian.

GOVERNMENT & LAW

Political Parties (12)

General Council of the Valleys	% of seats
Liberal Union (UL)	.57
National Democratic Group (AND)	.21
National Democratic Initiative (IDN)	.7
New Democracy (ND)	.7
Other	.8

Government Budget (13B)

Revenues . . . .$138 million

Expenditures . . . .$177 million

Capital expenditures . . . . .NA

Data for 1993. NA stands for not available.

Military Affairs (14A)

Defense is the responsibility of France and Spain.

Crime (15)

Crime rate (for 1997)

Crimes reported 1,950

Total persons convicted 850

Crimes per 100,000 population 2,950

Persons responsible for offenses

Total number of suspects 975

Total number of female suspects 175

Total number of juvenile suspects 175

LABOR FORCE

Unemployment Rate (17)

0%

PRODUCTION SECTOR

Electric Energy (18)

Capacity . . . . .35,000 kW (1992)

Production . . . . .140 million kWh (1992)

Consumption per capita . . . . .NA

Andorra exports most of its electricity to France and Spain.
NA stands for not available.

Transportation (19)

Highways:

total: 269 km

paved: 198 km

unpaved: 71 km (1991 est.)

Airports: none

Top Agricultural Products (20)

Small quantities of tobacco, rye, wheat, barley, oats,
vegetables; sheep raising.

FINANCE, ECONOMICS, & TRADE

Economic Indicators (22)

National product: GDP—purchasing power parity—
$1.2 billion (1995 est.)

National product real growth rate: NA%

National product per capita: $18,000 (1995 est.)

Inflation rate—consumer price index: NA%

Exchange Rates (24)

Exchange rates:	
French francs (F) per US$1	
January 1998	.6.0836
1997	.5.8367
1996	.5.1155
1995	.4.9915

1994	.5.5520
1993	.5.6632

Spanish pesetas (Ptas) per US$1

January 1998	.153.94
1997	.146.41
1996	.126.66
1995	.124.69
1994	.133.96
1993	.127.26

Top Import Origins (25)

$1 billion (1995).

Origins	%
France	.NA
Spain	.NA
United States	.4.2

NA stands for not available.

Top Export Destinations (26)

$47 million (f.o.b., 1995).

Destinations	%
France	.49
Spain	.47

Economic Aid (27)

None.

Import Export Commodities (28)

Import Commodities	Export Commodities
Consumer goods	Electricity
Food	Tobacco products
	Furniture

ANGOLA

Republic of Angola
República de Angola

CAPITAL: Luanda.

FLAG: The upper half is red, the lower half black; in the center, a five-pointed yellow star and half a yellow cogwheel are crossed by a yellow machete.

MONETARY UNIT: The Angolan escudo (AE) was the national currency until 1977, when the kwanza (Kw) of 100 lwei replaced it. There are coins of 50 lwei and 1, 2, 5, 10, and 20 kwanza, and notes of 20, 50, 100, 500, and 1,000 kwanza. Kw1 = $0.0334 (or $1 = Kw29.918).

WEIGHTS AND MEASURES: The metric system is used.

HOLIDAYS: New Year's Day, 1 January; Anniversary of Outbreak of Anti-Portuguese Struggle, 4 February; Victory Day, 27 March; Youth Day, 14 April; Workers' Day, 1 May; Armed Forces Day, 1 August; National Heroes' Day, 17 September; Independence Day, 11 November; Pioneers' Day, 1 December; Anniversary of the Foundation of the MPLA, 10 December; Family Day, 25 December.

TIME: 1 PM = noon GMT.

LOCATION AND SIZE: Angola is located on the west coast of Africa, south of the equator. Angola is slightly less than twice the size of Texas, with a total area of 1.2 million square kilometers (481,353 square miles), including Cabinda (7,270 square kilometers/2,810 square miles), the territory north of Angola which is surrounded by the Democratic Republic of the Congo (DROC) and the Republic of the Congo. Its total boundary length, including Cabinda's, is 6,798 kilometers (4,224 miles).

CLIMATE: Angola's climate varies considerably from the coast to the central plateau and even between the north coast and the south coast. There are two seasons: a dry, cool season from June to late September, and a rainy, hot season from October to April or May. The average temperature is 20°C (68°F). However, temperatures are warmer along the coast and cooler on the central plateau.

INTRODUCTORY SURVEY

RECENT HISTORY

Following World War II, Portuguese colonies began independence movements. In Angola, the major oppositions to Portugal were the Popular Movement for the Liberation of Angola (MPLA), the National Front for the Liberation of Angola (FNLA), and the National Union for the Total Independence of Angola (UNITA). Fourteen years after war broke out, Portugal granted independence to Angola in 1975. The MPLA controlled the country but civil war with UNITA began almost immediately. The Soviet Union and Cuba (with troops) supported the communist MPLA; the United States and South Africa supported UNITA. Angola thus became a cold war battle ground.

After Cuban troops left in 1989, the MPLA began to shift its support to a multiparty democracy. Free elections were held in 1992, and the MPLA won. UNITA charged election fraud and the civil war resumed. In 1997, Angola was heavily involved in the independence movements of the Republic of Congo and the Democratic Republic of the Congo. Helping the movements to win also helped destroy the UNITA strongholds in those countries.

Four years of relative peace followed the 1994 Lusaka peace accord, which was supported by the United Nations and $1.6 billion in aid. In 1997, a coalition government was announced with the MPLA and UNITA parties. By September 1998, the country was again in civil war. By September, 1999, UNITA had the upper hand and was in con-

trol of 70% of the country. The United Nations pulled out of the country. Massive starvation was the norm.

GOVERNMENT

The president of the republic is the president of the MPLA–Workers' Party. The president may rule by decree, exercising legislative functions delegated to him by the People's Assembly. A transitional government was set up in December 1992, dominated by the MPLA. UNITA had six cabinet posts and four other parties were represented. In 1997, an agreement was reached regarding UNITA's participation in the Government of National Unity and Reconciliation. UNITA nominated (and the government approved) officials for four government minister positions, as well as many deputy ministerial, governor, deputy governor, and ambassadorial posts. However, by late 1998, the agreement had broken.

Judiciary

The judicial system currently consists of municipal and provincial courts at the trial level and a

Supreme Court at the appellate level. Provincial court judges are nominated by the Supreme Court. The judge of the provincial court, along with two laymen, acts as a jury. As of September 1996, 12 of 16 seats on the Supreme Court were vacant. The judiciary system was largely destroyed during the civil war and was not functioning throughout much of the country as of 1997.

Political Parties

The three leading political organizations at the time of independence were the Popular Movement for the Liberation of Angola (Movimento Popular de Libertação de Angola—MPLA), founded in 1956; the National Front for the Liberation of Angola (Frente Nacional de Libertação de Angola—FNLA), founded in 1962; and the National Union for the Total Independence of Angola (União Nacional para a Independência Total de Angola—UNITA), founded in 1966.

DEFENSE

National defense is the responsibility of the Armed Popular Forces for the Liberation of Angola (Forças Amadas Populares de Libertação de Angola—FAPLA). In 1996, the army had 97,000 active soldiers with 500 tanks and other combat vehicles, the navy had 1,500–2,000 sailors and 17 vessels, and the air force had 5,500 personnel and 150 combat aircraft. There are probably no more than 28,000 UNITA soldiers.

ECONOMIC AFFAIRS

Angola is a potentially rich country of abundant natural resources, a surplus-producing agricultural sector and a sizable manufacturing potential. This promise has remained unfulfilled due to the effects of the 20-year-long civil war.

Cassava is the staple food crop. Petroleum production and diamond mining lead Angola's mineral industry. Angola also has significant deposits of high-grade iron ore, copper, manganese, phosphates, and uranium. Angola was the second-largest oil producer in sub-Saharan Africa in 1997, and oil exports accounted for 42% of the country's gross domestic product (GDP) that year.

Public Finance

Liberal monetary policies have financed large public sector deficits, which has led to high inflation and price distortions. In 1995, government revenues totaled approximately $928 million and expenditures $2.5 billion, including capital expen-

ditures of $963 million. External debt totaled $12 billion.

Government finances are precarious. Military expenditures continue to consume an enormous portion of the national budget. Since the 1970s, Angola has relied heavily on oil exports for revenue. However, revenues from oil sales fell in the 1990s as the result of a lower international oil price.

Income

In 1996, Angola's Gross Domestic Product (GDP) was estimated at $8.32 billion, with a per capita figure of just $800. Real growth was estimated at 9%; inflation was at 92% in mid 1997.

Industry

Industrial production consists of food processing and the production of textiles, soap, shoes, matches, paint, plastic bottles, and glues. Heavy industry (cement, steel, oil refining, vehicle assembly, and tire production) accounts for 15% of manufacturing output.

Banking and Finance

In 1976, the government nationalized the two major banks, the Bank of Angola and the Commercial Bank of Angola. The former became the central bank, renamed the National Bank of Angola; the latter was renamed the People's Bank of Angola. The Bank of Commercial and Industrial Commerce also operates, and in 1985 the Banque Paribas opened an office. There are no securities exchanges.

The opening in mid-November 1996 of the Banco Africano de Investimento (BAI) was Angola's first private bank launched since it gained independence in 1975. UK, Portuguese, South African and French interests hold shares in the bank, which is to concentrate mainly on project finance for privatization and infrastructure projects. It is also envisaged that the BAI will play a role in acquiring and helping to revive Angolan companies.

Economic Development

With the exception of the petroleum industry and possibly the fishing industry, economic development in Angola depends upon a political settlement of the civil war. The diamond industry is no exception to this rule. In June 1997, the Angolan state diamond enterprise, Endiama, provided for the establishment of a UNITA-backed mining company, SGM. Although the government has granted SGM rights to prospect, UNITA claims the government is redrawing the boundaries initially established for such prospecting.

SOCIAL WELFARE

Until recently, social services for most Africans were almost entirely the responsibility of the various tribal groups. The Roman Catholic Church also played an important part in welfare, health, and educational programs. The MPLA has established a number of self-help organizations. Women and children are often at high risk for mutilation by land mines because of their work in the fields tending crops and gathering firewood.

Healthcare

Only an estimated 30% of the population received even rudimentary medical attention during 1985–95. In 1990, there were 389 doctors, 8 pharmacists, and 6 dentists. Average life expectancy is estimated at only 47 years. During 1990–95, only 32% of the population had access to adequate sanitation.

Housing

The rapid growth of Angola's industrial centers has caused the rapid growth of urban slums. Demolition of shantytowns around Luanda is a principal aim of the government. According to the latest available figures, the total housing stock numbered 1.8 million units with 5.1 people per dwelling.

EDUCATION

In 1995 the adult illiteracy rate was estimated as 42%. Education for children between the ages of 7 and 15 years is compulsory and free. Primary education is for four years and secondary for seven years. Angolan primary schools had 990,155 pupils and 31,062 teachers in 1990. The secondary schools had 186,499 pupils. The University Agostinho Neto in Luanda was established in 1963.

1999 KEY EVENTS TIMELINE

January

- A United Nations–chartered plane is shot down in central Angola amid fighting between the National Union for the Total Independence of Angola (UNITA) rebels and government forces. The eight people on board are presumed dead. It is the second U.N.–chartered plane shot down in

a week. Neither UNITA nor the government claims responsibility.

- The U.N. orders its staff to evacuate areas in which fighting is taking place.

February

- The U.N. Security Council votes to end the U.N. peacekeeping operation in Angola because of renewed fighting. Secretary–General Kofi Annan said in a January report that there was no longer any hope of carrying out the 1994 Lusaka peace agreement.

- The attorney–general of Angola, Domingos Culolo, announces that legal action has been initiated against "terrorist" Jonas Malheiro Savimbi, UNITA president. The action accuses Savimbi of resuming the armed struggle against the government.

- The government decides to support a breakaway faction of UNITA based in Luanda, and no longer recognizes Savimbi, leader of the belligerent wing of UNITA.

- The U.N. Security Council authorizes the termination of MONUA, the United Nations Observer Mission in Angola, after the government fails to give its consent to retain the mission in the country. Kofi Annan projects a six-month period to complete shutting down of the mission.

March

- The government promises a final, decisive push to defeat the rebels, launching a new offensive to capture UNITA's headquarters at Andulo, in the central highlands.

- The U.N. estimates that the conflict has produced 750,000 homeless and displaced persons, about 460,000 of whom are receiving aid.

- Males born between 1979 and 1981 are being ordered to register for military call-up.

April

- The government requires all males born in 1978 to report at recruiting centers as part of its efforts to draft 21-year-olds in the fight against the UNITA rebels. This is the first time since 1991 that the government is drafting men.

May

- Angola is faced with a massive polio outbreak. Lord Snowden, a polio victim himself, unveils portraits of Angolan children stricken with polio. He appeals to various governments to rid the world of this disease, while South African diamond mining giant De Beers makes a $2.7 million donation to fund National Immunization Days in Angola.

June

- A driver and a nurse are killed and two other nurses are wounded when their vehicle is ambushed by armed men wearing UNITA uniforms. The Angolan health workers were conducting polio vaccinations for the Portuguese NGO, Instituto Portugues de Medicina Preventiva.

- The World Food Program (WFP) says 1,000,000 Angolans face starvation as food supplies diminish. Nearly 1.7 million Angolans have fled their homes since December, many having abandoned impending harvests.

- The nation is being strangled by run-away inflation. The "adjusted kwanza," (the local currency) which acts as a barometer of the civil strife in Angola, vastly depreciates against major international currencies. The official rate is 2.15 million to one U.S. dollar, while its black market value stands at more than 3 million to one U.S. dollar.

July

- The U.N. Fund for Population Activities announces that female condoms will be introduced in Luanda as part of events marking World Population Week. The condom may also supplement the male condom in the fight against HIV/AIDS.

- More than 1,000 cases of polio are reported in Luanda. Over 50 children have died and hundreds have been paralyzed for life.

- Kofi Annan inaugurates a 14-nation committee to promote peaceful settlement of the Angolan conflict. The members include the five permanent Security Council members and six African countries: Côte d'Ivoire, Gabon, Morocco, Namibia, Nigeria, and Zimbabwe. Brazil, Canada, and Portugal are also members.

- U.N. officials claim three out of four persons are dying of starvation in the besieged central city of Malanje. The town has been sheltering 130,000 displaced persons without regular relief supplies.

August

- Angola wins the 20th African men's basketball championship, and its fifth title over all, after beating Nigeria 79-72 in the final.

- De Beers announces plans to build a 12-story office complex in Luanda at a cost of $30 million.

- The government warns journalists against reporting anything detrimental to its image.

September

- President dos Santos celebrates his 57th birthday with a champagne toast to "the fight against poverty and misery."

- UNITA is estimated to control 70% of the country.

- Human Rights Watch releases a 200-page report documenting the UN-peacekeeping mission's deliberate overlooking of evidence showing rearmament and retraining in breach of the 1994 accords by both sides.

- The readjusted kwanza appears headed for a crash after depreciating by nearly 700,000 units in less than a month.

October

- The World Food Program (WFP) announces that it needs $158 million for year 2000.

- A United Nations sanctions team visits Angola, while South Africa announces its commitment to closing sanctions loopholes.

November

- Thousands flee across the southern border into Namibia to escape ongoing fighting between armed rebels and government forces.

December

- There is fighting between government troops and the rebel movement, UNITA, along the border with Namibia.

ANALYSIS OF EVENTS: 1999

BUSINESS AND THE ECONOMY

The year 1999 presents a very difficult financial outlook for Angola. Despite sanctions, the rebel movement UNITA controls the nation's diamond mining territory while the government controls the sites of oil production. A booming illicit weapons trade is squandering Angola's natural wealth, while huge humanitarian costs, which neither side is prepared to pay, continue to mount.

The appointment of a new economic team in January gave momentary hope that public finance policies would be improved. The widening gap in the exchange rate between the official and the actual exchange rates, however, and a World Bank announcement in May that it was discontinuing loans because of the war and rampant corruption, dimmed those hopes. The kwanza continued to slide against the dollar, and its accelerated depreciation in September foretold an imminent crash. In April reserves were on the verge of exhaustion with about a month of coverage.

Meanwhile, oil production was predicted to increase, while official diamond production was expected to decrease. The recent recovery of oil prices and the expected increase in output means that real Gross Domestic Growth (GDP) in 1999 will be about 2% and rise to 3% in 2000. In addition, the government awarded three major new oil prospecting licenses in ultra-deep water. This marked a new phase of exploration. A better-than-expected trade balance will narrow the current account deficit to $950 million in 1999 and $395 million in 2000. Despite higher oil prices, Angola's debt repayment eased only slightly, and new loans to be repaid with future oil sales were still in discussion at mid-year. World Bank data showed a total external debt of $10.2 billion at the end of 1997.

The government attempted to reorganize mining by appointing a new minister, but key mining areas remained under rebel control, or subject to rebel attacks. Nevertheless, De Beers announced its plans to build a $30 million diamond processing facility in Luanda. Transportation infrastructure continued to deteriorate and large domestic arrears to local contractors impeded development. Huge crop shortfalls and seedcorn shortages were expected into 2000 because of unharvested crops, and consumption of seed corn for survival. People fleeing their villages virtually left crops to be stolen, burned, or rot. Relief agencies expect to have to feed a vast proportion of them even if they return in time for planting in October-November.

GOVERNMENT AND POLITICS

The year 1999 saw the resumption of full-scale war, the departure of U.N. peacekeepers, a deteriorating humanitarian environment, and an awkward international relations scene. Despite assurances derived from the 1994 Lusaka accords, the renewed fighting clearly indicated massive violations of the accords, a lack of trust in stated intentions, and an unwillingness to share power on both sides. The failure of the U.N. peacekeeping mission to do its job gave the Security Council little choice but to close it down, with the exception of 30 human rights monitors.

A December 1998 offensive and a second government offensive in March 1999 left 1,000 government soldiers dead. In April, the government reinstated the draft for 21-year-olds, something it had not done since 1991. The third offensive was expected in May. UNITA's apparent strategy this year has attempted to make the government look bad by chasing people out of their villages into government-controlled cities, where insufficient public services and slow starvation was expected to turn them against the government. By the end of March, UNITA controlled the empty countryside, while the government had the overcrowded cities.

Both Jonas Savimbi and President dos Santos have used the war to entrench themselves. On the government side, dos Santos did away with the post of prime minister, vesting these powers in the director of his own office. He created a parallel ministry of defense within the presidency. He sacked a number of political figures who might have threatened his power. The government also cracked down on journalists who refused to pretend the government was winning the war. In Luanda 10 journalists were arrested and charged with undermining security for re-broadcasting an interview given by Savimbi to the BBC's Portuguese service.

In September, a Human Rights Watch report gave damning evidence of the cynicism generated by the war. The 200-page report documented how the U.N. peacekeeping mission deliberately turned a blind eye to overwhelming evidence of rearmament and retraining by both sides in breach of the 1994 accords. Both sides were found guilty of assaults on relief personnel, laying landmines, importing weapons, and forced recruitment of juvenile soldiers. Moreover, six nations, including Russia—a member of the National Security Council—were involved in arms sales and smuggling to the government, while two more did the same for the rebels. Several African countries and governments served as transshipment points.

If there was a bright spot, it was the emergence of a peace movement led by the Catholic Church.

The Church and other groups became far more outspoken in their criticism of the government and the rebels. By late October, the military situation was bringing all sides closer to peace talks.

CULTURE AND SOCIETY

Angola in 1999 presented the macabre characteristics of a Graham Greene novel. While the capital's elites hosted the Miss Luanda pageant at the Hotel Panorama, and while champagne toasts were made to the president on his 57th birthday, more than one in ten Angolans were being chased from their homes to face malnutrition, starvation, and disease. This year war-stricken Angola was having trouble containing the ravages if polio because of unsanitary conditions. While the rest of the world is only eighteen months away from eradicating polio, at least 1,000 people among Angola's internal refugees are estimated to have been infected with it. Squatter settlements in Luanda and in major towns have created conditions where one in four children under five years old are dying of preventable diseases. Land mines have maimed up to 50,000 victims, including women and children.

By 2001, Angola will have experienced forty years of civil war with innocent civilians having paid much of the costs. The current mitigation and recovery scenario for caring for some 2,000,000 displaced persons is precarious. Only $25 million of $67 million requested by the WFP had been donated by the end of May, and transportation of food stocks by air, required an additional $20 million. In June, the WFP estimated that the country's food import requirement for 1999–2000 would be more than half a million tons. In October the WFP predicted it would need $158 million for 2000. Complicating airlift operations is the risk of being shot down. Six cargo planes have been shot down since last December.

DIRECTORY

CENTRAL GOVERNMENT

Head of State

President
Jose Eduardo dos Santos, Office of the President, Gabinete do Presidente, Luanda, Angola

Ministers

Minister of Agriculture and Rural Development
Albino Malungo, Ministry of Agriculture and Rural Development

Minister of Assistance and Social Reintegration
Gilberto Lutucuta, Ministry of Assistance and Social Reintegration

Minister of Commerce
Victorino Domingos Hossi, Ministry of Commerce

Minister of Education and Culture
Antonio Burity da Silva Neto, Ministry of Education and Culture

Minister of Energy and Water
Luis Filipe da Silva, Ministry of Energy and Water

Minister of External Relations
Joao Bernardo de Miranda, Ministry of External Relations

Minister of Family and Women's Affairs
Candida Celeste da Silva, Ministry of Family and Women's Affairs

Minister of Finance
Joaquim Duarte da Costa David, Ministry of Finance

Minister of Fisheries and Environment
Maria de Fatima Monteiro Jardim, Ministry of Fisheries and Environment

Minister of Geology and Mines
Manuel Gunjo, Ministry of Geology and Mines

Minister of Health
Adelino Manacas, Ministry of Health

Minister of Hotels and Tourism
Jorge Alicerces Valentim, Ministry of Hotels and Tourism

Minister of Industry
Albina Faria de Assis ''Africano,'' Ministry of Industry

Minister of Interior
Fernando ''Nando'' da Piedade Dias dos Santos, Ministry of Interior

Minister of Justice
Paulo Tjipilica, Ministry of Justice

Minister of National Defense
Kundi Paihama, Ministry of National Defense

Minister of Petroleum
Jose Maria Botelho de Vasconcelos, Ministry of Petroleum

Minister of Posts and Telecommunications
Licinio Tavares Ribeiro, Ministry of Posts and Telecommunications

Minister of Public Administration, Employment, and Social Welfare
Antonio Domingos Pitra Neto Costa, Ministry of Public Administration, Employment, and Social Welfare

Minister of Public Works and Urban Affairs
Antonio Henriques da Silva, Ministry of Public Works and Urban Affairs

Minister of Science and Technology
Joao Baptista Nganda Gina, Ministry of Science and Technology

Minister of Social Communication
Pedro Hendrick Vaal Neto, Ministry of Social Communication

Minister of Territorial Administration
Fernando Faustino Muteka, Ministry of Territorial Administration

Minister of Transport
Andre Luis Brandao, Ministry of Transport

Minister of War Veterans
Pedro Jose van Dunem, Ministry of War Veterans

Minister of Youth and Sports
Jose Marcos Barrica, Ministry of Youth and Sports

Ambassador to the United States
Antonio dos Santos Franca ''N'dalu,''

Permanent Representative to the United Nations
Afonso Domingos Pedro van Dunem ''Mbinda,''

POLITICAL ORGANIZATIONS

Popular Movement for the Liberation of Angola (MPLA)

NAME: Jose Eduardo dos Santos

National Union for the Total Independence of Angola (UNITA)

NAME: Jonas Savimbi

DIPLOMATIC REPRESENTATION

Embassies in Angola

Austria
Luanda, Angola
PHONE: +244 394813

Brazil
Rua Pres. Houari Boumedienne 132, Miramar, CP 52, Luanda, Angola
PHONE: +244 342010; 342887

Canada (Consulate)
Rua Rei Katyavala 113, CP 3360, Luanda, Angola
PHONE: +244 330243

China
Rua Pres. Houari Boumedienne 196/200, Miramar, CP 52, Luanda, Angola
PHONE: +244 344185

Egypt
Rua Comandante Stona 247/9, Alvalade, Luanda, Angola
PHONE: +244 321593

European Union
Rua Rainha Ginga 6, 1o andar Luanda, Angola
PHONE: +244 391339
FAX: +244 392531

France
Rua Reverendo Pedro Agostinho Neto 31/3, 5o andar, Luanda, Angola
PHONE: +244 334841; 330065

Germany
Av. 4 de Fevereiro, 120, 5o andar, Luanda, Angola
PHONE: +244 334516; 334773

India
Predio dos Armazens Carrapas 81, 10 andar, Kinaxixi, Luanda, Angola
PHONE: +244 345398; 342061

Italy
Rua Rainha Ginga 12, 1o andar, Luanda, Angola
PHONE: +244 331245; 393533
FAX: +244 331245

Republic of Korea (South Korea)
Rua Cabral Moncada 116-118, Avalade CP 599, Angola
PHONE: +244 395575

Netherlands
Edificio Secil, Av. 4 de Fevereiro 42-6, 6o andar CP 3624, Luanda, Angola

PHONE: +244 333540; 333544
FAX: +244 333699

Nigeria
Rua Pres. Houari Boumedienne 120, 6o andar
CP 3624, Luanda, Angola
PHONE: +244 340084; 340861

Norway
Rua Ex-Jo o de Deus, Vila Alice, Angola
PHONE: +244 330899

Portugal
Rua Karl Marx 50, Vila Alice, Angola
PHONE: +244 333027; 333443

Russia
Rua Pres. Houari Boumedienne 170, Miramar,
CP 3141 Luanda, Angola
PHONE: +244 345028; 345038

South Africa
Rua Fernando Manuel Caldeiro, 63 Bairro
Coqueiros, CP 6212 Luanda, Angola
PHONE: +244 397391
FAX: +244 390149

United Kingdom
Rua Diogo Cao 4, Luanda, Angola
PHONE: +244 397391
FAX: +244 392991; 393345

United States
Pres. CP, Luanda, Angola
PHONE: +244 392498
FAX: +244 390515

JUDICIAL SYSTEM
Supreme Court

Provincial Court

FURTHER READING
Books

Africa on File. New York: 1995 Facts on File, 1995.

Angola. n.d. Paris: Editions Delroisse.

Broadhead, Susan H. *Historical Dictionary of Angola.* Metuchen, N.J. and London: The Scarecrow Press, 1992.

Federal Research Division, Library of Congress. *Angola: A Country Study.* Thomas Collelo, ed. Third Edition. Area Handbook Series. Washington, D.C.: Department of the Army, 1991.

Sommerville, Keith. *Angola: Politics, Economics, and Society.* Marxist Regimes Series. Boulder, Colorado: Lynne Rienner, 1986.

Internet

Africaonline. Available Online @ http://www.africaonline.com. (Accessed October 28, 1999).

Africa News Online. Available Online @ http://www.africanews.org/west/stories/1999_feat1.html. (Accessed October 28, 1999).

Integrated Regional Information Network (IRIN). Available Online @ http://www.reliefweb.int/IRIN. (Accessed October 28, 1999).

ANGOLA: STATISTICAL DATA

For sources and notes see "Sources of Statistics" in the front of each volume.

GEOGRAPHY

Geography (1)

Area:

Total: 1,246,700 sq km.

Land: 1,246,700 sq km.

Water: 0 sq km.

Area—comparative: slightly less than twice the size of Texas.

Land boundaries:

Total: 5,198 km.

Border countries: Democratic Republic of the Congo 2,511 km of which 220 km is the boundary of discontiguous Cabinda Province, Republic of the Congo 201 km, Namibia 1,376 km, Zambia 1,110 km.

Coastline: 1,600 km.

Climate: semiarid in south and along coast to Luanda; north has cool, dry season (May to October) and hot, rainy season (November to April).

Terrain: narrow coastal plain rises abruptly to vast interior plateau.

Natural resources: petroleum, diamonds, iron ore, phosphates, copper, feldspar, gold, bauxite, uranium.

Land use:

Arable land: 2%

Permanent crops: 0%

Permanent pastures: 23%

Forests and woodland: 43%

Other: 32% (1993 est.).

HUMAN FACTORS

Demographics (2A)

	1990	1995	1998	2000	2010	2020	2030	2040	2050
Population	8,429.9	9,877.5	10,864.5	11,486.7	14,932.0	19,207.4	24,093.7	29,255.8	34,465.1
Net migration rate (per 1,000 population)	NA	NA	NA	NA	NA	NA	NA	NA	NA
Births	NA	NA	NA	NA	NA	NA	NA	NA	NA
Deaths	NA	NA	NA	NA	NA	NA	NA	NA	NA
Life expectancy - males	41.9	44.2	45.6	46.6	51.6	56.8	61.6	66.0	69.7
Life expectancy - females	45.7	48.5	50.2	51.4	57.5	63.5	68.9	73.5	77.2
Birth rate (per 1,000)	46.9	45.1	43.6	42.6	38.0	33.2	27.9	23.6	20.4
Death rate (per 1,000)	20.3	18.2	16.8	15.9	12.1	9.0	6.9	5.8	5.4
Women of reproductive age (15-49 yrs.)	1,895.5	2,198.5	2,419.4	2,570.6	3,548.9	4,741.2	6,229.0	7,825.1	9,236.3
of which are currently married	NA	NA	NA	NA	NA	NA	NA	NA	NA
Fertility rate	6.7	6.4	6.2	6.1	5.2	4.2	3.4	2.8	2.4

Except as noted, values for vital statistics are in thousands; life expectancy is in years.

Health Personnel (3)

Total health expenditure as a percentage of GDP, 1990-1997[a]

Public sector 3.9

Private sector . . . . .NA

Total[b] . . . . .NA

Health expenditure per capita in U.S. dollars, 1990-1997[a]

Purchasing power parity .NA

Total . . . . .NA

Availability of health care facilities per 100,000 people

Hospital beds 1990-1997[a] .130

Doctors 1993[c] . . . . .NA

Nurses 1993[c] . . . . .NA

Health Indicators (4)

Life expectancy at birth

1980 41

1997 46

Daily per capita supply of calories (1996) 1,983

Total fertility rate births per woman (1997) 6.8

Maternal mortality ratio per 100,000 live births (1990-97) . . . . .1,500[c]

Safe water % of population with access (1995) 32

Sanitation % of population with access (1995) 15

Consumption of iodized salt % of households (1992-98)[a] 10

Smoking prevalence

Male % of adults (1985-95)[a] . . . .

Female % of adults (1985-95)[a] . . . .

Tuberculosis incidence per 100,000 people (1997) 238

Adult HIV prevalence % of population ages 15-49 (1997) 2.12

Infants and Malnutrition (5)

Under-5 mortality rate (1997) 292

% of infants with low birthweight (1990-97) 19

Births attended by skilled health staff % of total[a] . . .17

% fully immunized (1995-97)

TB 68

DPT 41

Polio 38

Measles 78

Prevalence of child malnutrition under age 5 (1992-97)[b] 35

Ethnic Division (6)

Ovimbundu 37%

Kimbundu 25%

Bakongo 13%

Mestico 2%

European 1%

Other 22%

Mestico are mixed European and Native African.

Religions (7)

Indigenous beliefs 47%

Roman Catholic 38%

Protestant 15%

Data are for 1998 est.

Languages (8)

Portuguese (official), Bantu and other African languages.

EDUCATION

Public Education Expenditures (9)

Public expenditure on education (% of GNP)

1980 . . . .

1996 . . . .

Expenditure per student

Primary % of GNP per capita

1980 . . . .

1996 . . . .

Secondary % of GNP per capita

1980 . . . .

1996 . . . .

Tertiary % of GNP per capita

1980 . . . .

1996 . . . .

Expenditure on teaching materials

Primary % of total for level (1996) . . . .

Secondary % of total for level (1996) . . . .

Primary pupil-teacher ratio per teacher (1996) . . . .

Duration of primary education years (1995) 4

Literacy Rates (11B)

Adult literacy rate

1980

Male 16%

Female 7%

1995

Male 56%

Female 29%

GOVERNMENT & LAW

Political Parties (12)

National Assembly	% of seats
Popular Movement for the Liberation of Angola (MPLA)	54
National Union for the Total Independence of Angola (UNITA)	34
Others	12

Government Budget (13B)

Revenues . . . .$928 million

Expenditures . . . .$2.5 billion

Capital expenditures . . . .$963 million

Data for 1992 est.

Crime (15)

Crime rate (for 1997)

Crimes reported 7,150

Total persons convicted 4,600

Crimes per 100,000 population 65

Persons responsible for offenses

Total number of suspects . . . . .NA

Total number of female suspects . . . . .NA

Total number of juvenile suspects . . . . .NA

Military Affairs (14B)

	1990	1991	1992	1993	1994	1995
Military expenditures						
Current dollars (mil.)	NA	NA	NA	NA	453	225
1995 constant dollars (mil.)	NA	NA	NA	NA	464	225
Armed forces (000)	115	150	128	128	120	82[e]
Gross national product (GNP)						
Current dollars (mil.)	6,903	7,048	7,549	5,511	6,197	7,400
1995 constant dollars (mil.)	7,933	7,788	8,120	5,778	6,352	7,400
Central government expenditures (CGE)						
1995 constant dollars (mil.)	4,229	NA	3,706	NA	NA	NA
People (mil.)	8.4	8.7	9.1	9.5	9.8	10.1
Military expenditure as % of GNP	NA	NA	NA	NA	7.3	3.0
Military expenditure as % of CGE	NA	NA	NA	NA	NA	NA
Military expenditure per capita (1995 $)	NA	NA	NA	NA	47	22
Armed forces per 1,000 people (soldiers)	13.6	17.3	14.1	13.4	12.2	8.1
GNP per capita (1995 $)	941	900	893	605	648	735
Arms imports[6]						
Current dollars (mil.)	525	50	40	280	700	90
1995 constant dollars (mil.)	603	55	43	294	718	90
Arms exports[6]						
Current dollars (mil.)	0	0	0	0	0	0
1995 constant dollars (mil.)	0	0	0	0	0	0
Total imports[7]						
Current dollars (mil.)	1,577	1,909[e]	1,600[e]	2,046[e]	NA	NA
1995 constant dollars (mil.)	1,812	2,109[e]	1,721[e]	2,145[e]	NA	NA
Total exports[7]						
Current dollars (mil.)	3,944	3,449	3,788	3,182[e]	NA	NA
1995 constant dollars (mil.)	4,533	3,811	4,075	3,336[e]	NA	NA
Arms as percent of total imports[8]	33.3	2.6	2.5	13.7	NA	NA
Arms as percent of total exports[8]	0	0	0	0	NA	NA

LABOR FORCE

Labor Force (16)

Total (million) 2.783

Agriculture 85%

Industry and services 15%

Data for 1997 est. Total shows economically active only.

Unemployment Rate (17)

Extensive unemployment and underemployment affecting more than half the population (1997 est.).

PRODUCTION SECTOR

Electric Energy (18)

Capacity .617,000 kW (1995)

Production . . . . .18.62 billion kWh (1995)

Consumption per capita . . . . .185 kWh (1995)

Transportation (19)

Highways:

total: 72,626 km

paved: 18,157 km

unpaved: 54,469 km (1996 est.)

Waterways: 1,295 km navigable

Pipelines: crude oil 179 km

Merchant marine:

total: 10 ships (1,000 GRT or over) totaling 48,384 GRT/78,357 DWT ships by type: cargo 9, oil tanker 1 (1997 est.)

Airports: 252 (1997 est.)

Airports—with paved runways:

total: 32

over 3,047 m: 4

2,438 to 3,047 m: 9

1,524 to 2,437 m: 12

914 to 1,523 m: 6

under 914 m: 1 (1997 est.)

Airports—with unpaved runways:

total: 220

over 3,047 m: 1

2,438 to 3,047 m: 4

1,524 to 2,437 m: 32

914 to 1,523 m: 101

under 914 m: 82 (1997 est.)

Top Agricultural Products (20)

Bananas, sugarcane, coffee, sisal, corn, cotton, manioc (tapioca), tobacco, vegetables, plantains; livestock; forest products; fish.

FINANCE, ECONOMICS, & TRADE

Economic Indicators (22)

National product: GDP—purchasing power parity— $8.2 billion (1996 est.)

National product real growth rate: 9% (1996 est.)

National product per capita: $800 (1996 est.)

Inflation rate—consumer price index: 92% (mid-1997 est.)

Exchange Rates (24)

Exchange rates:

Kwanza (NKz) per US$1

August 1997 265,000

November 1996 201,994

The exchange rate is set by the National Bank of Angola (BNA); adjusted by BNA on 19 July 1997 at 265,000 kwanzas per US$1; black market rate was then 360,000 kwanzas per US$1

Balance of Payments (23)

	1990	1991	1992	1993	1994
Exports of goods (f.o.b.)	3,884	3,449	3,833	2,900	3,017
Imports of goods (f.o.b.)	−1,578	−1,347	−1,988	−1,463	−1,454
Trade balance	2,306	2,102	1,845	1,438	1,562
Services - debits	−2,583	−2,896	−2,840	−2,389	−2,311
Services - credits	119	186	159	117	163
Private transfers (net)	−140	−1	55	136	85
Government transfers (net)	63	29	47	30	161
Overall balance	−236	−580	−735	−668	−340

Top Import Origins (25)

$1.7 billion (f.o.b., 1995 est.)

Origins	%
Portugal	NA
Brazil	NA
United States	NA
France	NA
Spain	NA

NA stands for not available.

Top Export Destinations (26)

$4 billion (f.o.b., 1996 est.).

Destinations	%
United States	70
European Union	NA

NA stands for not available.

Economic Aid (27)

Recipient: ODA, $451 million (1994).

Import Export Commodities (28)

Import Commodities	Export Commodities
Capital equipment (machinery and electrical equipment)	Crude oil 90%
	Diamonds
Vehicles and spare parts; medicines	Refined petroleum products
Food	Gas
	Coffee
Textiles and clothing; substantial military supplies	Sisal
	Fish and fish products
	Timber
	Cotton

ANGUILLA

INTRODUCTORY SURVEY

RECENT HISTORY

Uninhabited until the British colonized the island in 1650, the Leeward island of Anguilla passed through several variations of organization as a British territory for three hundred years. In 1958, the island was named a part of the Federation of the West Indies along with the islands of St. Christopher and Nevis. Opposition to any alignment with St. Christopher was long standing on the island, and in 1967, Anguilla ejected the St. Christopher police and declared its independence. The British negotiated the situation for two years, then in 1969, troops were sent in to restore the legal government and set up a temporary British commissioner.

The British Anguilla Act of July 1971 put the island under direct British control. In 1976, a constitution was established granting internal autonomy and kept the island subject to the Crown, but the island was still a part of the associated state with St. Christopher. This situation was rectified when Anguilla was formally separated from St. Christopher and Nevis on December 19, 1980. In 1982, a new Anguillan constitution was ratified.

Hurricane Luis severely damaged the island and its economy when it passed over the island in September or 1995. The island did recover, however, with tourism leading the way in economic growth.

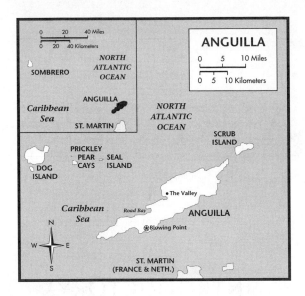

GOVERNMENT

Under the 1982 constitution, the British Crown appoints a governor to represent it on the island. This governor presides over a House of Assembly, an eleven member house, seven of whom are elected by universal suffrage and two of whom are appointed by the governor. The members of the House of Assembly serve for five year terms. The governor appoints an Executive Council which serves as his cabinet. The Executive Council consists of the chief minister, three members of the House of Assembly, the attorney general, and the secretary of finance.

As a British territory, the island is not a party to international agreements or representation of its own accord. The island's government does participate as an observer in several international organizations including Caricom, OECS, and ECLAC.

Judiciary

Justice on Anguilla is served by a magistrate's court, a Court of appeal, and a High Court. The High Court's judge is provided by the Eastern Caribbean Supreme Court on St. Lucia. English common law is the basis for the island's legal system.

Political Parties

Three political parties are active on Anguilla: The Anguilla National Alliance, the Anguilla United Party, and the Anguilla Democratic Party.

DEFENSE

The defense of the island is the responsibility of Great Britain. There is a small police force.

ECONOMIC AFFAIRS

Anguilla has limited natural resources, including fresh water. The island is relatively dry and has very little arable land. Some pigeon peas, corn, and sweet potatoes are grown. Sheep, goats, pigs, cattle, and poultry are raised, and some livestock is exported. Fish and lobster are abundant around the island and in the offshore reefs. Export of seafood provides one of the island's main sources of revenue. Several evaporation ponds produce salt, which is also exported.

The white sand beaches of Anguilla attract tourists along with good fishing. Hotels, restaurants, and other tourist-oriented facilities are major elements in the economy along with construction and boat building. Off shore banking is a growth industry. The island has 11 radio stations and one TV station. A modern telephone system connects the entire island.

Public Finance

Government expenditures in 1997 were $23.3 million while revenues were $20.4 million. The island was the recipient of $3.5 million in economic aid as late as 1995.

Income

Gross domestic product was estimated by the CIA in 1997 to be about $81 million. Per capita purchasing power was estimated in the same year to be $7,300.

Industry

Tourism, construction, fishing, salt, livestock, boat building, and offshore financing comprise the industries of the island. Exports include lobster, fish, salt, and livestock.

Banking and Finance

The East Caribbean dollar is the currency in use. Off shore financial services are a growth industry.

Economic Development

Economic development centers around tourism. Construction is an important spinoff of the growth in tourism. Limited fresh water is a problem as is a general lack of natural resources. Only half of the island's 105 km of roads are paved. There are two main seaports for shipping, and an airport with paved runway is located at Wallblake.

SOCIAL WELFARE

Anguilla is a relatively poor island with unsteady employment but good housing conditions.

The populace is primarily black and Protestant in their religion.

Healthcare

The island has one hospital, a cottage hospital with 36 beds. The health of the islanders is generally good.

Housing

Housing is good when compared to other Caribbean islands. The common home is built of concrete and is relatively spacious.

EDUCATION

All Anguillans are provided with free education from the ages of 5 to 14. Schooling is free, and virtually all adults are literate. The government operates six elementary schools and a secondary school. Advanced training and/or college must be pursued off the island.

1999 KEY EVENTS TIMELINE

January

- The annual Agricultural Exhibition was held January 29–30 on the grounds of the Agricultural Department.

February

- The third international conference on financial data security and digital commerce was held February 22–25.

March

- It is announced that Britain plans to grant citizenship to residents of its overseas territories, including Anguilla.

- March 4—General elections are held.

- March 5—Anguilla's two political parties again join to form a coalition government.

- March 9—The Ministers of Government are sworn into office.

May

- The Anguilla Community Foundation is launched.

July

- The second biennial Anguilla International Arts Festival is held.

August

- The Summer Festival 99 begins and features boat racing.

October

- The Red Stripe Bowl 1999 Cricket competition takes place, as does the annual Best Village competition. At the end of the month, a Road Relay is held, which showcases runners from Anguilla and St. Martin.

November

- The Anguilla Art Show opens in Barbados, and showcases the work of six Anguilla artists.

ANALYSIS OF EVENTS: 1999

BUSINESS AND THE ECONOMY

Anguilla is an overseas territory of the United Kingdom in the British West Indies, east of Puerto Rico. Its sunny climate is moderated by northeast trade winds, making it a preferred vacation spot. Life expectancy at birth stood at 77.71 years for the total population. The Anguillan economy depends on tourism. Events encompassing "Tourism Week," the annual week of activities that launches the tourism season, included an open house celebration at the tourist board offices, school visits to hotels, hotelier of the year award, hospitality staff awards, and the annual best village contest, which recognizes the most beautiful village in Anguilla. Residents spruced up their hometowns in anticipation of the judging and in hopes of winning U.S.$1,000 worth of plants.

The Anguilla Community Foundation was founded in May 1999. Established to garner long-term support for the island, it will also perform charitable services. A steering committee was organized early in the year to analyze the way the foundation should function, including identifying possible donors, alerting the community to their presence, coming up with a logo, and planning ways it can help the community. The steering committee, representing a broad range of Anguillans, became the permanent board members.

International phone rates from Anguilla were reduced by Anguilla Cable and Wireless, effective October 1, 1999. New prices, converted to U.S.

dollars at 2.7EC per U.S.$, were $1.20 per minute during the day, $1.00 per minute evenings, and 74 cents weekends. Compared to new, lower prices in the United States, which competition drove down to an average of 7 cents per minute, these rates are costly.

The Anguillan economy also hoped to attract more offshore banking. The third international conference on financial data security and digital commerce was held February 22–25, 1999. The conference, organized by the International Financial Cryptography Association, brings together those involved in the financial and data security fields as a means to boost collaboration and the mutual exchange of ideas.

In April a year of above-average hurricane activity and U.S. hurricane landfall was predicted by the Department of Atmospheric Science at Colorado State University for regions of the Atlantic, including Anguilla.

GOVERNMENT AND POLITICS

Anguilla is a British Dependent Territory, part of the British West Indies, which, however, holds democratic elections for its Ministers of Government. General elections were held on March 4, 1999, and 6,573 persons were eligible to vote. The results returned the incumbents to power, keeping the government as a coalition government comprised of the Anguilla Democratic Party (Victor Banks) and the Anguilla United Party (Hubert Hughes). Five days later the four ministers of government—Hubert Hughes, Chief Minister; Victor Banks, Finance; Edison Baird, Social Services; Albert Hughes, Infrastructure—were sworn in. The ministers took the Oath of Allegiance to Her Majesty the Queen and the Oath for the Due Execution of Office.

In April Chief Minister Hubert Hughes brought Caribbean concerns about the U.S.–European banana dispute to the attention of European Union (EU) officials. At issue is the World Trade Organization (WTO) ruling that the EU should stop favoring the marketing of bananas from other parts of the Caribbean. Hughes blamed the United States—which had a long-time interest in the Chiquita fruit-exporting corporation (with ties to the United Fruit Corporation) providing the fruit to the EU—for "destroying the economy of these islands." Hughes went on to ask the WTO to look into the U.S.-backing of cheap labor in Central America, which is harming the local banana industry.

In July Hughes called on the Caribbean Community (CARICOM) to intercede in an ongoing dispute between his administration and Governor Robert Harris. Harris and Hughes have long disagreed with each other's politics. Hughes has gone so far as to request that the governor's appointment be withdrawn.

CULTURE AND SOCIETY

Such weighty and contentious issues were generally overshadowed by the island's devotion to lighthearted entertainment. The annual Agricultural Exhibition was held in late January. The theme of the '99 exhibition was "Farm Today or Starve Tomorrow," with much emphasis on farming and agriculture within the nation. The event had the atmosphere of an American state fair, with farmers entering crops and livestock into competition, music stages, and food booths.

In an effort to raise money for the restoration of a local plantation house, a screen created by the individual paintings of nine Anguillan artists was auctioned in February. The screen was on display at the Loblolly Gallery in South Hill Plaza for three months leading up to the auction. The Wallblake Plantation House, the oldest building on Anguilla, was built in 1787 and has weathered hurricanes, droughts, famine, and war. The restoration effort was started to preserve the house as part of the cultural history of Anguilla.

In August, Kimdra Smith, the new Miss Anguilla 1999, was awarded a check for EU$15,000 by the National Bank of Anguilla.

In Anguillan sports, cricket is popular. The Red Stripe Bowl 1999, featuring first-class Regional One Day Cricket, took place in October; this featured playoffs among the teams of Trinidad and Tobago, Canada, the Leeward Islands, and Barbados.

DIRECTORY

CENTRAL GOVERNMENT
Head of State

Monarch
Elizabeth II, Queen of England

Governor

R.M. Harris, Office of the Governor, Government House, the Valley, Anguilla
PHONE: +(264) 4972621
FAX: +(264) 4973314

Chief Minister

Hubert Hughes, The Secretariat, The Valley, Anguilla
PHONE: +(264) 4972518
FAX: +(264) 4973389

Officers

Deputy Governor

R.G. Cousins, Office of the Governor, Government House, the Valley, Anguilla
PHONE: +(264) 4973312
FAX: +(264) 4973314

Staff Officer

D.A. Bicker, Office of the Governor, Government House, the Valley, Anguilla
PHONE: +(264) 4973315
FAX: +(264) 4973314

Defense Advisor

Captain P. Jackson, Office of the Defense Advisor

Executive Assistant to the Governor

M. Gallacher, Office of the Governor, Government House, the Valley, Anguilla
PHONE: +(264) 4972621
FAX: +(264) 4973314

Director, Anguilla Chamber of Commerce

Anguilla Chamber of Commerce, Box 321, The Valley, Anguilla
PHONE: +(264) 4972701

Director, Department of Tourism

Department of Tourism, The Secretariat, The Valley, Anguilla
PHONE: +(264) 4972759
FAX: +(264) 4972751

POLITICAL ORGANIZATIONS

Anguilla United Party

Anguilla Democratic Party

Anguilla National Alliance

DIPLOMATIC REPRESENTATION

Embassies in Anguilla

British High Commission
PHONE: +(264) 4620008

China
PHONE: +(264) 4621125

Denmark
PHONE: +(264) 4620183

Germany
PHONE: +(264) 4623174

Italian Consulate
PHONE: +(264) 4601915

Netherlands
PHONE: +(264) 4620308

United States
PHONE: +(264) 4623505

Venezuela
PHONE: +(264) 4621574

JUDICIAL SYSTEM

High Court

Magistrate's Court

FURTHER READING

Articles

"Europe, Britain: Citizenship Extended." *New York Times* (March 18, 1999).

Internet

Anguilla Calendar. Available Online @ http://news.ai/ref/calendar.html (November 1, 1999).

Anguilla Community Foundation. Available Online @ http://news.ai/ref/foundation.html (November 1, 1999).

Anguilla Elections. Available Online @ http://elections.ai (November 1, 1999).

Anguilla News. Available Online @ http://news.ai (November 1, 1999).

Caribbean Week. Available Online @ http://www.cweek.com (October 31, 1999).

Current Events Anguilla. Available Online @ http://www.net.ai/current.html (November 1, 1999).

Early April Forecast of Atlantic Seasonal Hurricane Activity and U.S. Landfall Strike Probabilities 1999. Available Online @ http://

typhoon.atmos.colostate.edu/forecasts/1999/
april99/ (November 2, 1999).

Financial Cryptography '99. Available Online @
http://fc99.ai/ (November 2, 1999).

Nine Artists on Art Screen for Wallblake House.
Available Online @ http://news.ai/
news981215.html#news (November 2, 1999).

*Wallblake House Anguilla. 1787 to the Present3/
4A Restoration in Progress.* Available Online
@ http://wallblake.ai/index.html (November 2,
1999).

ANGUILLA: STATISTICAL DATA

For sources and notes see "Sources of Statistics" in the front of each volume.

GEOGRAPHY

Geography (1)

Area:

Total: 91 sq km.

Land: 91 sq km.

Water: 0 sq km.

Area—comparative: about half the size of Washington, DC.

Land boundaries: 0 km.

Coastline: 61 km.

Climate: tropical; moderated by northeast trade winds.

Terrain: flat and low-lying island of coral and limestone.

Natural resources: salt, fish, lobster.

Land use:

Arable land: NA%

Permanent crops: NA%

Permanent pastures: NA%

Forests and woodland: NA%

Other: 100% (mostly rock with sparse scrub oak, few trees, some commercial salt ponds).

HUMAN FACTORS

Ethnic Division (6)

Black.

HUMAN FACTORS

Demographics (2A)

	1990	1995	1998	2000	2010	2020	2030	2040	2050
Population	8.3	10.1	11.1	11.9	14.4	15.7	16.7	17.1	17.0
Net migration rate (per 1,000 population)	NA	NA	NA	NA	NA	NA	NA	NA	NA
Births	NA	NA	NA	NA	NA	NA	NA	NA	NA
Deaths	NA	NA	NA	NA	NA	NA	NA	NA	NA
Life expectancy - males	72.5	73.4	74.4	75.1	77.4	78.8	79.7	80.3	80.6
Life expectancy - females	78.0	79.4	80.4	81.1	83.6	85.0	85.9	86.4	86.6
Birth rate (per 1,000)	20.6	18.2	17.0	16.3	14.3	12.7	11.3	10.5	10.2
Death rate (per 1,000)	6.8	5.9	5.5	5.2	4.7	5.3	7.1	9.6	11.8
Women of reproductive age (15-49 yrs.)	2.1	2.7	3.0	3.3	3.9	3.9	3.8	3.6	3.4
of which are currently married	NA	NA	NA	NA	NA	NA	NA	NA	NA
Fertility rate	2.4	2.1	2.0	1.9	1.8	1.8	1.8	1.8	1.8

Except as noted, values for vital statistics are in thousands; life expectancy is in years.

Religions (7)

Anglican 40%

Methodist 33%

Seventh-Day Adventist 7%

Baptist 5%

Roman Catholic 3%

Other 12%

Languages (8)

English (official).

GOVERNMENT & LAW

Political Parties (12)

House of Assembly	No. of seats
Anguilla National Alliance (ANA)	.2
Anguilla United Party (AUP)	.2
Anguilla Democratic Party (ADP)	.2
Independent	.1

Government Budget (13B)

Revenues . . . .$13.5 million

Expenditures . . . .$17.6 million

   Capital expenditures $740,000

Data for 1993. Data for 1995 est.

Military Affairs (14A)

Defense is the responsibility of the UK.

LABOR FORCE

Labor Force (16)

Total 4,400

Commerce 36%

Services 29%

Construction 18%

Transportation and utilities 10%

Manufacturing 3%

Agriculture/fishing/forestry/mining 4%

Data for 1992.

Unemployment Rate (17)

7% (1992 est.)

PRODUCTION SECTOR

Electric Energy (18)

No data available.

Transportation (19)

Highways:

total: 105 km

paved: 65 km

unpaved: 40 km (1992 est.)

Merchant marine: none

Airports: 3 (1997 est.)

Airports—with paved runways:

total: 1

914 to 1,523 m: 1 (1997 est.)

Airports—with unpaved runways:

total: 2

under 914 m: 2 (1997 est.)

Top Agricultural Products (20)

Pigeon peas, corn, sweet potatoes; sheep, goats, pigs, cattle, poultry; fishing (including lobster).

FINANCE, ECONOMICS, & TRADE

Economic Indicators (22)

National product: GDP—purchasing power parity—$75 million (1996 est.)

National product real growth rate: 3.4% (1996 est.)

National product per capita: $7,200 (1996 est.)

Inflation rate—consumer price index: 3.6% (1996 est.)

Balance of Payments (23)

	1990	1991	1992	1993	1994
Exports of goods (f.o.b.)	NA	NA	1	1	2
Imports of goods (f.o.b.)	−29	−28	−34	−34	−38
Trade balance	−28	−28	−33	−33	−37
Services - debits	−22	−23	−30	−35	−35
Services - credits	43	44	46	55	63
Private transfers (net)	NA	−2	−2	−2	−2
Government transfers (net)	NA	1	2	3	NA
Overall balance	−9	−8	−17	−13	−10

Exchange Rates (24)

Exchange rates: East Caribbean dollars (EC$) per US$1—2.7000 (fixed rate since 1976).

Top Import Origins (25)

$52.7 million (f.o.b., 1996).

Origins	%
NA	NA

NA stands for not available.

Top Export Destinations (26)

$1.8 million (f.o.b., 1996).

Destinations	%
NA	NA

NA stands for not available.

Economic Aid (27)

$NA. NA stands for not available.

Import Export Commodities (28)

Import Commodities	Export Commodities
NA	Lobster
	Fish
	Livestock
	Salt

ANTIGUA AND BARBUDA

INTRODUCTORY SURVEY

RECENT HISTORY

Antigua was first explored by Christopher Columbus, but was colonized by the English in 1632. The islands joined the West Indies Federation in 1958. When that federation broke up, the Antigua and Barbuda became one of the West Indies Associated States in 1967. A constitution was established in November of 1981 giving the islands self-determination.

Control of the islands has been in the hands of a single family for most of the time since World War II. The islands have had money laundering, drug trafficking, arms sales, and extortion activities alleged. The Russian Mafia is reputed to be in residence. The United States and the United Kingdom recognize the potential for massive money laundering, and are pressuring the country to halt illegal activities.

GOVERNMENT

The British monarch, as head of state, is represented in Antigua and Barbuda by a governor-general. The two-chamber legislature consists of a 17-member House of Representatives, elected for up to five years, and a 17-member Senate, appointed by the governor-general. The prime minister, who must have the support of a majority of the House, is appointed by the governor-general, as is the cabinet.

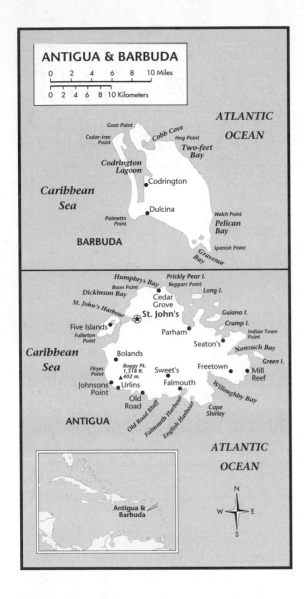

DEFENSE

Defense is the responsibility of the United Kingdom. There is a Royal Antigua and Barbuda Defense Force of some 150 personnel that forms a part of the Eastern Caribbean Regional Security System. The Royal Antigua Police Force has 250 personnel.

ECONOMIC AFFAIRS

Since the 1960s, tourism has dominated the economy. It now indirectly accounts for 60% of the gross domestic product (GDP). Antigua and Barbuda has the largest tourism industry in the Windward and Leeward Islands, with about 480,000 visitors annually. In spite of the growth of tourism, the country hasn't reduced its large foreign debt and trade deficit.

Public Finance

Since the abolition of income tax on residents, government revenues have been derived mainly from indirect taxes, principally customs and excise duties and consumption taxes. A major source of revenue is the EC$4.1 million paid by the U.S. for its two bases. The U.S. Central Intelligence Agency estimates that, in 1995, government revenues totaled approximately U.S.$134 million and expenditures U.S.$135.4 million. External debt totaled U.S.$377 million.

Income

In 1995, Antigua and Barbuda's gross domestic product (GDP) was estimated in 1997 to be $470 million. The per capita amount was estimated at $7,400. Real growth rate was 3.3%; inflation was 2.5% in 1996.

Industry

Industrial activity has shifted from the processing of local agricultural products to consumer and export industries using imported raw materials. Industrial products include rum, refined petroleum, pottery, paints, garments, furniture, and electrical components.

Banking and Finance

There were eight commercial banks in 1994, five of which were foreign, including the Bank of Antigua and the Stanford International Bank. Their liabilities and assets at that time stood at EC$113.4 million. The Antigua and Barbuda Development Bank, wholly owned by the government, began operations in 1975. Currency is issued by the Eastern Caribbean Central Bank.

Judiciary

The legal system is based upon English common law. Antigua and Barbuda is under the jurisdiction of the Eastern Caribbean Supreme Court, based in St. Lucia, which also provides a High Court and Court of Appeals. Final appeals may be made to the Queen's Privy council in the United Kingdom. A court of summary jurisdiction on Antigua deals with civil cases.

Political Parties

The Antigua Labour Party (ALP) has held power since 1946, except for a period from 1971 to 1976, when the Progressive Labour Movement (PLM) held a parliamentary majority. Other political groups include the Antigua Caribbean Liberation Movement, the United People's Movement, and the National Democratic Party.

Economic Development

Antigua is an excellent location for international business. The country offers a pleasant tropical atmosphere and adequate infrastructure in which to conduct business.

Although only 280 sq. km (108 sq. mi.), Antigua has the largest tourist sector in the Leeward and Windward Islands. Frequent cruise ship arrivals at the St. John's Harbour and the Deep Water Harbour also play a major part in boosting tourism. The opening of the Heritage Quay duty-free shopping complex provides tourists with the opportunity to shop at duty-free prices.

There has been a substantial decrease in agriculture's contribution to the country's GDP, falling from 40% to 12% since the 1960s. However, the Ministry of Agriculture has been implementing policies to encourage farmers to increase output in an effort to decrease imports of agricultural products.

In addition to local tax and duty concessions, manufacturers have access to the U.S., European, Canadian, and Caribbean markets through the Lome Convention, Caribbean Basin Initiative (CBI), CARICOM, and other agreements. The industrial park, located in the Coolidge Area, produces a range of products such as paints, furniture, garments, and galvanized sheets, mainly for export.

SOCIAL WELFARE

A social security fund provides compulsory coverage of persons between the ages of 16 and 60 years. Medical insurance includes maternity benefits. The government operates day care centers for children under five years of age.

Healthcare

Four hospitals care for the sick and aged, as well as 4 health centers and 16 dispensaries. There are three physicians for every 1,000 residents. The average life expectancy in 1996 was 75 years.

Housing

The Central Housing and Planning Authority rehabilitates houses in the event of disaster, develops new housing tracts, and redevelops deteriorating areas.

EDUCATION

Education for children between the ages of 5 and 16 years is compulsory. In 1995, there were 45 primary schools and 12 secondary schools. There were 9,298 students enrolled at the primary schools

and 5,845 students at the secondary schools. There currently are three colleges: the University of Health Sciences, the University of the West Indies School of Continuing Studies, and Antigua State College.

1999 KEY EVENTS TIMELINE

January

- Eighteenth-century prison burns down on Antigua.

- Attorneys general from twelve Caribbean nations, including Antigua and Barbuda, recommend that their governments withdraw from human rights pacts (of the Inter-American Human Rights Convention and the United Nations Treaty on Civil and Political Rights) that may delay executions.

March

- In preparation for a March 9 election, Prime Minister Lester Bird and parliamentarian Vere C. Bird, Jr., backed by the Antigua Labor Party (ALP), hold rallies.

- General election is held; Prime Minister Lester Bird is re-elected by a substantial majority.

- Unemployment is reported to be less than 5 percent.

- A Malaysian businessman plans a $300-million hotel-casino-golf complex on Antigua; an American developer has begun work on a $100 million retail-hotel-office center adjacent to the island's airport.

- Antigua breaks ground for a new hospital.

April

- The U.S. Treasury Department, fearing money-laundering in Antigua and Barbuda, issues a warning to banks that they should scrutinize any transactions routed through the island nation.

June

- Former Prime Minister Vere Cornwall Bird, 89, dies (June 28) in the capital of St. John's.

July

- The nation observes a moment of silence and more than 17,000 people pack the Antigua Recreation Ground (on July 10) to attend the funeral of Antiguan independence leader Vere C. Bird.

- Since March, nine of Antigua's offshore banks have been shut down due to international apprehension that drug money is being laundered through the island nation's financial institutions.

August

- Vancouver police release a statement saying that Antiguan authorities are cooperating with them in an investigation of Starnet Communications International Inc., an Internet gambling firm.

- The Antiguan director of offshore gaming announces that the statement saying her nation's government is working with Canadian investigators was inaccurate and that Antigua and Barbuda had received no request for information about Starnet.

September

- The Internet gaming company Starnet Communications International Inc. relocates its headquarters from Vancouver, British Columbia (Canada), to St. John's, Antigua.

- The Antigua Public Utilities Authority (APUA) makes improvements in its telecommunications systems and customer billing procedures.

- The population of Antigua and Barbuda is estimated at 68,000.

- The Crossroads Centre at Antigua, the drug and alcohol rehabilitation facility established by rock star Eric Clapton, announces the addition of new staff to accommodate the nonprofit center's growth.

- The U.N. holds a special General Assembly session on small island nations; Secretary-General Kofi Annan warns that the places most loved by tourists are becoming the "front-line zones of environmental hazard and economic plight."

- A World Bank official praises Antigua and Barbuda for the country's Y2K readiness; the nation's banks are reported to be fully prepared while the public utilities are making significant progress.

- Expanded and improved telephone service is announced for Barbuda; construction of a new system will be completed in 2000 and will offer cellular service to the island.

- The House of Representatives passes the Money Laundering Prevention Amendment Act; the move is praised by Prime Minister Lester Bird.

October

- The eye of Hurricane Jose, packing 100-mile-per-hour winds, moves over Antigua on October 22.

ANALYSIS OF EVENTS: 1999

BUSINESS AND THE ECONOMY

Economic growth was fueled by expansion of the nation's tourism industry. A Malaysian businessman announced plans to develop a $300-million hotel-casino-golf complex on Antigua and an American had already begun work on a $100-million retail-hotel-office complex adjacent to the island's airport. Unfortunately, however, the unwanted specter of the laundering of drug money began to plague the islands' financial industry during the year. The U.S. Treasury Department, fearing money laundering in Antigua and Barbuda, issued a warning to American banks that they should scrutinize any transactions routed through the island nation. The U.S. suspected that Latin American drug lords were laundering drug money throughout the Caribbean. The suspicion resulted in the closure of nine of Antigua's offshore banks. The government intervened by passing the Money Laundering Prevention Amendment, which the attorney general hailed as "a clear signal, not only to the international community, but to all would-be money launderers, that this activity will not be tolerated in this jurisdiction."

The islands' technology sector got a boost when Internet gaming company Starnet Communications International announced it would move its headquarters from Canada to St. John's, Antigua. On the heels of this statement, the company, considered a leader in the industry, also announced its new subsidiary WorldBroadcast.com, which will provide live audio and video coverage of sporting events to enhance online wagering. Also on the technology front, St. John's-based IndexTrade.com announced its launch of a new form of online trading. This would involve global equity indexes (such as the S and P 500, NASDAQ 100, German

DAX 30, and Britain's FTSE 100), as well as bonds, selected commodities, and currencies.

The Antigua Public Utilities Authority (APUA) worked to keep pace with the growing business sector on the islands; it placed an order for a module that will support improved billing for its new wireless telecommunications services. Construction on a new telephone system on Barbuda was expected to be completed in 2000.

Agriculture was the subject of a statement made by Antigua and Barbuda U.N. Ambassador Patrick Albert Lewis, who told the press that the World Trade Organization (WTO) and international lenders must "level the playing field" on behalf of the economies of small islands, many of which are highly dependent on agriculture. The ambassador was referring to regulations in industrialized nations that favor domestic farm products over imports. The statement came as part of a two-day session of the U.N. General Assembly, which was devoted to discussing the problems of small islands. Antigua and Barbuda was one of 43 island nations from around the world that banded together to request time during the General Assembly's annual debate.

Unemployment remained low and was reported to be less than 5 percent.

GOVERNMENT AND POLITICS

The attorneys general from 12 Caribbean nations, including Antigua and Barbuda, recommended that their governments withdraw from human rights pacts (of the Inter-American Human Rights Convention and the U.N. Treaty on Civil and Political Rights), which they claim unreasonably delay executions. The announcement was in response to pressure from Britain, which has been urging its former colonies to eliminate the death penalty. With some 250 people on death row in 1999, English-speaking nations of the Caribbean had one of the highest combined death sentence rates in the world. But most Caribbean nations view execution as an important deterrent to would-be drug traffickers.

In a general election in March, Prime Minister Lester Bird was re-elected by a substantial majority. The leader is one of three sons of Vere Cornwall Bird, who died in St. John's in late June. The senior Bird was the revered leader of the country from 1981 to 1994. He rose from the slums to a position of leadership in 1951 after heading a successful strike of sugar workers. In the following

decades, the British government, regarding him as a powerful leader on the islands, fostered an alliance with Bird and supported his political career. When Antigua gained independence in 1981, Bird became prime minister. His Antigua Labor Party (ALP) won all subsequent general elections. He stepped down in 1994 but his descendants—and the ALP—continue to dominate island politics. Antiguans and Barbudans regard Vere C. Bird as the leader of the independence movement; he was given a hero's burial on Antigua.

During the General Assembly's annual debate, the U.N. held a special session on small island nations. U.N. Secretary-General Kofi Annan warned that the places most loved by tourists are becoming the "front-line zones of environmental hazard and economic plight." The meeting was intended to be a wake-up call to industrialized nations on their dealings with the small island countries around the world.

CULTURE AND SOCIETY

The Crossroads Centre at Antigua, the drug and alcohol rehabilitation facility established by British rock star Eric Clapton, announced the addition of new staff to accommodate the nonprofit center's growth. The high-profile facility has made international news since it was founded in 1997.

The eye of Hurricane Jose, packing 100-mile-per-hour winds, moved over Antigua in late October; residents felt the full impact of the storm, which destroyed several homes, knocked down trees, and caused a suspension of water services to approximately 90 percent of the island. Damage, however, is considered minimal.

DIRECTORY

CENTRAL GOVERNMENT
Head of State

Monarch
Elizabeth II, Queen of England

Governor-General
James B. Carlisle

Prime Minister
Lester Bird, Office of the Prime Minister, Factory Road, St. John's, Antigua and Barbuda
PHONE: +(268) 4624965
FAX: +(268) 4623225
E-MAIL: pmo@candw.ag

Ministers

Minister of Agriculture, Lands, and Fisheries

John St. Luce, Ministry of Agriculture, Lands, and Fisheries, Nevis Street, St. John's, Antigua and Barbuda
PHONE: +(268) 4621007

Minister of Defense

Lester Bird, Ministry of Defense

Minister of Education, Youths, and Sports

Bernard Percival, Ministry of Education, Youths, and Sports, Church St., St. John's, Antigua and Barbuda
PHONE: +(268) 4620192

Minister of External Affairs

Lester Bird, Ministry of External Affairs, Factory Road, St. John's, Antigua and Barbuda
PHONE: +(268) 4624956
FAX: +(268) 4623225

Minister of Finance and Social Security

Ministry of Finance and Social Security, John St. Luce, High Street, St. John's, Antigua and Barbuda
PHONE: +(268) 4624860
FAX: +(268) 4621622

Minister of Health and Home Affairs

Sam Aymer, Ministry of Health and Home Affairs

Minister of Information

Lester Bird, Ministry of Information, Cross St., St. John's, Antigua and Barbuda
PHONE: +(268) 4624427; 4624428
FAX: +(268) 4624442

Minister of Justice and Legal Affairs

Radford Wentworth Hll, Ministry of Justice and Legal Affairs

Minister of Labor, Home Affairs, and Citizen Services

Adolphus Freeland, Ministry of Labor, Home Affairs, and Citizen Services

Minister of Planning and Implementation

Molwyn Joseph, Ministry of Planning and Implementation

Minister of Public Works, Utilities, Energy, and Local Transportation

Robin Yearwood, Ministry of Public Works, Utilities, Energy, and Local Transportation, Thames St., St. John's, Antigua and Barbuda
PHONE: +(268) 4623851

Minister of Telecommunications, Civil Aviation, International Transportation and Gaming

Lester Bird, Ministry of Telecommunications, Civil Aviation, International Transportation, and Gaming

Minister of Tourism, Culture, and Environmental Affairs

Rodney Williams, Ministry of Tourism, Culture, and Environmental Affairs

Minister of Trade, Industry, and Consumer Affairs

Hilroy Humhreys, Ministry of Trade, Industry, and Consumer Affairs

POLITICAL ORGANIZATIONS

Antigua Labour Party (ALP)

NAME: Lester Bird

Barbuda People's Movement (BPM)

United Progressive Party (UPP)

NAME: Baldwin Spencer

DIPLOMATIC REPRESENTATION

Embassies in Antigua and Barbuda

United Kingdom

Price Waterhouse Centre, 11 Old Parham Rd., St. John's, Antigua and Barbuda
TITLE: High Commissioner
NAME: G. M. Baker

Venezuela

Redcliffe And Cross Streets, St. John's, Antigua and Barbuda
PHONE: +(268) 4621574
FAX: +(268) 4621570
E-MAIL: venezuela@mail.candw.ag

JUDICIAL SYSTEM

East Caribbean Supreme Court

Saint Lucia

FURTHER READING

Government Publications

Central Intelligence Agency. *CIA World Factbook,* 1998. Washington, DC: GPO, 1999.

U.S. Department of State. *Background Notes: Antigua and Barbuda, 1997*. Washington, DC: GPO, 1998.

U.S. Department of State. *Antigua and Barbuda Reports on Human Rights Practices for 1997*. Washington, DC: GPO, 1998.

Articles

"Ah, Democracy—Antigua-style." *The Economist*, March 6, 1999.

"Antigua Hearing Adjourned in Scot's Killing." *Reuters*, August 31, 1999.

"Bursting at the Seams, Eric Clapton's Treatment Centre Hires New Staff." *Business Wire*, September 13, 1999.

"IndexTrade.com Launches World's First Index Trading Web Site." *PR Newswire*, September 27, 1999.

"Response from Antiguan Government to Media Reports Regarding Vancouver Police Investigation of Starnet." *Business Wire*, August 26, 1999.

"Starnet Establishes New Wholly Owned Subsidiary." *Business Wire*, September 28, 1999.

"Starnet Relocates Head Office to St. John's, Antigua." *Business Wire*, September 2, 1999.

"U.S. Warns on Antigua Money Laundering." *New York Times*, April 8, 1999.

"Veramark Receives Wireless Order from Antigua Public Utilities." *Business Wire*, September 8, 1999.

"Vere Bird." Obituary. *The Economist*, July 17, 1999.

"Vere Bird, 89, Who Led Antigua to Freedom." Obituary. *New York Times*, June 30, 1999.

Books

Kelly, Robert C. et. al., editors. *Antigua and Barbuda Country Review 1999–2000*. Houston, TX: Commercial Data International, 1999.

Internet

CIA World Factbook: Antigua and Barbuda. Available Online @: http://www.odci.gov/cia/publications/factbook/ac.html. (October 29, 1999).

The Commonwealth Online: Antigua and Barbuda. Available Online @ http://www.tcol.co.uk/antig/antigua.htm. (October 29, 1999).

News from Antigua and Barbuda. Available Online @ http://www.antigua-barbuda.com/newsfrom.html. (October 29, 1999).

The Source. Available Online @ http://www.antol.net/antol2.htm. (October 29, 1999).

ANTIGUA AND BARBUDA: STATISTICAL DATA

For sources and notes see "Sources of Statistics" in the front of each volume.

GEOGRAPHY

Geography (1)

Area:

Total: 440 sq km.

Land: 440 sq km.

Water: 0 sq km.

Note: includes Redonda.

Area—comparative: 2.5 times the size of Washington, DC.

Land boundaries: 0 km.

Coastline: 153 km.

Climate: tropical marine; little seasonal temperature variation.

Terrain: mostly low-lying limestone and coral islands with some higher volcanic areas.

Natural resources: negligible; pleasant climate fosters tourism.

Land use:

Arable land: 18%

Permanent crops: 0%

Permanent pastures: 9%

Forests and woodland: 11%

Other: 62% (1993 est.).

HUMAN FACTORS

Ethnic Division (6)

Black, British, Portuguese, Lebanese, Syrian.

Demographics (2A)

	1990	1995	1998	2000	2010	2020	2030	2040	2050
Population	62.7	63.1	64.0	64.5	65.8	66.0	64.1	59.0	51.4
Net migration rate (per 1,000 population)	NA	NA	NA	NA	NA	NA	NA	NA	NA
Births	NA	NA	NA	NA	NA	NA	NA	NA	NA
Deaths	NA	NA	NA	NA	NA	NA	NA	NA	NA
Life expectancy - males	66.8	68.1	68.8	69.3	71.5	73.3	74.8	76.1	77.1
Life expectancy - females	71.3	72.8	73.7	74.3	76.8	78.9	80.7	82.1	83.2
Birth rate (per 1,000)	20.5	18.4	16.7	15.7	13.1	11.7	10.4	9.6	9.3
Death rate (per 1,000)	6.9	6.2	5.9	5.7	5.3	5.8	8.8	13.5	16.3
Women of reproductive age (15-49 yrs.)	18.8	19.6	20.0	20.1	19.1	15.7	13.6	12.0	9.8
of which are currently married	NA	NA	NA	NA	NA	NA	NA	NA	NA
Fertility rate	1.9	1.8	1.7	1.7	1.7	1.7	1.7	1.7	1.7

Except as noted, values for vital statistics are in thousands; life expectancy is in years.

Religions (7)

Anglican (predominant), other Protestant sects, some Roman Catholic.

Languages (8)

English (official), local dialects.

GOVERNMENT & LAW

Political Parties (12)

House of Representatives	No. of seats
Antigua Labor Party (ALP)	11
United Progressive Party (UPP)	5
Independent	1

Government Budget (13B)

Revenues . . . .$107 million
Expenditures . . . .$132 million
  Capital expenditures . . . .$18 million
Data for 1995.

Military Affairs (14A)

Total expenditures (FY90/91) . . . .$1.4 million
Expenditures as % of GDP (FY90/91) 1%

LABOR FORCE

Labor Force (16)

Total 30,000
Commerce and services 82%
Agriculture 11%
Industry 7%
Data for 1983.

Unemployment Rate (17)

5%-10% (1995 est.)

PRODUCTION SECTOR

Electric Energy (18)

Capacity . . . . .26,000 kW (1995)
Production . . . . .95 million kWh (1995)
Consumption per capita . . . . .1,458 kWh (1995)

Transportation (19)

Highways:

total: 250 km (1996 est.)

paved: NA km

unpaved: NA km

Merchant marine:

total: 440 ships (1,000 GRT or over) totaling 2,025,920 GRT/2,690,028 DWT ships by type: bulk 12, cargo 295, chemical tanker 6, combination bulk 1, container 89, liquefied gas tanker 2, oil tanker 4, refrigerated cargo 10, roll-on/roll-off cargo 20, vehicle carrier 1 note: a flag of convenience registry: Germany owns 11 ships, Slovenia 3, Cyprus 2, and US 1 (1997 est.)

Airports: 3 (1997 est.)

Airports—with paved runways:

total: 2

2,438 to 3,047 m: 1

under 914 m: 1 (1997 est.)

Airports—with unpaved runways:

total: 1

under 914 m: 1 (1997 est.)

Top Agricultural Products (20)

Cotton, fruits, vegetables, bananas, coconuts, cucumbers, mangoes, sugarcane; livestock.

FINANCE, ECONOMICS, & TRADE

Balance of Payments (23)

	1990	1992	1994	1995	1996
Exports of goods (f.o.b.)	33	65	44	53	54
Imports of goods (f.o.b.)	−235	−273	−298	−302	−317
Trade balance	−202	−208	−254	−249	−263
Services - debits	−153	−156	−166	−175	−178
Services - credits	314	346	401	354	373
Private transfers (net)	9	−0	NA	69	29
Government transfers (net)	NA	−1	1	NA	−1
Overall balance	−31	−19	−18	−1	−40

FINANCE, ECONOMICS, & TRADE

Economic Indicators (22)

National product: GDP—purchasing power parity— $470 million (1997 est.)

National product real growth rate: 3.3% (1997 est.)

National product per capita: $7,400 (1997 est.)

Inflation rate—consumer price index: 2.5% (1996)

Exchange Rates (24)

Exchange rates: East Caribbean dollars (EC$) per US$1—2.7000 (fixed rate since 1976).

Top Import Origins (25)

$350.8 million (f.o.b., 1996 est.)

Origins	%
United States	.27
United Kingdom	.16
Canada	.4
OECS	.3
Other	.50

Top Export Destinations (26)

$45 million (f.o.b., 1996 est.).

Destinations	%
OECS	.26
Barbados	.15
Guyana	.4
Trinidad and Tobago	.2
United States	.0.3

Economic Aid (27)

$NA. NA stands for not available.

Import Export Commodities (28)

Import Commodities	Export Commodities
Food and live animals	Petroleum products 48%
Machinery and transport equipment	Manufactures 23%
	Food and live animals 4%
Manufactures	Machinery and transport equipment 17%
Chemicals	
Oil	

ARGENTINA

Argentine Republic
República Argentina

INTRODUCTORY SURVEY

RECENT HISTORY

Army Colonel Juan D. Peron emerged from World War II as the leader of Argentina, and he won elections to president in 1946 and 1951. His wins were aided by his popular second wife, Eva Duarte de Peron (Evita). Evita championed the working classes in establishing a national charitable organization, and awarding generous wage increases to the unions. Peron's increasing authoritarianism let to a coup by the armed forces, and Peron went into exile in 1955, three years after the death of Evita by cancer.

Argentina went through a period of military dictatorships punctuated by brief periods of constitutional government. Peron returned to power in 1973 with his third wife, Isabel Martinez de Peron as elected vice president. When he died in 1974, she became president, but was deposed in 1976 in a coup.

The military government invaded the Falkland Islands on April 2, 1982, after many decades of arguing with the United Kingdom over sovereignty. The war with the British lasted only 70 days before Argentina was defeated. The military government collapsed and constitutional government was restored.

Through the 1980s and 1990s, Argentina has struggled with high unemployment and high inflation rates. Government programs and economic development have concentrated on austere moves to bring these under control. Throughout this pe-

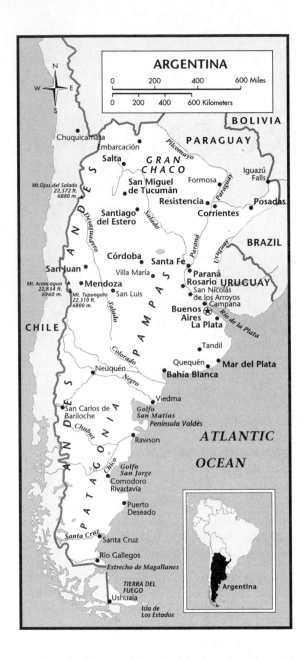

ARGENTINA

officials without the consent of the Senate. The president also possesses broad powers to declare a state of siege and suspend the constitution.

The president is commander-in-chief of the army, navy, and air force. The president and vice-president are elected by an electoral college for six-year terms. They must be Roman Catholics, and either they or their parents must be native-born citizens. Voting is compulsory for all citizens 18 to 70 years of age.

The constitution calls for a National Congress consisting of a 46-member Senate and a 254-member Chamber of Deputies.

Judiciary

The Supreme Court supervises and regulates all other federal courts. Other federal courts include nine appeals courts; single-judge district courts, at least one for each province; and one-judge territorial courts. Provincial courts include supreme courts, appeals courts, courts of first instance, and minor courts. In 1994, constitutional amendments authorized the creation of the Judicial Court, which will have the power to administrate the federal court and appoint and remove judges.

Political Parties

Due to the frequency of military takeovers, parties have often been banned. Still, several parties were formed in the 1980s and continued be active in the 1990s, including the party of Peron.

DEFENSE

The Argentine armed forces numbered 72,500 in 1996. The other services are the navy (which has air and marine units) of 28,000, a national police force of 17,000, a coast guard of 13,000, and an air force of 12,000. Required military service ended in 1995.

The navy has 4 submarines, 1 aircraft carrier, 7 frigates, and 6 missile-equipped destroyers. The air force has 174 combat aircraft. Defense spending has fallen from an estimated $4 billion to $700 million in the last decade.

ECONOMIC AFFAIRS

Argentina has one of the most highly developed economies and richest natural resource bases in Latin America, but political instability has kept the economy from realizing its full potential. The country has almost overcome its dependence on imported machinery and finished products, and

riod, periodic scandals, social disturbances and riots, and political corruption have shaken the government, but it has not fallen.

GOVERNMENT

Argentina is a federation of 22 provinces, the federal capital of Buenos Aires, and the territories of Tierra del Fuego, a claim to part of Antarctica, and the Isla de los Estados.

There is a separation of powers among the executive, legislative, and judicial branches, but the president is powerful within this arrangement. The president can draw up and introduce his own bills in Congress and appoint cabinet members and other

there is a great demand for parts and raw materials that are assembled or finished within the country.

In 1991, President Carlos Menem introduced an original stabilization and reform program. After three years of swift growth, the devaluation of the Mexican peso in December 1994 pushed the Argentine economy into recession, and the economy shrank by 4.4% in 1995. However, the economy began to recover by 1996, and grew by an estimated 5–6% in 1997.

Public Finance

Beginning in 1970, Argentina's budget picture steadily worsened. Since 1991, however, the government has considerably narrowed the deficit gap through structural reform efforts including stricter controls on public spending and more efficient tax collection. Although tax enforcement has improved, evasion is still a major problem.

In 1995, government revenues totaled approximately U.S.$48.6 billion and expenditures U.S.$46.5 billion, including capital expenditures of $3.5 billion. External debt totaled U.S.$90 billion.

Income

In 1995, Argentina's gross domestic product (GDP) was estimated in 1997 to be $348.2 billion; per capita income was estimated at $9,700. Real growth rate in 1997 was 8.4%; inflation was 0.3%. Unemployment stood at about 15%.

Industry

Argentina's principal industrial enterprises are meat packing, food processing, machinery manufacturing and assembly, flour milling, tanning and leather goods manufacturing, oil refining, oilseed milling, and textile, chemical, pharmaceutical, and cement manufacturing. Packing and processing of food products is the oldest and most important industry in Argentina. The textile industry was also developed quite early, making use of wool from the vast herds of sheep and cotton from the northeast. In addition to these traditional products, a variety of synthetic fibers are now produced.

Portland cement is the country's leading construction material, with 5.6 million tons produced in 1994. The output of crude steel totaled 3.3 million tons in 1994. Argentina's automotive industry manufactured 285,435 motor vehicles in 1995, including 226,656 passenger cars. Argentina also produces electric appliances, communications equipment—including radios and television sets—motors, watches, and numerous other items.

Banking and Finance

In 1935, the Central Bank of the Argentine Republic was established as a central reserve bank, having the sole right of note issue, with all capital held by the state. The Buenos Aires Stock Exchange is one of the 23 markets that form the Buenos Aires Commercial Exchange, which has over 12,000 members and is often confused with the Stock Exchange. The Commercial Exchange now includes a grain market, a foreign currency exchange, a general produce exchange, and the securities exchange.

Economic Development

Argentine economic policy has undergone several cycles of change since the 1940s. During World War II, the demand for Argentine beef and wheat boosted the country's exchange reserves to their highest point in history. Under the Perón regime, however, declining terms of trade and increasing state benefits and subsidies, as well as Perón's attempt to industrialize Argentina at the expense of the agrarian sector, disrupted the nation's economic system. When Perón fell, steps were taken to fund foreign obligations with long-term provisions for Argentine repayment and to create a climate favorable to private investment.

The 1970s brought a resurgence of economic and political instability. The return to constitutional government—and especially the return of the Perónists to power—brought a period of increased labor influence, extraordinary wage demands, accelerating inflation, and huge government deficits, largely financed through short-term borrowing.

Perón's death in July 1974 and the subsequent political instability aborted his programs and led to an economic crisis. In 1978, a medium-term economic adjustment plan led to triple-digit inflation and increasing unemployment. In the fall of 1982, the government committed itself to an austerity program, consisting of cuts in government spending, higher interest rates on bank loans to the private sector, and continuing regular devaluation.

The "Austral Plan," launched in June 1985, was the Alfonsín government's attempt to break out of the stagnation that has characterized the economy since 1982. Since then, the government has attempted to manage price and wage increases and has offered several public corporations for sale.

Argentina has recovered from the financial crisis and economic recession of 1994–95, yet its recovery is not immune to external threats. Sweeping privatization and a wave of investment, both foreign and local, have modernized old industries and nourished new ones.

SOCIAL WELFARE

In the 1940s, new provisions established salary increases, paid holidays, sick leave, job tenure, and many other benefits. By 1945, a National Social Security Institute administered social insurance programs and a pension system. In the early 1950s, these measures continued and were also extended to the rural sector. Most of the social legislation enacted during the Perón years has remained in effect.

Although guaranteed equality under the Constitution, women are fighting for equal advancement and pay in the labor force. In 1993, a presidential decree set a quota that 30% of political candidates must be female. The National Council on Children and Families develops child protection programs and legislation.

Healthcare

In the field of health care, Argentina compares favorably with other Latin American countries. Nutritional requirements are comfortably met.

Health and medical services for workers are provided by union clinics, and employers are usually required to provide free medical and pharmaceutical care for injured workers. It is estimated that 71% of the population has access to health services. Life expectancy averages 73 years.

Housing

Housing in Argentina reflects the Italian and Spanish ethnic backgrounds of the population. The total number of dwellings in 1992 was 9.2 million. As of 1993, there was a housing shortage of roughly 2.5 million houses in Argentina.

EDUCATION

Argentina has one of the highest literacy rates in Latin America, estimated in 1990 at 96.2%. Education is free and compulsory for all children at the primary level. Secondary education lasts for four to six years depending on the type of course. In 1994, there were 25,448 primary schools with 286,885 teachers and 5.2 million students enrolled. Argentina has 46 officially accredited universities with a total of 570,000 students (1988).

1999 KEY EVENTS TIMELINE

January

- Argentina announces it is thinking of replacing the Argentine peso with the United States dollar. This would take the already implemented plan of basing the peso one-to-one with the U.S. dollar, monitored by a currency union, one step further. The plan is greeted with some skepticism and uncertainty.

- The government of Argentina officially sells all but five percent of its stake in former state oil company YPF S.A. to Spain's Repsol.

- The devaluation of Brazil's *real* strains relations with Argentina. Diplomatic efforts begin to stabilize the tensions between Latin America's two largest economies.

- A UNESCO report cites that Argentina's retired population face problems that include poor medical services, little income, and general lack of respect by the rest of society. Recent economic measures have resulted in smaller pensions and cut backs medical services for Argentina's retired population.

- Police arrest over 1,000 suspected undocumented immigrants across Argentina for failing to produce legal identification documents.

February

- A team of paleontologists discovers thousands of fossilized dinosaur eggshells in the Patagonian desert of Argentina.

- Argentina's National Foreign Trade Commission proposes anti-dumping duties on some Brazilian steel imports.

March

- Former military ruler Jorge Acosta, once head of the Navy Mechanics School in Buenos Aires—a center for torture in the junta days—is placed on trial for crimes of abducting thousands of children born in captivity to dissident women.

- President Carlos Menem has been busy making promises across the provinces with cash, ambulances, school supplies and other gifts to win the votes of the rural populations for his Peronist party in the upcoming presidential elections.

• A judge freezes the Argentine assets of Royal Dutch/Shell Group and a German firm totaling $60 million after an oil spill in the River Plate of Argentina affects approximately 20 miles of coast line in the inlet that separates Argentina from Uruguay.

April

• Archaeologist Johan Reinhard discovers the remains of three children at Mount Llullaillaco in the Argentine Andes; theories propose they were probably sacrificed 500 years ago in an Incan ritual.

• President Carlos Menem proposes a series of laws aimed at cracking down on undocumented immigrants in Argentina.

• General Martin Balza, commander of the Argentine army, denounces his predecessors by accusing military officers of burning archives containing information on thousands of dissidents who disappeared during military rule 1976–83.

• Thousands of farmers conduct a three-day strike called by the Rural Society, made up of four rural associations, demanding financial aid from the Argentine government.

May

• For the first time since 1983, Argentines name crime as their most important public concern. In response, President Carlos Menem assigns additional border police and coast guards to Buenos Aires, where robberies and violent crime have doubled in recent years.

June

• The Economic Ministry announces this month that the Argentine economy is 11% smaller than previously thought.

• The GasAtacama pipeline goes into service. The pipeline is a new cross-Andes section designed to export natural gas from Argentina to northern Chile's Atacama mining region and is expected to cut electricity prices in the area by approximately 25%.

• A new Argentine law promotes the wood-processing industry to consume fiber grown in new plantations and offers a tax advantage for small and mid-sized landowners in domestic and foreign companies. The new law will ensure tax stability by reducing long-term burdens in expectations of future tax collection, when plantations are mature and operating well.

• Julio Miranda, candidate for the Menem's Peronist party, becomes the new governor of the poor northwest region of San Miguel de Tucuman.

• The Argentine Agricultural Department shows a drop in wheat and corn exports to Iran in 1998–99.

• Senate officials work to pass an anti-monopoly legislation this month to force Spain's Repsol, which just became the largest shareholder of Argentina's YPF SA oil company, to divest assets thus quelling the possibility the merger will dominate the country's oil market.

July

• A dreary economic situation spurs protests by 5,000 public employees in the northern province of Corrientes, including 270,000 truckers, causing numerous nationwide transport problems.

• Transportation resumes to normal service on July 8.

• The National Institute of Statistics and the Census releases staggering new figures for unemployment in Argentina estimating 14.5% of the population is unemployed while 13.2% are under-employed.

August

• Suffering from its second recession in four years, new figures show that the Argentine economy is expected to shrink by approximately 3% this year and the current unemployment rate of 14.5% is expected to rise.

• Petrolera Argentina San Jorge SA, Argentina's fourth largest oil producer, announces the discovery of new oil fields in one block of Rio Negro Norte and in the south-central province of Rio Negro.

• Jorge Luis Borges mania sweeps Argentina, as August marks the centenary of the author's birth.

September

• Tensions in the South American trade union Mercosur increase as Paraguay tries again, unsuccessfully, to extradite Lino Oviedo, a former Paraguayan general who fled to Argentina in

March and was given political asylum by President Menem.

- Opinion polls place leading presidential candidate Fernando de la Rua at a comfortable lead for the October elections. His main opposition candidate, Eduardo Duhalde, leading in the polls several weeks earlier, now trails.

- Argentine Catholics and Jews are up in arms over the construction of what will be the largest mosque in South America, being built in Buenos Aires by the Saudi embassy.

- Philippine president Joseph Estrada arrives in Argentina for a four-day visit to discuss economic possibilities offered by the Philippines with President Carlos Menem and business leaders.

- An Argentine contractor sues Pan American Energy, the joint endeavor between BP Amoco and Bridas corporation, for alleged environmental damage.

October

- Fernando de la Rua, center-left Alliance candidate and mayor of Buenos Aires, wins the presidency as Argentinian's discontent over unemployment, crime, scandals and Menem grows.

November

- Fernando de la Rua, Argentina's president-elect, reveals his list of cabinet appointments, entrusting at least four of the 12 jobs to economists.

- Colombian drug lord Pablo Escobar's widow and son are arrested in Argentina on suspicion of laundering drug money and falsifying documents.

December

- Fernando de la Rua takes office as Argentina's new president on December 10.

- President Fernando de la Rua initiates a federal takeover of the government of the province Corientes to stop protests by provincial workers who haven't been paid for months. The workers are blocking several important bridges, and threaten to expand their protests to disrupt international trade.

ANALYSIS OF EVENTS: 1999

BUSINESS AND THE ECONOMY

Evidence of the deep recession in Argentina was clear throughout 1999. Beginning the year with the devaluation of the Brazilian *real* negatively affected not only Argentina's economy, but also its relations with Brazil—a key trade partner and fellow member of the South American trade alliance Mercosur (along with Paraguay and Uruguay). As the largest economies in Latin America, diplomatic efforts have been underway to try and prevent serious crisis. So far, these efforts have been unsuccessful and Argentine exports have been pushed out of Brazil's fragile market. A new president taking office in Argentina and the weakened power of Brazil's President, Fernando Henrique Cardoso, as a result of the devaluation added to the tensions and made discussions difficult.

Evidence of the recession and widespread discontent was demonstrated among the mass populations as well; thousands of farmers conducted a three-day strike demanding financial aid from the Argentine government. The strike was called by the Rural Society, made up of four rural associations, and protested new income taxes, higher interest rates and a crash in international crop prices that have devastated many farmers across the country. An estimated 60% of Argentina's exports come from the agricultural sector. Many farmers unable to make mortgage payments were being forced to claim bankruptcy. A dreary economic situation spurred protests by 5,000 public employees in the northern province of Corrientes. Police fired rubber bullets and sprayed tear gas into the crowd while President Carlos Menem pledged $55 million to the province to pay the workers. Meanwhile in Buenos Aires, 300 schoolteachers were blocked by Menem from protesting for wages owed to them through an increased vehicle tax after 270,000 truckers protested against the tax.

The Economic Ministry's announcement that the Argentine economy is 11% smaller than previously thought may mean very little in terms of who is rich and who is poor. However, the negative impact of arriving at a higher foreign debt and fiscal deficit will do little to calm the already discontented Argentine population. Using a more recent date (1993) in calculating the size of the economy—taking into account the recent developments of hyperinflation, price stability and trade opening—resulted in the announcement. Previous calculations used 1986 as their base, a problem since Argentina's economy has suffered economically more recently. Some figures still show growth, however, including foreign investment (though less growth than before).

Adding to the bad news for Argentina's business and economic sector, the National Institute of Statistics and the Census released staggering new figures for unemployment—estimating that 14.5% of the population are unemployed while 13.2% are underemployed. An estimated 12 million out of a population 36 million are poverty-stricken. These figures placed additional pressure on politicians campaigning for the presidential elections in October, though the candidates lacked real ideas and reform plans to seriously address the recession and unemployment.

Senate officials worked to pass an anti-monopoly legislation to force Spain's Repsol, which became the largest shareholder of Argentina's YPF SA this year, to divest assets to quell the possibility that the merger will dominate the country's oil market. The government officially sold all but 5% of its stake in former state oil company, YPF S.A., to Repsol. Repsol's purchase for $2.01 billion place it as the largest share holder of YPF, and many expect Repsol to complete a takeover as soon as possible. In order to complete the sale, Repsol will have to negotiate changing the current law that prevents an acquisition using stock rather than cash. Eduardo de la Rua's Alliance Party, leading in the opinion polls of October's national elections, strongly opposed the takeover and instead supported YPF's merger with Brazil's Petroleo Brasileiro. Many feared the deal would detract from privatization efforts begun in the early 1990s and that Repsol would control 58% of retail gasoline sales, more than 50% of crude oil production and more than 70% of natural gas sales.

Some good news in the oil business, thanks to Petrolera Argentina San Jorge SA, Argentina's fourth largest oil producer, was the announcement of the discovery of new oil fields in one block of Rio Negro Norte and in the south-central province of Rio Negro. The finds were described by the company as ''one of the most important discoveries of the last ten years in Argentina'' and came at a time when the company was looking to sell and receiving offers following the sale of Argentina's largest oil company, YPF SA. After privatizing the state-run oil company in the early 1990s, oil production has increased significantly.

Finally, on the legal front, an Argentine contractor is suing PanAmerican Energy, the joint endeavor between BP Amoco and Bridas corporation, for alleged environmental damage. The case concerns a mandate issued several years ago by Argentina's energy secretary to the oil industry to clean up pits at oil drilling sites. Though largely followed, one contractor is claiming that PanAmerican contaminated land and water in cleaning up the pits. PanAmerican expects the charge to be dismissed.

GOVERNMENT AND POLITICS

The year 1999 was a troubling one for politics in Argentina: recent recession, high unemployment and increasing crime plague a country whose fiscal reforms only a few years ago were held up as a model in Latin America. In the final weeks before President Carlos Saul Menem stepped down as Argentina's leader, many contemplated and reflected on the ten years he was in power—longer than any other leader in Argentina, including dictators.

After being forbidden to run for a third presidential term by Congress and the Supreme Court, Menem's approval rates plunged, despite being largely credited for bringing the country out of social and economic chaos. Menem's successes include increasing foreign investment and installing free-market plans, while maintaining a steadfast commitment to democracy. He also increased diplomatic relations worldwide, ended a long-running dispute with Chile, and restored relations with Great Britain—a landmark event thought impossible since the 1982 war over the Falklands (Malvinas) Islands. His economic reforms included backing every Argentine peso with the U.S. dollar, a move that virtually stopped inflation. However, despite all the benefits Menem's reforms brought to the country, his flashy image, suspected scandals, acceptance of posh gifts, and plastic surgeries grew old as the country began feeling the effects of Mexico's devaluation of the peso (1994) and the more recent economic crisis in neighboring Brazil. Further, Menem seemed to accomplish most of his success during the first five years of his presidency and when things began to fall apart, many contest that he did as well.

When Menem left office in October, many expected his economic reforms to go unfinished.

Complicating the problems further, Argentina's currency board limits the government's ability to use new financial policy to rejuvenate the economy while it maintains the Argentine peso one-to-one with the U.S. dollar. After Menem won re-election in 1995, many believed his strident fiscal reforms—credited for cutting inflation from 20,000% to 4% in four years and eliminating many trade restrictions—would continue. Rather, Menem backed off in pursuing much needed labor, health and tax reforms that could have continued the success official reforms begun in his first term. The news does not add hope to Argentina's future; some analysts believe that the budget deficit could reach $7 billion in 1999, representing 2.3% of the country's gross domestic product, a disturbing figure for a country whose credibility for foreign investment is directly tied to its fiscal discretion.

Menem has frequently been criticized for his shady dealings and associations with corruption. One example took place in the poor northwest territory of San Miguel de Tucuman where Julio Miranda, candidate for the Menem's Peronist party, became the new governor of the region by beating Ricardo Bussi. Bussi's father, Antonio Domingo Bussi, was elected in 1995 and since has been plagued for allegations of corruption and tax evasion. With a political history full of corruption and scandal, the region has seen a steady rise in poverty, unemployment and the province's debt. Miranda's recent win is being protested as a fraud by his opposition. Ramon "Palito" Ortega, the running mate of presidential candidate Eduardo Duhalde of the Peronist party, once ruled the Tucuman region as well. Duhalde and Ortega secured the Peronist nomination when their only opponents withdrew from the race.

Another questionable deal that caused an international stir was Menem's granting of political asylum to Lino Oviedo, a former Paraguayan general who fled to Argentina in March. Oviedo, who has been relaxing on a country estate and has enjoying saunas and a hair transplant, is supposed to be serving a ten-year jail sentence for attempting to stage a coup in 1996. A judge in Paraguay ordered his extradition, accusing him of ordering the murder of Luis Maria Argana, the vice-president and his rival for leading the Colorado political party, who has ruled for a number of years. Fernando de la Rua, presidential candidate for Argentina's opposition Alliance, disapproved of Menem's refusal to extradite Oviedo. The Mercosur trade block, which includes Brazil, Argentina, Paraguay and Uruguay, has struggled with increasing tensions spurred by trade anxiety between Brazil and Argentina.

The chaotic political environment in Argentina has had a direct impact on its citizens. New laws were passed to fine employers who employ undocumented workers, targeting illegal immigration. Government officials claim illegal workers are stealing jobs from Argentines and are responsible for more than 60% of petty crime. Police officials, however, say that their involvement is actually around 5–7% of minor crimes. Large discontent over unemployment, cuts in health and social services, and the economic crisis in neighboring Brazil have spurred Argentines to issue blame on illegal immigrants.

For the first time since 1983, Argentines named crime as their most important public concern. In response, President Carlos Menem assigned additional border police and coast guards to Buenos Aires, where robberies and violent crime have doubled in recent years. Problems such as lack of crime data, police corruption, and an inefficient court system plague the South American country. Lacking long-term political commitment to fighting crime, many Argentines doubt that the situation will improve any time soon. The government has further complicated matters by denying the rising crime problem. Human rights observers have noted that most people don't trust the police to do anything; they seem to be part of the crime problem and are seemingly plagued with allegations of prostitution, illegal gambling, police torture and illegal detentions. Some officials claim that less than a third of crimes are actually reported and even less—one percent—are cleared up. But the police are not the only ones to blame; slow court systems investigating police corruption in several Buenos Aires districts are also part of the problem. In the election year of 1999, politicians scrambled to demonstrate their concern, but many question how far they can actually get. Police intelligence is said to include not-so-flattering information on public figures and most Argentines are skeptical that reforms are the answer. The dismal environment causes many Argentines to look to new leaders for hope.

Center-left Alliance candidate Fernando de la Rua, the former mayor of Buenos Aires, won the presidency as Argentine discontent over unemployment, crime and President Carlos Menem and his government grew. De la Rua profited from the scandals and mistakes which plagued Menem during the campaign. Though many experts maintained that de la Rua offered few ideas and policies to pull the South American country out of its second recession in four years, he was a welcome change for a population tired of Menem.

De la Rua will face serious problems—besides economic recession, crime, and unemployment, the new president will be challenged to maintain the peso one-to-one with the dollar while trying to restore economic growth and keeping up with foreign debt. Further, he will face a Peronist-majority Senate until 2001 and will inherit numerous reforms unfinished by his predecessor.

CULTURE AND SOCIETY

August marks the 100th anniversary of the birth of author and poet Jorge Luis Borges. Affectionately called ''Argentina's Shakespeare'' by many Argentines, ''Borges mania'' swept Argentina during 1999. To honor the anniversary, an exposition of his works will tour the Americas, Asia, and Europe beginning with an inauguration in mid-2000 in Venice, Italy. Maria Kodoma, Borges's widow, will be accompanying the exposition. Born in Argentina on August 24, 1899, Borges's popularity has grown to cult-status in Argentina, while there has been a resurgence in interest in his works worldwide. Seminars, debates, conferences, phone exhibitions, and fresh editions of his books are just a few of the events that will take place around the world to honor the poet who died in Geneva in 1986.

Key advances were made on scientific fronts in 1999, thanks to significant discoveries in the Argentine desert and mountains. A team of paleontologists discovered thousands of fossilized dinosaur eggshells in the Patagonian desert of Argentina. Approximately six inches in diameter, the scientists chiseled the eggs open. Much to their amazement, the team found unhatched embryos inside, among the rarest fossils in the world. The discovery of these dinosaur-egg deposits rates among the largest ever found. The embryos allowed researchers to identify the dinosaurs as part of a plant-eating group called sauropods with long necks and tails and large bodies. Sauropods are known to be among the largest land creatures ever to inhabit Earth, reaching lengths of up to 45 feet as adults. The nesting site where the eggs were found is estimated to be 79 to 90 million years old; researchers plan to return for further excavations.

The discovery of the remains of three children by archaeologist Johan Reinhard followed the dinosaur-egg find. Frozen solid hours after their burial, the two girls and one boy between the ages of 8–15 years are thought to have been sacrificed and entombed on the summit of Mount Llullaillaco in the Argentine Andes 500 years ago. This discovery accompanies recent finds totaling 15 bodies, but surpasses their significance in that the three children's bodies were almost perfectly preserved (the internal organs were intact and still contained blood). The children's bodies were found with gold and silver statues, necklaces and other artifacts. Some of the bodies were found with bundles of food wrapped in alpaca skin, indicating that they came from Incan social elite. Only Incans of elite class were considered for sacrifice. Experts will analyze the children's stomachs to determine what their last meal might have been and will also analyze their organs to investigate diet patterns. It is hoped that examining their DNA will also help link them with other ethnic groups.

The largest mosque in South America, which is being built in Buenos Aires, caused a stir among Argentines. The mosque, being financed by Saudi ruler King Fahn, is meant to give his estimated 900,000 followers a place to worship. President Carlos Menem gave the Saudi embassy in Buenos Aires permission to build the mosque in the wealthy district of Palermo. Argentine Catholics are somewhat on the defensive at the possible clash of cultures, while an estimated 300,000 Argentine Jews are also alarmed.

DIRECTORY

CENTRAL GOVERNMENT
Head of State

President
Fernando de la Rua, Office of the President, Casa de Gobierno, Balcarce 50, 1064 Buenos Aires, Argentina
PHONE: +54 (1) 3443600
FAX: +54 (1) 3316376

Ministers

Chief Cabinet Minister
Jorge Rodriguez, Chief of the Cabinet Ministry, Balcarce 50, 1064 Buenos Aires, Argentina

PHONE: +54 (1) 3749841; 3749849; 3433051

Minister of Foreign Relations and Culture
Guido Jose Maria Di Tella, Ministry of Foreign Relations and Culture, Ministerio de Relaciones Exteriores y Culto, Arenales 761, Buenos Aires CF, Argentina

Minister of the Interior
Carlos Corach, Ministry of the Interior, Casa de Gobierno, Balcarce 50, Buenos Aires CF, Argentina
PHONE: +54 (1) 3311156; 3129328

Minister of Justice
Raul Granillo Ocampo, Ministry of Justice, Sarmiento 329, 1041 Buenos Aires, Argentina
PHONE: +54 (1) 3283015; 3283019

Minister of Economics
Roque Fernandez, Ministry of Economics, Hipolito Yrigoyen 250, 1310 Buenos Aires, Argentina
PHONE: +54 (1) 3495000; 3495010; 3495020

Minister of Labor and Social Security
Jose A. Andres Uriburu, Ministry of Labor and Social Security, Av. Leandro N. Alem 650, 1001 Buenos Aires, Argentina
PHONE: +54 (1) 3106000

Minister of Culture and Education
Manuel G. Garcia Sola, Ministry of Culture and Education, Pizzurno 935, 1020 Buenos Aires, Argentina
PHONE: +54 (1) 8134551; 8134559

Minister of Defense
Jorge Dominguez, Ministry of Defense, Azopardo 250, 1328 Buenos Aires, Argentina
PHONE: +54 (1) 3468800

Minister of Health and Social Welfare
Alberto Mazza, Ministry of Health and Social Welfare, Avenida de Julio 1925, 1332 Buenos Aires, Argentina
PHONE: +54 (1) 3799000

POLITICAL ORGANIZATIONS

Frente del País Solidario-FrePaSo (Front for the Country in Solidarity)
E-MAIL: frepaso@sion.com

Frente Grande (Broad Front)
Franklin 545, 1405 CF, Buenos Aires, Argentina
PHONE: +54 (11) 49580066; 43436297
E-MAIL: J-Frente-Grande@iname.com
NAME: Carlos Alvarez

Partido Socialista Democrático (Social Democratic Party)
E-MAIL: cesode1@geocities.com
NAME: Guillermo Estévez Boero

Movimiento Popular Jujeño (Popular Movement of Jujuy)
Riobamba 25, 1025 CF, Buenos Aires, Argentina
PHONE: +54 (11) 43707100
FAX: +54 (11) 43707100
E-MAIL: mpj@mail.imagine.com.ar
NAME: María Cristina Guzmán

Unión Cívica Radical-UCR (Radical Civic Union)
E-MAIL: info@ucr.org.ar
NAME: Rodolfo Terragno

Movimiento al Socialismo (Trotskyist Party)
Chile 1362, 1098 CF, Buenos Aires, Argentina
PHONE: +54 3812718; 3812995
FAX: +54 3812976
E-MAIL: Mas@giga.com.a

Partido Obrero (Trotskyist Workers Party)
E-MAIL: ayacucho@po.org.ar

El Movimiento de Trabajadores Demócrata Cristianos de Argentina (Christian Democrats of Argentina)
PHONE: +54 (011) 43051229
FAX: +54 (011) 43068242
E-MAIL: info@mtdc.org.ar

Acción Por La República (Action for the Republic)
4 de Enero 1700, 2° Piso, Dpto. "A," 3000 Santa Fe, Argentina
PHONE: +54 (42) 597748; 593452
FAX: +54 (42) 600080
E-MAIL: accionrepublic@geocities.com
TITLE: Presidente
NAME: Domingo F. Cavallo

DIPLOMATIC REPRESENTATION
Embassies in Argentina

Australia
Villanueva 1400, 1426 Buenos Aires, Argentina

PHONE: +54 (1) 7715620; 7776580
FAX: +54 (1) 7723349

Belgium
Defensa 113, Piso 8, 1065 Buenos Aires,
Argentina
PHONE: +54 (1) 3310066; 3310069
FAX: +54 (1) 3310814

Bolivia
Corrientes 545, Piso 2, 1043 Buenos Aires,
Argentina
PHONE: +54 (1) 3946042; 3946640
FAX: +54 (1) 3220371

Brazil
Cerrito 1350, 1010 Buenos Aires, Argentina
PHONE: +54 (1) 8120035; 8120039
FAX: +54 (1) 8144687

Canada
Tagle 2828, 1425 Buenos Aires, Argentina
PHONE: +54 (1) 8053032
FAX: +54 (1) 8061209

Chile
Tagle 2762, 1425 Buenos Aires, Argentina
PHONE: +54 (1) 8027020; 8027028
FAX: +54 (1) 8045927

China
Crisólogo Larralde 5349, 1431 Buenos Aires,
Argentina
PHONE: +54 (1) 5438862, 5420054
FAX: +54 (1) 9534208

Colombia
Carlos Pellegrini 1363, Piso 3, 1011 Buenos
Aires, Argentina
PHONE: +54 (1) 3250494; 3250258
FAX: +54 (1) 3329370

Cuba
Virrey del Pino 1810, 1426 Buenos Aires,
Argentina
PHONE: +54 (1) 7829049; 7829089
FAX: +54 (1) 7867713

Denmark
Av. L.N. Alem 1074, Piso 9, 1001 Buenos
Aires, Argentina
PHONE: +54 (1) 3126901
FAX: +54 (1) 3127857

Ecuador
Av. Quintana 585, Piso 9 y 10, 1129 Buenos
Aires, Argentina
PHONE: +54 (1) 8040073; 8040074
FAX: +54 (1) 8040074

Egypt
Juez Tedín 2795, 1425 Buenos Aires, Argentina
PHONE: +54 (1) 8053913; 8053916
FAX: +54 (1) 8016145

France
Cerrito 1399, 1010 Buenos Aires, Argentina
PHONE: +54 (1) 3792930
FAX: +54 (1) 3931235

Germany
Villanueva 1055, 1426 Buenos Aires, Argentina
PHONE: +54 (1) 7715054; 7715059
FAX: +54 (1) 7759612

Greece
Av. Roque Sáenz Peña 547, Piso 4, 1035
Buenos Aires, Argentina
PHONE: +54 (1) 3424958
FAX: +54 (1) 3422838

India
Córdoba 950, Piso 4, 1054 Buenos Aires,
Argentina
PHONE: +54 (1) 3934001
FAX: +54 (1) 3934063

Indonesia
Mariscal Ramón Castilla 2901, 1425 Buenos
Aires, Argentina
PHONE: +54 (1) 8016622
FAX: +54 (1) 8024448

Ireland
Suipacha 1380, Piso 2, 1095 Buenos Aires,
Argentina
PHONE: +54 (1) 3258588; 3250849
FAX: +54 (1) 3257572

Israel
Av. Mayo 701, Piso 10, 1084 Buenos Aires,
Argentina
PHONE: +54 (1) 3421465
FAX: +54 (1) 3425307

Italy
Billinghurst 2577, 1425 Buenos Aires, Argentina
PHONE: +54 (1) 8020071; 8020074
FAX: +54 (1) 8044914

Japan
Av. Paseo Colón 275, Piso 9, 1063 Buenos
Aires, Argentina
PHONE: +54 (1) 3345203

Mexico
Larrea 1230, 1117 Buenos Aires, Argentina
PHONE: +54 (1) 8217136
FAX: +54 (1) 8217251

Netherlands
Av. de Mayo 701, Piso 19, 1084 Buenos Aires, Argentina
PHONE: +54 (1) 3343474
FAX: +54 (1) 3342717

Paraguay
Las Heras 2545, 1425 Buenos Aires, Argentina
PHONE: +54 (1) 8023826; 8020437

Peru
Av. Libertador 1720, 1425 Buenos Aires, Argentina
PHONE: +54 (1) 8022000
FAX: +54 (1) 8025887

Russia
Rodriguez Peña 1741, 1021 Buenos Aires, Argentina
PHONE: +54 (1) 421552; 428039

Spain
Mariscal Ramón Castilla 2720, 1425 Buenos Aires, Argentina
PHONE: +54 (1) 8026031; 8026033
FAX: +54 (1) 8020719

United Kingdom
Luis Agote 2412/52, Casilla 2050, 1425 Buenos Aires, Argentina
PHONE: +54 (1) 8037070; 8037071
FAX: +54 (1) 8031731

United States
Av. Colombia 4300, 1425 Buenos Aires, Argentina
PHONE: +54 (1) 7770197; 7754205
FAX: +54 (1) 7754205; 7770673

Uruguay
Av. Las Heras 1907, 1127 Buenos Aires, Argentina
PHONE: +54 (1) 8036030; 8036039
FAX: +54 (1) 8036038

Venezuela
Virrey Loreto 2035, 1428 Buenos Aires, Argentina
PHONE: +54(1) 5442618
FAX: +54 (1) 5446704

JUDICIAL SYSTEM
Corte Suprema de Justicia de la Nación
E-MAIL: webmaster@pjn.gov.ar

Court of Appeals
District Court
Territorial Court
Judicial Court

FURTHER READING
Articles
"Argentina, Not As Big As It Seemed." *The Economist* (June 19, 1999): 30.

"Argentina's Awkward Transition." *The Economist* (May 29, 1999): 31.

"Argentina's Mr. Boring Plods to Victory by Default." *The Economist* (September 4, 1999): 39.

"Brazil's Falling Currency Strains Relations with Argentina." *Journal of Commerce and Commercial* 419 (January 25, 1999): 2A.

"A Buoyant Ending." *Newsweek International*, 13 September 1999, p. 32.

"Cops and Robbers in Argentina." *The Economist* 351 (May 1, 1999): 33.

"Death in the Andes." *Time* 153 (April 19, 1999): 46.

Eisen, Peter. "PanAmerican Denies Envrionmental Charges." *The Oil Daily* (September 3, 1999).

———. "Repsol Plots Next Move After Winning YPF Bid." *The Oil Daily* (January 22, 1999).

Fuhr, Stefan. "South America's Largest Mosque Causing Stir in Argentina." *Deutsche-Presse Agentur*, September 20, 1999.

"GasAtacama Finally Starts Up." *The Oil Daily* (June 17, 1999).

Gottling, Jorge. "Argentina's Penniless Pensioners." *UNESCO Courier* (January 1999): 27.

Gray, Kevin. "Argentine Presidential Race Near." *Associated Press*, October 11, 1999.

"A Job Half Done." *Business Week* (August 30, 1999): 60.

"Justice at Last." *The Economist* (February 27, 1999): 34.

Kowalski, B.J. "Targeting Immigrants." *World Press Review* (April 1999): 23.

"Meanwhile, in the Provinces." *The Economist* (March 20, 1999): 40.

"The Month in Review." *Current History* (February 1999).

Moss, Chris. "Chris Moss Finds Borges Mania Sweeping Argentina." *The Guardian of London*, August 18, 1999.

"New Argentine Law Encourages Plantations." *Wood Technology* (June 1999): 12.

"No More Peso?" *The Economist* (January 23, 1999): 69.

"Paraguay's General in His Asylum." *The Economist* (September 11, 1999): 40.

"Philippine President Visits Argentina." *Xinhua News Agency*, September 18, 1999.

"Rebuke over Disappeared." *New York Times, World Briefs*, 29 April 1999, p. 6.

Rivera, Rachel. "Golden Eggs." *Science World* 55 (February 8, 1999): 4.

Robinson, Matthew; Jason Freer. "Argentina Rushes to Pass Anti-Monopoly Bill." *The Oil Daily* (June 15, 1999).

"San Jorge Reports 2 New Oil Discoveries on its Rio Norte Block." *The Oil Daily* (August 13, 1999).

"Shell's Argentine Assets Frozen." *The Oil Daily* (March 5, 1999).

"Sour Mercosur." *The Economist* (August 14, 1999): 13.

"Strike Ends for the Present; Threat of Renewal Remains." *Journal of Commerce and Commercial* (July 9, 1999): 15.

"Sweet and Sour Politics." *The Economist* (June 12, 1999): 32.

Valente, Marcela. "Jorge Luis Borges." *Inter Press Service*, January 12, 1999.

———. "Striking Farmers Demand Government Aid." *Inter Press Service*, April 20, 1999.

ARGENTINA: STATISTICAL DATA

For sources and notes see "Sources of Statistics" in the front of each volume.

GEOGRAPHY

Geography (1)

Area:

Total: 2,766,890 sq km.

Land: 2,736,690 sq km.

Water: 30,200 sq km.

Area—comparative: slightly less than three-tenths the size of the US.

Land boundaries:

Total: 9,665 km.

Border countries: Bolivia 832 km, Brazil 1,224 km, Chile 5,150 km, Paraguay 1,880 km, Uruguay 579 km.

Coastline: 4,989 km.

Climate: mostly temperate; arid in southeast; subantarctic in southwest.

Terrain: rich plains of the Pampas in northern half, flat to rolling plateau of Patagonia in south, rugged Andes along western border.

Natural resources: fertile plains of the pampas, lead, zinc, tin, copper, iron ore, manganese, petroleum, uranium.

Land use:

Arable land: 9%

Permanent crops: 1%

Permanent pastures: 52%

Forests and woodland: 19%

Other: 19% (1993 est.).

HUMAN FACTORS

Demographics (2A)

	1990	1995	1998	2000	2010	2020	2030	2040	2050
Population	32,634.4	34,877.2	36,265.5	37,214.8	41,975.0	46,344.8	50,250.1	53,616.8	56,258.5
Net migration rate (per 1,000 population)	NA	NA	NA	NA	NA	NA	NA	NA	NA
Births	NA	NA	NA	NA	NA	NA	NA	NA	NA
Deaths	259.7	NA	NA	NA	NA	NA	NA	NA	NA
Life expectancy - males	69.1	70.2	70.9	71.4	73.0	74.3	75.5	76.5	77.3
Life expectancy - females	76.0	77.7	78.3	78.8	80.7	82.3	83.5	84.4	85.0
Birth rate (per 1,000)	20.8	20.1	20.0	19.9	18.2	16.4	15.2	14.0	13.0
Death rate (per 1,000)	8.0	7.7	7.7	7.6	7.5	7.5	7.9	8.4	9.0
Women of reproductive age (15-49 yrs.)	7,777.1	8,527.2	8,928.9	9,148.8	10,220.3	11,342.4	11,998.1	12,470.2	12,779.2
of which are currently married	NA	NA	NA	NA	NA	NA	NA	NA	NA
Fertility rate	2.9	2.7	2.7	2.6	2.4	2.3	2.2	2.1	2.0

Except as noted, values for vital statistics are in thousands; life expectancy is in years.

Health Personnel (3)

Total health expenditure as a percentage of GDP, 1990-1997[a]

Public sector 4.3

Private sector 5.4

Total[b] 9.7

Health expenditure per capita in U.S. dollars, 1990-1997[a]

Purchasing power parity 931

Total 799

Availability of health care facilities per 100,000 people

Hospital beds 1990-1997[a] 460

Doctors 1993[c] 268

Nurses 1993[c] 54

Health Indicators (4)

Life expectancy at birth

1980 70

1997 73

Daily per capita supply of calories (1996) 3,136

Total fertility rate births per woman (1997) 2.6

Maternal mortality ratio per 100,000 live births (1990-97) . . . . .100[c]

Safe water % of population with access (1995) 65

Sanitation % of population with access (1995) 75

Consumption of iodized salt % of households (1992-98)[a] 90

Smoking prevalence

Male % of adults (1985-95)[a] 40

Female % of adults (1985-95)[a] 23

Tuberculosis incidence per 100,000 people (1997) 56

Adult HIV prevalence % of population ages 15-49 (1997) 0.69

Infants and Malnutrition (5)

Under-5 mortality rate (1997) 24

% of infants with low birthweight (1990-97) 7

Births attended by skilled health staff % of total[a] . . .97

% fully immunized (1995-97)

TB 100

DPT 86

Polio 92

Measles 92

Prevalence of child malnutrition under age 5 (1992-97)[b] 2

Ethnic Division (6)

White 85%

Mestizo, Amerindian, or other nonwhite groups . . .15%

Religions (7)

Nominally Roman Catholic 90%

Protestant 2%

Jewish 2%

Other 6%

Less than 20% of Roman Catholics practicing.

Languages (8)

Spanish (official), English, Italian, German, French.

EDUCATION

Public Education Expenditures (9)

Public expenditure on education (% of GNP)

1980 . . . . .2.7

1996 . . . . .3.5

Expenditure per student

Primary % of GNP per capita

1980 . . . . .6.5

1996 . . . . .8.3

Secondary % of GNP per capita

1980 . . . .

1996 . . . .

Tertiary % of GNP per capita

1980 . . . . .29.3

1996 . . . . .19.8[1]

Expenditure on teaching materials

Primary % of total for level (1996) . . . .

Secondary % of total for level (1996) . . . .

Primary pupil-teacher ratio per teacher (1996) 16

Duration of primary education years (1995) 7

Educational Attainment (10)

Age group (1991) . . . . .25+

Total population 17,340,713

Highest level attained (%)

No schooling 5.7

First level

Not completed 22.3

Completed 34.6

Entered second level

S-1 . . . . .25.3

S-2 . . . . .NA

Postsecondary 12.0

Literacy Rates (11A)

In thousands and percent[1]	1990	1995	2000	2010
Illiterate population (15+ yrs.)	983	935	891	808
Literacy rate - total adult pop. (%)	95.6	96.2	96.6	97.3
Literacy rate - males (%)	95.7	96.2	96.6	97.2
Literacy rate - females (%)	95.6	96.2	96.7	97.5

GOVERNMENT & LAW

Political Parties (12)

Chamber of Deputies	No. of seats
Justicialist Party (PJ)	119
Radical Civic Union (UCR)	69
Front for a Country in Solidarity (Frepaso)	36
Other	33

Military Affairs (14B)

	1990	1991	1992	1993	1994	1995
Military expenditures						
Current dollars (mil.)	3,436	2,769	4,500	4,282	4,724	4,684
1995 constant dollars (mil.)	3,949	3,060	4,841	4,489	4,842	4,684
Armed forces (000)	85	70	65	65	69	65
Gross national product (GNP)						
Current dollars (mil.)	181,400	207,900	234,300	256,800	278,400	271,200
1995 constant dollars (mil.)	208,500	229,700	252,000	269,200	285,400	271,200
Central government expenditures (CGE)						
1995 constant dollars (mil.)	9,387	11,780	14,680	18,110	17,960	NA
People (mil.)	32.4	32.8	33.2	33.5	33.9	34.3
Military expenditure as % of GNP	1.9	1.3	1.9	1.7	1.7	1.7
Military expenditure as % of CGE	42.1	26.0	33.0	24.8	27.0	NA
Military expenditure per capita (1995 $)	122	93	146	134	143	137
Armed forces per 1,000 people (soldiers)	2.6	2.1	2.0	1.9	2.0	1.9
GNP per capita (1995 $)	6,437	7,010	7,601	8,027	8,415	7,909
Arms imports[6]						
Current dollars (mil.)	20	10	10	20	10	40
1995 constant dollars (mil.)	23	11	11	21	10	40
Arms exports[6]						
Current dollars (mil.)	20	5	5	140	30	70
1995 constant dollars (mil.)	23	6	5	147	31	70
Total imports[7]						
Current dollars (mil.)	4,076	8,275	14,870	16,780	21,530	20,120
1995 constant dollars (mil.)	4,684	9,144	16,000	17,600	22,070	20,120
Total exports[7]						
Current dollars (mil.)	12,350	11,980	12,230	13,120	15,660	20,970
1995 constant dollars (mil.)	14,200	13,240	13,160	13,750	16,050	20,970
Arms as percent of total imports[8]	.5	.1	.1	.1	0	.2
Arms as percent of total exports[8]	.2	0	0	1.1	.2	.3

Government Budget (13A)

Year: 1996

Total Expenditures: 41,866.9 Millions of Pesos

Expenditures as a percentage of the total by function:

General public services and public order 13.39

Defense 4.81

Education 5.74

Health 2.53

Social Security and Welfare 53.36

Housing and community amenities 2.44

Recreational, cultural, and religious affairs 35

Fuel and energy 1.14

Agriculture, forestry, fishing, and hunting 89

Mining, manufacturing, and construction 29

Transportation and communication 3.36

Other economic affairs and services 60

Crime (15)

Crime rate (for 1997)

Crimes reported 338,100

Total persons convicted 164,400

Crimes per 100,000 population 1,000

Persons responsible for offenses

Total number of suspects 106,600

Total number of female suspects 9,700

Total number of juvenile suspects 18,500

LABOR FORCE

Labor Force (16)

Total (million) 14.5

Agriculture 12%

Industry 31%

Services 57%

Data for 1995 est. Percent distribution for 1985 est.

Unemployment Rate (17)

13.7% (October 1997)

PRODUCTION SECTOR

Electric Energy (18)

Capacity . . . . .19.61 million kW (1995)

Production . . . . .65.72 billion kWh (1995)

Consumption per capita . . . . .1,960 kWh (1995)

Transportation (19)

Highways:

total: 218,276 km

paved: 63,518 km (including 567 km of expressways)

unpaved: 154,758 km (1996 est.)

Waterways: 11,000 km navigable

Pipelines: crude oil 4,090 km; petroleum products 2,900 km; natural gas 9,918 km

Merchant marine:

total: 34 ships (1,000 GRT or over) totaling 268,492 GRT/388,524 DWT ships by type: cargo 11, container 2, oil tanker 13, railcar carrier 1, refrigerated cargo 6, roll-on/roll-off cargo 1 (1997 est.)

Airports: 1,411 (1997 est.)

Airports—with paved runways:

total: 137

over 3,047 m: 5

2,438 to 3,047 m: 25

1,524 to 2,437 m: 55

914 to 1,523 m: 44

under 914 m: 8 (1997 est.)

Airports—with unpaved runways:

total: 1,274

over 3,047 m: 2

2,438 to 3,047 m: 2

1,524 to 2,437 m: 65

914 to 1,523 m: 635

under 914 m: 570 (1997 est.)

Top Agricultural Products (20)

Wheat, corn, sorghum, soybeans, sugar beets; livestock.

MANUFACTURING SECTOR

GDP & Manufacturing Summary (21)

Detailed value added figures are listed by both International Standard Industry Code (ISIC) and product title.

	1980	1985	1990	1994
GDP ($-1990 mil.)[1]	154,859	139,450	141,353	190,518
Per capita ($-1990)[1]	5,508	4,599	4,343	5,574
Manufacturing share (%) (current prices)[1]	29.5	29.6	27.1	*25.0*
Manufacturing				
Value added ($-1990 mil.)[1]	43,566	37,054	37,868	*53,044*
Industrial production index	100	86	90	*126*

	1980	1985	1990	1994
Value added ($ mil.)	24,511	28,891	31,156	88,366
Gross output ($ mil.)	55,936	48,084	79,001	217,063
Employment (000)	1,346	1,174	942	982
Profitability (% of gross output)				
Intermediate input (%)	56	40	61	59
Wages and salaries inc. supplements (%)	10	11	8	6
Gross operating surplus	33	49	31	34
Productivity ($)				
Gross output per worker	41,553	34,798	83,878	220,539
Value added per worker	18,208	20,908	33,080	89,820
Average wage (inc. supplements)	4,302	4,411	6,767	13,818
Value added ($ mil.)				
311/2 Food products	3,544	4,912	4,695	13,932
313 Beverages	703	942	932	2,753
314 Tobacco products	498	719	480	1,454
321 Textiles	1,703	1,832	2,209	6,747
322 Wearing apparel	919	558	492	1,647
323 Leather and fur products	284	350	336	958
324 Footwear	245	240	190	433
331 Wood and wood products	363	283	255	370
332 Furniture and fixtures	226	185	246	648
341 Paper and paper products	554	763	882	2,628
342 Printing and publishing	679	800	695	2,147
351 Industrial chemicals	914	1,367	1,844	4,588
352 Other chemical products	1,206	1,916	1,791	3,094
353 Petroleum refineries	3,647	5,120	6,069	18,143
354 Miscellaneous petroleum and coal products	86	121	122	360
355 Rubber products	331	327	368	878
356 Plastic products	424	485	436	865
361 Pottery, china and earthenware	189	130	156	500
362 Glass and glass products	199	153	249	560
369 Other non-metal mineral products	659	587	932	2,542
371 Iron and steel	900	1,239	1,651	4,856
372 Non-ferrous metals	235	257	305	899
381 Metal products	1,272	1,499	1,611	4,924
382 Non-electrical machinery	1,358	930	835	2,718
383 Electrical machinery	902	936	1,025	2,655
384 Transport equipment	2,289	2,054	2,140	6,564
385 Professional and scientific equipment	86	95	112	347
390 Other manufacturing industries	96	92	97	154

FINANCE, ECONOMICS, & TRADE

Economic Indicators (22)

National product: GDP—purchasing power parity—$348.2 billion (1997 est.)

National product real growth rate: 8.4% (1997 est.)

National product per capita: $9,700 (1997 est.)

Inflation rate—consumer price index: 0.3% (1997)

Balance of Payments (23)

	1990	1992	1994	1995	1996
Exports of goods (f.o.b.)	12,354	12,235	15,840	20,964	23,811
Imports of goods (f.o.b.)	−3,726	−13,685	−20,078	−18,726	−22,189
Trade balance	8,628	−1,450	−4,238	2,238	1,622
Services - debits	−9,374	−9,262	−11,826	−12,463	−13,979
Services - credits	4,300	4,636	5,768	7,374	7,887
Private transfers (net)	998	729	423	475	360
Government transfers (net)	NA	−70	−105	−43	−26
Overall balance	4,552	−5,417	−9,978	−2,446	−4,136

Exchange Rates (24)

Exchange rates:

Pesos per US$1

January 1998 . . . . .0.99950

1997 . . . . .0.99950

1996 . . . . .0.99966

1995 . . . . .0.99975

1994 . . . . .0.99901

1993 . . . . .0.99895

Top Import Origins (25)

$30.3 billion (c.i.f., 1997). Data are for 1995.

Origins	%
Brazil	20.8
United States	20.7
Italy	6.3
Germany	6.2
France	5.2

Top Export Destinations (26)

$25.4 billion (f.o.b., 1997). Data are for 1995.

Destinations	%
Brazil	26.1
United States	8.5
Chile	7.0
Netherlands	5.7
Italy	3.5

Economic Aid (27)

$NA. NA stands for not available.

Import Export Commodities (28)

Import Commodities	Export Commodities
Machinery and equipment	Meat
Chemicals	Wheat
Metals	Corn
Transport equipment	Oilseed
Agricultural products	Manufactures
	Fuels

ARMENIA

Republic of Armenia
Hayastani Hanrapetut 'Yun

INTRODUCTORY SURVEY

RECENT HISTORY

Armenia is located at a crossroads of ancient history. It was the first country to be converted to Christianity. Armenia was annexed by the communist army of the Union of Soviet Socialist Republics in 1920. It became a separate constituent republic of the USSR in 1936, and it remained a part of the communist empire until it declared its independence on September 23, 1991.

Armenia has been embroiled in a territorial dispute with Azerbaijan since 1988, and Armenia has been successful in military actions against Azerbaijan. A cease fire was signed in 1994 over the disputed territory, but the issue is still unresolved.

Armenia's Prime Minister Vazgen Sarkisian and six others were assassinated on October 27, 1999. The prime minister's brother was appointed to succeed him. The assassins claimed the prime minister was corrupt.

GOVERNMENT

Armenia adopted its first post-Soviet constitution in July 1995, based on the French model with a strong presidency. Armenia has two branches of government, the executive and legislative, with elections held every five years. Armenia is divided into 11 provinces; each has its own legislative and executive bodies that control the provincial budget as well as residential and commercial affairs.

ARMENIA

GEORGIA

Kalinino • Alaverdi • Akstafa
Step'anavan • Ijevan • Tovuz
Kumayri • Kirovakan
Dilijan
Akhta
AZERBAIJAN
Mt. Aragats
13,419 ft.
4090 m.
Kamo
Sevana
Lich
Nagorno-Karabakh
boundary
Ejmiatsin • Arzni • Zod
Hoktemberyan • Yerevan • Basargech'ar
Garni • Martuni
Igdir • Artashat • Kälbäjär
Ararat
TURKEY • Arpa
Sisian
Shakhbus • Goris
AZERBAIJAN
Ghap'an
Armenia
Meghri
IRAN

Judiciary

The court system consists of district courts, a Supreme Court, and military tribunals. Criminal procedures include the right to an attorney, a public trial, and the right to appeal. New criminal and civil codes were under preparation in 1997. A Constitutional Court reviews the constitutionality of legislation and approves international agreements.

Political Parties

The former president, Levon Ter-Petrossyan, belonged to the Armenian Pan-National Movement (APNM), and was reelected in 1996. In March 1998, Prime Minister Robert Kocharian was elected president. There are seven opposition parties represented in parliament.

DEFENSE

The armed forces may number 57,400 regular soldiers and 30,000 militiamen, reinforced with 4,300 Russian soldiers.

ECONOMIC AFFAIRS

The Armenian economy is mainly agricultural, with agricultural products including fruits, vegetables, vineyards, and livestock. In December 1988, a severe earthquake seriously damaged the Armenian economy, which has also been severely disrupted by the break-up of the former Soviet Union. Economic growth has improved from −15% in 1993 to 7% in 1995.

Public Finance

The government's efforts to privatize the national industries started in 1994 and was scheduled for completion in 1997. Loans from the IMF, World Bank, EBRD, and other financial institutions and foreign countries are targeted at eliminating the government's budget deficit. By 1996, external public debt exceeded $353 million with annual debt service payments exceeding $55 million.

Income

In 1997, the Gross Domestic Product (GDP) was $9.5 billion, or about $2,750 per person. The real growth rate was 2.7%; inflation was 13.2%. Unemployment was 10.6% in 1997, but large numbers were underemployed.

Industry

The main industries are mechanical engineering, chemicals, textiles, and food processing. Since the collapse of the former Soviet Union, industrial production has been severely disrupted by political instability and shortages of power. A severe earthquake in December 1988 destroyed about one-tenth of the industrial capacity of the country. Much of the industrial sector has not been repaired.

Banking and Finance

The National Bank of the Republic of Armenia is the central bank of Armenia, charged with regulating the money supply, circulating currency, and regulating the commercial banks of the country. Commercial banks in Armenia include the Ardshinbank, Armagrobank, Armeconombank, Armimplexbank, Arminvestbank, Bank Armcommunication, Bank "Capital," Bank "Haykap," Central Bank of Armenia, Commercial Bank "Ardana," Commercial Bank Anelik, "Gladzor" Joint Stock Commercial Bank, Masis Commercial Bank, and the State Specialized Savings Bank of the Republic of Armenia.

The IMF has been concerned about the direction of policy taken by the National Bank of Armenia and the slow pace of financial reform. Armenia's financial sector is overbanked and beset with non-performing credits, mainly to large state enterprises. Armenia has been a model reforming country among the former Soviet republics, and multilateral creditors are worried that public pressure may now force the government to loosen monetary and fiscal policies.

It was revealed in January 1997 that the central bank's credits to finance the government's budget gap had surpassed their $100 million limit in the first ten months of 1996. The bank has been forced to intervene in the domestic markets, selling foreign exchange reserves to maintain the stability of the dram. The dram has lost some 14% in value since September 1996, when it stood at D412:$1. By the end of February 1997 the rate had gone down to almost D470:$1.

In 1995, market capitalization on the Yerevan Stock Exchange was $3.3.

Economic Development

The government's economic reform program was launched by its privatization of agricultural land in 1991, which boosted crop output 30% and resulted in a 15% increase in agricultural production. Privatization of input supplies, distribution, and marketing is in progress.

The republic has substantial deposits of gold, copper, zinc, bauxite, and other minerals, which could be developed with Western capital. The government is currently exploring alternative trade routes, and seeking export orders from the West to aid production and earn foreign exchange.

Armenia's determination to create a market-oriented economy and democratic society has engaged the IMF, World Bank, and EBRD as well as other financial institutions and foreign countries.

SOCIAL WELFARE

Women in Armenia largely occupy traditional roles defined by their families. A 1992 employment law does formally prohibit discrimination based on gender. Work injury legislation was updated in 1995 to provide comprehensive payments for disability. The government allows ethnic minorities the right to preserve their own cultures and languages.

Healthcare

Life expectancy averages 73 years (74 years for females and 71 years for males). Vaccination programs have been hampered by the war and earthquakes.

Housing

In 1990, Armenia had 15 square meters of housing space per person. As of 1 January 1991, there were 142,000 households on waiting lists for housing in urban areas, or 34.6% of all households. The 1988 earthquake is estimated to have destroyed up to 10% of the housing in Armenia.

EDUCATION

Adult literacy is estimated at 100%. Education is compulsory and free at the primary and secondary levels. There are two universities in Yerevan. In 1991, a total of 125,900 students were enrolled in all higher level institutions.

1999 KEY EVENTS
TIMELINE

May

- General elections result in a new government; Vazgen Sarkisian is the new prime minister. A former mayor of Yerevan is investigated for contracting murders during his term as minister of the interior.

June

- Catholicos Garegin, head of the Armenian Apostolic Church, dies of cancer.

July

- Armenia finalizes a cooperation pact with the European Union.

October

- Five gunmen storm the Armenian parliament, killing eight people, including Prime Minister Vazgen Sarkisian.

November

- Azerbaijani president Haidar Aliyev and Armenian president Robert Kocharyan fail to reach an agreement on peace in the Nagorno-Karabakh region; observers had speculated that the two would sign an agreement during the meeting of the Organization for Security and Cooperation in Europe (OCSE) in Istanbul, Turkey.

December

- Alexan Arutunian, a senior adviser to President Robert Kocharian, is detained by authorities because he is believed to have a connection with the attack on parliament in October.

ANALYSIS OF EVENTS: 1999

BUSINESS AND THE ECONOMY

The formation of a new government after general elections in May led to the ouster of economic reformer Armen Darbinyan as prime minister. Armenian leaders assured the president of the World Bank, who visited Yerevan in June, that the Armenian government is committed to continuing economic reform. Armenia was one of three nations in the Caucasus to finalize a pact with the European Union (EU) in July. The pact outlines a program of cooperation in politics and on matters of trade and investment. The foreign minister of Germany saw the agreement as a continuation of EU expansion into Eastern Europe and an indicator of the increasing importance of the countries in the regions of the Caucasus and the Black Sea.

GOVERNMENT AND POLITICS

General elections in May resulted in the victory of the Unity Bloc, headed by former defense minister Vazgen Sarkisian. Armen Darbinyan resigned as prime minister, and talks with president Robert Kocharyan led to the appointments of Sarkisian as prime minister and Soviet-era Communist Karen Demirchian as parliamentary speaker. Sarkisian was viewed as a hard-liner and was a close ally of Demirchian. The elections saw a 55% voter turnout, with the Unity Bloc garnering almost 45% of the total votes.

A former mayor of Yerevan was detained for four days in May while being investigated for contracting murders during his term as interior minister. The former mayor had fled Armenia in February when he was stripped of his immunity from prosecution as a parliamentary deputy and was released in this latest instance after the maximum period of detention allowed by Armenian law, since parliament had not lifted his immunity a second time.

In October, gunmen stormed the Armenian parliament during late afternoon debates, which are televised nationally. The gunmen killed eight people (including two of country's top leaders—Prime Minister Sarkisian and parliamentary Speaker Karen Demirchian, a leader of Armenia during the Soviet era) and wounded 30, taking dozens of hostages. Overnight talks with Armenia's president led

to the gunmen's surrender the following day. Statements were read on national television, in which Kocharyan promised a fair trial and no reprisals, and the gunmen submitted to the judgment of the nation and asked for a guarantee that they not be subjected to violence. The gunmen were members of the nationalist Dashnan party and intended a coup against the Armenian leadership, Sarkisian in particular, which the gunmen said was misleading the country. Various government ministries, including the ministries of defense and the interior and the National Security Force, called for a restructuring of the national government in the wake of the parliament crisis. The incident was condemned by the international community, and the United Nations observed a minute of silence in honor of the victims.

The attack renewed fears of instability in region, which for years has been plagued with violence over the disputed Nagorno-Karabakh region, where ethnic Armenian separatists fought to maintain their independence from Azerbaijan until a cease-fire in 1994. Political analysts at the close of October were inclined to expect a resolution to the conflict over Karabakh, even though Armenia has provided political and military aid to Karabakh; the Armenian government denies any direct involvement.

Armenia has also received support from Russia, which in March updated its missile capability on bases it maintains in Armenia. But the Azeri economy has suffered from low global oil prices, the disruption of oil production by the Karabakh situation (because of which roughly one million Azeris are still living in refugee camps outside Baku), and the failure to find new sources of oil. Hence, the Azeris have grown more inclined to forge a settlement, which will mean an influx of foreign aid and investment, especially from the United States, which has promised in the event of a settlement to repeal a law prohibiting direct aid to Azerbaijan.

U.S. Secretary of State Madeleine Albright met with the Armenian and Azeri foreign ministers at the U.N. General Assembly in September, after the two ministers had met at Yalta earlier in the month. U.S. Deputy Secretary of State Strobe Talbott met with the presidents of Armenia and Azerbaijan at the end of October. The presidents of the two nations met four times between August and October, and Azerbaijan returned all its Armenian prisoners of war in September, while Armenia has returned all but ten of the Azeris it holds captive. Armenia also agreed to cooperate with Azerbaijan in strengthening their mutual border, where skirmishes between Armenian and Azeri troops in June resulted in two deaths.

CULTURE AND SOCIETY

In April crowds at a monument in Yerevan commemorated the massacre of over a million Armenians by the Ottoman Empire between the years 1915 and 1923. While Turkish intellectuals have pressed for an acknowledgement of Ottoman atrocities, the government of Turkey counters Armenian charges of genocide by claiming that mass deportations from Turkey to Syria caused the deaths of some 300,000 Armenians.

Three days of mourning were declared in Armenia in July following the death of the head of the Armenian Apostolic Church, Catholicos Garegin, at the end of June. The patriarchs of Constantinople and Jerusalem attended the funeral of Garegin, who was buried in St. Etchmiadzin Cathedral, the country's main church, in Yerevan. The Syrian-born Garegin was the first Catholic installed in newly independent Armenia and had attended Oxford and ministered to Armenian communities in New York, Lebanon, and Iran. Pope John Paul II cancelled a proposed July visit to Armenia and visited instead the ailing Catholicos Garegin in June.

DIRECTORY

CENTRAL GOVERNMENT

Head of State

President
Robert Kocharian, Office of the President, President House, Marhshal Baghramyan Avenue, 19 Yerevan, Armenia
PHONE: +374 (2) 520656
FAX: +374 (2) 151152

Ministers

Prime Minister
Aram Sarkisian, Office of the Prime Minister, 1st Government House, Republic Square, 10 Yerevan, Armenia
PHONE: +374 (2) 520360
FAX: +374 (2) 151036

Minister of Agriculture and Food Supplies
Gagik Shahbazian, Ministry of Agriculture and Food Supplies, Government Building #2, Yerevan, Armenia 375010
PHONE: +374 (2) 524641
FAX: +374 (2) 523793

Minister of Communications
Ruben Tonoyan, Ministry of Communications, 22 Sarian Street, Yerevan, Armenia 375010
PHONE: +374 (2) 526632; 538645
FAX: +374 (2) 151446; 538645

Minister of Culture, Youth Issues and Sports
Roland Sharoyan, Ministry of Culture, Youth Issues and Sports, 5 Toumanian Street, Yerevan, Armenia 375010
PHONE: +374 (2) 561920; 526869
FAX: +374 (2) 523922

Minister of Defense
Vagharshak Arutyunyan, Ministry of Defense, Republic Square, Government Building #1, Yerevan, Armenia 375010
PHONE: +374 (2) 523332; 345656; 357911
FAX: +374 (2) 527537

Minister of Ecology and Underground Resources
Gevork Vardanyan, Ministry of Ecology and Underground Resources, 35 Moskovian Street, Yerevan, Armenia 375002
PHONE: +374 (2) 530741; 531862
FAX: +374 (2) 534902

Minister of Economy
Armen Darbinyan, Ministry of Economy, Republic Square, Government Building #1, Yerevan, Armenia 375010
PHONE: +374 (2) 527342; 529890
FAX: +374 (2) 151069; 151036; 524332

Minister of Education and Science
Eduard Ghazaryan, Ministry of Education and Science, 13 Movses Khorenatsi Street, Yerevan, Armenia 375010
PHONE: +374 (2) 524749; 580302; 525317
FAX: +374 (2) 567164

Minister of Energy
David Zadoyan, Ministry of Energy, Republic Square, Government Building #2, Yerevan, Armenia 375010
PHONE: +374 (2) 521964; 520998
FAX: +374 (2) 151045; 151154

Minister of Finance

Levon Barkhudaryan, Ministry of Finance, 1 Melik Adamian Street, Yerevan, Armenia 375010
PHONE: +374 (2) 527082; 522522
FAX: +374 (2) 523745; 151154

Minister of Foreign Affairs

Vartan Oskanyan, Ministry of Foreign Affairs, 10 Marshall Baghramian Avenue, Yerevan, Armenia 375019
PHONE: +374 (2) 523531; 588829
FAX: +374 (2) 151042; 527022

Minister of Health

Hayk Nikogosyan, Ministry of Health, 8 Tourmanian Street, Yerevan, Armenia 375019
PHONE: +374 (2) 580564; 582413
FAX: +374 (2) 151097; 562923

Minister of Industry

Hayk Gevorkyan, Ministry of Industry, Republic Square, Government Building #2, Yerevan, Armenia 375010
PHONE: +374 (2) 521877
FAX: +374 (2) 151084; 523564

Minister of Interior

Suren Abrahamyan, Ministry of Interior, 130 Nalbandian Street, Yerevan, Armenia
PHONE: +374 (2) 560908; 578430
FAX: +374 (2) 151137

Minister of Justice

David Artyunyan, Ministry of Justice, 8 Shahumian, Yerevan, Armenia
PHONE: +374 (2) 582157; 581943

Minister of National Security

Serzhik Sarkisyan, Ministry of National Security

Minister of Social Security, Employment and Refugee Affairs

Rafayel Bagoyan, Ministry of Social Security, Employment and Refugee Affairs, 18 Isahahian Street, Yerevan, Armenia 375025
PHONE: +374 (2) 565321; 226309; 565383
FAX: +374 (2) 565321; 226309; 565383

Minister of Trade, Services and Tourism

Hayk Gevorkyan, Ministry of Trade, Services and Tourism, 69 Terian Street, Yerevan, Armenia 375009
PHONE: +374 (2) 582157; 581943
FAX: +374 (2) 583521

Minister of Transport and Transportation

Ervand Lakhasian, Ministry of Transport and Transportation, 10 Zakian Street, Yerevan, Armenia 375015
PHONE: +374 (2) 563391
FAX: +374 (2) 525268

Minister of Urban Planning and Construction

Hrayr Hovhannisian, Ministry of Urban Planning and Construction, Republic Square, Government Building #3, Yerevan, Armenia 375010
PHONE: +374 (2) 589080; 528423
FAX: +374 (2) 523200

POLITICAL ORGANIZATIONS

Armenian Revolutionary Federation (ARF)

2 Myasnyak Avenue, Yerevan 375025, Armenia
TITLE: Chairmen
NAME: Ruben Hagobian, Vahan Hovhanissian

Armenian Christian Democratic Union

Nubarashen St., Yerevan, Armenia
PHONE: +374 (2) 476868
TITLE: Chairman
NAME: Azad Arshakian

Communist Party of Armenia

Marshal Baghramian St. 10, Yerevan, Armenia
PHONE: +374 (2) 567933
FAX: +374 (2) 53855
TITLE: Chairman
NAME: Sergei Badalian

Hnchak Armenian Social Democratic Party

Aghbiur Serob St. 7, Yerevan, Armenia
PHONE: +374 (2) 273315
TITLE: Chairman
NAME: Yeghia Najarian

Pan-Armenian National Movement (PNM)

14 Marshal Baghramian St., Yerevan 37500, Armenia
PHONE: +374 (2) 520331
TITLE: Chairman
NAME: Levon Ter-Petrossian

Republican Party of Armenia

23 Tumanian St., Yeravan, Armenia
PHONE: +374 (2) 581882

FAX: +374 (2) 566034
TITLE: Chairman
NAME: Ashot Navasardian

DIPLOMATIC REPRESENTATION

Embassies in Armenia

China
12 Baghramian Ave., Yerevan, Armenia
PHONE: +374 (7) 560067; 561234
FAX: +374 (7) 151143
TITLE: Ambassador
NAME: Yang Kerong

Egypt
Hotel Hrazdan,10th Floor, Yerevan, Armenia
PHONE: +374 (7) 537304; 537705
FAX: +374 (7) 151160
TITLE: Ambassador
NAME: Said Imam

France
8 Lousavoritch Street, Yerevan, Armenia
PHONE: +374 (7) 564667; 583511
FAX: +374 (7) 151105
TITLE: Ambassador
NAME: Michel Legras

Georgia
5 Nalbandian St., Yerevan, Armenia
PHONE: +374 (7) 564183; 585511; 505586
FAX: +374 (7) 151838
TITLE: Ambassador
NAME: Grigol Baramidze

Germany
Hotel Hrazdan, 7th Floor, Yerevan, Armenia
PHONE: +374 (7) 536774; 536773
FAX: +374 (7) 151112; 151709
TITLE: Ambassador
NAME: Carola Mueller-Holtkemper

Greece
Hotel Hrazdan, 5th Floor, Yerevan, Armenia
PHONE: +374 (7) 537103; 530051
FAX: +374 (7) 151170
TITLE: Ambassador
NAME: Iakovos Spetsios

Iran
1 Boudaghian Street, Yerevan, Armenia
PHONE: +374 (7) 529830; 280457
FAX: +374 (7) 151385
TITLE: Ambassador
NAME: Hamid Reza Nikkar-Esfahani

Lebanon
7 Vardanats St., Yerevan, Armenia
PHONE: +374 (7) 561327; 526540; 561296; 589874
FAX: +374 (7) 151838
TITLE: Charge d'Affaires
NAME: Saad Zakhia

Russian Federation
Hotel Hrazdan, 3rd Floor, Yerevan, Armenia
PHONE: +374 (7) 524464; 535483
FAX: +374 (7) 521378
TITLE: Ambassador
NAME: Andrei Ournov

Ukraine
14 Zarubian Street, Yerevan, Armenia
PHONE: +374 (7) 586787; 586856
FAX: +374 (7) 583156
TITLE: Ambassador
NAME: Olexander Bozhko

United Kingdom
1 Vramshapuh Arkai Street, Yerevan, Armenia
PHONE: +374 (7) 553081
FAX: +374 (7) 151842; 151841
TITLE: Ambassador
NAME: John Mitchiner

United States
18 Baghramian Ave., Yerevan, Armenia
PHONE: +374 (7) 524661; 521611
FAX: +374 (7) 151550; 151511
TITLE: Ambassador
NAME: Peter Tomsen

JUDICIAL SYSTEM

Supreme Court

Constitutional Court

FURTHER READING

Articles

"Armenians Try to Mend Fences with Turkey." *Times Higher Education Supplement* (May 12,1999): 13.

"A Quake's Bitter Aftershocks." *Christian Science Monitor* (August 31, 1999): 9-10.

"Racing for Arms." *The Economist* 351 (May 4, 1999): 50.

Tatevosyan, Ara. "Yerevan Denies Baku's Changes." *Current Digest of the Post Soviet Press* 51 (June 16, 1999): 19 (2).

Weir, Fred. ''Armenia's Troubled Present.'' *Christian Science Monitor* 91 (October 29, 1999): 1.

Wines, Michael. ''Prime Minister and Others Slain in Armenian Siege.'' *New York Times* (October 28, 1999): 1A.

Internet

Armenpress. Available Online @ http: // www.armenpress.am/ (November 13, 1999).

Asbarez Online. Available Online @ http: // www.asbarez.com/ (November 13, 1999).

ARMENIA: STATISTICAL DATA

For sources and notes see "Sources of Statistics" in the front of each volume.

GEOGRAPHY

Geography (1)

Area:

Total: 29,800 sq km.

Land: 28,400 sq km.

Water: 1,400 sq km.

Area—comparative: slightly smaller than Maryland.

Land boundaries:

Total: 1,254 km.

Border countries: Azerbaijan-proper 566 km, Azerbaijan-Naxcivan exclave 221 km, Georgia 164 km, Iran 35 km, Turkey 268 km.

Coastline: 0 km (landlocked).

Climate: highland continental, hot summers, cold winters.

Terrain: high Armenian Plateau with mountains; little forest land; fast flowing rivers; good soil in Aras River valley.

Natural resources: small deposits of gold, copper, molybdenum, zinc, alumina.

Land use:

Arable land: 17%

Permanent crops: 3%

Permanent pastures: 24%

Forests and woodland: 15%

Other: 41% (1993 est.).

HUMAN FACTORS

Demographics (2A)

	1990	1995	1998	2000	2010	2020	2030	2040	2050
Population	3,366.3	3,453.8	3,421.8	3,396.2	3,369.5	3,416.3	3,468.8	3,503.7	3,428.1
Net migration rate (per 1,000 population)	NA	NA	NA	NA	NA	NA	NA	NA	NA
Births	NA	NA	NA	NA	NA	NA	NA	NA	NA
Deaths	NA	NA	NA	NA	NA	NA	NA	NA	NA
Life expectancy - males	67.2	63.4	62.5	62.0	65.0	69.2	72.5	75.2	77.1
Life expectancy - females	74.0	71.6	71.2	71.0	73.3	76.8	79.6	81.8	83.5
Birth rate (per 1,000)	22.4	14.1	13.5	13.6	18.5	11.7	11.6	10.0	8.8
Death rate (per 1,000)	6.9	8.2	8.8	9.3	10.6	9.5	9.4	10.8	11.8
Women of reproductive age (15-49 yrs.)	850.9	911.5	934.1	948.6	915.1	834.4	858.4	758.5	741.2
of which are currently married	NA	NA	NA	NA	NA	NA	NA	NA	NA
Fertility rate	2.6	1.8	1.7	1.7	2.2	1.9	1.7	1.6	1.5

Except as noted, values for vital statistics are in thousands; life expectancy is in years.

Health Personnel (3)

Total health expenditure as a percentage of GDP, 1990-1997[a]

Public sector 3.1

Private sector 4.7

Total[b] 7.8

Health expenditure per capita in U.S. dollars, 1990-1997[a]

Purchasing power parity 156

Total 27

Availability of health care facilities per 100,000 people

Hospital beds 1990-1997[a] 7600

Doctors 1993[c] 312

Nurses 1993[c] 831

Health Indicators (4)

Life expectancy at birth

1980 73

1997 74

Daily per capita supply of calories (1996) 2,147

Total fertility rate births per woman (1997) 1.5

Maternal mortality ratio per 100,000 live births (1990-97) . . . . .21[b]

Safe water % of population with access (1995) . . . .

Sanitation % of population with access (1995) . . . .

Consumption of iodized salt % of households (1992-98)[a] . . . .

Smoking prevalence

Male % of adults (1985-95)[a] . . . .

Female % of adults (1985-95)[a] . . . .

Tuberculosis incidence per 100,000 people (1997) 44

Adult HIV prevalence % of population ages 15-49 (1997) 0.01

Infants and Malnutrition (5)

Under-5 mortality rate (1997) 30

% of infants with low birthweight (1990-97) 7

Births attended by skilled health staff % of total[a] . . .95

% fully immunized (1995-97)

TB 72

DPT 89

Polio 95

Measles 92

Prevalence of child malnutrition under age 5 (1992-97)[b] . . . . .NA

Ethnic Division (6)

Armenian 93%

Azeri 3%

Russian 2%

Other 2%

Other is mostly Yezidi Kurds. Data for 1989.

Religions (7)

Armenian Orthodox 94%.

Languages (8)

Armenian 96%, Russian 2%, other 2%.

EDUCATION

Public Education Expenditures (9)

Public expenditure on education (% of GNP)

1980 . . . .

1996 . . . . .2.0

Expenditure per student

Primary % of GNP per capita

1980 . . . .

1996 . . . .

Secondary % of GNP per capita

1980 . . . .

1996 . . . .

Tertiary % of GNP per capita

1980 . . . .

1996 . . . . .26.0

Expenditure on teaching materials

Primary % of total for level (1996) . . . .

Secondary % of total for level (1996) . . . .

Primary pupil-teacher ratio per teacher (1996) 19

Duration of primary education years (1995) 4

Literacy Rates (11B)

Adult literacy rate

1980

Male . . . .—

Female . . . .—

1995

Male 100

Female 99

GOVERNMENT & LAW

Political Parties (12)

National Assembly	No. of seats
Republican Bloc	159
Shamiram Women's Movement (SWM)	8
Armenian Communist Party (ACP)	7
National Democratic Union (NDU)	5
Union of National Self-Determination (NSDU)	3
Democratic Liberal Party (DLP)	1
Armenian Revolutionary Federation (ARF)	1
Other	4
Vacant	2

Government Budget (13B)

Revenues	$322 million
Expenditures	$424 million
Capital expenditures	$80 million

Data for 1998 est.

Military Affairs (14B)

	1992	1993	1994	1995
Military expenditures				
Current dollars (mil.)	NA	NA	71	79
1995 constant dollars (mil.)	NA	NA	73	79
Armed forces (000)	20	20	45	60
Gross national product (GNP)				
Current dollars (mil.)	8,846	7,760	8,187	8,498
1995 constant dollars (mil.)	9,515	8,135	8,393	8,498
Central government expenditures (CGE)				
1995 constant dollars (mil.)	4,650	NA	NA	NA
People (mil.)	3.5	3.5	3.5	3.5
Military expenditure as % of GNP	NA	NA	.9	.9
Military expenditure as % of CGE	NA	NA	NA	NA
Military expenditure per capita (1995 $)	NA	NA	21	23
Armed forces per 1,000 people (soldiers)	5.8	6.1	13.0	17.3
GNP per capita (1995 $)	2,758	2,348	2,422	2,453

Arms imports[6]				
Current dollars (mil.)	0	0	10	30
1995 constant dollars (mil.)	0	0	10	30
Arms exports[6]				
Current dollars (mil.)	0	0	0	0
1995 constant dollars (mil.)	0	0	0	0
Total imports[7]				
Current dollars (mil.)	328	191	345	661[e]
1995 constant dollars (mil.)	353	200	354	661[e]
Total exports[7]				
Current dollars (mil.)	256	57	196	248[e]
1995 constant dollars (mil.)	275	60	201	248[e]
Arms as percent of total imports[8]	0.0	0	2.9	4.5
Arms as percent of total exports[8]	0.0	0	0	0

Crime (15)

Crime rate (for 1997)

Crimes reported	12,400
Total persons convicted	10,500
Crimes per 100,000 population	325

Persons responsible for offenses

Total number of suspects	9,850
Total number of female suspects	700
Total number of juvenile suspects	675

LABOR FORCE

Labor Force (16)

Total (million)	1.6
Manufacturing, mining, and construction	25%
Agriculture	38%
Services	37%

Data for 1997.

Unemployment Rate (17)

10.6% officially registered unemployed, but large numbers of underemployed (June 1997).

PRODUCTION SECTOR

Electric Energy (18)

Capacity . . . . .2.768 million kW (1995)

Production . . . . .6.3 billion kWh (1996)

Consumption per capita . . . . .1,570 kWh (1995)

Transportation (19)

Highways:

total: 8,580 km

paved: 8,580 km

unpaved: 0 km (1996 est.)

Waterways: NA km

Pipelines: natural gas 900 km (1991)

Airports: 11 (1996 est.)

Airports—with paved runways:

total: 5

over 3,047 m: 2

1,524 to 2,437 m: 1

914 to 1,523 m: 2 (1996 est.)

Airports—with unpaved runways:

total: 6

1,524 to 2,437 m: 2

914 to 1,523 m: 3

under 914 m: 1 (1996 est.)

Top Agricultural Products (20)

Fruit (especially grapes), vegetables; vineyards near Yerevan are famous for brandy and other liqueurs; minor livestock sector.

MANUFACTURING SECTOR

GDP & Manufacturing Summary (21)

Detailed value added figures are listed by both International Standard Industry Code (ISIC) and product title.

	1980	1985	1990	1994
GDP ($-1990 mil.)[1]	5,227	6,971	7,650	2,689
Per capita ($-1990)[1]	1,702	2,157	2,282	758
Manufacturing share (%) (current prices)[1]	30.8	30.0	28.7	31.2
Manufacturing				
Value added ($-1990 mil.)[1]	NA	NA	2,199	866
Industrial production index	NA	NA	NA	NA
Value added ($ mil.)	1,350	1,212	907	368

Gross output ($ mil.)	12,433	8,917	5,419	962
Employment (000)	265	302	354	295
Profitability (% of gross output)				
Intermediate input (%)	89	86	83	60
Wages and salaries inc. supplements (%)	11	14	16	21
Gross operating surplus	0	0	1	19
Productivity ($)				
Gross output per worker	39,287	23,952	15,291	3,260
Value added per worker	4,350	3,460	2,696	1,324
Average wage (inc. supplements)	4,404	3,468	2,462	781
Value added ($ mil.)				
311/2 Food products	89	76	40	15
313 Beverages	11	38	15	58
314 Tobacco products	23	21	18	8
321 Textiles	102	99	78	46
322 Wearing apparel	139	132	101	69
323 Leather and fur products	NA	NA	38	NA
324 Footwear	NA	NA	NA	NA
331 Wood and wood products	35	30	16	6
332 Furniture and fixtures	38	33	31	7
341 Paper and paper products	2	2	1	1
342 Printing and publishing	4	4	3	1
351 Industrial chemicals	32	29	−46	20
352 Other chemical products	10	9	7	3
353 Petroleum refineries	−	−	−	−
354 Miscellaneous petroleum and coal products	3	3	2	2
355 Rubber products	10	9	−10	1
356 Plastic products	10	10	5	4
361 Pottery, china and earthenware	5	5	2	1
362 Glass and glass products	2	1	−	1
369 Other non-metal mineral products	97	76	56	8

371 Iron and steel	*3*	*3*	*1*	*1*
372 Non-ferrous metals	*60*	*50*	*23*	*12*
381 Metal products	*47*	*35*	*48*	*2*
382 Non-electrical machinery	*248*	*173*	*206*	*12*
383 Electrical machinery	*108*	*109*	*75*	*39*
384 Transport equipment	*9*	*9*	*4*	*1*
385 Professional and scientific equipment	*97*	*79*	*88*	*12*
390 Other manufacturing industries	*167*	*173*	*106*	*40*

FINANCE, ECONOMICS, & TRADE

Economic Indicators (22)

National product: GDP—purchasing power parity—$9.5 billion (1997 est.)

National product real growth rate: 2.7% (1997 est.)

National product per capita: $2,750 (1997 est.)

Inflation rate—consumer price index: 13.2% (1997 est.)

Exchange Rates (24)

Exchange rates:

Dram per US$1

November 1997	.499.89
1996	.414.04
1995	.405.91
1994	.288.65
1993	.9.11

Top Import Origins (25)

$727 million (c.i.f., 1996).

Origins	%
Iran	.NA
Russia	.NA
Turkmenistan	.NA
Georgia	.NA
United States	.NA
European Union	.NA

NA stands for not available.

Top Export Destinations (26)

$290 million (f.o.b., 1996).

Destinations	%
Iran	.NA
Russia	.NA
Turkmenistan	.NA
Georgia	.NA

NA stands for not available.

Economic Aid (27)

Recipient: ODA, $NA. Note: commitments (excluding Russia), $1,385 million ($675 million in disbursements) (1992-95). NA stands for not available.

Import Export Commodities (28)

Import Commodities	Export Commodities
Grain	Gold and jewelry
Other foods	Aluminum
Fuel	Transport equipment
Other energy	Electrical equipment
	Scrap metal

Balance of Payments (23)

	1990	1993	1994	1995	1995
Exports of goods (f.o.b.)	NA	156	238	271	290
Imports of goods (f.o.b.)	NA	−254	−419	−674	−760
Trade balance	NA	−98	−181	−403	−469
Services - debits	NA	−41	−44	−67	−163
Services - credits	NA	17	13	30	156
Private transfers (net)	NA	NA	11	18	67
Government transfers (net)	NA	55	95	142	117
Overall balance	NA	−67	−106	−279	−291

ARUBA

CAPITAL: Oranjestad.

FLAG: The flag of Aruba is blue with two horizontal yellow stripes across the lower portion and a red, four-pointed star outlined in white in the upper hoist-side corner.

ANTHEM: Aruba Dushi Tera (Aruba Precious Country).

MONETARY UNIT: 1 Aruban florin (Af.) = 100 cents.

WEIGHTS AND MEASURES: The metric system is used.

HOLIDAYS: New Year's Day, 1 January; Carnival Monday; Good Friday; Easter Monday; National Anthem and Flag Day, 18 March; Queen's Birthday, 30 April; Labor Day, 1 May; Ascension Day; Christmas Day, 25 December; and Boxing Day, 26 December.

TIME: 8 PM = noon GMT.

LOCATION AND SIZE: The island of Aruba is located off the north coast of South America, NW of Curaçao. As part of the West Indies in the Caribbean Sea, the island lies about 12° north of the equator, approximately 29 km (18 mi.) off the Paraguan Peninsula of Venezuela. One of the Lesser Antilles islands, Aruba is about 30 km (19 mi.) long and about 8 km (5 mi.) wide with an area of 193 sq. km (75 sq. mi.).

CLIMATE: The climate is tropical but not extreme, with practically constant temperature of 82°F (28°C). Rainfall averages about 18 inches a year, with a mild wet season from October through January. Aruba lies outside the hurricane belt and usually only experiences fringe effects of nearby heavy tropical storms.

INTRODUCTORY SURVEY

RECENT HISTORY

Originally occupied by the indigenous Arawak peoples, Aruba was claimed for Spain by explorer Alonzo de Ojeda in 1499. Under Spain, the island became a haven for piracy and smuggling. Following conclusion of the Eighty Year's War between Spain and Holland, the Dutch gained possession of Aruba in 1636, becoming one of six Dutch Caribbean islands. The British briefly gained control of Aruba between 1805 and 1816. Development of the island did not begin until later in the 19th century and by the 1920s the refining and storage of Venezuelan oil became Aruba's primary economic activity. A progression toward complete political independence began in 1986 with Aruba assuming its own internal affairs. Complete independence was sought by 1996, but in 1994 Aruba and Holland decided to further delay the process.

GOVERNMENT

A Dutch possession since 1636, Aruba was a member of the Netherlands Antilles federation until 1986 when it gained control over its internal affairs, including its own judiciary, revenue, currency, and civil service. The Kingdom of the Netherlands, which still administers Aruba's foreign affairs and defense, is an hereditary constitutional monarchy. Queen Beatrix Wilhelmina Armgard of the Netherlands has served as chief of state since April of 1980. The Queen's main representative on the island is the governor, appointed by the Dutch crown for six year terms. The executive power for

ARUBA

0   5   10 Miles

0   5   10 Kilometers

Druif

Caribbean
Sea

Oranjestad

Santa Cruz

Barcadera

Caribbean
Sea

Sint Nicolaas

Netherlands
American Dependencies

N
W   E
S

the parliamentary government is the Council of Ministers, elected by the Staten, which answers to an elected unicameral legislature. The single-chambered legislature consists of 21 members elected for four-year terms by popular vote of island residents having Dutch nationality and over eighteen years of age. The next election is July of 2001.

Judiciary

Based on a constitution adopted on January 1, 1986, the legal system is based on Dutch civil law with some English common law influences. Legal jurisdiction lies with justices on the Common Court of Justice, who are appointed by the monarch, and with the Supreme Court of Justice in the Netherlands.

Political Parties

The various political parties active in Aruba include the Electoral Movement Party (MEP), Aruban People's Party (AVP), National Democratic Action (AND), New Patriotic Party (PPN), Aruban Patriotic Party (PPA), Aruban Democratic Party (PDA), Democratic Action '86 (AD'86), Aruban Liberal Party (OLA), and For a Restructured Aruba Now (PARA).

DEFENSE

The Kingdom of the Netherlands still controls Aruba's defense and foreign affairs. Aruba was not involved in any critical international issues in the late 1990s except for drug smuggling related activities that drew the attention of the United States and

other countries. Military service is compulsory. A Dutch naval contingent is stationed on Aruba.

ECONOMIC AFFAIRS

Located on the southwestern extreme of the Lesser Antilles in the Carribean Sea, the tropical marine climate is extremely dry being in the rainshadow of other islands. Consequently, a plantation economy never developed and agriculture remains very limited, largely exporting aloes. Only 11% of the land is arable with no permanent crops, pastures, or forest and woodlands. Drinking water largely derives from one of the world's largest distillation plants which desalinates seawater.

A center of smuggling and piracy beginning with Spanish rule in the 16th century, cocaine, drug smuggling, and drug-money-laundering have been prominent in more recent times with the island located only 40 miles north of Venezuela and near Columbia. The Aruban government began introducing criminal procedure reforms in the late 1990s to strengthen police powers such as broadening search and seizure authorities.

Off-shore banking is another important economic activity in the surrounding Free Zone of Aruba. Export commodities, amounting to approximately $1.7 million in 1997, are mostly refined petroleum products with the United States the primary export partner and Europe a secondary partner. Most imports derive from the United States. The major trade association is Aruba Trade and Industry Association. A cooperative union known as the Union of the Netherlands Antilles and Aruba addresses economic and monetary affairs between Aruba and the other five Dutch Caribbean islands.

Public Finance

Aruba's annual revenues were over $345 million in 1997 with expenditures that year of over $378. Revenue derived primarily from income and profit taxes, excises, and import duties. In 1995 Aruba also received $26 million in economic aid. The following year the Netherlands provided $127 million in aid to both Aruba and Suriname.

Income

The GDP for purchasing power was $1.5 billion for 1997 at a 6% growth rate. The per capita rate that year was $22,000.

Industry

Principal industries are tourism, transshipment facilities, and oil refining. Petroleum processing and storage has been a major economic component of the island since the 1920s. The refining complex faced some temporary interruptions in production in the 1980s and early 1990s; however, production resumed again in the late 1990s.

The more recent mainstay of the island's economy is tourism, making use of its long white sandy beaches and year-round temperate climate. The deepwater harbors facilitate cruise ship visits. Queen Beatrix International Airport serves numerous airlines and Air Aruba, established in 1988, provides a link to U.S. markets from where most stop-over tourists come. Activity by the Aruba Hotel and Tourism Association (AHATA) and the government's Aruba Tourism Authority (ATA) led to a significantly expanded economy by the 1990s. Construction boomed as hotel capacity expanded from just over 2,000 rooms in 1986 to over 7,000 rooms in 1996. Attractions besides beaches and hotels include casinos, festivals, a bird sanctuary, Arikok National Park, scuba diving, and two golf courses. By the late 1990s, Aruba was spending approximately $1 million (U.S.) annually in tourism marketing.

Banking and Finance

The central bank of Aruba is Centrale Bank van Aruba. In addition to eight commercial banks on the island, off-shore banking is also authorized and an important facet of the island's economy.

SOCIAL WELFARE

Healthcare

Life expectancy in general is 77 years of age; for males it is 73 years, females almost 81.

EDUCATION

Aruba applies the same educational standards as the Netherlands and all instruction is primarily in Dutch. Other languages, such as English and Spanish, are offered in early student years. Education is not compulsory with primary education beginning at age six and secondary education extends up to eleven years later. The island has a secondary education system, a teacher's college, a law school, and five technical and vocational training schools. The University of Aruba held over 130 students in 1994. Scholarships are also awarded for further study in Holland. In 1995 almost 15% of Aruba's budget was devoted to education.

1999 KEY EVENTS TIMELINE

May

- Queen Beatrix of the Netherlands announces a visit to Aruba in November, 1999.

July

- A minor earthquake, the result of the shift in a "dead plate," rattles Aruba; however, geologists assure residents that Aruba is not in an active seismic zone and that it is nothing but a small tremor.

September

- The island celebrates the 500-year anniversary of its discovery by the Spaniard Alonso de Ojeda in 1499.

- Various unions and environmentalists protest the building of a racetrack in San Nicolas.

October

- The court in Aruba approves the construction of the racetrack.

- Three unions strike on October 25 and 26, suspending all activities in protest of the racetrack. The striking unions are SEPA, a government union; SADA, the customs workers' union; and the STT, the communications and telephone services union, plan to strike.

- The Aruban government plans the construction of a four-lane highway to connect San Nicolas to Oranjestad, the capital city of Aruba.

- DisneyWorld Caribbean plans a $750 million construction of a theme park in Aruba.

ANALYSIS OF EVENTS: 1999

BUSINESS AND THE ECONOMY

Aruba developed in the seventeenth and eighteenth centuries as a colony of the Netherlands. It is located in the Dutch Antilles Islands in the Caribbean Sea. In the recent past Aruba has experienced economic success mainly as a tourist attraction. Its wonderful beaches, casinos, and good restaurants have made Aruba an attractive place to visit. Also the climate, which is out of the hurricane zone, is pleasant year-round.

Aruba's economy also features off-shore banking, oil refining, and storage. Largely as a result of the tourism trade, Aruba's construction sector has also been booming. The island boasts an unemployment rate of less than one percent. The high demand for labor has stimulated an active trade union movement.

Aruba's tourism office succeeded in booking the 2001 meeting of the Florida Caribbean Cruise Association. The major development in the cruise industry has been the construction of mega cruise ships. The port city of Oranjestad is ideal as a debarkation port for these ships. The tourism industry also plans to add Formula One racing events, which are now generally run in Europe, to its list of attractions. Race enthusiasts are excited about this new venue and the racing events would no doubt bring fans and revenue to the island.

GOVERNMENT AND POLITICS

The promoters of the Formula One racetrack want it to be built in San Nicolas, Aruba's second largest city, which has been economically depressed for years. In spite of the island's idyllic surroundings, Aruba has experienced a contentious political life, mostly over the issues of the ecological impact of economic development. Many environmentalists, for instance, object to the building of a racetrack in San Nicolas because they fear that it would destroy the flora and fauna there. This is not the first time that the people of San Nicolas have opposed the promotional efforts of the country's leadership. They also protested the building of a four-lane highway that the government proposed in order to improve Aruba's transportation infrastructure to coincide with the booming economy.

Though the government and the courts approved the Formula One racetrack, the action sparked demonstrations, and some of the country's trade unions (syndicates) threatened to shut down the government and other services.

Aruba's political life also involves struggles over larger questions, such its relationship to its colonial past. Since 1986, Aruba has been a special entity of the Netherlands with its own identity and government except that it receives military aid from the Netherlands. This special accord is called "Status Aparte." Aruba no longer shares its status with Bonaire and Curaçao, other Dutch Antilles islands. The Governor-General is Olindo Koolman,

and the present prime minister is Jan (Henny) Eman. The main political party remains the MEP (Moviemiento Electoral del Pueblo) which presses for complete independence from the Netherlands.

CULTURE AND SOCIETY

The people of Aruba are of mostly Arawak Indian descent. There has been no history of a slave trade, so there are few people of African descent, and most people living in Aruba at the close of the twentieth century are of mixed Indian and European lineage. The mainstay of the island is tourism, and many of the natives work in the hotel and restaurant industry. The formal language is Dutch, but most of the inhabitants speak Papiamento (a dialect of Portuguese) and understand English and Spanish.

DIRECTORY

CENTRAL GOVERNMENT

Head of State

Monarch
Beatrix Wilhelmina Armgard, Queen of the Netherlands

Governor-General
Olindo Koolman

Prime Minister
Jan H. Eman

Ministers

Minister of General Affairs
Jan H. Eman, Ministry of General Affairs

Minister of Economy
Lilia G. Beke-Martínez, Ministry of Economy

Minister of Education and Labour
Mary Wever-Lacle, Ministry of Education and Labour

Minister of Finance
Robertico R. Crpes, Ministry of Finance

Minister of Health, Social Affairs, Culture and Sport
Israel Posner, Ministry of Health, Social Affairs, Culture and Sport

Minister of Justice and Public Works
Edgar J. Vos, Ministry of Justice and Public Works

Minister of Transport and Communications
Gilbert F. Croes, Ministry of Transport and
Communications

POLITICAL ORGANIZATIONS

Movimiento Electoral di Pueblo-MEP (Electoral Movement Party)

NAME: Nelson O. Oduber

Arubaanse Volkspartij-AVP (Aruban's People Party)

NAME: Jan Henny Eman

Acción Democratico Nacional-ADN (National Democratic Action)

NAME: Pedro Charro Kelly

Partido Patriotico Arubano-PPA (Aruban Patriotic Party)

NAME: Benny Nisbet

Organisacion Liberal Arubiano-OLA (Aruban Liberal Party)

NAME: Glenbert Croes

MEP (Electoral People's Movement)

NAME: Betico Croes

PARA (For a Restructured Aruba Now)

NAME: Urbana Lopez

JUDICIAL SYSTEM

Common Court of Justice (with the Netherlands Antilles)

FURTHER READING

Articles

"Aruba Posts 4% Tourism Increase." *Travel Weekly* (April 29, 1999): 2.

Books

Sedoc-Dahlberg, Betty, ed. *The Dutch Caribbean: Prospects for Democracy.* New York: Gordon and Breach, 1990.

Internet

Eddy's Aruba News. Available Online @ http://www.cyberdistrict.net/eddy (November 3, 1999).

Visit Aruba. Available Online @ http://www.visitaruba.com (November 3, 1999).

ARUBA:
STATISTICAL DATA

For sources and notes see "Sources of Statistics" in the front of each volume.

GEOGRAPHY

Geography (1)

Area:

Total: 193 sq km.

Land: 193 sq km.

Water: 0 sq km.

Area—comparative: slightly larger than Washington, DC.

Land boundaries: 0 km.

Coastline: 68.5 km.

Climate: tropical marine; little seasonal temperature variation.

Terrain: flat with a few hills; scant vegetation.

Natural resources: negligible; white sandy beaches.

Land use:

Arable land: 11%

Permanent crops: NA%

Permanent pastures: NA%

Forests and woodland: NA%

Other: 89% (1993 est.).

HUMAN FACTORS

Ethnic Division (6)

Mixed white/Caribbean Amerindian 80%.

Religions (7)

Roman Catholic 82%

Protestant 8%

Hindu, Muslim, Confucian, Jewish . . . .

HUMAN FACTORS

Demographics (2A)

	1990	1995	1998	2000	2010	2020	2030	2040	2050
Population	66.6	67.6	68.3	69.1	72.2	73.7	73.4	70.9	67.2
Net migration rate (per 1,000 population)	NA	NA	NA	NA	NA	NA	NA	NA	NA
Births	NA	NA	NA	NA	NA	NA	NA	NA	NA
Deaths	NA	NA	NA	NA	NA	NA	NA	NA	NA
Life expectancy - males	72.3	72.9	73.2	73.4	74.4	75.3	76.1	76.8	77.4
Life expectancy - females	79.7	80.4	80.8	81.1	82.2	83.2	83.9	84.5	85.0
Birth rate (per 1,000)	16.4	15.0	13.7	12.8	10.9	10.9	9.8	9.4	9.4
Death rate (per 1,000)	5.8	6.2	6.4	6.6	7.8	9.9	11.8	14.1	15.0
Women of reproductive age (15-49 yrs.)	19.1	19.0	18.8	18.7	17.7	15.3	14.9	14.4	13.2
of which are currently married	NA	NA	NA	NA	NA	NA	NA	NA	NA
Fertility rate	1.8	1.8	1.8	1.8	1.8	1.8	1.7	1.7	1.7

Except as noted, values for vital statistics are in thousands; life expectancy is in years.

Languages (8)

Dutch (official), Papiamento (a Spanish, Portuguese, Dutch, English dialect), English (widely spoken), Spanish.

EDUCATION

Educational Attainment (10)

Age group (1991)[8] . . . . .25+

Total population 41,180

Highest level attained (%)

No schooling 14.9

First level

Not completed 37.3

Completed . . . . .NA

Entered second level

S-1 . . . . .37.7

S-2 . . . . .NA

Postsecondary 7.0

GOVERNMENT & LAW

Political Parties (12)

Legislature	No. of seats
Aruban People's Party (AVP)	10
Electoral Movement Party (MEP)	9
Aruban Liberal Party (OLA)	2

Government Budget (13B)

Revenues . . . .$376 million

Expenditures . . . .$409 million

Capital expenditures . . . .$107 million

Data for 1997 est.

Military Affairs (14A)

Defense is the responsibility of the Kingdom of the Netherlands.

LABOR FORCE

Labor Force (16)

Most employment is in the tourist industry. Data for 1996.

Unemployment Rate (17)

0.6% (1996 est.)

PRODUCTION SECTOR

Electric Energy (18)

Capacity . . . . .90,000 kW (1995)

Production . . . . .340 million kWh (1995)

Consumption per capita . . . . .5,154 kWh (1995)

Transportation (19)

Highways:

total: NA km

paved: NA km

unpaved: NA km note: most coastal roads are paved, while unpaved roads serve large tracts of the interior

Merchant marine:

total: 2 cargo ships (1,000 GRT or over) totaling 18,365 GRT/29,170 DWT (1997 est.)

Airports: 2 (1997 est.)

Airports—with paved runways:

total: 2

2,438 to 3,047 m: 1

914 to 1,523 m: 1 (1997 est.)

Top Agricultural Products (20)

Aloes; livestock; fishing.

FINANCE, ECONOMICS, & TRADE

Economic Indicators (22)

National product: GDP—purchasing power parity—$1.4 billion (1996 est.)

National product real growth rate: 4% (1996 est.)

National product per capita: $21,000 (1996 est.)

Inflation rate—consumer price index: 3.2% (1996)

Exchange Rates (24)

Exchange rates: Aruban florins (Af.) per US$1—1.7900 (fixed rate since 1986)

Top Import Origins (25)

$2 billion (f.o.b., 1996)

Origins	%
United States	8
European Union	NA

NA stands for not available.

Top Export Destinations (26)

$1.7 billion (including oil re-exports) (f.o.b., 1996).

Destinations	%
United States	.64
European Union	.NA

NA stands for not available.

Economic Aid (27)

The Netherlands provided a 1996 aid package of $224 million to Aruba, the Netherlands Antilles, and Suriname.

Import Export Commodities (28)

Import Commodities	Export Commodities
Food	Mostly refined petroleum products
Consumer goods	
Manufactures	
Petroleum products	
Crude oil for refining and reexport	

Balance of Payments (23)

	1990	1992	1994	1995	1996
Exports of goods (f.o.b.)	156	1,069	12,975	1,347	1,736
Imports of goods (f.o.b.)	−581	−1,447	−1,607	−1,772	−2,043
Trade balance	−425	−377	−311	−425	−308
Services - debits	−158	−182	−251	−270	−547
Services - credits	426	586	634	661	789
Private transfers (net)	−9	10	NA	21	−2
Government transfers (net)	8	7	8	12	−2
Overall balance	−158	44	81	−0	−69

AUSTRALIA

Commonwealth of Australia

CAPITAL: Canberra.

FLAG: The flag has three main features: the red, white, and blue Union Jack in the upper left quarter, indicating Australia's membership in the Commonwealth of Nations; the white five-star Southern Cross in the right half; and the white seven-pointed federal star below the Union Jack. The flag has a blue ground. Of the five stars of the Southern Cross, four have seven points and one has five points.

ANTHEM: *Advance Australia Fair; God Save the Queen* is reserved for regal and state occasions.

MONETARY UNIT: The Australian dollar (A $) is a paper currency of 100 cents. There are coins of 5, 10, 20, and 50 cents and 1 and 2 dollars, and notes of 5, 10, 20, 50 and 100 dollars. A $1 = US $0.79177 (US $1 = A $1.263).

WEIGHTS AND MEASURES: Metric weights and measures are used.

HOLIDAYS: New Year's Day, 1 January; Australia Day, last Monday in January; Anzac Day, 25 April; Queen's Birthday, 2nd Monday in June; Christmas, 25 December; Boxing Day, 26 December. Movable religious holidays include Good Friday, Easter Saturday, and Easter Monday.

TIME: Western Australia, 8 PM = noon GMT; South Australia and Northern Territory, 9:30 PM; Victoria, New South Wales, Queensland, and Tasmania, 10 PM. Summer time is 1 hour later in all states except Western Australia, Queensland, and the Northern Territory.

LOCATION AND SIZE: Lying southeast of Asia, between the Pacific and Indian oceans, Australia is slightly smaller than the United States, with a total area of 7,686,850 square kilometers (2,967,909 square miles). Australia's capital city, Canberra, is located in the southeastern part of the country.

CLIMATE: Australia is generally warm and dry, with no extreme cold and little frost. July mean temperatures average 9°C (48°F) in Melbourne in the southeast and 25°C (77°F) in Darwin in the north. January mean temperatures average 20°C (68°F) in Melbourne and 30°C (86°F) in Darwin. Mean annual rainfall is 42 centimeters (17 inches). Droughts and floods occur frequently over large areas.

INTRODUCTORY SURVEY

RECENT HISTORY

Once an English penal colony, Australia is considered one of the freer countries in the world. Still a British Commonwealth Nation, Australia was brought closer to the United States as a result of its participation in Wold War II. Previously strict and discriminatory immigration laws were relaxed in the 1960s and 1970s, resulting in a more diverse population. An Aboriginal movement has grown since the 1960s, improving the education and granting full citizenship to the country's poorest group.

Australia has participated in many United Nations and other treaty-obligated police and military actions, from Korea to Vietnam, and in 1999, East Timor. (East Timor is a province of Indonesia where Indonesian militias were massacring civilians due to an independence referendum that overwhelmingly passed).

Australia had scheduled a referendum of its own for independence in November 1999, where the issue up for voter's approval would eliminate all formal allegiance to the British Crown and the country would become a republic.

GOVERNMENT

Australia is divided into six states and two territories. The government consists of the British sovereign, represented by a governor-general, and the Australian Parliament. Officially, executive power belongs to the governor-general and an executive council. In practice, however, it is normally

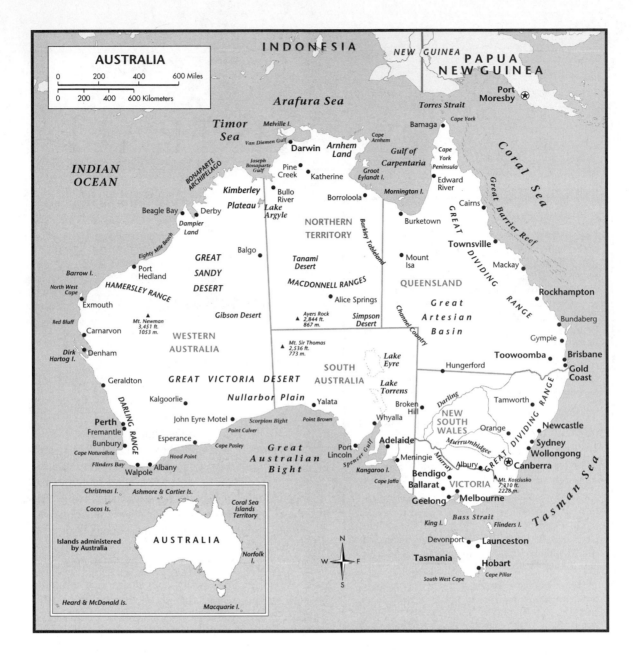

exercised by a cabinet chosen and presided over by a prime minister, representing the political party or coalition with a majority in the House of Representatives.

Legislative power is exercised by the Parliament, which is composed of a 76-member Senate, representing the states and territories, and a 148-member House of Representatives, representing electoral districts. Twelve senators are elected from each state and two senators each from the Northern Territory and Capital Territory. House membership is not quite double that of the Senate, with a minimum of five representatives for each state. There

are two members from the Australian Capital Territory and one from the Northern Territory. Parliament must meet at least once a year.

Voting is universal for all persons 18 years of age and older. Voting is compulsory in national and state parliamentary elections.

Judiciary

The High Court of Australia consists of a Chief Justice and six Associate Justices appointed by the governor general. It is the supreme authority on interpreting the Australian constitution and has the authority to decide whether state and federal legislation is constitutional. Special cases may be referred to a 25-member federal court which deals with commercial law, copyright law, taxation, and trade practices. There is also a family court. States and territories have their own court systems.

Political Parties

The Labour Party is a trade-union party, officially socialist in policy and outlook. The Liberal Party represents business interests, while the National Party (formerly the Country Party) is allied with farmers. Smaller parties include the Democratic Labour Party, the Communist Party, the Australian Democrats Party, and the Green Party.

DEFENSE

The all-volunteer Australian armed forces numbered 57,800 in 1996. The army had an official strength of 26,000; the navy, 14,700; the air force, 17,100; and reserve forces, 49,480 for all three services. The active forces include 7,260 women. Military weapons systems included 103 battle tanks, 5 submarines, 3 destroyers, 8 frigates, and 157 air force combat aircraft. Australia's defense expenditure in 1995 was $8.5 billion.

ECONOMIC AFFAIRS

Wool, food, and minerals provide raw materials for industry at home and around two-thirds of foreign earnings. Australia grows all needed basic foodstuffs and has large surpluses for export. Australia is the world's largest wool-producing country, as well as one of the world's great wheat exporters, and also exports large quantities of meat and dairy products. The country is also a major world supplier of iron ore, bauxite, lead, zinc, and copper. Coal, beach sand minerals, and nickel have become major industries.

Public Finance

Social security and welfare payments are the largest category of government expenditure. The central government has financed almost all its defense and capital works programs from revenue and has made available to the states money raised by public loans for public works programs. Deficits are common. In the latter half of the 1980s, however, five consecutive years of significant surpluses occurred as a result of expenditure restraints.

The U.S. Central Intelligence Agency estimates that, in 1995, government revenues totaled approximately U.S.$95.69 billion and expenditures U.S.$95.15 billion. External debt totaled U.S.$147.2 billion, approximately 30% of which was financed abroad.

Income

In 1997, Australia's Gross Domestic Product (GDP) was estimated at $394 billion, or a per capita of $21,400 per person. Real growth rate for 1997 was 3.3%; inflation was 1%. Unemployment was estimated at 8.4%.

Industry

In proportion to its total population, Australia is one of the world's most highly industrialized countries. The manufacturing sector has undergone significant expansion in recent years and turns out goods ranging from automobiles to chemicals and textiles. The leading industries are food processing, beverages, motor vehicles, metalworking, and paper and paper products.

Australia produces most of its own foods, as well as its beverages, building materials, many common chemicals, some domestic electrical appliances, radios, plastics, textiles, and clothing. In addition, most of its needed communications equipment, farm machinery (except tractors), furniture, leather goods, and metal manufactures are domestically produced. Recent years have seen the rapid growth of high-tech industries including aircraft, communications and other electronic equipment, electrical appliances and machinery, pharmaceuticals, and scientific equipment.

Banking and Finance

The Reserve Bank of Australia, the central bank, reconstituted in 1960, functions as a banker's bank and financial agent of the federal and some state governments, issuing notes, controlling interest and discount rates, mobilizing Australia's international reserves, and administering exchange controls and government loans.

Australia's net foreign debt broke through the A $200 billion barrier during the fourth quarter of 1996.

The Australian stock market is where equity (shares), units in listed trusts, options, government bonds, and other fixed-interest securities are traded. It is operated on a national basis by the Australian Stock Exchange (ASX), which is responsible for the day-to-day running and surveillance of stock market trading. The ASX was established on 1 April 1987, with the passage of the Australian National Guarantee Fund Act through the Commonwealth Parliament.

Economic Development

Commonwealth and state governments have devoted special attention to the production and marketing of main primary products, and since 1920, legislation has provided subsidies or other marketing aids to certain commodities. Direct subsidies, however, are not common, and butter, cheese, and cotton are among the few export commodities subsidized. Federal and state aid is given to industries established in approved fields of manufacture. The Export Market Development Grant Acts of 1974 provides government assistance in the development of export markets. Recipients are eligible for up to 50% reimbursement for expenses incurred establishing foreign markets for domestic goods. A one-year limit of a $200,000 in reimbursements is enforced. In 1975, the government set up the Export Finance and Insurance Corp. (replacing the Export Payments Insurance Corp.) to provide Australian exporters with insurance and other financial services not readily available commercially.

The government endeavors to prevent undue fluctuation in the economy. Price controls were in effect during World War II and part of the postwar period and are now imposed on a few essential household items. As an alternative to price controls, the Commonwealth government, in mid-1975, introduced a policy of wage indexation, allowing wages to rise as fast as, but no faster than, consumer prices; major labor unions, however, opposed this restraint, which was ended in 1981.

Monetary policy has supported recovery while resulting in low inflation. After August 1993, the focus of fiscal policy was expected to shift towards deficit reduction. In 1995, the national budget recorded a surplus of a $54 million.

SOCIAL WELFARE

The Commonwealth Social Services Act of 1947, as amended, provides for invalid and old age pensions and a variety of other benefits. The government provides allowances to families for every child born. Widows' pensions are also provided. The Sex Discrimination Act of 1984 bars discrimination on the basis of gender, marital status, or pregnancy. In 1992, the Parliament passed amendments that strengthened it significantly.

Healthcare

Australia is one of the healthiest countries in the world. The estimated life expectancy is 78 years. Under the Medicare national health insurance program, all Australians have access to free care at public hospitals. The plan also meets three-fourths of the bill for private hospital treatment, while patients pay the rest. In 1995, Australia had about 1,100 hospitals, of which 350 were private.

The federal government provides grants to the states and aboriginal organizations for the development of special health services for aboriginals, who are often reluctant to use general community health services.

Housing

In 1992, there were 6.3 million dwellings in Australia. A total of 132,000 new houses and apartments were completed the same year. Central heating, formerly available only in the most modern and expensive homes and apartments, is now generally available in the coldest areas of the country. Most apartments and houses are equipped with hot water, refrigeration, and indoor bath and toilet facilities.

EDUCATION

Illiteracy is practically nonexistent except among aborigines. Education is compulsory for children from the age of 6 to 15 (16 in Tasmania). Public education is provided in municipal kindergartens and in state primary, secondary, and technical schools. There are also state-regulated private schools. Correspondence courses and educational broadcasts are given for children living in the remote outback areas. The government expenditure on education in the 1995 was 7.6% of the total government spending.

Australia has 20 universities and more than 200 technical colleges. There is a state university in each capital city and each provincial area; a national post-graduate research institute in Canberra; and a university of technology in Sydney with a branch at Newcastle. There were 932,969 students in colleges and universities in 1994.

1999 KEY EVENTS TIMELINE

January

- Government introduces legislation to ensure that Australia remains on the cutting edge of information technology.

February

- Australia and five other nations reject treaty to regulate trade in genetically modified products.

March

- Australia opens National Portrait Gallery in Canberra.

- United States-based NTL Inc. acquires Australian National Transmission Network for $407 million.

April

- Australian representatives meet with delegates of 19 nations to discuss immigration issues.

May

- Researchers find Australia's oldest human remains.

- Australian Senate supports passage of the Online Services Bill.

June

- Committee drops plan to use foreign marching bands in opening ceremony of Sydney's 2000 Olympic Games.

July

- Australia opens first university for indigenous population.

- Report cites Australians as the biggest gamblers in the world.

August

- Prime Minister John Howard expresses public regret for Australia's past mistreatment of aborigines.

- Australian geologists discover molecular fossils, which demonstrate that life existed on earth more than a billion years earlier than previously thought.

September

- Australia leads peacekeeping force into East Timor.

- Australian telephone company Telstra expands into the United States.

October

- Australians prepare for vote on royalty referendum.

November

- Premier John Howard welcomes the referendum rejection of a plan to make the country a republic.

- Leaked Australian intelligence documents emerge as the strongest proof yet that the Indonesian government had closer ties than it has acknowledged to the violence carried out by its troops and their affiliates in East Timor.

- Almost 900 illegal immigrants, mostly Afghans and Iraqis, land on Australia's northern shores. Philip Ruddock, Australia's immigration minister, claims 10,000 more people from the Middle East are preparing to catch boats from Asia to Australia; in response, the government introduces measures to deter them.

December

- The Australian National Gallery cancels the British art exhibition, "Sensation," after the controversy it caused in New York.

ANALYSIS OF EVENTS: 1999

BUSINESS AND THE ECONOMY

To ensure that Australia remains on the cutting edge of information technology, the Australian government introduced a group of laws covering issues such as online content, privacy, and copyright. The Electronic Transactions Bill, released for comment in January, makes e-commerce the equivalent of Australian paper-based commerce.

Australia joined five other nations in February to reject a treaty that would require nations to provide advance approval of genetically altered imports. The nations claimed that the treaty would block millions of dollars in farm exports.

Television signals in Australia are now controlled by U.S.-based NTL Inc., which purchased the Australian National Transmission Network for $407 million in March.

Telstra, Australia's top telephone company, made its first foray into the American market in September, purchasing $20 million in long-distance phone service from Frontier Corporation.

GOVERNMENT AND POLITICS

Increasing numbers of illegal immigrants from Asia and the Middle East attempted to enter Australia in 1999. At an April conference in Bangkok, Australian representatives and delegates from 19 other nations discussed the need for harsher penalties and ways to end human trafficking.

The Australian Senate supported passage of the Broadcast Services Amendment, or Online Services Bill, to regulate racially or sexually offensive material on the Internet. The Australian Broadcasting Authority will enforce the new laws, which take effect on January 1, 2000.

In the first half of the century the Australian government attempted to assimilate aboriginal children by placing many of them with white families. Prime Minister John Howard presented a motion of reconciliation to Parliament in August to express public regret for Australia's past mistreatment of aborigines. Aboriginal leaders criticized Howard's motion because it did not include a full apology.

Australians led a United Nations-sanctioned peacekeeping force into East Timor in September to assist refugees and control the violence spread by pro-Indonesia militias. The effort followed Indonesia's cancellation of a security treaty with Australia, which would have made the two nations allies.

Australians prepared for the Parliament's November vote on the royalty referendum, which would determine whether the nation should become a republic or remain a monarchy.

CULTURE AND SOCIETY

Portraits representing a century of famous Australians are on display at the National Portrait Gallery in Canberra. The museum, which opened in March, celebrates the achievements of artists, scientists, politicians, athletes, and other citizens from ''Down Under,'' as Australia is often called.

The organizing committee for the Sydney Olympic Games became the subject of a lawsuit when it dropped a plan to include 1,300 American and 200 Japanese marching band members in the opening ceremony. World Projects Corporation, the American firm hired to provide the foreign bands, demanded that the members be allowed to perform as scheduled.

Recent discoveries in Australia led scientists to revise their theories regarding the dates on which life first appeared on earth. Geologists found molecular fossils in northwestern Australia which indicate that life existed on the planet 2.7 billion years ago. Researchers discovered a skeleton in Lake Mungo that is 62,000 years old, which places humans in Australia thousands of years earlier than archaeologists had thought.

Australia's first university for indigenous people, the Batchelor Institute of Indigenous Tertiary Education, opened in 1999. The university's programs incorporate the customs and traditions of the aborigines and other native peoples.

A thousand-page Productivity Commission report released in July claimed that Australians are the biggest gamblers in the world. Gambling is a $7.2 billion-per-year industry in Australia and accounts for 12 percent of state revenues. The report stated that approximately 330,000 Australians have a serious gambling problem.

DIRECTORY

CENTRAL GOVERNMENT

Head of State

Monarch
Queen Elizabeth II, The Visitor Office, Buckingham Palace, London SW1A 1AA, England
PHONE: +44 8391377
FAX: +44 9309625

Governor-General and Commander in Chief
Sir William Patrick Deane, Government House, Canberra ACT 2600, Australia
PHONE: +61 (02) 62833533

Ministers

Prime Minister
John Howard, Office of the Prime Minister, MG 8, Parliament House, Canberra ACT 2600, Australia
PHONE: +61 (02) 62777111
FAX: +61 (02) 62772058

Minister for Employment Services
Anthony John Abbott

Minister for Transport and Regional Development
John Duncan Anderson

Minister for Community Services
Lawrence James Anthony

Minister for Aged Care
Bronwyn Kathleen Bishop

Minister for Foreign Affairs
Alexander John Gosse Downer

Minister for Finance and Administration
Joseph Fahey

Minister for Financial Services and Regulation
Benedict Hocke

Minister for Sports and Tourism
Jacqueline Marie Kelly

Minister for Education, Training and Youth Affairs
David Alistair Kemp

Minister for the Arts
Peter John McGauran

Minister for Defence
John Colinton

Minister for Employment, Workplace Relations and Small Business
Peter Keaston Reith

Minister for Intergration and Multicultural Affairs
Philip Maxwell Ruddock

Minister for Forestry and Conservation
Charles Wilson Tuckey

Minister for Health and Aged Care
Michael Richard Lewis Woolridge

POLITICAL ORGANIZATIONS

Australian Democrats Party

National Office, P.O. Box 5089, Kingston ACT 2604, 10-12 Brisbane Avenue, Barton ACT 2600, Australia
PHONE: +61 (02) 62731059
FAX: +61 (02) 62731251
E-MAIL: inquiries@democrats.org.au
TITLE: Parliamentary Leader
NAME: Senator Meg Lees

Australian Labor Party

Parliament House, Canberra ACT 2600, Australia
PHONE: +61 (02) 62774022
FAX: +61 (02) 62778495
E-MAIL: Kim.Beazley.MP@aph.gov.au
TITLE: Leader of the Opposition
NAME: Kim Beazley

Communist Party of Australia

65 Campbell Street, Surrey Hills NSW 2010, Australia
PHONE: +61 (02) 92126855
FAX: +61 (02) 92815795
E-MAIL: cpa@zipworld.com.au
TITLE: President
NAME: Hannah Middleton

Liberal Party of Australia

Corner Blackall and Macquarie Sts., Barton ACT 2600, Australia
PHONE: +61 (02) 62732564
E-MAIL: libadm@liberal.org.au
TITLE: Federal Secretariat
NAME: Shane Stone

National Party of Australia

DIPLOMATIC REPRESENTATION
Embassies in Australia

Argentina
1st Fl, Suite 102 MLC Twr Woden ACT 2606, P.O. Box 262, Woden ACT 2606, Australia
PHONE: +61 (06) 2824855
FAX: +61 (06) 2853062

Austria
12 Talbot Street, Forrest ACT 2603, P.O. Box 3375, Manuka ACT 2603, Australia
PHONE: +61 (06) 2951533
FAX: +61 (06) 2396751

Bangledesh
35 Endeavor Street, Red Hill Australian Capital Territory 2603, P.O. Box 5, Monaro Crescent ACT 2603, Australia
PHONE: +61 (06) 2953328
FAX: +61 (06) 2953511

Barbados
4 Warren Road, Double Bay NSW 2028, Australia
PHONE: +61 (02) 93277009

Belgium
19 Arkuna Street, Yarralumla ACT 2600, Australia
PHONE: +61 (06) 2732501
FAX: +61 (06) 2733392

Brazil
19 Forster Cres., Yarralumla ACT 2600, Australia
PHONE: +61 (06) 2732372

FAX: +61 (06) 2732375

Brunei Darsallam
16 Bulwarra Close, O'Malley ACT 2603, P.O.
Box 3737, Manuka ACT 2606, Australia
PHONE: +61 (06) 2901801
FAX: +61 (06) 2901554

Bulgaria
Unit 2, 4 Carlotta Road, Double Bay NSW
2028, Australia
PHONE: +61 (02) 93277581
FAX: +61 (02) 93278067

Canada
Commonwealth Ave., Canberra ACT 2600,
Australia
PHONE: +61 (06) 2733844
FAX: +61(06) 2733285

Chile
10 Culgoa Cct, O'Malley ACT 2606, P.O. Box
69, Monaro Crescent ACT 2603, Australia
PHONE: +61 (06) 2862430
FAX: +61 (06) 2861289

China
15 Coronation Drive, Yarralumla ACT 2600,
Australia
PHONE: +61 (06) 2734780
FAX: +61 (06) 2734878

Columbia
2nd Fl., 101 Northbourne Ave., Turner ACT
2601, P.O. Box 2892, Canberra City ACT 2601,
Australia
PHONE: +61 (06) 2572027
FAX: +61 (06) 2571448

Indonesia
236 Marouba Rd., Maroubra NSW 2035,
Australia
PHONE: +61 (02) 93449933
FAX: +61 (02) 93496854

Solomon Islands
Traxview Towers Building, Suite 1, Lvl 4/97
Creek St, GPO Box 850, Brisbane Qld 4001,
Australia
PHONE: +61 (07) 32217899
FAX: +61 (07) 32212296

JUDICIAL SYSTEM
High Court of Australia

P.O. Box E435, Kingston, Canberra, Australian
Capital Territory, 2604
PHONE: +61 (2) 62706811

Federal Court of Australia

Principal Registry, Level 17, Law Courts
Building, Queens Square, Sydney NSW 2000,
Australia
PHONE: +61 (2) 92308281
FAX: +61 (2) 92237706
E-MAIL: query@fedcourt.gov.au

FURTHER READING
Articles

Argy, Philip. "Australia Introduces Technology-Friendly Legislation." *International Tax Review* (February 1999): 5+.

"Australia Acknowledges 'Injustices' to Aborigines." *New York Times*, 27 August 1999, p. A10.

"Bad Bets." *The Economist* (August 21, 1999): 34.

Carruthers, Fiona. "Escape at Any Price." *Time International* (June 7, 1999): 57+.

Dionne, E.J. "Australia's Royalty Referendum." *Washington Post*, 3 September 1999, p. A27.

Donnan, Shawn. "Australia Awakens to Gambling Habit." *Christian Science Monitor* (July 26, 1999): 1.

Fitzgerald, Michael. "Heads of State: A New National Portrait Gallery Traces the Features of Australia's Past and Present." *Time International* (April 12, 1999): 60+.

"Friends No More." *The Economist* (September 25, 1999): 44.

Lakshmanan, Indira A. "Australians Arrive in East Timor." *Boston Globe*, 20 September 20, 1999, p. A8.

Maslen, Geoffrey. "Australia Inaugurates Its First University for Indigenous People." *The Chronicle of Higher Education*, 30 July 1999, p. A42.

"NTL to Buy Australian TV Network for $407 Million." *New York Times*, 19 March 1999, p. C3.

"Olympic Discord." *The Economist* (August 7, 1999): 31+.

Pollack, Andrew. "U.S. Rejects Pact on Genetically Altered Goods: Treaty Called Insufficient, Restrictive." *Times-Picayune*, 25 February 25, 1999, p. A15.

"Rethinking the Origins of Life." *Maclean's* (August 23, 1999): p. 21.

"Sydney Easing Up on Bands." *New York Times*, 29 July 1999, p. D4.

"Telstra of Australia to Expand into the United States." *New York Times*, 16 September 1999, p. 4.

"The Hardest Word." *The Economist* (September 11, 1999): 48.

Zimmer, Carl. "New Date for the Dawn of Dream Time." *Science* (May 21, 1999): 1243.

Zinn, Christopher. "Protests at Porn Bill." *The Guardian*, 3 June 1999, p. 8.

AUSTRALIA: STATISTICAL DATA

For sources and notes see "Sources of Statistics" in the front of each volume.

GEOGRAPHY

Geography (1)

Area:

Total: 7,686,850 sq km.

Land: 7,617,930 sq km.

Water: 68,920 sq km.

Note: includes Lord Howe Island and Macquarie Island.

Area—comparative: slightly smaller than the US.

Land boundaries: 0 km.

Coastline: 25,760 km.

Climate: generally arid to semiarid; temperate in south and east; tropical in north.

Terrain: mostly low plateau with deserts; fertile plain in southeast.

Natural resources: bauxite, coal, iron ore, copper, tin, silver, uranium, nickel, tungsten, mineral sands, lead, zinc, diamonds, natural gas, petroleum.

Land use:

Arable land: 6%

Permanent crops: 0%

Permanent pastures: 54%

Forests and woodland: 19%

Other: 21% (1993 est.).

HUMAN FACTORS

Demographics (2A)

	1990	1995	1998	2000	2010	2020	2030	2040	2050
Population	17,033.2	18,079.3	18,613.1	18,950.1	20,433.7	21,695.9	22,541.3	22,860.3	22,846.5
Net migration rate (per 1,000 population)	NA	NA	NA	NA	NA	NA	NA	NA	NA
Births	NA	NA	NA	NA	NA	NA	NA	NA	NA
Deaths	NA	NA	NA	NA	NA	NA	NA	NA	NA
Life expectancy - males	74.2	76.2	76.9	77.5	79.2	80.1	80.5	80.8	80.9
Life expectancy - females	80.8	82.3	83.0	83.5	85.1	86.0	86.5	86.7	86.8
Birth rate (per 1,000)	15.4	14.2	13.5	13.0	11.7	11.1	10.2	9.8	9.6
Death rate (per 1,000)	7.1	6.9	6.9	6.9	7.4	8.3	10.0	11.5	12.4
Women of reproductive age (15-49 yrs.)	4,474.2	4,702.4	4,752.2	4,773.6	4,853.0	4,796.9	4,756.9	4,719.4	4,600.2
of which are currently married	6,483.3	NA	NA	NA	NA	NA	NA	NA	NA
Fertility rate	1.9	1.9	1.8	1.8	1.8	1.8	1.7	1.7	1.7

Except as noted, values for vital statistics are in thousands; life expectancy is in years.

Health Personnel (3)

Total health expenditure as a percentage of GDP, 1990-1997[a]

Public sector 5.8

Private sector 2.7

Total[b] 8.5

Health expenditure per capita in U.S. dollars, 1990-1997[a]

Purchasing power parity 1,786

Total 1,798

Availability of health care facilities per 100,000 people

Hospital beds 1990-1997[a] 8900

Doctors 1993[c] . . . . .NA

Nurses 1993[c] . . . . .NA

Health Indicators (4)

Life expectancy at birth

1980 74

1997 78

Daily per capita supply of calories (1996) 3,001

Total fertility rate births per woman (1997) 1.8

Maternal mortality ratio per 100,000 live births (1990-97) . . . . .9[c]

Safe water % of population with access (1995) 99

Sanitation % of population with access (1995) . . . .

Consumption of iodized salt % of households (1992-98)[a] . . . .

Smoking prevalence

Male % of adults (1985-95)[a] 29

Female % of adults (1985-95)[a] 21

Tuberculosis incidence per 100,000 people (1997) . . .8

Adult HIV prevalence % of population ages 15-49 (1997) 0.14

Infants and Malnutrition (5)

Under-5 mortality rate (1997) 6

% of infants with low birthweight (1990-97) 6

Births attended by skilled health staff % of total[a] . . .NA

% fully immunized (1995-97)

TB . . . . .NA

DPT 86

Polio . . . . .NA

Measles 87

Prevalence of child malnutrition under age 5 (1992-97)[b] 0

Ethnic Division (6)

Caucasian 92%

Asian 7%

Aboriginal and other 1%

Religions (7)

Anglican 26.1%

Roman Catholic 26%

Other Christian 24.3%

Non-Christian 11%

Languages (8)

English, native languages.

EDUCATION

Public Education Expenditures (9)

Public expenditure on education (% of GNP)

1980 . . . . .5.5

1996 . . . . .5.6[1]

Expenditure per student

Primary % of GNP per capita

1980 . . . .

1996 . . . . .17.4[1]

Secondary % of GNP per capita

1980 . . . . .44.7

1996 . . . . .18.8[1]

Tertiary % of GNP per capita

1980 . . . . .51.3

1996 . . . . .30.4[1]

Expenditure on teaching materials

Primary % of total for level (1996) . . . .

Secondary % of total for level (1996) . . . .

Primary pupil-teacher ratio per teacher (1996) 18

Duration of primary education years (1995) 7

GOVERNMENT & LAW

Political Parties (12)

House of Representatives	No. of seats
Liberal-National	.94
Labor	.49
Independent	.5

Government Budget (13A)

Year: 1997

Total Expenditures: 140,478 millions of Dollars

Expenditures as a percentage of the total by function:

General public services and public order 8.06

Defense 6.78

Education 7.53

Health 13.82

Social Security and Welfare 35.17

Housing and community amenities 1.03

Recreational, cultural, and religious affairs 94

Fuel and energy 74

Agriculture, forestry, fishing, and hunting 1.31

Mining, manufacturing, and construction 28

Transportation and communication 2.13

Other economic affairs and services 2.72

Crime (15)

Crime rate (for 1997)

Crimes reported 1,107,200

Total persons convicted ....NA

Crimes per 100,000 population 5,950

Persons responsible for offenses

Total number of suspects ....NA

Total number of female suspects ....NA

Total number of juvenile suspects ....NA

Military Affairs (14B)

	1990	1991	1992	1993	1994	1995
Military expenditures						
Current dollars (mil.)	5,866	5,719	7,065	7,994	8,358	8,401
1995 constant dollars (mil.)	6,741	7,425	7,599	8,381	8,567	8,401
Armed forces (000)	68	68	68	68	59	58
Gross national product (GNP)						
Current dollars (mil.)	250,400	262,900	280,700	300,400	323,800	342,100[e]
1995 constant dollars (mil.)	287,800	290,600	301,900	314,900	331,900	342,100[e]
Central government expenditures (CGE)						
1995 constant dollars (mil.)	73,320	78,770	83,820	88,340	91,480	95,150
People (mil.)	17.0	17.3	17.5	17.7	17.9	18.1
Military expenditure as % of GNP	2.3	2.6	2.5	2.7	2.6	2.5
military expenditure as % of CGE	9.2	9.4	9.1	9.5	9.4	8.8
Military expenditure per capita (1995 $)	396	430	434	473	479	465
Armed forces per 1,000 people (soldiers)	4.0	3.9	3.9	3.8	3.3	3.2
GNP per capita (1995 $)	16,900	16,900	17,260	17,790	18,550	18,920
Arms imports[6]						
Current dollars (mil.)	850	675	240	675	400	900
1995 constant dollars (mil.)	977	746	258	708	410	900
Arms exports[6]						
Current dollars (mil.)	60	20	50	40	20	50
1995 constant dollars (mil.)	69	22	54	42	21	50
Total imports[7]						
Current dollars (mil.)	41,290	41,700	43,810	45,580	53,420	61,290
1995 constant dollars (mil.)	47,450	46,080	47,120	47,780	54,760	61,290
Total exports[7]						
Current dollars (mil.)	39,750	41,850	42,820	42,720	47,540	52,690
1995 constant dollars (mil.)	45,680	46,250	46,060	44,790	48,730	52,690
Arms as percent of total imports[8]	2.1	1.6	.5	1.5	.7	1.5
Arms as percent of total exports[8]	.2	.0	.1	.1	0	.1

LABOR FORCE

Labor Force (16)

Total (million) 9.2

Services 73%

Industry 22%

Agriculture 5%

Data for 1997 est. Total for December 1997.

Unemployment Rate (17)

8.4% (1997)

PRODUCTION SECTOR

Electric Energy (18)

Capacity . . . . .38.83 million kW (1995)

Production . . . . .163.082 billion kWh (1995)

Consumption per capita . . . . .8,901 kWh (1995)

Transportation (19)

Highways:

total: 913,000 km

paved: 353,331 km (including 1,3630 km of expressways)

unpaved: 559,669 km (1996 est.)

Waterways: 8,368 km; mainly by small, shallow-draft craft

Pipelines: crude oil 2,500 km; petroleum products 500 km; natural gas 5,600 km

Merchant marine:

total: 64 ships (1,000 GRT or over) totaling 2,122,604 GRT/3,045,417 DWT ships by type: bulk 31, cargo 3, chemical tanker 4, combination bulk 1, container 5, liquefied gas tanker 4, oil tanker 10, passenger 1, roll-on/roll-off cargo 5 (1997 est.)

Airports: 419 (1997 est.)

Airports—with paved runways:

total: 259

over 3,047 m: 8

2,438 to 3,047 m: 13

1,524 to 2,437 m: 111

914 to 1,523 m: 119

under 914 m: 8 (1997 est.)

Airports—with unpaved runways:

total: 160

1,524 to 2,437 m: 22

914 to 1,523 m: 123

under 914 m: 15 (1997 est.)

Top Agricultural Products (20)

Wheat, barley, sugarcane, fruits; cattle, sheep, poultry.

MANUFACTURING SECTOR

GDP & Manufacturing Summary (21)

Detailed value added figures are listed by both International Standard Industry Code (ISIC) and product title.

	1980	1985	1990	1994
GDP ($-1990 mil.)[1]	215,620	251,024	289,788	324,841
Per capita ($-1990)[1]	14,800	16,049	17,159	18,195
Manufacturing share (%) (current prices)[1]	19.0	17.4	15.3	*14.5*
Manufacturing				
Value added ($-1990 mil.)[1]	40,263	40,619	44,683	52,061
Industrial production index	100	101	111	127
Value added ($ mil.)	29,173	26,900	54,097	*64,417*
Gross output ($ mil.)	75,474	69,330	128,983	*143,435*
Employment (000)	1,139	1,014	1,017	*916*
Profitability (% of gross output)				
Intermediate input (%)	61	61	58	*55*
Wages and salaries inc. supplements (%)	20	19	16	*16*
Gross operating surplus	18	20	26	*29*
Productivity ($)				
Gross output per worker	65,402	67,785	125,117	*156,517*
Value added per worker	25,280	26,301	52,475	*70,383*
Average wage (inc. supplements)	13,356	12,977	20,719	*25,067*
Value added ($ mil.)				
311/2 Food products	3,993	3,764	7,647	*10,043*
313 Beverages	785	847	1,723	*2,222*
314 Tobacco products	248	179	365	*373*
321 Textiles	1,050	955	1,673	*1,792*
322 Wearing apparel	821	722	1,223	*1,261*
323 Leather and fur products	93	77	105	*109*
324 Footwear	223	205	279	*272*
331 Wood and wood products	1,052	1,028	1,728	*1,942*
332 Furniture and fixtures	505	507	1,032	*1,130*

	1980	1985	1990	1994
341 Paper and paper products	744	704	1,302	*1,540*
342 Printing and publishing	1,818	2,131	4,058	*4,946*
351 Industrial chemicals	969	982	1,660	*1,998*
352 Other chemical products	1,186	1,191	2,291	*2,879*
353 Petroleum refineries	323	285	1,659	*1,990*
354 Miscellaneous petroleum and coal products	30	25	34	*39*
355 Rubber products	341	264	546	*631*
356 Plastic products	831	808	1,702	*2,311*
361 Pottery, china and earthenware	46	41	76	*76*
362 Glass and glass products	246	254	528	*598*
369 Other non-metal mineral products	1,183	1,085	2,170	*2,560*
371 Iron and steel	1,920	1,391	2,431	*2,637*
372 Non-ferrous metals	1,473	1,409	3,791	*4,624*
381 Metal products	2,467	2,040	4,215	*5,234*
382 Non-electrical machinery	2,091	1,575	3,070	*3,417*
383 Electrical machinery	1,351	1,329	2,466	*2,777*
384 Transport equipment	2,830	2,579	5,379	*5,860*
385 Professional and scientific equipment	290	279	498	*601*
390 Other manufacturing industries	263	246	445	*555*

FINANCE, ECONOMICS, & TRADE

Economic Indicators (22)

National product: GDP—purchasing power parity—$394 billion (1997 est.)

National product real growth rate: 3.3% (1997 est.)

National product per capita: $21,400 (1997 est.)

Inflation rate—consumer price index: 1% (1997 est.)

Exchange Rates (24)

Exchange rates:

Australian dollars ($A) per US$1.

February 1998	1.4865
1997	1.3439
1996	1.2773
1995	1.3486
1994	1.3668
1993	1.4704

Top Import Origins (25)

$67 billion (f.o.b., 1997 est.). Data are for 1994/95.

Origins	%
United States	.22
Japan	.17
United Kingdom	.6
China	.5
NZ	.5

Balance of Payments (23)

	1990	1992	1994	1995	1996
Exports of goods (f.o.b.)	39,642	42,816	47,331	53,146	60,065
Imports of goods (f.o.b.)	−39,284	−41,173	−50,611	−57,371	−60,957
Trade balance	358	1,643	−3,280	−4,225	−892
Services - debits	−30,095	−27,606	−32,387	−36,731	−39,857
Services - credits	13,386	14,921	18,582	21,377	24,535
Private transfers (net)	460	128	164	157	232
Government transfers (net)	13	−299	−547	−291	−126
Overall balance	−15,879	−11,213	−17,467	−19,713	−16,108

Top Export Destinations (26)

$68 billion (f.o.b., 1997 est.). Data are for 1997.

Destinations	%
Japan	.20
ASEAN	.16
South Korea	.9
United States	.9
NZ	.8
United Kingdom	NA
Taiwan	NA
Hong Kong	NA
China	NA

NA stands for not available.

Economic Aid (27)

Donor: ODA, $1.43 billion (FY97/98).

Import Export Commodities (28)

Import Commodities	Export Commodities
Machinery and transport equipment	Coal
Computers and office machines	Gold
	Meat
Telecommunication equipment and parts; crude oil and petroleum products	Wool
	Alumina
	Iron ore
	Wheat
	Machinery and transport equipment

AUSTRIA

Republic of Austria
Republik Österreich

CAPITAL: Vienna (Wien).

FLAG: The flag consists of a white horizontal stripe between two red stripes.

ANTHEM: *Land der Berge, Land am Ströme (Land of Mountains, Land on the River).*

MONETARY UNIT: The schilling (s) is a paper currency of 100 groschen. There are coins of 1, 2, 5, 10, and 50 groschen and 1, 5, 10, 20, 25, 50, 100, 500, 1,000, and 2,000 schillings, and notes of 20, 50, 100, 500, 1,000, and 5,000 schillings. s1 = $0.09391 (or $1 = s10.649).

WEIGHTS AND MEASURES: The metric system is in use.

HOLIDAYS: New Year's Day, 1 January; Epiphany, 6 January; May Day, 1 May; Assumption, 15 August; National Day, 26 October; All Saints' Day, 1 November; Immaculate Conception, 8 December; Christmas, 25 December; St. Stephen's Day, 26 December. Movable religious holidays include Easter Monday, Ascension, Whitmonday, and Corpus Christi. In addition, there are provincial holidays.

TIME: 1 PM = noon GMT.

LOCATION AND SIZE: Austria, with an area of 83,850 square kilometers (32,375 square miles), is a landlocked country in Central Europe. It is slightly smaller than the state of Maine and has a total boundary length of 2,564 kilometers (1,593 miles). Austria's capital city, Vienna, is located in the northeastern part of the country.

CLIMATE: Climatic conditions depend on location and altitude. Temperatures range from an average of about $-2°C$ (28°F) in January to about 19°C (66°F) in July. Rainfall ranges from more than 200 centimeters (80 inches) annually in the hills bordering the Alps to less than 60 centimeters (24 inches) in the driest region, east of the Neusiedler See.

INTRODUCTORY SURVEY

RECENT HISTORY

The struggles of maintaining the Austrian-Hungarian Empire were among the underlying causes of World War I. Defeat in the war led to the destruction of that empire and the establishment of an independent Austria in 1920 with the establishment of a constitution. Adolf Hitler invaded the country in 1938. England and the United States declared Austria liberated with the defeat of Nazi Germany in 1945, but Russian occupation troops failed to leave. Austria regained its independence on May 15, 1955, and was restored on the basis of the 1920 constitution.

Austria maintained independence and neutrality throughout the Cold War. Former United Nations Secretary-General Kurt Waldheim was elected to the mostly ceremonial office of president on June 8, 1986, even though controversial allegations of links to Nazi war crimes in Yugoslavia during World War II surfaced. Waldheim served until 1992. On January 1, 1995, Austria joined the European Union. However, Austria maintains its strict neutrality and refuses to allow the stationing of foreign troops on its soil.

More recently, debate and discussion has been engaged over the return of art objects owned by Austria but acquired after Nazis stole them from primarily Jewish owners. Austrian police arrested Bosnian Serb General Momir Talic in August of 1999. Talic was wanted by the United Nations on war crimes charges in the former Yugoslavia.

GOVERNMENT

Austria is a federal republic with a democratically elected parliament. The president, elected by popular vote for a six-year term, appoints a federal chancellor, usually the leader of the largest party in parliament. The president is limited to two terms of office.

The parliament, known as the Federal Assembly, consists of the 63 member National Council and 183 members Federal Council. All citizens 19 years of age or older may vote. Voting is compulsory for presidential elections.

Judiciary

As of 1985, Austria had about 200 local courts with civil jurisdiction. There were also 20 provincial and district courts with civil and criminal jurisdiction and four higher provincial courts with criminal jurisdiction, located in Vienna, Graz, Innsbruck, and Linz.

The Supreme Court, in Vienna, acts as the final appeals court for criminal and civil cases. The Constitutional Court has supreme jurisdiction over constitutional and civil rights issues. The Administrative Court ensures the legal functioning of public administration.

Criminal defendants are afforded a presumption of innocence, public trials, and jury trial for major offenses.

Political Parties

The principal political parties in Austria include: the Austrian People's Party, also referred to as Austria's Christian Democratic Party; the SPÖ, also known as the Social Democratic Party; the Freedom Party of Austria; and the Free Democratic Party, founded by dissidents from the SPÖ.

DEFENSE

In 1993, the Austrian armed forces totaled 52,000. The Austrian army had 51,500 members, and the air service 4,300, with 54 combat aircraft. Active reserve strength is 200,000 with 66,000 receiving annual training. Another 960,000 have had military training.

ECONOMIC AFFAIRS

The government plays a large role in the Austrian economy, although private enterprise continues to occupy a central position. Basic industries, including mineral production, heavy industry, rail and water transport, and utilities, were taken over by the government during 1946 and 1947. In 1970, they were reorganized under the Austrian Industrial Administration.

Public Finance

The government's proposed annual budget is submitted before the beginning of each calendar year. As a result of a mini-recession in 1993, the budget deficit widened in 1994. The increase in the budget deficit was mainly due to the government's decision to let automatic stabilizers work, when it became apparent that business activity was slowing down. Raising budget deficits presents an economic challenge to the government. Austria joined the European Monetary Union (EMU) in 1999.

Income

Austria's Gross Domestic Product (GDP) was estimated in 1997 to be $174.1 billion, with a per capita estimate of $21,400. Real growth was estimated at 2.1%, and inflation at 1.3%. Unemployment was 7.1% in 1997.

Industry

Major parts of the electric and electronics, chemical, iron and steel, and machinery industries are government controlled. However, a return to private ownership began for many companies in 1993. Textiles are an important industry, including embroidery, spinning, weaving, and knitting.

The chemical industry products include fertilizers, rubber and asbestos products, paints and coating compounds, soaps and scouring agents, pharmaceuticals. Petroleum refinery products include fuel oil, gasoline, and lubricants.

Other leading industries are electrical and electronic machinery and equipment, pulp and paper, ceramics, and especially foodstuffs and allied products. Austria has always been famous for its skilled glassblowers, goldsmiths, jewelers, lacemakers, potters, stonecutters, and woodcarvers.

Banking and Finance

The Austrian National Bank was reestablished in July 1945. The bank is a corporation with capital shares fixed by law; 50% of the shares are owned by the government. It is the central bank and the bank of issue. It sets reserve requirements for credit institutions.

The Austrian banking system also includes joint-stock banks, banking houses, and private banks, as well as postal savings banks, private savings banks, mortgage banks, building societies, and specialized cooperative credit institutions. The stock exchange in Vienna was the first in Europe.

Economic Development

The federal government has a majority share in two of the three largest commercial banks and all or most of the nation's electricity, coal and metal mining, and iron and steel production, as well as part of Austria's chemical, electrical, machine, and vehicle industries. The republic's share in the nationalized industries was handed over on 1 January 1970 to the Austrian Industrial Administration Co., of which the government is still the principal shareholder and maintains voting control. In line with the government's industrialization program, the nationalized industries have been regrouped into five sections: steel; metals; machinery and turnkey operations; electronics, petroleum, petrochemicals and plastics; and chemicals, pharmaceuticals, and fertilizers.

The nationalized establishments operate according to free-enterprise principles and do not receive tax concessions. The postal, telephone, and telegraph services and radio and television transmission are state monopolies, as is the trade in tobacco, alcohol, salt, and explosives.

Government planning and control remain key to the Austrian economy.

SOCIAL WELFARE

Austria has one of the most advanced and comprehensive systems of social legislation in the world. Health insurance is available to industrial and agricultural workers, federal and professional employees, and members of various other occupational groups. For those without insurance or adequate means, treatment is paid for by public welfare funds.

Family allowances are paid monthly, depending on the number of dependent children, with the amount doubled for any child who is severely handicapped. The state provides school lunches for more than 100,000 children annually.

The state also grants a special birth allowance and a payment for newlyweds setting up their first home. Unmarried people establishing a common household may apply for tax relief. A 1975 federal law provides for complete equality between husband and wife in maintaining the household and raising children.

Healthcare

Anyone is entitled to use the facilities provided by Austria's health service. The costs are borne by the social insurance plan, or, in cases of hardship, by the social welfare program. Life expectancy at birth in 1995 was 80 years for women and 73 years for men. Mandatory maternity leave (during which employment is prohibited by law) amounts to eight weeks before and eight weeks after birth. Vienna's medical school and research institutes are world famous.

Housing

The Housing Improvement Act of 1969 provides for government support for modernization of outdated housing. In 1990, 25% of Austria's housing stock had been built before 1919, and 19% between 1971 and 1980.

EDUCATION

All schools are coeducational, and education at state schools is free of charge. Financial support is provided for post-secondary schooling. There are 12 university-level institutions and six fine arts colleges. The literacy rate is 99%.

1999 KEY EVENTS TIMELINE

January

- Parliament passes law to allow the return of stolen art to Holocaust victims.

- Walter Kohn, an Austrian-born U.S. citizen, is awarded the Nobel Prize for Chemistry.

- Austria, Hungary and Slovakia leaders meet for Trilateral Summit in Budapest.

February

- Austrian women win 12 medals in ski events at the Alpine World Championships in Vail, Colorado.

- Thirty-eight people die in Austria as avalanches sweep Alpine resorts.

- Austrian government pledges to return 250 artworks stolen by the Nazis in World War II to the Rothschild family.

March

- Chinese President Jiang Zemin visits Austria.

- Far-right Freedom Party scores dramatic gains in provincial elections.

- Reforms proposed by Austria's Catholic Church are rejected in letter from Vatican.

April

- Austria seeks extradition of the terrorist "Carlos the Jackal" from France.

- Former Nazi doctor, Heinrich Gross, is charged with murder of nine children during World War II.

May

- The NATO/Serbia conflict, by halting Danube River shipments, inflicts heavy losses on Austrian exporters and shippers.

- The Cabinet approves a law to streamline the statute books.

June

- EU elections in Austria: Social Democratic Party (SPÖ) wins an additional seat.

- Karl Wlaschek is awarded the Austrian Cross of Honor for Science and Art, 1st class.

- Appointment of Seiji Ozawa as new director of the Vienna State Opera is announced.

July

- Austria and Germany boycott meeting of EU Industry Ministers in Finland because Finland provides translation only in English, French, and Finnish.

- Molecular biologist Kim Ashley Nasmyth wins the 1999 Wittgenstein Prize.

- Austrian Parliament passes a bill affirming that Austria will not develop or test nuclear weapons.

August

- Austrian police arrest senior Bosnian military official charged with war crimes by the international tribune in The Hague.

September

- With general elections only two weeks away, right-wing Freedom Party records big gains in regional voting.

October

- Jörg Haider's far-right Freedom Party comes in second in general parliamentary election, edging out the conservative People's Party by only 400 votes. This causes Chancellor Viktor Klima, leader of the Social Democrat-People's Party co-alition government, to resign and the process of forming a new government to begin.

December

- Five people are trampled to death when a barrier gives way under the crush of spectators at a snowboarding event in Innsbruck.

ANALYSIS OF EVENTS: 1999

BUSINESS AND THE ECONOMY

In 1999 Austria was one of Europe's most prosperous countries. It had low unemployment, a negligible inflation rate, a reasonable budget deficit, and a generous social welfare program. Its banking sector was eyeing expansion into Eastern Europe and regrouping in the wake of two recent major bank mergers: Bank Austria's takeover of Creditanstalt Investment Bank, and the merger of First Austrian and GiroCredit into Erste Bank. In January, Austria became one of eleven European Union countries to officially adopt the euro.

In the spring, the NATO bombing of Yugoslavia in response to Serb attacks on ethnic Albanians in Kosovo stopped shipping on the Danube River between Hungary and the Black Sea, resulting in heavy financial losses for both Austrian and Romanian exporters and shippers.

GOVERNMENT AND POLITICS

The major political story of 1999 was the growing power of the far-right Freedom Party, led by Jörg Haider. Following notable gains in March provincial elections and September regional voting, Haider's party upset the country's traditional balance of power on the national level in October's parliamentary elections by edging out the conservative People's Party for second place in the polls with 27 percent of the vote. Although Austria's stable government and economy are not the kind of circumstances which ordinarily provide fertile ground for the growth of far-right sentiment, Haider, who has been known to make pro-Nazi statements, skillfully capitalized on anti-foreigner and anti-immigrant sentiment. Haider adopted an "outsider" stance from which he critiqued the deeply entrenched national system of political patronage by the two major parties, called the *Pro-*

porz system. He also adopted a strong law-and-order position and opposed the country's high taxes and austerity budget.

This victory cast doubt on the future of the nation's ruling "grand coalition" between the People's Party and the Social Democrats. Between them, the two parties had ruled Austria for most of the postwar period. Austrian chancellor Viktor Klima had declared that his Social Democrats would never form a coalition with the Freedom Party. The leader of the People's Party, Wolfgang Schussel, had declared that if his party came in third, they would not be a part of a coalition government. To further complicate matters, the nation of Israel has stated that they will not maintain diplomatic relations with Austria if Haider, who Israel considers a neo-Nazi, is given a place in a new government.

Chancellor Klima was officially given the task of forming a new government in December. Unless the Social Democrats wish to form a minority government either Klima or Schussel will have to go against their earlier declarations. The fact that, for all intents and purposes, the People's Party and the Freedom Party tied in the general election would seem to leave an opening for the People's Party and the Social Democrats to maintain their coalition.

On the international front, Chancellor Klima met with the leaders of Hungary and Slovakia for Trilateral Summit in Budapest in January. The Social Democrats strengthened their position in the European Union by gaining an additional seat in elections to the EU's parliamentary body in June. In July, Austria's parliament passed a bill affirming that Austria would not develop or test nuclear weapons. General Momir Talic, the chief of staff of the Bosnian Serb army, who had been charged as a war criminal by the international tribune in The Hague, was arrested in August in Vienna for the ethnic cleansing of Bosnian Muslims and Croats from the Krajina region during the 1992–95 war. Talic was the first alleged Bosnian war criminal arrested outside the borders of the former Yugoslavia.

CULTURE AND SOCIETY

Natural disaster exacted a toll in the Austrian resort town of Valzur at the beginning of the year, when unusually heavy snowfalls combined with high winds to trigger a wave of avalanches throughout the Alps, both in Austria and neighboring countries. Thirty-eight people, including at least 19 foreign tourists, were killed when an avalanche struck the village in February.

In January Austria's parliament passed legislature providing for the return of hundreds of artworks stolen from Holocaust victims during the Nazi era. The following month the government announced the return of some 250 works of art housed in state-owned museums to the Rothschild family, from whom they had been appropriated between 1938 and 1945. The World War II era also made headlines in charges filed against Heinrich Gross, an Austrian physician who performed wartime research at the Am Steinhof Children's Hospital, where hundreds of handicapped children were killed in the name of Nazi ''research.'' Through renewed investigations spearheaded by the British and Austrian media, Gross, who had shaken off early postwar criminal charges and later risen to the highest ranks of his profession, was linked to the deaths of nine children through wartime records from the hospital.

Prospects for church reform in Austria dimmed with the March publication of a confidential letter containing the Vatican's rejection of reforms proposed the previous autumn by a national assembly of Catholics, including greater decentralization and an expanded role for women in the church.

Austrians garnered significant honors in 1999. The Nobel Prize for Chemistry was awarded to Walter Kohn, an Austrian-born U.S. citizen. Austrian women earned twelve medals at the Alpine World Championship skiing competition in Vail, Colorado, including two gold medals won by Alexandra Meissnitzer for the super-G and the giant slalom.

In June it was announced that internationally recognized conductor Seiji Ozawa would leave his post at the Boston Symphony Orchestra in 2002 to become the director of the Vienna State Opera.

DIRECTORY

CENTRAL GOVERNMENT
Head of State

President
Thomas Klestil, Office of the President, Prasidentschaftskanzlei, Hofburg, Bellariator, Ballhausplatz 2, A-1010, Vienna, Austria
E-MAIL: thomas.klestil@hofburg.at

Ministers
Federal Chancellor
Viktor Klima, Office of the Federal Chancellor, Bundeskanzleramt, Ballhausplatz 2, A-1014, Vienna, Austria
PHONE: +43 (1) 531152446
FAX: +43 (1) 531152705
E-MAIL: vklima@spoe.or.at

Vice Chancellor
Wolfgang Schuessel, Office of the Vice Chancellor

Federal Minister for Women's Affairs and Consumer Protection
Barbara Prammer, Ministry of Women's Affairs and Consumer Protection
PHONE: +43 (1) 711724759
FAX: +43 (1) 7155831

Minister of Agriculture and Forestry
Wilhelm Molterer, Ministry of Agriculture and Forestry, Stubenring 1, A-1012 Vienna, Austria
PHONE: +43 (1) 711000

Minister of Defense
Werner Fasslabend, Ministry of Defense, Bürgerservicestelle, Mariahilfer Straße 24, A-1070 Vienna, Austria
PHONE: +43 (1) 810200106
FAX: +43 (1) 878381250
E-MAIL: direktion@fbva.bmlf.gv.at

Minister of Economic Affairs
Hannes Farnleiter, Ministry of Economic Affairs, Stubenring 1, A-1010 Vienna, Austria
E-MAIL: minister@bmwa.gv.at

Minister of Education and Cultural Affairs
Elisabeth Gehrer, Ministry of Education and Cultural Affairs

Minister of Environment, Youth and Family
Martin Bartenstein, Ministry of Environment, Youth and Family

Minister of Finance
Rudolf Edlinger, Ministry of Finance

Minister of Foreign Affairs
Wolfgang Schuessel, Ministry of Foreign Affairs, Ballhausplatz 2, A-1014 Vienna, Austria

Minister of Interior
Karl Schlögl, Ministry of Interior, Postfach 100, A-1014 Vienna, Austria
E-MAIL: heder@oebfa.co.at

Minister of Justice
Nikolaus Michalek, Ministry of Justice

Minister of Labor, Health and Social Affairs

Lore Hostasch, Ministry of Labor, Health and Social Affairs, Stubenring 1, A-1010 Vienna, Austria

E-MAIL: heder@oebfa.co.at

Minister of Science and Transport

Caspar Einem, Ministry of Science and Transport, Radetzkystrasse 2, A-1030 Vienna, Austria

PHONE: +43 (1) 711628000

E-MAIL: minister@bmwf.gv.at

State Secretary in the Finance Ministry

Wolfgang Ruttensdorfer, Secretariat of Finance

State Secretary for Foreign Ministry

Benita Ferrero-Waldner, Secretariat for Foreign Ministry

POLITICAL ORGANIZATIONS

Christlich Soziale Allianz-CSA (Christian Social Alliance)

Landstrasser-Hauptstrasse 63, A-1030 Vienna, Austria

PHONE: +43 (1) 7181866

FAX: +43 (1) 718186618

E-MAIL: csa@tclcweb

Demokraten (Democrats)

Kommunistische Partei Österreichs (Communist Party of Austria)

Weyringergasse 33/5, A-1040 Vienna, Austria

PHONE: +43 (1) 5036580

FAX: +43 (1) 5036580411

E-MAIL: kpoe@magnet.at

TITLE: Party Leader

NAME: Walter Baier

Freedom Party of Austria

Rathausplatz 8-3-9, A-1010 Vienna, Austria

PHONE: +43 (1) 4057560

FAX: +43 (1) 405756023

E-MAIL: kpoe@magnet.at

TITLE: Party Leader

NAME: Jörg Haider

Grüne Alternative Liste (Green Alternative List)

TITLE: Party Spokesman

NAME: Alexander Van Der Bellen

Österreichische Volkspartei (Austrian People's Party)

Lichtenfelsgasse 7, A-1010 Vienna, Austria

PHONE: +43 (1) 401260

NAME: Wolfgang Schüssel

Liberales Forum (Liberal Forum)

Reichsratsstraße 7-10, A-1010 Vienna, Austria

PHONE: +43 (1) 4027881

FAX: +43 (1) 4027889

NAME: Heide Schmidt

Österreichische Naturgesetz-Partei (Austrian Natural Law Party)

Postfach 395, A-1010 Vienna, Austria

PHONE: +43 (1) 5126612

FAX: +43 (1) 5139660

NAME: Lothar Krenner

E-MAIL: lothar.krenner@telecom.at

Sozialdemokratische Partei Österreichs-SPÖ (Social Democratic Party of Austria)

Löwelstraße 18, A-1014 Vienna, Austria

PHONE: +43 (1) 53427

FAX: +43 (1) 5359683

TITLE: Party Leader

NAME: Andreas Rudas

DIPLOMATIC REPRESENTATION

Embassies in Austria

Brazil

Lugeck 1/V/15, A-1010 Vienna, Austria

PHONE: +43 (1) 5120631

FAX: +43 (1) 5135056

China

Metternichgasse 4, A-1030 Vienna, Austria

PHONE: +43 (1) 7143149

FAX: +43 (1) 7136816

Egypt

Hohe Warte 52, A-1190 Vienna, Austria

PHONE: +43 (1) 3708104

FAX: +43 (1) 370810427

France

Technikerstraße 2, A-1040 Vienna, Austria

PHONE: +43 (1) 5054747

FAX: +43 (1) 505639268

Germany

Metternichgasse 3, A-1030 Vienna, Austria

PHONE: +43 (1) 71154

FAX: +43 (1) 7138366

Greece
Argentinierstraße 14, A-1040 Vienna, Austria
PHONE: +43 (1) 5055791
FAX: +43 (1) 5056217

India
Kärntner Ring 2, A-1015 Vienna, Austria
PHONE: +43 (1) 5058666
FAX: +43 (1) 5059219

Italy
Rennweg 27, A-1030 Vienna, Austria
PHONE: +43 (1) 7125121
FAX: +43 (1) 7139719

Japan
Heßgasse 6, A-1010 Vienna, Austria
PHONE: +43 (1) 531920
FAX: +43 (1) 5320590

Kenya
Neulinggasse 29/8, A-1030 Vienna, Austria
PHONE: +43 (1) 7123919
FAX: +43 (1) 7123922

Mexico
Türkenstraße 15, A-1090 Vienna, Austria
PHONE: +43 (1) 3107383
FAX: +43 (1) 3107387

Netherlands
Opernring 3-5/7. und 8. Stock, A-1010 Vienna, Austria
PHONE: +43 (1) 58939200
FAX: +43 (1) 58939265
E-MAIL: nlgovwen@cso.co.at

Poland
Hietzinger Hauptstraße 42c, A-1130 Vienna, Austria
FAX: +43 (1) 87015128

Portugal
Opernring 3, Stiege 1, A-1010 Vienna, Austria
FAX: +43 (1) 5867536
PHONE: +43 (1) 5875839

Russia
Reisnerstraße 45-47, A-1030 Vienna, Austria
PHONE: +43 (1) 7123388
FAX: +43 (1) 7121229; 7131215

South Africa
Mattiellistraße 2/III, A-1040 Vienna, Austria
PHONE: +43 (1) 5041178
FAX: +43 (1) 5128580; 5129710

South Korea
Laurenzerberg 2/III, A-1010 Vienna, Austria

PHONE: +43 (1) 531383321
FAX: +43 (1) 531380

Spain
Argentinier Straße 34, A-1040 Vienna, Austria
PHONE: +43 (1) 5055788
FAX: +43 (1) 5055780; 5055788; 5055789

Switzerland
Prinz-Eugen-Straße 7, A-1030 Vienna, Austria
FAX: +43 (1) 7950521

Turkey
Prinz-Eugen-Straße 40, A-1040 Vienna, Austria
PHONE: +43 (1) 5057338
FAX: +43 (1) 5053660

United Kingdom
Jauresgasse 12, A-1030 Vienna, Austria
PHONE: +43 (1) 716130
FAX: +43 (1) 716132999

United States
Boltzmanngasse 14/3 und 16, A-1090 Vienna, Austria
PHONE: +43 (1) 31339
FAX: +43 (1) 3100682

Venezuela
Marokkanergasse 22/4, A-1030 Vienna, Austria
PHONE: +43 (1) 7122638
FAX: +43 (1) 7153219

JUDICIAL SYSTEM
Austrian Constitutional Court
Judenplatz 11, A-1010 Vienna, Austria
PHONE: +43 (1) 531220
FAX: +43 (1) 53122499

FURTHER READING
Articles
''Anti-Immigrant Rightists Gain in Austrian Province.'' *The New York Times*, 20 September 1999, p. A8.

Blanden, Michael. ''Look East and West.'' *The Banker*, August 1999, p. 31.

''Europe's Year of the Avalanche.'' *U. S. News and World Report*. (March 8, 1999): 44.

''Far-right Turn.'' *The Economist* (October 9, 1999): 4.

''Fascism Resurgent?'' *The Economist* (October 9, 1999): 57.

''Heil Haider?'' *The Economist* (March 13, 1999): 61.

Kielmas, Maria. ''Blocked River Causing Trade, Shipping Losses.'' *Business Insurance* (May 3, 1999): 15.

''Who Next?'' *The Economist* (September 25, 1999): 60.

Books

Brook-Shepherd, Gordon. *The Austrians: A Thousand-Year Odyssey*. New York: Carroll and Graf Publishers, 1997.

Mason, John W. *The Dissolution of the Austro-Hungarian Empire 1867–1918*. 2nd ed. New York: Longman, 1997

Sandford, John, ed. *Encyclopedia of Contemporary German Culture*. New York: Routledge, 1999.

Strong, George V. *Seedtime for Fascism: The Disintegration of Austrian Political Culture, 1867–1918*. Armonk, N.Y.: M.E. Sharpe, 1998.

AUSTRIA:
STATISTICAL DATA

For sources and notes see "Sources of Statistics" in the front of each volume.

GEOGRAPHY

Geography (1)

Area:

Total: 83,858 sq km.

Land: 82,738 sq km.

Water: 1,120 sq km.

Area—comparative: slightly smaller than Maine.

Land boundaries:

Total: 2,562 km.

Border countries: Czech Republic 362 km, Germany 784 km, Hungary 366 km, Italy 430 km, Liechtenstein 35 km, Slovakia 91 km, Slovenia 330 km, Switzerland 164 km.

Coastline: 0 km (landlocked).

Climate: temperate; continental, cloudy; cold winters with frequent rain in lowlands and snow in mountains; cool summers with occasional showers.

Terrain: in the west and south mostly mountains (Alps); along the eastern and northern margins mostly flat or gently sloping.

Natural resources: iron ore, oil, timber, magnesite, lead, coal, lignite, copper, hydropower.

Land use:

Arable land: 17%

Permanent crops: 1%

Permanent pastures: 23%

Forests and woodland: 39%

Other: 20% (1996 est.).

HUMAN FACTORS

Demographics (2A)

	1990	1995	1998	2000	2010	2020	2030	2040	2050
Population	7,717.9	8,101.4	8,133.6	8,148.0	8,182.5	8,005.8	7,567.3	6,919.5	6,135.6
Net migration rate (per 1,000 population)	NA	NA	NA	NA	NA	NA	NA	NA	NA
Births	NA	NA	NA	NA	NA	NA	NA	NA	NA
Deaths	83.0	NA	NA	NA	NA	NA	NA	NA	NA
Life expectancy - males	72.4	73.6	74.1	74.5	76.0	77.3	78.3	79.1	79.7
Life expectancy - females	79.1	80.2	80.7	81.0	82.4	83.5	84.4	85.2	85.7
Birth rate (per 1,000)	11.7	10.9	9.9	9.4	7.8	7.4	6.3	5.8	5.6
Death rate (per 1,000)	10.8	10.1	10.1	10.0	10.7	11.7	13.7	16.2	19.0
Women of reproductive age (15-49 yrs.)	1,966.1	2,007.8	2,004.8	1,994.1	1,924.9	1,628.7	1,432.1	1,228.3	1,013.3
of which are currently married	NA	NA	NA	NA	NA	NA	NA	NA	NA
Fertility rate	1.5	1.4	1.4	1.4	1.3	1.3	1.3	1.3	1.3

Except as noted, values for vital statistics are in thousands; life expectancy is in years.

Health Personnel (3)

Total health expenditure as a percentage of GDP, 1990-1997[a]

Public sector 5.7

Private sector 2.2

Total[b] 7.9

Health expenditure per capita in U.S. dollars, 1990-1997[a]

Purchasing power parity 1,747

Total 2,012

Availability of health care facilities per 100,000 people

Hospital beds 1990-1997[a] 930

Doctors 1993[c] 327

Nurses 1993[c] 530

Health Indicators (4)

Life expectancy at birth

1980 73

1997 77

Daily per capita supply of calories (1996) 3,343

Total fertility rate births per woman (1997) 1.4

Maternal mortality ratio per 100,000 live births (1990-97) . . . . .10[c]

Safe water % of population with access (1995) . . . .

Sanitation % of population with access (1995) . . . .

Consumption of iodized salt % of households (1992-98)[a] . . . .

Smoking prevalence

Male % of adults (1985-95)[a] 42

Female % of adults (1985-95)[a] 27

Tuberculosis incidence per 100,000 people (1997) 19

Adult HIV prevalence % of population ages 15-49 (1997) 0.18

Infants and Malnutrition (5)

Under-5 mortality rate (1997) 5

% of infants with low birthweight (1990-97) 6

Births attended by skilled health staff % of total[a] . . .NA

% fully immunized (1995-97)

TB . . . . .NA

DPT 90

Polio 95

Measles 90

Prevalence of child malnutrition under age 5 (1992-97)[b] . . . . .NA

Ethnic Division (6)

German 99.4%

Croatian 0.3%

Slovene 0.2%

Other 0.1%

Religions (7)

Roman Catholic 78%

Protestant 5%

Other 17%

Languages (8)

German.

EDUCATION

Public Education Expenditures (9)

Public expenditure on education (% of GNP)

1980 . . . . .5.4

1996 . . . . .5.6[1]

Expenditure per student

Primary % of GNP per capita

1980 . . . . .15.7

1996 . . . . .23.1

Secondary % of GNP per capita

1980 . . . .

1996 . . . . .25.1[1]

Tertiary % of GNP per capita

1980 . . . . .37.3

1996 . . . . .37.6[1]

Expenditure on teaching materials

Primary % of total for level (1996) . . . .

Secondary % of total for level (1996) . . . .

Primary pupil-teacher ratio per teacher (1996) . . . . .12[1]

Duration of primary education years (1995) 4

Educational Attainment (10)

Age group (1991) . . . . .25+

Total population 5,288,032

Highest level attained (%)

No schooling 0

First level

Not completed 0

Completed . . . . .NA

Entered second level

S-1 . . . . .94.0

S-2 . . . . .NA

Postsecondary 6.1

GOVERNMENT & LAW

Political Parties (12)

National Council—	% of seats
Social Democratic Party of Austria (SPOe)	.38.3
Austrian People's Party (OeVP)	.28.3
Freedom Party of Austria (FPOe)	.22.1
Liberal Forum (LF)	.5.3
The Greens (GA)	.4.6
Other	.1.4

Government Budget (13A)

Year: 1996

Total Expenditures: 1,009.89 Billions of Schillings

Expenditures as a percentage of the total by function:

General public services and public order	.13.57
Defense	.2.02
Education	.9.19
Health	.12.95
Social Security and Welfare	.41.20
Housing and community amenities	.2.70
Recreational, cultural, and religious affairs	..52
Fuel and energy	..01
Agriculture, forestry, fishing, and hunting	.1.94
Mining, manufacturing, and construction	.1.15
Transportation and communication	.4.60
Other economic affairs and services	..61

Military Affairs (14A)

Military age	19 years of age
Availability of manpower	
Males age 15-19 (1998 est.)	.2,098,409
Fit for military service	
Males (1998 est.)	.1,744,035
Reaching military age annually	
Males (1998 est.)	.46,854
Total expenditures (1998 est.)	.$1.8 billion
Expenditures as % of GDP (1998 est.)	.0.83%

Crime (15)

Crime rate (for 1997)

Crimes reported	.481,500
Total persons convicted	.241,700
Crimes per 100,000 population	.6,000
Persons responsible for offenses	
Total number of suspects	.203,100
Total number of female suspects	.41,200
Total number of juvenile suspects	.27,600

LABOR FORCE

Labor Force (16)

Total (million)	.3.646
Services	.66.1%
Industry and crafts	.29.6%
Agriculture and forestry	.1.3%

Data for 1996 for salaried employees. Percent distribution for 1996. An estimated 150,000 Austrians are employed abroad; foreign laborers in Austria number 298,000.

Unemployment Rate (17)

7.1% (January 1998)

PRODUCTION SECTOR

Electric Energy (18)

Capacity	.15.65 million kW (1996)
Production	.54.8 billion kWh (1996)
Consumption per capita	.6,900 kWh (1996)

Transportation (19)

Highways: 129,055 km

paved: 129,055 km (including 1,607 km of expressways)

unpaved: 0 km (1996 est.)

Waterways: 356 km (1996)

Pipelines: crude oil 777 km; natural gas 909.1 km

Merchant marine:

total: 25 ships (1,000 GRT or over) totaling 84,103 GRT/114,616 DWT ships by type: bulk 1, cargo 19, combination bulk 2, container 1, refrigerated cargo 2 (1997 est.)

Airports: 55 (1997 est.)

Airports—with paved runways:

total: 20

over 3,047 m: 1

2,438 to 3,047 m: 5

1,524 to 2,437 m: 1

914 to 1,523 m: 3

under 914 m: 10 (1997 est.)

Airports—with unpaved runways:

total: 35

914 to 1,523 m: 4

under 914 m: 31 (1997 est.)

Top Agricultural Products (20)

Grains, potatoes, sugar beets, wine, fruit, dairy products; cattle, pigs, poultry; sawn wood.

MANUFACTURING SECTOR

GDP & Manufacturing Summary (21)

Detailed value added figures are listed by both International Standard Industry Code (ISIC) and product title.

	1980	1985	1990	1994
GDP ($-1990 mil.)[1]	127,712	136,332	158,427	172,084
Per capita ($-1990)[1]	16,918	18,038	20,562	21,733
Manufacturing share (%) (current prices)[1]	29.1	28.3	26.7	24.4
Manufacturing				
Value added ($-1990 mil.)[1]	32,106	34,533	40,785	42,856
Industrial production index	100	111	138	147
Value added ($ mil.)	15,949	13,394	31,318	33,721
Gross output ($ mil.)	48,872	41,230	90,474	96,296
Employment (000)	699	654	642	562
Profitability (% of gross output)				
Intermediate input (%)	67	68	65	65
Wages and salaries inc. supplements (%)	24	23	23	25
Gross operating surplus	9	10	11	10
Productivity ($)				
Gross output per worker	69,500	62,508	139,901	170,107
Value added per worker	22,681	20,307	48,427	61,797
Average wage (inc. supplements)	16,754	14,288	33,021	42,899
Value added ($ mil.)				
311/2 Food products	1,240	1,073	2,302	2,849
313 Beverages	454	368	841	1,166
314 Tobacco products	807	728	1,417	1,546
321 Textiles	852	623	1,291	1,279
322 Wearing apparel	447	303	547	449
323 Leather and fur products	51	37	82	82
324 Footwear	209	146	213	199
331 Wood and wood products	192	298	879	828
332 Furniture and fixtures	539	407	994	1,428
341 Paper and paper products	631	500	1,333	1,229
342 Printing and publishing	624	513	1,163	1,274
351 Industrial chemicals	638	555	1,277	1,176
352 Other chemical products	534	398	1,070	1,374
353 Petroleum refineries	80	72	489	492
354 Miscellaneous petroleum and coal products	32	24	65	65
355 Rubber products	230	168	311	326
356 Plastic products	281	215	545	768
361 Pottery, china and earthenware	63	42	112	121
362 Glass and glass products	235	229	518	606
369 Other non-metal mineral products	815	652	1,473	1,628
371 Iron and steel	1,223	1,051	2,088	1,570
372 Non-ferrous metals	280	241	434	378
381 Metal products	1,283	942	2,534	2,711
382 Non-electrical machinery	1,656	1,400	3,292	3,160
383 Electrical machinery	1,579	1,430	3,926	4,589
384 Transport equipment	709	743	1,652	1,858
385 Professional and scientific equipment	130	115	222	282
390 Other manufacturing industries	136	123	249	289

FINANCE, ECONOMICS, & TRADE

Economic Indicators (22)

National product: GDP—purchasing power parity—$174.1 billion (1997 est.)

National product real growth rate: 2.1% (1997 est.)

National product per capita: $21,400 (1997 est.)

Inflation rate—consumer price index: 1.3% (1997)

Exchange Rates (24)

Exchange rates:

Austrian schillings (AS) per US$1

January 1998	12.776
1997	12.204
1996	10.587
1995	10.081
1994	11.422
1993	11.632

Top Import Origins (25)

$67.3 billion (1996). Data are for 1996.

Origins	%
European Union	70.7
Germany	42.8
Italy	8.7
Eastern Europe	10
Japan	2.4
United States	4.5

Top Export Destinations (26)

$57.8 billion (1996). Data are for 1996.

Destinations	%
European Union	64.7%
Germany	37.7
Italy	8.5
Eastern Europe	14.9
Japan	1.5
United States	3.1

Economic Aid (27)

Donor: ODA, $480 million; assistance to central and eastern Europe $400 million. (1996).

Import Export Commodities (28)

Import Commodities	Export Commodities
Petroleum	Machinery and
Foodstuffs	equipment
Machinery and	Iron and steel
equipment	Lumber
Vehicles	Textiles
Chemicals	Paper products
Textiles and clothing	Chemicals US 3.1%
Pharmaceuticals US 4.5%	

Balance of Payments (23)

	1990	1992	1994	1995	1996
Exports of goods (f.o.b.)	40,414	43,929	44,645	55,826	55,915
Imports of goods (f.o.b.)	−47,383	−52,332	−53,373	−63,028	−63,701
Trade balance	−6,969	−8,403	−8,727	−7,203	−7,786
Services - debits	−24,284	−28,321	−30,384	−40,375	−43,606
Services - credits	32,424	37,628	37,957	44,961	48,386
Private transfers (net)	102	−493	−428	−368	−343
Government transfers (net)	−108	−490	−626	−1,856	−641
Overall balance	1,166	−79	−2,208	−4,841	−3,990

AZERBAIJAN

Azerbaijan Republic
Azarbaichan Respublikasy

INTRODUCTORY SURVEY

RECENT HISTORY

A part of ancient Albania, Azerbaijan was acquired by Russia from Persia in 1813 and 1828. Attempting independence in 1918, the Red Army conquered the country in 1920 and it was integrated into the communist Union of Soviet Socialist Republic (USSR). Azerbaijan was reestablished as a separate Soviet Republic in 1936. On August 30, 1991, Azerbaijan declared independence from the Soviet Union as it collapsed.

Azerbaijan and Armenia continue a feud over territory begun in 1983. The territory's residents are primarily Armenian Christians seeking to shed Islamic Azeri rule. War broke out in 1988, but the 1994 cease fire did not settle the issue.

Azerbaijan was not strong economically under communist rule, but expectations are that Western investment in oil resources will turn the economy around. The state oil company (SOCAR) has signed several billion-dollar agreements with international oil companies since 1994. Foreign investors are more interested in Azerbaijan than other oil-rich Caspian countries due to a pro-Western attitude and careful economic management.

The country has undergone rapid privatization since independence was declared. The IMF has given it high marks as one of the more successful economic overhauls. Azerbaijan's economic boon has been stalled to some degree due to negotiations over the construction of a pipeline required to move oil to western markets. An announcement of agree-

AZERBAIJAN

ments routing the pipeline to avoid Iraq and Iran was made in November 1999.

GOVERNMENT

Azerbaijan adopted its present constitution on 12 November 1995. Its system of government is based on a division of powers between a strong presidency, a legislature with the power to approve the budget and impeach the president, and a judiciary. The Soviet-era legislature has been replaced by a 125-member National Assembly. The country is divided into 11 cities, 59 regions, and one autonomous republic (Nakhichevan).

Judiciary

The 1995 constitution provides for a judiciary with limited independence. The court system includes district courts and municipal courts that hear cases for the first time, and a Supreme Court which hears appeals. Criminal defendants have the right to an attorney and to an appointed lawyer, the right to a public trial, the right to be present at trial, and the right to confront witnesses. Lower level judges are appointed directly by the president. Constitu-

tional Court and Supreme Court judges are also appointed by the president, with confirmation by parliament.

Political Parties

In March 1994, there were 22 political parties registered in Azerbaijan. The most important is probably the New Azerbaijan Party of President Heydar Aliev. The Azerbaijan Popular Front is the main opposition party. Two other opposition parties are the Milli Istiglal (National Independence Party) and the Musavat. There are also separatist parties advocating independence for three ethnic groups: the Armenians, the Talysh, and the Lezghins.

DEFENSE

As a member of the Commonwealth of Independent States (CIS), naval forces are under CIS (Russian) control. The navy has 2,200 personnel, the army has 57,300, and the air force has 11,200. Azerbaijan also has 40,000 people serving in two separate paramilitary units.

ECONOMIC AFFAIRS

Azerbaijan is one of the oldest oil-producing regions of the world. Remaining oil reserves are estimated at about 1 billion tons, and gas reserves at about 6 trillion cubic feet. Azerbaijan has varied industry and agriculture and a well-developed transport network. Like those of other post-Soviet republics, Azerbaijan's economy has been severely affected by the break-up of its traditional trading arrangements within the former Soviet Union, a steep drop in consumer buying power, and the decline in military-related industrial activity. Conflicts over the provinces of Nagorno-Karabakh and Nakhichevan have added to the republic's economic troubles. In 1994, Russia closed all rail service to Azerbaijan. Between 1991 and 1995, the economy declined by about 60%. Economic growth in the long term depends on developing the oil reserves in the Caspian Sea basin and implementing economic reforms.

Public Finance

The U.S. Central Intelligence Agency estimates that, in 1995, government revenues totaled approximately $465 million and expenditures $488 million. External debt totaled $100 million. The government has been working with the International Monetary Fund (IMF) to constrain state credit and consolidate control over the state budget.

In response, the parliament passed a restricted budget for 1996.

Income

In 1997, Azerbaijan's Gross Domestic Product (GDP) was estimated at $11.9 billion; per capita estimates were $1,460. Real growth rate was estimated at 5.8%, and inflation at 3.7%. Unemployment was estimated in 1996 at 20%.

Industry

The oil and gas industry has traditionally been important to the wider industrial sector in Azerbaijan. Total oil refinery output averaged 185,000 barrels per day in 1995. Output of residual fuels was 78,460 barrels per day in 1994; distillate, 46,660; and gasoline, 27,720. Other important industrial areas in the Azerbaijani economy include finished food products, metal goods, machine tools, chemicals and petrochemicals, and some electronics.

Banking and Finance

The National Bank of Azerbaijan is the central bank of Azerbaijan. The central bank is charged with regulating the money supply, circulating currency, and regulating the commercial banks of the country. The dual currency units are the manat and the ruble, although the government is shifting official currency to the manat. Commercial banks in Azerbaijan include: the Agricultural Bank (1988); the Bank for Industry and Construction (1899); and the International Bank (1992).

The manat is expected to maintain a new-found stability in 1997. As in 1996, government finances will benefit from external funds associated with oil deals. The budget deficit is estimated by the IMF to have fallen from around 11% of GDP in 1994 to 7% in 1995, and according to official statistics, is reported to have narrowed to some 2.9% of GDP in the first nine months of 1996.

Economic Development

Rapid development of the Azeri economy in the former USSR was based on the expansion of both its industrial sector, led by oil-related industries, and its agricultural sector, led by grape, tobacco, and cotton production. With grape and wine production weakened by the effects of Gorbachev's anti-alcoholism campaign in the 1980s, and much of the country's industrial sector afflicted by technological obsolescence, overall economic growth in the republic had already begun to decline by 1989, when NMP dropped 6%. Key strategies of the Azeri government to bring about economic revitalization have included both an economic restructuring program as well as efforts to expand its economic ties to countries beyond the former Soviet Union.

To the latter end, Azerbaijan joined the Economic Cooperation Organization set up by Iran, Pakistan, and Turkey to promote trade among Muslim countries. It was also the first of the former Soviet republics to become a member of the Islamic Development Bank, which provides potential access to financing for programs related to agriculture, construction, training, and food aid.

The restructuring program in Azerbaijan has been similar to those of other countries in the former USSR. Its main points include stabilization measures (price liberalization, introduction of national currency, and establishment of an exchange rate stabilization fund); introduction of new legislation regarding privatization, foreign investment, and employment; fiscal and monetary reform (including introduction of a value-added tax and controls on government expenditures); civil service reform; and development of the banking sector. Four committees on antitrust, support for enterprises, state property, and land reform have been established to oversee the implementation of reform legislation. Particular attention is being directed at modernizing those strategic sectors of the economy with the greatest potential for export growth, particularly the oil industry and, to a lesser extent, textile production; the role of foreign investment is seen as pivotal in these areas.

SOCIAL WELFARE

The minimum wage was raised several times in 1992, but it still does not provide adequately for a worker and family. A decent living can only be assured by the "safety net" of the extended family structure. Health and safety standards are often ignored in the workplace. Women have the same legal status as men.

Healthcare

Azerbaijan's infant mortality rate for 1994 was 25 per 1,000 live births. The overall death rate in 1993 was 7 per 1,000 inhabitants.

Housing

In 1990, Azerbaijan had 12.5 square meters of housing space per person. As of 1 January 1991, 138,000 households (or 15.6%) were on waiting lists for housing in urban areas.

EDUCATION

The educational system is extensive and illiteracy is practically unknown. In 1995, the adult illiteracy rate was estimated at 0.4% (males: 0.3%; females: 0.5%). The usual language of instruction is Azerbaijani, although Russian, Armenian, and Georgian are also offered by some schools.

There are two universities: the Azerbaijan Polytechnic Institute, located in Baku, has an enrollment of 12,000 students; the State University, also located at Baku, was founded in 1919. In 1994 there were 120,870 students enrolled in institutions of higher education.

1999 KEY EVENTS TIMELINE

January

- President Heidar Aliev is admitted to a Turkish hospital supposedly for treatment of bronchitis, but more serious health problems are suspected.

February

- The United States government announces that it foiled terrorist bomb plots against its embassies in seven countries, including Azerbaijan.

April

- A $4.5 billion offshore exploration deal with Exxon and Mobil is announced.

- Azeri president Heidar Aliev attends the NATO conference in Washington, D.C.

May

- The North Absheron exploration consortium led by BP and Amoco announces that it will close down operations.

June

- The Azeri government leaks news of a major new natural gas discovery.

July

- A U.S. Senate appropriations bill extends foreign-aid sanctions against Azerbaijan.

August

- The government announces plans to resume privatization auctions.

- Azerbaijan increases security along its border with Dagestan.

September

- The creation of an Azerbaijan stock exchange in 2000 is announced.

- The Azeri and Armenian presidents hold talks at Yalta.

- Azerbaijan frees remaining Armenian prisoners of war.

October

- President Heyder Aliyev travels to Turkey October 31 for a two-day visit to discuss the possible construction of a pipeline from Baku, the capital, to the Turkish port city of Cayhan.

November

- Russian officials are directed to begin talks with Georgia and Azerbaijan to implement a program requiring visas for travel into and out of the two countries to help keep dangerous militants from moving freely through the region.

- Azerbaijan, Turkey, and Georgia agree to cooperate to build an oil pipeline from Baku through Georgia to the Turkish port of Cayhan.

- Officials from Azerbaijan and Iran sign an extradition agreement in Baku, the capital.

December

- The first local elections since the breakup of the former Soviet Union in 1981 are held on December 12. Thirty-five thousand candidates run for twenty-one thousand local government offices.

ANALYSIS OF EVENTS: 1999

BUSINESS AND THE ECONOMY

As it approached its first decade of independence from the Union of Socialist Soviet Republics (USSR), the west Caspian Sea nation of Azerbaijan was betting that development of its oil reserves by Western European and U.S. petroleum companies would catapult it out of chronic underdevelopment and into the twenty-first century. Initial results in oil exploration during 1999, however, were disappointing. The failure of recent oil exploration ventures to discover major new oil reserves resulted in the dissolution of two international consortiums. In February the Caspian International Petroleum Company (CIPCO), led by Pennzoil, discontinued operations in the Karabakh region. This was followed in May by the BP Amoco-led North Absheron Operating Company (NAOC), which pulled up stakes in the Dan Ulduzu block northeast of the capital city of Baku. The interruption of these explorations idled a variety of professionals providing services to the consortia some of which left the country.

Discouragement with Azerbaijan's offshore exploration prospects was not universally shared. Some foreign oil companies stated their intentions of exploring in different regions. In April, while on a visit to the United States, President Heidar Aliev signed exploration contracts worth $4.5 billion with representatives of the Exxon and Mobil corporations to explore different offshore blocks in joint "production sharing arrangements" with the Azeri state-owned oil company, SOCAR. In addition to prospecting in untested deepwater areas, Azerbaijan sought foreign investment in five partially developed oil and gas fields with more predictable yields and total remaining reserves estimated at 450 million bbl of oil.

This optimistic view of the country's economic future was reflected in the words of a government spokesman who announced plans to establish the country's own stock exchange early in the year 2000. Thus far, Azerbaijan's securities market, founded in 1996, functioned mainly as a symbol of economic development and offered only government treasury bills. In addition to expanded securities trading, Azerbaijan also planned to launch a bond market after the stock exchange began operations.

GOVERNMENT AND POLITICS

Although aging and in declining health, Azerbaijan's longtime leader, 76-year-old President Heidar Aliev, retained a firm grasp on power, and the country's ruling party was advancing the prospect that Aliev's only son, Ilham, might succeed him in office, creating a political dynasty. In spite of the younger Aliev's evident lack of political aptitude or experience, observers deemed such a succession possible due to the lack of strong contenders to oppose him.

In the United States, the oil lobby once again attempted to end the seven-year ban on direct U.S. government aid to Azerbaijan under Section 907 of the Freedom Support Act. Enacted during the six-year conflict between Azerbaijan and Armenia over the status of the disputed Nagorno-Karabakh re-gion, the measure had been kept in place to avoid U.S. involvement in the continuing tensions in the region. Although the legislation allowed private U.S. investment in Azerbaijan, the U.S. oil industry had hoped that allowing a presidential repeal of the sanctions would result in closer ties between the two nations and improve access to Azerbaijan's substantial oil and gas resources. But in spite of lobbying efforts, and before it passed the Senate in July 1999, the Foreign Operations Appropriations bill was stripped of language allowing a presidential waiver of the sanctions.

Meanwhile, Azerbaijan and Armenia continued trying to resolve their long-standing dispute over Nagorno-Karabakh, which is located within Azerbaijan's borders but has a predominantly Armenian population. During a summit of Baltic and Black Sea political leaders held in Yalta in September 1999, President Aliev met with Armenia's president, Robert Kocharyan. The two leaders attempted to arrive at an agreement on the official status of the region. The Armenians wanted the region to be granted de facto independence, while the Azeris proposed making it an autonomous republic, basically the same designation accorded to it when it was part of the former Soviet Union. Although no new agreement was reached, the two leaders agreed to hold direct talks again in October at the Commonwealth of Independent States summit in Ukraine. In addition, each nation demonstrated its goodwill in September by releasing prisoners of war to the opposing side.

The continued threat of violence in the region was underscored by the U.S. State Department announcement early in the year that it had foiled a planned car-bomb attack on its embassy in Azerbaijan. Azeri security was also strengthened along the nation's border with the Russian province of Dagestan following hostilities between Russian soldiers and Islamic guerrilla forces.

CULTURE AND SOCIETY

As the decade drew to a close, President Heidar Aliev remained a dominating presence on the social and cultural landscape of his country through a deeply entrenched cult of personality. Pictures of the longtime leader abounded in both public and private places, and his name graced everything from buildings to mountaintops. Between April and September alone, two museums were named for him. Celebrations of Aliev's birthday, May 10th, extended up to the July festivities commemorating the 30th anniversary of his rise to power during the Communist era. During these celebrations the aging leader himself was actually out of the country, recuperating from heart surgery in the U.S., and his September return was lavishly feted.

In August Azerbaijan sent doctors and other aid workers to assist relief efforts in Turkey after that nation suffered an earthquake which killed thousands. The two nations share strong cultural and linguistic ties.

DIRECTORY

CENTRAL GOVERNMENT

Head of State

President
Heydar Aliyev, Office of the President, Ulitsa Levmontova 63, Baku, Azerbaijan
PHONE: +994 (12) 983365
FAX: +994 (12) 920625
E-MAIL: president@gov.az

Prime Minister
Artur Tairoghlu Rasizade, Office of the Prime Minister, Mermontov Str 68, 370066 Baku, Azerbaijan
PHONE: +994 (12) 983365

Ministers

Minister of Agriculture and Food
Irshad Aliyev, Ministry of Agriculture and Food, 4 Sh. Gurbanov, Baku, Azerbaijan
PHONE: +994 (12) 945355
FAX: +994 (12) 944334

Minister of Communications
Nadyr Akhmadov, Ministry of Communications, 33 Azerbaijan Avenue, Baku, Azerbaijan
PHONE: +994 (12) 930004
FAX: +994 (12) 934480

Minister of Culture
Polad Byul-Byul, Ministry of Culture, Government House, Baku, Azerbaijan
PHONE: +994 (12) 934398
FAX: +994 (12) 935605

Minister of Defense
Safar Abiyev, Ministry of Defense, 3 Azizbayov Avenue, Baku, Azerbaijan
PHONE: +994 (12) 929250
FAX: +994 (12) 980879

Minister of Economy
Namiq Nasrullayev, Ministry of Economy, Government House, Baku, Azerbaijan
PHONE: +994 (12) 936920
FAX: +994 (12) 932025

Minister of Education
Misir Mardanov, Ministry of Education, Government House, Baku, Azerbaijan
PHONE: +994 (12) 937266
FAX: +994 (12) 984207

Minister of Finance
Avaz Alekperov, Ministry of Finance, 6 S. Vurgun, Baku, Azerbaijan
PHONE: +994 (12) 933012
FAX: +994 (12) 987969

Minister of Foreign Affairs
Tofiq Zulfiqarov, Ministry of Foreign Affairs, 3 Gyanjlik Square, Baku, Azerbaijan
PHONE: +994 (12) 923401
FAX: +994 (12) 988480

Minister of Health
Ali Insanov, Ministry of Health

Minister of Internal Affairs
Ramil Usubov, Ministry of Internal Affairs, 7 H. Hajiyev, Baku, Azerbaijan
PHONE: +994 (12) 909222

Minister of Justice
Sudaba Hasanova, Ministry of Justice, 13 Bul-Bul Avenue, Baku, Azerbaijan
PHONE: +994 (12) 984941
FAX: +994 (12) 985931

Minister of Labor and Social Security
Ali Nagiyev, Ministry of Labor and Social Security, Government House, Baku, Azerbaijan
PHONE: +994 (12) 930542
FAX: +994 (12) 939472

Minister of Material Resources
Ministry of Material Resources, 83/23 Alekperov, Baku, Azerbaijan
PHONE: +994 (12) 394296
FAX: +994 (12) 399176

Minister of National Security
Namiq Abbasov, Ministry of National Security, 2 Parlamentsky Avenue, Baku, Azerbaijan
PHONE: +994 (12) 950491
FAX: +994 (12) 936296

Minister of Information and Press

Siruz Tabrizili, Ministsry of Information and Press, 12 A. Javad, Baku, Azerbaijan
PHONE: +994 (12) 926357
FAX: +994 (12) 929333

Minister of Public Health

Namiq Abbasov, Ministry of Public Health, 4 Kichic Sahil, Baku, Azerbaijan
PHONE: +994 (12) 932977
FAX: +994 (12) 934646

Minister of Trade

Namiq Abbasov, Ministry of Trade, 23 Niyazi, Baku, Azerbaijan
PHONE: +994 (12) 921531
FAX: +994 (12) 987431

Minister of Youth and Sports

Abulfaz Harayev, Ministry of Youth and Sports, 98a F. Khoisky Avenue, Baku, Azerbaijan
PHONE: +994 (12) 981426
FAX: +994 (12) 643650

POLITICAL ORGANIZATIONS

Yeni Azerbaijan Party

Uzeir Hacibekova 28, Baku, Azerbaijan
PHONE: +994 (12) 935488; 934276; 938254
TITLE: Chairman
NAME: Heydar Alirza oglu Aliev

Azerbaijan Xalq Cabhasi (Popular Front)

33 Khagani Street, Baku, Azerbaijan
PHONE: +994 (12) 980794
TITLE: Chairman
NAME: Abulfaz Elchibey

Azerbaijan Milli Istiglal-AMIP (National Independence Party)

179 Azadlyg Street, Baku, Azerbaijan
PHONE: +994 (12) 627576; 622917
TITLE: Chairman
NAME: Ehtibar Salidar oglu Mamedov

Musavat (Equality Party)

Prospect Azerbaijan, Baku, Azerbaijan
PHONE: +994 (12) 981870; 983163
TITLE: Chairman
NAME: Isa Gambar

Azerbaijan Democratic Party-ADIP

PHONE: +994 (12) 667971; 664059; 935741
TITLE: Chairman

NAME: Ilyas Ismailov

Yurddash (Compatriot Party)

Matbuat St., Azerbaijan Publishing House, Baku, Azerbaijan
PHONE: +994 (12) 321047; 323978
TITLE: Chairman
NAME: Mais Safarli

Ana Vatan (Motherland Party)

Mardanov Gardashlary St., 14, Baku, Azerbaijan
PHONE: +994 (12) 938297; 938539; 931345
TITLE: Chairman
NAME: Fazail Rahim oglu Agamanli

National Statehood Party

PHONE: +994 (12) 677174; 677054; 667524
TITLE: Chairman
NAME: Neymat Panahov

Vatandash Hamirali (Citizens' Solidarity Party)

4 H. Hajiev Street, Baku, Azerbaijan
PHONE: +994 (12) 935683
TITLE: Chairman
NAME: Sabir Rustamkhanli

Alliance for Azerbaijan

Prospect Azizbeyov, Baku, Azerbaijan
PHONE: +994 (12) 325453
TITLE: Chairman
NAME: Abutalib Samedov

Azerbaijan Communist Party

TITLE: Chairman
NAME: Firuddun Hasanov

Ehrar (Freedom Party)

24 Matbuat Avenue, Baku, Azerbaijan
PHONE: +994 (12) 395427; 755163; 2142620
TITLE: Chairman
NAME: Vagif M. Hadjibayli

Umid (Hope)

24 Matbuat Avenue, Baku, Azerbaijan
TITLE: Chairman
NAME: Huseyn Artikoglu

United Azerbaijan Party

Sabir Kazimov Street, Lenkoran, Azerbaijan
TITLE: Chairman

NAME: Hadjibaba Azimov

Demokratik Azerbaycan Dunyasi (Democratic Azerbaijan World Party)

73 Saint Petersburg Street, Baku, Azerbaijan
PHONE: +994 (12) 383297
TITLE: Chairman
NAME: Mammad Alizadeh

Azerbaijan Independence Party

1128 Kecid, Baku, Azerbaijan
PHONE: +994 (12) 393851; 394602
TITLE: Chairman
NAME: Nizami Suleimanov

Azerbaijan Islamic Party

14 Askerov Street, Baku, Azerbaijan
PHONE: +994 (12) 937261; 938946; 935465
TITLE: Chairman
NAME: Aliakram Ismail oglu Aliev

Labour Party

14 Askerov Street, Baku, Azerbaijan
TITLE: Chairman
NAME: Sabutay Mamedov

Vahdat Party

PHONE: +994 (12) 948937
TITLE: Chairman
NAME: Tahir Kerimli

Azerbaijan Milli Tarragi (National Progress Party)

Room 209, Government House, Baku, Azerbaijan
PHONE: +994 (12) 932727
TITLE: Chairman
NAME: Mammad Alizadeh

Azerbaijan Cagdas Turan (Modern Turan Party)

PHONE: +994 (12) 731679
TITLE: Chairman
NAME: Arif Islam oglu Tagiev

Azerbaijan National Movement Party

PHONE: +994 (12) 385696
TITLE: Chairman
NAME: Samir Jafarov

Milli Demokratik Idrak (National Democratic Will Party)

68 Tagizadeh Street, Baku, Azerbaijan
PHONE: +994 (12) 315031
TITLE: Chairman
NAME: Osman Efendiev

Azerbaijan Dircalis ve Tarragi (Renaissance and Progress Party)

1 Nakhchivan St., Apt. 23, Baku, Azerbaijan
PHONE: +994 (12) 387390; 621758
TITLE: Chairman
NAME: Azad Nabiev

Elin Sasi Party (People's Voice)

PHONE: +994 (12) 966984
TITLE: Chairman
NAME: Haji Xanahmad oglu Novruzov

Azerbaijan Hummet (Enlightenment Party)

Room 117, Government House, Baku, Azerbaijan
PHONE: +994 (12) 935309; 934967
TITLE: Chairman
NAME: Kuzasaf Zaman oglu Amirov

Azerbaijan Republican Party

161 Azadlyg Street, Baku, Azerbaijan
PHONE: +994 (12) 619819
TITLE: Chairman
NAME: Fargan Qanbar oglu Aliev

Azerbaijan National Equality Party

PHONE: +994 (12) 600521
TITLE: Chairman
NAME: Faxriddin Aydayev

DIPLOMATIC REPRESENTATION

Embassies in Azerbajan

China
Room 831 Azerbaijan Hotel, 1 Azadlig Prospect, Baku, Azerbaijan
PHONE: +994 (12) 989001; 989002; 989003
FAX: +994 (12) 980010

Egypt
Moscow Avenue 50, Baku, Azerbaijan
PHONE: +994 (12) 987906
FAX: +994 (12) 987954

France
R. Rza 7, Baku, Azerbaijan
PHONE: +994 (12) 928977
FAX: +994 (12) 928144

Georgia
Rooms 1323 and 1325, Azerbaijan Hotel, 1
Azadlig Prospect, Baku, Azerbaijan
PHONE: +994 (12) 939184; 989004
E-MAIL: emb@georgian.baku.az

Germany
15 Mamedaliyev Street, Baku, Azerbaijan
PHONE: +994 (12) 987918; 987819
FAX: +994 (12) 985419

Greece
Istiglaliyat 15, Baku, Azerbaijan
PHONE: +994 (12) 980811; 987813
FAX: +994 (12) 989184

Iran
4b Sardarov Street, Baku, Azerbaijan
PHONE: +994 (12) 921932
FAX: +994 (12) 926453

Iraq
9 Khagani Street, Baku, Azerbaijan
PHONE: +994 (12) 981447
FAX: +994 (12) 981437

Israel
1 Inshaatcilar Prospect, Baku, Azerbaijan
PHONE: +994 (12) 385282; 380519
FAX: +994 (12) 989283

Italy
44 Kichic Gala Kuchesi, Baku 370004,
Azerbaijan
PHONE: +994 (12) 975133; 975135; 975258
FAX: +994 (12) 975202; 975258
E-MAIL: ambbaku@azeuro.net

Kazakhstan
Inglab 82, Baku, Azerbaijan
PHONE: +994 (12) 906521; 906248
FAX: +994 (12) 906249

Libya
Azerbaijan Hotel, 1 Azadlig Prospect, Baku,
Azerbaijan
PHONE: +994 (12) 938548
FAX: +994 (12) 981247

Norway
40 Boyuk Gala Street, Baku, Azerbaijan
PHONE: +994 (12) 926601

Pakistan
Rooms 534 and 541 Azerbaijan Hotel, 1 Azadlig
Prospect, Baku, Azerbaijan
PHONE: +994 (12) 989004 ext. 534; 539; 541

Russia
Rooms 1102, 1104 and 1123 Azerbaijan Hotel, 1
Azadlig Prospect, Baku, Azerbaijan
PHONE: +994 (12) 989004
FAX: +994 (12) 986083
E-MAIL: embrus@embrus.baku.az

Slovakia
12 Mukhtarov Street, Apt. 17, Baku, Azerbaijan
PHONE: +994 (12) 920308
FAX: +994 (12) 923566

Sudan
60 Neftcilar Prospect, Baku, Azerbaijan
PHONE: +994 (12) 984361
FAX: +994 (12) 984897

Turkey
57 Khagani Street, Baku, Azerbaijan
PHONE: +994 (12) 988133; 988134; 988135
FAX: +994 (12) 98834

Ukraine
1 Azadlig prospekt 1, Baku, Azerbaijan
PHONE: +994 (12) 982742
FAX: +994 (12) 98276

United Kingdom
2 Izmir Street, Baku 370065, Azerbaijan
PHONE: +994 (12) 975188; 975189; 975190
FAX: +994 (12) 922739
E-MAIL: office@britemb.baku.az

United States
Azadlyg Avenue 83, Baku 370007, Azerbaijan
PHONE: +994 (12) 980335; 9803356
FAX: +994 (12) 983755; 906671

JUDICIAL SYSTEM
Supreme Court

FURTHER READING
Articles

"Aliev and Son." *The Economist* (March 6,
1999): 51.

"Baba of Baku." *The Economist* (September 11,
1999): 56.

Beckman, Jeremy. "Azerbaijan Courting
Investors for Rehabilitation of Five Fields."
Offshore (March 1999): 38.

"The Caspian's Black Holes." *The Economist* (March 13, 1999): 78.

Kronenwetter, Eric. "Senate Bill Keeps Unilateral Sanctions Against Azerbaijan in Place." *The Oil Daily* (July 7, 1999).

Books

Baddeley, John F. *The Russian Conquest of the Caucasus*. Richmond, U.K.: Curzon Press, 1999.

Carley, Patricia. *Nagorno-Karabakh: Searching for a Solution*. A United States Institute of Peace roundtable report. Washington, D.C.: U.S. Institute of Peace, 1998.

Hxiris, Ole, ed. *Contrasts and Solutions in the Caucasus*. Oakville, Conn.: Aarhus Univ. Press, 1998.

Leeuw, Charles van der. *Azerbaijan: A Quest for Identity*. New York: St. Martin's Press, 1998.

AZERBAIJAN: STATISTICAL DATA

For sources and notes see "Sources of Statistics" in the front of each volume.

GEOGRAPHY

Geography (1)

Area:

Total: 86,600 sq km.

Land: 86,100 sq km.

Water: 500 sq km.

Note: includes the exclave of Naxcivan Autonomous Republic and the Nagorno-Karabakh region; the region's autonomy was abolished by Azerbaijani Supreme Soviet on 26 November 1991.

Area—comparative: slightly smaller than Maine.

Land boundaries:

Total: 2,013 km.

Border countries: Armenia (with Azerbaijan-proper) 566 km, Armenia (with Azerbaijan-Naxcivan exclave) 221 km, Georgia 322 km, Iran (with Azerbaijan-proper) 432 km, Iran (with Azerbaijan- Naxcivan exclave) 179 km, Russia 284 km, Turkey 9 km.

Coastline: 0 km (landlocked).

Note: Azerbaijan borders the Caspian Sea (800 km, est.).

Climate: dry, semiarid steppe.

Terrain: large, flat Kur-Araz Lowland (much of it below sea level) with Great Caucasus Mountains to the north, Qarabag (Karabakh) Upland in west; Baku lies on Abseron (Apsheron) Peninsula that juts into Caspian Sea.

Natural resources: petroleum, natural gas, iron ore, nonferrous metals, alumina.

Land use:

Arable land: 18%

Permanent crops: 5%

Permanent pastures: 25%

Forests and woodland: 11%

Other: 41% (1993 est.).

HUMAN FACTORS

Demographics (2A)

	1990	1995	1998	2000	2010	2020	2030	2040	2050
Population	7,199.8	7,663.7	7,855.6	7,955.8	8,420.9	9,082.0	9,746.1	10,255.6	10,585.0
Net migration rate (per 1,000 population)	NA	NA	NA	NA	NA	NA	NA	NA	NA
Births	NA	NA	NA	NA	NA	NA	NA	NA	NA
Deaths	NA	NA	NA	NA	NA	NA	NA	NA	NA
Life expectancy - males	64.3	60.0	59.0	58.5	62.0	67.0	71.1	74.3	76.7
Life expectancy - females	72.8	68.5	67.8	67.4	70.2	74.7	78.2	81.0	83.1
Birth rate (per 1,000)	27.2	24.4	22.2	21.0	18.8	16.7	13.7	12.7	11.6
Death rate (per 1,000)	7.3	9.1	9.4	9.6	8.8	7.9	7.6	8.5	9.5
Women of reproductive age (15-49 yrs.)	1,823.9	1,986.5	2,081.0	2,141.6	2,351.2	2,377.6	2,491.4	2,469.6	2,347.6
of which are currently married	NA	NA	NA	NA	NA	NA	NA	NA	NA
Fertility rate	2.9	2.9	2.7	2.6	2.2	2.0	1.9	1.9	1.8

Except as noted, values for vital statistics are in thousands; life expectancy is in years.

Health Personnel (3)

Total health expenditure as a percentage of GDP, 1990-1997[a]

Public sector 1.1

Private sector 5.0

Total[b] 6.2

Health expenditure per capita in U.S. dollars, 1990-1997[a]

Purchasing power parity 92

Total 31

Availability of health care facilities per 100,000 people

Hospital beds 1990-1997[a] 990

Doctors 1993[c] 390

Nurses 1993[c] 1,081

Health Indicators (4)

Life expectancy at birth

1980 68

1997 71

Daily per capita supply of calories (1996) 2,139

Total fertility rate births per woman (1997) 2.1

Maternal mortality ratio per 100,000 live births (1990-97) . . . . .44[b]

Safe water % of population with access (1995) . . . .

Sanitation % of population with access (1995) 36

Consumption of iodized salt % of households (1992-98)[a] . . . .

Smoking prevalence

Male % of adults (1985-95)[a] . . . .

Female % of adults (1985-95)[a] . . . .

Tuberculosis incidence per 100,000 people (1997) 58

Adult HIV prevalence % of population ages 15-49 (1997) . . . .<0.005

Infants and Malnutrition (5)

Under-5 mortality rate (1997) 45

% of infants with low birthweight (1990-97) 6

Births attended by skilled health staff % of total[a] . . .99

% fully immunized (1995-97)

TB 94

DPT 95

Polio 98

Measles 97

Prevalence of child malnutrition under age 5 (1992-97)[b] 10

Ethnic Division (6)

Azeri 90%

Dagestani Peoples 3.2%

Russian 2.5%

Armenian 2.3%

Other 2%

Note: almost all Armenians live in the separatist Nagorno-Karabakh region. Data for 1995 est.

Religions (7)

Muslim 93.4%

Russian Orthodox 2.5%

Armenian Orthodox 2.3%

Other 1.8%

Note: Data for 1995. Religious affiliation is still nominal in Azerbaijan; actual practicing Adherents are much lower.

Languages (8)

Azeri 89%, Russian 3%, Armenian 2%, other 6% (1995 est.)

EDUCATION

Public Education Expenditures (9)

Public expenditure on education (% of GNP)

1980 . . . .

1996 . . . . .3.3

Expenditure per student

Primary % of GNP per capita

1980 . . . .

1996 . . . . .16.9[1]

Secondary % of GNP per capita

1980 . . . .

1996 . . . .

Tertiary % of GNP per capita

1980 . . . .

1996 . . . . .14.9

Expenditure on teaching materials

Primary % of total for level (1996) . . . .

Secondary % of total for level (1996) . . . .

Primary pupil-teacher ratio per teacher (1996) . . . . .21[1]

Duration of primary education years (1995) 4

Literacy Rates (11B)

Adult literacy rate

1980

Male . . . . -

Female . . . . -

1995

Male 100

Female 99

GOVERNMENT & LAW

Political Parties (12)

National Assembly	No. of seats
New Azerbaijan Party (YAP) and allies	.115
Azerbaijan Popular Front (AXC)	.4
Party for National Independence of Azerbaijan (AMIP)	.3
Musavat Party (YMP)	.1
Vacant	.2

Government Budget (13B)

Revenues . . . .$565 million
Expenditures . . . .$682 million
  Capital expenditures . . . . .NA

Data for 1996 est. NA stands for not available.

Military Affairs (14B)

	1992	1993	1994	1995
Military expenditures				
Current dollars (mil.)	208	540	257	304
1995 constant dollars (mil.)	224	566	263	304
Armed forces (000)	13	63	50	87
Gross national product (GNP)				
Current dollars (mil.)	18,380	16,580	12,850	10,960
1995 constant dollars (mil.)	19,770	17,380	13,170	10,960
Central government expenditures (CGE)				
1995 constant dollars (mil.)	5,952	NA	NA	NA
People (mil.)	7.4	7.5	7.6	7.6
Military expenditure as % of GNP	1.1	3.3	2.0	2.8
Military expenditure as % of CGE	3.8	NA	NA	NA
Military expenditure per capita (1995 $)	30	76	35	40
Armed forces per 1,000 people (soldiers)	5.7	8.4	6.6	11.4
GNP per capita (1995 $)	2,669	2,323	1,745	1,440
Arms imports[6]				
Current dollars (mil.)	0	10	60	0
1995 constant dollars (mil.)	0	10	62	0
Arms exports[6]				
Current dollars (mil.)	0	0	0	0
1995 constant dollars (mil.)	0	0	0	0
Total imports[7]				
Current dollars (mil.)	875	490	781	682[e]
1995 constant dollars (mil.)	941	514	801	682[e]
Total exports[7]				
Current dollars (mil.)	1,284	626	621	550
1995 constant dollars (mil.)	1,381	656	637	550
Arms as percent of total imports[8]	0.0	2.0	7.7	0
Arms as percent of total exports[8]	0.0	0	0	0

Crime (15)

Crime rate (for 1997)
  Crimes reported 16,400
  Total persons convicted 15,000
  Crimes per 100,000 population 225
Persons responsible for offenses
  Total number of suspects 15,400
  Total number of female suspects 1,350
  Total number of juvenile suspects 700

LABOR FORCE

Labor Force (16)

Total (million) 2.789
Agriculture and forestry .32%
Industry and construction 26%
Other 42%

Data for 1990.

Unemployment Rate (17)

20% (1996 est.)

PRODUCTION SECTOR

Electric Energy (18)

Capacity . . . . .5.239 million kW (1995)

Production . . . . .16.051 billion kWh (1995)

Consumption per capita . . . . . . .2,200 kWh (1996 est.)

Transportation (19)

Highways:

total: 57,770 km

paved: 54,188 km

unpaved: 3,582 km (1995 est.)

Pipelines: crude oil 1,130 km; petroleum products 630 km; natural gas 1,240 km

Airports: 69 (1996 est.)

Airports—with paved runways:

total: 29

over 3,047 m: 2

2,438 to 3,047 m: 6

1,524 to 2,437 m: 17

914 to 1,523 m: 3

under 914 m: 1 (1996 est.)

Airports—with unpaved runways:

total: 40

914 to 1,523 m: 7

under 914 m: 33 (1996 est.)

Top Agricultural Products (20)

Cotton, grain, rice, grapes, fruit, vegetables, tea, tobacco; cattle, pigs, sheep, goats.

FINANCE, ECONOMICS, & TRADE

Economic Indicators (22)

National product: GDP—purchasing power parity— $11.9 billion (1997 est.)

National product real growth rate: 5.8% (1997 est.)

National product per capita: $1,460 (1997 est.)

Inflation rate—consumer price index: 3.7% (1997 est.)

Exchange Rates (24)

Exchange rates:

Manats per US$1

September 1997 . . . . .3,936.00

1996 . . . . .4,301.26

1995 . . . . .4,413.54

1994 . . . . .1,570.23

1993 . . . . .99.98

Top Import Origins (25)

$1.3 billion (c.i.f., 1996 est.).

Origins	%
CIS	NA
European countries	NA
Turkey	NA

NA stands for not available.

MANUFACTURING SECTOR

GDP & Manufacturing Summary (21)

	1980	1985	1990	1992	1993	1994
Gross Domestic Product						
Millions of 1990 dollars	7,470	10,051	9,740	5,439	4,732	3,696
Growth rate in percent	10.13	4.61	−9.79	−35.20	−13.00	−21.90
Per capita (in 1990 dollars)	1,213.2	1,509.3	1,368.5	745.5	640.9	494.6
Manufacturing Value Added						
Millions of 1990 dollars	NA	NA	1,657	1,750	*1,356*	*1,017*
Growth rate in percent	NA	NA	NA	−4.35	−22.50	−24.98
Manufacturing share in percent of current prices	21.5	20.5	*17.0*	*27.5*	*22.5*	*22.5*

FINANCE, ECONOMICS, & TRADE

Top Export Destinations (26)

$789 million (f.o.b., 1996 est.).

Destinations	%
CIS	NA
European countries	NA
Turkey	NA

NA stands for not available.

Economic Aid (27)

Recipient: ODA, $14 million (1993). Note: commitments, 1992-95, $1,000 million ($185 million in disbursements); wheat from Turkey.

Import Export Commodities (28)

Import Commodities	Export Commodities
Machinery and parts	Oil and gas
Consumer durables	Chemicals
Foodstuffs	Oilfield equipment
Textiles	Textiles
	Cotton

BAHAMAS

Commonwealth of the Bahamas

INTRODUCTORY SURVEY

RECENT HISTORY

The Bahamas held Arawak Indians until discovered by Christopher Columbus in 1492. The English first established settlements on the islands in the 17th century. From 1717 until 1964, the islands were a British Crown Colony. Internal self-government was granted in 1964 and a new constitution established in 1969.

Although the Bahamas joined the British Commonwealth in just 1969, they became an independent nation on July 10, 1973.

Subject to south Atlantic and Caribbean hurricanes, the islands were severely damaged by Hurricane Floyd in September 1999.

GOVERNMENT

The Bahamas has a republican form of government, formally headed by the British sovereign, who is represented by a governor-general. A prime minister and a cabinet have executive authority. The two-chamber legislature consists of a 16-member Senate appointed by the governor-general and an elected 49-member House of Assembly. The prime minister is the leader of the majority party in the House.

Judiciary

The legal system is based upon English common law. The highest court is the Court of Appeal, consisting of three judges. Ultimate appeals go to the Privy Council of the UK. Lower courts include three magistrates' courts on New Providence and

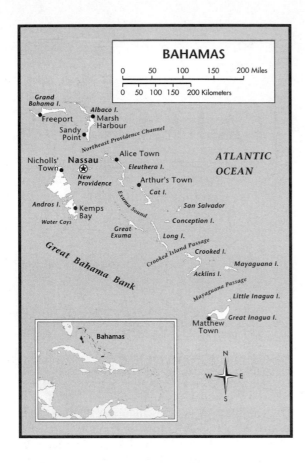

BAHAMAS

0   50   100   150   200 Miles

0   50 100 150 200 Kilometers

Grand Bahama I.
Freeport • Albaco I.
• Marsh Harbour
Sandy Point •
Northeast Providence Channel
Alice Town •
Nicholls' Town •
Nassau ⊛
New Providence
Eleuthera I.
Arthur's Town •
Cat I.
ATLANTIC OCEAN
Andros I. • Kemps Bay
Water Cays
Exuma Sound
San Salvador
Conception I.
Great Exuma
Long I.
Crooked Island Passage
Crooked I.
Great Bahama Bank
Acklins I.
Mayaguana I.
Mayaguana Passage
Little Inagua I.
Matthew Town
Great Inagua I.

Bahamas

N / W / E / S

cline which began in 1990, due to the U.S. recession and competition from other Caribbean nations.

Public Finance

The U.S. Central Intelligence Agency estimates that, in 1995, government revenues totaled approximately $665 million and expenditures $725 million, including capital expenditures of $94 million. External debt totaled $408 million, approximately 10% of which was financed abroad.

Income

In 1997, Bahamas' Gross Domestic Product (GDP) was estimated at $5.36 billion, with the per capita figure at $19,400. Real growth in 1997 was estimated at 3.5%, and inflation at 0.4%. Unemployment in 1997 was 10%.

Industry

Refined petroleum, cement, and rum production are important, and enterprises producing pharmaceuticals and steel pipe have been developed. Heineken, Europe's largest beer company, constructed a brewery in Nassau in 1985 with an annual production capacity of 1.2 million cases of beer.

Banking and Finance

Banking started in the Bahamas in 1837, when the first commercial bank opened in New Providence. The Central Bank of the Bahamas, established in 1973, is the central issuing and regulatory authority. Funds for local development are made available through the Bahamas Development Bank.

Low taxation and lenient regulations have encouraged the establishment of about 400 financial institutions in the country. As of 1993 there were 274 domestic and foreign institutions, allowed to deal with both residents and nonresidents; the remainder were offshore banks, dealing exclusively with nonresidents. Many of the loans of domestic banks are denominated in foreign currency. According to Central Bank data, accelerating economic activity led commercial banks to reduce their holdings of short-term government paper in the third quarter of 1996, in favor of increased lending to the private sector. As a result, the commercial banks' excess liquid assets ratio and overall bank liquidity fell. Increased competition to attract new loans reduced the interest rate spread.

There is no securities exchange in the Bahamas, but trading in both foreign securities and currencies is permitted under the authority of the Central Bank.

one on Freeport. Police abuse of suspects has been a serious problem. In 1993, a coroner's court was established to investigate cases in which criminal suspects die while in police custody.

Political Parties

The Progressive Liberal Party (PLP) emerged as the Bahamas' majority party in the early 1970s. The Free Progressive Liberal Party, a splinter group formed in 1970, merged with another opposition group, the United Bahamian Party, to form the Free National Movement (FNM). After years of loyal opposition, the FNM took power in 1992, winning 32 seats, compared to 17 for the PLP.

DEFENSE

Defense of the islands is the responsibility of the United Kingdom. The Royal Bahamas Defense Force of 700 sailors is responsible for external security. Defense expenditures were $19 million in 1995.

ECONOMIC AFFAIRS

Tourism, the mainstay of the economy, directly or indirectly involves most of the population. Tourism in the Bahamas is recovering from a de-

Economic Development

The promotion of tourism and financial activity by foreign firms continues as a basic tenet of the Bahamas government. Since the late 1960s, increased emphasis has been focused on development of local industry, with the liberal tax structure remaining the key incentive. In 1976, the government began a series of measures to foster greater participation by Bahamians in the economy. The new ruling included increased working-permit fees for foreigners and sharp rises in property-transfer taxes and business licensing for non-Bahamians. Since late 1979, government permission has been required for the sale of land to non-Bahamians. The Bahamas Development Bank helps provide financing for non-Bahamian entrepreneurs. The government is attempting to diversify the economy and attract new industry, as well as to conserve and develop the country's 800,000 acres of forest to build a lumber industry.

A number of policy measures were introduced that will have repercussions in the Bahamian economy. First, a change took effect on 1 July 1996 that modified the customs coding system. At the same time, the number of rates were reduced from 123 to 29, and the rates themselves were lowered as well. Second, at a time when private sector activities are up, the government awarded increases in public sector wages across the board. Third, a minimum public sector wage policy was implemented. Fourth, all temporary civil service workers with at least 5 years of continuous service were made permanent. Most of the additional wage costs, although implemented in 1996, would not fully impact the government budget until 1997 and beyond.

SOCIAL WELFARE

Workers' compensation and retirement, maternity, survivors', and funeral benefits are provided. Bahamian women are well represented in business, the professions, and government.

Healthcare

The government operates the 478-bed Princess Margaret Hospital in Nassau and 4 other hospitals. In 1993 there were 800 persons per physician and 200 patients per hospital bed. Average life expectancy in 1994 was 74 years. The country is free from tropical diseases.

Housing

Overcrowding is a problem on New Providence, and decent low-cost housing is in short supply. The Bahamas Housing Authority was established in 1983 to develop housing for low-income people.

EDUCATION

Government expenditure on education in 1994 amounted to 3.9% of the GNP. Education is compulsory for children aged 5 to 14. In 1993, 115 primary schools enrolled 33,343 pupils. Secondary schools enrolled 28,532 students that year. Higher education is provided by the College of the Bahamas, with an enrollment of about 2,050 students. Over 98% of Bahamians are reported literate.

1999 KEY EVENTS TIMELINE

January

- The attorneys general from twelve Caribbean nations, including the Bahamas, recommend that their governments withdraw from human rights pacts (of the Inter-American Human Rights Convention and the U.N. Treaty on Civil and Political Rights) that they say delay executions.

- A high-speed ferry between Florida and Nassau begins service.

March

- The new session of parliament opens with a speech by the Governor General; the focus is on prosperity in the islands.

- Tourism officials estimate that Nassau and Paradise Island have a total inventory of 8,005 hotel rooms.

- TWA, Delta, British Airways, and other carriers expand service to the Bahamas.

June

- Dairy Queen announces a licensing agreement with independent businessmen to develop stores in the Bahamas; the first two restaurants are slated to open in July.

August

- The Grand Bahamas Port Authority joins with the German shipyard company Lloyd Werft to build a ship repair depot in Freeport; it will be capable of servicing the world's largest cruise and cargo vessels.

- Bahamian finance officials announce the late-1999 launch of the island chain's first stock exchange. The Bahamas International Securities Exchange will open in two phases.

- The Bahamian government announces plans to sell 49 percent of BaTelCo, Bahamas Telecommunications Corp., on the Bahamas International Securities Exchange.

- Hurricane Dennis hits the Bahamas (August 28) with sustained winds near 100 mph.

- Bahamian field and track athletes claim a gold medal at the World Athletics Championships.

September

- Bahamian government representatives defend their country's taxation policies in the face of international criticism.

- Category-4 Hurricane Floyd hits the northern and central islands of the Bahamas on September 14. The Abacos, Eleuthra, and Grand Bahama see severe damage.

- Bahamian police and immigration authorities search for 47 Cuban immigrants who broke out of Nassau's main prison; the fugitives were transferred to that site for safety reasons in preparation for Hurricane Floyd; seventeen escapees are recaptured.

October

- Officials announce that Hurricane Floyd cost the islands $70 million in tourism, accounting for less than 5 percent of the total revenue expected to be generated by island visitors this year.

- Hurricane Irene drenches the Bahamas with heavy rains.

- A high-speed ferry, which will shuttle passengers between Nassau and Harbour Island begins service.

- Hilton International opens its first hotel in the Bahamas; the British Colonial Hilton is located in Nassau.

ANALYSIS OF EVENTS: 1999

BUSINESS AND THE ECONOMY

The year 1999 was a good one for Bahamian tourism despite the fact that Hurricane Floyd lashed the northern islands (in October). Transportation to and among the islands was upgraded. A high-speed ferry between Port of Miami (Florida) and Nassau began making daily runs. Another high-speed ferry, which shuttles passengers between the islands of the Bahamas, began service. The $5.2-million catamaran can carry up to 177 people and makes twice-daily trips from Nassau to Harbour Island and nearby Eleuthra. The inter-island transport takes about two hours and costs slightly less than flying, making it an attractive option for tourists. Several air carriers, including TWA, Delta, and British Airways, expanded service to the islands; tourism officials claimed the 25 percent increase in airline capacity mirrors the increase in hotel space, supporting the islands' "ongoing tourism renaissance." The improvements are aimed at making it easier to get to and from the country's 700 islands. In the tourist meccas of Nassau and Paradise Island, Bahamian officials estimate the total inventory of hotel rooms was 8,005 as of March—an increase of 26 percent over the previous year.

Ship operators are expected to benefit from a joint project between Grand Bahamas Port Authority and German shipyard company Lloyd Werft; together they plan to build a $75-million ship repair depot in Freeport. The facility, adjacent to a new container port, will be capable of servicing the world's largest cruise and cargo vessels, reducing turnaround time for ship operators that are currently sending their vessels to U.S. coastal facilities. The first repair dock of the facility was expected to be in place by 2000.

While category-4 Hurricane Floyd caused great destruction in the Abacos and Eleuthra, the other islands in the archipelago did not see significant damage, allowing most hotels to resume normal operations within days of the storm. Sizing up the cost to tourism, which accounts for roughly half the nation's Gross Domestic Product and employs half its workers, officials estimated the hurricane put a dent of $70 million in the $1.4 billion expected to be generated by island visitors during the year. The Ministry of Tourism, anticipating robust growth, projected stopover visitors will spend $2 billion in the Bahamas in 2000.

Bahamian finance officials announced the late-1999 launch of the island chain's first stock exchange. The Bahamas International Securities Exchange was slated to open in two phases; domestic stocks (from about 20 companies listing an estimated $30 billion in shares) will be followed in 2000 by international offerings. In preparation for the stock exchange, which is part of the Bahamian government's plan to grab a bigger share of the global financial services industry, fraud and money laundering laws were tightened and securities and mutual fund regulations were overhauled.

GOVERNMENT AND POLITICS

The attorneys general from 12 Caribbean nations, including the Bahamas, recommended that their governments withdraw from human rights pacts (of the Inter-American Human Rights Convention and the U.N. Treaty on Civil and Political Rights), which they claim delay executions. The announcement was in response to pressure from Britain, which has been urging its former colonies to eliminate the death penalty. With some 250 people on death row in 1999, English-speaking nations of the Caribbean had one of the highest combined death sentence rates in the world. But most Caribbean nations view execution as an important deterrent to would-be drug traffickers and other criminals.

At the opening of parliament (March 17), the Governor General of the Bahamas, Sir Orville Turnquest, stated that during the late 1990s domestic and foreign investments combined to produce economic growth exceeding four percent annually, unemployment was reduced to single digits, an overall increase in household incomes was seen, and low inflation was realized. He hailed tourism and financial services as the "bulwarks of our economy."

Bahamian government representatives defended their country's taxation policies in the face of international criticism; an OECD (Paris) report criticized the archipelago, calling it a "harmful tax haven" since the Bahamian government does not tax income or capital.

Government recovery efforts in the wake of Hurricane Floyd included special assistance for the elderly and indigent; 200 Royal Bahamas Defense Force troops and boats filled with food and medical supplies were dispatched to the northern islands, which suffered the brunt of the storm's fury.

CULTURE AND SOCIETY

The Bahamian population was affected by several tropical storms. Hurricane Dennis hit the islands (August 28) with sustained winds near 100 mph, heavy rains, and pounding surf; trees were damaged, water supplies cut off, and telephone and electrical lines downed by the storm. Two weeks later Hurricane Floyd hit the northern and central islands of the Bahamas. The powerful storm, estimated to have covered a territory roughly the size of Texas and one of the strongest storms ever recorded in the Atlantic, wrought considerable damage to the Abacos, Eleuthra, and Grand Bahama, which were left without drinking water, telephone service, and power. One death was reported. In the northern islands, beaches, homes, and an entire village were wiped out by the storm, which also ravaged banana crops, killed more than a million chickens, and caused losses for the crawfish industry. While the Freeport International Airport was closed during the storm, the heavily visited areas of the Bahamas received only moderate damage. In October, with some areas still recovering from Floyd, Hurricane Irene drenched the islands with heavy rains, and claimed four lives.

Bahamian track and field athletes competing at the World Athletics Championships in Seville, Spain, claimed a surprise win in the women's 4x100 meters relay. The gold medalists set a year's best record of 41.92 seconds.

DIRECTORY

CENTRAL GOVERNMENT

Head of State

Monarch
Elizabeth II, Queen of England

Governor-General
Sir Orville Turnquest

Prime Minister
Hubert Alexander Ingraham, Office of the Prime Minister, Cecil Wallace Whitfield Centre, West Bay St, PO Box CB-10980, Nassau, New Providence, Bahamas
PHONE: +(809) 3275826
FAX: +(809) 3275806

Ministers

Minister of Foreign Affairs
Janet Bostwick, Ministry of Foreign Affairs, PO Box N-3746, Nassau, Bahamas
PHONE: +(809) 3227624
FAX: +(809) 3288212

Minister of Agriculture and Fisheries
Earl Deveaux, Ministry of Agriculture and
Fisheries, Levy Building, East Bay St., Nassau,
Bahamas
PHONE: +(809) 3257502
FAX: +(809) 3251767

Minister of Consumer Welfare and Aviation
Pierre Dupuch, Ministry of Consumer Welfare
and Aviation, Commission of Inquiry Building,
Thompson Blvd, Oakfield, Nassau, Bahamas
PHONE: +(809) 3264550
FAX: +(809) 3281160

Minister of Education
Ivy L. Dumont, Ministry of Education, Shirley
St., Nassau, Bahamas
PHONE: +(809) 225495
FAX: +(809) 3226327

Minister of Youth, Sports, and Culture
Ivy L. Dumont, Ministry of Youth, Sports, and
Culture, Gold Circle House, East Bay St.,
Nassau, Bahamas

Minister of Finance and Planning
William Allen, Ministry of Finance and
Planning, Sir Cecil V Wallace Whitfield Centre,
West Bay St., Nassau, Bahamas
PHONE: +(809) 3271530
FAX: +(809) 3271618

Minister of Economic Development
William Allen, Ministry of Economic
Development, Cecil V Wallace Whitfield Centre,
West Bay St., Nassau, Bahamas

Minister of Health and the Environment
Ronald Knowles, Ministry of Health and the
Environment, Ministry of Health Building, Royal
Victoria Gardens, Shirley St., Nassau, Bahamas
PHONE: +(809) 3227425
FAX: +(809) 3227788

Minister of Housing and Social Development
Algernon Allen, Ministry of Housing and Social
Development, Frederick House, Frederick St.,
Nassau, Bahamas
PHONE: +(809) 3560765; 3560766
FAX: +(809) 3233883

Minister of Justice
Tebbyson Wells, Ministry of Justice, Post Office
Building, East Hill St., Nassau, Bahamas

Minister of Labor, Immigration, and Training
Theresa Moxey-Ingraham, Ministry of Labor,
Immigration, and Training, Post Office Building,
East Hill St., Nassau, Bahamas

PHONE: +(809) 3226250
FAX: +(809) 3226546

Minister of Public Works
Tommy Turnquest, Ministry of Public Works,
Ministry of Works Building, John F. Kennedy
Dr., Nassau, Bahamas
PHONE: +(809) 3237240
FAX: +(809) 3267344

Minister of Tourism
Cornelius A. Smith, Ministry of Tourism,
Market Plaza, Bay St., Nassau, Bahamas
PHONE: +(809) 3227500
FAX: +(809) 3224041

Minister of Transport
James Knowles, Ministry of Transport, Post
Office Building, East Hill St., Nassau, Bahamas
PHONE: +(809) 3237814
FAX: +(809) 3252016

POLITICAL ORGANIZATIONS

Progressive Liberal Party-PLP

Farrington Rd., PO Box N-547, Nassau,
Bahamas
PHONE: +(809) 3252900; 3269668
NAME: Perry Christie

Free National Movement-FNM

#144 Mackey St., PO Box N-10713, Nassau,
Bahamas
PHONE: +(809) 3937853; 3937863
FAX: +(809) 3937914
TITLE: Leader
NAME: Hubert Alexander Ingraham

Bahaman Freedom Alliance

Wulff Road, PO Box CB-12412, Nassau,
Bahamas
PHONE: +(809) 3242948; 3560423
FAX: +(809) 3560423
TITLE: Leader
NAME: Holston Moultry

Survivors Party

Jasmine Drive High Vista, PO Box N-1703,
Nassau, Bahamas
PHONE: +(809) 3266191; 3242580
TITLE: Leader
NAME: Kenneth Taylor

DIPLOMATIC REPRESENTATION

Embassies in the Bahamas

Antigua and Barbuda
c/o The Ministry of Foreign Affairs, PO Box N-3746, Nassau, Bahamas
PHONE: +(809) 3227624; 3227625
TITLE: High Commissioner
NAME: A. Leonard Archer

Argentina
c/o The Ministry of Foreign Affairs, PO Box N-3746, Nassau, Bahamas
PHONE: +(809) 3227624; 3227625
TITLE: Ambassador
NAME: Geoffrey Johnstone

Barbados
c/o The Ministry of Foreign Affairs, PO Box N-3746, Nassau, Bahamas
PHONE: +(809) 3227624; 3227625
TITLE: High Commissioner
NAME: A. Leonard Archer

Belize
c/o The Ministry of Foreign Affairs, PO Box N-3746, Nassau, Bahamas
PHONE: +(809) 3227624; 3227625
TITLE: High Commissioner
NAME: A. Leonard Archer

Brazil
c/o The Ministry of Foreign Affairs, PO Box N-3746, Nassau, Bahamas
PHONE: +(809) 3227624; 3227625
TITLE: Ambassador
NAME: Geoffrey Johnstone

Chile
c/o The Ministry of Foreign Affairs, PO Box N-3746, Nassau, Bahamas
PHONE: +(809) 3227624; 3227625
TITLE: Ambassador
NAME: Geoffrey Johnstone

China
Sandyport, PO Box CB-13500, Nassau, Bahamas
PHONE: +(809) 3275206
TITLE: Ambassador
NAME: Ma Shuxue

Costa Rica
c/o The Ministry of Foreign Affairs, PO Box N-3746, Nassau, Bahamas
PHONE: +(809) 3227624; 3227625
TITLE: Ambassador Designate
NAME: Peter Galanos

Cuba
c/o The Ministry of Foreign Affairs, PO Box N-3746, Nassau, Bahamas
PHONE: +(809) 322-7624; 3227625
TITLE: Ambasador
NAME: Davidson L Hepburn

Dominica
c/o The Ministry of Foreign Affairs, PO Box N-3746, Nassau, Bahamas
PHONE: +(809) 3227624; 3227625
TITLE: High Commissioner
NAME: A. Leonard Archer

The Gambia
Coral Harbour, PO Box N-8851, Nassau, Bahamas
PHONE: +(809) 3621145; 3621262
TITLE: Consul-General
NAME: Irving Gould

Grenada
c/o The Ministry of Foreign Affairs, PO Box N-3746, Nassau, Bahamas
PHONE: +(809) 3227624; 3227625
TITLE: High Commissioner
NAME: A. Leonard Archer

Guatemala
c/o The Ministry of Foreign Affairs, PO Box N-3746, Nassau, Bahamas
PHONE: +(809) 3227624; 3227625
TITLE: Ambassador Designate
NAME: Peter Galanos

Guyana
c/o The Ministry of Foreign Affairs, PO Box N-3746, Nassau, Bahamas
PHONE: +(809) 322-7624; 3227625
TITLE: High Commissioner
NAME: A. Leonard Archer

Haiti
Roberts Building, Room 203, East and Bay Sts., PO Box N-666, Nassau, Bahamas
PHONE: +(809) 3260325
TITLE: Consul-General
NAME: Joseph J'Étienne

Honduras
c/o The Ministry of Foreign Affairs, PO Box N-3746, Nassau, Bahamas
PHONE: +(809) 3227624; 3227625
TITLE: Ambassador Designate
NAME: Peter Galanos

Jamaica

c/o The Ministry of Forcign Affairs, PO Box N-3746, Nassau, Bahamas
PHONE: +(809) 3227624; 3227625
TITLE: High Commissioner
NAME: A. Leonard Archer

Japan

c/o The Ministry of Foreign Affairs, PO Box N-3746, Nassau, Bahamas
PHONE: +(809) 3227624; 3227625
TITLE: Ambassador
NAME: Sidney Poitier

Nicaragua

c/o The Ministry of Foreign Affairs, PO Box N-3746, Nassau, Bahamas
PHONE: +(809) 3227624; 3227625
TITLE: Ambassador Designate
NAME: Peter Galanos

Panama

c/o The Ministry of Foreign Affairs, PO Box N-3746, Nassau, Bahamas
PHONE: +(809) 3227624; 3227625
TITLE: Ambassador Designate
NAME: Peter Galanos

St. Kitts and Nevis

c/o The Ministry of Foreign Affairs, PO Box N-3746, Nassau, Bahamas
PHONE: +(809) 3227624; 3227625
TITLE: High Commissioner
NAME: A. Leonard Archer

St. Lucia

c/o The Ministry of Foreign Affairs, PO Box N-3746, Nassau, Bahamas
PHONE: +(809) 3227624; 3227625
TITLE: High Commissioner
NAME: A. Leonard Archer

St. Vincent and the Grenadines

c/o The Ministry of Foreign Affairs, PO Box N-3746, Nassau, Bahamas
PHONE: +(809) 3227624; 3227625
TITLE: High Commissioner
NAME: A. Leonard Archer

Suriname

c/o The Ministry of Foreign Affairs, PO Box N-3746, Nassau, Bahamas
PHONE: +(809) 3227624; 3227625
TITLE: High Commissioner
NAME: A. Leonard Archer

Trinidad

c/o The Ministry of Foreign Affairs, PO Box N-3746, Nassau, Bahamas
PHONE: +(809) 3227624; 3227625
TITLE: High Commissioner
NAME: A. Leonard Archer

United Kingdom

Ansbacher House, 3rd Floor, East St., PO Box N-7516, Nassau, Bahamas
PHONE: +(809) 3257471
TITLE: High Commissioner
NAME: Peter Heigel

United States

Queen St., PO Box N-8197, Nassau, Bahamas
PHONE: +(809) 3221181
FAX: +(809) 3560222
TITLE: Ambassador
NAME: Sidney Williams

Uruguay

c/o The Ministry of Foreign Affairs, PO Box N-3746, Nassau, Bahamas
PHONE: +(809) 3227624; 3227625
TITLE: Ambassador
NAME: Geoffrey Johnstone

JUDICIAL SYSTEM

Supreme Court

Shirley St., Nassau, Bahamas

FURTHER READING

Government Publications

Central Intelligence Agency. *CIA World Factbook*, 1998. Washington, DC: GPO, 1999.

U.S. Department of State. *Background Notes: Bahamas*, 1997. Washington, DC: GPO, 1998.

U.S. Department of State. *Bahamas Reports on Human Rights Practices for 1997.* Washington, DC: GPO, 1998.

Articles

''Bahamas Aims to Launch Stock Exchange by Year-End.'' Reuters, August 13, 1999.

''Bahamas Lacking Power, Water after Floyd.'' Reuters, September 20, 1999.

''Bahamas Plans Repair Yard for Cruise Ships, Cargo Vessels.'' *Knight-Ridder/Tribune Business News*, August 10, 1999.

"Bahamas Swept Underwater by Hurricane Floyd." *Knight-Ridder/Tribune Business News*, September 15, 1999.

"Bahamas Win Surprise Women's 4x100 Gold." Reuters, August 29, 1999.

"Commonwealth of the Bahamas Speech from the Throne Delivered at the Opening of Parliament." (Press Release), March 17, 1999.

"Cuban Migrants Escape from Bahamas Prison." Reuters, September 24, 1999.

"Dennis Hits Bahamas, Strengthens as it Eyes U.S." Reuters, August 28, 1999.

"DQ Scals Bahamas Development Pact." *Nation's Restaurant News*, June 7, 1999.

"An Executive Summary of the Government of the Bahamas' Statement to the OECD." *PR Newswire*, September 3, 1999.

"Grim Picture of Bahamas Storm Destruction Emerges." Reuters, September 16, 1999.

"Hilton International Opens First Bahamas Hotel:" Reuters, October 25, 1999.

"Hurricane Floyd Roars over Bahamas, toward Florida." Reuters, September 14, 1999.

Books

Kelly, Robert C. et. al., editors. *Bahamas Country Review 1999–2000*. Houston, TX: Commercial Data International, 1999.

1999 Bahamas Handbook and Businessman's Annual. (Serial.) International Publications Service, 1999.

Internet

CIA World Factbook: The Bahamas. Available Online @ http://www.odci.gov/cia/publications/factbook/bf.html. (October 29, 1999).

WashingtonPost.com International: The Bahamas. Available Online @ http://www.washingtonpost.com/wpsrv/inatl/longterm/worldref/country/bahamas.htm. (October 29, 1999).

BAHAMAS: STATISTICAL DATA

For sources and notes see "Sources of Statistics" in the front of each volume.

GEOGRAPHY

Geography (1)

Area:

Total: 13,940 sq km.

Land: 10,070 sq km.

Water: 3,870 sq km.

Area—comparative: slightly smaller than Connecticut.

Land boundaries: 0 km.

Coastline: 3,542 km.

Climate: tropical marine; moderated by warm waters of Gulf Stream.

Terrain: long, flat coral formations with some low rounded hills.

Natural resources: salt, aragonite, timber.

Land use:

Arable land: 1%

Permanent crops: 0%

Permanent pastures: 0%

Forests and woodland: 32%

Other: 67% (1993 est.).

HUMAN FACTORS

Ethnic Division (6)

Black 85%

White 15%

HUMAN FACTORS

Demographics (2A)

	1990	1995	1998	2000	2010	2020	2030	2040	2050
Population	251.3	268.1	279.8	287.5	323.6	354.9	380.7	397.1	404.1
Net migration rate (per 1,000 population)	NA	NA	NA	NA	NA	NA	NA	NA	NA
Births	NA	NA	NA	NA	NA	NA	NA	NA	NA
Deaths	NA	NA	NA	NA	NA	NA	NA	NA	NA
Life expectancy - males	68.6	69.8	70.7	71.2	73.7	75.6	77.0	78.1	78.9
Life expectancy - females	75.9	76.8	77.4	77.9	79.8	81.3	82.6	83.5	84.3
Birth rate (per 1,000)	24.6	22.4	21.0	20.1	16.1	14.5	13.3	12.0	11.4
Death rate (per 1,000)	5.3	5.5	5.4	5.4	5.6	6.4	7.6	9.2	10.6
Women of reproductive age (15-49 yrs.)	71.1	76.9	80.6	82.6	86.7	89.5	90.2	91.0	88.6
of which are currently married	NA	NA	NA	NA	NA	NA	NA	NA	NA
Fertility rate	2.6	2.4	2.3	2.3	2.1	2.0	1.9	1.9	1.8

Except as noted, values for vital statistics are in thousands; life expectancy is in years.

Religions (7)

Baptist	.32%
Anglican	.20%
Roman Catholic	.19%
Methodist	.6%
Church of God	.6%
Other Protestant	.12%
None or unknown	.3%
Other	.2%

Languages (8)

English, Creole (among Haitian immigrants).

EDUCATION

Educational Attainment (10)

Age group (1990)	.25+
Total population	.104,472
Highest level attained (%)	
No schooling	.3.5
First level	
Not completed	.25.4
Completed	.NA
Entered second level	
S-1	.57.7
S-2	.NA
Postsecondary	.13.5

Literacy Rates (11A)

In thousands and percent[1]	1990	1995	2000	2010
Illiterate population (15+ yrs.)	4	3	3	3
Literacy rate - total adult pop. (%)	97.9	98.2	98.5	98.9
Literacy rate - males (%)	98.3	98.5	96.7	99.1
Literacy rate - females (%)	97.5	98.0	98.3	98.8

GOVERNMENT & LAW

Political Parties (12)

Parliament	No. of seats
Free National Movement (FNM)	.35
Progressive Liberal Party (PLP)	.5

Government Budget (13B)

Revenues	.$687.5 million
Expenditures	.$827 million
Capital expenditures	.$112 million

Data for FY96/97 est.

Military Affairs (14A)

Total expenditures (FY96/97)	.$22.9 million
Expenditures as % of GDP (FY95/96)	.3.8%

Crime (15)

Crime rate (for 1997)

Crimes reported	.16,600
Total persons convicted	.3,400
Crimes per 100,000 population	.6,500

Persons responsible for offenses

Total number of suspects	.3,000
Total number of female suspects	.125
Total number of juvenile suspects	.200

LABOR FORCE

Labor Force (16)

Total	.146,600
Government	.30%
Tourism	.40%
Business services	.10%
Agriculture	.5%

Data for 1996, distribution for 1995 est.

Unemployment Rate (17)

10% (1997 est.)

PRODUCTION SECTOR

Electric Energy (18)

Capacity	.401,000 kW (1995)
Production	.1.29 billion kWh (1996)
Consumption per capita	.4,100 kWh (1996)

Transportation (19)

Highways:
total: 2,693 km
paved: 1,546 km
unpaved: 1,147 km (1997 est.)

Merchant marine:
total: 1,024 ships (1,000 GRT or over) totaling 24,674,594 GRT/38,334,892 DWT

Airports: 62 (1997 est.)

Airports—with paved runways:
total: 32
over 3,047 m: 2
2,438 to 3,047 m: 1

1,524 to 2,437 m: 15

914 to 1,523 m: 12

under 914 m: 2 (1997 est.)

Airports—with unpaved runways:

total: 30

1,524 to 2,437 m: 1

914 to 1,523 m: 8

under 914 m: 21 (1997 est.)

Top Agricultural Products (20)

Citrus, vegetables; poultry.

FINANCE, ECONOMICS, & TRADE

Economic Indicators (22)

National product: GDP—purchasing power parity—$5.36 billion (1997 est.)

National product real growth rate: 3.5% (1997 est.)

National product per capita: $19,400 (1997 est.)

Inflation rate—consumer price index: 0.4% (1997)

Exchange Rates (24)

Exchange rates: Bahamian dollar (B$) per US$1—1.000 (fixed rate pegged to the dollar).

Top Import Origins (25)

$1.26 billion (c.i.f., 1996).

Origins	%
United States	.29
Finland	.10
Iran	.10
Denmark	.8

Top Export Destinations (26)

$201.7 million (f.o.b., 1996). Data are for 1995 est.

Destinations	%
United States	.24
Spain	.14
United Kingdom	.7
Norway	.7
France	.6
Italy	.5

Balance of Payments (23)

	1990	1992	1994	1995	1996
Exports of goods (f.o.b.)	283	217	199	255	273
Imports of goods (f.o.b.)	−1,080	−984	−1,014	−1,157	−1,263
Trade balance	−796	−768	−815	−931	−990
Services - debits	−978	−701	−826	−850	−972
Services - credits	1,732	1,493	1,572	1,617	1,699
Private transfers (net)	−3	−3	−2	−3	−3
Government transfers (net)	9	15	29	21	20
Overall balance	−37	36	−42	−146	−246

MANUFACTURING SECTOR

GDP & Manufacturing Summary (21)

	1980	1985	1990	1992	1993	1994
Gross Domestic Product						
Millions of 1990 dollars	1,603	2,075	3,134	3,068	3,130	3,139
Growth rate in percent	−3.56	13.51	0.97	0.11	2.00	0.30
Per capita (in 1990 dollars)	7,631.1	8,869.1	12,242.2	11,622.4	11,677.7	11,540.5
Manufacturing Value Added						
Millions of 1990 dollars	NA	NA	NA	NA	NA	NA
Growth rate in percent	NA	NA	NA	NA	NA	NA
Manufacturing share in percent of current prices	7.5	NA	3.2	4.0	*3.4*	NA

FINANCE, ECONOMICS, & TRADE

Economic Aid (27)

$NA. NA stands for not available.

Import Export Commodities (28)

Import Commodities	Export Commodities
Foodstuffs	Pharmaceuticals
Manufactured goods	Cement
Crude oil	Rum
Vehicles	Crawfish
Electronics products	Refined petroleum products

BAHRAIN

State of Bahrain
Dawlat al-Bahrayn

CAPITAL: Manama (Al-Manamah).

FLAG: Red with a white vertical stripe on the hoist, the edge between them being saw-toothed.

ANTHEM: Music without words.

MONETARY UNIT: The Bahrain dinar (BD) is divided into 1,000 fils. There are coins of 5, 10, 25, 50, and 100 fils and notes of 500 fils and 1, 5, 10, and 20 dinars. BD1 = $2.6596 (or $1 = BD0.3760).

WEIGHTS AND MEASURES: The metric system is used; local measures are also used.

HOLIDAYS: New Year's Day, 1 January; National Day, 16 December. Movable Muslim religious holidays include Hijra (Muslim New Year), 'Ashura, Prophet's Birthday, 'Id al-Fitr, and 'Id al-'Adha'.

TIME: 3 PM = noon GMT.

LOCATION AND SIZE: The State of Bahrain consists of a group of 33 islands (6 inhabited) in the western Persian Gulf, with a total area of 620 square kilometers (239 square miles), slightly less than 3.5 times the area of Washington, D.C. Bahrain, the main island, is linked by bridges to Al Muharraq and Sitra islands and to Saudi Arabia. Other islands include the Hawar group (off the west coast of Qatar), Nabih Salih, Umm an-Na'san, and Jidda. The total coastline is 161 kilometers (100 miles). Bahrain's capital, Manama, is located on the northeastern coast.

CLIMATE: Summers in Bahrain are hot and humid, and winters are relatively cool. Daily average temperatures in July range from a minimum of 29°C (84°F) to a maximum of 37°C (99°F). In January, the minimum is 14°C (57°F); the maximum 20°C (68°F). Rainfall averages less than 10 centimeters (4 inches) annually.

INTRODUCTORY SURVEY

RECENT HISTORY

The Portuguese occupied Bahrain, known as Dilmun, from 1522 to 1602. The present ruling family, the Khalifa, captured Bahrain in 1782. Contact with the British followed in the nineteenth century, concluding in an 1861 treaty of protection. After a plan to federate the nine sheikhdoms of the southern Gulf failed, Bahrain became a sovereign state on 15 August 1971.

Owing to its small size, Bahrain generally takes its lead in foreign affairs from its Arab neighbors on the Gulf. During the 1980–88 Iran-Iraq War, Bahrain joined most other Arab states in supporting Iraq. However, when Iraq invaded Kuwait in 1990, Bahrain stood with the United States and its Middle Eastern allies, contributing military support to the defeat of Iraq. Bahrain has long assisted the American naval presence in the Persian Gulf. In 1991, the U.S. signed an agreement giving the Department of Defense access to facilities on the island.

GOVERNMENT

Bahrain is a constitutional monarchy headed by an emir. A council of ministers, appointed by the emir, acts as a legislature (the constitution provides for a National Assembly, but none has existed since 1975). Bahrain consists of six major towns and five rural communities.

BAHRAIN

0 2 4 6 8 Miles

0 2 4 6 8 Kilometers

Persian Gulf

Jazīrat al Muḥarraq
Al Qalālī
Al Muḥarraq
Ad Dirāz
Manama
Al Ḥadd
Al Budayyi'
Al Jufayr
Jiddah
Jidd Ḥafṣ
Mina Salmon
Marqūbān
Umm an Na'sān
Sitrah
Karzakkān
Al Rifā' ash Sharqi
Al Mālikōyah
'Awālō
Az Zallāq
'Askar
Ra's Ḥayyan
Jabal ad Dukhān 400 ft. 122 m.
Jaww
Ad Dūr
Gulf of Bahrain
Ar Rumaythah
Al Mamṭalah

Ra's al Barr

Bahrain

N / W E / S

Judiciary

The law of Bahrain represents a mixture of Islamic religious law (Shari'a) and government decrees dealing with criminal and commercial matters. In ordinary civil and criminal courts, there are open trials, a right to counsel, and a right to appeal.

Political Parties

Political parties are illegal in Bahrain. Several underground groups, including pro-Iranian militant Islamic groups, have been active and are vigorously opposed by the government.

DEFENSE

The Bahraini armed forces in 1995 had 11,000 personnel. Bahrain sent troops to Sa'udi Arabia during the 1991 Gulf War. Defense expenditures in 1995 were $261 million.

ECONOMIC AFFAIRS

Bahrain's economy has been based on oil for the last six decades. However, its present oil supply is expected to be soon exhausted, so the government has developed other areas, such as petroleum refining, and increased natural gas production.

Public Finance

The budget is presented biennially and regularly updated, and represents a large section of economic activity. The U.S. Central Intelligence Agency estimates that, in 1995, government revenues totaled approximately $1.38 billion and expenditures $1.7 billion. External debt totaled $2.6 billion, approximately 16% of which was financed abroad.

Income

In 1998, Bahrain's gross national product (GNP) was $5.2 billion, or $8,640 per person. For the period 1985–95, the average inflation rate was 0.4%, resulting in a real growth rate in gross national product of 0.6%.

Industry

Petroleum refining was Bahrain's first modern industrial enterprise. A total of 251,300 barrels per day of petroleum products were produced in 1995. Aluminum production was 450,000 tons in 1993.

Banking and Finance

Bahrain is considered the pre-eminent financial services center in the Middle East. The Bahrain Monetary Agency (BMA) issues and redeems bank notes, regulates the value of the Bahrain dinar, supervises interest rates, and licenses and monitors the activities of money changers. Contributing to Bahrain's growth as a Middle Eastern financial services center is that no serious religious opposition exists to western banking practices. There are, however, several large Islamic banks in Bahrain. The giant, U.S.-headquartered Citibank opened an Islamic bank in Bahrain in July 1997. In 1992, the government created the Bahrain Development Bank (BDB) to help stimulate economic growth through the provision of loans for new manufacturing and service businesses.

Total commercial bank loans declined in the third quarter of 1996 for the fourth consecutive quarter. At BD2.53 billion (US $6.73 billion), they were below the total of BD2.55 billion recorded in the first quarter of 1995.

The value of assets held by Bahrain's offshore banking units (DBUs) rose by 9% between the second and third quarter of 1996. Assets in Bahrain's 50 or so DBUs stood at $67.1 billion in the third quarter compared with $61.5 billion in the second, and equal to the third quarter of 1995. The BMA is anxious to maintain Bahrain's premier banking position in the face of regional competition and domestic political uncertainty. In April 1996, Bahrain was home to 19 full commercial banks, 2 specialized banks, 41 representative offices, 28 investment banks, 6 foreign exchange and money brokers, and 27 money-changing companies.

The Bahrain Stock Exchange (BSE) has become an important Gulf center of share trading. Beginning in 1995, the BSE listed foreign companies, bonds, and investment funds. Trading in foreign investment vehicles was made open to all Bahrainis in late 1996.

Economic Development

Since the late 1960s, the government has concentrated on policies and projects that will provide sufficient diversification in industrial, commercial, and financial activities to sustain growth in income, employment, and exports into the post-oil era. Despite diversification efforts, the oil and gas sectors remain the cornerstone of the economy.

SOCIAL WELFARE

Impoverished families receive survival allowances from the government. Since 1976, a social security fund has provided old age, disability, survivor, and accident insurance.

Healthcare

There are 4 government-operated hospitals and 19 health care centers. In 1991, Bahrain had 668 physicians. Life expectancy is approximately 73 years.

Housing

At the 1981 census, roughly 45% of all homes were traditional dwellings. A major program for low- and middle-income housing, costing $195 million, was inaugurated in 1987 with Saudi aid.

EDUCATION

In 1995, the illiteracy rate was estimated by UNESCO at 15% (11% for males, 21% for females). Primary education lasts for six years, intermediate for three, and secondary for three. The University of Bahrain was founded in 1986, and the Arabian Gulf University in 1980.

1999 KEY EVENTS TIMELINE

February

- Bahrain condemns the United States and British air assault on Iraq.

March

- The emir of Bahrain dies of a heart attack after a 38-year reign; he is succeeded by his son, Sheik Hamad bin Isa al-Khalifa.

May

- The Bahrain-based Gulf International Bank merges with Saudi International Bank.

July

- A high-profile Shiite dissident, Sheik Abdul Amir al-Jamri, is released from prison.

August

- Bahrain boycotts a youth hand ball championship due to Israeli participation.

- The new emir welcomes an invitation to visit Iran.

September

- Bahrain will resume the transport of passengers and cargo to Iraq as United Nations sanctions are retracted.

- Bahrain becomes the first Gulf state to sign an investment treaty with the U.S.

November

- Sheikh Hamad al-Khalifa pardons two hundred citizens for participating in anti-government demonstrations during the last decade. Some are citizens living abroad, and the pardon paves the way for their return to Bahrain.

December

- Sheikh Hamad al-Khalifa announces that he will revive democratically elected municipal councils which were banned during the 1970s.

- Bahrain and Qatar establish new relations, agreeing to exchange ambassadors and establishing a special committee charged with resolving the dispute over territories that is currently the subject of a case before the International Court of Justice in the Hague, Netherlands. The case will be withdrawn if the countries can negotiate a settlement on their own.

ANALYSIS OF EVENTS: 1999

BUSINESS AND THE ECONOMY

Although it remains the premier financial center of the Gulf region, Bahrain, like its neighbors, suffered from low worldwide oil prices in 1999. However, the ups and downs of the oil market had a less drastic effect on Bahrain than on some other Gulf countries due to the relatively diverse nature of its economy. Nevertheless, the Bahraini government, which receives 50 percent of its revenue from oil, was forced to curtail spending, and unemployment reached 15 percent.

The ascent of Sheik Hamad Bin Isa al-Khalifa to the throne was expected to help boost the nation's economy, which had been stagnant in the final years of his father's reign. In addition to low oil prices, the economy had been negatively affected by the illness of the former emir and by civil unrest caused by Shiite dissidents. Sheik Hamad's moves to improve diffuse regional tensions by improving ties between Bahrain and Iran were also seen as positive indicators for the Bahraini economy.

A major development in the nation's important offshore banking sector was the merger of Bahrain-based Gulf International Bank (GIB) with Saudi International Bank, whose headquarters are in London, creating a new financial entity with assets valued at over $14 billion. The Gulf International Bank also took advantage of by a Gulf Cooperation Council (GCC) ruling of the previous year to open a new branch in Saudi Arabia.

Bahrain's intention to continue developing its oil industry was indicated by an oil and gas exploration agreement with U.S.–based Texaco Inc., as well as by the state-owned Bahrain Petroleum Company's announcement of a planned series of upgrades at the country's sole oil refinery to improve production of its major petroleum products. The improvements, expected to total some $800 million, were to include projects to streamline production of jet fuel, significantly reduce the sulfur content of diesel fuel, and introduce production of unleaded gasoline. The various projects were scheduled for completion between 2000 and 2002. In addition, work on a new $5 billion oil refining and petrochemical complex was slated to begin in September.

In other industries, a $400 million expansion and upgrade of the state-owned aluminum company's marine terminal was under way.

GOVERNMENT AND POLITICS

The year 1999 brought a political milestone to the small Gulf nation of Bahrain. The country's emir, Sheik Isa bin Sulman al-Khalifa, who had ruled the country since 1961, died of a heart attack and was succeeded on the throne by his son, Sheik Hamad bin Isa al-Khalifa. The elder al-Khalifa had suspended the nation's democratic constitution and dissolved its parliament shortly after Bahrain won independence its from Great Britain in 1971. He had proceeded to rule by decree, maintaining firm control over Bahrain's Shiite Muslim majority (the ruling family are Sunni Muslims) through a repressive system under which persons could be detained for three years without a trial.

In his first months as emir, Sheik Hamad took several liberalizing steps that made observers hope he might eventually move the country toward true democracy. He made several overtures to the beleaguered Shiite majority, including allowing Shiites into the army for the first time and releasing hundreds of Shiite political prisoners, most notably Sheik Abdul Amir al-Jamri, the country's best-known Shiite dissident.

In August, Sheik Hamad responded positively to an invitation to visit Iran by that country's president, Mohammad Khatami. The 1980 Muslim revolution in Iran, a predominantly Shiite country, had strained relations between the two nations, as Bahrain's rulers feared it might incite a similar revolt by Shiites in their own country.

Sheik Hamad was also expected to continue Bahrain's close ties with the United States, which has its Gulf fleet anchored there. Earlier in the year, however, his father's government had protested U.S. and British air strikes against Iraq provoked by Saddam Hussein's refusal to cooperate with

U.N. weapons monitors and UNSCOM (UN Special Commission) demilitarization measures.

CULTURE AND SOCIETY

Bahrain has received high rankings in the areas of health, education, per capita income, and life expectancy from the United Nations Human Development Report, but its human rights record has come under scrutiny, especially since 1994, for the repression of dissent by the country's Shiite Muslims. With the succession to the throne of a new emir, Sheik Hamad bin Isa al-Khalifa, there were prospects of improved tolerance. Sheik Hamad's release of hundreds of Shiite political prisoners, including the most prominent one— Sheik Abdul Amir al-Jamri—was a cause for optimism, as was his agreement to allow observers from Amnesty International into the country to investigate alleged human rights abuses by security forces.

DIRECTORY

CENTRAL GOVERNMENT

Head of State

Amir of Bahrain
Shaikh Hamad bin Isa al-Khalifa, Office of the Amir, Bahrain Amiri Court, West Rafaa, Bahrain
PHONE: +973 666666

Ministers

Prime Minister
Sheikh Khalifah bin Salman al-Khalifa, Office of the Prime Minister

Minister of Foreign Affairs
Muhammad bin Mubarak al-Khalifa, Ministry of Foreign Affairs, P.O. Box 547, Manama, Bahrain
PHONE: +973 262277
FAX: +973 210575

Minister of Justice and Islamic Affairs
Abdallah bin Khalid al-Khalifa, Ministry of Justice and Islamic Affairs, P.O. Box 450, Manama, Bahrain
PHONE: +973 531333
FAX: +973 536343

Minister of Cabinet Affairs
Muhammad bin Ibrahim al-Mutawa, Ministry of Cabinet Affairs, P.O. Box 100, Manama, Bahrain

PHONE: +973 262266
FAX: +973 277730

Minister of Defense
Khalifa bin Ahmad al-Khalifa, Ministry of Defense, P.O. Box 245, Manama, Bahrain
PHONE: +973 665599
FAX: +973 663923

Minister of Housing
Khalid bin Abdallah al-Khalifa, Ministry of Housing, Municipalities, and Environment, P.O. Box 5802, Manama, Bahrain
PHONE: +973 533000
FAX: +973 534115

Minister of Finance and National Economy
Abdallah Hasan al-Saif, Ministry of Finance and National Economy, P.O. Box 333, Manama, Bahrain
PHONE: +973 530800
FAX: +973 532853

Minister of Transportation and Communication
Ali Bin Khalifa bin Salman al-Khalifa, Ministry of Transportation, P.O. Box 10325, Manama, Bahrain
PHONE: +973 534534
FAX: +973 534140

Minister of Health
Faysal Radhi al-Musawi, Ministry of Health, P.O. Box 12, Manama, Bahrain
PHONE: +973 255555
FAX: +973 252569

Minister of Interior
Muhammad Bin Khalifa bin Hamad al-Khalifa, Ministry of Interior, P.O. Box 13, Manama, Bahrain
PHONE: +973 272111
FAX: +973 2262169

Minister of Education
Abd Al-Aziz bin Muhammad al-Fadhil, Ministry of Education, P.O. Box 43, Manama, Bahrain
PHONE: +973 680161
FAX: +973 261836

Minister of Amiri Court Affairs
Ali bin Isa bin Salman al-Khalifa, Ministry of Amiri Court Affairs

Minister of Commerce
ali Salih Abdallah al-Salih, Ministry of Commerce

Minister of Electricity and Water
Abdallah bin Muhammad Juma, Ministry of
Electricity and Water

Minister of Labor and Social Affairs
Abd al-Nabi al-Shuala, Ministry of Labor and
Social Affairs

Minister of Oil and Industry
Isa bin Ali bin Hamad al-Khalifa, Ministry of
Oil and Industry

Minister of Public Works and Agriculture
Majid Jawad al-Jishi, Ministry of Public Works
and Agriculture

Minister of State
Jawad Salim al-Urayid, Ministry of State

DIPLOMATIC REPRESENTATION
Embassies in Bahrain

United Kingdom
21 Government Avenue, P.O. Box 114, Manama
306, Bahrain

PHONE: +973 534404
FAX: +973 531273

JUDICIAL SYSTEM
High Civil Appeals Court

FURTHER READING
Articles

Marks, Jon. "Will the Son Shine?" *The Banker*
(June 1999): 59.

"Mourning, and Questioning, in Bahrain." *The
Economist* (March 13, 1999): 56.

"Suddenly, It's Time for Charm." *The
Economist* (July 17, 1999): 41.

"Whitewash." *The Economist* (January 23,
1999): 42.

Books

al-Khalifah, Hamad ibn 'Isa. *First Light: Modern
Bahrain and Its Heritage*. London: Kegan
Paul International, 1994.

BAHRAIN: STATISTICAL DATA

For sources and notes see "Sources of Statistics" in the front of each volume.

GEOGRAPHY

Geography (1)

Area:

Total: 620 sq km.

Land: 620 sq km.

Water: 0 sq km.

Area—comparative: 3.5 times the size of Washington, DC.

Land boundaries: 0 km.

Coastline: 161 km.

Climate: arid; mild, pleasant winters; very hot, humid summers.

Terrain: mostly low desert plain rising gently to low central escarpment.

Natural resources: oil, associated and nonassociated natural gas, fish.

Land use:

Arable land: 1%

Permanent crops: 1%

Permanent pastures: 6%

Forests and woodland: 0%

Other: 92% (1993 est.).

HUMAN FACTORS

Infants and Malnutrition (5)

Under-5 mortality rate (1997) 22

% of infants with low birthweight (1990-97) 6

Births attended by skilled health staff % of total[a] . . .NA

Continued on next page.

Demographics (2A)

	1990	1995	1998	2000	2010	2020	2030	2040	2050
Population	501.7	575.9	616.3	641.5	758.7	870.2	969.6	1,041.7	1,098.0
Net migration rate (per 1,000 population)	NA	NA	NA	NA	NA	NA	NA	NA	NA
Births	NA	NA	NA	NA	NA	NA	NA	NA	NA
Deaths	NA	NA	NA	NA	NA	NA	NA	NA	NA
Life expectancy - males	69.6	71.5	72.4	73.1	75.6	77.4	78.6	79.4	80.0
Life expectancy - females	74.3	76.5	77.6	78.3	81.2	83.2	84.6	85.4	86.0
Birth rate (per 1,000)	26.7	24.1	22.4	21.3	18.3	17.4	15.5	14.5	13.9
Death rate (per 1,000)	3.7	3.3	3.3	3.2	3.7	4.8	6.6	8.6	9.1
Women of reproductive age (15-49 yrs.)	117.2	137.0	147.6	154.7	182.4	199.2	220.8	239.0	246.8
of which are currently married	NA	NA	NA	NA	NA	NA	NA	NA	NA
Fertility rate	3.4	3.1	3.0	2.9	2.7	2.4	2.3	2.2	2.1

Except as noted, values for vital statistics are in thousands; life expectancy is in years.

Infants and Malnutrition (5) cont.

% fully immunized (1995-97)

TB . . . . .NA

DPT 98

Polio 98

Measles 95

Prevalence of child malnutrition under age 5
(1992-97)[b] . . . . .NA

Ethnic Division (6)

Bahraini 63%

Asian 13%

Other Arab 10%

Iranian 8%

Other 6%

Religions (7)

Shi'a Muslim 75%

Sunni Muslim 25%

Languages (8)

Arabic, English, Farsi, Urdu.

EDUCATION

Educational Attainment (10)

Age group (1991) . . . . .25+

Total population 263,720

Highest level attained (%)

No schooling 38.4

First level

    Not completed 26.2

    Completed . . . . .NA

Entered second level

    S-1 . . . . .25.1

    S-2 . . . . .NA

Postsecondary 10.3

Literacy Rates (11A)

In thousands and percent[1]	1990	1995	2000	2010
Illiterate population (15+ yrs.)	59	56	52	42
Literacy rate - total adult pop. (%)	82.3	85.2	87.9	92.5
Literacy rate - males (%)	87.0	89.1	91.0	94.1
Literacy rate - females (%)	75.0	79.4	83.4	90.3

GOVERNMENT & LAW

Political Parties (12)

The unicameral National Assembly was dissolved 26
August 1975 and legislative powers were assumed by
the Cabinet appointed Advisory Council established 16
December 1992.

Government Budget (13A)

Year: 1997

Total Expenditures: 620.00 Millions of Dinars

Expenditures as a percentage of the total by function:

General public services and public order 26.65

Defense 17.58

Education 13.68

Health 9.87

Social Security and Welfare 3.94

Housing and community amenities 3.60

Recreational, cultural, and religious affairs 1.69

Fuel and energy 14.37

Agriculture, forestry, fishing, and hunting 71

Mining, manufacturing, and construction 56

Transportation and communication 3.77

Other economic affairs and services 11

LABOR FORCE

Labor Force (16)

Total 140,000

Industry, commerce, and service 78%

Government 21%

Agriculture 1%

Data for 1994. 44% of the population in the 15-64 age group is
non-national (July 1998 est.)

Unemployment Rate (17)

15% (1996 est.)

PRODUCTION SECTOR

Electric Energy (18)

Capacity . . . . .1.05 million kW (1995)

Production . . . . .4.4 billion kWh (1995)

Consumption per capita . . . . .7,640 kWh (1995)

GOVERNMENT & LAW

Military Affairs (14B)

	1990	1991	1992	1993	1994	1995
Military expenditures						
Current dollars (mil.)	216	237	252	251	256	273
1995 constant dollars (mil.)	248	262	271	263	263	273
Armed forces (000)	8	8	7	7	8	8
Gross national product (GNP)						
Current dollars (mil.)	3,448	3,583	3,835	4,006	4,006	5,053
1995 constant dollars (mil.)	3,963	3,959	4,125	4,200	4,107	5,053
Central government expenditures (CGE)						
1995 constant dollars (mil.)	1,829	1,698	1,764	1,577	1,560	1,837
People (mil.)	.5	.5	.5	.5	.6	.6
Military expenditure as % of GNP	6.3	6.6	6.6	6.3	6.4	5.4
Military expenditure as % of CGE	13.6	15.4	15.3	16.7	16.8	14.8
Military expenditure per capita (1995 $)	495	507	509	482	468	473
Armed forces per 1,000 people (soldiers)	15.9	15.5	13.2	12.8	14.3	13.9
GNP per capita (1995 $)	7,898	7,662	7,765	7,690	7,319	8,774
Arms imports[6]						
Current dollars (mil.)	280	60	110	70	80	40
1995 constant dollars (mil.)	322	66	118	73	82	40
Arms exports[6]						
Current dollars (mil.)	0	0	0	0	0	0
1995 constant dollars (mil.)	0	0	0	0	0	0
Total imports[7]						
Current dollars (mil.)	3,711	4,115	4,263	3,858	3,737	3,626
1995 constant dollars (mil.)	4,265	4,547	4,585	4,045	3,831	3,626
Total exports[7]						
Current dollars (mil.)	3,761	3,513	3,464	3,710	3,454	4,044
1995 constant dollars (mil.)	4,322	3,882	3,726	3,889	3,541	4,044
Arms as percent of total imports[8]	7.5	1.5	2.6	1.8	2.1	1.1
Arms as percent of total exports[8]	0	0	0	0	0	0

PRODUCTION SECTOR

Transportation (19)

Highways:

total: 3,013 km

paved: 2,284 km

unpaved: 729 km (1996 est.)

Pipelines: crude oil 56 km; petroleum products 16 km; natural gas 32 km

Merchant marine:

total: 6 ships (1,000 GRT or over) totaling 131,919

GRT/212,510 DWT ships by type: bulk 2, cargo 3, oil tanker 1 (1997 est.)

Airports: 3 (1997 est.)

Airports—with paved runways:

total: 2

over 3,047 m: 2 (1997 est.)

Airports—with unpaved runways:

total: 1

1,524 to 2,437 m: 1 (1997 est.)

Top Agricultural Products (20)

Fruit, vegetables; poultry, dairy products; shrimp, fish.

MANUFACTURING SECTOR

GDP & Manufacturing Summary (21)

	1980	1985	1990	1992	1993	1994
Gross Domestic Product						
Millions of 1990 dollars	3,748	3,607	4,032	4,699	5,087	5,202
Growth rate in percent	2.58	−2.04	1.23	7.80	8.25	2.27
Per capita (in 1990 dollars)	10,801.3	8,713.6	8,229.5	9,036.5	9,507.9	9,475.7
Manufacturing Value Added						
Millions of 1990 dollars	509	559	672	852	*914*	*947*
Growth rate in percent	26.25	−10.51	5.23	22.17	*7.26*	*3.57*
Manufacturing share in percent of current prices	14.8	8.5	15.4	14.2	16.5	*16.5*

FINANCE, ECONOMICS, & TRADE

Economic Indicators (22)

National product: GDP—purchasing power parity— $8.2 billion (1997 est.)

National product real growth rate: 2.7% (1997 est.)

National product per capita: $13,700 (1997 est.)

Inflation rate—consumer price index: -0.2% (1996 est.)

Exchange Rates (24)

Exchange rates: Bahraini dinars (BD) per US$1— 0.3760 (fixed rate)

Top Import Origins (25)

$3.7 billion (f.o.b., 1996) Data are for 1995.

Origins	%
Saudi Arabia	.40
United States	.13
United Kingdom	.7
Japan	.5
Switzerland	.5

Top Export Destinations (26)

$4.6 billion (f.o.b., 1996) Data are for 1995.

Destinations	%
India	.22
Japan	.12
Saudi Arabia	.6
United States	.6
UAE	.5

Economic Aid (27)

$NA. NA stands for not available.

Import Export Commodities (28)

Import Commodities	Export Commodities
Nonoil 63%	Petroleum and petroleum products 61%
Crude oil 37%	
	Aluminum 7%

Balance of Payments (23)

	1990	1992	1993	1994	1995
Exports of goods (f.o.b.)	3,761	3,464	3,723	3,617	4,113
Imports of goods (f.o.b.)	−3,340	−3,837	−3,472	−3,373	−3,344
Trade balance	420	−372	251	244	769
Services - debits	−1,558	−1,716	−1,573	−1,489	−1,658
Services - credits	1,198	1,505	1,477	1,454	1,669
Private transfers (net)	−272	−271	−323	−329	−379
Government transfers (net)	457	100	202	319	157
Overall balance	245	−754	34	198	557

BANGLADESH

People's Republic of Bangladesh
Gana-Prajatantri Bangladesh

CAPITAL: Dhaka (formerly Dacca).

FLAG: The national flag is a red circle against a dark green background.

ANTHEM: *Amar Sonar Bangla (My Golden Bengal).*

MONETARY UNIT: The taka (T) of 100 poisha is a paper currency set on a par with the Indian rupee. There are coins of 1, 2, 5, 10, 25, and 50 poisha, and notes of 1, 5, 10, 20, 50, and 100 taka. T1 — $0.02356 (or $1 =T42.45).

WEIGHTS AND MEASURES: Bangladesh adopted the metric system as of 1 July 1982. Customary numerical units include the lakh (equal to 100,000) and the crore (equal to 10 million).

HOLIDAYS: New Year's Day, 1 January; National Mourning Day (Shaheel Day), 21 February; Independence Day, 26 March; May Day, 1 May; Victory Day, 16 December; Christmas, 25 December; Boxing Day, 26 December. Movable religious holidays include Good Friday, Jamat Wida, Shab-i-Bharat, 'Id al-Fitr, 'Id al-'Adha', and Durga Puja.

TIME: 6 PM = noon GMT.

LOCATION AND SIZE: Located in South Asia, Bangladesh is slightly smaller than the state of Wisconsin, with a total area of 144,000 square kilometers (55,599 square miles). It has a total boundary length of 4,826 kilometers (2,999 miles). Bangladesh's capital city, Dhaka, is located near the center of the country.

CLIMATE: Bangladesh has a tropical monsoon climate. Annual rainfall is high, averaging from about 119 centimeters (47 inches) up to 145 centimeters (57 inches). There are three distinct seasons. The winter, which lasts from November through February, is cool and dry, with average temperatures for most of the country at about 7°C (45°F). Temperatures rise rapidly in early March, and during the summer season—March through May—average about 32°C (90°F). From June to October, temperatures drop somewhat, seldom exceeding 31°C (88°F). For parts of the year, tropical cyclones, accompanied by high seas and heavy flooding, are common. Storms and floods in 1970, 1974, 1980, 1983, and 1993 devastated the country and caused many deaths.

INTRODUCTORY SURVEY

RECENT HISTORY

The area now known as Bangladesh was home to a flourishing civilization in the fourth century BC. The region, then called Bengal, was eventually conquered by the Hindu Maurya empire that reached its height under Emperor Asoka around 207 BC.

Islam came to South Asia in the years following AD 800 but did not reach Bengal until Muslim invaders from the west secured a foothold there around AD 1200. In the thirteenth and fourteenth centuries, after waves of Turkish, Persian, and Afghan invaders, the religion began to take a firm hold in the area.

By the middle of the eighteenth century, the British established themselves in Calcutta and expanded into what is now Bangladesh. British traders and officials gained control of most of the Indian subcontinent by 1859. Hindus in Bengal prospered under the British. The Muslim aristocracy of eastern Bengal, however, resisted British rule. By the turn of the twentieth century, both communities united in anti-British feeling.

The subcontinent's demand for independence from Britain grew under the leadership of Gandhi in the early 1930s. Finally, in 1947, Britain granted independence to the Indian subcontinent. British India was partitioned into a predominately Hindu India and a predominately Muslim Pakistan.

However, the new state of Pakistan was made up of Muslim-majority districts at both the eastern

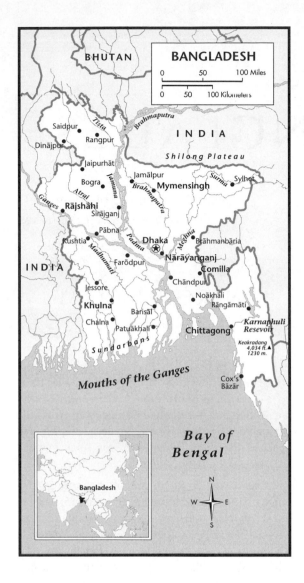

BANGLADESH

0   50   100 Miles

0   50   100 Kilometers

BHUTAN

INDIA

Shilong Plateau

Saidpur

Rangpur

Dinājpur

Jaipurhāt

Bogra

Jamālpur

Mymensingh

Surmā

Sylhet

Brahmaputra

Tista

Jamuna

Atrai

Ganges

Rājshāhi

Sirājganj

Pābna

Kushtia

Farōdpur

Madhumati

Padma

Meghna

Dhaka

Brāhmanbāria

Narāyanganj

Comilla

Chāndpur

Jessore

Noākhāli

Rāngāmāti

Khulna

Barisāl

Chālna

Patuākhāli

Chittagong

Karnaphuli
Resevoir

Keakradang
4,034 ft.
1,230 m.

Sundarbans

Mouths of the Ganges

Cox's
Bāzār

Bay of
Bengal

Bangladesh

N W E S

and western ends of formerly British India. These two distinct territories were separated by 1600 kilometers (1000 miles) of predominantly Hindu India. The division cut across long-established lines of trade and communication, divided families, and started a mass movement of refugees caught on the ''wrong'' side of the partition markers.

In language, culture, and ethnic background, East and West Pakistan were totally different—the main bonds being Islam and a fear of potential Indian (Hindu) expansion. Pakistan's early years as a nation were dominated by unsuccessful attempts to create a nation that would somehow bridge these differences, but they persisted and demands for a separate state in the east began to mount.

After continued refusal by West Pakistan to grant East Pakistan's requests for independence, civil war broke out in 1971. Swamped with a mil-

lion refugees from the fighting, India intervened militarily on behalf of those seeking a separate state. India's intervention helped create the independent nation of Bangladesh in 1972. Sheikh Mujibur (Mujib) Rahman, a leader of the fight for autonomy, was released from prison in West Pakistan and became prime minister of the new nation.

The civil war was a disaster for Bangladesh, undoing much of the limited progress East Pakistan had made in recovering from the social disruption of the 1947 partition. The nation's new leader faced a task for which his administrative and political experience was not enough. He fought and won a massive victory in the 1973 election, but two years later, he suspended the political process and took power into his own hands.

With this move, public opinion turned against Mujib. On 15 August 1975, a group of young military officers seized power. They killed Mujib and many of his family members and imposed martial law. A succession of military takeovers and new governments followed until General Hussain Mohammad Ershad seized power in 1981.

In 1982, Ershad declared Bangladesh an Islamic republic. This move angered the Hindu minority, and in 1990, Ershad was forced to resign the presidency.

A temporary government scheduled elections for February 1991, and the Bangladesh National Party (BNP) won control of the government. By March 1994, the BNP lost its popular support when opposition parties walked out of parliament and boycotted the government. They claimed the BNP had rigged a regional election. The main opposition groups boycotted the February 1996 elections, and the BNP won the majority. With further charges of vote-rigging, Prime Minister Khaleda Zia resigned, and the BNP dissolved the parliament. New elections were held in June 1996, and the Awami League gained control of the parliament.

GOVERNMENT

The constitution of December 1972 established a democratic republic, with an indirectly elected president as official head of state and a prime minister as head of government and chief executive. The prime minister and the administration are responsible to a single-chamber legislature—the National Assembly.

Judiciary

The judicial system consists of a Low Court and a Supreme Court, both of which hear civil and criminal cases.

Political Parties

The June 1996 elections brought Sheikh Hasina Wajid and the Awami League (AL) to a majority role in the parliament, with 140 of 330 seats. The Bangladesh National Party (BNP) held 116 seats.

DEFENSE

In 1995, Bangladesh had an army of 101,500 men, a navy of 10,000, and an air force of 6,500.

ECONOMIC AFFAIRS

Bangladesh is a poor country with few natural resources and an economy dominated by agriculture. Bangladesh has suffered from the 1971 war with Pakistan, a severe famine in 1971, and a series of weather-related disasters. However, measures taken by the government in 1991 brought inflation to a record low of 1.4% in 1993. Political instability and a lack of economic reforms pushed inflation to 5.2% in 1995, but as stability returned, the gross domestic product (GDP) grew by 4.7% in 1996.

Public Finance

In 1993, Bangladesh successfully completed a three-year IMF structural adjustment program. This program resulted in a growth in money supply of 11% in 1993, 15% in 1994, and 16% in 1995. In addition, government spending was curbed by a decline in subsidies to money-losing parastatals, and the value-added tax (VAT) continued to generate higher than predicted government revenues.

In 1996, the government reported that exports were up, the GDP grew by 4.4%, and that tax revenues climbed 9% to $3.06 billion. Encouraged by the good news, the government proposed a 1997 budget that would reduce domestic taxes, further cut import duties, and provide special incentives for foreign investors.

Income

In 1998, Bangladesh's gross national product (GNP) was $44 billion at current prices, or $350 per person.

Industry

Major industries include the manufacture of jute textiles, garments, cotton yarn, cotton cloth, and fertilizer. Paper, newsprint, tea, and sugar are also manufactured.

Banking and Finance

Central banking is conducted by the Bangladesh Bank, which is responsible for the circulation of money, supervision of commercial banks, and control of credit and foreign exchange.

Economic Development

The major objectives of planned development have been increased national income, rural development, self-sufficiency in food, and increased industrial production.

In 1991, a newly elected government instituted another economic initiation that included financial sector reform and liberalization measures to encourage investment, government revenue improvement efforts, and tight monetary policy. Income transfer measures, Food-for-Work, and other programs were also implemented to help protect the poorest segments of the population from the transitional effects of structural reform.

SOCIAL WELFARE

In 1976, the National Population Council was formed to develop a population control program. While women have and exercise full voting rights, they receive unequal treatment in many areas, including education, employment, and family matters such as divorce and inheritance.

Evidence suggests that children are sold for their labor to the Middle East, India, Pakistan, and Southeast Asia. The use of child labor within Bangladesh is the result of widespread poverty and economic deprivation; there may be as many as 10 million child laborers. Discrimination against Hindus has led to violence and conflict.

Healthcare

Malaria, tuberculosis, and other serious diseases remain widespread, and public health problems are aggravated by widespread malnutrition and periodic natural disasters. In 1994, 84% of children under age 5 were malnourished. Average life expectancy at birth is about 58 years.

Housing

The government maintains an urban housing program but does not have any housing development program for villages. As of 1981, 63% of all housing units were straw or bamboo, 20% were mud or unburnt brick, 12% were cement or wood roofed with iron sheets, and 5% were cement or brick.

EDUCATION

About 62% of the adult population of Bangladesh cannot read. Bangladesh has five years of compulsory education. In 1990, the number of primary schools was 45,917, with 189,508 teachers and 11.9 million students. At the secondary level, there were 130,949 teachers and 3.6 million students.

1999 KEY EVENTS TIMELINE

January

- A human rights group reports that more than 200,000 Bangladeshi women have been smuggled into Pakistan to work as prostitutes.

- Feminist writer Taslima Nasreen returns to exile in Sweden.

April

- Bangladesh is one of the countries affected by the Chernobyl computer virus.

July

- Bangladesh buys MiG-29 jets from Russia for $120 million, provoking protest from the United States.

- Floods leave 10 percent of Bangladesh under water.

August

- Opposition parties call a general strike to protest government's decision to allow passage of Indian goods through Bangladesh.

- Bangladesh and India exchange gunfire over a disputed border region.

September

- A general strike led by political opposition paralyzes Bangladesh for three days; the government offers to meet with opposition leaders.

November

- During a meeting of the parliament, Bangladeshi prime minister Sheikh Hasina Wajed attacks opposition leader Khaleda Zia, charging that the unrelenting campaign of strikes that has brought the country to a halt for 25 days this year is

disrupting school and university examinations and that Zia wants to deprive others of education; in a retaliatory response, Zia calls for yet another strike.

ANALYSIS OF EVENTS: 1999

BUSINESS AND THE ECONOMY

Political strife and ineffectual economic management by Bangladesh's government prompted concern by investing nations, who expressed dissatisfaction with the slow pace of economic reform and privatization, the inadequacy of social services, and the country's continued widespread poverty. Officially, 35.6 percent of the population of Bangladesh lives below the poverty line. The 1996 official unemployment rate was an astounding 35.2 percent. Inflation hovers around 7 percent. Citing these problems, as well as the country's chaotic political situation and its frequent work stoppages, the World Bank reduced its aid package to Bangladesh. Most of Bangladesh's industries are staple agricultural products or unsophisticated technology-based manufacturing. Its current mix of Gross Domestic Product (30% agriculture; 17% industry; 53% service) does not appear to be going anywhere. Finally, the periodic depredations of cyclones and floods is a drag on economic development.

One of the major resources with potential to improve Bangladesh's economy and lessen its trade deficit is its reserves of natural gas, thought to be among the most plentiful in Asia. In April the United States agreed to provide technical assistance to help the country develop these resources.

GOVERNMENT AND POLITICS

Turmoil and confrontation continued to characterize Bangladesh's politics in 1999, with opposition leaders calling strikes that crippled transport and brought economic activity to a halt throughout the country. The opposition also boycotted the opening of the autumn session of Bangladesh's parliament over a controversial government plan to allow Indian goods to be transported through the country. Opposition leader Begum Khaleda Zia, head of the Bangladesh Nationalist Party, condemned the measure in spite of the millions of dollars in income it would bring in annually, declaring Indian passage through the country a threat to Bangladeshi security and sovereignty. The plan also provoked a three-day general strike by opposition groups. During roughly the same period, about 5,000 temporary workers at Chittagong port staged a weeklong walkout, which led to clashes with police; the workers were demanding permanent positions.

Tensions over the Bangladeshi border with India erupted into violence for the first time since 1996 as gunfire was exchanged between the Bangladesh rifle corps and India's border security force in a disputed area 210 kilometers (130 miles) southeast of Dhaka. Three civilian injuries were reported and nearby villages were evacuated.

In September Bangladeshi police conducted the biggest drug raid in the country's history, nabbing three Pakistanis in a Dhaka hotel with 24 kilograms of pure heroin worth over $5 million. The size of the heist underscored Bangladesh's popularity as a transit point for drug trade between Asia and the West. The government moved to curb political violence and organized crime by arresting over 50,000 people between May and July, which brought a decrease in lawlessness, although it was suspected that some perpetrators had taken refuge in India.

CULTURE AND SOCIETY

Separate events at the beginning of the year drew attention to the rights of women in Bangladesh. In January, feminist author Taslima Nasreen returned to exile in Sweden when Islamic militants renewed their death threats against her. Nasreen, who had advocated revising the Koran to change Muslim practices toward women, had returned to the country from Sweden to spend time with her ailing mother. The same month, a report by an international women's rights group stated that over 200,000 Bangladeshi women, mostly minors, had been transported to Pakistan since the late 1980s to work as prostitutes there.

The human rights focus shifted to children with a September report on child labor by UNICEF that estimated the number of child workers under the age of 14 in Bangladesh at 6.3 million or more; 12 percent were thought to be under 9 years old. The Bangladesh government, which had ratified a UN convention on children's rights in 1990, pledged that it would eradicate child labor by 2005.

In April Bangladesh was one of the countries affected by the "Chernobyl" computer virus; there was no estimate of the magnitude of the damage by the program, which was reported to have disabled at least 10,000 computers in neighboring India. Viruses of a different sort were one focus of a six-day regional meeting of Asian health officials sponsored by the World Health Organization in Dhaka, the Bangladeshi capital, in September. The meeting addressed regional health problems including AIDS, malnutrition, and vitamin deficiencies. In particular, Bangladesh was cited for the success of its campaign against polio, which had been eradicated from much of the world ten years earlier but had remained a problem on the Indian subcontinent. (The subcontinent accounted for 70 percent of polio victims worldwide.) Bangladesh's polio vaccination program, begun in 1995, virtually eradicated the disease from that country. The number of polio cases in children plummeted from 2,300 to 50. A new vaccination program, targeting young children in remote areas of the country, was expected to help WHO reach its goal of eradicating the disease worldwide by 2000.

DIRECTORY

CENTRAL GOVERNMENT
Head of State

President
Justice Shahabuddin Ahmed, Office of the President, Bangabhaba, Dhaka, Bangladesh
PHONE: +880 832066

Ministers

Prime Minister
Sheikh Hasina, Office of the Prime Minister
PHONE: +880 815100

Minister of Foreign Affairs
Abdus Samad Azad, Ministry of Foreign Affairs
PHONE: +880 9562852

Minister of LGRD and Co-operatives
Zillur Rahman, Ministry of LGRD and Co-operatives
PHONE: +880 864255; 869176

Minister of Finance
Sams Kibria, Ministry of Finance
PHONE: +880 864444; 865950

Minister of Education
A.S.H.K. Sadek, Ministry of Education
PHONE: +880 861395

Minister of Water Resources
Abdur Razzak, Ministry of Water Resources
PHONE: +880 861201; 862640

Minister of Industries and Commerce
Tofael Ahmed, Ministry of Industries and
Commerce
PHONE: +880 869679; 9563549

Minister of Science and Technology
Nooruddin Khan, Ministry of Science and
Technology
PHONE: +880 866484; 872422

Minister of Home Affairs and Post
Md. Nasim, Ministry of Home Affairs and Post
PHONE: +880 864800; 860690; 842858

**Minister of Agriculture, Food, Disaster
Management and Relief**
Matia Chowdhury, Ministry of Agriculture,
Food, Disaster Management and Relief
PHONE: +880 869277; 862240

Minister of Communication
Anwar Hossain, Ministry of Communication
PHONE: +880 864977; 814715

Minister of Health and Family Welfare
Salahuddin Yusuf, Ministry of Health and
Family Welfare
PHONE: +880 868008; 868188

Minister of Fisheries and Livestock
A.S.M. Abdur Rab, Ministry of Fisheries and
Livestock
PHONE: +880 862430; 872211

**Minister of Law, Justice and Parliament
Affairs**
Abdul Matin Khasru, Ministry of Law, Justice
and Parliament Affairs
PHONE: +880 860577; 860627

Minister of Environment and Forest
Syeda Sazeda Chowdhury, Ministry of
Environment and Forest
PHONE: +880 860587; 9342727

Minister of Labour and Employment
M.A. Mannan, Ministry of Labour and
Employment
PHONE: +880 868845; 842866

**Minister of Civil Aviation and Tourism and
Homing and Works**
Mosharrof Hossain, Ministry of Civil Aviation
and Tourism and Homing and Works
PHONE: +880 868070; 861141

Minister of Chittagong Hill Tracks Affairs
Kalpa Ranjan Chakma, Ministry of Chittagong
Hill Tracks Affairs
PHONE: +880 9129982

State Minister of Social Welfare
Mozammel Hossain, State Ministry of Social
Welfare
PHONE: +880 869766; 842722

State Minister of Primary and Mass Education
Satish Chandra Roy, State Ministry of Primary
and Mass Education
PHONE: +880 863461; 842818

**State Minister of Youth, Sports and Cultural
Affairs**
Obaidul Kader, State Ministry of Youth, Sports
and Cultural Affairs
PHONE: +880 864299; 860683

State Minister of Foreign Affairs
Abdul Hasan Chowdhury, State Ministry of
Foreign Affairs
PHONE: +880 9562104; 842699

State Minister of Religious Affairs
Maulana Md. Nurul Islam, State Ministry of
Religious Affairs
PHONE: +880 860761; 860682

State Minister of Jute, Textiles
A.K. Faizul Haque, State Ministry of Jute,
Textiles
PHONE: +880 861643; 860661

State Minister of Land
Hajee Rashed Mosharraf, State Ministry of Land
PHONE: +880 869644; 842899

State Minister of Information
Abu Sayeed, State Ministry of Information
PHONE: +880 862440; 860474

State Minister of Planning
Mohiuddin Khan Alamgir, State Ministry of
Planning
PHONE: +880 815175; 9883737

State Minister of Women and Child Affairs
Jinatunnesa Talukder, State Ministry of Women
and Child Affairs
PHONE: +880 861396; 9129010

State Minister of Health and Family Welfare
M. Amanullah, State Ministry of Health and
Family Welfare
PHONE: +880 865515; 9118520

State Minister of Disaster Management and Relief

Talukder Abdul Khaleque, State Ministry of Disaster Management and Relief
PHONE: +880 866262

State Minister of Shipping

Mofajjal Hossain Chowdhury Maya, State Ministry of Shipping
PHONE: +880 868155; 896882

State Minister of Power, Energy and Mineral Resources

Rafiqul Islam, State Ministry of Power, Energy and Mineral Resources
PHONE: +880 860568

State Minister of Textile

Akm Jahangir Hossain, State Ministry of Textile
PHONE: +880 860661

State Minister of Water Resources

Md. Alauddin, State Ministry of Water Resources
PHONE: +880 866851; 9350740

POLITICAL ORGANIZATIONS

Bangladesh Jatiyatabadi Dal-BJD (Bengal Nationalist Party)

NAME: Khaleda Zia

Jatiyo Dal-JD (Nationalist Party)

NAME: Hossain Mohammad Ershad

BAL (Awami League)

NAME: Sheikh Hasina Wajed

DIPLOMATIC REPRESENTATION

Embassies in Bangladesh

Nepal

UN Road, #2, Baridhara Diplomatic Enclave, Dhaka, Bangladesh
PHONE: +880 601890; 601790
E-MAIL: rnedhaka@bdmail.net
TITLE: Royal Nepalese Ambassador
NAME: Madhu Raman Acharya

United States

Diplomatic Enclave Madani Ave., Baridhara
G.P.O. Box 323, Dhaka 1212 Bangladesh
PHONE: +880 (2) 884700
FAX: +880 (2) 883744
TITLE: Ambassador
NAME: John C. Holzman

JUDICIAL SYSTEM

Supreme Court

FURTHER READING

Articles

"Bangladesh: Concern over Violence." *The New York Times*, 3 March 1999, p. A8.

"Bangladesh: International Prostitution." *The New York Times*, 29 January 1999, p. A9.

"Bangladesh: Writer Flees Again to Sweden." *The New York Times*, 27 January 1999, p. A9.

"Heavens Above." *The Economist* (July 17, 1999): 38.

Books

Baxter, Craig. *Bangladesh: From a Nation to a State*. Boulder, Colo.: Westview Press, 1997.

Choudhury, Dilara. *Constitutional Development in Bangladesh: Stresses and Strains*. New York: Oxford University Press, 1994.

BANGLADESH: STATISTICAL DATA

For sources and notes see "Sources of Statistics" in the front of each volume.

GEOGRAPHY

Geography (1)

Area:

Total: 144,000 sq km.

Land: 133,910 sq km.

Water: 10,090 sq km.

Area—comparative: slightly smaller than Wisconsin.

Land boundaries:

Total: 4,246 km.

Border countries: Burma 193 km, India 4,053 km.

Coastline: 580 km.

Climate: tropical; cool, dry winter (October to March); hot, humid summer (March to June); cool, rainy monsoon (June to October).

Terrain: mostly flat alluvial plain; hilly in southeast.

Natural resources: natural gas, arable land, timber.

Land use:

Arable land: 73%

Permanent crops: 2%

Permanent pastures: 5%

Forests and woodland: 15%

Other: 5% (1993 est.).

HUMAN FACTORS

Demographics (2A)

	1990	1995	1998	2000	2010	2020	2030	2040	2050
Population	NA	119,188.3	125,105.0	129,146.7	150,635.4	170,879.0	186,829.1	200,996.9	211,020.0
Net migration rate (per 1,000 population)	NA	NA	NA	NA	NA	NA	NA	NA	NA
Births	NA	NA	NA	NA	NA	NA	NA	NA	NA
Deaths	NA	NA	NA	NA	NA	NA	NA	NA	NA
Life expectancy - males	NA	59.0	60.3	61.2	65.2	68.7	71.6	73.9	75.7
Life expectancy - females	NA	58.0	59.8	61.1	66.9	72.0	76.1	79.3	81.6
Birth rate (per 1,000)	NA	26.6	25.5	24.8	22.2	17.0	15.2	14.1	12.6
Death rate (per 1,000)	NA	9.4	8.7	8.3	6.9	6.3	6.5	7.3	8.6
Women of reproductive age (15-49 yrs.)	NA	27,754.2	30,998.5	33,498.3	42,381.2	47,624.6	50,922.5	47,626.5	47,723.3
of which are currently married	NA	NA	NA	NA	NA	NA	NA	NA	NA
Fertility rate	NA	3.2	3.0	2.8	2.2	2.1	2.0	2.0	2.0

Except as noted, values for vital statistics are in thousands; life expectancy is in years.

Health Personnel (3)

Total health expenditure as a percentage of GDP, 1990-1997[a]

Public sector 1.2

Private sector 1.3

Total[b] 2.4

Health expenditure per capita in U.S. dollars, 1990-1997[a]

Purchasing power parity 24

Total 6

Availability of health care facilities per 100,000 people

Hospital beds 1990-1997[a] 30

Doctors 1993[c] 18

Nurses 1993[c] 5

Health Indicators (4)

Life expectancy at birth

1980 48

1997 58

Daily per capita supply of calories (1996) 2,105

Total fertility rate births per woman (1997) 3.2

Maternal mortality ratio per 100,000 live births (1990-97) . . . . .850[c]

Safe water % of population with access (1995) 84

Sanitation % of population with access (1995) 35

Consumption of iodized salt % of households (1992-98)[a] 78

Smoking prevalence

Male % of adults (1985-95)[a] 60

Female % of adults (1985-95)[a] 15

Tuberculosis incidence per 100,000 people (1997) 246

Adult HIV prevalence % of population ages 15-49 (1997) 0.03

Infants and Malnutrition (5)

Under-5 mortality rate (1997) 109

% of infants with low birthweight (1990-97) 50

Births attended by skilled health staff % of total[a] 8

% fully immunized (1995-97)

TB 91

DPT 68

Polio 68

Measles 62

Prevalence of child malnutrition under age 5 (1992-97)[b] 56

Ethnic Division (6)

Bengali 98%

Biharis 250,000

Tribals . . . .<1 million

Religions (7)

Muslim 88.3%

Hindu 10.5%

Other 1.2%

Languages (8)

Bangla (official), English.

EDUCATION

Public Education Expenditures (9)

Public expenditure on education (% of GNP)

1980 . . . . .1.5

1996 . . . . .2.9

Expenditure per student

Primary % of GNP per capita

1980 . . . . .4.8

1996 . . . .

Secondary % of GNP per capita

1980 . . . . .14.1[1]

1996 . . . .

Tertiary % of GNP per capita

1980 . . . . .46.7

1996 . . . .

Expenditure on teaching materials

Primary % of total for level (1996) . . . .

Secondary % of total for level (1996) . . . .

Primary pupil-teacher ratio per teacher (1996) . . . .

Duration of primary education years (1995) 5

Educational Attainment (10)

Age group (1981) . . . . .25+

Total population 31,593,122

Highest level attained (%)

No schooling 70.4

First level

Not completed 16.7

Completed . . . . .NA

Entered second level

S-1 . . . . .7.4

Literacy Rates (11A)

In thousands and percent[1]	1990	1995	2000	2010
Illiterate population (15+ yrs.)	40,704	45,082	49,983	58,616
Literacy rate - total adult pop. (%)	35.3	38.1	40.9	46.1
Literacy rate - males (%)	46.7	49.4	51.9	56.6
Literacy rate - females (%)	23.2	26.1	29.1	34.9

GOVERNMENT & LAW

Political Parties (12)

National Parliament	No. of seats
Awami League (AL) 178	
Bangladesh Nationalist Party (BNP) 113	
Jatiyo Party (JP) 33	
Jamaat-E-Islami (JI) 3	
Other 2	

Government Budget (13B)

Revenues . . . .$3.6 billion
Expenditures . . . .$5.3 billion
  Capital expenditures . . . .$3 billion
Data for FY96/97.

Military Affairs (14B)

	1990	1991	1992	1993	1994	1995
Military expenditures						
Current dollars (mil.)	317	304	345	433	475	502
1995 constant dollars (mil.)	365	336	372	454	486	502
Armed forces (000)	103	107	107	107	113	115
Gross national product (GNP)						
Current dollars (mil.)	20,580	22,150	23,720	25,420	27,130	29,010
1995 constant dollars (mil.)	23,650	24,480	25,510	26,650	27,810	29,010
Central government expenditures (CGE)						
1995 constant dollars (mil.)	NA	3,989	4,071	4,579[e]	NA	NA
People (mil.)	110.1	112.2	114.3	116.4	118.6	120.8
Military expenditure as % of GNP	1.5	1.4	1.5	1.7	1.7	1.7
Military expenditure as % of CGE	NA	8.4	9.1	9.9	NA	NA
Military expenditure per capita (1995 $)	3	3	3	4	4	4
Armed forces per 1,000 people (soldiers)	.9	1.0	.9	.9	1.0	1.0
GNP per capita (1995 $)	215	218	223	229	235	240
Arms imports[6]						
Current dollars (mil.)	40	80	40	30	30	60
1995 constant dollars (mil.)	46	88	43	31	31	60
Arms exports[6]						
Current dollars (mil.)	0	0	0	0	0	0
1995 constant dollars (mil.)	0	0	0	0	0	0
Total imports[7]						
Current dollars (mil.)	3,598	3,401	3,888	4,001	4,701	6,496
1995 constant dollars (mil.)	4,135	3,758	4,182	4,195	4,819	6,496
Total exports[7]						
Current dollars (mil.)	1,671	1,689	2,098	2,272	2,661	3,173
1995 constant dollars (mil.)	1,920	1,866	2,257	2,382	2,728	3,173
Arms as percent of total imports[8]	1.1	2.4	1.0	.7	.6	.9
Arms as percent of total exports[8]	0	0	0	0	0	0

Crime (15)

Crime rate (for 1997)

Crimes reported 102,200

Total persons convicted 94,400

Crimes per 100,000 population 82

Persons responsible for offenses

Total number of suspects 370,500

Total number of female suspects 8,950

Total number of juvenile suspects 375

LABOR FORCE

Labor Force (16)

Total (million) 56

Agriculture 63%

Services 25%

Industry and mining 10%

Extensive export of labor to Saudi Arabia, Kuwait, UAE, and Oman. Data for 1996. Percent distribution for 1996.

Unemployment Rate (17)

35.2% (1996).

PRODUCTION SECTOR

Electric Energy (18)

Capacity . . . . .2.978 million kW (1995)

Production . . . . .11.5 billion kWh (1997)

Consumption per capita . . . . .71 kWh (1997 est.)

Transportation (19)

Highways:

total: 223,391 km

paved: 16,084 km

unpaved: 207,307 km (1995 est.)

Waterways: 5,150-8,046 km navigable waterways (includes 2,575-3,058 km main cargo routes)

Pipelines: natural gas 1,220 km

Merchant marine:

total: 39 ships (1,000 GRT or over) totaling 310,728 GRT/444,245 DWT ships by type: bulk 2, cargo 31, oil tanker 2, refrigerated cargo 2, roll-on/roll-off cargo 2 (1997 est.)

Airports: 16 (1997 est.)

Airports—with paved runways:

total: 15

over 3,047 m: 1

2,438 to 3,047 m: 2

1,524 to 2,437 m: 4

914 to 1,523 m: 1

under 914 m: 7 (1997 est.)

Airports—with unpaved runways:

total: 1

over 3,047 m: 1 (1997 est.)

Top Agricultural Products (20)

Rice, jute, tea, wheat, sugarcane, potatoes; beef, milk, poultry.

MANUFACTURING SECTOR

GDP & Manufacturing Summary (21)

Detailed value added figures are listed by both International Standard Industry Code (ISIC) and product title.

	1980	1985	1990	1994
GDP ($-1990 mil.)[1]	14,177	17,610	21,336	25,269
Per capita ($-1990)[1]	161	179	197	215
Manufacturing share (%) (current prices)[1]	11.0	9.9	8.7	10.4
Manufacturing				
Value added ($-1990 mil.)[1]	1,374	1,523	1,866	2,647
Industrial production index	100	100	116	148
Value added ($ mil.)	834	863	1,759	2,576
Gross output ($ mil.)	2,253	2,497	5,504	7,430
Employment (000)	412	469	1,028	1,240
Profitability (% of gross output)				
Intermediate input (%)	63	65	68	65
Wages and salaries inc. supplements (%)	12	10	16	17
Gross operating surplus	25	24	16	18
Productivity ($)				
Gross output per worker	5,466	5,191	4,418	4,966
Value added per worker	2,023	1,793	1,412	1,722
Average wage (inc. supplements)	639	557	859	1,016
Value added ($ mil.)				
311/2 Food products	78	98	265	359
313 Beverages	7	6	4	6
314 Tobacco products	111	109	153	225
321 Textiles	336	230	439	617
322 Wearing apparel	—	8	158	225

	1980	1985	1990	1994
323 Leather and fur products	18	14	42	62
324 Footwear	4	10	21	34
331 Wood and wood products	3	10	14	21
332 Furniture and fixtures	1	2	6	9
341 Paper and paper products	23	19	53	86
342 Printing and publishing	6	8	23	36
351 Industrial chemicals	33	70	134	199
352 Other chemical products	97	85	166	274
353 Petroleum refineries	2	75	9	16
354 Miscellaneous petroleum and coal products	1	2	1	1
355 Rubber products	4	1	5	8
356 Plastic products	—	2	14	19
361 Pottery, china and earthenware	2	4	10	15
362 Glass and glass products	4	4	7	10
369 Other non-metal mineral products	14	7	31	46
371 Iron and steel	39	35	43	69
372 Non-ferrous metals	—	—	—	—
381 Metal products	9	13	22	32
382 Non-electrical machinery	4	17	7	12
383 Electrical machinery	19	18	60	88
384 Transport equipment	11	10	56	80
385 Professional and scientific equipment	—	—	—	—
390 Other manufacturing industries	8	7	18	27

FINANCE, ECONOMICS, & TRADE

Economic Indicators (22)

National product: GDP—purchasing power parity—$167 billion (1997 est.)

National product real growth rate: 5.5% (1997 est.)

National product per capita: $1,330 (1997 est.)

Inflation rate—consumer price index: 2.5% (1996)

Exchange Rates (24)

Exchange rates:

Taka (Tk) per US$1

January 1998	45.450
1997	43.892
1996	41.794
1995	40.278
1994	40.212
1993	39.567

Top Import Origins (25)

$6.9 billion (1996) Data are for FY95/96 est.

Origins	%
India	21
China	10
Western Europe	8
Hong Kong	7
Singapore	6

Balance of Payments (23)

	1990	1992	1994	1995	1996
Exports of goods (f.o.b.)	1,672	2,098	2,934	3,733	4,009
Imports of goods (f.o.b.)	−3,259	−3,354	−4,350	−6,057	−6,264
Trade balance	−1,587	−1,256	−1,416	−2,324	−2,255
Services - debits	−880	−955	−1,214	−1,733	−1,347
Services - credits	456	583	740	968	734
Private transfers (net)	852	1,047	1,349	1,454	1,617
Government transfers (net)	762	761	740	811	292
Overall balance	−398	181	199	−824	−958

Top Export Destinations (26)

$3.9 billion (1996). Data are for FY95/96 est.

Destinations	%
Western Europe	.42
United States	.30
Hong Kong	.4
Japan	.3

Economic Aid (27)

Recipient: $1.475 billion (FY96/97).

Import Export Commodities (28)

Import Commodities	Export Commodities
Capital goods	Garments
Textiles	Jute and jute goods
Food	Leather
Petroleum products (FY95/96 est.)	Frozen fish and seafood

BARBADOS

CAPITAL: Bridgetown.

FLAG: The national flag has three equal vertical bands of ultramarine blue, gold, and ultramarine blue and displays a broken trident in black on the center stripe.

ANTHEM: *National Anthem of Barbados,* beginning "In plenty and in time of need, when this fair land was young. . . ."

MONETARY UNIT: Officially introduced on 3 December 1973, the Barbados dollar (BDS $) of 100 cents is a paper currency officially pegged to the U.S. dollar. There are coins of 1, 5, 10, and 25 cents and 1 dollar, and notes of 1, 2, 5, 10, 20, 50, and 100 dollars. BDS $1 = US $0.49772 (or US $1 = BDS $2.011)

WEIGHTS AND MEASURES: The metric system is used.

HOLIDAYS: New Year's Day, 1 January; Errol Barrow Day, 23 January; May Day, 1 May; Kadooment Day, 1st Monday in August; CARICOM Day, 1 August; UN Day, 1st Monday in October; Independence Day, 30 November; Christmas Day, 25 December; Boxing Day, 26 December. Movable religious holidays are Good Friday, Easter Monday, and Whitmonday.

TIME: 8 AM = noon GMT.

LOCATION AND SIZE: Barbados has an area of 430 square kilometers (166 square miles), slightly less than 2.5 times the area of Washington, D.C., and a total coastline of 101 kilometers (63 miles). The capital city of Barbados, Bridgetown, is located on the country's southwestern coast.

CLIMATE: The tropical climate is tempered by an almost constant sea breeze. Temperatures range from 24° to 29°C (75–84°F). Annual rainfall ranges from about 100 centimeters (40 inches) to 230 centimeters (90 inches).

INTRODUCTORY SURVEY

RECENT HISTORY

When the British landed on Barbados in 1625, the island was uninhabited. Almost 2,000 English settlers landed in 1627–28. Soon afterward, the island developed a sugar-based economy, supported by a slave population. Slavery was abolished in 1834, and the last slaves were freed in 1838.

During the following 100 years, the economic fortunes of Barbados rose and fell with alternating booms and slumps in the sugar trade. In the 1930s, the dominance of plantation owners and merchants was challenged by a labor movement. The gradual introduction of social and political reforms led to the granting of universal adult suffrage in 1950.

The island was proclaimed an independent republic on 30 November 1966. Political stability has been maintained since that time. In 1973, the nation began issuing its own currency. The country was a staging area in October 1983 for the U.S.-led invasion of Grenada, in which Barbadian troops took part.

Laws enacted in the early 1980s led to the development of Barbados as an offshore business center. The international recession of the early 1990s negatively affected the economy, which led to a lack of support for the government. In June 1994, Prime Minister Erskine Sandiford dissolved the House of Assembly, the first time since independence that such an action had been taken.

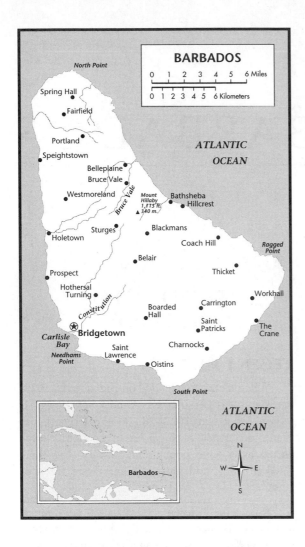

BARBADOS

GOVERNMENT

Barbados has a crown-appointed governor-general (who in turn appoints an advisory privy council) and independent executive, legislative, and judicial bodies. The two-chamber legislature consists of a 21-member appointed Senate and a 28-member elected House of Assembly. Voting is universal at age 18. The governor-general appoints as prime minister a member of the House of Assembly.

Judiciary

The Supreme Court of Judicature sits as a high court and court of appeal. Magistrate courts have both civil and criminal jurisdiction. Final appeals are brought to the Committee of Her Majesty's Privy Council in the United Kingdom.

Political Parties

The leading parties are the Barbados Labor Party (BLP), the Democratic Labour Party (DLP),

and the National Democratic Party (NDP). After the legislature was dissolved in June 1994, the elections of September 1994 gave the BLP the majority, with 19 of 28 seats.

DEFENSE

The Barbados Defense Force and the Royal Barbados Police Force number about 1,000. The defense budget was US $14 million in 1996.

ECONOMIC AFFAIRS

The economy has traditionally depended on the production of sugar, rum, and molasses. In recent years, however, tourism and manufacturing have surpassed the sugar industry in importance.

The gross domestic product (GDP) grew by 4.4% in 1996, compared to an annual average of 3.4% during 1994–95. Barbados was in an economic recession during 1990–94.

Public Finance

Revenues are derived mostly from import duties, internal consumption taxes, and income tax. Public sector deficits grew during the 1980s as the economy weakened. The international recession of 1990–91 magnified problems of debt service and debt management. By the end of 1990, the national debt was U.S.$928.3 million, 9.5% higher than 1989. By 1991, the fiscal deficit had become unsustainable; in February 1992, the government began a stabilization program in fiscal policies with assistance from the IMF. The U.S. Central Intelligence Agency estimates that, in 1995, government revenues totaled approximately U.S.$550 million and expenditures U.S.$710 million, including capital expenditures of U.S.$86 million. External debt totaled U.S.$405 million.

Income

In 1996, Barbados' gross national product (GNP) was US $1.99 billion at current prices, or US $7,538 per person.

Industry

Traditionally, sugar production and related enterprises were Barbados' primary industry, but light industry has become more important. Items manufactured for export include soap, glycerin, pharmaceuticals, furniture, household appliances, plastic products, fabricated metal products, and cotton garments.

Banking and Finance

The bank of issue is the Central Bank of Barbados. The fiscal deficit for the first three-quarters of 1996 was BD $73.2 million (US$36.6 million), or 2.5% of GDP. Capital expenditure appears to have been the key to the growth of the deficit. Bank claims on the central government, according to the IMF, rose from BD $714 million at the end of 1995 to BD $889 million at the end of September 1996. The total value of Treasury bills outstanding also increased by BD $100 million between January and April 1996, reaching BD $595.5 million.

There is no stock exchange in Barbados, although the Central Bank has established the Barbados Securities Marketing Corp. in anticipation of the future development of a securities exchange.

Economic Development

The government has been making efforts to relieve the island's economic dependence on sugar by establishing industries and encouraging tourism. In 1957, the Barbados Development Board (now the Barbados Industrial Development Corp.) was established. The development plan for 1979–83 called for expansion of the construction sector. During 1962–86, multilateral aid to Barbados totaled U.S.$123.1 million, of which 24% was from the IDB and 57% from the World Bank.

The island's economy has been growing since the mid-1980s. GDP growth was 4.5% in 1996. Total tourist numbers rose by 3.3%, with 5% growth in cruise business and a 1% increase in stayover arrivals. Sugar rebounded from the 1995 drought to record a 52% increase. Unemployment fell to an average of 16.2% of the labor force in the first three-quarters of 1996, from 20.7% in the comparable period of the previous year. A major share of the new jobs, as much as one third, were created in the public sector. Employment creation in 1996 did not lead to a significant change in the overall gender gap in employment opportunities. The existing incomes policy, as contained in the tripartite (labor, management, government) 1995–97 Wages and Prices Protocol, held back wage inflation in 1996; but, unlike the case in the years since 1993, when the current incomes policy was put in place, wage pressures unrelated to productivity changes were strongly felt because of a salary increase for public sector workers.

SOCIAL WELFARE

A national social security system provides old age and survivors' pensions, sickness, disability, maternity benefits, and employment injury benefits. The Family Planning Association receives government support. The 1992 Domestic Violence law requires a police response to violence against women and children.

Healthcare

In 1993, there were 1,100 people per physician, and 100% of the population had access to health care services. Life expectancy during 1994 was 76 years.

Housing

The Barbados Housing Authority constructs housing projects, and redevelops overcrowded areas. In 1980, 90% of all housing consisted of detached homes and 6% of apartments.

EDUCATION

Education is compulsory for children between the ages of 5 and 16. In 1991, children in 106 primary schools numbered 26,662. The Barbados branch of the University of the West Indies opened in 1963, and the Barbados Community College was established in 1968. Barbados' adult illiteracy rate in 1995 was 3%.

1999 KEY EVENTS TIMELINE

February

- A World Bank study finds Barbados only partially Y2K compliant.

June

- Prime Minister Arthur announces the establishment of the Institute for Solar Research.

July

- The United Nations names Barbados the best place to live in Caribbean.

August

- The prime minister's budget focuses on economic competitiveness.

October

- The anti-AIDS drug AZT is made more available and affordable.

- Dead fish, including snapper, parrotfish, and angelfish among others, are washing up on beaches around the Caribbean, especially in Barbados, St. Vincent and the Grenadines, Grenada, and Trinidad and Tobago. Health inspectors and scientists are searching for an explanation.

ANALYSIS OF EVENTS: 1999

BUSINESS AND THE ECONOMY

In February a World Bank study warned Barbados that many of its important computer systems were not Y2K compliant. (The Y2K millennium bug arose because old computer programs, when reading the date, see the year as only two numbers; therefore, when seeing 00 for the year 2000, computers could interpret this as 1900.) The study said that Barbados had only a "medium awareness" of the problem, with almost no media coverage of Y2K in Barbados. If uncorrected, the Y2K millennium bug could affect banking, transportation, and personal computers. Immediately after the World Bank report, the Barbados Mutual Life Assurance Society formed a Y2K Project Team to update their computer systems, and in May one of the largest banks in Barbados, Canadian Imperial Bank of Commerce, completed the installation of new Y2K-compliant integrated banking systems. These steps were seen as a positive improvement, though overall preparedness lagged seriously behind that of developed countries.

During a visit to Havana, Cuba in June, Prime Minister Owen Arthur announced the establishment of the Institute for Solar Research. Arthur said, "Solar research is an area of tremendous potential for the future." While meeting with Fidel Castro, Arthur also laid the groundwork for exporting solar energy to Cuba.

In July Roy Ward, chairman of the West Indies Sea Island Cotton Association, predicted a gloomy future for Barbados' cotton growers. With worldwide prices depressed, Ward said that most cotton producers in Barbados were operating at a loss and would likely decide against planting cotton in the future.

GOVERNMENT AND POLITICS

On August 24, Prime Minister Owen Arthur delivered a budget that focused on stimulating foreign trade. Arthur said that his aim was to make Barbados the most competitive Caribbean country by the year 2005, when the Carricom Single Market takes effect. The Carricom Single Market agreement will ease tariffs and other market protections. Looking ahead to 2005, Arthur announced that he had already begun negotiations with the European Union and the North American Free Trade Area. In his annual televised speech to the House of Assembly, Arthur said that for Barbados to compete on the world market, it must curtail excessive consumer demand driven by easy access to credit, and Barbados must seek to reverse the trend of falling exports and declining tourism.

On June 23, Barbados signed a new Air Services Agreement with the United Kingdom, replacing an agreement signed in 1971. The new agreement will expand coverage and improve the transport of people, cargo and mail. The agreement is part of the government's ongoing effort to stimulate trade and tourism.

In yet another step towards a single Caribbean market, Prime Minister Arthur announced in July that Barbados would lift the ban against importing foreign soft drinks. Later, in August, Prime Minister Arthur pressured Trinidad and Tobago to lower oil prices. Because of treaties, Barbados is locked into buying oil from within the region, and Prime Minister Arthur complained that Trinidad and Tobago were charging above world market prices for gasoline and diesel fuel.

CULTURE AND SOCIETY

The Pan American Health Organization (PAHO) announced a plan to make the anti-AIDS drug AZT more available and affordable in developing countries. The plan focused on pregnant women. Medical researchers suspect that AZT lowers the chances that an HIV-positive woman will pass the virus on to her baby. The plan will help the anti-AIDS efforts already in place in Barbados. Over the last few years, the government spent approximately $150,000 to treat 32 HIV-positive pregnant women. More than half of the babies born to those women did not contract HIV.

In July the United Nations announced that Barbados was the best place to live in the Caribbean. The U.N. Human Development report considered such factors as health care, life expectancy, education, and income. Overall, Barbados placed twenty-ninth on the list of the world's most livable countries. (Topping the list were Canada, the United States, Norway, and Japan. Sierra Leone placed last.)

Later in the year, however, the U.N. released less favorable news regarding Barbados. The U.N. Environmental Program (UNEP) warned that small-island developing states, like Barbados, would face serious ecological problems in the future unless steps are taken to protect against land degradation, water shortages, and pollution. Five years ago, at a conference held in Barbados, the forty-three-member Alliance of Small Island States pledged to more actively engage in environmental protection. So far, though, the reality has fallen short of the conference pledges. Overpopulation, unsustainable consumption, poverty, and climate change all contributed to environmental decline.

DIRECTORY

CENTRAL GOVERNMENT

Head of State

Monarch
Elizabeth II, Queen of England

Governor-General
Clifford Straughn Husbands

Prime Minister
Owen Seymour Arthur, Office of the Prime Minister, Government Headquarters, Bay St., St Michael, Barbados
PHONE: +(246) 4363179
FAX: +(246) 4369280
E-MAIL: office@primeminister.gov.bb

Ministers

Minister of Defense and Security
Owen Seymour Arthur, Ministry of Defense and Security, Government Headquarters, Bay St., St Michael, Barbados
PHONE: +(246) 4366435

Minister of Finance and Economic Affairs
Owen Seymour Arthur, Ministry of Finance and Economic Affairs, Government Headquarters, Bay St., St Michael, Barbados
PHONE: +(246) 4262814
FAX: +(246) 4294032

Minister of Foreign Affairs and Foreign Trade
Billie A. Miller, Ministry of Foreign Affairs and Foreign Trade, 1 Culloden Rd., St. Michael, Barbados
PHONE: +(246) 4362990
FAX: +(246) 4296652; 2280838
E-MAIL: foreign@foreign.barbadosgov.org

Minister of Home Affairs
David A.C. Simmons, Ministry of Home Affairs, Level 5, General Post Office Building, Cheapside, Bridgetown, St. Michael, Barbados
PHONE: +(246) 2288950
FAX: +(246) 4373794

Minister of Agriculture and Rural Development
Anthony Wood, Ministry of Agriculture and Rural Development, Graeme Hall, Christ Church, Barbados
PHONE: +(246) 4284061
FAX: +(246) 4208444

Minister of Education, Youth Affairs and Culture
Mia A. Mottley, Ministry of Education, Youth Affairs and Culture, Dame Elsie Payne Complex, Constitution Rd., St. Michael, Barbados
PHONE: +(246) 426 5416
FAX: +(246) 436 2411

Minister of Health
H. Elizabeth Thompson, Ministry of Health

Minister of Labour, Sports and Public Reform
Rudolph N. Greenridge, Ministry of Labour, Sports and Public Reform, Dockland Place, Cavans Lane, Bridgetown, Barbados
PHONE: +(246) 4277550
FAX: +(246) 4268959
E-MAIL: mrsumlc@sunbeach.net

Minister of Transport and Public Works
Phillip C. Goddard, Ministry of Transport and Public Works, The Pine, St. Michael, Barbados
PHONE: +(246) 4264452
FAX: +(246) 4378133

Minister of Tourism and International Transport
George W. Payne, Ministry of Tourism and International Transport

Minister of Environment, Energy and Natural Resources
Rawle C. Eastmond, Ministry of Environment, Energy and Natural Resources

Minister of Industry and International Business
Reginald R. Farley, Ministry of Industry and International Business, The Business Centre, Upton, St. Michael, Barbados
PHONE: +(246) 4302200
FAX: +(246) 2286167

Minister of Government Headquarters

Glyne Murray, Ministry of Government
Headquarters, Bay Street, St. Michael, Barbados
PHONE: +(246) 4366435
FAX: +(246) 4369280

Minister of Consumer Affairs and Business Development

Ronald Toppin, Ministry of Commerce,
Consumer Affairs and Business Development,
Reef Road, Fontabelle, St. Michael, Barbados
PHONE: +(246) 4264452
FAX: +(246) 4310056

Minister of Social Transformation

Hamilton Lashley, Ministry of Social
Transformation

Minister of Housing and Lands

Gline Arley Clarke, Ministry of Housing and
Lands

POLITICAL ORGANIZATIONS

Barbados Labour Party-BLP

Grantley Adams House, 111 Roebuck St.,
Bridgetown, Barbados
PHONE: +(246) 4291990; 4378980
E-MAIL: hq@blp.org.bb
NAME: Owen S. Arthur

Democratic Labour Party-DLP

George St., Beleville, St. Michael, Barbados
PHONE: +(246) 4293104
FAX: +(246) 4293007
E-MAIL: dlp@dlpbarbados.bb
NAME: David Thompson

National Democratic Party-NDP

3 Sixth Avenue, Belleville, Barbados
PHONE: +(246) 4296882
NAME: Richard Haynes

DIPLOMATIC REPRESENTATION

Embassies in Barbados

Australia

Bishop's Court Hill, St. Michael, Barbados
PHONE: +(246) 4352834
FAX: +(246) 4352896
E-MAIL: paul.smith@dsat.gov.au

Brazil

3rd Floor, Sunjet House, Fairchild Street,
Bridgetown, Barbados
PHONE: +(246) 4271735
FAX: +(246) 4295563; 4325566
E-MAIL: brembarb@sunbeach.net

Canada

P.O. Box 404, Bishops Court Hill, Barbados
PHONE: +(246) 4293550
FAX: +(246) 4293780
E-MAIL: shirley.hardy@dfait-maeci.gc.ca

People's Republic of China

17 Golf View Terrace, Rockley, Christ Church,
Barbados
PHONE: +(246) 4356890
FAX: +(246) 4358300
E-MAIL: chineseembbds@caribsurf.com

Colombia

P.O. Box 37W, Rockley, Christ Church,
Barbados
PHONE: +(246) 4296821
FAX: +(246) 4295563; 4325566
E-MAIL: colombiaembassy@sunbeach.net

Costa Rica

105 F Durants South, Christ Church, Barbados
PHONE: +(246) 4320194
FAX: +(246) 4295563; 4325566
E-MAIL: ember@sunbeach.net

Cuba

Erin Court, Ground Floor, Bishops Court Hill,
St. Michael, Barbados
PHONE: +(246) 4352769; 4352772
FAX: +(246) 4352534
E-MAIL: embacuba@sunbeach.net

Guatemala

2nd Floor, Trident House, Lower Broad Street,
Bridgetown, Barbados
PHONE: +(246) 4352542
FAX: +(246) 4352638
E-MAIL: embaguatebar@sunbeach.net

United Kingdom

Lower Collymore Rock, St. Michael, Barbados
PHONE: +(246) 4366694
FAX: +(246) 4365398
E-MAIL: britishhc@sunbeach.net

United States

Canadian Imperial Bank of Commerce Building,
Broad Street, Bridgetown, Barbados
PHONE: +(246) 4364950
FAX: +(246) 4295246
E-MAIL: mpobarbados@yahoo.com

Venezuela

Hastings Main Road, Christ Church, Barbados

PHONE: +(246) 4357619
FAX: +(246) 4357830
E-MAIL: embaven@sunbeach.net

JUDICIAL SYSTEM
Supreme Court

Judiciary Office, Bridgetown, Barbados
PHONE: +(246) 4262461

FURTHER READING
Articles

Ail, Ken. "Study Finds Barbados and TT Only Partially Y2K Compliant." *The Broad Street Journal*, 3 February 1999.

———. "UN HD Report: Barbados the Best Caribbean Country in which to Live." *The Broad Street Journal*, 26 July 1999.

Hoyos, Patrick. "Ward: Barbados Cotton Crop in Jeopardy." *The Broad Street Journal*, 9 July 1999.

———. "Arthur: Budget Aims to Make Barbados More Competitive." *The Broad Street Journal*, 26 August 1999.

Ljunggren, David. "Small Island States Face Ecological Woes—U.N." *Reuters*, 28 September 1999.

BARBADOS:
STATISTICAL DATA

For sources and notes see "Sources of Statistics" in the front of each volume.

GEOGRAPHY

Geography (1)

Area:

Total: 430 sq km.

Land: 430 sq km.

Water: 0 sq km.

Area—comparative: 2.5 times the size of Washington, DC.

Land boundaries: 0 km.

Coastline: 97 km.

Climate: tropical; rainy season (June to October).

Terrain: relatively flat; rises gently to central highland region.

Natural resources: petroleum, fish, natural gas.

Land use:

Arable land: 37%

Permanent crops: 0%

Permanent pastures: 5%

Forests and woodland: 12%

Other: 46% (1993 est.).

HUMAN FACTORS

Demographics (2A)

	1990	1995	1998	2000	2010	2020	2030	2040	2050
Population	255.0	257.9	259.0	259.2	264.8	275.3	279.9	275.9	265.9
Net migration rate (per 1,000 population)	NA	NA	NA	NA	NA	NA	NA	NA	NA
Births	NA	NA	NA	NA	NA	NA	NA	NA	NA
Deaths	2.2	NA	NA	NA	NA	NA	NA	NA	NA
Life expectancy - males	69.6	71.5	72.0	72.4	74.1	75.4	76.6	77.5	78.2
Life expectancy - females	75.2	77.1	77.6	78.0	79.7	81.0	82.2	83.1	83.9
Birth rate (per 1,000)	18.3	16.3	14.9	14.0	12.4	11.5	10.4	9.9	9.6
Death rate (per 1,000)	9.2	8.3	8.2	8.1	7.9	8.5	10.3	12.7	13.9
Women of reproductive age (15-49 yrs.)	70.1	71.3	71.8	71.6	67.3	62.9	60.7	58.1	53.7
of which are currently married	43.8	NA	NA	NA	NA	NA	NA	NA	NA
Fertility rate	2.0	1.9	1.9	1.8	1.8	1.8	1.7	1.7	1.7

Except as noted, values for vital statistics are in thousands; life expectancy is in years.

Infants and Malnutrition (5)

Under-5 mortality rate (1997) 12

% of infants with low birthweight (1990-97) 10

Births attended by skilled health staff % of total[a] . . .NA

% fully immunized (1995-97)

TB . . . . .NA

DPT 96

Polio 96

Measles 92

Prevalence of child malnutrition under age 5
(1992-97)[b] . . . . .NA

Ethnic Division (6)

Black 80%

White 4%

Other 16%

Religions (7)

Protestant 67%

Anglican 40%

Pentecostal 8%

Methodist 7%

Other 12%

Roman Catholic 4%

None 17%

Unknown 3%

Other 9%

Data for 1980.

Languages (8)

English.

EDUCATION

Educational Attainment (10)

Age group (1980) . . . . .25+

Total population 116,874

Highest level attained (%)

No schooling 0.8

First level

Not completed 63.5

Completed . . . . .NA

Entered second level

S-1 . . . . .32.3

S-2 . . . . .NA

Postsecondary 3.3

Literacy Rates (11A)

In thousands and percent[1]	1990	1995	2000	2010
Illiterate population (15+ yrs.)	6	5	4	3
Literacy rate - total adult pop. (%)	96.8	97.4	97.9	98.6
Literacy rate - males (%)	97.7	98.0	98.4	98.8
Literacy rate - females (%)	95.9	96.8	97.4	98.4

GOVERNMENT & LAW

Political Parties (12)

House of Assembly	No. of seats
Barbados Labor Party (BLP)	19
Democratic Labor Party (DLP)	8
National Democratic Party (NDP)	1

Government Budget (13B)

Revenues . . . .$600 million

Expenditures . . . .$645 million

Capital expenditures . . . .$80 million

Data for FY96/97 est.

Crime (15)

Crime rate (for 1997)

Crimes reported 10,200

Total persons convicted 3,900

Crimes per 100,000 population 3,850

Persons responsible for offenses

Total number of suspects 4,050

Total number of female suspects 275

Total number of juvenile suspects 125

LABOR FORCE

Labor Force (16)

Total 68,900

Services 75%

Industry 15%

Agriculture 10%

Data for 1996. Percent distribution for 1996 est.

Unemployment Rate (17)

16.2% (1996)

GOVERNMENT & LAW

Military Affairs (14B)

	1990	1991	1992	1993	1994	1995
Military expenditures						
Current dollars (mil.)	NA	NA	NA	12	13	13
1995 constant dollars (mil.)	NA	NA	NA	12	13	13
Armed forces (000)	0	0	0	0	0	0
Gross national product (GNP)						
Current dollars (mil.)	1,487	1,489	1,477	1,515	1,617	1,690[e]
1995 constant dollars (mil.)	1,709	1,645	1,589	1,589	1,657	1,690[e]
Central government expenditures (CGE)						
1995 constant dollars (mil.)	588[e]	545[e]	522[e]	548[e]	542[e]	554[e]
People (mil.)	.3	.3	.3	.3	.3	.3
Military expenditure as % of GNP	NA	NA	NA	.8	.8	.8
Military expenditure as % of CGE	NA	NA	NA	2.3	2.4	2.3
Military expenditure per capita (1995 $)	NA	NA	NA	49	50	50
Armed forces per 1,000 people (soldiers)	1.8	1.6	1.6	1.6	0	0
GNP per capita (1994 $)	6,716	6,460	6,231	6,221	6,478	6,593
Arms imports[6]						
Current dollars (mil.)	0	0	0	0	0	0
1995 constant dollars (mil.)	0	0	0	0	0	0
Arms exports[6]						
Current dollars (mil.)	0	0	0	0	0	0
1995 constant dollars (mil.)	0	0	0	0	0	0
Total imports[7]						
Current dollars (mil.)	700	694	521	574	611	763
1995 constant dollars (mil.)	804	767	560	602	626	763
Total exports[7]						
Current dollars (mil.)	209	205	191	179	185	235
1995 constant dollars (mil.)	240	227	205	188	190	235
Arms as percent of total imports[8]	0	0	0	0	0	0
Arms as percent of total exports[8]	0	0	0	0	0	0

PRODUCTION SECTOR

Electric Energy (18)

Capacity . . . . .140,000 kW (1995)

Production . . . . .591.5 million kWh (1996)

Consumption per capita . . . . .2,145 kWh (1995)

Transportation (19)

Highways:

total: 1,640 km

paved: 1,573 km

unpaved: 67 km (1996 est.)

Merchant marine:

total: 57 ships (1,000 GRT or over) totaling 869,363 GRT/1,365,640 DWT ships by type: bulk 15, cargo 30, container 1, combination bulk 4, multifunction large-load carrier 1, oil tanker 4, refrigerated cargo 1, roll-on/roll-off cargo 1 note: a flag of convenience registry; includes ships of 2 countries: Canada owns 2 ships, Hong Kong 1 (1997 est.)

Airports: 1 (1997 est.)

Airports—with paved runways:

total: 1

over 3,047 m: 1 (1997 est.)

Top Agricultural Products (20)

Sugarcane, vegetables, cotton.

MANUFACTURING SECTOR

GDP & Manufacturing Summary (21)

Detailed value added figures are listed by both International Standard Industry Code (ISIC) and product title.

	1980	1985	1990	1994
GDP ($-1990 mil.)[1]	1,506	1,447	1,743	1,691
Per capita ($-1990)[1]	6,049	5,720	6,783	6,478
Manufacturing share (%) (current prices)[1]	11.9	10.6	7.8	8.8
Manufacturing				
Value added ($-1990 mil.)[1]	127	110	118	107
Industrial production index	100	87	88	80
Value added ($ mil.)	53	90	95	100
Gross output ($ mil.)	241	383	412	434
Employment (000)	8	9	7	6
Profitability (% of gross output)				
Intermediate input (%)	78	77	77	78
Wages and salaries inc. supplements (%)	14	18	16	14
Gross operating surplus	8	5	7	8
Productivity ($)				
Gross output per worker	31,297	41,552	60,974	74,716
Value added per worker	6,853	9,724	13,984	16,472
Average wage (inc. supplements)	4,336	7,725	9,537	10,684
Value added ($ mil.)				
311/2 Food products	12	25	30	27
313 Beverages	6	12	10	16
314 Tobacco products	1	2	1	2
321 Textiles	—	—	1	1
322 Wearing apparel	6	7	5	2
323 Leather and fur products	—	—	—	—
324 Footwear	—	—	—	—
331 Wood and wood products	—	—	—	—
332 Furniture and fixtures	1	2	2	1
341 Paper and paper products	—	1	1	1
342 Printing and publishing	4	8	10	10
351 Industrial chemicals	—	1	2	2
352 Other chemical products	1	3	4	3
353 Petroleum refineries	—	—	—	—
354 Miscellaneous petroleum and coal products	—	—	—	—
355 Rubber products	2	2	4	4
356 Plastic products	1	3	4	6
361 Pottery, china and earthenware	—	—	—	—
362 Glass and glass products	—	—	1	—
369 Other non-metal mineral products	3	−3	5	2
371 Iron and steel	—	—	—	—
372 Non-ferrous metals	—	—	—	—
381 Metal products	3	5	10	9
382 Non-electrical machinery	5	11	3	5
383 Electrical machinery	3	8	1	4
384 Transport equipment	1	2	1	2
385 Professional and scientific equipment	—	—	—	—
390 Other manufacturing industries	3	1	1	—

FINANCE, ECONOMICS, & TRADE

Economic Indicators (22)

National product: GDP—purchasing power parity—$2.8 billion (1997 est.)

National product real growth rate: 3% (1997 est.)

National product per capita: $10,900 (1997 est.)

Inflation rate—consumer price index: 2.4% (1996)

Exchange Rates (24)

Exchange rates: Barbadian dollars (Bds$) per US$1—2.0000 (fixed rate pegged to the dollar)

Top Import Origins (25)
$763 million (c.i.f., 1995)

Origins	%
United States	.37
Trinidad and Tobago	.11
United Kingdom	.10
Japan	.7

Top Export Destinations (26)
$235 million (f.o.b., 1995).

Destinations	%
United States	.15
United Kingdom	.15
Trinidad and Tobago	.9
Windward Islands	.8

Economic Aid (27)
$NA. NA stands for not available.

Import Export Commodities (28)

Import Commodities	Export Commodities
Consumer goods	Sugar and molasses
Machinery	Rum
Foodstuffs	Other foods and beverages
Construction materials	Chemicals
Chemicals	Electrical components
Fuel	Clothing
Electrical components	

Balance of Payments (23)

	1990	1992	1994	1995	1996
Exports of goods (f.o.b.)	219	190	190	245	287
Imports of goods (f.o.b.)	−628	−468	−545	−691	−743
Trade balance	−409	−278	−355	−446	−456
Services - debits	−326	−276	−408	−459	−493
Services - credits	684	657	860	962	1,014
Private transfers (net)	39	41	40	35	42
Government transfers (net)	4	−1	−5	−1	−2
Overall balance	−8	143	132	90	104

BELARUS

Republic of Belarus
Respublika Belarus

INTRODUCTORY SURVEY

CAPITAL: Minsk.

FLAG: Two horizontal bands of red (top) and green, with the red band twice as wide as the green. At the hoist is a vertical band showing a traditional Belarusan ornamental pattern.

ANTHEM: *Maladaya Belarus.*

MONETARY UNIT: The Belarus ruble (BR) circulates along with the Russian rouble (R). The government has a varying exchange rate for trade between Belarus and Russia. BR1 = $0.00002 (or $1 = BR41,000).

WEIGHTS AND MEASURES: The metric system is in force.

HOLIDAYS: New Year's Day, 1 January; Orthodox Christmas, 7 January; International Women's Day, 8 March; Labor Day, 1 May; Victory Day, 9 May; Independence Day, 27 July; Day of Commemoration, 2 November; Christmas, 25 December.

TIME: 2 PM = noon GMT.

LOCATION AND SIZE: Belarus is a landlocked nation located in eastern Europe, between Poland and Russia. Comparatively, the area occupied by Belarus is slightly smaller than the state of Kansas, with a total area of 207,600 square kilometers (80,154 square miles). The boundary length of Belarus totals 3,098 kilometers (1,925 miles).

The capital city of Belarus, Minsk, is located near the center of the country.

CLIMATE: The mean temperature is 19.4°C (67°F) in July and −5°C (23°F) in January. Rainfall averages between 57 centimeters (22.5 inches) and 61 centimeters (26.5 inches) annually.

RECENT HISTORY

The Belarusans are the descendants of Slavic tribes that migrated into the region in the ninth century AD. They trace their distinct identity from the thirteenth century, when the Mongols conquered Russia and parts of Ukraine. During this period, Belarus managed to maintain its identity as part of the Grand Duchy of Lithuania. The combining of the Grand Duchy with Poland in 1569 put the territory of Belarus under Polish rule. After the division of Poland in the late eighteenth century, Belarus fell to the Russian Empire.

The Belarusan National Republic was formed in March 1918 with German military assistance. However, after the German government collapsed in November 1918, Bolshevik troops moved in and set up the Byelorussian Soviet Socialist Republic in January 1919. In 1922, the Belarus SSR became one of the 15 socialist republics to form the Union of Soviet Socialist Republics. Belarus, located between Germany and Russia, was devastated by World War II.

Throughout the early 1990s, the Belarusan leadership wanted to keep the Soviet Union intact. However, shortly after the failed August 1991 takeover attempt against Mikhail Gorbachev, the independence of Belarus was declared on 26 August 1991.

Since independence, Belarus has made scant progress toward economic and political reform. The economy is failing, and Soviet-era party bosses are struggling to hold power. President Aleksandr Lukashenka has stopped economic and political reform since his election in 1994. In 1996, Lukashenka signed into law a new constitution that expanded his power.

In December 1998, Lukashena and Russian President Boris Yeltsin announced their intention

BELARUS

to forge common defense, economic, and foreign policies.

GOVERNMENT

A new constitution was adopted on 15 March 1994. Until mid-1994, Belarus was the only former Soviet republic not to have a president. In elections held on 19 July 1994, Aleksandr Lukashenka was elected after promising to clear out the communist establishment ruling Belarus. However, in 1996, Lukashenka signed into law a new constitution that gave the presidency greater power. In March 1997, President Lukashenka disbanded parliament and replaced it with his loyal followers. He also increased restrictions on freedoms of speech, the press, and peaceful assembly.

Judiciary

The government continues to operate under the judicial system of the former Soviet Union. The courts system consists of district courts, city or province courts, and republic courts. The judicial system is not independent and operates under the influence of the government.

Political Parties

The Communist Party was declared illegal after the failed August 1991 takeover attempt, but was re-legalized in February 1993. It and two other pro-communist parties merged into one political party called the People's Movement of Belarus in May 1993. The primary opposition party is the Belarusan Popular Front.

DEFENSE

Belarus's armed forces number 84,200. It has an army of 50,500 troops with 1,850 tanks, an air force of 25,700 personnel with 502 aircraft, and an air defense force of 10,000 personnel with 115 interceptors. The defense budget for 1996 was about $458 million.

ECONOMIC AFFAIRS

Belarus's economy is geared toward industrial production, mostly in machinery and metallurgy with a significant weapons industry.

Belarus's economy is closely tied in with those of Eastern Europe and the other republics of the former Soviet Union.

The annual inflation rate was 2,220% in 1994, but dropped to 244% in 1995. An overvalued Belarusan ruble has limited Belarus's exports. The government stopped accepting payment of its own currency for exports.

Public Finance

In 1995, the Belarussian government began to enact structural reforms in accordance with a previous IMF agreement, including tax reform and a cut in subsidies to state supported enterprises. The government limits its budget deficit to no more than 6% of government expenditures, and under the terms of the IMF agreement the deficit cannot exceed 3.2% of the budget.

The U.S. CIA estimates that, in 1995, government revenues totaled approximately $4.95 billion and expenditures $5.47 billion. External debt totaled $2 billion, approximately 52% of which was financed abroad.

Income

In 1998, the gross national product (GNP) was $22.5 billion, or $2,200 per person. For the period 1985–95, the average inflation rate was 309.4%, and the average annual real growth rate per person was −5.2%.

Industry

Belarus's main industries are engineering, machine tools, agricultural equipment, chemicals, motor vehicles, and some consumer goods. In 1995, industrial production declined by about 11%.

Banking and Finance

The National Bank of Belarus is the central bank of Belarus, charged with regulating the money supply, circulating currency, and regulating the commercial banks of the country. The currency unit is the ruble.

Economic Development

In the summer of 1995, the Belarussian president announced the policy of "market socialism." The government still controls key market sectors as the private sector only makes up 20% of the economy. Most of the heavy industry in Belarus remains state owned.

SOCIAL WELFARE

The government has provided inhabitants with food and other basic goods to preserve social stability. There are no legal restrictions on women's participation in public life. However, social customs discourage participation by women in politics and business.

Healthcare

The factor most affecting the health of the Belarusan population is the accident at the Chernobyl nuclear power plant in April 1986. An estimated 2.2 million Belarusans were directly affected by radioactive fallout. Continuing radiation weakens the immune systems of individuals in contaminated areas. Many are said to suffer from "Chernobyl AIDS."

Housing

In 1990, Belarus had 17.9 square meters of housing space per capita and, as of 1 January 1991, 635,000 households (or 28.8%) were on waiting lists for housing in urban areas.

EDUCATION

The adult illiteracy rate is estimated at 2%. Education is compulsory for children between the ages of 6 and 15. Secondary education lasts for five years. In 1994, there were 5,000 primary level schools with 125,300 teachers and 636,300 students.

There are three universities in Belarus. The largest is the Belarusan State University. All higher level institutions combined had 229,640 students and 39,200 teaching staff in 1994.

1999 KEY EVENTS TIMELINE

April

- The lower house of the Russian parliament approves a union with Belarus and Yugoslavia.

May

- The Belarusian parliament votes to include Yugoslavia in the proposed union with Russia.

- Fifty-four die in Minsk in an underground tunnel stampede following a rock concert.

July

- Opposition leader Semyon Sharetsky flees to Lithuania as the government begins a crackdown on dissidents.

August

- Exiled opposition leader Semyon Sharetsky proclaims himself Belarus's leader.

September

- Opposition politician Victor Gonchar is reported missing.

- Russian president Boris Yeltsin approves the publication of a document outlining a proposed merger of the two nations.

December

- Belarus and Russia agree in principle to form an economic alliance. All 101 members of parliament vote to approve the alliance. Leaders of the two countries—Boris Yeltsin of Russia and Aleksandr Lukashenko of Belarus—sign the treaty, and the Russian Parliament also approves it.

ANALYSIS OF EVENTS: 1999

BUSINESS AND THE ECONOMY

Structural reform of the Belarus economy ground to a halt in 1995. Former manager of a collective farm, Belarus president Lukashenko imposed a tightly controlled Communist-style economy in Belarus. This set-up was not to the liking of international investors and the result was hyperinflation. The government began printing million-ruble notes—worth about $3 apiece—in May. By September, notes were issued in the amount of five million rubles, worth only about $10. In addition, shortages of consumer goods were frequent. In September vodka shortages were reported throughout the country, and fears of shortages of basic items like meat and butter were so widespread that President Lukashenko toured provincial shops to check on stocks, while declaring that the alleged shortages were a creation of the media.

Exacerbating the situation was a poor grain harvest, the worst in 20 years for Belarus. Crop failure was so serious that a harvest festival that had been planned for a year in President Lukashenko's hometown was cancelled, and the government sought a lean from the International Monetary Fund. Authorities estimated that the nation would need to import at least $100 million worth of grain to feed its population, and the World Bank stated that it would not lend any more money to the beleaguered country unless the Belarusian government instituted market reforms.

Discouraged by the slow pace of progress toward a political and economic union with Russia, Belarus's financial authorities announced in September that they would take steps to peg the Belarusian ruble to the euro. It had previously been thought that Belarus and Russia might adopt a common currency by 2000, but prospects for this seemed dim.

GOVERNMENT AND POLITICS

The major issue dominating Belarusian politics in 1999 was the adoption of closer ties or even the formation of a political union with Russia, Belarus's fellow republic in the former Soviet Union. Belarus, economically ailing and politically isolated, stood to gain clear benefits from an alliance with its larger, wealthier, and more powerful neighbor. The advantages for Russia were less immediate, and some observers cited the drawbacks posed by the weak Belarusian economy and the unsatisfactory human rights record of its autocratic president, Alexander Lukashenko.

However the majority of the Russian population was in favor of the move, largely for nationalistic reasons: the two peoples have strong cultural, linguistic, and religious ties, and many in both nations who were nostalgic for the Soviet era re-

garded the proposed union as a way to recapture some of the stability and international political status of the Soviet days. Flanking Russia on the west, Belarus could also be considered a possible buffer against NATO expansion. Some observers warned that if Russia and Belarus formed a new political entity, Russian president Boris Yeltsin might try to take advantage of the situation by attempting to remain in power after the expiration in 2000 of his last allowable term as president. However, these warnings did not gain wide credence, and by September President Yeltsin approved publication of a document outlining a proposed merger of the two nations, and it was submitted to Belarus for approval and feedback in October.

The political situation in Belarus, meanwhile, remained repressive under the regime of President Lukashenko, who had disbanded the country's parliament when he came to power in 1996 and appointed a Soviet-style "rubber-stamp" assembly in its place. He had also rewritten the constitution to give himself sweeping powers over the judiciary and the central bank. Lukashenko's government maintained tight control of the media and used strong-arm methods to repress dissent. By 1998 it was estimated that Belarus had thousands of political detainees. In foreign affairs, Lukashenko aligned himself vigorously against the United States and NATO and favored the rebirth of an isolationist pan-Slavism in Russia.

In 1999 Lukashenko's political opponents took strong, if largely symbolic, steps to protest his hard-line rule. In the spring they launched an "alternative" presidential election campaign, citing the fact that Lukashenko's presidential term was to have expired in July before he pushed through a two-year extension in 1996. Semyon Sharetsky, who had been speaker of the disbanded parliament, was "elected" acting president but was forced into exile in Lithuania for fear of government persecution. In August, from exile, he proclaimed himself the nation's legitimate ruler, but his action was expected to have little effect on the actual state of political affairs in the country. In September another prominent opposition leader, Viktor Gonchar, mysteriously disappeared amid a crackdown on opposition political figures.

CULTURE AND SOCIETY

Living conditions in Belarus in 1999 resembled life under the former Soviet regime, with strict control of political dissent, a centralized economy with shortages of consumer items, and political isolation from the West.

In May the capital city of Minsk was the scene of a senseless tragedy as 54 persons—most of them teenagers—died and over 100 more were injured as a crowd stampeded into an underground passenger tunnel in a downpour following a rock concert.

DIRECTORY

CENTRAL GOVERNMENT

Head of State

President
Aleksandr Lukashenko, Office of the President

Ministers

Prime Minister
Sergey Ling, Office of the Prime Minister

First Deputy Prime Minister
Vasiliy Dolgolev, Office of the Deputy Prime Minister

Deputy Prime Minister
Boris Batura, Office of the Deputy Prime Minister

Deputy Prime Minister
Valeriy Kokorev, Office of the Deputy Prime Minister

Deputy Prime Minister
Leonid Kozik, Office of the Deputy Prime Minister

Deputy Prime Minister
Ural Latypov, Office of the Deputy Prime Minister

Deputy Prime Minister
Gennadiy Novitskiy, Office of the Deputy Prime Minister

Deputy Prime Minister
Aleksandr Popkov, Office of the Deputy Prime Minister

Deputy Prime Minister
Vladimir Zametalin, Office of the Deputy Prime Minister

Minister of Agriculture and Food
Yuriy Maroz, Ministry of Agriculture and Food

Minister of Architecture and Construction
Henadz Kurachkin, Ministry of Architecture and Construction

Minister of Communications
Vladimir Goncharenko, Ministry of Communications

Minister of Culture
Aleksandr Sosnovskiy, Ministry of Culture

Minister of Defense
Aleksandr Chumakov, Ministry of Defense

Minister of Economy
Vladimir Shimov, Ministry of Economy

Minister of Education
Vasiliy Strazhev, Ministry of Education

Minister of Emergency Situations
Valery Astapov, Ministry of Emergency Situations

Minister of Enterprise and Investment
Aleksandr Sazonov, Ministry of Enterprise and Investment

Minister of Finance
Nikolay Korbut, Ministry of Finance

Minister of Foreign Affairs
Ural Latypov, Ministry of Foreign Affairs

Minister of Forestry
Valentin Zorin, Ministry of Forestry

Minister of Health
Igor Zelenkevich, Ministry of Health

Minister of Housing and Municipal Services
Boris Batura, Ministry of Housing and Municipal Services

Minister of Industry
Anatoliy Kharlap, Ministry of Industry

Minister of Internal Affairs
Yuriy Sivakov, Ministry of Internal Affairs

Minister of Justice
Gennadiy Vorontsov, Ministry of Justice

Minister of Labor
Ivan Lyakh, Ministry of Labor

Minister of Natural Resources and Environmental Protection
Mikhail Rusyy, Ministry of Natural Resources and Environmental Protection

Minister of Social Security
Olga Dargel, Ministry of Social Security

Minister of Sports and Tourism
Yavhen Vorsin, Ministry of Sports and Tourism

Minister of State Property and Privitization
Vasiliy Novak, Ministry of State Property and Privitization

Minister of Statistics and Analysis
Mr. Zinowski, Ministry of Statistics and
Analysis

Minister of Trade
Petr Kozlov, Ministry of Trade

Minister of Transport
Aleksandr Lukashev, Ministry of Transport

POLITICAL ORGANIZATIONS

Party of Communists Belarusian (PKB)

NAME: Sergei Kalyakin

Belarusian Communist Party (KPB)

NAME: Yetrem Sokolov

Agrarian Party

NAME: Aleksandr Pavlov

Belarusian Popular Front (BNF)

NAME: Levon Barshevskiy

Civic Accord Bloc (CAB)

NAME: Stanislav Bogdankevich

Liberal-Democratic Party (LDPB)

NAME: Sergei Gaydukevich

Belarusian Patriotic Movement (BPR)

NAME: Anatoliy Barankevich

Belarusian Labor Party (BPP)

NAME: Aleksandr Bukhvostov

Party of All-Belarusian Unity And Concord (UPNAZ)

NAME: Dmitriy Bulakov

Belarusian Social-Democrat Hramada (SDBP)

NAME: Nikolay Statkevich

Women's Party Nadezhda

NAME: Valentina Polevikova

Green Party of Belarus (BPZ)

NAME: Nikolay Kartash

Belarus Peasants

NAME: Yevgeniy Lugin

Party of Common Sense

NAME: Ivan Karavaichik

Belarusian Humanitarian Party

NAME: Yevgeniy Novikov

DIPLOMATIC REPRESENTATION

Embassies in Belarus

Armenia
Kirova 17, Minsk, Belarus
PHONE: +7 506560; 223072
FAX: +7 231321

Bulgaria
Bronevoy per. 5, Minsk, Belarus
PHONE: +7 367056
FAX: +7 365661

China
Berestyanskaya 22, Minsk, Belarus
PHONE: +7 768641
FAX: +7 768643

Estonia
Varvasheni 17, Minsk, Belarus
PHONE: +7 346486

France
Svoboda sq. 11, Minsk, Belarus
PHONE: +7 236229; 267522
FAX: +7 102548

Germany
Zaharova 26, Minsk, Belarus
PHONE: +7 330752; 332714
FAX: +7 368552

India
Kolcova 4/5, Minsk, Belarus
PHONE: +7 629399; 261210
FAX: +7 629799

Italy
K. Marksa 37, Minsk, Belarus
PHONE: +7 292001; 292004
FAX: +7 343046

Japan
Engelsa 13, hotel Oktyabrskaya, Minsk, Belarus
PHONE: +7 274718
FAX: +7 274319

Kazakstan
Ivanovskaya 56, Minsk, Belarus
PHONE: +7 355943; 369401
FAX: +7 358452

Kyrgyzstan
Starovilenskaya 57, Minsk, Belarus
PHONE: +7 349103; 769709
FAX: +7 341602

Latvia
Storozhevskaya 15, hotel Belarus, Minsk,
Belarus
PHONE: +7 391631; 391612
FAX: +7 506784

Lithuania
Varvasheni 17, Minsk, Belarus
PHONE: +7 769472; 347784
FAX: +7 769471

Moldova
Drozdi, building 32, Minsk, Belarus
PHONE: +7 506579; 503952
FAX: +7 506573

Poland
Rumyanceva 6, Minsk, Belarus
PHONE: +7 331114; 332516
FAX: +7 364992

Romania
Moskvina per. 4, Minsk, Belarus
PHONE: +7 238097

Russia
Starovilenskaya 48, Minsk, Belarus
PHONE: +7 503665; 345497
FAX: +7 503664

Turkey
Kirova 17, Minsk, Belarus
PHONE: +7 271408
FAX: +7 272746; 768674

Turkmenistan
Kirova 17, Minsk, Belarus
PHONE: +7 223367

Ukraine
Kirova 17, Minsk, Belarus
PHONE: +7 272796; 272354
FAX: +7 272861

United Kingdom
K. Marksa 37, Minsk, Belarus
PHONE: +7 292303
FAX: +7 368552

United States
Starovilenskaya 46, Minsk, Belarus
PHONE: +7 315000; 347761
FAX: +7 347853

JUDICIAL SYSTEM
Supreme Court
Constitutional Court

FURTHER READING
Articles
"In Big Daddy's Shadow: Belarus Dictator Alexander Lukashenko Maintains a Soviet-Style Grip on His Long-Suffering People." *Time International* (May 17, 1999): 153.

"Russia and Belarus Reunite." *The Economist* (January 9, 1999): p. 47.

"Slavic Disunion?" *The Economist* (July 24, 1999): 45.

Books
Fedor, Helen, ed. *Belarus and Moldova: Country Studies*. Federal Research Division, Library of Congress. Washington, D.C.: U.S. Government Printing Office, 1995.

Marples, David R. *Belarus: From Soviet Rule to Nuclear Disaster*. New York: St. Martin's Press, 1996.

Zaprudnik, I. A. *Belarus: At a Crossroads in History*. Boulder: Westview Press, 1993.

Internet
Central Intelligence Agency. *World Factbook, 1998*. Available Online @ http://www.odci.gov/cia/publications/factbook/bo/html (December 13, 1999).

BELARUS:
STATISTICAL DATA

For sources and notes see "Sources of Statistics" in the front of each volume.

GEOGRAPHY

Geography (1)

Area:

Total: 207,600 sq km.

Land: 207,600 sq km.

Water: 0 sq km.

Area—comparative: slightly smaller than Kansas.

Land boundaries:

Total: 3,098 km.

Border countries: Latvia 141 km, Lithuania 502 km, Poland 605 km, Russia 959 km, Ukraine 891 km.

Coastline: 0 km (landlocked).

Climate: cold winters, cool and moist summers; transitional between continental and maritime.

Terrain: generally flat and contains much marshland.

Natural resources: forests, peat deposits, small quantities of oil and natural gas.

Land use:

Arable land: 29%

Permanent crops: 1%

Permanent pastures: 15%

Forests and woodland: 34%

Other: 21% (1993 est.).

HUMAN FACTORS

Demographics (2A)

	1990	1995	1998	2000	2010	2020	2030	2040	2050
Population	10,215.2	10,404.0	10,409.0	10,390.7	10,441.3	10,387.2	10,100.7	9,720.3	9,100.1
Net migration rate (per 1,000 population)	NA	NA	NA	NA	NA	NA	NA	NA	NA
Births	NA	NA	NA	NA	NA	NA	NA	NA	NA
Deaths	NA	NA	NA	NA	NA	NA	NA	NA	NA
Life expectancy - males	66.2	63.1	62.3	61.8	65.3	69.4	72.7	75.2	77.2
Life expectancy - females	75.8	74.7	74.6	74.5	76.2	78.8	80.9	82.6	83.9
Birth rate (per 1,000)	14.0	10.0	9.7	9.7	12.8	9.2	9.0	7.8	6.8
Death rate (per 1,000)	10.9	12.7	13.5	13.9	13.3	12.0	11.8	13.1	14.4
Women of reproductive age (15-49 yrs.)	2,461.8	2,623.4	2,711.1	2,746.8	2,699.0	2,481.5	2,324.8	1,960.0	1,810.2
of which are currently married	NA	NA	NA	NA	NA	NA	NA	NA	NA
Fertility rate	1.9	1.4	1.3	1.3	1.7	1.6	1.5	1.4	1.4

Except as noted, values for vital statistics are in thousands; life expectancy is in years.

Health Personnel (3)

Total health expenditure as a percentage of GDP, 1990-1997[a]

Public sector 5.2

Private sector 1.1

Total[b] 6.4

Health expenditure per capita in U.S. dollars, 1990-1997[a]

Purchasing power parity 269

Total 134

Availability of health care facilities per 100,000 people

Hospital beds 1990-1997[a] 1230

Doctors 1993[c] 379

Nurses 1993[c] 1,160

Health Indicators (4)

Life expectancy at birth

1980 71

1997 68

Daily per capita supply of calories (1996) 3,101

Total fertility rate births per woman (1997) 1.2

Maternal mortality ratio per 100,000 live births (1990-97) . . . . .22[b]

Safe water % of population with access (1995) . . . .

Sanitation % of population with access (1995) . . . .

Consumption of iodized salt % of households (1992-98)[a] 37

Smoking prevalence

Male % of adults (1985-95)[a] . . . .

Female % of adults (1985-95)[a] . . . .

Tuberculosis incidence per 100,000 people (1997) 65

Adult HIV prevalence % of population ages 15-49 (1997) 0.17

Infants and Malnutrition (5)

Under-5 mortality rate (1997) 18

% of infants with low birthweight (1990-97) . . . . . .NA

Births attended by skilled health staff % of total[a] . . .NA

% fully immunized (1995-97)

TB 98

DPT 47

Polio 47

Measles 74

Prevalence of child malnutrition under age 5 (1992-97)[b] . . . . .NA

Ethnic Division (6)

Byelorussian 77.9%

Russian 13.2%

Polish 4.1%

Ukrainian 2.9%

Other 1.9%

Religions (7)

Eastern Orthodox 80%

Other . . . . .20% (1997 est.)

Other includes Roman Catholic, Protestant, Jewish, and Muslim.

Languages (8)

Byelorussian, Russian, other.

EDUCATION

Public Education Expenditures (9)

Public expenditure on education (% of GNP)

1980 . . . .

1996 . . . . .6.1

Expenditure per student

Primary % of GNP per capita

1980 . . . .

1996 . . . . .47.4[1]

Secondary % of GNP per capita

1980 . . . .

1996 . . . . .9.2[1]

Tertiary % of GNP per capita

1980 . . . .

1996 . . . . .19.3

Expenditure on teaching materials

Primary % of total for level (1996) . . . .

Secondary % of total for level (1996) . . . .

Primary pupil-teacher ratio per teacher (1996) . . . . .20[1]

Duration of primary education years (1995) 4

Educational Attainment (10)

Age group (1989) . . . . .25+

Total population .6,401,777

Highest level attained (%)

No schooling 9.4

First level

Not completed 32.5

Completed . . . . .NA

Entered second level

S-1 . . . . .45.8

S-2 . . . . .NA

Postsecondary 12.5

Literacy Rates (11B)

Adult literacy rate

1980

   Male ....-

   Female ....-

1995

   Male 100

   Female 99

GOVERNMENT & LAW

Political Parties (12)

Parliament	No. of seats
Belarusian Communist Party (KPB) 42	
Agrarian 33	
Agrarian Party Civic Accord Bloc (CAB) 9	
Party of People's Concord 8	
Party of All-Belarusian Unity and Concord (UPNAZ) 2	
Belarusian Social-Democrat Hramada (SDBP) 2	
Other 7	
Independents 95	
Vacant 62	

Government Budget (13A)

Year: 1996

Total Expenditures: 62,514.7 Millions of Rubels

Expenditures as a percentage of the total by function:

General public services and public order 8.33

Defense 3.59

Education 5.20

Health 3.50

Social Security and Welfare 34.49

Housing and community amenities 2.49

Recreational, cultural, and religious affairs 1.49

Fuel and energy 55

Agriculture, forestry, fishing, and hunting 5.85

Mining, manufacturing, and construction 03

Transportation and communication 6.06

Other economic affairs and services 2.86

Military Affairs (14B)

	1992	1993	1994	1995
Military expenditures				
Current dollars (mil.)	NA	NA	491	331
1995 constant dollars (mil.)	NA	NA	503	331
Armed forces (000)	102[e]	102[e]	108	115
Gross national product (GNP)				
Current dollars (mil.)	70,010	65,630	50,920	43,630
1995 constant dollars (mil.)	75,310	68,800	52,190	43,630
Central government expenditures (CGE)				
1995 constant dollars (mil.)	37,280	NA	NA	NA
People (mil.)	10.3	10.4	10.4	10.4
Military expenditure as % of GNP	NA	NA	1.0	.8
Military expenditure as % of CGE	NA	NA	NA	NA
Military expenditure per capita (1995 $)	NA	NA	48	32
Armed forces per 1,000 people (soldiers)	9.9	11.1	10.4	11.1
GNP per capita (1995 $)	7,307	6,642	5,028	4,196
Arms imports[6]				
Current dollars (mil.)	0	0	0	0
1995 constant dollars (mil.)	0	0	0	0
Arms exports[6]				
Current dollars (mil.)	0	0	0	170
1995 constant dollars (mil.)	0	0	0	170
Total imports[7]				
Current dollars (mil.)	2,929	4,654	4,296	4,600[e]
1995 constant dollars (mil.)	3,150	4,879	4,404	4,600[e]
Total exports[7]				
Current dollars (mil.)	3,064	3,659	2,413	4,200[e]
1995 constant dollars (mil.)	3,296	3,836	2,473	4,200[e]
Arms as percent of total imports[8]	0.0	0	0	0
Arms as percent of total exports[8]	0.0	0	0	4.0

Crime (15)

Crime rate (for 1997)

Crimes reported 128,400

Total persons convicted 86,400

Crimes per 100,000 population 1,250

Persons responsible for offenses

Total number of suspects 67,900

Total number of female suspects 14,000

Total number of juvenile suspects 7,600

LABOR FORCE

Labor Force (16)

Total (million) 4.3

Industry and construction 40%

Agriculture and forestry .19%

Services 41%

Data for 1997 est.

Unemployment Rate (17)

3.3% officially registered unemployed (July 1997); large numbers of underemployed workers.

PRODUCTION SECTOR

Electric Energy (18)

Capacity . . . . .7.21 million kW (1997)

Production . . . . .23.7 billion kWh (1996)

Consumption per capita . . . . .3,144 kWh (1996)

Transportation (19)

Highways:

total: 52,131 km

paved: 36,544 km

unpaved: 15,587 km (1996 est.)

Waterways: NA km; note—Belarus has extensive and widely used canal and river systems

Pipelines: crude oil 1,470 km; refined products 1,100 km; natural gas 1,980 km (1992)

Merchant marine: note: claims 5% of former Soviet fleet (1995 est.)

Airports: 118 (1996 est.)

Airports—with paved runways:

total: 36

over 3,047 m: 2

2,438 to 3,047 m: 18

1,524 to 2,437 m: 5

under 914 m: 11 (1996 est.)

Airports—with unpaved runways:

total: 82

over 3,047 m: 1

2,438 to 3,047 m: 6

1,524 to 2,437 m: 4

914 to 1,523 m: 9

under 914 m: 62 (1996 est.)

Top Agricultural Products (20)

Grain, potatoes, vegetables; meat, milk.

MANUFACTURING SECTOR

GDP & Manufacturing Summary (21)

	1980	1985	1990	1992	1993	1994
Gross Domestic Product						
Millions of 1990 dollars	22,472	29,438	34,188	30,313	27,434	21,535
Growth rate in percent	4.17	3.97	−1.40	−8.59	−9.50	−21.50
Per capita (in 1990 dollars)	2,334.2	2,956.2	3,347.8	2,969.0	2,692.7	2,119.0
Manufacturing Value Added						
Millions of 1990 dollars	NA	NA	8,902	8,801	8,881	7,167
Growth rate in percent	NA	NA	NA	−1.83	0.91	−19.30
Manufacturing share in percent of current prices	30.2	24.7	35.6	28.0	28.3	32.1

FINANCE, ECONOMICS, & TRADE

Economic Indicators (22)

National product: GDP—purchasing power parity—$50.4 billion (1997 est.)

National product real growth rate: 8.5% (1997 est.)

National product per capita: $4,800 (1997 est.)

Inflation rate—consumer price index: 65% (1997 est.)

Exchange Rates (24)

Exchange rates:

Belarusian rubels per US$1

19 January 1998 official Belarusian exchange rate . . . 31,030

October 1997 end of period 28,800

Yearend 1996 15,500

Yearend 1995 11,500

Yearend 1994 10,600

Yearend 1993 699

Top Import Origins (25)

$6.7 billion (c.i.f., 1996)

Origins	%
Russia	NA
Ukraine	NA
Poland	NA
Germany	NA

NA stands for not available.

Top Export Destinations (26)

$5.4 billion (f.o.b., 1996).

Destinations	%
Russia	NA
Ukraine	NA
Poland	NA
Germany	NA

NA stands for not available.

Economic Aid (27)

Recipient: ODA, $186 million (1993). Note: commitments, $3,930 million ($1,845 million disbursements), 1992-95.

Import Export Commodities (28)

Import Commodities	Export Commodities
Fuel	Machinery and transport equipment
Natural gas	
Industrial raw materials	Chemicals
Textiles	Foodstuffs
Sugar	

BELGIUM

Kingdom of Belgium
Dutch—*Koninkrijk België*
French—*Royaume de Belgique*

CAPITAL: Brussels (Brussel, Bruxelles).

FLAG: The flag, adopted in 1831, is a tricolor of black, yellow, and red vertical stripes.

ANTHEM: *La Brabançonne (The Song of Brabant),* named after the Duchy of Brabant.

MONETARY UNIT: The Belgian franc (BFr) is a paper currency of 100 centimes. There are coins of 50 centimes and 1, 5, 20, 50, and 500 francs, and notes of 100, 500, 1,000, and 5,000 francs. BFr1 = $0.03211 (or $1 = BFr31.147).

WEIGHTS AND MEASURES: The metric system is the legal standard.

HOLIDAYS: New Year's Day, 1 January; Labor Day, 1 May; Independence Day, 21 July; Assumption Day, 15 August; All Saints' Day, 1 November; Armistice Day, 11 November; Dynasty Day, 15 November; and Christmas, 25 December. Movable holidays are Easter Monday, Ascension, and Whitmonday.

TIME: 1 PM = noon GMT.

LOCATION AND SIZE: Situated in northwestern Europe, Belgium has an area of 30,510 square kilometers (11,780 square miles), slightly larger than the state of Maryland. Belgium has a total boundary length of 1,446 kilometers (899 miles).

Belgium's capital city, Brussels, is located in the north central part of the country.

CLIMATE: In the coastal region, the climate is mild and humid. Except in the highlands, rainfall is seldom heavy. The average annual temperature is 8°C (46°F). In Brussels, the mean temperature ranges from 2.2°C (36°F) in January to 18°C (64°F) in July. Average annual rainfall is 76.6 centimeters (30.2 inches).

INTRODUCTORY SURVEY

RECENT HISTORY

Belgium is named after the Belgae, a Celtic people whose territory Julius Caesar conquered in 57 BC and ruled as Gallia Belgica. In the fifth century AD, it was overrun by the Franks, and in the eighth century, it became part of Charlemagne's empire. By the tenth century this empire had declined, and feudal powers ruled the land. During the next three centuries, trade flourished. Antwerp, Bruges, Ypres, and Ghent became especially prosperous.

The territories that currently form Belgium, the Netherlands, and Luxembourg—now called the Benelux countries—have been called the Low Countries. Beginning in the 15th century, these territories, or parts of them, were ruled at various times by France, Austria, and Spain for some 400 years.

On 4 October 1830, Belgium was declared independent. The following year its parliament chose Prince Leopold of Saxe-Coburg-Gotha (Leopold I) as ruler of the new kingdom. In 1865, Leopold I was followed by Leopold II (r.1865–1909), who financed exploration and settlement in the Congo River Basin of Africa, laying the foundations of Belgium's colonial empire.

When World War I (1914–18) broke out, German troops invaded Belgium (4 August 1914). The Belgian army offered fierce resistance, but by the end of November 1914, most of the country was occupied by the Germans. Belgium, on the side of

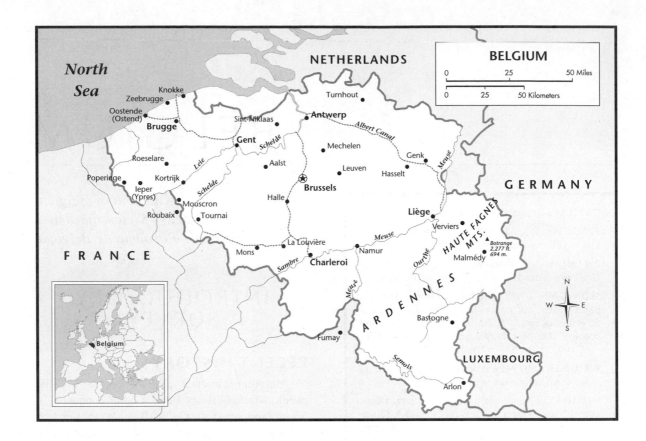

the Allies, continued to struggle against the occupation. Ypres (Ieper), in particular, was the scene of fierce fighting. Nearly 100,000 men lost their lives at a battle near there in April and May 1915.

The Allies won the war, and under the Treaty of Versailles (1919), Belgium acquired the German-speaking districts of Eupen, Malmédy, St. Vith, and Moresnet. The country made a remarkable recovery from the war, and by 1923, manufacturing industries were nearly back to normal.

Belgium was again attacked early in World War II (1939–45). On 10 May 1940, without warning, the Germans invaded the country and bombed Belgian airports, railroad stations, and communications centers. King Leopold III surrendered unconditionally on 28 May and was taken prisoner of war. The country was liberated from the Germans in 1944, and the Belgian government returned to Brussels in September of that year.

The country was economically better off after World War II than after World War I. However, a split had developed during the war years between Leopold III, who had surrendered to the Germans, and the Belgian government-in-exile, operating from London. The government-in-exile had rejected the king's surrender to Germany. On 22 July

1950, Leopold came back from exile, but much of the country opposed his return. On 1 August 1950, he agreed to give up the throne in favor of his son, Baudouin I.

In 1960, the Belgian Congo (later Zaire and then the Democratic Republic of the Congo), a major portion of Belgium's colonial empire, became independent. The event was followed by two years of brutal civil war, involving mercenaries from Belgium and other countries. Another Belgian territory in Africa, Ruanda-Urundi, became independent as the two states of Rwanda and Burundi in 1962.

Belgium shared fully in the European prosperity of the first three postwar decades. However, domestic political conflict during this period centered on the unequal distribution of wealth and power between Flemings (Dutch speakers) and Walloons (French speakers). Today, the country is divided into three regions (Flanders, Wallonia, and Brussels) and three linguistic communities (Flemish, French, and German).

King Baudouin died suddenly on 31 July 1993, while vacationing in Spain. Since he had no children, he was succeeded by his brother, Prince Albert of Liège.

GOVERNMENT

Belgium is a hereditary monarchy governed under the constitution of 1831. This document has been frequently amended in recent years to grant recognition and autonomy to the Dutch- and French-speaking communities. Executive power is held by the king, who also holds legislative power jointly with the two-chamber Parliament. The Chamber of Representatives has 150 members, and the Senate, 71 members.

In the constitutional reform of 1980, three communities—the Dutch-, the French-, and the German-speaking—were established. Each has independent responsibility for cultural affairs and for matters concerning the individual. There are also three regions in the northwest that have partial responsibility for economic, energy, housing, environmental, and other matters.

Belgium is divided into nine provinces. Each has a council of 50 to 90 members and a governor appointed by the king.

Judiciary

Belgian law is modeled on the French legal system. The judiciary is an independent branch of government on an equal footing with the legislative and the executive branches.

The highest courts are five civil and criminal courts of appeal and the supreme Court of Cassation, which must verify that the law has been properly applied and interpreted.

Political Parties

The Belgian political system operates through "twin" sets of French- and Dutch-speaking parties. Each French-speaking group has a Dutch-speaking counterpart. The three major political alliances are the Christian Social parties, consisting of the Parti Social Chrétien (PSC) and the Christelijke Volkspartij (CVP); the Socialist parties, the Parti Socialiste (PS) and Socialistische Partij (SP); and the Liberal parties, Parti Réformateur et Liberal (PRL) and Flemish Liberal Party (VLD).

The People's Union (Volksunie, or VU) is the Flemish nationalistic party, while the French-speaking Democratic Front (Front Démocratique des Francophones—FDF) affirms the rights of the French-speaking population of Brussels. Ecology parties (ECOCO/AGALEV) have become important political actors by gaining seats in the Chamber and Senate.

After the elections of 21 May 1995, party representation in the Chamber of Representatives was as follows: CVP, 17.2%; PS, 11.9%; SP, 12.6%; VLD, 13.1%; PRL, 10.3%; PSC, 7.7%; and five other parties, 27.2%. Following the election, Jean-Luc Dehaene was reappointed prime minister.

DEFENSE

Belgium's active armed forces in 1995 numbered 46,300, including 32,300 draftees and 2,950 women. In 1994, Belgium abolished the draft. Combat forces include one armored brigade, two mechanized infantry brigades, and a parachute–commando regiment, which together form an important part of NATO forces in Western Europe.

In 1995, the army had 30,100 personnel, the air force 12,300, and the navy 2,650. In 1995, Belgium spent $3.2 billion on defense, but almost half of the budget comes from NATO allies.

ECONOMIC AFFAIRS

In relation to its size and population, Belgium is among the most highly industrialized countries in Europe. Poor in natural resources, it imports raw materials in great quantity and processes them largely for export. Belgium's highly developed transportation systems are closely linked with those of its neighbors. Its chief port, Antwerp, is one of the world's busiest. Exports and imports accounted for 65% of the country's gross domestic product (GDP) in 1994.

Public Finance

The government's budgetary year coincides with the calendar year. In the final months of the year, the minister of finance places before Parliament a budget containing estimated revenues and expenditures for the following year.

Improvements in fiscal and external balances in the early 1990s and a slowdown in external debt growth enables the Belgian government to easily obtain loans on the local credit market. As a member of the G-10 group of leading financial nations, Belgium participates in the IMF, World Bank, and the Paris Club. Belgium is a leading donor nation, and it closely follows development and debt issues, particularly with respect to Zaire and other African nations.

Income

In 1996, Belgium's gross national product (GNP) was $250.7 billion at current prices, or $26,440 per person. For the period 1985–95 the average inflation rate was 3.1%, resulting in a real growth rate in gross national product (GNP) of 2.2% per person.

Industry

Steel production is the single most important type of industry, with Belgium ranking high among world producers of iron and steel. In 1994, Belgium produced 371,152 tons of refined copper, 306,200 tons of zinc, and 123,500 tons of refined lead.

The textile industry, dating from the Middle Ages, produces cottons, woolens, linens, and synthetic fibers.

The chemical industry manufactures a wide range of products, from heavy chemicals and explosives to pharmaceuticals and photographic supplies.

The diamond-cutting industry in Antwerp supplies most of the U.S. industrial diamond requirements. Belgium has one of the largest glass industries in the world, and is especially known for its fine crystal glassware.

Banking and Finance

The National Bank of Belgium (Banque Nationale de Belgique–BNB, founded in 1850), the sole bank of issue, originally was a joint-stock institution. In Belgium, most regulatory powers are vested in the Banking Commission, an autonomous administrative body that monitors compliance of all banks with national banking laws.

The primary surplus—exchequer revenue less government spending excluding interest payments—rose from BFr394 billion to BFr425 billion (from 5% to 5.2% of GDP0 in 1996. Although Belgium's primary surplus is one of the largest in the EV, Belgian debt continued to be a burden on the federal fiscal position, since Belgium's interest bill remained large enough to turn the primary surplus into a deficit of 3.4% of GDP.

The Brussels Stock Exchange was founded in 1801 after Napoleon, then Consul of the Republic, issued a decree of the 13th Messidor in the 9th year that ''There shall be an exchange in Brussels, in the Department of the Dyle.'' The law of 30 December 1867 completely abolished the provisions then in force controlling the profession of broker, the organization of the exchanges, and the operations transacted there. After the crisis of 1929 through 1933, a commission was created to assure investors of greater security. The Commercial Code of 1935 still controls the organization of the stock exchange

in large measure. Since the law of 4 December 1990, the Société de la Bourse de valeirs mobiliéres de Bruxelles (SBVMB) is organized under the form of a cooperative society.

Economic Development

Belgian economic policy is based upon the encouragement of private enterprise, with very little government intervention in the economy. Also, as a country heavily dependent upon foreign trade, Belgium has traditionally favored the freest exchange of goods, without tariffs or other limitations. Restrictions on free enterprise and free trade have always been due to external pressure and abnormal circumstances, as in time of war or economic decline.

SOCIAL WELFARE

Belgium has a highly developed social security system dating back to mutual benefit societies begun in 1894. The central coordinating organ for welfare is the National Social Security Office. It collects all workers' and employers' contributions for old age pensions and life insurance. It also collects management's payments for family allowances, paid vacations, and other benefits.

The government, which promotes women's rights, provided for a National Women's Center in its 1994 budget. In 1992, a royal decree was issued barring sexual harassment in both the public and private sectors.

Healthcare

Every city or town in Belgium has a committee in charge of health and hospital services. These committees organize clinics and visiting nurse services, run public hospitals, and pay for relief patients in private hospitals. There is a national health insurance plan, membership in which includes practically the whole population. Average life expectancy in 1995 was 77 years (80 years for females and 73 years for males).

Housing

Public funds have been made available in increasing amounts to support the construction of low-cost housing, with low-interest mortgages. Housing starts totaled 46,645 in 1992, up from 44,484 in 1991. The total number of dwellings in 1991 was 4,198,000.

EDUCATION

Adult illiteracy is practically nonexistent. Education is free and compulsory for children between the ages of 6 and 16. The teaching language is that of the region, for example, French, Dutch, or German.

More than half the school population is in private schools, largely Roman Catholic. Both public and private systems are presently financed with government funds. In 1991, Belgium had 4,158 primary schools with 72,589 teachers and 711,521 students. Secondary level schools had 765,672 students and 110,599 teachers.

Higher education centers on the eight main universities. The higher level institutions had 276,248 students in 1990.

1999 KEY EVENTS TIMELINE

January

- European finance ministers announce the rates at which national currencies convert to Europe's single currency; one euro is equal to 40 Belgian francs.

- German drug company Braun Mclsungcn AG accepts responsibility for the deaths of two babies in January who were given a lethal dose of potassium chloride instead of glucose.

February

- Riot police clash with 30,000 farmers from all fifteen EU countries who are demonstrating against cuts in food prices and farm subsidies.

- Police arrest a dozen anti-nuclear protestors who force their way into a NATO base near the border with the Netherlands.

- The Belgian government prevents a private plane, suspected of carrying Turkey's most wanted fugitive, the Kurdish rebel leader Abdulla Ocalan, from landing in the country.

March

- Belgium expresses astonishment at the decision to clear a U.S. marine pilot of responsibility for 20 deaths in a Italian cable car disaster in 1998.

- A United Nations tribunal on the genocide in Rwanda orders the release of a suspect accused of murdering ten Belgian peacekeepers in 1994.

- Eleven suspected Islamic militants, associated with the Algerian Armed Islamic Group, go on trial in Belgium.

April

- The United States decides against imposing trade sanctions on Belgium in the wake of the ongoing quarrel with respect to EU's banana policy.

May

- The Royal Museum of Fine Art in Antwerp opens a major exhibition of the Flemish painter Antoon Van Dyck.

- Belgium declares the Hell's Angels an illegal organization.

- High levels of a cancer-causing chemical dioxin found in some chicken and eggs. All sales of chicken and eggs are banned and 350 farms are placed under surveillance.

June

- The country's contaminated feed scandal deepens as it is discovered that thousands of farms have used dioxin-contaminated feed.

- Two government ministers (Public Health and Agriculture) are forced to resign because of an alleged three-month delay in publicizing the contamination.

- The European Union orders the destruction of millions of pounds of chickens and eggs and also ordered the removal from sale and destruction of pork and cattle products.

- The parliamentary election of June 13 ends the political career of Prime Minister Jean-Luc Dehaene, the Flemish Christian Democrat who has led a center-left coalition of Francophone and Flemish socialists and his Francophone Christian Democratic party.

- More than 100 children fall ill after drinking Coca-Cola containing the wrong carbon dioxide gas. Coca-Cola recalls 2.5 million bottles of Coke, Diet Coke, and Fanta bottled in Belgium.

July

- The "rainbow" coalition of Flemish Liberals, Socialists, and Greens and their French-speaking counterparts are installed as the new government under the leadership of Guy Verhofstadt.

- Another food scare erupts after it appears that 200 pig farms have used contaminated feed. The government recalls all pork products with more than 20 percent fat.

August

- Two Guinean teenagers die while trying to reach Belgium on the wheel bay of a Belgian plane that flew from Conakry (Guinean capital) to Brussels.

- The government enacts tough food laws following the long-running crisis surrounding the presence of cancer-causing chemicals.

September

- A parliamentary commission begins a dioxin inquiry.

- Soviet KGB equipment is found hidden in woods outside Brussels.

- The country's immigration laws are radically reformed following a public outcry over the death last year of a young Nigerian woman during her forced deportation.

October

- The deportation of more than seventy gypsies back to Slovakia provokes a political row after one of the Green parties in the coalition harshly condemns the police decision.

- The Gent film festival opens.

- The Center for the Study of Enterprise and the Stock Exchange at the University of Antwerp has launched the creation of a digital archive, containing information on the economic performance of every Belgian firm starting from 1832 until today.

November

- The European Commission in Brussels gives France an eight-day deadline to end its ban on British beef, indicating it will launch legal action unless the demand is met.

ANALYSIS OF EVENTS: 1999

BUSINESS AND THE ECONOMY

The economic news was dominated by the food scandal. Belgium's prosperous farming sector was paralyzed by the dioxin scare for more than two months and lost probably more than 1.5 billion dollars in exports and destroyed food products. It also led to the closure of more than 1,200 farms. The event began on May 27 after the Belgian government alerted the European Commission to the fact that high levels of dioxins had been found in eggs and chickens. The scare quickly widened to include pork and the commission ordered the destruction of all beef, chicken, eggs, milk, or products made from them. It also prohibited the sale of these products without a certificate guaranteeing that they were safe to eat. The Commission is threatening Belgium with legal action and a failure to protect European consumers. Laboratory results had revealed the presence of carcinogen in early April yet the authorities kept silent until the end of May.

In early August, Belgium appeared to be on a renewed collision course with the European Union, as the cabinet warned that it might refuse to implement instructions to test all exported foods with a fat content of more than 2% for potentially carcinogenic dioxin contamination. The regulations, required by the EU's committee of scientific experts, would have the effect of bringing the export of almost all Belgian foods to a halt because of the impossibility of carrying out tests on such a vast scale. The Belgian government insisted that the regulations were unnecessarily harsh.

In September, most of the issues between the Belgian authorities and the European Commission were finally settled and cleared and Belgian food products were given a clean bill of health.

Otherwise, the actual economic situation in Belgium is sound. The economic growth rate is projected to be 1.7 percent in 1999. The budget deficit has been brought down to 1.3 percent of gross domestic product (GDP) and the current account still shows a healthy surplus of 4.6 percent of GDP. The only economic indicator which has barely improved over the last few years is the unemployment rate. Officially, unemployment is 12 percent, yet a large proportion of working-age people are not active in the labor market. Less than half of those aged fifty and over still have a job since many older workers are phased into early retirement. Although around 120,000 jobs have been created between 1994 and 1998, most of these are part-time jobs in the service sector and mainly employ women. This means that the actual labor force participation rate (proportion of people aged 15 to 65 years employed) is only 57 percent and very low compared to other European countries. The non-working population, which depends on state allowances and social security, is very high and complicates the search for an acceptable reform of the social security system. Many voters have a direct stake in maintaining the system as it is.

GOVERNMENT AND POLITICS

The June 1999 parliamentary election was a watershed event. The food safety scandal was the last straw for many voters, already disgusted with the numerous scandals that have come to light in the last few years. The Flemish Christian Democratic Party received only 21.5 percent of the vote and the Flemish socialist suffered their worst defeat by receiving a disappointing 15.7 percent of the regional vote. The biggest gains were for the Dutch- and French-speaking Green parties and the Dutch-speaking Liberal party, which obtained an astonishing 22.7 percent of the Flemish vote.

The traditional supporters of the Christian Democratic Party clearly had enough of the endless scandals such as a bungled inquiry into child murders in 1996, bribery and corruption revelations, and the death of a Nigerian refugee while being deported. Some voters supported the radical right-wing Flemish Union, which became Flanders' third largest party with 15.5 percent of the vote. More moderate voters gave support to the green parties and the French-speaking Ecolo obtained 11.3 percent of the regional vote while the Dutch-speaking Agalev garnered 18.3 percent of the regional Flemish vote.

In French-speaking Belgium, the largest party continues to be the Socialists, who enjoy the support of a little less than a third of the electorate while the French-speaking Liberals received a quarter of the vote.

Six parties (French-speaking and Dutch-speaking branches of the Liberal, Socialist and Green parties) reached a core agreement only three weeks after the election on forming a "blue-red-green" coalition government. It is Belgium's first government in 40 years not to include the Christian Democrats, the first to include the Greens, and the first led by a Liberal prime minister (Guy Verhofstadt) since 1884.

The presence of the Greens includes a commitment to a progressive withdrawal from nuclear energy, starting with gradual decommissioning of nuclear power stations more than 40 years old. The coalition agreement also includes a pledge to accelerate the pace of electricity liberalization, allowing sources of power to be diversified, and to invest BFr40bn ($1.05b) in the rail network.

Reflecting the right-leaning program of the Liberals, the coalition plans to reduce social charges to employers by an annual BFr80bn ($2.16b) by 2001—twice the target of the outgoing Christian Democrat—Socialist coalition. The program will be partly paid for by privatization of state-owned assets.

The food safety crisis overshadowed many other issues that were traditionally fought in parliamentary elections. For the first time in recent memory, the split between Dutch and French-speaking communities did not influence the election. At the same time, the racist Flemish Union—boycotted by the mainstream parties—emerged to be the third largest political party in Flanders and is the largest party in Antwerp, Flanders' main commercial and cultural center. The Flemish Union, among other things, advocates the expulsion of foreigners and an independent Flanders. The latter proposal is meant to keep tax money, raised from Flemish business and households, in Flanders by cutting all ties with the French-speaking region.

CULTURE AND SOCIETY

The division between the Flemish and French speaking regions, although it did not dominate the June 1999 election, is as wide as ever. Flemish politicians (and electorate) are still suspicious of Francophone motives while the French-speaking region fears the prosperity and assertiveness of the Flemish region. The regional Flemish parties are seeking further discussions on constitutional amendments to achieve greater autonomy, especially in the critical area of social security. The French-speaking regional parties refuse to entertain any further thought on devolution out of fear that they will lose access to Belgium's social security fund. The struggle focuses on social security because Flanders pays more into the general budget than the French-speaking region and is less dependent on public transfers. Non-employment is nearly twice as high in Wallonia (Francophone region) than Flanders.

The inability of the dominant political forces to deal with the unequal economic trajectory of each region in addition to the string of scandals opens space for small parties with more radical programs to capture the hearts and minds of the voter. An example of this is the Flemish Union, a radical right-wing party which is explicitly anti-Francophone. Although the mainstream parties try to ignore the Flemish Union, its language permeates the political discourse and lifts a taboo on the controversial topic of an independent Flanders in a united Europe. Certainly, the popularity of the Flemish Union keeps the idea of an independent Flanders alive.

DIRECTORY

CENTRAL GOVERNMENT

King
Albert II, Monarch, Palais Royal, rue de Brederode 16, B-1000 Brussels, Belgium

Prime Minister
Guy Verhofstadt, Office of the Prime Minister, Wetstraat 16, rue de la Loi, B-1000 Brussels, Belgium
PHONE: +32 (2) 5010211
FAX: +32 (2) 5126953; 5115021

Ministers

Minister for Agriculture and the Middle Class
Jaak Gabriels, Ministry of Agriculture and the Middle Class, Maria-Theresiastraat 1, rue Marie-Thérèse, B-1000 Brussels, Belgium
PHONE: +32 (2) 2110611
FAX: +32 (2) 2196130

Minister for the Budget, Social Integration and Social Economy
Johan Vande Lanotte, Ministry of the Budget, Social Integration and Social Economy, Koningsstraat 180, rue Royale, B-1000 Brussels, Belgium
PHONE: +32 (2) 2101911
FAX: +32 (2) 2173328

Minister for Civil Service and Modernization of Public Administration
Luc Van Den Bossche, Ministry of Civil Service and Modernization of Public, Residence Palace (9th floor), Wetstraat 155, rue de la Loi, B-1040 Brussels, Belgium
PHONE: +32 (2) 2330511
FAX: +32 (2) 2330590
E-MAIL: kabinet-cabinet@mazfp.fgov.be

Minister for Consumer Interests, Health and Environment
Magda Aelvoet, Ministry for Consumer Interests, Health and Environment, Bischoffsheimlaan 33, boulevard Bischoffsheim, B-1000 Brussels, Belgium
PHONE: +32 (2) 2202011

FAX: +32 (2) 2202067

Minister for Defense
André Flahaut, Ministry for Defense, Lambermontstraat 8, rue Lambermont, B-1000 Brussels, Belgium
PHONE: +32 (2) 5502811
FAX: +32 (2) 5502919

Minister for Employment
Laurette Onkelinx, Ministry for Employment, Belliardstraat 51-53, rue Belliard, B-1040 Brussels, Belgium
PHONE: +32 (2) 2335111
FAX: +32 (2) 2301067

Minister for Economy and Scientific Research
Rudy Demotte, Ministry for Economy and Scientific Research, de Meeûssquare 23, square de Meeûs, B-1000 Brussels, Belgium
PHONE: +32 (2) 5065111
FAX: +32 (2) 5144683

Minister for Finance
Didier Reynders, Ministry for Finance, Wetstraat 12, rue de la Loi, B-1000 Brussels, Belgium
PHONE: +32 (2) 2338111
FAX: +32 (2) 2338003

Minister for Foreign Affairs
Louis Michel, Ministry for Foreign Affairs, Karmelietenstraat 15, rue des Petits Carmes, B-1000 Brussels, Belgium
PHONE: +32 (2) 5018211
FAX: +32 (2) 5116385

Minister for the Home Department
Antoine Duquesne, Ministry of the Home Department, Koningsstraat 60-62, rue Royale, B-1000 Brussels, Belgium
PHONE: +32 (2) 5048511
FAX: +32 (2) 5048500; 5048580

Minister of Justice
Marc Verwilghen, Ministry of Justice, Waterloolaan 115, boulevard de Waterloo, B-1000 Brussels, Belgium
PHONE: +32 (2) 5427911
FAX: +32 (2) 5380767

Minister for Labor and Employment
Laurette Onkelinx, Ministry of Labor and Employment, rue Belliard 51, B-1040 Brussels, Belgium
PHONE: +32 (2) 2335111
FAX: +32 (2) 2331067
E-MAIL: info@cabmeta.fgov.be

Minister for Mobility and Transport
Isabelle Durant, Ministry of Mobility and
Transport, Wetstraat 63-65, rue de la Loi,
B-1040 Brussels, Belgium
PHONE: +32 (2) 2376711
FAX: +32 (2) 2301824

**Secretary General of the Ministry for
Communications and Infrastructure**
Véronique Scalais, Ministry of Communication
and Infrastructure, rue d'Arlon 104, B-1040
Brussels, Belgium
PHONE: +32 (2) 2331507
FAX: +32 (2) 2311833
E-MAIL: +32 (2) 2311833

Minister for Social Affairs and Pensions
Frank Vandenbroucke, Ministry of Social Affairs
and Pensions, Wetstraat 66, rue de la Loi,
B-1040 Brussels, Belgium
PHONE: +32 (2) 2382811
FAX: +32 (2) 2303895

**Minister for Telecommunications, Public
Enterprises and Participations**
Rik Daems, Ministry of Telecommunications,
Public Enterprises and Participations,
Queteletplein 7, place Quetelet, B-1210 Brussels,
Belgium
PHONE: +32 (2) 2500303
FAX: +32 (2) 2190914

POLITICAL ORGANIZATIONS
Christelijke Volkspartij-CVP (Christian People's Party)

rue de la Loi 89, B-1040 Brussels, Belgium
PHONE: +32 (2) 2383814
FAX: +32 (2) 2304360
TITLE: President
NAME: Stefaab De Clercq

Vlaamse Liberalen en Democraten-VLD (Flemish Liberals and Democrats)

rue Melsens 34, B-1000 Brussels, Belgium
PHONE: +32 (2) 5490020
FAX: +32 (2) 5126025
TITLE: President
NAME: Karel De Gucht

Socialistische Partij-SP (Socialist Party)

boulevard de l'Empereur 13, B-1000 Brussels,
Belgium
PHONE: +32 (2) 5483211
FAX: +32 (2) 5483590

TITLE: President
NAME: Patrick Janssens

Parti Socialiste-PS (Socialist Party)

Boulevard de l'Empereur 13, B-1000 Brussels,
Belgium
PHONE: +32 (2) 5483211
FAX: +32 (2) 5483590
TITLE: President
NAME: Elio Di Rupo

Parti Socialiste-Fédération de Mons-Borinage (ASBL)

25, rue de Dinant, B-7000 Mons, Belgium
TITLE: President
NAME: Claude Durciux

Parti réformateur libéral-PRL (Liberal Reform Party)

rue de Naples 41, Brussels, Belgium
PHONE: +32 (2) 5003511
FAX: +32 (2) 5003500
TITLE: President
NAME: Daniel Ducarme

Front démocratique des Francophones (FDF)

Chaussée de Charleroi 127, B-1060 Brussels,
Belgium
PHONE: +32 (2) 5388320
FAX: +32 (2) 5393650
TITLE: President
NAME: Olivier Maingain

Vlaams Blok (Flemish Bloc)

place Madou 8, bte 9, B-1210 Brussels, Belgium
PHONE: +32 (2) 2196009
FAX: +32 (2) 2175275
TITLE: President
NAME: Frank Vanhecke

Parti social chrétien-PSC (Christian Social Party)

rue des Deux Églises 41, B-1000 Brussels,
Belgium
PHONE: +32 (2) 2380111
FAX: +32 (2) 2380129
TITLE: President
NAME: Joëlle Milquet

Volksunie-Vlaamse Vrije Democraten-VU (People's Union-Flemish Free Democrats)

place des Barricades 12, B-1000 Brussels, Belgium
PHONE: +32 (2) 2194930
FAX: +32 (2) 2173510
TITLE: President
NAME: Patrik Vankrunkelsven

Anders gaan Leven (AGALEV)

P/A Brialmontstraat 23, B-1210 Brussels, Belgium
PHONE: +32 (2) 2191919
FAX: +32 (2) 2231090
E-MAIL: luc.lemiengre@agalev.be
TITLE: Secretary
NAME: Luc Lemiengre

Écologistes confédérés pour l'Organisation de Luttes originales (ÉCOLO)

Maison bruxelloise de l'Écologie, rue Charles VI, 12, B-1210 Brussels, Belgium
PHONE: +32 (2) 2183035
FAX: +32 (2) 2175290
TITLE: Secretary
NAME: Jacky Morael

Front National (National Front)

Clos du Parnasse, 12/8, B-1050 Brussels, Belgium
PHONE: +32 (2) 5117577
TITLE: President
NAME: Daniel Féret

Workers' Party of Belgium (WPB)

171, boulevard Lemonnier, B-1050 Brussels, Belgium
PHONE: +32 (2) 5137760
FAX: +32 (2) 5139831
TITLE: President
NAME: Daniel Féret

Parti Social Démocrate-PSD (Social Democrat Party)

Partei der Deutschsprachigen Belgier-PDB (Party of the German-speaking Belgians)

TITLE: President
NAME: Guido Breuer

Parti Humaniste de Belgium

131, rue du Noyer, B-1000 Brussels, Belgium
PHONE: +32 (2) 7343784
FAX: +32 (2) 4260378
E-MAIL: parti.humaniste@euronet.be

Natuurwetpartij Vlaandern-NWP (Natural Law Party Flanders)

DIPLOMATIC REPRESENTATION

Embassies in Belgium

Austria
Marsveld plein 5, B-1050 Brussels, Belgium
PHONE: +32 (2) 2890700
FAX: +32 (2) 5136641

Brazil
avenue Louise, 350, 6ème étage, Bte 5, B-1050 Brussels, Belgium
PHONE: +32 (2) 6402015
FAX: +32 (2) 6408134

Canada
avenue de Tervuren, 2, B-1040 Brussels, Belgium
PHONE: +32 (2) 7410611
FAX: +32 (2) 7410643

China
avenue de Tervuren 443-445, B-1150 Brussels, Belgium
PHONE: +32 (2) 7713309
FAX: +32 (2) 7715857

Egypt
Leo Erreralaan, 44, B-1180 Brussels, Belgium
PHONE: +32 (2) 3455015
FAX: +32 (2) 3436533

France
65, rue Ducale, B-1000 Brussels, Belgium
PHONE: +32 (2) 5488711
FAX: +32 (2) 5136871

Germany
avenue de Tervuren 190, B-1150 Brussels, Belgium
PHONE: +32 (2) 7741911
FAX: +32 (2) 7723692

India
Vleurgatsesteenweg 217, B-1050 Brussels, Belgium
PHONE: +32 (2) 6409140
FAX: +32 (2) 6489638

Israel
Sterrewachtlaan 40, B-1040 Brussels, Belgium
PHONE: +32 (2) 3735500
FAX: +32 (2) 3735617

Italy
rue Emile Claus 28, B-1050 Brussels, Belgium
PHONE: +32 (2) 6499700
FAX: +32 (2) 6485485

Japan
avenue des Arts, 58, 6e Et., Btes 17-18, B-1000
Brussels, Belgium
PHONE: +32 (2) 5132340
FAX: +32 (2) 5131556

Netherlands
Hermann-Debrouxlaan, 48, B-1160 Brussels,
Belgium
PHONE: +32 (2) 6791711
FAX: +32 (2) 6791775

Poland
avenue des Gaulois, 29, B-1040 Brussels,
Belgium
PHONE: +32 (2) 7337340
FAX: +32 (2) 7361881

Portugal
F.D. Rooseveltlaan, 71, B-1050 Brussels,
Belgium
PHONE: +32 (2) 6402900
FAX: +32 (2) 6484078

Russia
avenue de Fré, 66, B-1180 Brussels, Belgium
PHONE: +32 (2) 3743400
FAX: +32 (2) 3742613

South Africa
rue de la Loi, 26, Btes 7-8, B-1180 Brussels,
Belgium
PHONE: +32 (2) 2854400
FAX: +32 (2) 2854402

Spain
Wetenschapsstraat, 19, B-1040 Brussels,
Belgium
PHONE: +32 (2) 2300340
FAX: +32 (2) 2309380

Switzerland
Wetstraat, 26, Bus 9, B-1040 Brussels, Belgium
PHONE: +32 (2) 2854350
FAX: +32 (2) 2303781

Turkey
rue Montoyer 4, B-1040 Brussels, Belgium
PHONE: +32 (2) 5134095
FAX: +32 (2) 5140748

United Kingdom
PHONE: +32 (2) 2876211
FAX: +32 (2) 2876355

United States
Regentlaan 27, B-1000 Brussels, Belgium
PHONE: +32 (2) 5082111
FAX: +32 (2) 5112725

JUDICIAL SYSTEM
Supreme Administrative Court (Council of State)

Wetenschapstraat 33, B-1040 Brussels, Belgium
PHONE: +58 (2) 2619397
FAX: +58 (2) 2611333
E-MAIL: webmaster@raadvst-consetat.be

FURTHER READING
Articles
"Belgium's Rotten Food." *The Economist* (June 5, 1999): 50.

Buckley, Neil. "Belgian Parties Reach Coalition Accord." *Financial Times* (July 5, 1999): 3.

"Economic Indicators." *The Economist* (October 23, 1999): 120–21.

Books
Fitzmaurice, John. *The Politics of Belgium.* Boulder, Colo.: Westview, 1996.

Jones, Erik. *The Politics of Economic and Monetary Union.* Boulder: Rowman and Littlefield, 2000.

OECD. *Economic Surveys of Belgium-Luxemburg 1999.* Paris: OECD, 1999.

Internet
BBC News "Belgian Chickens Come Home to Roost." Available Online @ http://news2.thls.bbc.co.uk/hi/english/world/europe/newsid%5F367000/367791.stm (December 8, 1999).

BBC News "Belgian Liberals Move to Form Government." Available Online @ http://news2.thls.bbc.co.uk/hi/english/world/europe/newsid%5F376000/376383.stm (December 8, 1999).

Belgian Tourist Office. Available Online @ http://www.visitbelgium.com/ (November 12, 1999).

BBC News "Belgium's Split Personality." Available Online @ http://news2.thls.bbc.co.uk/hi/english/

special%5Freport/1998/11/98/ crossing%5Fcontinents/newsid%5F292000/ 292956.stm (December 8, 1999).

BBC News ''Farmers Clash in Brussels.'' Available Online@ http:// news2.thls.bbc.co.uk/hi/english/world/europe/ newsid%5F283000/283803.stm (December 8, 1999).

BBC News ''U.S. Bans Euro Meat.'' Available Online @ http://news2.thls.bbc.co.uk/hi/ english/world/europe/newsid%5F360000/ 360583.stm (December 8, 1999).

Welcome to Brussels. Available Online @ http:// www.a-1.be/site/bxlnew/ (November 11, 1999).

BELGIUM: STATISTICAL DATA

For sources and notes see "Sources of Statistics" in the front of each volume.

GEOGRAPHY

Geography (1)

Area:

Total: 30,510 sq km.

Land: 30,230 sq km.

Water: 280 sq km.

Area—comparative: about the size of Maryland.

Land boundaries:

Total: 1,385 km.

Border countries: France 620 km, Germany 167 km, Luxembourg 148 km, Netherlands 450 km.

Coastline: 64 km.

Climate: temperate; mild winters, cool summers; rainy, humid, cloudy.

Terrain: flat coastal plains in northwest, central rolling hills, rugged mountains of Ardennes Forest in southeast.

Natural resources: coal, natural gas.

Land use:

Arable land: 24%

Permanent crops: 1%

Permanent pastures: 20%

Forests and woodland: 21%

Other: 34%

HUMAN FACTORS

Demographics (2A)

	1990	1995	1998	2000	2010	2020	2030	2040	2050
Population	9,962.2	10,133.8	10,174.9	10,185.9	10,075.5	9,762.3	9,241.5	8,486.8	7,608.5
Net migration rate (per 1,000 population)	NA	NA	NA	NA	NA	NA	NA	NA	NA
Births	NA	NA	NA	NA	NA	NA	NA	NA	NA
Deaths	60.3	NA	NA	NA	NA	NA	NA	NA	NA
Life expectancy - males	72.7	73.6	74.1	74.5	76.0	77.3	78.3	79.1	79.7
Life expectancy - females	79.6	80.3	80.7	81.1	82.4	83.5	84.4	85.2	85.7
Birth rate (per 1,000)	12.4	11.0	10.2	9.7	8.4	7.9	6.7	6.1	5.9
Death rate (per 1,000)	10.5	10.4	10.4	10.5	11.3	12.2	13.7	16.0	17.8
Women of reproductive age (15-49 yrs.)	2,438.1	2,481.7	2,460.7	2,438.4	2,291.7	2,016.8	1,792.2	1,562.0	1,308.4
of which are currently married	NA	3,976.0	NA	NA	NA	NA	NA	NA	NA
Fertility rate	1.6	1.5	1.5	1.5	1.4	1.3	1.3	1.3	1.3

Except as noted, values for vital statistics are in thousands; life expectancy is in years.

Health Personnel (3)

Total health expenditure as a percentage of GDP, 1990-1997[a]

Public sector	.6.7
Private sector	.0.9
Total[b]	.7.6

Health expenditure per capita in U.S. dollars, 1990-1997[a]

Purchasing power parity	.1,748
Total	.1,816

Availability of health care facilities per 100,000 people

Hospital beds 1990-1997[a]	.7.60
Doctors 1993[c]	.365
Nurses 1993[c]	.NA

Ethnic Division (6)

Fleming	.55%
Walloon	.33%
Mixed or other	.12%

Religions (7)

Roman Catholic	.75%
Protestant or other	.25%

Languages (8)

Flemish 56%, French 32%, German 1%, legally bilingual 11%.

EDUCATION

Literacy Rates (11B)

Adult literacy rate

1980

Male	.99%
Female	.99%

1995

Male	.-
Female	.-

GOVERNMENT & LAW

Political Parties (12)

Chamber of Deputies—	% of seats
Flemish Christian Democrats (CVP)	.17.2
Francophone Socialist Party (PS)	.11.9
Flemish Socialist Party (SP)	.12.6
Flemish Liberal Democrats (VLD)	.13.1
Francophone Liberal Reformation Party (PRL)	.10.3
Francophone Christian Democrats (PSC)	.7.7
Vlaams Blok (VB)	.7.8
Volksunie (VU)	.4.7
ECOLO (Francophone Greens)	.4.0
AGALEV (Flemish Greens)	.4.4
National Front (FN)	.2.3

Government Budget (13B)

Revenues	.NA
Expenditures	.NA
Capital expenditures	.NA

NA stands for not available.

Crime (15)

Crime rate (for 1994)

Crimes reported	.577,902
Total persons convicted	.40,056
Crimes per 100,000 population	.5,733

Persons responsible for offenses

Total number of suspects	.NA
Total number of female suspects	.NA
Total number of juvenile suspects	.NA

LABOR FORCE

Labor Force (16)

Total (million)	.4.283
Services	.69.7%
Industry	.27.7%
Agriculture	.2.6%

Data for 1997. Percent distribution for 1992.

Unemployment Rate (17)

12.75% (1997)

PRODUCTION SECTOR

Electric Energy (18)

Capacity	.13.592 million kW (1995)
Production	.69.56 billion kWh (1995)
Consumption per capita	.7,306 kWh (1995 est.)

Transportation (19)

Highways:

total: 143,175 km

paved: 143,175 km (including 1,674 km of expressways)

unpaved: 0 km (1996 est.)

Waterways: 2,043 km (1,528 km in regular commercial use)

Pipelines: crude oil 161 km; petroleum products 1,167 km; natural gas 3,300 km

Merchant marine:

total: 25 ships (1,000 GRT or over) totaling 60,082 GRT/93,973 DWT ships by type: bulk 2, cargo 7, chemical tanker 5, liquefied gas tanker 1, oil tanker 10 (1997 est.)

Airports: 42 (1997 est.)

Airports—with paved runways:

total: 24

over 3,047 m: 6

2,438 to 3,047 m: 9

1,524 to 2,437 m: 2

914 to 1,523 m: 1

under 914 m: 6 (1997 est.)

Airports—with unpaved runways:

total: 18

914 to 1,523 m: 3

under 914 m: 15 (1997 est.)

Top Agricultural Products (20)

Sugar beets, fresh vegetables, fruits, grain, tobacco; beef, veal, pork, milk.

GOVERNMENT & LAW

Military Affairs (14B)

	1990	1991	1992	1993	1994	1995
Military expenditures						
Current dollars (mil.)	5,356	5,520	4,612	4,426	4,498	4,449
1995 constant dollars (mil.)	6,155	6,099	4,961	4,640	4,611	4,449
Armed forces (000)	106	101	79	70	53	47
Gross national product (GNP)						
Current dollars (mil.)	219,300	234,800	245,200	249,900	261,700	269,100[e]
1995 constant dollars (mil.)	252,100	259,400	263,800	262,000	268,200	269,100[e]
Central government expenditures (CGE)						
1995 constant dollars (mil.)	126,300	130,100	134,400	133,400	133,600	NA
People (mil.)	10.0	10.0	10.0	10.1	10.1	10.1
Military expenditure as % of GNP	2.4	2.4	1.9	1.8	1.7	1.7
Military expenditure as % of CGE	4.9	4.7	3.7	3.5	3.5	NA
Military expenditure per capita (1995 $)	618	610	494	461	456	439
Armed forces per 1,000 people (soldiers)	10.6	10.1	7.9	6.9	5.2	4.6
GNP per capita (1995 $)	25,300	25,960	26,290	26,010	26,540	26,550
Arms imports[6]						
Current dollars (mil.)	310	310	140	280	160	340
1995 constant dollars (mil.)	356	343	151	294	164	340
Arms exports[6]						
Current dollars (mil.)	190	80	390	50	40	130
1995 constant dollars (mil.)	218	88	419	52	41	130
Total imports[7]						
Current dollars (mil.)	119,700	120,200	125,000	112,000	128,400	155,100
1995 constant dollars (mil.)	137,600	132,800	134,500	117,400	131,700	155,100
Total exports[7]						
Current dollars (mil.)	117,700	118,200	123,100	119,300	138,400	169,700
1995 constant dollars (mil.)	135,300	130,600	132,400	125,100	141,900	169,700
Arms as percent of total imports[8]	.3	.3	.1	.2	.1	.2
Arms as percent of total exports[8]	.2	.1	.3	0	0	.1

MANUFACTURING SECTOR

GDP & Manufacturing Summary (21)

Detailed value added figures are listed by both International Standard Industry Code (ISIC) and product title.

	1980	1985	1990	1994
GDP ($-1990 mil.)[1]	158,406	164,715	192,174	200,488
Per capita ($-1990)[1]	16,079	16,710	19,312	19,890
Manufacturing share (%) (current prices)[1]	25.5	24.6	23.8	22.1

Manufacturing

	1980	1985	1990	1994
Value added ($-1990 mil.)[1]	32,018	36,333	43,280	39,724
Industrial production index	100	108	128	118
Value added ($ mil.)	28,130	18,229	42,213	44,163
Gross output ($ mil.)	94,373	67,382	148,452	155,650
Employment (000)	872	755	735	676

Profitability (% of gross output)

	1980	1985	1990	1994
Intermediate input (%)	70	73	72	72
Wages and salaries inc. supplements (%)	15	12	11	12
Gross operating surplus	15	15	17	17

Productivity ($)

	1980	1985	1990	1994
Gross output per worker	102,512	84,112	190,250	216,108
Value added per worker	30,556	22,755	54,098	61,596
Average wage (inc. supplements)	16,066	10,617	22,774	26,600

Value added ($ mil.)

	1980	1985	1990	1994
311/2 Food products	3,991	2,863	5,814	6,574
313 Beverages	549	359	678	730
314 Tobacco products	199	123	310	340
321 Textiles	1,445	937	2,065	2,056
322 Wearing apparel	671	392	914	1,069
323 Leather and fur products	136	93	143	163
324 Footwear	67	35	56	40
331 Wood and wood products	226	131	503	447
332 Furniture and fixtures	1,123	614	1,613	1,632
341 Paper and paper products	612	441	1,042	929
342 Printing and publishing	926	602	1,677	1,968
351 Industrial chemicals	2,401	2,250	4,483	4,771
352 Other chemical products	665	467	1,199	1,491
353 Petroleum refineries	465	197	383	353
354 Miscellaneous petroleum and coal products	124	51	91	82
355 Rubber products	193	130	272	285
356 Plastic products	819	633	1,716	2,045
361 Pottery, china and earthenware	107	61	150	177
362 Glass and glass products	516	289	761	881
369 Other non-metal mineral products	654	307	872	1,000
371 Iron and steel	2,294	985	2,305	2,040
372 Non-ferrous metals	487	417	1,140	787
381 Metal products	2,071	1,228	2,954	2,755
382 Non-electrical machinery	2,490	1,556	3,826	3,906
383 Electrical machinery	2,303	1,451	3,034	2,919
384 Transport equipment	1,892	1,217	3,329	3,632
385 Professional and scientific equipment	170	106	282	493
390 Other manufacturing industries	537	294	603	598

FINANCE, ECONOMICS, & TRADE

Economic Indicators (22)

National product: GDP—purchasing power parity—$236.3 billion (1997 est.)

National product real growth rate: 2.3% (1997 est.)

National product per capita: $23,200 (1997 est.)

Inflation rate—consumer price index: 1.7% (1997 est.)

Exchange Rates (24)

Exchange rates:

Belgian francs (BF) per US$1

January 1998	.37.459
1997	.35.774
1996	.30.962
1995	.29.480
1994	.33.456
1993	.34.597

Top Import Origins (25)

$158.5 billion (c.i.f., 1997) Belgium-Luxembourg Economic Union. Data are for 1997.

Origins	%
European Union	75
Germany	.22.1
United States	.5
Former Communist countries	.0.8

Top Export Destinations (26)

$172 billion (f.o.b., 1997) Belgium-Luxembourg Economic Union (BLEU) Data are for 1996.

Destinations	%
Netherlands	.50
Brazil	.13
Canada	.6

Economic Aid (27)

Donor: ODA, $808 million (1993).

Import Export Commodities (28)

Import Commodities	Export Commodities
Fuels	Reexports of pharmaceuticals
Grains	
Chemicals	
Foodstuffs	

Balance of Payments (23)

	1990	1992	1994	1995	1996
Exports of goods (f.o.b.)	110,188	116,841	122,795	154,708	154,101
Imports of goods (f.o.b.)	−108,517	−113,141	−115,895	−1,452,457	−145,586
Trade balance	1,671	3,700	6,901	9,463	8,516
Services - debits	−89,809	−116,308	−120,666	−99,839	−87,805
Services - credits	93,961	121,953	129,843	109,106	97,479
Private transfers (net)	−1,038	−1,123	−1,018	−1,074	−1,051
Government transfers (net)	−1,158	−1,572	−2,489	−3,246	−3,139
Overall balance	3,627	6,650	12,571	14,410	14,000

BELIZE

CAPITAL: Belmopan.

FLAG: The national flag consists of the Belize coat of arms on a white disk centered in a blue rectangular field with a narrow red stripe at the top and the bottom.

ANTHEM: *Land of the Free.*

MONETARY UNIT: The Belize dollar (B $), formerly tied to the UK pound sterling and now pegged to the U.S. dollar, is a paper currency of 100 cents. There are coins of 1, 5, 10, 25, 50 cents and 1 dollar, and notes of 1, 5, 10, 20, 50, and 100 dollars. B $1 = US $0.50 (or US $1 = B $2).

WEIGHTS AND MEASURES: Imperial weights and measures are used. The exception is the measuring of petroleum products, for which the U.S. gallon is standard.

HOLIDAYS: New Year's Day, 1 January; Baron Bliss Day, 9 March; Labor Day, 1 May; Commonwealth Day, 24 May; National Day, 10 September; Independence Day, 21 September; Columbus Day, 12 October; Garifuna Day, 19 November; Christmas, 25 December; Boxing Day, 26 December. Movable holidays are Good Friday and Easter Monday.

TIME: 6 AM = noon GMT.

LOCATION AND SIZE: Belize (formerly British Honduras), on the Caribbean coast of Central America, has an area of 22,960 square kilometers (8,865 square miles), slightly larger than the state of Massachusetts. Belize has a total boundary length of 902 kilometers (560 miles). The capital city of Belize, Belmopan, is located in the center of the country.

CLIMATE: The climate is tempered by northeast trade winds that keep temperatures between 16° and 32°C (61–90°F) in the coastal region. Annual rainfall averages vary from 127 centimeters (50 inches) to more than 380 centimeters (150 inches).

INTRODUCTORY SURVEY

RECENT HISTORY

The area now called Belize was once heavily populated by Maya Indians, whose civilization collapsed around AD 900. The first permanent European settlement was established in 1638 by shipwrecked English seamen. Later immigrants included African slaves and British sailors.

England struggled with Spain over possession of the area and gained control in the nineteenth century. In 1862, they created the colony of British Honduras. For the next century, forestry was the main enterprise until eventually replaced by the sugar industry.

After attaining self-government on 1 January 1964, the country adopted Belize as its official name in 1973, although not yet fully independent. The United Kingdom granted Belize independence on 21 September 1981. Guatemala, which claimed the southern quarter of the area, refused to recognize the new nation and severed diplomatic relations with the United Kingdom. In December 1986 the United Kingdom and Guatemala resumed full diplomatic ties, but an 1,800-member British garrison remained in Belize. The United Kingdom withdrew its troops in 1994.

GOVERNMENT

Governmental authority is vested in a governor-general appointed by the British monarch, a cabinet headed by a prime minister, and a two-chamber National Assembly. The National Assembly consists of a 28-member House of Representa-

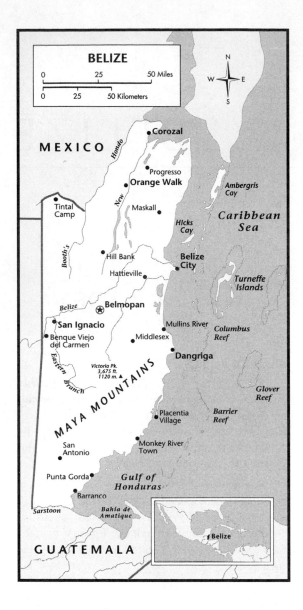

BELIZE

0 — 25 — 50 Miles

0 — 25 — 50 Kilometers

MEXICO

Corozal

Progresso
Orange Walk

Ambergris
Cay

Tintal
Camp

Maskall

*Hicks
Cay*

*Caribbean
Sea*

Hill Bank

**Belize
City**

Hattieville

*Turneffe
Islands*

Belize

Belmopan

San Ignacio

Mullins River

*Columbus
Reef*

Benque Viejo
del Carmen

Middlesex

Dangriga

Victoria Pk.
3,675 ft.
1120 m. ▲

*Glover
Reef*

MAYA MOUNTAINS

Placentia
Village

*Barrier
Reef*

San
Antonio

Monkey River
Town

Punta Gorda

*Gulf of
Honduras*

Barranco

Sarstoon

*Bahía de
Amatique*

Belize

GUATEMALA

tives elected by universal adult voting, and a Senate of eight members appointed by the governor-general. The voting age is eighteen, and parliamentary elections are held at least once every five years. Belize is divided into six administrative districts.

Judiciary

Belize's judiciary system includes a Supreme Court and a court of appeals. Final appeals are made to the UK Privy Council. Magistrates preside over six summary jurisdiction courts (criminal) and six district courts (civil).

Political Parties

The two major political parties in Belize are the majority United Democratic Party (UDP) and the People's United Party (PUP).

DEFENSE

The Belize Defense Force was established in 1973. Its members serve in regular and reserve companies, as well as a training organization. The British Kingdom maintains the British Army Training Support Unit Belize. The Belize Defense Force receives military assistance from the United Kingdom, the United States, and others.

ECONOMIC AFFAIRS

By 1995 tourism had surpassed the sugar industry as the leading source of foreign exchange. The economy also relies on agriculture and fishing. Belize continues to import most of its consumer goods, including much of its food and all of its petroleum requirements.

The government has chosen to concentrate on developing agriculture, livestock, forestry, fishing, and tourism as foreign exchange earners. The main sources of bilateral aid are the United States and the United Kingdom. Belize joined the OAS and IDG in 1992 in a move to increase its access to developing financing and external technical cooperation.

Public Finance

About half of Belize's recurrent expenditures are financed by customs duties; nearly all capital spending is funded by foreign loans and grants.

Since an International Monetary Fund standby stabilization program was implemented in 1985, fiscal responsibility has improved. The government typically budgets over 50% of projected spending to capital development, and raises 60% of current revenues from trade taxes.

Income

In 1998, Belize's gross national product (GNP) was U.S. $630 million at current prices, or U.S. $2,740 per capita.

Industry

Industrial activities include sugar and citrus processing, textiles and garments, and fertilizers. Other industries include plywood and veneer manufacturing, matches, beer and other beverages, furniture, boat building, and batteries. The garment industry faces heavy competition from the United States and Mexico.

Banking and Finance

The bank of issue in Belize is the Central Bank of Belize. Four foreign banks, including the Atlantic Bank and the Belize Bank, conduct commercial banking. Belize's Banking Ordinance has been amended to authorize offshore banking. There is no securities exchange in Belize.

SOCIAL WELFARE

Workers' compensation in Belize covers agricultural workers. A social security system is in effect, and employed persons aged 14 to 64 are eligible to make contributions for old age, disability, survivor, and health benefits. Women are active in all areas of national life, but they may face domestic violence and discrimination in the business sector.

Healthcare

Belize is relatively free of widespread diseases. Since 1976, however, there has been an increase in reported malaria cases. The government maintains a hospital in Belize City and rural health centers throughout the country. Life expectancy was averaged at 69.2 years for the total population in 1999; men have a life expectancy of 67.23 years and women, 71.26 years.

Housing

Housing in Belize is inadequate, and the situation has been aggravated by hurricane devastation. The government has put aside small sums for low-cost housing programs.

EDUCATION

The total literacy rate was estimated at 70.3% in early 1999, although some sources place the literacy rate as high as 75%. Primary education is free and compulsory for children between the ages of six and fourteen. The University College of Belize was opened in 1986. There are also several colleges providing specialized training.

1999 KEY EVENTS TIMELINE

February

- Belize and Honduras announce they are open and eager for tourist business. Belize suffered little damage during Hurricane Mitch in October 1998, and its tourist infrastructure was nearly untouched.

June

- The Belizean magistrate says there is enough evidence to hold a trial for two men facing charges of murdering a British aid worker in August 1998.

July

- The body of a young girl is found. She is the fourth girl found dead since September 1998. Authorities suspect a serial killer may be responsible for the abductions and killings. Belizeans demand answers from police.

- The United Nations issues an international quality-of-life report for the nations of the world. Belize ranks 83rd among 174 countries as the best place to live.

- A high-ranking British politician sues the *Times of London* for publishing stories suggesting he is involved in money laundering or drug dealing in Belize. The stories have international repercussions and involve England, Belize, and the United States.

August

- Belize supports Taiwan's efforts to rejoin the United Nations.

- Hundreds of school teachers protest the death of colleague who was shot and killed in Belize City during an attempted robbery.

September

- A U.S. Rotary Club donates a fifteen-passenger bus worth $23,000 to the Mercy Kitchen in Belize to help with its charitable causes.

December

- The Dangriga supreme court issues a guilty verdict on the charges of murder against Alan Cal, 20, and Estevan Sho, 21. The two are convicted of killing a 27-year-old UK aid worker last August. Both men are sentenced to death, the mandatory sentence for the crime of murder.

ANALYSIS OF EVENTS: 1999

BUSINESS AND THE ECONOMY

Belize is another of the fragile young nations buffeted by its exposure to the catastrophes of the economic world as much as by the catastrophes of the natural world. A year after hurricane Mitch, Belize is caught between a robust population growth and sluggish economic performance. In

1977 its debt level stood at $21 million. This grew to $137 million in 1987 and $383 million in 1997. In 1998 the per capita Gross National Product of Belize was only $2,610, compared to $3,940 for Latin America and the Caribbean as a whole. This lack of ready resources did not deter the population boom: the average annual growth in Belize's population in 1992–98 was 2.8 percent, compared to 1.6 percent for Latin America and the Caribbean.

In the face of this grim picture, Belize like many of its under-developed neighbors has turned to tourism. In fact, tourism has become one of Belize's top industries during the 1990s. While the first two months of 1999 were sluggish, The Belize Tourist Board reported that 12,130 visitors arrived at the country's international airport in March, an increase of 5 percent from the previous year. It was also the first time that arrivals broke the 12,000 mark for a month. The tourist board said a $1 million ad campaign in the United States, with advertising in some of the most prominent travel magazines, helped boost tourism. Officials also said they were receiving 100 calls per day from potential visitors, and their Internet site was generating 3,000 visitors per week. Despite the higher number of travelers, the Central American airline TACA suspended its non-stop Miami-Belize service in April, citing tough competition from American and Continental airlines. In June, TACA resumed its non-stop service from Miami.

The government was also considering new laws to entice retirees from the United States, the United Kingdom, Northern Ireland and Canada. The new measures would allow retirees to bring— tax-free—a vehicle, household goods, and personal effects into the country. Retirees would have to prove they have a guaranteed monthly income of about $1,000 per month.

GOVERNMENT AND POLITICS

One of the most controversial political issues affecting Belize during 1999 began to unravel in England. Michael Ashcroft, Belize high commissioner to the United Nations and England's Conservative Party treasurer, came under fire for his offshore banking activities in Belize, including generous tax exemptions, the sale of Belize passports through one of his companies, and his considerable influence over the small Central American Nation. Ashcroft, a multimillionaire, is considered the wealthiest man in Belize. During the year, the Times of London wrote a series of articles focusing on Ashcroft's complex business interests in Belize. Those articles were followed by other critical media reports focusing on Ashcroft and his activities in the small country. The Times claimed the U.S. Drug Enforcement Agency mentioned Ashcroft in four separate investigations into drug trafficking and money laundering in Belize. The articles led many prominent British politicians to ask for Ashcroft's resignation as Conservative Party Treasurer.

George Bruno, who left his post as U.S. Ambassador to Belize in 1997, came to Ashcroft's defense, saying American authorities had no evidence of wrongdoing against the Belizean businessman. Ashcroft filed a lawsuit against the Times, and a court hearing is expected sometime in 2000.

In July, the Belizean government sought to distance itself from the Ashcroft crisis. In a statement, Belize government officials said investors were shying away from the country because of the bad publicity generated by English press accounts. Prime Minister Said Musa said his country could be damaged in the long term by any suggestions that its offshore facilities were attracting drug traffickers and money launderers.

In the past, Musa has praised Ashcroft for his contributions to the country's economy. Ashcroft built a business empire in Belize based on tax-free banking, telecommunications and an agricultural empire. Musa insisted Ashcroft had not influenced his nation's economic policies. Former Prime Minister Manuel Esquivel was more critical. He told a Belize television station that Ashcroft "stops at nothing" to get his way.

CULTURE AND SOCIETY

While Hurricane Mitch caused little damage to Belize, its citizens remained concerned that homeless Hondurans and Guatemalans would cross the border looking for work. Illegal immigration became a sensitive issue after robberies and attacks on buses were blamed on Guatemalan gangs. A prominent Mennonite businessman was kidnapped in March, allegedly by a band of Salvadorans and Guatemalans. Belizeans began to experience a crime wave in 1998 that was spilling into 1999. The kidnapping and murder of four girls between 1998, and June 1999, possibly by a serial killer, enraged Belizeans. So did the murder of a teacher, and the murders of three Chinese businessmen in Belize City.

In July 19, new gun control rules went into effect. Anyone who wants to buy a gun has to attend a training session, and supply samples of test-fire bullets, cartridges and casings to ease linking guns to their owners. Buyers also have to wait four weeks to receive a weapon after making a purchase. Gun owners also will be required to carry a license.

Aware of the fact that tourism will not grow in a nation lacking the amenities of the developed world, the World Bank Group is funding the Belize City Infrastructure Project. This project is focused on upgrading the delivery of city services. It hopes to put tourism on a more solid foundation by addressing the ''quality of life'' issues associated with maintaining the delicate balance between the charms of an exotic location and the security and comforts that the discriminating vacationer demands.

DIRECTORY

CENTRAL GOVERNMENT

Head of State

Monarch
Elizabeth II, Queen, Buckingham Palace, The Visitor Center, London SW1A 1AA, England
PHONE: +44 (0171) 8391377
FAX: +44 (0171) 9309625

Governor-General
Sir Colville Young, Office of the Governor-General

Prime Minister
Said Musa, Office of the Prime Minister

Ministers

Minister of Education and Sports
Cordel Hyde, Ministry of Education and Sports, Ministry of Education, Belmopan, Cayo District, Belize
PHONE: +501 (08) 22329; 22380
FAX: +501 (08) 23389
E-MAIL: educate@btl.net

Minister of Works, Transport, Citrus and Banana Industries
Henry Canton, Ministry of Works, Transport, Citrus and Banana Industries
PHONE: +501 (08) 22136; 22139

Minister of Agriculture, Fisheries and Cooperatives
Daniel Silva, Ministry of Agriculture, Fisheries and Cooperatives, 2nd Floor, West Block Building, Belmopan, Belize C.A
PHONE: +501 (08) 22241; 22242
FAX: +501 (08) 22409
E-MAIL: mafpaeu@btl.net

Minister of Health, Public Services, Labour and Civil Society
Jose Coye, Ministry of Health, Public Services, Labour and Civil Society
PHONE: +501 (08) 22326; 22325
FAX: +501 (08) 22942
E-MAIL: mintrade@btl.net

Minister of Human Development and Women
Dolores Baldcramos Garcia, Ministry of Human Development and Women, West Block, Independence Hill, Belmopan, Belize
PHONE: +501 (08) 22161; 22684
FAX: +501 (08) 23175

Minister of Sugar Industry, Local Government and Latin American Affairs
Florencio Marin, Ministry of Sugar Industry, Local Government and Latin American Affairs, New Administrative Building, Belmopan, Cayo District, Belize
PHONE: +501 (08) 22167; 22322
FAX: +501 (08) 22854; 23365

Minister of Budget Planning and Management, Economic Development, Investment and Trade
Ralph Fonseca, Ministry of Budget Planning and Management, Economic Development, Investment and Trade, New Administration Building, Belmopan, Cayo District, Belize
PHONE: +501 (08) 22218; 22231
FAX: +501 (08) 22195

Minister of National Security and Immigration
Jorge Espat, Ministry of National Security and Immigration, Curl Osmond Thompson Building, Belmopan, Cayo District, Belize
PHONE: +501 (08) 22225
FAX: +501 (08) 22615
E-MAIL: mnsi@btl.net

Minister of Public Utilities, Transport and Communications
Maxwell Samuels, Ministry of Public Utilities, Transport and Communications, Power Lane, Belmopan, Belize
PHONE: +501 (08) 22817; 22435

FAX: +501 (08) 23317; 23677

Minister of Natural Resources, the Environment and Industry

John Briceno, Ministry of Natural Resources, the Environment and Industry, Permanent Secretary, Belmopan, Belize
PHONE: +501 (08) 22630
FAX: +501 (08) 22333

Minister of Foreign Affairs

Said Musa, Ministry of Foreign Affairs, P.O. Box 174, New Administration Building, Belmopan, Belize
PHONE: +501 (08) 22167; 22322
FAX: +501 (08) 22854
E-MAIL: belizemfa@btl.net

Minister of Finance

Said Musa, Ministry of Finance, New Administration Building, Belmopan, Belize
PHONE: +501 (08) 22158; 22152
FAX: +501 (08) 23317
E-MAIL: finsecmof@btl.net

Minister of Rural Development and Culture

Marcial Mes, Ministry of Rural Development and Culture
PHONE: +501 (08) 22444; 20326
FAX: +501 (08) 20317
E-MAIL: ruraldev@btl.net

Minister of Tourism and Youth

Mark Espat, Ministry of Tourism and Youth, Constitution Drive, Belmopan, Belize
PHONE: +501 (08) 23393; 23394
FAX: +501 (08) 23815
E-MAIL: tourismdpt@btl.net

Ministry of Housing, Urban Renewal and Home Affairs

Dickie Bradley, Ministry of Housing, Urban Renewal and Home Affairs
PHONE: +501 (08) 22680; 22016
FAX: +501 (08) 23337

Minister of Education and Sports

Cordel Hyde, Ministry of Education and Sports
PHONE: +501 (08) 22329; 22380
FAX: +501 (08) 23389
E-MAIL: educate@btl.net

Minister of Works, Transport, Citrus and Banana Industries

Henry Canton, Ministry of Works, Transport, Citrus and Banana Industries
PHONE: +501 (08) 22136; 22139; 22131

POLITICAL ORGANIZATIONS

United Democratic Party

UDP Secretariat, South End Bel-China Bridge, P.O. Box 1898, Belize City, Belize
PHONE: +501 (2) 72576; 76440
FAX: +501 (2) 76441
E-MAIL: secretary@udp.org.bz

DIPLOMATIC REPRESENTATION

Embassies in Belize

Canada

Consulate of Canada, 83 North Front Street, Belize City, Belize
PHONE: +501 (2) 33722
FAX: +501 (2) 30060
TITLE: Honorary Consul
NAME: L. Young

Mexico

20 North Park Street, Belize City, Belize C.A.
PHONE: +501 (2) 30193
FAX: +501 (2) 78742
E-MAIL: embamexbze@btl.net
TITLE: Ambassador
NAME: Enrique Hubbard Urrea

Sweden

Consulate of Sweden, 2 Daly street, Postadr P.O. Box 94, Belize City, Belize
PHONE: +501 (2) 45178; 45658
FAX: +501 (2) 31843
E-MAIL: gayuso@btl.net
TITLE: Konsul
NAME: Oskar Miquel Ayuso, Jr.

United States

29 Gabourel Lane, P.O. Box 286, Belize City, Belize
PHONE: +501 (2) 77161
FAX: +501 (2) 30802
E-MAIL: embbelize@state.gov
TITLE: Ambassador
NAME: Carolyn Curiel

Venezuela

Unity Boulevard, N° 18/20, P.O. Box 49, Belmopan, Belize
PHONE: +501 (8) 22384
FAX: +501 (08) 822022
E-MAIL: embaven@bt1.net
TITLE: Ambassador
NAME: Christian vna der Ree Paris

JUDICIAL SYSTEM
Supreme Court

FURTHER READING

"Serial Killer is Stalking the Oasis," *Los Angeles Times*, 22 September 1999.

"Belize's Capital is Clean, Safe—But Few Want to Live There," *Los Angeles Times*, 11 September.

"Taiwan Seeks to Rejoin U.N. Wins Support From Belize," *The Seattle Times*, 11 August 1999.

"Loneliness of the Belize Long Jumper," *Associated Press*, 26 July 1999.

"Travel Advisory: After Mitch, Overtures from Central America," *The New York Times*, 28 February 1999.

"Former U.S. Ambassador to Belize Defends British Official," *The Guardian Unlimited* (London), 15 August 1999.

"The Billionaire who Bought Belize," *The Guardian Unlimited* (London), 11 April 1999.

"First Among Equals, Cacao Farmers in Belize," *The Guardian Unlimited* (London), 11 March.

BELIZE: STATISTICAL DATA

For sources and notes see "Sources of Statistics" in the front of each volume.

GEOGRAPHY

Geography (1)

Area:

Total: 22,960 sq km.

Land: 22,800 sq km.

Water: 160 sq km.

Area—comparative: slightly smaller than Massachusetts.

Land boundaries:

Total: 516 km.

Border countries: Guatemala 266 km, Mexico 250 km.

Coastline: 386 km.

Climate: tropical; very hot and humid; rainy season (May to February).

Terrain: flat, swampy coastal plain; low mountains in south.

Natural resources: arable land potential, timber, fish.

Land use:

Arable land: 2%

Permanent crops: 1%

Permanent pastures: 2%

Forests and woodland: 92%

Other: 3% (1993 est.).

HUMAN FACTORS

Demographics (2A)

	1990	1995	1998	2000	2010	2020	2030	2040	2050
Population	189.8	214.1	230.2	241.5	299.5	356.5	408.8	453.4	489.1
Net migration rate (per 1,000 population)	NA	NA	NA	NA	NA	NA	NA	NA	NA
Births	NA	NA	NA	NA	NA	NA	NA	NA	NA
Deaths	NA	NA	NA	NA	NA	NA	NA	NA	NA
Life expectancy - males	65.2	66.4	67.0	67.4	69.4	71.2	72.8	74.1	75.2
Life expectancy - females	69.2	70.4	71.0	71.5	73.6	75.5	77.2	78.7	79.9
Birth rate (per 1,000)	38.7	33.7	31.0	29.4	23.9	20.2	17.1	15.3	13.9
Death rate (per 1,000)	6.6	5.9	5.5	5.3	4.7	4.7	5.2	6.3	7.7
Women of reproductive age (15-49 yrs.)	42.0	49.4	55.0	59.1	80.7	97.4	110.8	116.5	117.3
of which are currently married	NA	NA	NA	NA	NA	NA	NA	NA	NA
Fertility rate	4.9	4.3	3.9	3.6	2.7	2.3	2.1	2.0	2.0

Except as noted, values for vital statistics are in thousands; life expectancy is in years.

Infants and Malnutrition (5)

Under-5 mortality rate (1997) 43

% of infants with low birthweight (1990-97) 4

Births attended by skilled health staff % of total[a] . . .NA

% fully immunized (1995-97)

TB 95

DPT 86

Polio 85

Measles 98

Prevalence of child malnutrition under age 5

(1992-97)[b] . . . . .NA

Ethnic Division (6)

Mestizo 44%

Creole 30%

Maya 11%

Garifuna 7%

Other 8%

Religions (7)

Roman Catholic 62%

Protestant 30%

Anglican 12%

Methodist 6%

Mennonite 4%

Seventh-Day Adventist 3%

Pentecostal 2%

Jehovah's Witnesses .1%

Other 2%

None 2%

Other 6%

Data for 1980.

Languages (8)

English (official), Spanish, Mayan, Garifuna (Carib).

EDUCATION

Educational Attainment (10)

Age group (1991) . . . . .25+

Total population 66,520

Highest level attained (%)

No schooling 13.0

First level

Not completed 64.3

Completed . . . . .NA

Entered second level

S-1 . . . . .14.9

S-2 . . . . .NA

Postsecondary 6.6

GOVERNMENT & LAW

Political Parties (12)

National Assembly	No. of seats
People's United Party (PUP)	13
United Democratic Party (UDP)	15
National Alliance for Belizean Rights (NABR)	1

Government Budget (13A)

Year: 1996

Total Expenditures: 362,261 Thousands of Dollars

Expenditures as a percentage of the total by function:

General public services and public order 23.77

Defense 5.02

Education 20.39

Health 8.27

Social Security and Welfare 5.93

Housing and community amenities 2.77

Recreational, cultural, and religious affairs 1.02

Fuel and energy 1.20

Agriculture, forestry, fishing, and hunting 4.77

Mining, manufacturing, and construction . . . .-

Transportation and communication 14.13

Other economic affairs and services 2.25

Crime (15)

Crime rate (for 1997)

Crimes reported 3,750

Total persons convicted . . . . .NA

Crimes per 100,000 population 1,500

Persons responsible for offenses

Total number of suspects . . . . .NA

Total number of female suspects . . . . .NA

Total number of juvenile suspects . . . . .NA

LABOR FORCE

Labor Force (16)

Total 71,000

Agriculture 30%

Services 16%

Government 15.4%

Commerce 11.2%

Manufacturing 10.3%

Shortage of skilled labor and all types of technical personnel
(1997 est.)

Unemployment Rate (17)

13% (1997 est.)

PRODUCTION SECTOR

Electric Energy (18)

Capacity . . . . .23,000 kW (1995)

Production . . . . .105 million kWh (1995)

Consumption per capita . . . . .491 kWh (1995)

Transportation (19)

Highways:

total: 2,248 km

paved: 427 km

unpaved: 1,821 km (1996 est.)

Waterways: 825 km river network used by shallow-draft craft; seasonally navigable

Merchant marine:

total: 265 ships (1,000 GRT or over) totaling 1,298,562 GRT/2,055,027 DWT ships by type: bulk 26, cargo 184, chemical tanker 4, combination bulk 1, container 6, liquefied gas tanker 1, oil tanker 26, passenger-cargo 2, refrigerated cargo 8, roll-on/roll-off cargo 4, specialized tanker 2, vehicle carrier 1

Airports: 44 (1997 est.)

Airports—with paved runways:

total: 3

GOVERNMENT & LAW

Military Affairs (14B)

	1990	1991	1992	1993	1994	1995
Military expenditures						
Current dollars (mil.)	5	5	6	7	8	9
1995 constant dollars (mil.)	6	5	6	7	9	9
Armed forces (000)	1	1	1	1	1	1
Gross national product (GNP)						
Current dollars (mil.)	408	434	482	499	533	555
1995 constant dollars (mil.)	469	479	519	523	546	555
Central government expenditures (CGE)						
1995 constant dollars (mil.)	129	146	169	191	176	178
People (mil.)	.2	.2	.2	.2	.2	.2
Military expenditure as % of GNP	1.2	1.1	1.2	1.4	1.6	1.6
Military expenditure as % of CGE	4.5	3.6	3.7	3.7	4.9	5.0
Military expenditure per capita (1995 $)	30	27	31	35	41	41
Armed forces per 1,000 people (soldiers)	5.2	5.0	5.0	4.9	4.8	4.7
GNP per capita (1994 $)	2,470	2,466	2,606	2,566	2,613	2,593
Arms imports[6]						
Current dollars (mil.)	0	0	0	0	0	0
1995 constant dollars (mil.)	0	0	0	0	0	0
Arms exports[6]						
Current dollars (mil.)	0	0	0	0	0	0
1995 constant dollars (mil.)	0	0	0	0	0	0
Total imports[7]						
Current dollars (mil.)	211	251	273	281	260	259
1995 constant dollars (mil.)	242	277	294	295	267	259
Total exports[7]						
Current dollars (mil.)	105	99	116	119	128	143
1995 constant dollars (mil.)	121	109	125	125	131	143
Arms as percent of total imports[8]	0	0	0	0	0	0
Arms as percent of total exports[8]	0	0	0	0	0	0

1,524 to 2,437 m: 1
under 914 m: 2 (1997 est.)
Airports—with unpaved runways:
total: 41
2,438 to 3,047 m: 1
914 to 1,523 m: 10
under 914 m: 30 (1997 est.)

Top Agricultural Products (20)

Bananas, coca, citrus, sugarcane; lumber; fish, cultured shrimp.

FINANCE, ECONOMICS, & TRADE

Economic Indicators (22)

National product: GDP—purchasing power parity—$680 million (1997 est.)

National product real growth rate: 2.9% (1997 est.)

National product per capita: $3,000 (1997 est.)

Inflation rate—consumer price index: 1% (1997 est.)

Exchange Rates (24)

Exchange rates: Belizean dollars (Bz$) per US$1—2.0000 (fixed rate)

Top Import Origins (25)

$262 million (c.i.f., 1996) Data are for 1997.

Origins	%
United States	.55
Mexico	.12
United Kingdom	.5

MANUFACTURING SECTOR

GDP & Manufacturing Summary (21)

	1980	1985	1990	1992	1993	1994
Gross Domestic Product						
Millions of 1990 dollars	249	253	396	456	475	483
Growth rate in percent	4.37	1.02	8.49	9.15	4.22	1.60
Per capita (in 1990 dollars)	1,705.6	1,525.9	2,097.6	2,291.9	2,330.0	2,299.6
Manufacturing Value Added						
Millions of 1990 dollars	44	41	53	60	59	*60*
Growth rate in percent	14.91	0.96	4.89	12.79	−1.29	*2.03*
Manufacturing share in percent of current prices	23.1	16.3	15.0	13.9	13.4	*11.4*

FINANCE, ECONOMICS, & TRADE

Balance of Payments (23)

	1990	1992	1993	1994	1995
Exports of goods (f.o.b.)	129	141	132	157	165
Imports of goods (f.o.b.)	−188	−245	−251	−232	−231
Trade balance	−59	−104	−119	−75	−66
Services - debits	−81	−104	−116	−116	−120
Services - credits	126	149	156	124	136
Private transfers (net)	16	18	15	15	17
Government transfers (net)	13	13	14	13	16
Overall balance	15	−29	−49	−40	−17

Top Export Destinations (26)

$166 million (f.o.b., 1996) Data are for FY95/96 est.

Destinations	%
Western Europe	.42
United States	.30
Hong Kong	.4
Japan	.3

Economic Aid (27)

Recipient: ODA, $NA. NA stands for not available.

Import Export Commodities (28)

Import Commodities	Export Commodities
Machinery and transportation equipment	Sugar
	Citrus fruits
Food	Bananas
Manufactured goods	Clothing
	Fish products
Fuels	Molasses
Chemicals	Wood
Pharmaceuticals	

BENIN

Republic of Benin
République du Bénin

INTRODUCTORY SURVEY

RECENT HISTORY

The French ruled Benin (formerly Dahomey) until 1 August 1960, when the country proclaimed its independence. After independence, the country suffered from extreme political instability, with military coups in 1963, 1965 (twice), 1967, 1969, and 1972. The coup on 26 October 1972 established Major Mathieu Kérékou as the leader of a military regime. It represented a clear break with all earlier Dahomeyan governments, introducing revolutionary changes in the political and economic life of the country. In late 1974, President Kérékou said that the national revolution would follow a Marxist-Leninist course, and the state took over many industries. On 1 December 1975, the country's name was changed to the People's Republic of Benin.

In 1980, Kérékou made an official visit to Libya. During the visit, he converted to the Islamic faith in the presence of the Libyan leader, Colonel Mu'ammar al-Qadhafi, and accordingly took the first name Ahmed. The two countries then signed a major bilateral cooperation agreement.

Through the years, hundreds of government opponents have been imprisoned, often without trial. Opposition came mostly from the banned Communist Party (Parti Communiste du Dahomey—PCT) and student protesters. However, in 1989 Kérékou announced that the country would no longer follow a Marxist-Leninist philosophy. Democratic reforms were instituted and on 2 December 1990, a new constitution was adopted by

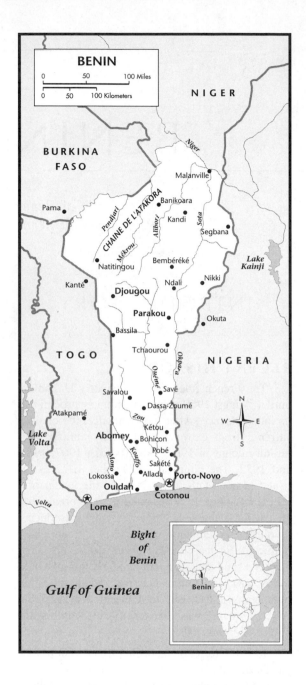

BENIN

NIGER

BURKINA FASO

Malanville

Pama

Banikoara

Kandi

CHAINE DE L'ATAKORA

Segbana

Natitingou

Bembéréké

Lake Kainji

Kanté

Ndali

Nikki

Djougou

Parakou

Okuta

Bassila

NIGERIA

TOGO

Tchaourou

Savalou

Savé

Dassa-Zoumé

Atakpamé

Kétou

Lake Volta

Abomey

Bohicon

Pobé

Sakété

Lokossa

Allada

Porto-Novo

Ouidah

Cotonou

Lome

Bight of Benin

Gulf of Guinea

Benin

runoff presidential election by his old rival Kérékou.

GOVERNMENT

The 1990 Constitution led to multiparty elections. The president is elected by popular vote for a five-year term. A directly elected National Assembly has a maximum term of four years.

Judiciary

Each district has a court with the power to try cases, and each province has a court to handle appeals. At the lowest level, each commune, village, and city ward has its own court. The highest court is the Supreme Court. Under the 1990 constitution, people who are arrested must be brought before a magistrate (judge) within 48 hours.

Political Parties

Partisan politics are characterized by frequent splits and mergers. As of 1996, there were over 80 recognized political parties. Party allegiances in the National Assembly are fluid. The 1995 multiparty general elections produced a National Assembly in which the largest bloc of votes (20 of 83) were held by the Party for the Renaissance of Benin (PRB). Parties allied with the PRB won 13 seats, and the remainder were split among 25 other parties.

DEFENSE

In 1995, the armed forces had some 4,800 personnel. There were 150 personnel in the air force, and an equal number in the navy. A paramilitary police force totaled 2,500.

ECONOMIC AFFAIRS

Benin's economy is recovering from the economic problems that led to the collapse of the socialist government in power between 1974 and 1989. Companies that were state owned are being returned to private ownership. However, recovery efforts are complicated by the fact that Benin's economy is strongly influenced by economic trends in Nigeria.

Agriculture is the most important sector in the Benin economy, accounting for some 36.8% of gross domestic product in 1996. About 90% of this output is produced on family farms using little technology.

Public Finance

Benin has both an ordinary and a development budget. High personnel costs have been a continuing problem in Benin, which has a surfeit of civil

popular referendum. The country's name was changed from People's Republic of Benin to Republic of Benin. Presidential and parliamentary elections were held on 10 March 1991. This was Benin's first free election in 30 years. Kérékou lost the presidential election to his opponent Nicephore Soglo. However, no one party was able to gain control of the National Assembly. A working coalition was formed to run the government, but in 1993, it fell apart. Soglo's administration lost popular support due to economic mismanagement. In September 1996, he was narrowly defeated in a

servants. Many government-backed enterprises are near bankruptcy, and some are barely functioning.

Most investment expenditure is financed by foreign loans and grants. The U.S. CIA estimates that, in 1993, government revenues totaled approximately $272 million and expenditures $375 million, including capital expenditures of $84 million. External debt totaled $1.5 billion.

Income

In 1996, Benin's gross national product (GNP) was $2.034 billion at current prices, or $350 per person. During 1985–95, the average annual inflation rate was 2.9% and the real growth rate of GNP was −0.4% per person.

Industry

Benin's industrial sector accounts for 9% of gross domestic product and centers primarily on construction materials and the processing of agricultural products. In 1994, Benin's industrial sector produced 380,000 tons of cement and 3,000 tons of raw sugar.

Banking and Finance

In 1959, the Central Bank of the West African States (Banque Centrale des États de l'Afrique de l'Ouest—BCEAO) succeeded the Currency Board of French West Africa and Togo as the bank of issue for the former French West African territories.

In December 1974, the government nationalized the banking sector, amalgamating the three main commercial banks into the Commercial Bank of Benin.

Economic Development

Benin's economic development program is conducted within the context of an IMF structural adjustment program. The recent devaluation of the CFA franc, the local currency, has made imports more expensive and brought the CFA closer in value to the Nigerian currency.

SOCIAL WELFARE

All public employees receive family allowances for up to six children. There is also a system of old-age benefits, and medical care is free. Female circumcision is still legal and is practiced in Benin.

Healthcare

Most serious epidemic diseases have been brought under control by mobile health units and other facilities. In 1993, 42% of the population had access to health services. During 1989–95, 36% of children under 5 years old suffered from malnutrition. Estimated average life expectancy is only 55 years.

Housing

In rural areas, the typical dwelling of northern Benin is a round hut of beaten mud with a cone-shaped thatch roof. In southern Benin, rectangular huts with sloping roofs of palm or straw thatch are more usual. Along the coastal lagoons, houses are often built on stilts.

EDUCATION

Since 1975, all education has been free, public, secular, and compulsory from ages 6 to 12. Adult illiteracy was 63% in 1995. In 1991, enrollment of children at the primary level was 53%.

1999 KEY EVENTS TIMELINE

January

- The energy crisis carries over from 1998, which has an adverse impact on industry, and lowers economic forecasts for 1999.

- Ismael Soumanou, the first Beninois to publish a weekly private newspaper (1988), makes Benin's first private FM radio station, Golfe FM (105.7), the most listened to radio station in the country.

February

- Parliament unanimously adopts a new law that would impose harsh penalties on journalists for defaming the head of state, foreign heads of state, and foreign ministers.

- Agricultural workshop on agronomic research opens in Cotonou.

March

- Legislative elections are held.

April

- Parliament elects its president, choosing a member of the opposition, PRD leader and former prime minister Adrien Houngbedji.

- The regional central bank, the BCEAO, estimates that the primary rural sector accounts for 38% of the GDP and provides livelihoods for 70% of the population (based on 1998 data).

May

- The mandate of the national elections commission, CENA, expires May 10. Despite its attempt to prolong its mandate via an ad hoc committee, the permanent secretariat (SAP), appointed by the head of state, takes over.

- Six ministers of government leave their posts to take up their seats in parliament.

- Two of three main teachers' trade unions agree to return to work.

- Government lowers the value-added tax on cement by 50% to encourage imports.

June

- Kérékou reappoints his cabinet, and announces his new government on the 22nd.

- The World Bank announces an urban decentralization initiative financed by $25.5 million in credit. The French Agency for development and government is co-financing the project.

- Denmark approves a $14 million grant for transport for improving rural roads and tracks in the Zou region.

- Benin withdraws its 140 troops from Guinea-Bissau.

July

- The government sets up a code of ethics to curb corruption among public bidders in the country.

- Police intercept 174 children being smuggled out of the country.

August

- Independence Day is celebrated on August 1.

- Tutsi detainees are flown into Benin from the Democratic Republic of the Congo.

- The government agrees to accommodate ICTR genocide convicts.

September

- Specialists join forces to eradicate the Guinea worm in Benin.

October

- The American international relief and development agency, CARE, begins operations in Benin. Its first project will be to help improve access for women to reproductive health services.

- The government sends troops to Couffo and Mano, regions in the southwest where vigilantes are reportedly burning alleged criminals alive. The vigilante group leader calls himself Civilian Colonel, and has held rallies reportedly attended by 20,000 supporters.

ANALYSIS OF EVENTS: 1999

BUSINESS AND THE ECONOMY

Benin was in a classic profile of under-development. Its birth rate was forty-five per thousand population; its death rate was twelve per thousand; its population was growing at an annual rate of 3.3 percent. Women in Benin gave birth to an average of 6.4 children. Almost half (48 percent) of its population was under fifteen years old, even though its infant mortality rate was almost ten percent (97.76 per thousand live births). Benin's economy was not able to cope with the social problems produced by this overpopulation crisis. Less than half of its population was literate (48.7 percent of the males; 25.8 percent of women).

In spite of these encumbrances, Benin's financial performance in 1999 was fairly good with a real GDP growth rate of 5%, expected to rise to 5.5% in 2000. Thanks to outstanding rains, an increase in crop production was expected, but without power from Ghana's Akosomba Dam, an energy crunch hurt industry. Energy matters worsened further as oil production from the Seme oil fields tapered off from 8,000 barrels a day in the 1980s, to 5,000 barrels a day (1994), down to a trickle in 1999. Current reserves are estimated at 100 million barrels of crude.

President Kérékou also was accused of failing to deliver on campaign promises to provide jobs. In his defense, he has been handicapped by a hostile parliament, and militant trade unions demanding higher spending, wages, and more jobs. But he will have a delicate balancing act next year when these political pressures will have to be traded against the IMF's ESAF, which expires in early 2000.

Economic recovery is predicted for 2000 given increases in cotton production, which accounted for $212 million in exports two years ago. Cotton is by far the mainstay of the export economy. The Economist Intelligence Unit predicts a decrease in inflation from 5.6% in 1998 to 3% in 1999. It also sees growth in the informal sector relieving pressure on the formal economy. Some 45,000 "Zem" (motor-bike) drivers in Cotonou make on average $2 to $3 a day—not bad for services and trades workers.

GOVERNMENT AND POLITICS

Beninese politics are confusing, but never dull. Having gained its independence in 1960, Benin has withstood six military coups, a socialist revolution, a state-run economy, near economic disaster, and a national conference, which ended General Kérékou's 18-year rule. In 1991, Nicéphore Soglo won the presidency in competitive elections. He restructured the economy and armed forces. But Soglo was beaten by Kérékou at the polls in 1996, making Benin one of two African states where voters have thrown out an elected government only to vote it back in again. The other is Madagascar.

Now a little more than halfway through his term, Kérékou is in a political deadlock. He has failed to make a deal with minority parties to win a parliamentary majority, and has not seated a Kerekiste candidate as president of the National Assembly. There has been considerable in-fighting among pro-Kérékou parties following their performance in March where they took 41 out of 83 seats. Legislative action is stalled until the government and the opposition find agreement over the composition of lists for parliamentary committees.

Kérékou may also be losing ground for having tightened libel laws. In November last year, the Higher Audiovisual and Communication Authority (HAAC) authorized eight commercial and seven non commercial radio stations along with one TV station and three satellite-TV stations. The decision reflected the will of the 1991 National Conference to break the state monopoly on airwaves. However, stations must subscribe to the state-owned Benin News Agency (ABP), which distributes national and international news at exorbitant rates. Furthermore, under a new defamation law, journalists face up to five years in prison or a fine up to 10 million CFA ($17,000) for libel.

Curiously, Soglo appears to be making his comeback as the RB candidate in 2001. His party won 27 seats in the March legislative elections, and it has gained popularity by accusing Kérékou of breaking his campaign promises. Given a history of mutinies in the military, sluggish economic growth, and routine strikes, constant political turnover in Benin could become a way of life.

CULTURE AND SOCIETY

Since colonial times, Beninese schools have graduated thousands of gifted writers, scholars, teachers, and statesmen, earning Benin the nickname of the "Quartier Latin," named for Parisian Sorbonne district. Unfortunately, the economy has not kept pace with graduation rates, producing a culture of underemployed intellectuals, as well as general unemployment. One bright development has been the privatization of the sugar company, which will be rehabilitated and is expected to require up to 2,000 workers to fill permanent and seasonal jobs.

Creative Beninese have found ways to survive. In June, police intercepted 174 children being smuggled out of the country. These children were believed destined for employment as domestic workers, farm labor, or petty trade. Apparently thousands are smuggled each year into Côte d'Ivoire, Nigeria, Cameroon, and Congo. Traffickers pay about 15,000 CFA ($25) per head to the children's families, and then sell them for between 200,000 to 300,000 CFA. The government intends to increase border surveillance and to sensitize embassies and populations in the countries of destination.

While capital crimes such as murder are rare, Benin's crime rate is expected to rise given its role as a prime transshipment point for illicit drugs destined for Europe and the U.S. In 1999, the World Bank announced an urban decentralization initiative financed by $25.5 million in credit that will address some of the problems caused by rural-urban migration and unemployment.

DIRECTORY

CENTRAL GOVERNMENT

Head of State

President
Mathieu Kerekou, Office of the President, Place de l'Independance, Boite Postale 08 0612, Conotou, Benin
PHONE: +229 312363; 301243
FAX: +229 300636

Ministers

Minister of Civil Service, Labor, and Administrative Reform
Ousmane Batoko, Ministry of Civil Service, Labor, and Administrative Reform
PHONE: +229 315084

Minister of Commerce, Handicrafts, and Tourism
Marie-Elise Gbedo, Ministry of Commerce, Handicrafts, and Tourism
PHONE: +229 315801

Minister of Culture and Communications
Severin Adjovi, Ministry of Culture and Communications
PHONE: +229 315729; 303417

Minister of Education and Scientific Research
Damien Zinsou Alahassa, Ministry of Education and Scientific Research
PHONE: +229 301991; 301698

Minister of Energy, Mining, and Water Resources
Felix Essou Dansou, Ministry of Energy, Mining, and Water Resources
PHONE: +229 314119; 312736

Minister of Finance and Economy
Abdoulaye Bio Tchane, Ministry of Finance and Economy
PHONE: +229 315145; 306105

Minister of Foreign Affairs and Cooperation
Antoine Kolawole Idji, Ministry of Foreign Affairs and Cooperation
PHONE: +229 300906; 306015

Minister of Health
Marina D'Almeida-Massougbodji, Ministry of Health
PHONE: +229 330464

Minister of Industry and Small to Medium-Sized Businesses
Pierre John Igue, Ministry of Industry and Small to Medium-Sized Businesses
PHONE: +229 301646

Minister of Interior, Security, and Territorial Administration
Daniel Tawema, Ministry of Interior, Security, and Territorial Administration
PHONE: +229 300153; 301030

Minister of Justice, Legislative Affairs, and Human Rights
Joseph H. Gnonlonfoun, Ministry of Justice, Legislative Affairs, and Human Rights
PHONE: +229 315145; 316329

Minister of National Defense
Pierre Osho, Ministry of National Defense
PHONE: +229 301243

Minister of Public Works and Transportation
Joseph Sourou Attin, Ministry of Public Works and Transportation
PHONE: +229 313841

Minister for Relations with Institutions and Government Spokesman
Sylvain Adekpedjou Akindes, Ministry of Relations with Institutions and Government
PHONE: +229 314129

Minister of Rural Development
Saka Saley, Ministry of Rural Development
PHONE: +229 301087; 300496

Minister of Social Welfare and Women's Affairs
Ramatou Baba-Moussa, Ministry of Social Welfare and Women's Affairs
PHONE: +229 300333

Minister of Youth, Sports, and Leisure
Christian Lagnide, Ministry of Youth, Sports, and Leisure
PHONE: +229 30-36-00

POLITICAL ORGANIZATIONS

Front d'Action pour le Rénouveau et le Développement-FARD (Action for Renewal and Development)
NAME: Mathieu Kérékou

Rassemblement Africain pour le Progrès et la Solidarité-RAP (African Rally for Progress and Solidarity)

Alliance pour la Démocratie et le Progrès-ADP (Alliance for Democracy and Progress)
NAME: Adekpedjon Akindes

Alliance pour la Social-Démocratie-ASD (Alliance for Social Democracy)
NAME: Robert Dossou

Alliance Caméléon-AC (Chameleon Alliance)

Parti Communiste du Bénin-PCB (Communist Party of Benin)

TITLE: Secretary
NAME: Pascal Fatondji

Parti du Renouveau Démocratique PRD (Democratic Renewal Party)

NAME: Pascal Chabi Kao

Impulsion au Progrès et la Démocratie-IPD (Impulse to Progress and Democracy)

Mouvement Nationale pour la Démocratie et le Développement-MNDD (National Movement for Democracy and Development)

Union Nationale pour la Démocratie et le Progrès-UNDP (National Union for Democracy and Progress)

Nouvelle Généeration-NG (New Generation)

Notre Cause Commune (Our Common Cause)

NAME: Albert Tevoedjre

Rassemblement pour la Démocratie et le progrès-RDP (Rally for Democracy and Progress)

Rassemblement des Démocrates Libéraux-RDL (Rally of Liberal Democrats)

NAME: Severin Adjovi

Parti Social-Démocrate-PSD (Social Democratic Party)

NAME: Bruno Amoussou

Parti de la Renaissance du Bénin-PRB (The Renaissance Party)

NAME: Nicéphore Soglo

Union pour la Démocratie et la Solidarité Nationale-UDSN (Union for Democracy and National Solidarity)

DIPLOMATIC REPRESENTATION

Embassies in Benin

Denmark
B.P. 04-1223, Cotonou, Benin
PHONE: +229 303862
FAX: +229 303860

France
PHONE: +229 312638

United Kingdom
BP 147, Sobepat, Cotonou, Benin
PHONE: +229 313342

United States
Rue Caporal Bernard Anani, Cotonou, B. P. 2012, Benin
PHONE: +229 300650; 300513; 301792
FAX: +229 301439; 301974
TITLE: Ambassador
NAME: Robert C. Felder

JUDICIAL SYSTEM

Supreme Court

PHONE: +229 314888; 303794

Constitutional Court

PHONE: +229 311992; 224870

Haute Cour de Justice

FURTHER READING
Books

Africa on File. New York: 1995 Facts on File, 1995.

Air Afrique. *Guides Touristiques de l'Afrique: Côte d'Ivoire, Haute-Volta, Benin, Togo.* Vol. 2. Paris: Hatier, 1976.

Cohen, William. *Rulers of Empire: The French Colonial Service in Africa.* Stanford: Hoover Institute Press, 1971.

Decalo, Samuel. *Historical Dictionary of Benin.* Third Edition. Lanham, Md., and London: The Scarecrow Press, 1995.

Duignan, Peter, and Lewis Henry Gann. *Colonialism in Africa, 1870–1960.* New York: Cambridge University Press, 1973.

Foltz, William J. *From French West Africa to the Mali Federation.* New Haven: Yale University Press, 1965.

Miller, Susan Katz. ''Sermon on the Farm.'' *International Wildlife.* March/April 1992, pp. 49-51.

Morgenthau, Ruth Schachter. *Political Parties in French-speaking West Africa.* Oxford: Oxford University Press, 1964.

Suret-Canal, Jean. *The Colonial Era in French West and Central Africa, 1900–1945.* London: C. Hurst, 1970.

Internet

Africaonline. Available Online @ http://www.africaonline.com (October 28, 1999).

Africa News Online. Available Online @ http://www.africanews.org/west/stories/1999_feat1.html (October 28, 1999).

Integrated Regional Information Network (IRIN). Available Online @ http://www.reliefweb.int/IRIN (October 28, 1999).

BENIN: STATISTICAL DATA

For sources and notes see "Sources of Statistics" in the front of each volume.

GEOGRAPHY

Geography (1)

Area:

Total: 112,620 sq km.

Land: 110,620 sq km.

Water: 2,000 sq km.

Area—comparative: slightly smaller than Pennsylvania.

Land boundaries:

Total: 1,989 km.

Border countries: Burkina Faso 306 km, Niger 266 km, Nigeria 773 km, Togo 644 km.

Coastline: 121 km.

Climate: tropical; hot, humid in south; semiarid in north.

Terrain: mostly flat to undulating plain; some hills and low mountains.

Natural resources: small offshore oil deposits, limestone, marble, timber.

Land use:

Arable land: 13%

Permanent crops: 4%

Permanent pastures: 4%

Forests and woodland: 31%

Other: 48% (1993 est.).

HUMAN FACTORS

Demographics (2A)

	1990	1995	1998	2000	2010	2020	2030	2040	2050
Population	4,675.9	5,522.7	6,100.8	6,516.6	8,955.1	11,920.0	15,223.8	18,690.9	22,171.1
Net migration rate (per 1,000 population)	NA	NA	NA	NA	NA	NA	NA	NA	NA
Births	NA	NA	NA	NA	NA	NA	NA	NA	NA
Deaths	NA	NA	NA	NA	NA	NA	NA	NA	NA
Life expectancy - males	48.3	50.3	51.6	52.4	56.5	60.4	63.9	67.0	69.6
Life expectancy - females	51.6	54.2	55.7	56.8	61.8	66.5	70.7	74.3	77.1
Birth rate (per 1,000)	49.5	47.2	45.8	44.9	39.5	33.6	28.2	23.9	20.8
Death rate (per 1,000)	16.2	13.9	12.8	12.0	9.1	7.0	5.8	5.3	5.3
Women of reproductive age (15-49 yrs.)	1,064.3	1,249.2	1,379.0	1,475.1	2,100.8	2,953.4	3,965.6	5,032.0	5,985.8
of which are currently married	NA	NA	NA	NA	NA	NA	NA	NA	NA
Fertility rate	7.1	6.7	6.5	6.3	5.3	4.3	3.5	2.9	2.6

Except as noted, values for vital statistics are in thousands; life expectancy is in years.

Health Personnel (3)

Total health expenditure as a percentage of GDP, 1990-1997[a]

Public sector 1.7

Private sector . . . . .NA

Total[b] . . . . .NA

Health expenditure per capita in U.S. dollars, 1990-1997[a]

Purchasing power parity . . . . .NA

Total . . . . .NA

Availability of health care facilities per 100,000 people

Hospital beds 1990-1997[a] 0.20

Doctors 1993[c] 6

Nurses 1993[c] 33

Health Indicators (4)

Life expectancy at birth

1980 48

1997 53

Daily per capita supply of calories (1996) 2,415

Total fertility rate births per woman (1997) 5.8

Maternal mortality ratio per 100,000 live births (1990-97) . . . . .500[d]

Safe water % of population with access (1995) 72

Sanitation % of population with access (1995) 24

Consumption of iodized salt % of households (1992-98)[a] 79

Smoking prevalence

Male % of adults (1985-95)[a] . . . .

Female % of adults (1985-95)[a] . . . .

Tuberculosis incidence per 100,000 people (1997) 220

Adult HIV prevalence % of population ages 15-49 (1997) 2.06

Infants and Malnutrition (5)

Under-5 mortality rate (1997) 167

% of infants with low birthweight (1990-97) . . . . . .NA

Births attended by skilled health staff % of total[a] . . .60

% fully immunized (1995-97)

TB 89

DPT 78

Polio 78

Measles 82

Prevalence of child malnutrition under age 5 (1992-97)[b] 29

Ethnic Division (6)

African (42 ethnic groups, most important Fon, Adja Yoruba, Bariba) 99%

Europeans 1%

Religions (7)

Indigenous beliefs 70%

Muslim 15%

Christian 15%

Languages (8)

French (official), Fon and Yoruba (most common vernaculars in south), tribal languages (at least six major ones in north).

EDUCATION

Public Education Expenditures (9)

Public expenditure on education (% of GNP)

1980 . . . .

1996 . . . . .3.2[1]

Expenditure per student

Primary % of GNP per capita

1980 . . . .

1996 . . . . .11.8[1]

Secondary % of GNP per capita

1980 . . . .

1996 . . . .

Tertiary % of GNP per capita

1980 . . . .

1996 . . . . .249.1[1]

Expenditure on teaching materials

Primary % of total for level (1996) . . . .

Secondary % of total for level (1996) . . . .

Primary pupil-teacher ratio per teacher (1996) . . . . .52[1]

Duration of primary education years (1995) 6

Educational Attainment (10)

Age group (1992) . . . . .25+

Total population 1,700,914

Highest level attained (%)

No schooling 78.5

First level

Not completed 10.8

Completed . . . . .NA

Entered second level

S-1 . . . . .8.2

S-2 . . . . .NA

Postsecondary 1.3

Literacy Rates (11A)

In thousands and percent[1]	1990	1995	2000	2010
Illiterate population (15+ yrs.)	1,722	1,792	1,839	1,845
Literacy rate - total adult pop. (%)	30.2	37.0	44.5	59.7
Literacy rate - males (%)	41.6	48.7	56.0	69.4
Literacy rate - females (%)	19.3	25.8	33.5	50.3

Military Affairs (14B)

	1990	1991	1992	1993	1994	1995
Military expenditures						
Current dollars (mil.)	28	NA	21e	26e	41	24e
1995 constant dollars (mil.)	32	NA	22e	27e	43	24e
Armed forces (000)	6	7	6	6	6	6
Gross national product (GNP)						
Current dollars (mil.)	1,371	1,503	1,586	1,700	1,795	2,013
1995 constant dollars (mil.)	1,576	1,661	1,706	1,782	1,840	2,013
Central government expenditures (CGE)						
1995 constant dollars (mil.)	NA	316e	NA	320e	NA	NA
People (mil.)	4.7	4.8	5.0	5.2	5.3	5.5
Military expenditure as % of GNP	2.0	NA	1.3	1.5	2.3	1.2
Military expenditure as % of CGE	NA	NA	NA	8.6	NA	NA
Military expenditure per capita (1995 $)	7	NA	4	5	8	4
Armed forces per 1,000 people (soldiers)	1.3	1.4	1.2	1.2	1.1	1.1
GNP per capita (1995 $)	337	344	341	345	344	365
Arms imports[6]						
Current dollars (mil.)	5	0	0	0	0	0
1995 constant dollars (mil.)	6	0	0	0	0	0
Arms exports[6]						
Current dollars (mil.)	0	0	0	0	0	0
1995 constant dollars (mil.)	0	0	0	0	0	0
Total imports[7]						
Current dollars (mil.)	265	241	615	614	493	794e
1995 constant dollars (mil.)	305	266	662	644	505	794e
Total exports[7]						
Current dollars (mil.)	122	21	88	181	163	79e
1995 constant dollars (mil.)	140	23	95	190	167	79e
Arms as percent of total imports[8]	1.9	0	0	0	0	0

GOVERNMENT & LAW

Political Parties (12)

National Assembly	No. of seats
The Renaissance Party of Benin (RB)	20
Democratic Renewal Party (PRD)	19
Action for Renewal and Development (FARD-ALAFIA)	10
Alliance of the Social Democratic Party (PSD)	7
Our Common Cause (NCC)	3
Liberal Democrats' Rally for National Reconstruction-Vivoten (RDL-Vivoten)	3
Communist Party of Benin (PCB)	2
Alliance Chameleon (AC)	1
Rally for Democracy and Progress (RDP)	1
Other	17

Government Budget (13B)

Revenues	$299 million
Expenditures	$445 million
Capital expenditures	$14 million

Data for 1995 est.

Crime (15)

Crime rate (for 1997)

Crimes reported	20,700
Total persons convicted	18,400
Crimes per 100,000 population	350

Persons responsible for offenses

Total number of suspects	3,300
Total number of female suspects	150
Total number of juvenile suspects	90

LABOR FORCE

Unemployment Rate (17)

Rate not available.

PRODUCTION SECTOR

Electric Energy (18)

Capacity	15,000 kW (1995)
Production	6 million kWh (1995)
Consumption per capita	45 kWh (1995)

Transportation (19)

Highways:
total: 6,787 km
paved: 1,357 km (including 10 km of expressways)
unpaved: 5,430 km (1996 est.)

Waterways: navigable along small sections, important only locally

Merchant marine: none

Airports: 6 (1997 est.)

Airports—with paved runways:
total: 2
2,438 to 3,047 m: 1
1,524 to 2,437 m: 1 (1997 est.)

Airports—with unpaved runways:
total: 4
1,524 to 2,437 m: 1
914 to 1,523 m: 3 (1997 est.)

Top Agricultural Products (20)

Corn, sorghum, cassava (tapioca), yams, beans, rice, cotton, palm oil, peanuts; poultry, livestock.

MANUFACTURING SECTOR

GDP & Manufacturing Summary (21)

	1980	1985	1990	1992	1993	1994
Gross Domestic Product						
Millions of 1990 dollars	1,336	1,735	1,845	1,961	2,026	2,123
Growth rate in percent	9.42	7.53	3.29	4.16	3.31	4.80
Per capita (in 1990 dollars)	386.2	435.1	398.2	397.8	398.4	404.8
Manufacturing Value Added						
Millions of 1990 dollars	127	115	145	170	174	*180*
Growth rate in percent	−4.38	11.85	0.85	11.56	2.39	*3.79*
Manufacturing share in percent of current prices	12.9	8.2	8.2	8.2	8.2	*7.8*

FINANCE, ECONOMICS, & TRADE

Economic Indicators (22)

National product: GDP—purchasing power parity—$11.3 billion (1997 est.)
National product real growth rate: 5.8% (1997 est.)
National product per capita: $1,900 (1997 est.)
Inflation rate—consumer price index: 3.5% (1997 est.)

Exchange Rates (24)

Exchange rates:

CFA francs (CFAF) per US$1

January 1998	608.36
1997	583.67
1996	511.55
1995	499.15
1994	555.20
1993	283.16

Beginning 12 January 1994 the CFA franc was devalued to CFAF 100 per French franc from CFAF 50 at which it had been fixed since 1948

Top Import Origins (25)

$693 million (c.i.f., 1995)

Origins	%
France	27
Thailand	9

China	NA
Hong Kong	NA

NA stands for not available.

Top Export Destinations (26)

$192 million (f.o.b., 1995).

Destinations	%
Brazil	18
Portugal	14
Morocco	NA
Libya	NA
France	NA

NA stands for not available.

Economic Aid (27)

Recipient: ODA, $NA. NA stands for not available.

Import Export Commodities (28)

Import Commodities	Export Commodities
Foodstuffs	Cotton
Beverages	Crude oil
Tobacco	Palm products
Petroleum products	Cocoa
Intermediate goods	
Capital goods	
Light consumer goods	

Balance of Payments (23)

	1990	1991	1992	1993	1994
Exports of goods (f.o.b.)	287	337	371	341	301
Imports of goods (f.o.b.)	−428	−482	−561	−539	−366
Trade balance	−141	−146	−189	−198	−65
Services - debits	−174	−169	−220	−193	−152
Services - credits	115	123	143	137	104
Private transfers (net)	86	84	95	94	65
Government transfers (net)	133	102	132	144	84
Overall balance	19	−7	−39	−14	36

BERMUDA

INTRODUCTORY SURVEY

RECENT HISTORY

Reportedly discovered by Spanish explorer Juan Bermudez in 1503, the coral islands known today as Bermuda were first inhabited by 150 shipwrecked English travelers in 1609. England took control of the islands and in the early years, and Bermuda has retained its status as a British territory throughout. England used it as part of its slave trade until slavery was abolished in 1834. The current population is nearly 60% African, descendants of those slaves. Taking advantage of its location 650 miles due east of North Carolina, the islands were used as a staging area for both blockade running during the American Civil War and for rum running during the American Prohibition era.

This location brought Bermuda attention again during World War II, when the U.S. government traded surplus destroyers to England for a 99 year lease for military bases. The U.S. put a naval base and naval air station on the islands during World War II, and kept them until 1995. The only U.S. government installation remaining is a tracking station operated by NASA. A British army garrison was closed in 1957, the Canadians closed a World War II era base in 1993, and the British Royal Navy closed its base in 1995.

Bermuda has always enjoyed a measure of self government within the set of English colonies and territories. Indicative of the times, however, political parties were only formed in the 1960s, with the first formed to represent non-whites. Shortly after, the racial turbulence in the United States and North

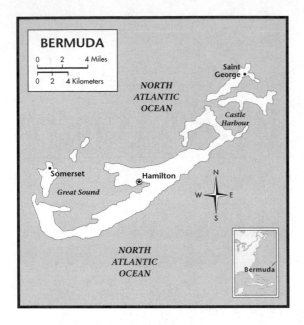

America was felt in Bermuda. In 1973, the British governor, Sir Richard Sharples, was assassinated along with four others. Tensions escalated until 1977 when the assassins were executed and civil unrest and rioting occurred. Shortly afterwards, the government began efforts to end de facto racial discriminations. Independence talks followed and a referendum on independence was held in August of 1995. Independence failed in this election, with nearly three-fourths of those voting in opposition. The failure of the independence movement was attributed to a general fear that the island's special economic circumstances (tourism and off shore banking) would be compromised.

GOVERNMENT

Bermuda is a self-governing overseas territory of the United Kingdom. As such, the head of state is the British monarch, who is represented on the islands by an appointed governor. The government of Bermuda in its present form was established by a constitution enacted in 1968. The executive branch is headed by the governor with a cabinet nominated by the premier and appointed by the governor. There are no elections for executive branch members.

The legislative branch of the government consists of a bicameral parliament, with a 40-seat house of assembly, which is popularly elected to five year terms and an 11-member appointed senate. The premier is the elected head of the majority party in the elected house of assembly. The constitution provides for a premier with strong powers.

The senate appointments are made by the governor, with five on the advice of the premier, three on the advice of the opposition leader, and three at the discretion of the governor.

Eligible voters are all legal residents over the age of eighteen. Bermudian local government is in the nine parishes of St. Georges, Hamilton, Smiths, Devonshire, Pembroke, Paget, Warwick, Southampton, and Sandy's. There are two municipalities: Hamilton and Saint George.

Foreign relations and defense are the responsibility of the United Kingdom. Bermuda does, however, participate as an observer in many regional and international organizations such as Caricom and the IOC. Bermuda maintains offices of their Department of Tourism in New York, Atlanta, Chicago, and Boston.

Judiciary

The judicial system is based upon English common law. The courts are headed by a Supreme Court appointed by the governor. The court is composed of a chief justice and associate judges.

Political Parties

Political parties are a recent development in Bermuda's history. The first party, the Progressive Labor Party, was established in 1963 of predominantly black followers. Other parties include the United Bermuda Party and the National Liberal Party. The 1998 elections found the Progressive Labor Party as the party of the majority, ending a thirty year period where the United Bermuda Party was the majority party. Although not technically political parties, two organizations wield some influence: the Bermuda Industrial Union and the Bermuda Public Services Association.

DEFENSE

National defense of the islands is the responsibility of the United Kingdom. There is no standing army, although there is a police force.

ECONOMIC AFFAIRS

Bermuda has successfully taken advantage of its location and developed a strong financial services industry and a strong luxury tourist industry. It has also become a location of choice for those looking to register shipping. As a result, Bermuda has one of the stronger economies in the world with one of the highest per capita incomes, estimated in 1997 to be $30,000. Gross Domestic Product in 1997 was estimated by the CIA at $1.9 billion.

The tourist industry draws primarily from North America, and is the major source of income for Bermuda. More than 500,000 tourists visit annually; tourists arrive either by air or cruise ship. Financial services for international firms is another major source of income as off shore banking with associated tax benefits are more and more important to international firms. Insurance and investment companies are also located in Bermuda. Registered ships of major tonnage (1,000 GRT or over) numbered 97 in 1998. Together, these industries account for more than enough income annually to offset an annual trade imbalance of over $500 million.

With only 6% of the land arable, agriculture is not significant on the island. Over 80% of all food consumed on the islands is imported. Locally grown agricultural products include bananas, vegetables, citrus fruits, honey, flowers, and dairy products. The fishing industry is small, but includes recreational fishing for the tourists. Most building materials are imported, although sand and limestone quarried for construction is available on the islands.

Light manufacturing is established on the islands: paint, pharmaceuticals, electronic wares, and printed materials. Exports of $57 million (estimated for 1997) include pharmaceuticals, cut flowers, essences, and brass electrical contacts. Imports of $617 million (estimated for 1997) include machinery and transport equipment, manufactured goods, food and animals, chemicals, and petroleum products. Bermuda's trading partners are primarily Canada, the United Kingdom, Caribbean countries, and the United States. Oil is primarily provided to the islands from the Netherlands Antilles.

There are seven radio stations and three television stations on the islands.

Public Finance

The monetary system in Bermuda is based upon the Bermudian dollar (Bd$) which is pegged to the U.S. dollar (US$) at a fixed rate, 1:1. Taxes are principally raised through import duties, a small property tax, and taxes on tourism. Government expenditures in fiscal year 1998 were $537 million on revenues of $505 million. Economic aid of nearly $28 million was received in 1995. The large and unfavorable balance of payments is covered by an influx of foreign exchange through the tourist and off shore banking services industries.

Income

There is very little unemployment in Bermuda, and that situation has existed for some time. The per capita income on the islands is $30,000, among the highest in the world. Many Bermudians work more than one job. Poverty is virtually non-existent.

Industry

Industrial activities include tourism, finance, insurance, structural concrete products, paints, furniture, perfumes, pharmaceuticals, and ship repairing.

Banking and Finance

Bermuda has local banking services as well as a large off shore banking, financial services, investments, and insurance industry.

Economic Development

Economic growth is limited due to the small land mass and a general lack of arable land and natural resources. Economic development activities are focused on the tourist and off shore banking industries. Bermuda will continue to be a registry location for shipping. Fear of disturbing these sources of income led to the defeat of the independence initiative in 1995.

SOCIAL WELFARE

The government is not heavily involved in social welfare programs due to the high per capita income and general lack of poverty. However, a social security program was enacted in 1965 that provides old-age, disability, and survivor pensions. Hospitalization insurance is also compulsory for all citizens.

Healthcare

Healthcare on the islands is through private sources, although the hospital with more than 230 single beds on the islands receives some government support. Health insurance is compulsory for all citizens. The quality of healthcare meets a high standard.

Housing

Housing for the permanent residents is adequate. Building materials other than concrete and limestone must be imported.

EDUCATION

Education is compulsory and free for all residents between the ages of 5 and 16. There are eighteen primary and 14 secondary schools on the island, and one junior college. To upgrade the educational system, a program is in place to add five middle schools and two high schools by 2002. Technical training is available at the one junior college. Higher education is generally pursued in the United Kingdom or the United States. Government scholarships are available for higher education.

1999 KEY EVENTS TIMELINE

February

- New labor government submits its first budget.

May

- High-profile court case involving 1993 collapse of Bermuda Fire and Marine Insurance goes to trial.

- Bermuda launches $15 million ad campaign to boost U.S. tourism.

July

- Bermuda's hotels launch new "cruise welcome program" to attract more cruise passengers for overnight stays on the island.

August

- Bank of Bermuda launches new $250,000 on-line security system to bolster e-commerce capacity.

October

- New session of parliament begins amid public ceremonies led by island's governor.

ANALYSIS OF EVENTS: 1999

BUSINESS AND THE ECONOMY

Tourism and insurance continued to be the mainstays of Bermuda's economy in 1999, with insurance the stronger of the two sectors. Although the tourist industry still employed more than twice as many local residents as insurance companies did, tourism has been on the decline for over a decade due to increasing competition, high prices, and changing tastes. Bermuda's new government pledged that it would take steps to reverse this trend. In May the Department of Tourism launched a new $15 million advertising campaign, for which it hired the U.S. ad agency J. Walter Thompson. Targeted at both print and broadcast media markets in the eastern United States, the ads were aimed at boosting awareness of Bermuda by focusing on the island's cultural features rather than exclusively on tourist attractions such as recreational activities.

The real economic success story in Bermuda remained the insurance sector, which has grown into a world leader on a par with London and New York thanks to the absence of corporate income taxes on the island and its reputation for a laissez-faire regulatory style. Insurance revenues in Bermuda have surpassed those from tourism since 1996 (in the 1998/99 fiscal year, insurance generated $757.6 million, compared with $472.3 million from tourism). After starting out primarily as a site for captive insurance companies in the 1970s, Bermuda has evolved into a center for insurers selling high-risk policies covering major international corporations for multimillion-dollar losses in such areas as product liability and catastrophe reinsurance (a sector that experienced rapid growth following a series of natural disasters in the early 1990s, including Hurricane Andrew). With the nation's new government committed to maintaining the success of this sector, prospects for continued growth are excellent.

GOVERNMENT AND POLITICS

For Bermudians, the last year of the 20th century marked a new beginning—it was their first year of rule by the labor government swept into office in the electoral upset of November 1998, which ended 30 years of dominance by the conservative United Bermuda Party. It also brought the island its first elected female prime minister, Progressive Labor Party leader Jennifer Smith. In spite of its more liberal orientation, the new government pledged to maintain the favorable business climate that had made Bermuda a world leader in the insurance industry in recent years and took a first step in this direction by easing the island's work-permit regulations, making it easier for businesses to bring qualified individuals into the country to work for them. The new government signaled its intention of insuring an open dialogue among government, business, and organized labor by creating the National Tripartite Commission, with representatives of all three interests. Perhaps most importantly, the government extended the island's corporate tax exemption—a major attraction for insurers and other businesses—from the year 2016 to 2020.

The PLP government also indicated its intention of improving Bermuda's telecommunications infrastructure with an eye toward expansion of e-commerce. Reorganization of the nation's civil service to achieve greater effectiveness and lower costs was also indicated as a high priority by the new government.

An important aspect of maintaining the island's status as a major international business center was establishing credibility with foreign governments. In the course of the year, parliament unanimously passed three laws to enhance cooperation between Bermuda's government and foreign regulatory authorities: the USA-Bermuda Tax Convention Act of 1999, the Proceeds of Crime Amendment Act of 1999, and the Taxes Management Act of 1999.

CULTURE AND SOCIETY

Among the goals articulated by Bermuda's new prime minister, Jennifer Smith, was that of including all Bermudians in the economic success brought to the island by tourism and international business. While many of the new jobs created in business were professional and managerial, there was a shortage of native Bermudians to fill them, and companies based on the island brought in many employees from outside— insurance industry employees were mostly white males from the United States and Europe, and there were no blacks at the CEO level in any of Bermuda's insurance companies. However, rather than blaming the situation on racism, Smith cited a lack of management-level skills among the local population.

In its first year, Smith's new government took an important step in developing a better-qualified local work force through its education initiatives, responding to reports that nearly half of all Bermudian students graduated from high school with substandard reading skills. The government's first budget increased education spending by 8 percent, to $85 million, to hire better-qualified teachers, reduce class sizes, and decrease the dropout rate.

DIRECTORY

CENTRAL GOVERNMENT

Head of State

Queen
Elizabeth II, Monarch, Buckingham Palace, The Visitor Center, London SW1A 1AA, England
PHONE: +44 (0171) 8391377
FAX: +44 (0171) 9309625

Governor-General
Thorold Masefield

Premier
Jennifer Smith, Office of the Governor, Government House, 11 Langton Hill, Pembroke, HM 13 Bermuda
PHONE: +(809) 2923600
FAX: +(809) 2953823

Ministers

Deputy Premier
Terry Lister, Ministry of Development, Opportunity and Government

Minister of Technology and Information
Maurine Renee Webb, Ministry of Technology and Information, Melbourne House, 3rd Floor, Parliament St., POB HM 2552, Hamilton HM KX Bermuda
PHONE: +(809) 2960609
FAX: +(809) 2960616

Minister of Education and Libraries
Milton Scott, Ministry of Education, POB HM 1185, Hamilton HM EX Bermuda
PHONE: +(809) 2955151
FAX: +(809) 2922349

Minister of Works, Engineering, Parks and Housing
Alex Scott, Ministry of Works, Engineering, Parks and Housing, Post Office Bldg., 56 Church Street, POB 525, Hamilton HM 12 Bermuda
PHONE: +(809) 2955151
FAX: +(809) 2950170

Minister of Youth Development, Sport, Parks and Recreation
Dennis Lister, Ministry of Youth Development, Sport, Parks and Recreation, Old Fire Station Bldg., 81 Court Street, Hamilton HM 12 Bermuda
PHONE: +(809) 2950855
FAX: +(809) 2956292

Minister of Environment, Planning and Natural Resources

Arthur Hodgson, Ministry of Environment, Planning and Natural Resources, Government Administration Bldg., 30 Parliament Street, Hamilton HM 12 Bermuda
PHONE: +(809) 2955151
FAX: +(809) 2922349

Minister of Labor, Home Affairs and Public Safety

Paula Cox, Ministry of Labor, Home Affairs and Public Safety, Government Administration Bldg, 30 Parliament Street, Hamilton HM 12 Bermuda
PHONE: +(809) 2955151
FAX: +(809) 2954780

Minister of Legislative Affairs and Attorney-General

Lois Browne-Evans, Ministry of Legislative Affairs and Attorney-General, Old Fire Station Bldg., 8 Court Street, Hamilton HM 12 Bermuda
PHONE: +(809) 2950855
FAX: +(809) 2956292

Minister of Transport, Aviation and Marine Services

Ewart Brown, Ministry of Transport, Aviation and Marine Services, Global House, 43 Church Street, Hamilton HM 12 Bermuda
PHONE: +(809) 2953130
FAX: +(809) 2951013

Minister of Health and Family Services

Nelson Bascome, Ministry of Health and Family Services, Old Hospital Bldg., 7 Point Finger Road, Paget DV 04 Bermuda
PHONE: +(809) 2360224
FAX: +(809) 2363971

Minister of Tourism

David Allen, Ministry of Tourism, Global House, 43 Church Street, Hamilton HM 12 Bermuda
PHONE: +(809) 2920023
FAX: +(809) 2927537

Minister of Finance

Eugene Cox, Ministry of Finance, Government Administration Bldg., 30 Parliament Street, Hamilton HM 12 Bermuda
PHONE: +(809) 2955151
FAX: +(809) 2955727

POLITICAL ORGANIZATIONS

United Bermuda Party-UBP

Central Office, 87 John F Burows Bldg., Chancery Lane, POB HM 715, Hamilton HM CX Bermuda
PHONE: +(809) 2950729

Progressive Labour Party-PLP

Court Street, POB HM 1367, Hamilton HM FX Bermuda
PHONE: +(809) 2922264
FAX: +(809) 2957890
NAME: Jennifer Smith

National Liberal Party-NLP

POB HM 1794, Hamilton HM HX Bermuda
NAME: Charles Jeffers

DIPLOMATIC REPRESENTATION

Embassies in Bermuda

Austria
P.O. Box 761 WK06, Bermuda
PHONE: +(809) 2363300
FAX: +(809) 2366100
E-MAIL: vienna@ibl.bm
TITLE: Consul
NAME: Leopold Kuechler

JUDICIAL SYSTEM

Supreme Court

FURTHER READING

Articles

Allen, Michael. ''Bermuda's Business Elites Go to Court Today as Creditors Sue over Insurance Firm's Collapse.'' *The Wall Street Journal*, 4 May 1999, p. A14.

McIntyre, Kathryn. ''Bermuda Attains Predicted Stature.'' *Business Insurance* (March 22, 1999): 21.

''New Bermuda Premier Works with Insurers.'' *National Underwriter Property and Casualty-Risk and Benefits Management* (March 1, 1999): 4.

Power, Carol. ''Bank of Bermuda Rolls Out Entrust Web Security System as Institution Positions Itself for International E-Commerce.'' *American Banker* (August 13, 1999): 10.

Snyder, Beth. ''Bermuda Ads from JWT Recast Isle in New Light: Unique Culture Highlighted in Effort to Combat Dip in Air Travel.'' *Advertising Age* (May 10, 1999): 12.

Treaster, Joseph B. ''Bermuda Takes the Risk: From Tourist Paradise to Haven for Insurance Business.'' *The New York Times*, 28 April 1999, p. C1.

BERMUDA: STATISTICAL DATA

For sources and notes see "Sources of Statistics" in the front of each volume.

GEOGRAPHY

Geography (1)

Area:

Total: 50 sq km.

Land: 50 sq km.

Water: 0 sq km.

Area—comparative: about 0.3 times the size of Washington, DC.

Land boundaries: 0 km.

Coastline: 103 km.

Climate: subtropical; mild, humid; gales, strong winds common in winter.

Terrain: low hills separated by fertile depressions.

Natural resources: limestone, pleasant climate fostering tourism.

Land use:

Arable land: 6%

Permanent crops: NA%

Permanent pastures: NA%

Forests and woodland: NA%

Other: NA (1997 est.).

Note: developed (55%), and rural and open space (39%) comprise 94% of Bermudian land area.

HUMAN FACTORS

Demographics (2A)

	1990	1995	1998	2000	2010	2020	2030	2040	2050
Population	NA	60.5	62.0	62.9	66.3	68.2	67.9	65.0	60.8
Net migration rate (per 1,000 population)	NA	NA	NA	NA	NA	NA	NA	NA	NA
Births	NA	NA	NA	NA	NA	NA	NA	NA	NA
Deaths	NA	NA	NA	NA	NA	NA	NA	NA	NA
Life expectancy - males	NA	74.4	75.0	75.4	76.9	78.1	78.9	79.5	80.0
Life expectancy - females	NA	78.1	78.6	79.0	80.7	82.1	83.1	84.0	84.7
Birth rate (per 1,000)	NA	13.5	12.2	11.5	10.2	9.9	9.0	8.8	8.9
Death rate (per 1,000)	NA	7.2	7.2	7.3	8.4	10.1	12.6	15.3	15.7
Women of reproductive age (15-49 yrs.)	NA	16.8	16.8	16.8	15.6	13.7	13.3	12.5	11.4
of which are currently married	NA	NA	NA	NA	NA	NA	NA	NA	NA
Fertility rate	NA	1.7	1.7	1.7	1.7	1.7	1.7	1.7	1.7

Except as noted, values for vital statistics are in thousands; life expectancy is in years.

Ethnic Division (6)

Black 61%

White and other 39%

Religions (7)

Anglican 28%

Roman Catholic 15%

African Methodist

Episcopal (Zion) 12%

Seventh-Day Adventist 6%

Methodist 5%

Other 34% (1991)

Languages (8)

English (official), Portuguese.

EDUCATION

Educational Attainment (10)

Age group (1991) . . . . .25+

Total population 38,873

Highest level attained (%)

No schooling 0.5

First level

Not completed 18.2

Completed . . . . .NA

Entered second level

S-1 . . . . .63.0

S-2 . . . . .NA

Postsecondary 18.4

GOVERNMENT & LAW

Political Parties (12)

Parliament	% of seats
United Bermuda Party (UBP)	.50
Progressive Lab Party (PLP)	.46
Independents	.4

Government Budget (13B)

Revenues . . . .$430.9 million

Expenditures . . . .$452.9 million

Capital expenditures . . . .$50 million

Data for FY95/96 est.

Military Affairs (14A)

Total expenditures . . . .$NA

Expenditures as % of GDP . . . . .NA%

Defense is the responsibility of the UK. NA stands for not available.

Crime (15)

Crime rate (for 1997)

Crimes reported 7,500

Total persons convicted 3,150

Crimes per 100,000 population 12,400

Persons responsible for offenses

Total number of suspects . . . . .NA

Total number of female suspects . . . . .NA

Total number of juvenile suspects . . . . .NA

LABOR FORCE

Labor Force (16)

Total 34,633

Clerical 23%

Services 22%

Laborers 17%

Professional and technical 17%

Administrative and managerial 12%

Sales 7%

Agriculture and fishing 2%

Data for 1996.

Unemployment Rate (17)

Negligible. (1995)

PRODUCTION SECTOR

Electric Energy (18)

Capacity . . . . .145,000 kW (1996)

Production . . . . .527,526,728 kWh (1996)

Consumption per capita . . . . .7,856 kWh (1996)

Transportation (19)

Highways:

total: 225 km

paved: 225 km

unpaved: 0 km (1997 est.) note: in addition, there are 232 km of paved and unpaved roads that are privately owned

Merchant marine:

total: 91 ships (1,000 GRT or over) totaling 4,590,132 GRT/7,440,524 DWT ships by type: bulk 18, chemical tanker 1, container 18, liquefied gas tanker 7, oil tanker

26, refrigerated cargo 15, roll-on/roll-off cargo 3, short-sea passenger 2, vehicle carrier 1 note: a flag of convenience registry; includes ships from 8 countries among which are UK 31, Canada 13, US 10, Norway 2, Hong Kong 1, Nigeria 4, Sweden 4, and Mexico 1 (1997 est.)

Airports: 1 (1997 est.)

Airports—with paved runways:

total: 1

2,438 to 3,047 m: 1 (1997 est.)

Top Agricultural Products (20)

Bananas, vegetables, citrus, flowers; dairy products.

FINANCE, ECONOMICS, & TRADE

Economic Indicators (22)

National product: GDP—purchasing power parity—$1.8 billion (1996 est.)

National product real growth rate: 2.4% (1996 est.)

National product per capita: $29,000 (1996 est.)

Inflation rate—consumer price index: 1.8% (November 1997)

Exchange Rates (24)

Exchange rates: Bermudian dollar (Bd$) per US$1—1.0000 (fixed rate)

Top Import Origins (25)

$569 million (f.o.b., 1996 est.) Data are for 1996 est.

Origins	%
United States	.73
United Kingdom	.5
Canada	.4

Top Export Destinations (26)

$67.7 million (f.o.b., 1996 est.) Data are for 1996.

Destinations	%
Netherlands	.50
Brazil	.13
Canada	.6

Economic Aid (27)

$NA. NA stands for not available.

Import Export Commodities (28)

Import Commodities	Export Commodities
Miscellaneous manufactured articles	Reexports of pharmaceuticals
Machinery and transport equipment	
Food and live animals	
Chemicals	

MANUFACTURING SECTOR

GDP & Manufacturing Summary (21)

	1980	1985	1990	1992	1993	1994
Gross Domestic Product						
Millions of 1990 dollars	1,541	1,548	1,635	1,528	1,574	1,613
Growth rate in percent	2.51	6.69	−2.50	−1.70	3.00	2.50
Per capita (in 1990 dollars)	28,544.2	27,645.6	26,801.6	24,648.2	25,387.6	25,609.3
Manufacturing Value Added						
Millions of 1990 dollars	101	98	103	100	103	*105*
Growth rate in percent	4.52	2.80	−3.79	−1.38	2.60	*2.24*
Manufacturing share in percent of current prices	NA	NA	NA	NA	NA	NA

BHUTAN

Kingdom of Bhutan
Druk-Yul

INTRODUCTORY SURVEY

RECENT HISTORY

In the 1960s, India helped Bhutan prepare economic plans to modernize the country and end its isolation. Relations with Nepal have grown difficult in recent years because of tensions surrounding ethnic Nepalese living in Bhutan. Cross-border attacks between Bhutan and Nepal through a narrow corridor of India have forced thousands of ethnic Nepalese—both illegal immigrants and Bhutanese citizens—to migrate in recent years.

GOVERNMENT

Bhutan has functioned as a limited monarchy since 1969. The king, who is chief of state and head of government, may be removed at any time by a two-thirds vote of the National Assembly. The Royal Advisory Council is the country's chief administrative body. There is also a seven-member Council of Ministers. The National Assembly, known as the Tsongdu, consists of 151 members. The country is divided into 4 regions, 18 districts (*dzongkhas*), and 192 blocks (*gewog*).

Judiciary

Local headmen and magistrates (*thrimpon*) hear original cases. Appeals may be made to an eight-member High Court. From here, a final appeal may be made to the king.

Political Parties

Political parties are illegal in Bhutan. Opposition groups, composed mainly of ethnic Nepalese, include the Bhutan State Congress (BSC), the People's Forum for Democratic Rights, and the Bhutan People's Party (BPP), a militant group.

DEFENSE

India is responsible for Bhutan's defense. The army consists of about 4,000 lightly armed soldiers in the army and palace guard.

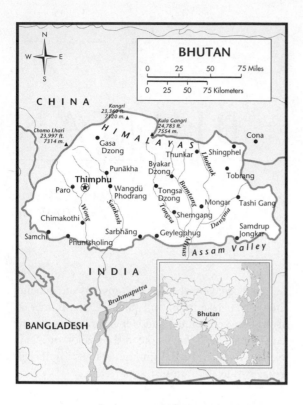

ECONOMIC AFFAIRS

Isolated Bhutan has one of the smallest economies in the world. Farming or herding supports 91% of the labor force, who produce 42% of the gross national product. The country supplies most of its food needs through the production of grains, fruits, some meat, and yak butter.

Public Finance

The largest category of annual current expenditure is public works, which presumably includes the maintenance of monasteries. Most of the annual budget deficit is covered by grants from India and from the UN and other international agencies.

The U.S. CIA estimates that, in 1995, government revenues totaled approximately $52 million and expenditures $150 million, including capital expenditures of $95 million. External debt totaled $141 million, approximately 91% of which was financed abroad.

Income

Bhutan's gross national product (GNP) was estimated to be about $301 million in 1998, or about $430 per person. During 1985–95, inflation averaged 8.4% per year and the real growth rate of the GNP was 4% per person.

Industry

Manufacturing accounted for 10.3% of the gross domestic product (GDP) in 1994. Crafts are the principal industrial occupation. Homespun textiles—woven and embroidered cottons, wools, and silks—are the most important products. Also produced in Bhutan are cement, carbide, and particle board. A large number of sawmills operate throughout the country.

Banking and Finance

Bhutan's central bank is the Royal Monetary Authority, established in 1982 to manage currency and foreign exchange. Its agent, the Bank of Bhutan, founded in 1968, has its main office at Phuntsholing and 25 branches (as of 1993) throughout the country. Bank reserves in 1992 were $192.7 million. In January 1995, the exchange rate to the dollar has Nu (ngultrum) 31.374. Securities are not traded.

Economic Development

Under Bhutan's first four development plans, considerable improvements were made in agriculture and irrigation, road transportation, forestry, and electric power generation. The plans were underwritten by India, which contributed more than $197 million over the twenty-year period.

Under the fifth economic plan (1981–87), total investments were projected at N 4,338.1 million, with almost 31% of the outlays financed by India and with some 30% provided by the UN and other foreign sources. This plan aimed to increase the GNP by 6-8% annually, with priority given to agriculture and animal husbandry (14% of the outlays) and public works (13%).

The sixth plan (1987–92), with a projected outlay of N 8,200 million, included among its goals encouragement of the private sector, revision of the tax system, greater decentralization to the district (dzongkha) level, and improvement of education and personnel training. The GDP was expected to grow by 6.9% annually, and priority was given to industry, trade, and commerce (20% of the outlays) and power (13%).

For 1992–97, the seventh plan reaffirmed basic goals of economic self-sufficiency, preserving national identity, and human resource development. In addition, the plan strengthened the government's emphasis on development of the private sector as well as its commitment to environmental preservation. Privatization of public sector manufacturing firms and other measures expanded the role of private manufacturing and services firms, especially within export-oriented manufacturing and mining industries as well as the tourist sector. Specific environmental objectives included the promotion of sustainable agriculture through soil erosion control as well as the setting aside of 20% of the country's land area as nature reserves and other areas protected from commercial timber extraction. Ambitious targets were set for meeting all recurrent expenditures from domestic revenues by the end of the plan period. Bhutan seeks to end its over-dependence on Indian financing for balancing its current fiscal debt. The expenditures required to meet other targets however, make it unlikely that much progress will be achieved in this area in the near future.

SOCIAL WELFARE

There is no national social welfare system, except for a modest maternal and child welfare program begun in the early 1980s, which includes family planning. Bhutan's culture does not isolate or disenfranchise women. Discriminatory policies against Nepalese Hindus in the 1980s led to the cultural repression of Hindus, but there are now a growing number of Nepalese employed in the public sector.

Healthcare

Bhutan suffers from a shortage of medical personnel. Only 65% of the population has access to any form of medical care. In 1990, there were 141 doctors. The average life expectancy is only 53 years. Malaria, tuberculosis, and venereal disease remain widespread.

Housing

Traditional houses are built of blocks or layers of stone set in clay mortar, with roofs formed of pine shingles kept in place by heavy stones. As of 1990, 60% of urban and 30% of rural dwellers had access to a public water supply.

EDUCATION

Bhutan's estimated rate of adult illiteracy in 1995 was 58%. In 1993, primary schools numbered 235 with 1,859 teachers and 56,773 pupils. There was one junior college, two teacher training colleges, and one college affiliated with the university at Delhi in India.

1999 KEY EVENTS TIMELINE

January

- Bhutan introduces a personal income tax. Bhutanese must now pay a 5 to 30 percent tax if they earn more than $100 per month.

- Bhutan authorities say that a leading radio broadcaster, and leading member of the minority ethnic Nepalese community, is seeking political asylum in the Netherlands.

- Amnesty International, the London-based human rights organization, completes its first visit to Bhutan in six years to investigate allegations of human rights abuses. A member of the organization says Bhutan is more open than in past years.

February

- Ethnic Nepalese groups in Bhutan claim the country's police prevented them from holding a pro-democracy rally in the southern town of Phuentsoling. Bhutan authorities deny the charges.

March

- Dr. Michael Aris, a leading British scholar in Tibetan and Himalayan studies, and an expert on Bhutan, dies of cancer at age 53. Among his published works are *The Early History of a Himalayan Kingdom*; *Views of Medieval Bhutan: The Diary And Drawings Of Samuel Davis, 1783*; and *Sources For The History Of Bhutan*.

May

- Bhutan installs a $48 million digital telephone network, which rivals those of Singapore and Hong Kong.

June

- King Jigme Singye Wangchuk celebrates 25 years on the throne.

- Bhutan ends its ban on television. Bhutan Broadcasting Service's first evening program includes news in Dzongkha, the national language, and English, followed by a recording of the morning jubilee celebrations.

- Queen Ashi Dorji Wangmo Wangchuk launches the country's first Internet and e-mail service with a mouse-click, following an elaborate Buddhist ceremony in the capital Thimphu. It beats television transmissions by a few hours.

September

- India refuses to intervene to resolve Nepal's Bhutanese refugee problem.

- Bhutan and Nepal fail to resolve a nine-year-old refugee problem after three days of talks between their foreign ministers.

October

- Bhutan makes a formal request to become member of World Trade Organization. Bhutan became an observer in 1998.

December

- King Jigme Singye Wangchuck releases about 200 prisoners, many of whom were considered political prisoners by human rights groups.

ANALYSIS OF EVENTS: 1999

BUSINESS AND THE ECONOMY

In January, Bhutan introduced a personal income tax for all Bhutanese earning more than $1,200 a year. Finance minister Yeshey Zimba said the tax would help boost revenue and ensure a more equitable distribution of wealth. Even though the government reassured its citizens that the tax is one of the lowest anywhere in the world, foreign correspondents reported that many people began to withdraw bank deposits to avoid paying the tax.

About 85 percent of Bhutanese practice subsistence farming, and the per-capita gross domestic product is about $520. The kingdom has been offering more services to their citizens, which is why they claim they need to raise more revenues to make the country self-sufficient. Bhutan has not exploited its tourism potential, and few foreigners are allowed to visit. Only 6,000 visitors were allowed in 1998.

Bhutan has relied on corporate taxes, corporate dividends, and revenue from mining, energy, and tourism for its operating budget. In 1998, Bhutan reported expenditures of $65 million. The first tax returns are due in February 2000.

GOVERNMENT AND POLITICS

In October, Nepal and Bhutan spent three days discussing the fate of 100,000 people who claim to be Bhutanese citizens, but have been living in refugee camps in Nepal for nine years. The talks between the foreign ministers of both nations were the first in more than three years, and were supposed to focus on the issue of verification of the refugees. But little was accomplished, and the fate of the refugees remained uncertain. Verification has been a difficult issue for both countries, with seven rounds of talks that ended in failure. Nepal claims that all refugees living in camps in eastern Nepal are Bhutanese citizens and must return to Bhutan. But Bhutan says only a few thousand are citizens and the rest are prohibited from returning. The refugees have been living in camps run with the assistance of the United Nations refugee agency. The refugees said they left Bhutan because of ethnic cleansing and political repression. Bhutan denies these allegations.

In June, thousands of refugees demonstrated in eastern Nepal, and pleaded with King Jigme Singye Wangchuk to allow them to return. The refugees said celebrations marking the 25th anniversary of the coronation of the king were not complete without the participation of what they say is one-sixth of the country's population.

CULTURE AND SOCIETY

For centuries, Bhutan's citizens were kept isolated from the rest of the world. The kingdom's leaders feared that outside influences would undermine the monarchy and the culture. Surrounded by the more powerful nations of China and India, the Bhutanese didn't want to end up like the Buddhist kingdoms of Tibet, Sikkim and Ladakh, which were once independent states.

But in the past two years, the kingdom has gone through major changes, signaling an end to its deliberate policy of isolation. In 1998, King Jigme Singye Wangchuk gave the legislature the power to fire him and yielded to Parliament the right to choose his cabinet, sharply curtailing the powers of the monarchy.

The king, a British-educated National Basketball Association fan, celebrated his 25th anniversary on the throne in June 1999 by allowing his subjects to watch television and connecting to the Internet. Queen Ashi Tshering Pem Wangchuk, the second oldest of King Wangchuk's four wives, said the time had come for Bhutan to be connected to the outside world, but that the Bhutanese would not compromise their culture.

Writing about the occasion for the New York Times Magazine, reporter Peter de Jonge said television was not really bringing the world to Bhutan. "In fact, the country's tortured decision to set up its own television network—called the Bhutan Broadcasting Service, or BBS—has not been made as a concession to western culture but as an attempt to thwart it. For now at least, the BBS will be broadcast only in Thimphu, be limited to a few hours a day and will consist entirely of national news and documentaries about the Bhutanese themselves. The hope is that television will paradoxically help remind the ancient people of the Dragon Kingdom who they are, not who they aren't." Before television officially arrived in Bhutan, most Bhutanese already owned a television. The sets were used to watch videos or foreign satellite channels.

DIRECTORY

CENTRAL GOVERNMENT

Head of State

King
Jigme Singye Wangchuck, Monarch

Ministers

Minister of Agriculture
Kinzang Dorji, Ministry of Agriculture

Minister of Education and Health
Kinzang Dorji, Ministry of Education and Health

Minister of Finance
Hishey Zimba, Ministry of Finance

Minister of Foreign Affairs
Jigme Thinley, Ministry of Foreign Affairs

Minister of Home Affairs
Thinley Gyamtso, Ministry of Home Affairs

Minister of Law
Sonam Tobgye, Ministry of Law

Minister of Trade and Industry
Khandu Wangchuk, Ministry of Trade and Industry

POLITICAL ORGANIZATIONS
United Front for Democracy

JUDICIAL SYSTEM
Supreme Court of Appeal
High Court

FURTHER READING
Articles

"Bhutan is Ending Centuries of Isolation." *The Seattle Times*, May 21, 1999.

"The Himalayas: Masked Dances and Mixed Blessings." *UNESCO Courier* (July-August 1999): 28.

"India Refuses to Intervene to Resolve Nepal's Bhutanese Refugee Problem." The Associated Press, September 11, 1999.

"Michael Aris, Loyalty, Learning and Love." *The Guardian of London*, 29 March 1999.

"South Asian Nations Discuss Landmine Elimination." Reuters, August 20, 1999.

"Television's Final Frontier." *The New York Times Magazine* (August 22, 1999): 42.

BHUTAN: STATISTICAL DATA

For sources and notes see "Sources of Statistics" in the front of each volume.

GEOGRAPHY

Geography (1)

Area:

Total: 47,000 sq km.

Land: 47,000 sq km.

Water: 0 sq km.

Area—comparative: about half the size of Indiana.

Land boundaries:

Total: 1,075 km.

Border countries: China 470 km, India 605 km.

Coastline: 0 km (landlocked).

Climate: varies; tropical in southern plains; cool winters and hot summers in central valleys; severe winters and cool summers in Himalayas.

Terrain: mostly mountainous with some fertile valleys and savanna.

Natural resources: timber, hydropower, gypsum, calcium carbide.

Land use:

Arable land: 2%

Permanent crops: 0%

Permanent pastures: 6%

Forests and woodland: 66%

Other: 26% (1993 est.).

HUMAN FACTORS

Demographics (2A)

	1990	1995	1998	2000	2010	2020	2030	2040	2050
Population	1,584.9	1,780.6	1,908.3	1,996.2	2,474.5	3,034.6	3,655.3	4,294.4	4,935.4
Net migration rate (per 1,000 population)	NA	NA	NA	NA	NA	NA	NA	NA	NA
Births	NA	NA	NA	NA	NA	NA	NA	NA	NA
Deaths	NA	NA	NA	NA	NA	NA	NA	NA	NA
Life expectancy - males	49.5	51.6	52.8	53.6	57.6	61.5	65.0	68.2	70.8
Life expectancy - females	48.3	50.5	51.8	52.8	57.4	61.9	66.3	70.2	73.6
Birth rate (per 1,000)	40.3	39.0	37.3	36.3	32.1	29.0	25.3	22.2	19.7
Death rate (per 1,000)	17.2	15.6	14.6	13.9	11.2	9.3	7.9	7.2	6.9
Women of reproductive age (15-49 yrs.)	371.0	412.3	441.1	461.6	583.7	731.7	900.1	1,081.7	1,241.2
of which are currently married	NA	NA	NA	NA	NA	NA	NA	NA	NA
Fertility rate	5.5	5.4	5.2	5.1	4.5	3.8	3.3	2.8	2.5

Except as noted, values for vital statistics are in thousands; life expectancy is in years.

Infants and Malnutrition (5)

Under-5 mortality rate (1997) 121

% of infants with low birthweight (1990-97) . . . . . .NA

Births attended by skilled health staff % of total[a] . . .NA

% fully immunized (1995-97)

TB 92

DPT 87

Polio 87

Measles 84

Prevalence of child malnutrition under age 5
(1992-97)[b] . . . . .NA

Ethnic Division (6)

Bhote 50%

Ethnic Nepalese 35%

Indigenous or migrant tribes 15%

Religions (7)

Lamaistic Buddhism 75%

Indian- and Nepalese-influenced Hinduism 25%

Languages (8)

Dzongkha (official), Bhotes speak various Tibetan
dialects, Nepalese speak various Nepalese dialects

EDUCATION

Literacy Rates (11A)

In thousands and percent[1]	1990	1995	2000	2010
Illiterate population (15+ yrs.)	575	558	574	600
Literacy rate - total adult pop. (%)	37.2	42.2	47.3	57.6
Literacy rate - males (%)	51.2	56.2	61.0	70.0
Literacy rate - females (%)	23.2	28.1	33.6	45.3

GOVERNMENT & LAW

Political Parties (12)

Legislative branch is a unicameral National Assembly
(150 seats 105 elected from village constituencies, 10
represent religious bodies, and 35 are designated by the
king to represent government and other secular
interests; members serve three-year terms).

Government Budget (13A)

Year: 1997

Total Expenditures: 4,630.6 Millions of Ngultrum

Expenditures as a percentage of the total by function:

General public services and public order 23.99

Defense . . . .-

Education 11.18

Health 10.12

Social Security and Welfare . . . .-

Housing and community amenities 3.56

Recreational, cultural, and religious affairs 1.83

Fuel and energy 11.48

Agriculture, forestry, fishing, and hunting 14.85

Mining, manufacturing, and construction 30

Transportation and communication 17.86

Other economic affairs and services 48

LABOR FORCE

Labor Force (16)

Agriculture 93%

Services 5%

Industry and commerce .2%

Massive lack of skilled labor.

Unemployment Rate (17)

Rate not available.

PRODUCTION SECTOR

Electric Energy (18)

Capacity .361,000 kW (1995)

Production . . . . .1.707 billion kWh (1995)

Consumption per capita . . . . .143 kWh (1995)

Exports electricity to India.

Transportation (19)

Highways:

total: 3,285 km

paved: 1,994 km

unpaved: 1,291 km (1996 est.)

Airports: 2 (1997 est.)

Airports—with paved runways:

total: 1

1,524 to 2,437 m: 1 (1997 est.)

Airports—with unpaved runways:

total: 1

914 to 1,523 m: 1 (1997 est.)

Top Agricultural Products (20)

Rice, corn, root crops, citrus, foodgrains; dairy
products, eggs.

GOVERNMENT & LAW

Military Affairs (14B)

	1990	1991	1992	1993	1994	1995
Military expenditures						
Current dollars (mil.)	NA	NA	NA	NA	NA	NA
1995 constant dollars (mil.)	NA	NA	NA	NA	NA	NA
Armed forces (000)	NA	NA	5	5	5	5
Gross national product (GNP)						
Current dollars (mil.)	207	226	241	259	278	304
1995 constant dollars (mil.)	238	250	259	271	285	304
Central government expenditures (CGE)						
1995 constant dollars (mil.)	87	81	89	95	115	145
People (mil.)	1.6	1.6	1.7	1.7	1.7	1.8
Military expenditure as % of GNP	NA	NA	NA	NA	NA	NA
Military expenditure as % of CGE	NA	NA	NA	NA	NA	NA
Military expenditure per capita (1995 $)	NA	NA	NA	NA	NA	NA
Armed forces per 1,000 people (soldiers)	NA	NA	3.0	2.9	2.9	2.8
GDP per capita (1995 $)	150	154	156	160	164	170
Arms imports[6]						
Current dollars (mil.)	0	0	0	0	0	0
1995 constant dollars (mil.)	0	0	0	0	0	0
Arms exports[6]						
Current dollars (mil.)	0	0	0	0	0	0
1995 constant dollars (mil.)	0	0	0	0	0	0
Total imports[7]						
Current dollars (mil.)	108	94	134	100	114	114[e]
1995 constant dollars (mil.)	124	104	144	105	117	114[e]
Total exports[7]						
Current dollars (mil.)	75	72	71	69	71	71[e]
1995 constant dollars (mil.)	86	80	76	72	73	71[e]
Arms as percent of total imports[8]	0	0	0	0	0	0
Arms as percent of total exports[8]	0	0	0	0	0	0

MANUFACTURING SECTOR

GDP & Manufacturing Summary (21)

	1980	1985	1990	1992	1993	1994
Gross Domestic Product						
Millions of 1990 dollars	142	197	283	311	327	344
Growth rate in percent	17.63	3.69	4.90	4.50	5.20	5.10
Per capita (in 1990 dollars)	114.6	143.0	183.6	196.6	205.0	213.1
Manufacturing Value Added						
Millions of 1990 dollars	5	11	23	27	30	*32*
Growth rate in percent	35.27	12.20	15.55	11.84	10.06	*8.46*
Manufacturing share in percent of current prices	3.2	5.3	8.1	10.4	11.3	NA

FINANCE, ECONOMICS, & TRADE

Economic Indicators (22)

National product: GDP—purchasing power parity—$1.3 billion (1995 est.)

National product real growth rate: 6.9% (1995 est.)

National product per capita: $730 (1995 est.)

Inflation rate—consumer price index: 7% (FY96/97 est.)

Exchange Rates (24)

Exchange rates:

Ngultrum (Nu) per US$1

January 1998	.39.358
1997	.36.313
1996	.35.433
1995	.32.427
1994	.31.374
1993	.30.493

The Bhutanese ngultrum is at par with the Indian rupee

Top Import Origins (25)

$104.1 million (c.i.f., 1996 est.)

Origins	%
India	.77
Japan	.NA
United Kingdom	.NA
Germany	.NA
United States	.NA

NA stands for not available.

Top Export Destinations (26)

$77.4 million (f.o.b., 1996 est.).

Destinations	%
India	.94
Bangladesh	.NA

NA stands for not available.

Economic Aid (27)

Recipient: $NA. NA stands for not available.

Import Export Commodities (28)

Import Commodities	Export Commodities
Fuel and lubricants	Cardamom
Grain	Gypsum
Machinery and parts	Timber
Vehicles	Handicrafts
Fabrics	Cement
Rice	Fruit
	Electricity (to India)
	Precious stones
	Spices

BOLIVIA

Republic of Bolivia
República de Bolivia

INTRODUCTORY SURVEY

RECENT HISTORY

World War II (1939–45) brought many strains to Bolivia. In December 1943, a coalition of the army and the Nationalist Revolutionary Movement (Movimiento Nacionalista Revolutionario—MNR) engineered a successful takeover of the government. However, the tin market collapsed at the war's end, weakening the new government's power base. The new government, in turn, was overthrown, and a conservative government favoring the wealthy mine and land owners was installed.

The MNR returned to power in the early 1950s, dominating Bolivian politics from 1952 to 1964. Its first government, led by Víctor Paz Estenssoro, made dramatic moves to transform Bolivian society. The tin holdings of the three dominant families were taken over by the government, and a comprehensive land reform program was begun, along with large-scale welfare and literacy programs. Industry was encouraged, and the search for oil deposits was hastened.

In addition, a new policy gave Amerindians the right to vote and tried to integrate the Amerindian community more fully into the national economy. The right to vote, previously restricted to literate Bolivian males (who constituted less than 10% of the population), was made universal for all Bolivians over 21.

After his initial term in office, Paz became more and more dictatorial, and divisions within the MNR worsened. After Paz tried to rig the presiden-

tial elections in June 1964, he was removed from office by a military takeover. For the next 20 years, a series of military and civilian governments ruled Bolivia.

In 1985, former prime minister Paz, now 77, was returned to office. Faced with runaway inflation, which reached an annual rate of 14,000% in August 1985, the two leading parties agreed to cooperate, allowing a comprehensive economic reform package to pass through the legislature. Inflation and interest rates fell and the economy stabilized.

More importantly, Paz got competing political parties to cooperate in support of a continuing

democracy. Paz's successor, Jaime Paz Zamora, who took office in 1989, was able to hold together a coalition and serve a full four-year presidential term.

Following the 1993 elections, Gonzalo Sánchez de Lozada assumed the presidency. His vice president, Victor Hugo Cárdenas, is the first Amerindian in Bolivian history to hold that office. The administration began a reform program that included selling public enterprises. State enterprises that were privatized included the national railroad, the state-owned airline, and electricity generation facilities. In June 1997, General Hugo Banzer, the former dictator, won the presidential election and pledged to stop the privatization program.

GOVERNMENT

The constitution of 3 February 1967 provides for a representative democracy, with its government divided into an executive branch, a two-chamber legislature (consisting of a Chamber of Deputies and a Senate), and the judiciary. Bolivia is divided into nine administrative departments but there are no local legislatures.

In practice, the constitution has not been consistently observed. Military takeovers and states of siege have been frequent. Congress was dissolved by the armed forces from 1969–79 and again between 1980 and 1982. Between 1966 and 1978, no presidential elections were held.

Judiciary

Judicial power is exercised by the Supreme Court, the superior district courts in each department, and the local courts. The Supreme Court, which sits at Sucre, is divided into four chambers: two deal with civil cases, one with criminal cases, and one with administrative, mining, and social cases.

Political Parties

The right-wing Democratic Nationalist Alliance (Alianza Democrática Nacionalista—ADN) is closely tied to President Hugo Banzer Suarez. After the June 1997 elections, the ADN formed a coalition government with the Movement of the Revolutionary Left (Movimiento de la Izquierda Revolucionaria—MIR), Civic Solidarity Union (UCS), and the far-right "Conscience of the Fatherland" party (CONDEPA).

The Nationalist Revolutionary Movement (Movimiento Nacionalista Revolucionario—MNR) was originally a militant organization, but is now considered a left-of-center party.

DEFENSE

As of 1995, armed strength totaled 33,500 men (army, 25,000; a navy for lake and river patrol, 4,500; air force, 4,000), and paramilitary police of 30,600. Defense expenditures in 1995 were $146 million.

ECONOMIC AFFAIRS

As of 1996, Bolivia was in its second decade of democratic rule and its tenth consecutive year of economic expansion. Market reforms are firmly in place, investment is growing steadily, and inflation is under control. Real gross domestic product grew by 4.5% in 1995. Growth was led by construction, manufacturing, and services. Inflation was reduced from the amazing 14,000% in 1985 to only 12.5% in 1995.

Public Finance

Since April 1992, comprehensive privatization has helped decrease the need for public sector expenses. The U.S. CIA estimates that, in 1995, government revenues totaled approximately $3.75 billion and expenditures $3.75 billion, including capital expenditures of $556.2 million. External debt totaled $4.4 billion, approximately 82% of which was financed abroad.

Income

In 1996, Bolivia's gross national product (GNP) was $5.9 billion at current prices, or $830 per person. During 1985–95, the real growth rate of the GNP per person was 1.7%.

Industry

Industrial development has been severely restricted by political instability, the small domestic market, the uncertain supply of raw materials, and the lack of technically trained labor. Over one-half of output is in nondurable consumer goods—food, beverages, tobacco, and coffee. Handicrafts and hydrocarbons account for much of the remainder.

Banking and Finance

The Central Bank of Bolivia, established in 1928 and reorganized in 1945, is the sole bank of issue and operates as a commercial bank. The Superintendent of Banks was set up to regulate the operations of banks and finance companies. There are five state-owned development banks, including the Mining Bank and the Agricultural Bank. The Bolivian Development Corp. channels credits from the Inter-American Development Bank into industrial expansion projects.

The Bolivian Stock Exchange is the main stock exchange, with seven listed companies trading in 1995.

Economic Development

In 1985, Bolivia was one of the first Latin American countries to institute market liberalizations, following the model set by Chile years earlier. In 1993, newly elected President Lazada, furthered these liberalizations by increasing privatizations (called capitalizations in order to deflect criticism), increasing money spent on education and decreasing the federal government's regulatory power.

Privatizations have continued under President Hugo Bonzer, a former military dictator who was elected in 1997. Between 1993 and 1997, growth has averaged 4.2% a year and exports have climbed 25% a year. Bolivia's continued economic development appears assured, the only obstacles being the possibility of intensified unrest among the large indigenous population, and, more seriously, if the country fails to adequately—as judged by the U.S.—crack down on cocoa leaf production.

SOCIAL WELFARE

Social security coverage is compulsory for both salaried employees and rural workers. Those covered by the program receive medical, hospital, dental, and pharmaceutical care for themselves and their families. The government also provides old-age pensions, survivors' benefits, maternity benefits, and family allowances.

Although women are guaranteed equal protection under the Constitution, in most cases, they earn less than men for doing similar work.

Healthcare

Health conditions have been notably poor, owing to poor hygiene and an insufficient number of doctors and hospitals, especially in rural areas. The most common disorders are acute respiratory diseases, tuberculosis, malaria, hepatitis, and Chagas' disease. Malnutrition is a serious and growing problem, with 13% of children under age five considered malnourished during 1989–95. Life expectancy in 1995 was estimated at 61 years.

Housing

As of 1988, 67% of all housing units were detached private dwellings, 25% were detached rooms for rent with common facilities, 5% were huts, and 2% were apartments. Only about 50% of the population had access to piped indoor water, and about 26% lived in dwellings with adequate sanitary facilities.

EDUCATION

Bolivia's estimated adult illiteracy rate was 17% (males, 10%; females, 25%). Primary education, which lasts for eight years, is compulsory and free of charge. Secondary education lasts for another four years. In 1994, the government's expenses for education amounted to 5.4% of Bolivia's gross national product.

Bolivia has eight state universities, one in each departmental capital except Cobija. There are also two private universities.

1999 KEY EVENTS TIMELINE

January

- Bolivia reports 33 cases of yellow fever; 13 are fatal.

- United States officials hail an "astonishing" drop in coca cultivation in Peru and Bolivia, where it has dropped by 22 percent in the past three years.

- Bolivia decides to send to a Spanish judge a list of citizens who disappeared under Chile's dictatorship of Augusto Pinochet.

February

- Bolivia and Brazil inaugurate a gas pipeline running between their nations.

March

- Past repression could lead to indictment of President Hugo Banzer.

- President Banzer and cabinet members will take a drug test to prove they do not consume cocaine.

May

- The World Bank authorizes $80 million for Bolivian farmers who are experiencing a sharp economic recession.

- President Banzer said he hopes neighboring Chile will eventually negotiate and give Bolivia access to the Pacific Ocean.

June

- President Banzer announces that a huge field of natural gas has been found near the Argentine border which could produce more than two million cubic meters per day.

- Bolivian authorities identify the remains of seven guerrillas who fought alongside Ernesto Che Guevara. Four are Bolivians and three are Cuban.

August

- Barry McCaffrey, the White House's senior anti-narcotics official, praises Bolivia for its efforts to curtail coca leaf production.

- A bus accident kills 23 people in Central Bolivia.

- Wind-charged fires destroy more than 350,000 acres of farmland and at least 500 homes in central Bolivia. Thousands are homeless while the fires blanket the country's lowlands with smoke.

September

- Bolivia is among the poorest nations eligible for U.S. debt relief.

- Bolivians say they have set coca leaf destruction record: Army and police teams eradicate 28,825 acres through mid-September

- Higher prices for bread, fuel and transportation lead to general strike. La Paz is virtually shut down.

October

- A British explorer claims he has found Atlantis somewhere in the Bolivian Altiplano.

- Bolivia's foreign minister promises his country will eradicate coca leaf plantations and take itself out of the international cocaine trade within three years.

December

- UK Chancellor Gordon Brown reports that the UK is implementing a program to cancel millions of pounds of debt for some of the world's most indebted nations. The first four countries on the list, Uganda, Mozambique, Bolivia, and Mauritania, are expected to qualify for the debt forgiveness program by the end of January 2000.

- Members of the bus drivers' union stage a two-day protest over a 4 percent increase in fuel prices. Drivers say bus fares must increase in line with the increase in gasoline costs. Santa Cruz is paralyzed and traffic is affected everywhere in the country.

ANALYSIS OF EVENTS: 1999

BUSINESS AND THE ECONOMY

Bolivia is a poor country. The at-birth life expectancy for males is only 58.5 years. Its underdevelopment makes it more vulnerable to changes in the economic climate. Thus, an increase in the price of oil in 1999 hit Bolivia hard. Although in no way

as disruptive as the hyperinflation of the mid-1980s, the price for bread, fuel and transportation in Bolivia rose and the economy exhibited a chronic inability to provide jobs for its population. The price hikes, as much as 20 percent for public transportation and 12 percent for fuel, led to a general strike which virtually shut down the capital city of La Paz for one day. In 1997 the unemployment rate stood at 11.4 percent. Poverty also stalked the countryside. The United States praised Bolivia for a dramatic drop in coca leaf production, but impoverished Bolivian farmers who for generations had depended on the illicit crop were angry. They charged that the United States and Bolivia had done nothing to replace coca with other crops, driving farmers further into poverty. Some help was on the way as the World Bank authorized $80 million in aid for farmers, and the United States announced Bolivia was eligible for debt relief. There was a further flicker of hope when Bolivian authorities announced the discovery of massive natural gas reserves and began planning to attract foreign drilling.

GOVERNMENT AND POLITICS

The 1998 arrest of former Chilean dictator Augusto Pinochet in Britain for alleged human rights violations focused unwanted attention on other former South American dictators, including Bolivian president Hugo Banzer. Banzer was dictator from 1971–78. Evidence presented against Pinochet linked Banzer to Operation Condor, the code name given to the repressive collaboration between South American dictatorships during the 1970s. Under Operation Condor military regimes maintained an information network and returned political refugees to their home countries. There, many were imprisoned, tortured, and killed. Banzer, who was elected president in 1997, has denied knowledge of the operation despite the evidence. So far, he has managed to stay clear of the controversy, although many Bolivian legislators are pressing for investigations. The Bolivian president could someday face charges at home for human rights violations during his regime, when as many as 200 Bolivians disappeared.

In a controversial move, Banzer decided to put soldiers in the streets to help police battle crime, a move that was criticized by many Bolivians mindful of military regimes in the past. Less controversial at home has been Banzer's decision to revive an old border dispute with Chile, and to press for what he called a frank and open dialogue with

Chilean authorities. His goal is to achieve some accommodation which would allow land-locked Bolivia a corridor of access to a South Pacific ocean port. But Banzer does not control this issue. Ever since it lost access to the Pacific Ocean to Chile in 1879 the Bolivian authorities have been unable to convince Chile's government to listen to their claims. Both nations have commercial agreements, but they have not had diplomatic relations since 1978.

CULTURE AND SOCIETY

Bolivians, like many poor populations in Latin America, have a deep distrust of the nation's law enforcement apparatus. But remarkable reforms that started in 1999, when Congress approved a new criminal code, may bring a greater measure of trust to Bolivia. The new law code is part of a number of dramatic changes taking place in Bolivia's old institutions. The entire justice system is being revamped and old laws are being discarded. New approaches are being tried to bring Bolivia into step with modern nations of the world. Recently improvised institutions like the federal Defender of the People and a human rights division under the jurisdiction of the Justice Ministry are mandated to secure the rights of all Bolivians.

Some of the proposed reforms may seem familiar to Americans: an independent judicial system, government-paid attorneys for indigent defendants, presumption of innocence, and oral arguments in an open court. But they are revolutionary in Bolivia, where cases have been tried by an investigating judge who acted as final arbiter against a defendant. Under such a secretive system, judges were open to bribes and abuse.

Under the new criminal law, independent prosecutors will have investigative powers, and police will be expected to present evidence to them. Bolivians opted for a five-member judicial panel of three citizens and two professional judges to hear a case instead of 12-member juries. Courts will be required to use interpreters and court officials who speak the native languages Quechua and Aymara, and may, in some cases, be allowed to defer to the decisions of tribal justice councils. It will take at least two years to implement all the changes, and perhaps longer to retrain police, judges and other people involved in the justice system. But many observers say the country is finally on the right path.

DIRECTORY

CENTRAL GOVERNMENT

Head of State

President
Hugo Banzer Suárez, Office of the President

Vice President
Jorge Quiroga Ramírez, Office of the Vice President, Ayacucho y Mercado N° 308, La Paz, Bolivia
PHONE: +591 (02) 391520; 302042
E-MAIL: prescong@congreso.gov.bo

Ministries

Minister of the Presidency
Franz Ondarza Linares, Ministry of the Presidency, Palacio de Gobierno, Plaza Murillo, Casilla: 3278, La Paz, Bolivia
PHONE: +591 (02) 371082; 391285
FAX: +591 (02) 371388

Minister of Foreign Affairs
Javier Murillo de la Rocha, Ministry of Foreign Affairs, Av. Busch esq. Héroes del Pacífico, Pliegos Oficiales, La Paz, Bolivia
PHONE: +591 (02) 371150; 371151
FAX: +591 (02) 371150
E-MAIL: mreuno@rree.gov.bo

Minister of the Government
Wálter Guiteras Dennis, Ministry of the Government, Av. Arce No. 2314, Casilla: 7110, La Paz, Bolivia
PHONE: +591 (02) 431708; 431851
FAX: +591 (02) 371334; 371352

Minister of Defense
Jorge Crespo Velasco, Ministry of Defense, Av. Busch No. 909 esq. Honduras-Miraflores, Pliegos Oficiales, La Paz, Bolivia
PHONE: +591 (02) 431364; 431183
FAX: +591 (02) 433159
E-MAIL: mindef2@ceibo.entelnet.bo

Minister of Labor
Herbert Müller Costas, Ministry of Labor, c. Bolívar No. 688, Casilla: 3744, La Paz, Bolivia
PHONE: +591 (02) 391234; 392220
FAX: +591 (02) 392999; 359955

Minister of Justice and Human Rights
Juan Antonio Chahín Lupo, Ministry of Justice and Human Rights, Av. 16 de Julio No 1679, Casilla: 6966, La Paz, Bolivia
PHONE: +591 (02) 373620; 361037

FAX: +591 (02) 392982
E-MAIL: minjust@caoba.entelnet.bo

Minister of Economic Development
José Luis Lupo, Ministry of Economic Development, Av. Camacho No. 1488 esq. Bueno, Casilla: 2088, La Paz, Bolivia
PHONE: +591 (02) 356741; 375000
FAX: +591 (02) 368788

Minister of Education, Culture and Sports
Tito Hoz de Vila Quiroga, Ministry of Education, Culture and Sports, Av. Arce No. 2408 esq. Belisario Salinas, Casilla: 3116, La Paz, Bolivia
PHONE: +591 (02) 372145; 372060
FAX: +591 (02) 371376

Minister of Health and Social Welfare
Guillermo Cuentas, Ministry of Health and Social Welfare, c. Capitán Ravelo No. 2199, Casilla: Pliegos Oficiales, La Paz, Bolivia
PHONE: +591 (02) 371373
FAX: +591 (02) 391590

Minister of Labor and Small Business
Luis Angel Vasquez Villamor, Ministry of Labor and Small Business, Yanacocha esq. Mercado 3er. Piso, La Paz, Bolivia
PHONE: +591 (02) 364164; 39449
FAX: +591 (02) 371387

Minister of Agriculture and Rural Development
Oswaldo Antenza Vaca Diez, Ministry of Agriculture and Rural Development, Obrajes Av. 14 de Septiembre entre c. 7 y 8, Casilla: 4536, La Paz, Bolivia
PHONE: +591 (02) 367968; 361348
FAX: +591 (02) 359480

Minister of Sustainable Development and Planning
Erick Reyes Villa Bacigalupi, Ministry of Sustainable Development and Planning, Av. 20 de Octubre No. 2230, Casilla: 12814, La Paz, Bolivia
PHONE: +591 (02) 363331; 372063
FAX: +591 (02) 392892

Minister of Foreign Trade and Investment
Carlos Saavedra Bruno, Ministry of Foreign Trade and Investment, Av. Mcal. Santa Cruz, Palacio de las Comunicaciones, Piso 17, La Paz, Bolivia
PHONE: +591 (02) 377222
FAX: +591 (02) 377451
E-MAIL: despacho@mcei-bolivia.com

Minister of Housing and Basic Services
Ruben Poma, Ministry of Housing and Basic Services, Avenida 20 de Octubre No. 2230 P. 4, La Paz, Bolivia
PHONE: +591 (02) 352841; 372241
FAX: +591 (02) 371335

Minister at Large, for Governmental Information
Jorge Landivar Roca, Ministry of Governmental Information, Av. Camacho 1485, Edif. La Urbana P. 4 y 5, La Paz, Bolivia
PHONE: +591 (02) 339027; 376352; 376353
FAX: +591 (02) 391607

POLITICAL ORGANIZATIONS
MIR Nueva Mayoria
E-MAIL: mir@cibergallo.com
TITLE: El Jefe de Nacionale
NAME: Jaime Paz Zamoria

Condepa
PHONE: +591 (02) 377134

Partido Democratico Boliviano (Bolivian Democratic Party)
Acción Democrática Nacionalista-ADN (National Democratic Alliance)
PHONE: +591 (02) 392658
FAX: +591 (02) 392384
TITLE: El General
NAME: Hugo Banzer Suarez

DIPLOMATIC REPRESENTATION
Embassies in Bolivia

France
Le Conseiller Economique et Commercial, Calle 5 de Obrajes n° 590, La Paz-Casilla 23609 (Obrajes), Bolivia
PHONE: +591 (02) 786610
FAX: +591 (02) 786715
E-MAIL: lapaz@dree.org

United States
Consular Section, Banco Popular Del Peru Building Corner of Calles Mercado and Colon, P.O. Box 425, La Paz, APO AA 3403, Bolivia
PHONE: +591 (02) 350251
FAX: +591 (02) 359875

JUDICIAL SYSTEM

Supreme Court

FURTHER READING

"Bolivia, at Risk of Some Unrest, is Making Big Gains in Eradicating Coca." *The New York Times,* 9 May 1999.

"Bolivia: Clashes to Come." *The Economist* (February 20, 1999): 34.

"Bolivia Promises to End Coca Leaf Production in Three Years." The Associated Press, 1 October 1999.

"Bolivia: Tin Soldiers." *The Economist* (January 9, 1999): 32.

"Bolivia's Dark Past Begins to Catch Up with Him." *The New York Times,* 14 March 1999.

"Copacabana Journal; Auto Insurance for All Comers, Yours for a Prayer." *The New York Times,* 26 March 1999.

"Drop in Coca Production Hailed, but Cocaine Plant Thrives Elsewhere." *The Seattle Times,* 7 January 1999.

"Go South, Young Child." *The Economist* (May 15, 1999): 38.

"Lake Titicaca: A Mountain Lake Teeming with Myths." *The New York Times,* 10 January 1999.

"A New Breed of Justice Reshaping Latin America. Watchdogs in Bolivia Help Change Archaic Law System." *Los Angeles Times,* 10 October 1999.

"Struggling Bolivian Mining Town Cashes in on Tourism." *The Miami Herald,* 10 May 1999.

"An Overdue Reform of Justice." *The Economist* (April 10, 1999): 32.

BOLIVIA: STATISTICAL DATA

For sources and notes see "Sources of Statistics" in the front of each volume.

GEOGRAPHY

Geography (1)

Area:

Total: 1,098,580 sq km.

Land: 1,084,390 sq km.

Water: 14,190 sq km.

Area—comparative: slightly less than three times the size of Montana.

Land boundaries:

Total: 6,743 km.

Border countries: Argentina 832 km, Brazil 3,400 km, Chile 861 km, Paraguay 750 km, Peru 900 km.

Coastline: 0 km (landlocked).

Climate: varies with altitude; humid and tropical to cold and semiarid.

Terrain: rugged Andes Mountains with a highland plateau (Altiplano), hills, lowland plains of the Amazon Basin.

Natural resources: tin, natural gas, petroleum, zinc, tungsten, antimony, silver, iron, lead, gold, timber.

Land use:

Arable land: 2%

Permanent crops: 0%

Permanent pastures: 24%

Forests and woodland: 53%

Other: 21% (1993 est.).

HUMAN FACTORS

Demographics (2A)

	1990	1995	1998	2000	2010	2020	2030	2040	2050
Population	NA	7,357.6	7,826.4	8,139.2	9,698.5	11,245.2	12,742.2	14,088.3	15,240.5
Net migration rate (per 1,000 population)	NA	NA	NA	NA	NA	NA	NA	NA	NA
Births	NA	NA	NA	NA	NA	NA	NA	NA	NA
Deaths	NA	NA	NA	NA	NA	NA	NA	NA	NA
Life expectancy - males	NA	56.4	58.0	59.0	63.9	68.1	71.5	74.2	76.2
Life expectancy - females	NA	62.3	63.9	65.1	70.2	74.5	77.9	80.5	82.4
Birth rate (per 1,000)	NA	33.6	31.4	30.0	24.3	20.3	17.4	15.4	14.0
Death rate (per 1,000)	NA	10.8	9.9	9.3	7.4	6.4	6.2	6.5	7.2
Women of reproductive age (15-49 yrs.)	NA	1,795.6	1,941.8	2,043.8	2,565.4	3,072.0	3,444.1	3,630.0	3,678.7
of which are currently married	NA	NA	NA	NA	NA	NA	NA	NA	NA
Fertility rate	NA	4.4	4.1	3.8	2.9	2.3	2.1	2.0	2.0

Except as noted, values for vital statistics are in thousands; life expectancy is in years.

Health Personnel (3)

Total health expenditure as a percentage of GDP, 1990-1997[a]

Public sector 3.8

Private sector 2.7

Total[b] 6.5

Health expenditure per capita in U.S. dollars, 1990-1997[a]

Purchasing power parity 194

Total 54

Availability of health care facilities per 100,000 people

Hospital beds 1990-1997[a] 140

Doctors 1993[c] 51

Nurses 1993[c] 25

Health Indicators (4)

Life expectancy at birth

1980 52

1997 61

Daily per capita supply of calories (1996) 2,170

Total fertility rate births per woman (1997) 4.4

Maternal mortality ratio per 100,000 live births (1990-97) . . . . .370[d]

Safe water % of population with access (1995) 70

Sanitation % of population with access (1995) 41

Consumption of iodized salt % of households (1992-98)[a] 92

Smoking prevalence

Male % of adults (1985-95)[a] 50

Female % of adults (1985-95)[a] 21

Tuberculosis incidence per 100,000 people (1997) 253

Adult HIV prevalence % of population ages 15-49 (1997) 0.07

Infants and Malnutrition (5)

Under-5 mortality rate (1997) 96

% of infants with low birthweight (1990-97) 12

Births attended by skilled health staff % of total[a] . . .46

% fully immunized (1995-97)

TB 93

DPT 82

Polio 82

Measles 98

Prevalence of child malnutrition under age 5 (1992-97)[b] 8

Religions (7)

Roman Catholic 95%

Protestant (Evangelical Methodist) . . . .

Languages (8)

Spanish (official), Quechua (official), Aymara (official).

EDUCATION

Public Education Expenditures (9)

Public expenditure on education (% of GNP)

1980 . . . . .4.4

1996 . . . . .5.6

Expenditure per student

Primary % of GNP per capita

1980 . . . . .13.7

1996 . . . .

Secondary % of GNP per capita

1980 . . . . .15.2

1996 . . . .

Tertiary % of GNP per capita

1980 . . . .

1996 . . . .

Expenditure on teaching materials

Primary % of total for level (1996) . . . .

Secondary % of total for level (1996) . . . .

Primary pupil-teacher ratio per teacher (1996) . . . .

Duration of primary education years (1995) 8

Educational Attainment (10)

Age group (1992)[14] . . . . .25+

Total population 2,533,393

Highest level attained (%)

No schooling 23.5

First level

Not completed 20.4

Completed 6.6

Entered second level

S-1 . . . . .15.2

S-2 . . . . .15.7

Postsecondary 9.9

Literacy Rates (11A)

In thousands and percent[1]	1990	1995	2000	2010
Illiterate population (15+ yrs.)	809	745	676	543
Literacy rate - total adult pop. (%)	79.1	83.1	86.6	91.7
Literacy rate - males (%)	87.7	90.5	92.8	95.9
Literacy rate - females (%)	70.8	76.0	80.6	87.6

GOVERNMENT & LAW

Political Parties (12)

Chamber of Deputies	No. of seats
Nationalist Democratic Action (ADN)	32
Nationalist Revolutionary Movement (MNR)	26
Movement of the Revolutionary Left (MIR)	23
Civic Solidarity Union (UCS)	21
Conscience of the Fatherland (CONDEPA)	19
Free Bolivia Movement (MBL)	5
United Left (IU)	4

Government Budget (13A)

Year: 1997

Total Expenditures: 9,489.6 Millions of Bolivianos

Expenditures as a percentage of the total by function:

General public services and public order	21.11
Defense	8.26
Education	19.29
Health	3.48
Social Security and Welfare	26.81
Housing and community amenities	.79
Recreational, cultural, and religious affairs	.37
Fuel and energy	.15
Agriculture, forestry, fishing, and hunting	.95
Mining, manufacturing, and construction	.50
Transportation and communication	6.04
Other economic affairs and services	4.29

Military Affairs (14B)

	1990	1991	1992	1993	1994	1995
Military expenditures						
Current dollars (mil.)	145	116	104	124	133	132
1995 constant dollars (mil.)	166	128	112	130	137	132
Armed forces (000)	30	33	32	32	28	28
Gross national product (GNP)						
Current dollars (mil.)	4,095	4,475	4,780	5,100	5,454	5,810
1995 constant dollars (mil.)	4,707	4,945	5,142	5,347	5,591	5,810
Central government expenditures (CGE)						
1995 constant dollars (mil.)	886	917	1,188	1,382	1,416	1,386
People (mil.)	6.4	6.5	6.6	6.8	6.9	7.0
Military expenditure as % of GNP	3.5	2.6	2.2	2.4	2.4	2.3
Military expenditure as % of CGE	18.8	14.0	9.4	9.4	9.6	9.5
Military expenditure per capita (1995 $)	26	20	17	19	20	19
Armed forces per 1,000 people (soldiers)	4.7	5.1	4.8	4.7	4.1	4.0
GNP per capita (1995 $)	737	759	774	789	810	826
Arms imports[6]						
Current dollars (mil.)	10	20	10	10	0	10
1995 constant dollars (mil.)	11	22	11	10	0	10
Arms exports[6]						
Current dollars (mil.)	0	0	0	0	0	0
1995 constant dollars (mil.)	0	0	0	0	0	0
Total imports[7]						
Current dollars (mil.)	687	970	1,090	1,206	1,209	1,424
1995 constant dollars (mil.)	790	1,072	1,172	1,264	1,239	1,424
Total exports[7]						
Current dollars (mil.)	926	849	710	728	1,032	1,101
1995 constant dollars (mil.)	1,064	938	764	763	1,058	1,101
Arms as percent of total imports[8]	1.5	2.1	.9	.8	0	.7
Arms as percent of total exports[8]	0	0	0	0	0	0

Crime (15)

Crime rate (for 1994)

Crimes reported 57,081

Total persons convicted .NA

Crimes per 100,000 population 789

Persons responsible for offenses

Total number of suspects 84,366

Total number of female suspects 27,812

Total number of juvenile suspects 5,957

LABOR FORCE

Labor Force (16)

Total (million) 2.5

Agriculture . . . . .NA

Services and utilities . . . . .NA

Manufacturing, mining and

construction . . . . .NA

NA stands for not available.

Unemployment Rate (17)

10%

PRODUCTION SECTOR

Electric Energy (18)

Capacity .786,000 kW (1995)

Production . . . . .2.9 billion kWh (1995)

Consumption per capita . . . . .370 kWh (1995)

Transportation (19)

Highways:

total: 52,216 km

paved: 2,872 km (including 27 km of expressways)

unpaved: 49,344 km (1995 est.)

Waterways: 10,000 km of commercially navigable waterways

Pipelines: crude oil 1,800 km; petroleum products 580 km; natural gas 1,495 km

Merchant marine:

total: 1 cargo ship (1,000 GRT or over) totaling 4,214 GRT/6,390 DWT (1997 est.)

Airports: 1,153 (1997 est.)

Airports—with paved runways:

total: 11

over 3,047 m: 4

2,438 to 3,047 m: 3

1,524 to 2,437 m: 4 (1997 est.)

Airports—with unpaved runways:

total: 1,142

2,438 to 3,047 m: 3

1,524 to 2,437 m: 73

914 to 1,523 m: 229

under 914 m: 837 (1997 est.)

Top Agricultural Products (20)

Coffee, coca, cotton, corn, sugarcane, rice, potatoes; timber.

MANUFACTURING SECTOR

GDP & Manufacturing Summary (21)

Detailed value added figures are listed by both International Standard Industry Code (ISIC) and product title.

	1980	1985	1990	1994
GDP ($-1990 mil.)[1]	5,445	4,943	5,373	6,169
Per capita ($-1990)[1]	1,017	839	817	852
Manufacturing share (%) (current prices)[1]	15.2	11.8	*16.0*	NA
Manufacturing				
Value added ($-1990 mil.)[1]	953	715	862	*1,029*
Industrial production index	100	65	77	*92*
Value added ($ mil.)	619	394	640	*847*
Gross output ($ mil.)	1,698	1,078	1,417	*1,907*
Employment (000)	43	28	28	*34*
Profitability (% of gross output)				
Intermediate input (%)	64	64	55	*56*
Wages and salaries inc. supplements (%)	8	6	6	*6*
Gross operating surplus	28	31	39	*38*
Productivity ($)				
Gross output per worker	38,348	38,228	49,821	*54,533*
Value added per worker	13,977	13,947	22,468	*24,238*
Average wage (inc. supplements)	3,147	2,129	3,149	*3,399*
Value added ($ mil.)				
311/2 Food products	93	193	104	*162*

	1980	1985	1990	1994
313 Beverages	57	34	51	99
314 Tobacco products	21	4	5	8
321 Textiles	34	26	18	23
322 Wearing apparel	6	3	3	3
323 Leather and fur products	5	2	5	6
324 Footwear	24	14	8	7
331 Wood and wood products	15	5	11	14
332 Furniture and fixtures	2	1	1	2
341 Paper and paper products	—	1	1	4
342 Printing and publishing	14	9	12	19
351 Industrial chemicals	3	2	2	2
352 Other chemical products	16	11	15	15
353 Petroleum refineries	159	29	336	375
354 Miscellaneous petroleum and coal products	—	—	—	—
355 Rubber products	1	—	—	—
356 Plastic products	11	4	7	12
361 Pottery, china and earthenware	1	—	—	—
362 Glass and glass products	6	6	3	4
369 Other non-metal mineral products	21	28	29	36
371 Iron and steel	1	1	—	3
372 Non-ferrous metals	89	14	10	18
381 Metal products	14	4	5	8
382 Non-electrical machinery	16	—	1	1
383 Electrical machinery	3	1	2	4
384 Transport equipment	5	—	2	2
385 Professional and scientific equipment	1	1	1	1
390 Other manufacturing industries	2	—	8	17

FINANCE, ECONOMICS, & TRADE

Economic Indicators (22)

National product: GDP—purchasing power parity— $23.1 billion (1997 est.)

National product real growth rate: 4.4% (1997 est.)

National product per capita: $3,000 (1997 est.)

Inflation rate—consumer price index: 7% (1997)

Exchange Rates (24)

Exchange rates:

Bolivianos ($B) per US$1

January 1998	5.3724
1997	5.2543
1996	5.0746
1995	4.8003
1994	4.6205
1993	4.2651

Balance of Payments (23)

	1990	1992	1994	1995	1996
Exports of goods (f.o.b.)	831	608	985	1,041	1,173
Imports of goods (f.o.b.)	−776	−1,041	−1,015	−1,224	−1,362
Trade balance	55	−432	−30	182	189
Services - debits	−599	−554	−565	−604	−629
Services - credits	165	182	241	226	259
Private transfers (net)	21	22	23	19	16
Government transfers (net)	138	221	243	226	272
Overall balance	−220	−561	−539	−315	−272

Top Import Origins (25)

$1.7 billion (c.i.f. 1997)

Origins	%
NA	NA

NA stands for not available.

Top Export Destinations (26)

$1.4 billion (f.o.b., 1997).

Destinations	%
NA	NA

NA stands for not available.

Economic Aid (27)

Recipient: ODA, $588 million (1997).

Import Export Commodities (28)

Import Commodities	Export Commodities
Capital goods 48%	Metals 34%
Chemicals 11%	Natural gas 9.4%
Petroleum 5%	Soybeans 8.4%
Food 5%	Jewelry 11%
	Wood 6.9%

BOSNIA AND HERZEGOVINA

Republic of Bosnia and Herzegovina
Republika Bosnia i Herzegovina

INTRODUCTORY SURVEY

RECENT HISTORY

Josip Broz-Tito, communist president of Yugoslavia from 1953 to his death in 1980, managed to maintain peace among the Croats, Serbs, and Muslims. After his death, there was an economic crisis that led to tensions between the different groups. They demanded a reorganization of the Yugoslav federation into a confederation of sovereign states and a shift to a market economy.

On 1 August 1990, Bosnia and Herzegovina declared itself a "sovereign and democratic state." However, by 1991 Yugoslavia was dissolved, as Slovenia, Croatia, Bosnia and Herzegovina, and Macedonia declared independence individually, leaving only Serbia and Montenegro together in a new Federal Republic of Yugoslavia, which remains unrecognized by the U.S. as a successor to the former Yugoslavia.

The coalition government of Bosnia and Herzegovina had a very difficult time maintaining the spirit of ethnic cooperation. The Serbian and Croatian parties each wanted a temporary confederation as a transition to unification with their "mother state" of Serbia or Croatia. The Muslim party favored a united Bosnia and Herzegovina. Ultimately war broke out among the parties.

War spread in Bosnia in mid-1992. While Serbs took over control of some 70% of the country, Croats kept control of western Herzegovina. Their Muslim allies tried to resist Serbian attacks on mostly Muslim cities and towns full of refugees. Peacekeeping efforts were made by the European Community, the United States, the United Nations (UN), and the North Atlantic Treaty Organization (NATO). In July 1995, Bosnian Serbs overran areas under UN protection. In retaliation, NATO forces began air raids on Bosnian Serb positions in August 1995. The Bosnian Serb forces then started lifting their siege of Sarajevo, and agreed to negotiate over Bosnia's future.

On 21 November 1995, Serb, Croat, and Bosnian authorities signed an agreement known as the Dayton Accords. The agreement recognized Bosnia and Herzegovina as a single state with two legal entities: the Federation of Bosnia and Herzegovina (FBH), and the Republika Srpska (RS). The FBH covers 51% of the territory and has a Bosnian Muslim and Croat majority. The RS occupies 49% of the area and has a Serb majority. NATO forces assisted with the military aspects of the agreement in order to provide stability during reconstruction.

In March 1996, the International War Crimes Tribunal filed its first charges against Serb soldiers who were accused of committing crimes against humanity during the civil war. Bosnian Muslim and Croat soldiers were also charged with crimes committed at a prison camp.

GOVERNMENT

Under the Dayton Accords, a constitution for Bosnia and Herzegovina recognizes a single state with two constituencies. The Federation of Bosnia and Herzegovina (FBH) covers 51% of the territory and has a Bosnian Muslim and Bosnian Croat majority. The Republika Srpska (RS) covers the 49% of the country with a Bosnian Serb majority. The FBH government has a mixed system of a president and a parliament that must approve the president's choice for prime minister. The RS government operates with a president, two vice-presidents, and a legislative branch.

Judiciary

The 1995 constitution provides for an independent judiciary. Federal courts include the Constitutional Court, the Supreme Court, and the Human Rights Court. Municipal courts have jurisdiction over most civil and criminal cases.

Political Parties

Presidential elections were held for the three-member presidency on September 12-13, 1998. Alija Izetbegovic won the Bozniak (Bosnian Muslim) contest, Ante Jelavic easily captured the Croat seat by unseating Kresimir Zubak, while Zivko Radisic unseated Momcilo Krajisnik for the Serb seat. In elections for the 42-seat House of Representatives for Bosnia and Herzegovina, the Coalition for a Whole and Democratic Bosnia and Herzegovina won the largest share with 17 seats. The Croatian Democratic Union came in second with 6 seats.

DEFENSE

The Serbs control most of the Russian weapons abandoned by the former Yugoslavian army. About 30,000 United Nations peacekeepers remain in Bosnia and Herzegovina.

ECONOMIC AFFAIRS

Bosnia and Herzegovina ranked next to Macedonia as the poorest republic of the former Yugoslav federation. Although industry accounts for over 50% of its income, Bosnia and Herzegovina is primarily agricultural. Farms have been small and inefficient, making it necessary to import food. Metallic ore and coal production, timber production, and textiles are also important.

The civil war caused the gross domestic product (GDP) to drop by 75%.

Public Finance

The breakup of the Yugoslav SFR and the ongoing civil war have severely disrupted the government's ability to account for revenues and expenditures.

Income

In 1999, Bosnia and Herzegovina's gross national product (GNP) was an estimated $750 per person.

Industry

Mining and mining-related activities make up the bulk of Bosnia and Herzegovina's industry. Steel production, vehicle assembly, textiles, tobacco products, wooden furniture, and domestic appliances are also important industries.

Banking and Finance

The central bank of Bosnia and Herzegovina is the National Bank of Bosnia and Herzegovina. In June 1992, Yugoslavia's central bank refused to issue Yugoslavian dinars in Bosnia and Herzegovina.

In 1996, Croatian dinars were used in Croat-held areas for currency, presumably to be replaced by new Croatian Kuna. Old and new Serbian dinars were used in Serb-held areas. Hard currencies supplanted local currencies in areas held by the Bosnian government. In April 1997, the presidential council agreed on a single currency for both the Muslim/Croat and Bosnian Serb parts of the country.

Economic Development

As of 1997, the World Bank had spent only one-third of the $1.8 billion it raised for Bosnia and Herzegovina because of repeated failures to institute economic reforms or honor the terms of the 1995 peace agreement. Reconstruction work will require an estimated $5 billion over the next few years. The actual distribution of assistance to particular entities or areas depends on compliance with the Dayton Accords, including the turnover of persons indicted for war crimes to the International Criminal Tribunal for the Former Yugoslavia.

SOCIAL WELFARE

Bosnia's economy and social fabric have been devastated by the war. Despite minimum wage guarantees, delays and partial payments are widespread. Enforcement of sick leave and other benefit programs, as well as occupational health and safety measures, has been inadequate.

By 1995, some two-thirds of the country's prewar population had become refugees or displaced within the country.

Healthcare

There were over 200,000 war-related deaths during the civil war. Many hospitals were destroyed, and people lost access to the health care system that was available before the war.

Housing

About 60% of all homes were destroyed during the civil war. There is now a serious housing shortage, and returning refugees are often housed in the abandoned homes of other refugees.

EDUCATION

Education at the elementary level is free and compulsory for eight years. At the secondary level, children have the option to take up general, vocational, or technical education. General secondary education lasts for four years and qualifies the students for university education.

1999 KEY EVENTS TIMELINE

March

- The chief international mediator dismisses Bosnian Serb president Nikola Poplasen for violation of Dayton peace accords.

- International authorities rule that the disputed northern city of Brcko should be shared by Bosnia's two sectors.

June

- United States aid agency triggers a run on the Bosnia and Herzegovina Bank (BiH) when it calls in its loans, leading to the bank's collapse.

July

- Bosnian deputy prime minister Radoslav Brdjanin becomes the highest-ranking Bosnian Serb official arrested for war crimes.

- Leaders of Bosnia and Croatia sign an agreement resolving remaining border disputes.

August

- Austrians arrest the top Bosnian Serb general for war crimes against Muslims and Croats.

- The *New York Times* publishes an article alleging widespread corruption among Bosnian officials.

- The remains of 250 people killed in Srebrenica are discovered in a mass grave.

September

- The top Western envoy dismisses the Croatian justice minister for obstructing the peace process.

- U.S. and international authorities announce plans to investigate widespread bureaucratic corruption said to be costing Bosnia millions of dollars in aid funds.

- NATO announces plans to reduce its peacekeeping force by one-third over the next six months.

December

- The United Nations' war crimes tribunal in the Hague, Netherlands, sentences Serb Goran Jelisic to 40 years in prison. Jelisic is found guilty on 31 counts of war crimes and crimes against humanity. The charges relate to the torture and murder of 13 Muslims and Croats during the war in May 1992 while Jelisic was a prison camp official.

ANALYSIS OF EVENTS: 1999

BUSINESS AND THE ECONOMY

The nation of Bosnia-Herzgovina is partially industrialized but poor. Industrial production accounts for 23 percent of the nation's Gross Domestic Product (GDP). It has always suffered from poverty. The per capita GDP in Bosnia-Herzgovina in 1998 was only $1,720—smaller even than Belize. In 1996 the unemployment rate in Bosnia hovered at between 40 percent and 50 percent. The recent war between Serbia and Bosnia compounded the problems of underdevelopment. In June the U.S. Agency for International Development (USAID) called in its loans to the Bosnia and Herzegovina Bank (BiH Bank), leading to a run on the bank and its financial collapse the same month. Commenting on allegations of official corruption in the *New York Times,* U.S. officials disclosed in August that USAID had called in the loans due to suspicions of fraudulent reporting by the bank.

Free market reformers intent on dismantling the socialist economies of Eastern Europe consolidated their influence at the close of the Balkan wars of 1992–95 and destabilized certain financial structures in the Bosnian economy. In June 1999 the U.S. Agency for International Development

(USAID) called in its loans to the Bosnia and Herzegovina Bank (BiH Bank), leading to a run on the bank and its financial collapse the same month. Commenting on allegations of official corruption in the *New York Times,* U.S. officials disclosed in August that USAID had called in the loans due to suspicions of fraudulent reporting by the bank.

In 1999 representatives of international bodies devoted to free market economic principles called for a faster pace of economic reform in Bosnia. UN envoy Carl Bildt criticized the fact that Bosnia had received large amounts of foreign aid that were not conditional on economic reforms, as well as the country's excessive reliance on aid and the reluctance of its leaders to undertake reforms. A World Bank official noted that the pace of privatization needed to be accelerated. After a long initial delay, the sell-off of state-owned assets—estimated to total some 26 billion marka (the Bosnian currency)—was only begun during the past year. In the Muslim-Croat federation, the privatization effort, begun in May, had yielded only about 13 million marka ($6.9 million) in its first few months. In the Serb part of the country, the sell-off, which began over the summer, was expected to turn about 1,700 companies over to the private sector in 2000.

GOVERNMENT AND POLITICS

In 1999 the four-year-old peace in Bosnia-Herzegovina remained stable enough for NATO to begin reducing the 25-nation peacekeeping force that had been in place since the 1995 Dayton peace accords. Modest reductions were carried out early in the year, and in September NATO announced that the remaining 31,000-member force would shrink by one-third over the next six months. The reduction also made more troops available for deployment in the current Balkan hot spot of Kosovo.

In spite of the NATO troop reduction, political tensions continued between Bosnia's rival ethnic groups, and representatives of the international community continued to play a major role in administering Bosnia, which had been divided into two political entities—the Republika Srpska and the Muslim-Croat federation—by the 1995 peace agreement. In March western envoy Carlos Westendorp dismissed Bosnian Serb president Nikola Poplasen for failing to carry out provisions of the peace accord. At the same time, a ruling by a representative of the International Court of Justice in The Hague mandated that the strategically located city of Brcko, which had been administered

as a de facto Serbian district, be shared between the country's two sectors. The loss of control over the city provoked anger and protest by Bosnian Serbs. But some of the rulings went the other way, as when in September the new top western envoy, Austrian diplomat Wolfgang Petritsch, removed a justice minister in the Muslim-Croat federation for failing to implement provisions of the peace accord.

Another major problem addressed by the international community was corruption. In August, the *New York Times* published an article alleging that up to $1 billion in foreign-aid funds for Bosnia had been embezzled by government officials and reporting a widespread network of graft at the highest levels of government. A U.S. congressional fact-finding team was dispatched to Bosnia to investigate, and international agencies began coordinating efforts to rectify the situation.

The aftermath of the bitter warfare of 1992–95 remained in the news with the arrest of Bosnian military and political figures accused of war crimes for trial before the tribunal in The Hague. Radoslav Brdjanin, a deputy prime minister of Republika Srpska, was arrested by NATO troops in July. In August General Momir Talic, the head of the Bosnian Serb army, was taken into custody in Austria, becoming the highest-ranking officer arrested thus far.

At a Balkan summit held in Sarajevo in July, Bosnia and Croatia signed an agreement resolving all remaining border disputes between the two countries.

CULTURE AND SOCIETY

Four years after a brutal war Bosnians were still working to repair not only the physical but also the social and psychological ravages of the fighting. In an attempt at healing the divided country Bosnia's leaders proposed that November 21—the anniversary of the signing of the Dayton peace accords—be celebrated as the country's new national holiday. The proposal, made by the nation's collective presidency, was submitted to the parliament for approval. In another attempt to overcome the country's ethnic divisions, education officials agreed to have the nation's textbooks reviewed for inflammatory language against any of the three major ethnic and religious groups, and to have such language removed.

The divisive memory of the war would not go away, however. Searchers in northeastern Bosnia reported the discovery of a mass grave containing the bodies of about 250 people believed to have been murdered following the fall of Srebrenica in 1995. This brought to 1,650 the total number of people known to have died in that city. A UN spokesperson said that the discovery of this latest execution site helps fill in the gaps in what is known about the events that occurred there. Searchers found 56 more bodies in two smaller grave pits near Sarajevo and Teslic. The total number of people killed in the three-and-a-half-year war now stood at over 200,000.

The return of refugees to their former homes continued to pose political and logistical challenges. Of the more than 2 million Bosnians torn from their homes during the war, some 840,000 were still displaced within the country, while over 300,000 refugees remained abroad. Bosnians were particularly reluctant to return to homes in areas where they were now an ethnic minority, and only about 100,000 had done so.

DIRECTORY

CENTRAL GOVERNMENT

The 1995 Dayton Accords ended war and recognized Bosnia and Herzegovina as a single state with two legal entities, the Federation of Bosnia and Herzegovina (FBH) and the Republika Srpska (RS). A new government structure was implemented to reflect the single state and the two separate entities. Elected for a four-year term, the state of Bosnia and Herzegovina's presidency is rotated between three elected individuals from each of the country's main ethnic groups. As for the separate entities, the Federation rotates its presidency between a Bosnian and a Croat, while the Republika Srpska's presidency is held by a single individual, a Serb. This type of division is held throughout the nation's government. The following information represents both the single state of Bosnia and Herzegovina and the representation of its two legal entities, the Federation of Bosnia and Herzegovina and the Republika Srpska.

Head of State

Member of the Presidency (Bosnian Serb)
Zivko Radisic, Office of the Presidency
PHONE: +387 (71) 672474
FAX: +387 (71) 672473

Member of the Presidency (Croat)
Ante Jelavic, Office of the Presidency, Save Kavacevica Ulica 6, 71000 Sarajevo, Bosnia and Herzegovina
PHONE: +387 (71) 471213
FAX: +387 (71) 206656; +387 (71) 470002
E-MAIL: info@mvp.gov.ba

Member of the Presidency (Bosnian Serb)
Alija Izetbegovic, Office of the Presidency
PHONE: +387 (71) 664941
FAX: +387 (71) 472491

Ministers

Co-Chairman of the Council of Ministers
Haris Silajdzic, Council of Ministers
PHONE: +387 (71) 664930
FAX: +387 (71) 443446

Co-Chairman of the Council of Ministers
Suetozar Mihajlovic, Council of Ministers

Co-Chairman of the Council of Ministers
Boro Bosic, Council of Ministers
PHONE: +387 (71) 786947
FAX: +387 (71) 786824

Vice-Chair Council of Ministers
Neven Tomic
PHONE: +387 (71) 471630
FAX: +387 (71) 206140

Minister of Foreign Affairs
Jadranko Prlic, Ministry of Foreign Affairs, Musala 3, 71000 Sarajevo, Bosnia and Herzegovina
PHONE: +387 (71) 667979
FAX: +387 (71) 444766

Minister of Foreign Trade and Economic Relations
Mirsad Kurtovic, Ministry of Foreign Trade and Economic Relations
PHONE: +387 (71) 473123
FAX: +387 (71) 445911

Minister of Civil Affairs and Communications
Spasoje Albijanic, Ministry of Civil Affairs and Communications
PHONE: +387 (71) 786822
FAX: +387 (71) 786942

Minister of Finance
Drago Bilandzija, Ministry of Finance
PHONE: +387 (71) 203149
FAX: +387 (71) 664863

Minister of Defense
Ante Jelavic, Ministry of Defense

PHONE: +387 (71) 664926
FAX: +387 (71) 663785

Minister of Internal Affairs
Mehmed Zilic, Ministry of Internal Affairs
PHONE: +387 (71) 667246
FAX: +387 (71) 472946

Minister of Justice
Mato Tadic, Ministry of Justice
PHONE: +387 (71) 656743
FAX: +387 (71) 656743

Minister of Energy, Mining and Industry
Mirsad Salkic, Ministry of Energy, Mining and Industry
PHONE: +387 (71) 663779
FAX· +387 (71) 642064

Minister of Transport and Communications
Kemal Bubalo, Ministry of Transport and Communications
PHONE: +387 (71) 668907
FAX: +387 (71) 667866

Minister of Social Policy, Diplaced Persons and Refugees
Rasim Kadic, Ministry of Social Policy, Diplaced Persons and Refugees
PHONE: +387 (71) 204552
FAX: +387 (71) 663977

Minister of Health
Bozo Ljubic, Ministry of Health
PHONE: +387 (71) 664246
FAX: +387 (71) 664245

Minister of Education, Science, Culture and Sport
Fahrudin Rizvanbegovic, Ministry of Education, Science, Culture and Sport
PHONE: +387 (71) 202750
FAX: +387 (71) 664381

Minister of Trade
Ile Krezo, Ministry of Trade
PHONE: +387 (88) 312191
FAX: +387 (88) 312191

Minister of Physical Planning and Environment
Ibrahim Morankic, Ministry of Physical Planning and Environment
PHONE: +387 (71) 473124
FAX: +387 (71) 663548

GOVERNMENT OF THE FEDERATION OF BOSNIA AND HERZEGOVINA

Head of State

President
Ivo Andric-Luzanski

Vice President
Ejup Ganic

Prime Minister
Edhem Bicakcic

Ministers

Deputy Prime Minister
Dragan Covic

Minister of Agriculture, Water Management, and Forestry
Ahmed Smajic

Minister of Defense
Miroslav Prce

Minister of Education, Science, Culture, and Sports
Fahrudin Rizvanbegovic

Minister of Energy, Mining, and Industry
Mirsad Salkic

Minister of Finance
Dragan Colic

Minister of Health
Bozo Ljubic

Minister of Interior
Mehmed Zilic

Minister of Justice
Ignjac Dodik

Minister of Refugees, Displaced Persons, and Social Welfare
Sulejman Garib

Minister of Trade
Branko Ivkovic

Minister of Transport and Communications
Besim Mehmedic

Minister of Urban Planning and Environmental Protection
Ramiz Mehmedovic

Minister Without Portfolio
Nikola Antunovic

Minister Without Portfolio
Nedeljko Despotovic

GOVERNMENT OF REPUBLIKA SRPSKA (BOSNIAN SERBS)

Head of State

President
Nikola Poplasen

Vice President
Mirko Sarovic

Prime Minister
Milorad Dodik

Ministers

Deputy Prime Minister
Djuradj Banjac

Deputy Prime Minister
Ostoja Kremenovic

Deputy Prime Minister
Savo Loncar

Deputy Prime Minister
Tihomir Gligoric

Minister of Administration and Local Self-Administration
Ostoja Kremenovic

Minister of Agriculture, Water Management, and Forestry
Milenko Savic

Minister in Charge of Veterans and Victims of War and Labor
Tihomir Gligoric

Minister of Defense
Manojlo Milovanovic

Minister of Education
Nenad Suzic

Minister of Finance
Novak Kondic

Minister of Foreign Trade Relations
Savo Loncar

Minister of Health and Social Welfare
Zeljko Rodic

Minister of Industry and Technology
Djuradj Banjac

Minister of Information
Rajko Vasic

Minister of Internal Affairs
Sredoje Novic

Minister of Justice
Milan Trbojevic

Minister of Power Industry and Mining
Vladimir Dokic

Minister of Refugees and Displaced Persons
Miladin Dragicevic

Minister of Religion
Jovo Turanjanin

Minister of Science and Culture
Zivojin Eric

Minister of Sports and Youth
Milorad Karalic

Minister of Trade and Tourism
Nikola Kragulj

Minister of Transportation and Communications
Marko Pavic

Minister of Urban Planning and Construction
Jovo Basic

POLITICAL ORGANIZATIONS

Bosnian Party of Rights-BSP

Bosnian Party (BOSS)
NAME: Mirnes Ajanovic

Bosnian Patriotic Party (GPS)
NAME: Sefer Halilovic

Center Coalition (KC)

Civic Democratic Party (GDS)
NAME: Ibrahim Spahic

Coalition for King and Fatherland (KKO)
NAME: Dugravko Prstojevic

Croatian Democratic Union of BiH (HDZ-BiH)
NAME: Ante Jelavic

Croatian Party of Rights (HSP)
NAME: Zdravko Hrstic

Croatian Peasants Party of BiH (HSS-BiH)
NAME: Ilija Simic

Democratic Party for Banja Luka and Krajina
NAME: Nikola Spiric

Democratic Party of Pensioners (DSP)
NAME: Alojz Knezovic

Democratic Peoples Union (DNZ)

NAME: Fikret Abdic

Liberal Bosniak Organization (LBO)

NAME: Muhamed Filipovic

Liberal Party (LS)

TITLE: President
NAME: Rasim Kadic

Muslim-Bosnia Organization (MBO)

NAME: Salih Burek

New Croatian Initiative (NHI)

NAME: Kresimir Zubak

Party for Bosnia and Herzegovina (SBH)

NAME: Haris Silajdzic

Party for Democratic Action (SDA)

NAME: Alija Izetbegovic

Party of Independent Social Democrats (SNSD)

NAME: Milorad Dodik

Radical Party Republika Srpska (RSRS)

NAME: Miroslav Radovanovic

Republican Party (RS)

NAME: Sjepan Kjlujic

Serb Coalition for Republika Srpska (SKRS)

NAME: Predrag Lazerevic

Serb Democratic Party or Serb Lands (SDS)

NAME: Dragan Kalinic

Serb National Alliance (SNS)

NAME: Biljana Plavsic

Serb Radical Party-Republika Srpska (SRS-RS)

NAME: Nikola Poplasen

Sloga (Unity)

NAME: Biljana Plavsic

Social Democratic Party BIH (SDP)

NAME: Zlatko Lagumdzija

Socialist Party of Republika Srpska (SPRS)

NAME: Zivko Radisic

DIPLOMATIC REPRESENTATION

Embassies in Bosnia and Herzegovina

United States
Alipasina 43, 71000 Sarajevo, Bosnia and
Herzegovina
PHONE: +387 (71) 445700
FAX: +387 (71) 659722
TITLE: Ambassador
NAME: Richard D. Kauzlarich

JUDICIAL SYSTEM

Constitutional Court

FURTHER READING

Articles

Becker, Elizabeth. "Citing Gains, NATO Plans to Cut Back Bosnia Force." *The New York Times*, 14 July 1999, p. A10.

"Better Luck Next Time." *The Economist* (May 1, 1999): 47.

Hedges, Chris. "Up to $1 Billion Reported Stolen by Bosnia Leaders." *The New York Times*, 17 August 1999, p. A1.

Holbrooke, Richard. "Battles After the War." *The New York Times*, 14 September 1999, p. A31.

Neuffer, Elizabeth. "Bosnia Dispatch: Homecoming." *The New Republic* (August 23, 1999): 15.

Thurow, Roger. "Another Country: 'If You Rebuild Our Houses, You Can't Just Drop Us Back Here.'" *The Wall Street Journal*, 24 August 1999, p. A1.

"Two on the Chin." *The Economist* (March 13, 1999): 61.

Zagorin, Adam. "More Losses in Bosnia: This Time It's Aid Money." *Time* (September 20, 1999): 18.

Books

Black, Eric. *Bosnia: Fractured Region*. Minneapolis, Minn.: Lerner Publications, 1999.

Bosnia and Herzegovina: Toward Economic Recovery. Prepared by the World Bank, the European Commission, and the European Bank for Reconstruction and Development. Washington, D.C.: World Bank, 1996.

Burg, Steven L., and Paul S. Shoup. *The War in Bosnia-Herzegovina: Ethnic Conflict and International Intervention.* Armonk, N.Y.: M.E. Sharpe, 1999.

Friedman, Francine. *The Bosnian Muslims: Denial of a Nation.* Boulder, Colo.: Westview Press, 1996.

Holbrooke, Richard C. *To End a War.* 1st ed. New York: Random House, 1998.

BOSNIA AND HERZEGOVINA: STATISTICAL DATA

For sources and notes see "Sources of Statistics" in the front of each volume.

GEOGRAPHY

Geography (1)

Area:

Total: 51,233 sq km.

Land: 51,233 sq km.

Water: 0 sq km.

Area—comparative: slightly smaller than West Virginia.

Land boundaries:

Total: 1,459 km.

Border countries: Croatia 932 km, Serbia and Montenegro 527 km (312 km with Serbia, 215 km with Montenegro).

Coastline: 20 km.

Climate: hot summers and cold winters; areas of high elevation have short, cool summers and long, severe winters; mild, rainy winters along coast.

Terrain: mountains and valleys.

Natural resources: coal, iron, bauxite, manganese, forests, copper, chromium, lead, zinc.

Land use:

Arable land: 14%

Permanent crops: 5%

Permanent pastures: 20%

Forests and woodland: 39%

Other: 22% (1993 est.).

HUMAN FACTORS

Demographics (2A)

	1990	1995	1998	2000	2010	2020	2030	2040	2050
Population	NA	3,282.2	3,365.7	3,591.6	3,736.7	3,564.8	3,379.9	3,149.2	2,833.5
Net migration rate (per 1,000 population)	NA	NA	NA	NA	NA	NA	NA	NA	NA
Births	NA	NA	NA	NA	NA	NA	NA	NA	NA
Deaths	NA	NA	NA	NA	NA	NA	NA	NA	NA
Life expectancy - males	NA	51.2	58.3	67.2	72.6	74.8	76.5	77.9	78.9
Life expectancy - females	NA	61.4	68.0	75.7	80.1	81.7	83.1	84.2	85.1
Birth rate (per 1,000)	NA	7.7	8.7	10.0	10.3	7.2	7.1	6.3	5.6
Death rate (per 1,000)	NA	14.9	12.3	9.3	9.8	11.3	12.8	15.1	17.5
Women of reproductive age (15-49 yrs.)	NA	854.6	898.9	975.7	954.9	795.6	690.8	550.7	505.7
of which are currently married	NA	NA	NA	NA	NA	NA	NA	NA	NA
Fertility rate	NA	1.0	1.1	1.3	1.4	1.4	1.3	1.3	1.3

Except as noted, values for vital statistics are in thousands; life expectancy is in years.

Health Indicators (4)

Life expectancy at birth

1980 70

1997 . . . .

Daily per capita supply of calories (1996) . . . .

Total fertility rate births per woman (1997) 1.6

Maternal mortality ratio per 100,000 live births
(1990-97) . . . .

Safe water % of population with access (1995) . . . .

Sanitation % of population with access (1995) 41

Consumption of iodized salt % of households
(1992-98)[a] . . . .

Smoking prevalence

Male % of adults (1985-95)[a] . . . .

Female % of adults (1985-95)[a] . . . .

Tuberculosis incidence per 100,000 people
(1997) 81

Adult HIV prevalence % of population ages
15-49 (1997) 0.04

Infants and Malnutrition (5)

Under-5 mortality rate (1997) 16

% of infants with low birthweight (1990-97) . . . . . .NA

Births attended by skilled health staff % of total[a] . . .NA

% fully immunized (1995-97)

TB 97

DPT 79

Polio 80

Measles 85

Prevalence of child malnutrition under age 5
(1992-97)[b] . . . . .NA

Ethnic Division (6)

Serb 40%

Muslim 38%

Croat 22%

Religions (7)

Muslim 40%

Orthodox 31%

Catholic 15%

Protestant 4%

Other 10%

Languages (8)

Serbo-Croatian (often called Bosnian) 99%.

EDUCATION

Public Education Expenditures (9)

Public expenditure on education (% of GNP)

1980 . . . .

1996 . . . .

Expenditure per student

Primary % of GNP per capita

1980 . . . .

1996 . . . .

Secondary % of GNP per capita

1980 . . . .

1996 . . . .

Tertiary % of GNP per capita

1980 . . . .

1996 . . . .

Expenditure on teaching materials

Primary % of total for level (1996) . . . .

Secondary % of total for level (1996) . . . .

Primary pupil-teacher ratio per teacher (1996) . . . .

Duration of primary education years (1995) . . . .

GOVERNMENT & LAW

Political Parties (12)

National Assembly	No. of seats
Serb Democratic Party (SDS)	.24
Serb Radical Party	.15
Serb National Alliance	.15
Socialist Party	.9
Independent Social Democrats	.2
Coalition for United Bosnia and Herzegovina and others	.18

82 parties participated in the September 1997 municipal
elections.

Government Budget (13B)

Revenues . . . . .NA

Expenditures . . . . .NA

Capital expenditures . . . . .NA

NA stands for not available.

Military Affairs (14A)

Military age . . . . .19 years of age

Availability of manpower

Males age 15-49 (1998 est.) 912,536

Fit for military service

Males (1998 est.) 733,931

Military Affairs (14A)

Reaching military age annually

Males (1998 est.) 26,114

Total expenditures . . . .$NA

Expenditures as % of GDP . . . . .NA%

NA stands for not available.

Crime (15)

Crime rate (for 1997)

Crimes reported 12,400

Total persons convicted 8,600

Crimes per 100,000 population . . . . .NA

Persons responsible for offenses

Total number of suspects 9,150

Total number of female suspects . . . . .NA

Total number of juvenile suspects 1,350

LABOR FORCE

Labor Force (16)

Total 1,026,254.

Unemployment Rate (17)

40%-50% (1996 est.)

PRODUCTION SECTOR

Electric Energy (18)

Capacity . . . . .2.339 million kW (1995)

Production . . . . .1.4 billion kWh (1995)

Consumption per capita . . . . .506 kWh (1995)

Transportation (19)

Highways:

total: 21,846 km

paved: 11,425 km

unpaved: 10,421 km (1996 est.) note: roads need maintenance and repair

Waterways: NA km; Sava blocked by downed bridges

Pipelines: crude oil 174 km; natural gas 90 km (1992); note—pipelines now disrupted

Merchant marine: none

Airports: 26 (1997 est.)

Airports—with paved runways:

total: 9

2,438 to 3,047 m: 4

1,524 to 2,437 m: 2

914 to 1,523 m: 1

under 914 m: 2 (1997 est.)

Airports—with unpaved runways:

total: 17

1,524 to 2,437 m: 1

914 to 1,523 m: 9

under 914 m: 7 (1997 est.)

Top Agricultural Products (20)

Wheat, corn, fruits, vegetables; livestock.

MANUFACTURING SECTOR

GDP & Manufacturing Summary (21)

Detailed value added figures are listed by both International Standard Industry Code (ISIC) and product title.

	1980	1985	1989	1990
GDP ($-1980 mil.)	69,958	71,058	72,234	66,371
Per capita ($-1980)	3,136	3,073	3,050	2,786
Manufacturing share (%) (current prices)	30.6	37.2	39.5	42.0
Manufacturing				
Value added ($-1981 mil.)	19,526	22,283	24,021	21,703
Industrial production index	100	116	120	108
Value added ($ mil.)	21,750	17,171	30,245	27,660
Gross output ($ mil.)	72,629	57,020	65,078	62,136
Employment (000)	2,106	2,467	2,658	2,537
Profitability (% of gross output)				
Intermediate input (%)	70	70	54	55
Wages and salaries inc. supplements (%)	14	12	12e	18
Gross operating surplus	15	18	34e	26
Productivity ($)				
Gross output per worker	34,487	23,113	24,484	24,248
Value added per worker	10,328	6,960	11,379	10,796
Average wage (inc. supplements)	4,991	2,703	2,986	4,488
Value added ($ mil.)				
311 Food products	1,897	1,458	3,916	3,484
313 Beverages	459	353	663	589
314 Tobacco products	184	221	344	308

MANUFACTURING SECTOR

GDP & Manufacturing Summary (21)

	1980	1985	1989	1990
321 Textiles	1,759	1,428	2,881	2,663
322 Wearing apparel	903	718	1,593	1,427
323 Leather and fur products	226	231	383	340
324 Footwear	482	503	1,022	899
331 Wood and wood products	977	530	794	706
332 Furniture and fixtures	730	438	1,030	1,065
341 Paper and paper products	529	394	759	674
342 Printing and publishing	876	462	761	678
351 Industrial chemicals	694	631	1,107	992
352 Other chemical products	681	525	1,419	1,315
353 Petroleum refineries	454	415	260	233
354 Miscellaneous petroleum and coal products	101	101	104	91
355 Rubber products	276	269	479	456
356 Plastic products	413	258	397	350
361 Pottery, china and earthenware	128	72	162	144
362 Glass and glass products	163	113	224	204
369 Other non-metal mineral products	906	513	683	604
371 Iron and steel	1,221	1,000	1,343	1,171
372 Non-ferrous metals	480	509	944	927
381 Metal products	2,105	1,577	1,293	1,130
382 Non-electrical machinery	1,828	1,463	2,372	2,378
383 Electrical machinery	1,600	1,544	2,640	2,334
384 Transport equipment	1,441	1,263	2,389	2,241
385 Professional and scientific equipment	101	93	154	146
390 Other manufacturing industries	134	88	128	114

FINANCE, ECONOMICS, & TRADE

Economic Indicators (22)

National product: GDP—purchasing power parity—$4.41 billion (1997 est.)

National product real growth rate: 35% (1997 est.)

National product per capita: $1,690 (1997 est.)

Inflation rate—consumer price index: NA%

Exchange Rates (24)

Exchange rates: NA

Top Import Origins (25)

$1.1 billion (1995 est.)

Origins	%
NA	NA

NA stands for not available.

Top Export Destinations (26)

$152 million (1995 est.).

Destinations	%
NA	NA

NA stands for not available.

Economic Aid (27)

Recipient: $1.2 billion (1997 pledged).

Import Export Commodities (28)

Import Commodities	Export Commodities
NA	NA

BOTSWANA

Republic of Botswana

CAPITAL: Gaborone.

FLAG: The flag of Botswana consists of five horizontal stripes. The top and bottom stripes are light blue and wider than the middle stripe, which is black. The blue stripes are separated from the black by thin white stripes.

ANTHEM: *Fatshe La Rona (Blessed Country)*.

MONETARY UNIT: On 23 August 1976, the pula (P) of 100 thebe replaced the South African rand (R) as Botswana's legal currency. There are coins of 1, 2, 5, 10, 25, 50 thebe and 1 pula, and notes of 2, 5, 10, 20, 50 and 100 pula. P1 = $0.27278 (or $1 = P3.666).

WEIGHTS AND MEASURES: The metric system is the legal standard.

HOLIDAYS: New Year's Day, 1 January; Good Friday; Easter Monday; Ascension; President's Day, 15 July; Botswana Days, 30 September–1 October; Christmas, 25 December; Boxing Day, 26 December.

TIME: 2 PM = noon GMT.

LOCATION AND SIZE: Botswana is a landlocked country in southern Africa. It covers an area of 600,370 square kilometers (231,804 square miles). Comparatively, Botswana is slightly smaller than the state of Texas. It meets Zambia at a point in the north and is bordered on the northeast by Zimbabwe, on the southeast and south by South Africa, and on the west and north by Namibia (South West Africa). Its total boundary length is 4,013 kilometers (2,490 miles).

CLIMATE: Most of the country has a subtropical climate, with cooler temperatures at higher altitudes. Winter days are warm and nights are cool, with heavy frost common in the desert. Temperatures range from average maximums of 33°C (91°F) in January and 22°C (72°F) in July to average minimums of 18°C (64°F) in January and 5°C (41°F) in July. Beginning in August, seasonal winds blow from the west and carry sand and dust across the country. Rainfall normally averages 45 centimeters (18 inches), ranging from 69 centimeters (27 inches) in the north to less than 25 centimeters (10 inches) in the Kalahari. Drought conditions prevailed in the early and mid-1980s.

INTRODUCTORY SURVEY

RECENT HISTORY

On 30 September 1966, under the leadership of President Khama, the new named Republic of Botswana came into being. During this first decade of independence, Botswana refused to support UN sanctions against South Africa. Although officially opposed to apartheid, Botswana was economically dependent on South Africa. After the 1969 elections, President Khama banned imports from white-minority-ruled Rhodesia (now Zimbabwe). Tensions were high in the 1970s as Botswana sheltered 20,000 refugees from Rhodesia, and Rhodesian armed forces crossed into Botswana on raids against guerrillas.

South Africa accused Botswana of allowing rebels to terrorize South Africa. In 1985, South African commandos killed several South African refugees in Gaborone. Further South African border violations and attacks in Botswana continued, but by 1992, the two countries established formal diplomatic relations.

The economy in Botswana was declining in 1995. There were protests from citizens who needed jobs and government help to live. The government announced a plan of reforms to try to improve economic and living conditions.

GOVERNMENT

Botswana is a republic. Under its constitution, the president is elected by the National Assembly and is chief of state, chief executive, and commander-in-chief of the armed forces. The

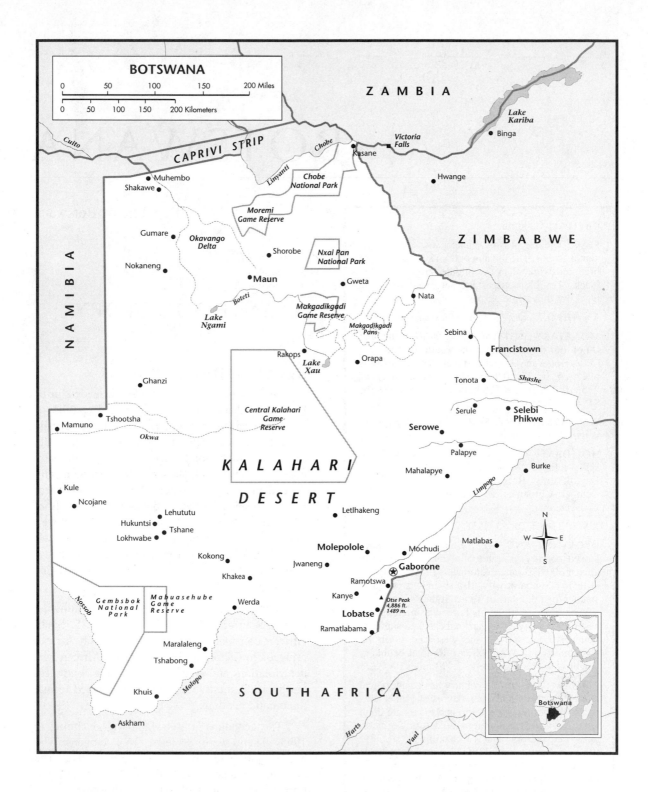

president appoints a cabinet from among the National Assembly members. The president can veto any bill, but if it is passed again within six months, the president must either sign it or dissolve the Assembly. All citizens over the age of 21 can vote.

The House of Chiefs consists of the chiefs of the eight principal tribes, and four chiefs elected from minority districts. Botswana has both a High Court and traditional village councils, called *kgotla*, where villagers can express opinions. Botswana is one of Africa's few stable multiparty democracies and has a commendable human rights record.

Judiciary

The constitution provides for a high court, a court of appeal, and lower courts. The African Courts Proclamation of 1961 provides for courts knowledgeable in tribal law and custom, presided over by chiefs. The judiciary is independent of the executive and the legislative branches.

Political Parties

Botswana's leading party, the Botswana Democratic Party (BDP), was founded in late 1961, pledging itself to democracy, nonracialism, and a multiparty state. Other parties include the Botswana People's Party (BPP), the Botswana Independence Party (BIP), and the Botswana National Front (BNF).

DEFENSE

The Botswana Defense Force (ground and air units) is estimated at over 6,000 members, armed with North Atlantic Treaty Organization (NATO) weapons in 1993. There are about 1,000 paramilitary police.

ECONOMIC AFFAIRS

Botswana's economy depended almost entirely on livestock production until the 1970s, when the country became an important exporter of diamonds and other minerals. Foreign investment in agriculture, tourism, and industry, together with the rapid growth in diamond production, helped Botswana achieve average annual economic growth of 8.4% from independence through 1984. Real growth of 10% was recorded between 1985 and 1987. However, it slowed to 8.7% in the following two years (1987–89). Agriculture employed an estimated 80% of the labor force in 1996.

Public Finance

The U.S. CIA estimates that, in 1995, government revenues totaled approximately $1.7 billion and expenditures $1.99 billion, including capital expenditures of $652 million. External debt totaled $691 million, approximately 100% of which was financed abroad.

Income

In 1996, Botswana's gross national product (GNP) was $4.5 billion at current prices, or $3,020 per person.

Industry

Botswana has a small manufacturing sector, which produces textiles, beverages, chemicals, metals, plastics, and electrical products.

Banking and Finance

Prior to 1976, Botswana belonged to the South African Monetary Area. Its currency, like those of Lesotho and Swaziland, was issued by the South African Reserve Bank. On 23 August 1976, however, the Bank of Botswana was established, and Botswana began issuing its own currency. The Bank of Botswana has responsibility for administering exchange control delegated for it by the Ministry of Finance and Development Planning.

The policy of the Bank of Botswana in 1996 was to maintain the relative international prices, and hence competitiveness, of non-mineral tradeables against its most important trading partners, notably South Africa. Given the high level of reserves and the continuing current-account surplus, there was little necessity for the Bank of Botswana to raise domestic interest rates to the real levels of South Africa in an attempt to attract portfolio capital.

In November, 1996, the Bank of Botswana further relaxed controls that prevented the dual listing of foreign companies on the Botswana Stock Exchange (BSE).

Economic Development

As in the 1986–91 development plan, which called for spending of P1.2 billion, Botswana has made job creation a top priority of government planning in the past few years. Though formal sector employment expanded at a 10% annual rate over much of the last decade, job growth in 1995 was just 1.4%. Over 20% of 20-24 year olds are unemployed.

The government has a long-standing policy of promoting human capital development and health care. All education through the university level is free. Great importance is placed on the development of rural areas so as to reduce rural-urban migration.

In light of the limited resources, Botswana's government now follows "food security" agricultural policy of promoting only those foodstuffs that can be grown economically.

SOCIAL WELFARE

Many social welfare needs are provided by tribal custom. Social security on a national scale has not yet been introduced. Drinking water supplies, public schools, and health clinics have been established in almost every village. Women are not given the same legal rights as men. Women require their husband's permission to buy or sell property, get a loan, or sign a contract.

Healthcare

In 1993, fifteen general hospitals provided comprehensive health services for about 86% of the population, with one doctor for every 5,151 people. Tuberculosis is a major health problem, as is malnutrition, which in 1993 affected 15% of children under 5 years of age. The average life expectancy is estimated to be 51 years. The infant mortality rate in 1994 was 54 per 1,000 live births.

Housing

There is no overcrowding in tribal villages, but slums have developed in the larger towns. The Botswana Housing Corporation, a public enterprise, concentrates its efforts on major urban areas.

EDUCATION

Education, not compulsory, lasts for seven years at the primary level, followed by five years of secondary school. In 1994, Botswana had 669 primary schools, with 310,050 students and 11,726 teachers. Secondary schools had 93,057 students and 5,678 teachers in 1994. There were 3,567 pupils and 376 teachers at the university level in 1991. The University of Botswana offers studies in social sciences, education, sciences, agriculture, and humanities.

1999 KEY EVENTS TIMELINE

January

- The International Court of Justice reaffirms its decision to hear submissions on the Kasikili island dispute between Namibia and Botswana from February 15 to March 5, 1999.

- Over 2,000 Namibian refugees who fled the Caprivi Strip during a recent crackdown on secessionists are to know soon if they are to be granted political in Botswana.

- The United Nations High Commissioner for Refugees plans to reopen its office in Gaborone to cope with Namibians continuing to flee to Botswana.

- A Botswana judge grants an eleventh hour stay of execution for two men sentenced to be hanged.

February

- The former president of Botswana, Ketumile Masire, will head a 23-member Commonwealth observer team to oversee national assembly and presidential elections in Nigeria on February 20 and 27 respectively.

- Botswana grants political asylum to fifteen Namibians who crossed into the country illegally, fearing persecution in their home country.

- Parties release the names of candidates who will vie for four council seats in the February by-election.

- The Botswana government and conservation societies are hopeful that the Convention on International Trade and Endangered Spices (CITES) would soon change its decision to maintain the ban on the country's elephant ivory trade.

- Botswana, renowned for its stable diamond-driven economy, faces a budget deficit for the first time in 15 years.

March

- Presidents Sam Nujoma of Namibia and Festus Mogae of Botswana declare their continued support for efforts to find peaceful solutions to the conflicts in Angola and the Democratic Republic of Congo (DRC).

- Botswana's trade balance for 1998 is at a positive 733.9 million pula (976.1 million South African Rands) at the end of the third quarter.

- The Botswana government is lobbied to allow its new television station, the existing Daily News and Radio Botswana, to become parastatal organizations with some degree of autonomy from the State.

- Botswana decides to pull out its remaining element of the Southern African Development Community peacekeeping force in Lesotho by the end of April.

- Botswana is given the go-ahead by the Conference on International Trade in Endangered Species (CITES) to sell 20 tons of stockpiled ivory.

April

- Botswana grants asylum to a further 1,116 Namibian nationals, part of 2,000 who fled to

Botswana claiming they were facing persecution in their home country.

- President Festus Mogae announces that Botswana's economy is not doing well due to a downfall in mineral sales at Asian markets.

- Botswana's assistant Finance and Development Planning minister and cabinet member, Jacob Nkate, resigns in the wake of his links to a construction company implicated in a scandal.

- Botswana sells 17.8 tons of ivory by auction to a group of Japanese buyers.

- Botswana President Festus Mogae, on an investment promotion mission to the United States, talks to five major corporations on their possible involvement in Botswana.

May

- Botswana grants asylum to 2,232 Namibian refugees believed to be from a group seeking the secession of the Caprivi Strip from Namibia.

- For the first time in Botswana, a minority tribe installs its own paramount chief; this act is in line with the Chieftainship Act, but possibly out of line with the constitution.

- The first independent radio station license issued in Botswana is granted to YaronaFM, which will broadcast within a 40-km radius of the capital, Gaborone, ending a 33-year government monopoly on broadcasting in Botswana.

- Botswana's first representative in the Miss Universe beauty pageant is crowned as the new Miss Universe.

- Tuberculosis rises rapidly in Botswana.

June

- Botswana President Festus Mogae praises democratic achievements in SADC states, noting that southern Africa had made great strides in promoting democracy through the holding of free and fair elections and would continue in that direction.

- Botswana President Festus Mogae visits Mozambique on a two-day state visit in which economic and political cooperation are discussed.

July

- The Botswana Defense Force and the United States armed forces conduct a series of military exercises, as well as civil and humanitarian assistance programs in Botswana.

August

- The Botswana Centre for Human Rights in Gabarone challenges the constitutionality of the death penalty handed down to two condemned men.

- The Botswana government launches a new loan guarantee scheme for entrepreneurs who want to start small businesses.

- An Act of Parliament allowing the release of terminally ill prisoners is tabled in Botswana as one way of addressing prison overcrowding.

- The president of Botswana, Festus Mogae, calls for a new approach toward debt alleviation in Africa.

September

- President Festus Mogae announces the lifting of the state of emergency and says elections are to go ahead.

- Vice President Ian Khama faces an abuse of office probe by the office of the Ombudsman.

- The latest bulletin of the Botswana Food Security notes that malnutrition among children under the age of five years surged from 11.7 percent to 13.1 percent between June and July this year.

- Botswana expresses its readiness to resume the repatriation of Namibians living in that country's Dukwe refugee Camp.

October

- Economists warn Botswana about the consequences of over-dependence on its vast diamond wealth and urge a diversification of its industrial base.

- The ruling Botswana Democratic Party (BDP) win by a wide majority in both Parliament and council elections and incumbent Festus Mogae is declared elected President.

- The University of Botswana, the nation's only university, awards its first doctorate in its 19 years of existence.

- South Africa Express has come to the rescue of Air Botswana after a pilot on an apparent suicide mission wiped out 75% of Air Botswana's fleet at Sir Seretse Khama Airport.

- Livestock, including cattle, sheep and goats die in Botswana as a drought tightens its grip on Botswana, while a growing number of children suffer malnutrition, according to the latest quarterly Botswana Food Security report.

December

- The World Court rules that an 1.4-square-mile uninhabited island, known as Kasikili or Sedudu, between Botswana and Namibia belongs to Botswana.

ANALYSIS OF EVENTS: 1999

BUSINESS AND THE ECONOMY

Within the southern African region Botswana was one of two countries boasting a thriving and healthy economy by the start of 1999 with South Africa as the other country. Indeed since independence in 1966 Botswana has had an impressive economic growth rate, averaging over 10 percent per year between 1976 and 1991. Recent economic indicators have also been impressive with an annual growth rate of 6.9% between 1996 and 1998; a per capita gross domestic product of about $3,000 and one of the lowest inflation rates in the southern African region, estimated at 10%. In addition to these healthy economic indicators, the country has enjoyed budget surpluses and substantial foreign exchange reserves. Botswana's impressive economic growth has been built on a single but lucrative commodity, diamonds.

At the end of the third quarter in 1998 Botswana's trade balance was at a positive 733.9 million pula (976.1 million South African rands). However, 1999 saw Botswana's economic fortunes begin to decline as the country faced a budget deficit for the first time in fifteen years. Early in the year President Festus Mogae announced that Botswana's economy was not doing well due to a downfall in mineral sales at Asian markets that were themselves undergoing an unprecedented economic crisis. Economists were quick to warn Botswana about the consequences of over-dependence on its vast diamond wealth and urged a diversification of its industrial base. Botswana President Festus Mogae quickly arranged an investment promotion mission to the United States to hold talks with a number of major corporations on their possible involvement in Botswana. As *Barnett* (1999) notes, while lauded internationally as a low-corruption, stable democracy which has spent its money wisely since discovering diamonds in 1969, the government of President Festus Mogae has been slow to attract industry to enable it to diversify and tackle an unemployment rate which is currently running at twenty percent.

GOVERNMENT AND POLITICS

Botswana has enjoyed a flourishing multiparty constitutional democracy since its independence from Great Britain in 1964. Elections have always been free and fair. The openness of the country's political system has been a significant factor in Botswana's stability and economic growth. The most recent elections were held on October 17, 1999, in which two main rival parties and a number of smaller parties competed for Parliament and council seats. In these latest elections the ruling Botswana Democratic Party (BDP) won by a wide majority in both parliament and council elections and the incumbent president, Festus Mogae, was declared elected president. Corruption is not as rampant as in neighboring countries. Government officials are often investigated if suspected of involvement in corrupt activities. For example in 1999 Botswana's assistant Finance and Development Planning minister and cabinet member, Jacob Nkate, was forced to resign in the wake of his links to a construction company implicated in a tender scandal. Vice President Ian Khama also faced an abuse of office probe by the office of the Ombudsman.

The country faced a number of international disputes with surrounding Namibia, Zambia, Zimbabwe and Lesotho. A dispute with Namibia over uninhabited Kasikili (Sidudu) Island in Linyanti (Chobe) River remains unresolved. A short section of the boundary with Namibia is also in dispute and the quadripoint with Namibia, Zambia, and Zimbabwe is in disagreement. The International Court of Justice held a hearing on the Kasikili island dispute between Namibia and Botswana from February 15 to March 5 of 1999. In December 1999 the International Court of Justice ruled that the island belonged to Botswana.

Tensions with Namibia rose as more than 3,000 Namibian refugees who fled Namibia's Caprivi Strip during a crackdown on secessionists flocked into Botswana and many of them received political asylum. However, relations began to thaw as Botswana indicated its willingness to repatriate most of the refugees. Botswana was also involved in a peace keeping mission in Lesotho where it joined South African forces to quell a mutiny in the Lesotho defense forces. However, Botswana began to pull out its peacekeeping force in Lesotho at the end of April, 1999.

CULTURE AND SOCIETY

A major cultural event caused much celebration in Botswana in 1999; the crowning of Botswana's first representative in the Miss Universe beauty pageant as the new Miss Universe. The people of Botswana, joined by the rest of Africa, were ecstatic and joyful. Miss Universe (Miss Kwelagobe) was welcomed back home with a red carpet and a reception at State House, and a celebration ball in her honor. The University of Botswana, the nation's only university, also scored another first for Botswana by awarding its first ever doctorate in its nineteen years of existence.

A rather controversial request made by Botswana to the Convention on International Trade and Endangered Spcies (CITES) was high on Botswana's agenda during 1999. The Botswanan government and conservation societies hoped that CITES would change its decision to maintain the ban on the country's elephant ivory trade. The request was granted in March of 1999 for Botswana to sell twenty tons of stockpiled ivory. The following April Botswana sold 17.8 tons of ivory by auction to a group of Japanese buyers.

The Botswana government was lobbied to allow its new television station, the existing Daily News and Radio Botswana, to become parastatal organizations with some degree of autonomy from the State. The government responded to this request by issuing the first independent radio station license in Botswana to YaronaFM, which now broadcasts within a 40-km radius of the capital, Gaborone, ending a 33-year government monopoly on broadcasting in Botswana.

Other noteworthy events included the installation of a paramount chief by a minority tribe, which is in line with the Chieftainship Act, but possibly out of line with the constitution. Tuberculosis and AIDS continued to be the major killers of young adults and the economically active with Botswana ranking among the most afflicted nations worldwide. Drought, a constant environmental problem for Botswana, tightened its grip during 1999 resulting in the death of livestock, including cattle, sheep and goats. The deleterious effects of drought were seen in the rise of malnutrition among children and women. The latest bulletin from the Botswana Food Security noted that malnutrition among children under the age of five years surged from 11.7

percent to 13.1 percent between June and July this year.

DIRECTORY

CENTRAL GOVERNMENT
Head of State

President
Festus Mogae, Office of the President, P/Bag 001, Gaborone, Botswana
PHONE: +267 350800
FAX: +267 312525

Ministers

Minister of Agriculture
Ronald K. Sebego, Ministry of Agriculture, P/Bag 003, Gaborone, Botswana
PHONE: +267 350603
FAX: +267 356027

Minister of Commerce and Industry
George Kgoroba, Ministry of Commerce and Industry
PHONE: +267 3601200
FAX: +267 371538

Minister of Education
Gaositwe K.T. Chiepe, Ministry of Education, P/Bag 005, Gaborone, Botswana
PHONE: +267 3655400
FAX: +267 365-5458

Minister of Finance and Development Planning
Ponteshego Kedikilwe, Ministry of Finance and Development Planning, P/Bag 008, Gaborone, Botswana
PHONE: +267 350100

Minister of Foreign Affairs
Mompati Merahfe, Ministry of Foreign Affairs, P/Bag 00368, Gaborone, Botswana
PHONE: +267 3600700
FAX: +267 313366

Minister of Health
Chapson Butale, Ministry of Health, P/Bag 0038, Gaborone, Botswana
PHONE: +267 352000
FAX: +267 353100

Minister of Labor and Home Affairs
Bahiti Temane, Ministry of Labor and Home Affairs, P/Bag 002, Gaborone, Botswana
PHONE: +267 611100

Minister of Local Government, Lands, and Housing

Daniel Kwelagobe, Ministry of Local Government, Lands, and Housing, P/Bag 006, Gaborone, Botswana

PHONE: +267 354100

Minister of Mineral Resources and Water Affairs

Margaret Nasha, Ministry of Mineral Resources and Water Affairs, P/Bag 0018, Gaborone, Botswana

PHONE: +267 3656600

FAX: +267 372738

Minister of Presidential Affairs and Public Administration

Seretse Ian Khama, Ministry of Presidential Affairs and Public Administration, P/Bag 001, Gaborone, Botswana

PHONE: +267 350800

Minister of Works, Transport, and Communications

David Magang, Ministry of Works, Transport, and Communications, P/Bag 007, Gaborone, Botswana

PHONE: +267 358500

FAX: +267 313303

POLITICAL ORGANIZATIONS

Botswana Democratic Party (BDP)

NAME: Festus Mogae

Botswana National Front (BNF)

NAME: Kenneth Koma

Botswana People's Party (BPP)

DIPLOMATIC REPRESENTATION

Embassies in Botswana

United States

P.O. Box 90, Gaborone, Botswana

PHONE: +267 353982

FAX: +267 356947

JUDICIAL SYSTEM

High Court

P/Bag 009, Gaborone, Botswana

PHONE: +267 354700

FAX: +267 357089

Court of Appeals

P/Bag 009, Gaborone, Botswana

PHONE: +267 354700

FAX: +267 357089

FURTHER READING

Books

Economist Intelligence Unit. *Country Report: Botswana, Lesotho.* London: The Economist Intelligence Unit, 1999.

Hope, Kempe R. *AIDS and Development in Africa: A Social Science Perspective.* New York: Haworth Press, 1999.

O'Malley, Padraig. *Southern Africa, the People's Voices: Perspectives on Democracy.* Bellville, South Africa: National Democratic Institute for International Affairs, School of Government, University of the Western Cape, 1999.

Pickford, Peter and Pickford, Beverly. *The Okavango and Chobe of Botswana.* London: New Holland, 1999.

Swaney, Deanna. *Zimbabwe, Botswana and Namibia.* Hawthorn, Vic.: Lonely Planet, 1999.

Thomas, Duncan and Muvandi, Ityai. *The Demographic Transition in Southern Africa: Reviewing the Evidence From Botswana and Zimbabwe.* Santa Monica, CA: RAND, 1995.

Internet

Botswana Economic Policy Documents. Available Online @ http://www.bidpa.bw/econ.htm#Economic

Botswana Government: Official Site of the Government. Available Online @ http://www.gov.bw/home.html.

Botswana Institute for Development Policy Analysis (BIDPA). Available Online @ http://www.bidpa.bw.

Botswana Online. Available Online @ http://www.botswana-online.com/.

BOTSWANA: STATISTICAL DATA

For sources and notes see "Sources of Statistics" in the front of each volume.

GEOGRAPHY

Geography (1)

Area:

Total: 600,370 sq km.

Land: 585,370 sq km.

Water: 15,000 sq km.

Area—comparative: slightly smaller than Texas.

Land boundaries:

Total: 4,013 km.

Border countries: Namibia 1,360 km, South Africa 1,840 km, Zimbabwe 813 km.

Coastline: 0 km (landlocked).

Climate: semiarid; warm winters and hot summers.

Terrain: predominately flat to gently rolling tableland; Kalahari Desert in southwest.

Natural resources: diamonds, copper, nickel, salt, soda ash, potash, coal, iron ore, silver.

Land use:

Arable land: 1%

Permanent crops: 0%

Permanent pastures: 46%

Forests and woodland: 47%

Other: 6% (1993 est.).

HUMAN FACTORS

Health Personnel (3)

Total health expenditure as a percentage of GDP, 1990-1997[a]

Public sector 1.8

Private sector 1.4

Total[b] 3.1

HUMAN FACTORS

Demographics (2A)

	1990	1995	1998	2000	2010	2020	2030	2040	2050
Population	1,303.9	1,397.1	1,448.5	1,479.0	1,569.7	1,600.6	1,697.5	1,907.0	2,146.2
Net migration rate (per 1,000 population)	NA	NA	NA	NA	NA	NA	NA	NA	NA
Births	NA	NA	NA	NA	NA	NA	NA	NA	NA
Deaths	NA	NA	NA	NA	NA	NA	NA	NA	NA
Life expectancy - males	40.5	39.6	39.5	39.4	37.6	42.0	55.4	68.9	73.3
Life expectancy - females	44.5	41.9	40.7	40.0	38.0	42.9	59.7	76.4	81.3
Birth rate (per 1,000)	35.5	33.7	32.0	30.9	26.2	23.3	21.0	18.1	15.7
Death rate (per 1,000)	21.0	20.8	20.9	21.1	23.8	20.8	11.4	5.5	4.9
Women of reproductive age (15-49 yrs.)	310.5	345.3	364.3	375.5	412.8	440.3	481.7	541.6	576.2
of which are currently married	NA	NA	NA	NA	NA	NA	NA	NA	NA
Fertility rate	4.8	4.4	4.0	3.8	2.9	2.4	2.2	2.1	2.0

Except as noted, values for vital statistics are in thousands; life expectancy is in years.

Health Personnel (3)

Health expenditure per capita in U.S. dollars, 1990-1997[a]

Purchasing power parity . . . . .NA

Total . . . . .NA

Availability of health care facilities per 100,000 people

Hospital beds 1990-1997[a] 160

Doctors 1993[c] . . . . .NA

Nurses 1993[c] . . . . .NA

Health Indicators (4)

Life expectancy at birth

1980 58

1997 47

Daily per capita supply of calories (1996) 2,272

Total fertility rate births per woman (1997) 4.3

Maternal mortality ratio per 100,000 live births
(1990-97) . . . . .250[c]

Safe water % of population with access (1995) 70

Sanitation % of population with access (1995) 55

Consumption of iodized salt % of households
(1992-98)[a] 27

Smoking prevalence

Male % of adults (1985-95)[a] . . . .

Female % of adults (1985-95)[a] . . . .

Tuberculosis incidence per 100,000 people
(1997) 503

Adult HIV prevalence % of population ages
15-49 (1997) 25.10

Infants and Malnutrition (5)

Under-5 mortality rate (1997) 49

% of infants with low birthweight (1990-97) 11

Births attended by skilled health staff % of total[a] . . .77

% fully immunized (1995-97)

TB 59

DPT 76

Polio 80

Measles 79

Prevalence of child malnutrition under age 5
(1992-97)[b] 27

Ethnic Division (6)

Batswana 95%

Kalanga, Basarwa,
and Kgalagadi 4%

White 1%

Religions (7)

Indigenous beliefs 50%

Christian 50%

Languages (8)

English (official), Setswana.

EDUCATION

Public Education Expenditures (9)

Public expenditure on education (% of GNP)

1980 . . . . .6.0

1996 . . . . .10.4

Expenditure per student

Primary % of GNP per capita

1980 . . . . .12.5[1]

1996 . . . .

Secondary % of GNP per capita

1980 . . . .

1996 . . . .

Tertiary % of GNP per capita

1980 . . . . .611.7[1]

1996 . . . .

Expenditure on teaching materials

Primary % of total for level (1996) . . . .

Secondary % of total for level (1996) . . . .

Primary pupil-teacher ratio per teacher (1996) 25

Duration of primary education years (1995) 7

Educational Attainment (10)

Age group (1993) . . . . .All ages

Total population .1,350,899

Highest level attained (%)

No schooling 20.4

First level

Not completed 44.1

Completed . . . . .NA

Entered second level

S-1 . . . . .19.8

S-2 . . . . .NA

Postsecondary 1.4

Literacy Rates (11A)

In thousands and percent[1]	1990	1995	2000	2010
Illiterate population (15+ yrs.)	242	255	265	275
Literacy rate - total adult pop. (%)	65.5	69.8	73.6	80.2
Literacy rate - males (%)	77.6	80.5	83.0	87.1
Literacy rate - females (%)	54.5	59.9	64.8	73.5

GOVERNMENT & LAW

Political Parties (12)

National Assembly	No. of seats
Botswana Democratic Party (BDP)	27
Botswana National Front (BNF)	13

Government Budget (13A)

Year: 1996

Total Expenditures: 5,764.0 Millions of Pula

Expenditures as a percentage of the total by function:

General public services and public order 19.86

Defense 8.13

Education 26.34

Health 5.19

Social Security and Welfare 1.13

Housing and community amenities 11.56

Recreational, cultural, and religious affairs 1.67

Fuel and energy 29

Agriculture, forestry, fishing, and hunting 8.91

Mining, manufacturing, and construction 50

Transportation and communication 5.04

Other economic affairs and services 2.23

Military Affairs (14B)

	1990	1991	1992	1993	1994	1995
Military expenditures						
Current dollars (mil.)	151	170	177	234	235	225[e]
1995 constant dollars (mil.)	173	188	190	245	241	225[e]
Armed forces (000)	6	7	6	6	8	8
Gross national product (GNP)						
Current dollars (mil.)	2,755	3,197	3,709	3,675	3,911	4,217
1995 constant dollars (mil.)	3,166	3,533	3,990	3,853	4,009	4,217
Central government expenditures (CGE)						
1995 constant dollars (mil.)	1,604	1,717	1,847	2,026	1,653	1,779[e]
People (mil.)	1.3	1.3	1.4	1.4	1.4	1.5
Military expenditure as % of GNP	5.5	5.3	4.8	6.4	6.0	5.3
Military expenditure as % of CGE	10.8	11.0	10.3	12.1	14.6	12.7
Military expenditure per capita (1995 $)	133	141	139	176	169	155
Armed forces per 1,000 people (soldiers)	4.6	4.9	4.4	4.3	5.6	5.2
GNP per capita (1994 $)	2,428	2,646	2,920	2,758	2,812	2,903
Arms imports[6]						
Current dollars (mil.)	20	20	20	20	20	0
1995 constant dollars (mil.)	23	22	22	21	21	0
Arms exports[6]						
Current dollars (mil.)	0	0	0	0	0	0
1995 constant dollars (mil.)	0	0	0	0	0	0
Total imports[7]						
Current dollars (mil.)	1,946	1,947	1,861	1,771	1,638	1,907
1995 constant dollars (mil.)	2,236	2,151	2,002	1,857	1,679	1,907
Total exports[7]						
Current dollars (mil.)	1,784	1,849	1,742	1,780	1,845	2,143
1995 constant dollars (mil.)	2,050	2,043	1,874	1,866	1,891	2,143
Arms as percent of total imports[8]	1.0	1.0	1.1	1.1	1.2	0
Arms as percent of total exports[8]	0	0	0	0	0	0

LABOR FORCE

Labor Force (16)

Total 235,000 formal sector employees, 100,000 public sector; 135,000 private sector, including 14,300 who are employed in various mines in South Africa; most others engaged in cattle raising and subsistence agriculture.

Unemployment Rate (17)

20-40% (1997 est.)

PRODUCTION SECTOR

Electric Energy (18)

Capacity .217,000 kW (1995)

Production . . . . .1 billion kWh (1995)

Consumption per capita . . . . .962 kWh (1995)

Transportation (19)

Highways:

total: 18,482 km

paved: 4,343 km

unpaved: 14,139 km (1996 est.)

Airports: 92 (1997 est.)

Airports—with paved runways:

total: 12

over 3,047 m: 1

2,438 to 3,047 m: 1

1,524 to 2,437 m: 9

914 to 1,523 m: 1 (1997 est.)

Airports—with unpaved runways:

total: 80

1,524 to 2,437 m: 3

914 to 1,523 m: 55

under 914 m: 22 (1997 est.)

Top Agricultural Products (20)

Sorghum, maize, millet, pulses, groundnuts (peanuts), beans, cowpeas, sunflower seed; livestock.

MANUFACTURING SECTOR

GDP & Manufacturing Summary (21)

Detailed value added figures are listed by both International Standard Industry Code (ISIC) and product title.

	1980	1985	1990	1994
GDP ($-1990 mil.)[1]	1,298	2,119	3,296	3,940
Per capita ($-1990)[1]	1,433	1,968	2,583	2,731
Manufacturing share (%) (current prices)[1]	4.0	5.1	4.6	*3.9*
Manufacturing				
Value added ($-1990 mil.)[1]	62	74	144	*175*
Industrial production index	100	169	290	*352*
Value added ($ mil.)	41	46	*140*	186
Gross output ($ mil.)	149	169	*552*	794
Employment (000)	5	10	24	22
Profitability (% of gross output)				
Intermediate input (%)	73	73	*75*	77
Wages and salaries inc. supplements (%)	*14*	*11*	*10*	*12*
Gross operating surplus	*14*	*16*	*15*	*11*
Productivity ($)				
Gross output per worker	27,102	16,581	*22,719*	*35,784*
Value added per worker	7,445	4,518	*5,773*	8,386
Average wage (inc. supplements)	*3,664*	*1,880*	*2,293*	*4,354*
Value added ($ mil.)				
311/2 Food products	13	14	*45*	61
313 Beverages	4	10	*30*	24
314 Tobacco products	—	—	—	—
321 Textiles	*4*	*2*	*8*	*21*
322 Wearing apparel	*2*	*1*	*2*	*4*
323 Leather and fur products	—	—	*1*	*2*
324 Footwear	*1*	—	*2*	*3*
331 Wood and wood products	—	—	*2*	*3*
332 Furniture and fixtures	—	—	*2*	*3*
341 Paper and paper products	—	*1*	*2*	*5*
342 Printing and publishing	—	*1*	*2*	*5*
351 Industrial chemicals	—	*1*	*3*	*2*
352 Other chemical products	—	*1*	*6*	*3*
353 Petroleum refineries	—	—	—	—

	1980	1985	1990	1994
Value added ($ mil.)				
354 Miscellaneous petroleum and coal products	—	—	—	—
355 Rubber products	—	—	2	1
356 Plastic products	—	—	2	1
361 Pottery, china and earthenware	—	—	—	—
362 Glass and glass products	—	—	—	—
369 Other non-metal mineral products	—	—	—	—
371 Iron and steel	—	—	—	—
372 Non-ferrous metals	—	—	—	—
381 Metal products	1	2	6	6
382 Non-electrical machinery	1	1	2	2
383 Electrical machinery	—	1	2	1
384 Transport equipment	1	1	2	2
385 Professional and scientific equipment	—	—	—	—
390 Other manufacturing industries	12	8	19	37

FINANCE, ECONOMICS, & TRADE

Economic Indicators (22)

National product: GDP—purchasing power parity—$5 billion (1997 est.)

National product real growth rate: 6% (1997 est.)

National product per capita: $3,300 (1997 est.)

Inflation rate—consumer price index: 10% (1996 est.)

Exchange Rates (24)

Exchange rates:

Pula (P) per US$1

January 1998	3.8547
1997	3.6508
1996	3.3242
1995	2.7716
1994	2.6831
1993	2.4190

Top Import Origins (25)

$1.6 billion (c.i.f., 1996 est.).

Origins	%
United States	37
Trinidad and Tobago	11
United Kingdom	10
Japan	7

Top Export Destinations (26)

$2.31 billion (f.o.b. 1996 est.).

Destinations	%
Europe	74
Southern African Customs Union (SACU)	22
Zimbabwe	3

Economic Aid (27)

Recipient: ODA, $189 million (1993).

Import Export Commodities (28)

Import Commodities	Export Commodities
Foodstuffs	Diamonds 71%
Vehicles and transport equipment	Copper and nickel 5%
Textiles	Meat 3%
Petroleum products	

Balance of Payments (23)

	1990	1992	1993	1994	1995
Exports of goods (f.o.b.)	1,795	1,744	1,722	1,878	2,164
Imports of goods (f.o.b.)	−1,611	−1,557	−1,455	−1,350	−1,579
Trade balance	184	187	267	528	586
Services - debits	−898	−790	−586	−777	−960
Services - credits	626	731	746	417	744
Private transfers (net)	−31	−26	−73	−91	−158
Government transfers (net)	161	142	151	166	130
Overall balance	42	244	503	243	342

BRAZIL

Federative Republic of Brazil
República Federativa do Brasil

CAPITAL, FLAG, etc.

CAPITAL: Brasília.

FLAG: The national flag consists of a green field upon which is a large yellow diamond twice as wide as it is high. Centered within the diamond is a blue globe showing constellations of the southern skies dominated by the Southern Cross. Encircling the globe is a white banner bearing the words *Ordem e Progresso*.

ANTHEM: *Hino Nacional Brasileiro*

MONETARY UNIT: On 1 July 1994, the real (R $), a paper currency of 100 centavos, replaced the cruzeiro real (CR $) at the rate of R $1: CR $2,750. R $1 = US $0.975 (or US $1 = R $1.026).

WEIGHTS AND MEASURES: The metric system is the legal standard, local units are also used.

HOLIDAYS: New Year's Day, 1 January; Tiradentes, 21 April; Labor Day, 1 May; Independence Day, 7 September; Our Lady of Aparecida (Patroness of Brazil), 12 October; All Souls' Day, 2 November; Proclamation of the Republic, 15 November; Christmas, 25 December. Movable holidays include the pre-Lenten Carnival, usually in February, Good Friday, and Corpus Christi.

TIME: At noon GMT, the time in Fernando de Noronha is 10 AM; Rio de Janeiro, 9 AM; Manaus, 8 AM; Rio Branco, 7 AM.

LOCATION AND SIZE: Situated in east-central South America, Brazil is the largest country in Latin America and the fourth-largest in the world in continuous area. It covers an area of 8,511,965 square kilometers (3,286,488 square miles). Bordering on all South American countries except Ecuador and Chile, Brazil has a total boundary length of 22,182 kilometers (13,783 miles). Brasília is located in the southeastern part of the country.

CLIMATE: Brazil is primarily a tropical country. The Amazon Basin has a typically hot, tropical climate. The Brazilian Highlands are subtropical. The narrow coastal lowland area ranges from tropical in the north to temperate in the south. The cool upland plains of the south have a temperate climate. Rainfall is heavy in the lowlands and in the upper Amazon Basin, along the northern coast, and in the southern interior, while there are periodic droughts in the northeast.

INTRODUCTORY SURVEY

RECENT HISTORY

In the early twentieth century, Brazil entered a period of economic and political turmoil, aggravated by regional and military rivalries. By 1930, a military takeover with widespread civilian support placed into power Getúlio Vargas. Vargas' government sought reforms for Brazil's middle and lower classes, but discouraged dissent.

Vargas was ousted by the military in 1946 but returned to the presidency in 1950. He was succeeded from 1955 to 1961 by Juscelino Kubitschek de Oliveira, whose most ambitious project was building a new federal capital, Brasília, in the highlands of central Brazil.

Ten years of military government, starting in 1964, brought Brazil rapid economic expansion, but there was a dramatic reversal during the oil crisis of 1973–74. During the late 1970s, continuing economic difficulties led to labor unrest and numerous strikes. In November 1982, Brazil had its first democratic elections since 1964. Opposition parties won the governorships of ten heavily populated states and a majority in the lower house of Congress.

In January 1985, the electoral college chose Tancredo Neves as Brazil's first civilian president in a generation. When Neves fell gravely ill and died just before his inauguration, Vice-President José Sarney was allowed to take office as president. A new constitution, passed in 1988, was followed by elections a year later. Brazil's first direct presi-

dential elections in twenty-nine years resulted in the victory of Fernando Collor de Mello.

Collor took office in March 1990, and launched a major economic reform program. However, Collor was forced to resign in December 1992 after massive corruption was revealed inside his administration. Itamar Franco took over, promising to continue Collor's programs. Brazil's chronic inflation was finally brought under control in 1994 through the introduction of a new currency linked to the U.S. dollar that was launched by finance minister Fernando Enrique Cardoso. Through that success, Cardoso was elected president in 1994. His policies continued to keep inflation in check, reduced tariffs, and included selling off public enterprises to private companies. The Asian financial crisis in 1997 caused the Brazilian stock market to plunge and the country's economic recovery remained fragile.

GOVERNMENT

The Federative Republic of Brazil is a constitutional republic comprising twenty-six states and a Federal District, which surrounds the federal capital, Brasília. The constitution of October 1988 established a strong presidential system.

The president is the head of the armed forces and is in charge of the executive branch, assisted in that task by a cabinet of ministers. He also appoints justices to the Supreme Federal Tribunal, the highest court in Brazil. The Congress consists of the 81-member Senate and the 517-member Chamber of Deputies.

Judiciary

The Supreme Federal Court comprises eleven justices. It has final jurisdiction, especially in cases involving the constitution and the acts of state and local authorities. The Federal Appeals Court deals with cases involving the federal government. Immediately below it are federal courts located in the state capitals and in the Federal District, as well as military and labor courts. Each state and municipality has its own judicial system.

Political Parties

In 1985, the Liberal Front Party (PFL) and the Party of the Brazilian Democratic Movement (Partido de Movimento Democrático Brasileiro–PMDB) formed the National Alliance, a coalition that won the 1985 elections. The Brazilian Social Democracy Party (PSDB) was formed in 1988 by former PMDB members, including the future President Cardoso.

DEFENSE

The Brazilian armed forces had a total strength of 265,000 (132,000 draftees) in 1996. Military service for a minimum of one year is compulsory. Draftees are inducted at the age of 18.

The army, with about 60 brigades, had 195,000 personnel in 1996; the navy, 50,000 (including 15,000 marines and 700 naval airmen); air force personnel totaled 50,000, with 307 combat aircraft. In 1995, Brazil spent $6.9 billion on defense.

ECONOMIC AFFAIRS

Attempts to diversify the economy through rapid industrialization have made Brazil one of the two leading industrial nations of South America, but uncontrolled inflation—close to 500% in 1986—offset many of the economic advances.

The Brazilian economy was hit by a deep recession and record inflation in 1990. In March 1990, upon assuming office, President Collor announced sweeping economic reforms designed to stop inflation and integrate Brazil into the developed world economy. By mid-1990, the monthly inflation rate was around 10%, but by the end of the year it was in the 20% range.

After a second government economic program in 1991 failed to reduce inflation, high interest rates, combined with worsening inflation and political uncertainty, produced another recession in 1992.

In 1994, a new economic program was introduced. It featured a new currency linked to the U.S. dollar, privatization of state-owned industries, lowering tariffs, and an end to having inflation rates determine prices. With the end of hyperinflation, the standard of living for Brazilians was greatly improved. Businesses and individuals can now make financial plans in a stable economy.

In 1997, Brazil was the world's eighth largest economy, with a gross domestic product (GDP) estimated at US $781.1 billion.

Public Finance

The budget, prepared under the supervision of the Ministry of Planning and Economic Coordination, represents the government's plans for financing administrative operations and capital expenditures. Budgetary deficits increased considerably in the 1960s, rising from CR$102.5 million in 1961 to CR$775 million in 1965.

Increases in both revenues and expenditures were rapid during the 1970s, but the pattern of decreasing deficits continued. There was a budget deficit of CR$3.2 billion in 1975, but surpluses were recorded annually during 1976–80. One of the principal causes of Brazil's financial instability in the 1980s has been the rate at which public spending has exceeded revenues. Following another stabilization program in 1990, a budget surplus of 1.4% of GDP was recorded, but deteriorated to a deficit of 1.7% of GDP by 1992. At the beginning of 1994, the public deficit was estimated at $22 billion. The U.S. CIA estimates that, in 1995, government revenues totaled approximately $58.7 billion and expenditures $54.9 billion. External debt totaled $94 billion.

Income

In 1999, Brazil's gross national product (GNP) was US $758 billion at current prices, or about US $4,750 per person. For the period 1985–95, the average inflation rate was 873.8%, resulting in a decline in real growth in gross national product of 0.7% per person.

Industry

Major industries include iron and steel, automobiles, petroleum processing, chemicals, and cement. The Brazilian automotive industry is the major producer of vehicles in Latin America and the sixth-largest producer in the world.

Petroleum products include diesel oils, gasoline, and fuel oil. Brazil's developing petrochemical industry emphasizes the production of synthetic rubber. Other chemical products include distilled alcohol used for the nation's burgeoning alcohol-fuel fleet.

Banking and Finance

A banking reform enacted in December 1964 provided for the establishment of the Central Bank of the Republic of Brazil (changed in 1967 to the Central Bank of Brazil), with powers to regulate the banking system and the stock market. The Central Bank serves as the financial agent of the federal government and functions as a depository for the reserves of private banks. The reform also created the National Monetary Council, which formulates monetary policies for the Central Bank.

The recent rise in international reserves and the fall of the dollar against the real in the futures market reveal greater calm in the financial market than in late 1996 when October's record trade deficit was announced. In an attempt to calm the financial markets' worries about exchange rate risk, the government began issuing bonds indexed to the exchange rate. The bonds are supposed to be a guarantee that exchange rate policy is not going to change.

The stock market is a source of financing for all listed companies in Brazil, regardless of ownership. All public issues require the approval of the Securities Commission (CVM). There are nine regional stock exchanges, although as of 1994, over 90% of transactions were carried out in São Paulo and Rio de Janeiro.

Economic Development

Economic policy since the late 1960s has had three prime objectives: control of inflation, gradual improvement of the welfare of the poorest sector, and a high economic growth rate.

The policy of the new civilian government, couched in the First National Plan of the New Republic (1986–89), sought to maintain high levels of economic growth, introduce a wide range of basic institutional and fiscal reform in the public sector, and reduce poverty significantly. When in-flation continued to mount, however, the "Cruzado Plan" was introduced; it froze wages and prices for a year, and introduced a new unit of currency, the cruzado. While inflation did drop dramatically, the ensuing consumer spending boom, caused by the desire to take advantage of the price freeze, re-kindled inflation. By 1987, Brazil had reverted to orthodox austerity and "monetary correction" in an attempt to bring the economy under control.

In 1994, finance minister (and later president) Fernando Enrique Cardoso implemented the "Real Plan," an economic liberalization named for the newly launched currency, the real. The plan called for the abolition of state control of wages and all indexing to inflation, lowering of tariffs and barriers to international investment, and a massive sell-off of state-owned enterprises in nearly every sector. The plan was almost immediately successful, and attracted huge amounts of international investment while raising the living standards of million of Brazilians.

SOCIAL WELFARE

In 1977, the National System of Social Security and Welfare was established. Benefits include modest insurance against accidents; old age, invalids', and survivors' pensions; funeral insurance; and medical, dental, and hospital coverage. Maternity benefits were introduced under the new constitution in 1988.

Healthcare

In 1993, Brazil's national health care system came to an end, chiefly due to widespread fraud by hospitals, physicians, and state and municipal agencies. The new Brazilian Minister of Health planned to introduce a new system.

The large cities have competent physicians, generally with advanced training abroad, but there is a shortage of doctors, hospitals, and nurses in most towns in the interior.

There are approximately 1.4 physicians per 1,000 people. The infant mortality rate in 1995 was 44 per 1,000 live births. The average life expectancy is estimated to be 67 years.

Housing

Despite major urban developments, both the housing supply and living conditions in Brazil remain inadequate. Large, sprawling slums are widespread in the major cities, while most rural dwellers live without conveniences such as piped water and electricity. In 1992, there were 32.7 million residences.

EDUCATION

Public education is free at all levels and non-profit private schools also receive public funding. In 1994, there were 31.2 million students at the elementary level; 4.5 million at the secondary level; and 1.7 million at the university level.

In 1990, there were 93 universities, including the Federal University of Rio de Janeiro.

Although millions of Brazilians have received literacy training, adult illiteracy in 1995 was still about 17% (males, 16.7%; females, 16.8%).

1999 KEY EVENTS TIMELINE

January

- The government devalues Brazil's currency, the *real*.

- Gustavo Franco resigns as head of the Central Bank and is replaced by Francisco Lopes.

- Governor Itamar Franco announces moratorium on repayment of Minas Gerais state's debt to Federal Government.

- The World Bank freezes development loans to the Minas Gerais and Rio Grande de Sul states in attempt to pressure debt payments; Rio Grande do Sul complies.

- Unemployment, reported at 8%, is at its highest since 1983.

February

- President Cardoso appoints the second new Central Bank president in three weeks; the new president is Arminio Fraga.

- Financial markets are temporarily calmed by Carnival.

March

- The *real* takes another dive, settling in the range 2.10-2.25 to the dollar, 40% below its pre-devaluation level.

April

- The *real* rises to 1.66 to the dollar; 27% devaluation since January 12.

May

- Currency has regained stability, and interest rates are at their lowest level in nine months.

- The economy is recovering, but job creation is not. Union leaders press the government for job-creation programs.

- Police raid the home of Francisco Lopes, finding a note suggesting Lopes has $1.6 million in a small bank abroad.

- Lopes is called to testify to a senate committee; he appears but is arrested upon refusing to sign an oath swearing to tell the truth.

June

- The government asks the World Bank to finance a $1 billion *real* loan fund for new student loans.

- Education minister Paulo Renato Souza attempts to improve educational standards by introducing the Provao, a national exam aimed at testing universities by testing their final year students.

- A multiple shooting in Sao Paulo prompts the Cardoso government to propose a complete ban on private ownership of all firearms.

July

- A pilot scheme to be known as Banco da Terra (Land Bank) requires landless peasants in Brazil to borrow money for their own resettlement as farmers; the Brazilian federal government and the World Bank agree to sign a deal under which each will provide $1 billion over five years in loans and grants for families to buy land and begin farming.

- A controversy arises over soy bean farmers' use of genetically modified seeds.

- Jose Pio Borges resigns as president of the Brazilian National Development Bank.

- Controversy erupts over the privatization of Brazilian Federal Banks.

August

- The *real* drops once again to its lowest level since March 15th.

- The conservative president of Brazil's senate, Antonio Carlos Malgalhaes, sets up congressional hearings to discuss anti-poverty proposals. The alliance between Malgalhaes and President Cardoso becomes an issue of political upheaval.

- In the biggest criminal trial in Brazil's history, 150 policemen are accused of murdering 19 protestors from the landless farmers' movement; however, in the trial's verdict on August 19, three senior officers are acquitted.

- Punishment for police violence becomes an issue of national concern; the public calls for a new human rights monitoring group to make it easier to punish cases of police violence.

September

- Dr. Jorge Pagura attempts to reform Sao Paulo's health system; hospitals should remain as co-ops but neighborhood clinics are to be run by the city council. New supervisory body will qualify system for federal and state money and buildings.

- Judge Leopoldino Marques do Amaral is found dead six weeks after he exposed corruption among his colleagues.

- On September 14, congressional leaders present a revised set of proposed judicial reforms to Congress.

November

- Brazil's plans to streamline its complex and inefficient tax system are upset after the administration and legislature clash over draft legislation.

- A parliamentary committee of inquiry into drug-dealing and organized crime being held by Brazil's lower house of Congress experiences unexpected success as it is finding, naming, and arresting leaders of an infamous network of criminal activity ranging from cargo theft to murder in at least 14 of Brazil's 27 states.

- In response to a serious housing shortage, Sao Paulo's Union of Housing Movements organizes a campaign of mass invasions of disused buildings by homeless families; the government responds by signing 87 contracts to build 10,300 homes, but bureaucracy slows the building process.

December

- Gunmen storm a low-security prison, releasing more than 100 inmates; it is suspected that the motive might have been to help them make it home in time for Christmas.

- A federal judge issues a ban on six popular video games (Duke Nukem, Blood, Doom, Mortal Kombat, Postal, and Requiem) after a student, claiming that he was inspired by the video game Duke Nukem, opens fire in a movie theater in Sao Paulo, killing three.

ANALYSIS OF EVENTS: 1999

BUSINESS AND THE ECONOMY

Brazil started the year announcing a devaluation of its national currency. The Government announced that from January on, the *real* would not longer be pegged to the U.S. dollar. Immediately after the announcement the *real* lost more than 30% of its value. During the year, the *real* recovered some lost ground, but subsequent devaluations made the *real* lose about 40% of its value during the year. One of the immediate effects of a currency devaluation is inflationary pressures. Imported goods are more expensive, interest rates increase and the real value of wages decrease. Political upheaval usually follows a currency devaluation. Brazil was no exception, the January devaluation intensified social tensions and further hurt the popularity of President Cardoso.

In order to tighten control over monetary police, President Cardoso appointed a new president for the Central Bank in January. Three weeks later, a new Central Bank president was appointed. Arminio Fraga was brought in because he had excellent relations with the international financial community and could restore trust on Brazil's economic team.

Brazil worked towards recovering from the crisis caused by devaluation, but social problems have worsened. The government, in an effort to attract foreign investors, attempted to move forward with its modernization and privatization plan, but opposition in congress and in state governments prevented president Carodoso from meeting the demands of potential foreign investors.

The international community, including foreign lenders and investors, supported Cardoso throughout the crisis and Brazil was expected to begin showing positive economic numbers in early 2000.

GOVERNMENT AND POLITICS

President Cardoso was reelected for a second term in 1998. He won the 1994 presidential elections after having served as Minister of Finance since 1993 and having successfully implemented the *real* program. With the adoption of the *real* program, Brazil was able to control the 4-digit inflation that had characterized that country in the late 80s and early 90s. Previous attempts had enjoyed temporary success, but chronic inflation had returned. When Cardoso became president, controlling inflation became the center of his economic program. The *real* was pegged to the U.S. dollar and that became President Cardoso's main electoral platform in 1998.

Despite the continuous efforts made to resist the runs against the Brazilian currency made by international speculators, Brazil eventually had to budge and let its currency float against the dollar. Support from the International Monetary Fund and other financial institutions came to rescue President Cardoso, but the political momentum he had gained after the election was lost.

Some of the state governors, particularly former president and current Minas Gerais governor Itamar Franco, led their state governments in defaulting on loans owned to the federal government. President Carodoso attempted to reform the constitution to restrict borrowing power to state governments, but political patronage and clientlism did not allow him to muster a sufficient majority in congress to carry out his reforms.

The economic crisis of 1999 came to worsen the situation of millions of impoverished Brazilians who suffer from unemployment, underemployment and poverty. Among them, the Landless Peasants movement gained international recognition in their effort to secure arable land for agricultural production. Because President Cardoso relies on an unstable congressional majority to govern, he has lacked enough room to negotiate with the Landless Peasants and with other social and political organizations that demand government programs to help them combat poverty and provide opportunities for the poor.

President Cardoso has vowed continuous support for the Mercosur international trade alliance, but the January devaluation deteriorated Mercosur relations significantly. Because Argentina's currency continues to be pegged to the U.S. dollar, Brazilian products in Argentina are much cheaper. The trade between the two countries favors Brazil as its products are cheaper in Argentina and Argentina's exports are more expensive in Brazil. President Cardoso has worked with Argentina's president Carlos Menen to find ways to strengthen Mercosur, and the recently elected Argentine president Fernando de la Rua has announced that his first trip abroad will be to Brazil to strengthen the Mercosur alliance. If Mercosur survives the 1999 crisis, President Cardoso will have obtained a major political victory.

CULTURE AND SOCIETY

Brazil has witnessed an unequal development process over the years. The industrialized state of Sao Paulo has led the economic development for decades. Northeastern states have lagged significantly behind. Because Brazil constitutes a federal system, northeastern states hold more political power than Sao Paulo in the senate. Those states have continuously pressured the government to provide them with subsidies and financial support. However, because educational, health access and employment opportunities are almost absent in those states, many Brazilians have chosen to migrate south and seek employment in the states of Sao Paulo, Rio de Janeiro and other southern regions. The long-term effects of this internal migration remain to be seen, but some evidence of racial tension has surfaced in recent months. A majority of the population in the northeast is black, while the south has a larger percentage of descendants of 19th century European immigrants.

DIRECTORY

CENTRAL GOVERNMENT
Head of State

President
Fernando Henrique Cardoso, Office of the President

Vice President
Marco Maciel, Office of the Vice President

Ministers

Minister of Administration and Reform of the State
Claudia Costin, Ministry of Administration and Reform of the State

Minister of Aeronautics
Brigadeiro Walter Werner Bráuer, Ministry of Aeronautics
E-MAIL: cecomsaer@cecomsaer.maer.mil.br

Minister of Agriculture
Francisco Sergio Turra, Ministry of Agriculture

Minister of the Armed Forces Joint Staff
Benedito Onofre Bezerra Leonel, Ministry of the Armed Forces

Minister of Army
Gleuber Vieira, Ministry of Army
E-MAIL: webmaster@exercito.gov.br

Minister of Commerce, Industry, and Tourism
Jose Botafogo Goncalves, Ministry of Commerce, Industry, and Tourism

Minister of Communications
João Pimenta da Veiga Filho, Ministry of Communications
E-MAIL: webmaster@mc.gov.br

Minister of Culture
Francisco Correa Weffort, Ministry of Culture
E-MAIL: gm@minc.gov.br

Minister of Education
Paulo Renato de Souza, Ministry of Education
E-MAIL: webmc@mec.gov.br

Minister of Environment, Water Resources, and the Amazon
Gustavo Krause, Ministry of Environment, Water Resources, and the Amazon

Minister of Finance
Pedro Malan, Ministry of Finance
E-MAIL: acs@fazenda.gov.br

Minister of Foreign Affairs
Luiz Felipe Palmeira Lampreia, Ministry of Foreign Affairs
E-MAIL: acs@mre.gov.br

Minister of Health
Jose Serra, Ministry of Health

Minister of Institutional Reforms
Antonio de Almendra Freitas Neto, Ministry of Institutional Reforms

Minister of Justice
José Carlos Dias, Ministry of Justice
E-MAIL: webmaster@mj.gov.br

Minister of Labor
Eduardo Amadeo, Ministry of Labor

Minister of Mines and Energy
Rodolpho Tourinho Neto, Ministry of Mines and Energy
E-MAIL: webmaster@mme.gov.br

Minister of the Navy
Sérgio Gitirana Florencio Chagasteles, Ministry of the Navy
E-MAIL: srpm@gmm.mar.mil.br

Minister of Planning
Paulo Paiva, Ministry of Planning

Minister of Science and Technology
Jose Israel Vargas, Ministry of Science and Technology

Minister of Social Security
Waldeck Vieira Ornellas, Ministry of Social Security
E-MAIL: Webmaster.mpas@rjo.dataprev.gov.br

Minister of Transport
Eliseu Padilha, Ministry of Transport
E-MAIL: comsock@transportes.gov.br

Special Minister of Agrarian Reform
Raul Jungmann, Ministry of Agrarian Reform
E-MAIL: webmaster@incra.gov.br

POLITICAL ORGANIZATIONS

Brazilian Democratic Movement Party (PMDB)

TITLE: President
NAME: Paes de Andrade

Liberal Front Party (PFL)

TITLE: President
NAME: Jose Jorge

Workers' Party (PT)

TITLE: President
NAME: Jose Dirceu

Brazilian Workers' Party (PTB)

Sede Nacional Scln 303, Bloco C, Sala 105, Asa Norte, 70735-530 Brasília, DF, Brazil
PHONE: +55 (61) 2260477
FAX: +55 (61) 2254757
E-MAIL: ptb@ptb.org.br
TITLE: President
NAME: Rodrigues Palma

Democratic Labor Party (PDT)

TITLE: President
NAME: Leonel Brizola

Brazilian Progressive Party (PPB)

TITLE: President
NAME: Espiridiao Amin

Brazilian Social Democracy Party (PSDB)

TITLE: President
NAME: Artur da Tavola

Popular Socialist Party (PPS)

TITLE: President

NAME: Roberto Freire

Communist Party of Brazil

TITLE: Chairman
NAME: Joao Amazonas

Liberal Party (PL)

TITLE: President
NAME: Alvaro Valle

DIPLOMATIC REPRESENTATION

Embassies in Brazil

Finland
Av. das Nacoes, Lote 27, 70417-900 Brasilia, DF, Brazil
PHONE: +55 (61) 4437151
FAX: +55 (61) 4433315
E-MAIL: suomi@tba.com.br

France
Av. das Nacoes, Lote 4, 70401-90 Brasilia, DF, Brazil
PHONE: +55 (61) 3129100
FAX: +55 (61) 3129158
E-MAIL: france@ambafrance.o

Russia
Av. das Nacoes, Lote A, Brasilia, DF, Brazil
PHONE: +55 (61) 2233094; 2234095
FAX: +55 (61) 2267319
E-MAIL: embrus@brnet.com.br

United States
Av. das Nacoes, Quadra 801, Lote 03, 70403-900 Brasilia, DF, Brazil
PHONE: +55 (61) 3217272

FAX: +55 (61) 2259136

JUDICIAL SYSTEM
Supreme Federal Tribunal
Superior Court of Justice

FURTHER READING
Articles

"Brazil and the IMF. First Steps to Safety." *The Economist* (March 13, 1999).

"Brazil Democracy Gets Back to Business." *The Economist* (April 17, 1999).

"Brazil Matters of Tax." *The Economist* (June 12, 1999).

"Brazil Sick System." *The Economist* (September 11, 1999).

"Brazil Work Cut Out." *The Economist* (May 22, 1999).

"Brazil's Railways: Trucks to Trains." *The Economist* (October 23, 1999).

"Brazil's Unsteady Recovery." *The Economist* (August 28, 1999).

"Brazilian Banking Federal Offenses." *The Economist* (July 31, 1999).

"Cardoso's Reform Puzzle." *The Economist* (July 24, 1999).

Internet

Brazil. Available Online @ http: // www.brazzil.com/ (November 17, 1999).

Gazeta Mercantil. Available Online @ http: // www.gazeta.com.br/default.asp (November 1/, 1999).

BRAZIL: STATISTICAL DATA

For sources and notes see "Sources of Statistics" in the front of each volume.

GEOGRAPHY

Geography (1)

Area:

Total: 8,511,965 sq km.

Land: 8,456,510 sq km.

Water: 55,455 sq km.

Note: includes Arquipelago de Fernando de Noronha, Atol das Rocas, Ilha da Trindade, Ilhas Martin Vaz, and Penedos de Sao Pedro e Sao Paulo.

Area—comparative: slightly smaller than the US.

Land boundaries:

Total: 14,691 km.

Border countries: Argentina 1,224 km, Bolivia 3,400 km, Colombia 1,643 km, French Guiana 673 km, Guyana 1,119 km, Paraguay 1,290 km, Peru 1,560 km, Suriname 597 km, Uruguay 985 km, Venezuela 2,200 km.

Coastline: 7,491 km.

Climate: mostly tropical, but temperate in south.

Terrain: mostly flat to rolling lowlands in north; some plains, hills, mountains, and narrow coastal belt.

Natural resources: bauxite, gold, iron ore, manganese, nickel, phosphates, platinum, tin, uranium, petroleum, hydropower, timber.

Land use:

Arable land: 5%

Permanent crops: 1%

Permanent pastures: 22%

Forests and woodland: 58%

Other: 14% (1993 est.).

HUMAN FACTORS

Demographics (2A)

	1990	1995	1998	2000	2010	2020	2030	2040	2050
Population	151,039.8	163,113.4	169,806.6	173,790.8	190,960.3	204,187.0	214,475.0	222,865.1	228,144.9
Net migration rate (per 1,000 population)	NA	NA	NA	NA	NA	NA	NA	NA	NA
Births	NA	NA	NA	NA	NA	NA	NA	NA	NA
Deaths	847.6	NA	NA	NA	NA	NA	NA	NA	NA
Life expectancy - males	63.0	59.5	59.4	59.3	63.8	66.2	71.3	76.4	78.8
Life expectancy - females	71.1	71.4	69.6	68.4	71.8	74.0	78.6	83.1	85.3
Birth rate (per 1,000)	22.4	22.2	20.9	19.9	16.6	14.5	13.0	11.8	10.9
Death rate (per 1,000)	6.5	7.8	8.5	9.1	8.5	8.9	8.6	8.6	9.5
Women of reproductive age (15-49 yrs.) of which are currently married	39,564.7	44,412.9	47,091.2	48,345.7	52,575.2	54,256.0	53,684.8	51,884.1	49,835.0
	NA	NA	NA	NA	NA	NA	NA	NA	NA
Fertility rate	2.6	2.5	2.3	2.2	2.0	1.9	1.8	1.8	1.8

Except as noted, values for vital statistics are in thousands; life expectancy is in years.

Health Personnel (3)

Total health expenditure as a percentage of GDP, 1990-1997[a]

Public sector 1.9

Private sector 4.9

Total[b] 6.8

Health expenditure per capita in U.S. dollars, 1990-1997[a]

Purchasing power parity 382

Total 351

Availability of health care facilities per 100,000 people

Hospital beds 1990-1997[a] 300

Doctors 1993[c] 134

Nurses 1993[c] 41

Health Indicators (4)

Life expectancy at birth

1980 63

1997 67

Daily per capita supply of calories (1996) 2,938

Total fertility rate births per woman (1997) 2.3

Maternal mortality ratio per 100,000 live births (1990-97) ....160[d]

Safe water % of population with access (1995) 69

Sanitation % of population with access (1995) 67

Consumption of iodized salt % of households (1992-98)[a] 95

Smoking prevalence

Male % of adults (1985-95)[a] 40

Female % of adults (1985-95)[a] 25

Tuberculosis incidence per 100,000 people (1997) 78

Adult HIV prevalence % of population ages 15-49 (1997) 0.63

Infants and Malnutrition (5)

Under-5 mortality rate (1997) 44

% of infants with low birthweight (1990-97) 8

Births attended by skilled health staff % of total[a] ...88

% fully immunized (1995-97)

TB 100

DPT 71

Polio 84

Measles 100

Prevalence of child malnutrition under age 5 (1992-97)[b] 6

Ethnic Division (6)

White 55%

Mixed white and black 38%

Black 6%

Other 1%

While includes Portuguese, German, Italian, Spanish, Polish. Other includes Japanese, Arab, Amerindian.

Religions (7)

Roman Catholic (nominal) 70%.

Languages (8)

Portuguese (official), Spanish, English, French.

EDUCATION

Public Education Expenditures (9)

Public expenditure on education (% of GNP)

1980 ....3.6

1996 ....5.5[1]

Expenditure per student

Primary % of GNP per capita

1980 ....8.7

1996 ....

Secondary % of GNP per capita

1980 ....11.0

1996 ....

Tertiary % of GNP per capita

1980 ....58.6

1996 ....

Expenditure on teaching materials

Primary % of total for level (1996) ....

Secondary % of total for level (1996) ....

Primary pupil-teacher ratio per teacher (1996) .....23[1]

Duration of primary education years (1995) 8

Educational Attainment (10)

Age group (1989)[15] ....10+

Total population 110,157,487

Highest level attained (%)

No schooling 18.7

First level

Not completed 57.0

Completed 6.9

Entered second level

S-1 ....11.9

S-2 ....5.5

Postsecondary ....NA

Literacy Rates (11A)

In thousands and percent[1]	1990	1995	2000	2010
Illiterate population (15+ yrs.)	18,514	18,331	17,842	16,438
Literacy rate - total adult pop. (%)	81.0	83.3	85.4	88.8
Literacy rate - males (%)	81.5	83.3	85.1	87.9
Literacy rate - females (%)	80.1	83.2	85.7	89.6

GOVERNMENT & LAW

Political Parties (12)

Chamber of Deputies—	% of seats
Brazilian Democratic Movement Party (PMDB)	12
Liberal Front Party (PFL)	18
Democratic Labor Party (PDT)	7
PSDB	12
Brazilian Workers' Party (PTB)	6
Workers' Party (PT)	10
Other	16

Party totals since the fall of 1994 have changed considerably due to extensive party-switching.

Military Affairs (14B)

	1990	1991	1992	1993	1994	1995
Military expenditures						
Current dollars (mil.)	8,555	7,021	6,204	7,913	7,185	10,900
1995 constant dollars (mil.)	9,832	7,758	6,674	8,296	7,365	10,900
Armed forces (000)	295	295	296	296	296	285
Gross national product (GNP)						
Current dollars (mil.)	501,500	524,200	533,800	574,400	610,200	656,500
1995 constant dollars (mil.)	576,400	579,200	547,200	602,100	625,500	656,500
Central government expenditures (CGE)						
1995 constant dollars (mil.)	214,100	159,900	188,100	246,600	237,900[e]	276,800[e]
People (mil.)	150.1	152.3	154.5	156.7	158.7	160.7
Military expenditure as % of GNP	1.7	1.3	1.2	1.4	1.2	1.7
Military expenditure as % of CGE	4.6	4.9	3.5	3.4	3.1	3.9
Military expenditure per capita (1995 $)	66	51	43	53	46	68
Armed forces per 1,000 people (soldiers)	2.0	1.9	1.9	1.9	1.9	1.8
GNP per capita (1994 $)	3,841	3,803	3,716	3,844	3,940	4,084
Arms imports[6]						
Current dollars (mil.)	150	150	120	160	100	170
1995 constant dollars (mil.)	172	166	129	168	103	170
Arms exports[6]						
Current dollars (mil.)	60	80	180	100	190	10
1995 constant dollars (mil.)	69	88	194	105	195	10
Total imports[7]						
Current dollars (mil.)	22,520	22,960	23,070	27,740	36,000	53,780
1995 constant dollars (mil.)	25,890	25,370	24,810	29,080	36,900	53,780
Total exports[7]						
Current dollars (mil.)	31,410	31,620	35,790	38,600	43,560	46,510
1995 constant dollars (mil.)	36,100	34,940	38,500	40,460	44,650	46,510
Arms as percent of total imports[8]	.7	.7	.5	.6	.3	.3
Arms as percent of total exports[8]	.2	.3	.5	.3	.4	0

Government Budget (13A)

Year: 1994

Total Expenditures: 117,905.6 Millions of Reais

Expenditures as a percentage of the total by function:

General public services and public order 10.06

Defense 3.13

Education 3.64

Health 6.27

Social Security and Welfare 30.42

Housing and community amenities 18

Recreational, cultural, and religious affairs 08

Fuel and energy 1.23

Agriculture, forestry, fishing, and hunting 2.86

Mining, manufacturing, and construction 05

Transportation and communication 96

Other economic affairs and services 41

LABOR FORCE

Labor Force (16)

Total (million) 57

Services 42%

Agriculture 31%

Industry 27%

Data for 1989 est.

Unemployment Rate (17)

7% (1997 est.)

PRODUCTION SECTOR

Electric Energy (18)

Capacity . . . . .57.64 million kW (1995)

Production . . . . .264.895 billion kWh (1995)

Consumption per capita . . . . .1,878 kWh (1995)

Imported about 36.95 billion kWh of electricity from Paraguay.

Transportation (19)

Highways:

total: 1.98 million km

paved: 184,140 km

unpaved: 1,795,860 km (1996 est.)

Waterways: 50,000 km navigable

Pipelines: crude oil 2,000 km; petroleum products 3,804 km; natural gas 1,095 km

Merchant marine:

total: 188 ships (1,000 GRT or over) totaling 4,498,081 GRT/7,279,945 DWT ships by type: bulk 37, cargo 26, chemical tanker 9, combination ore/oil 11, container 16, liquefied gas tanker 10, multifunction large-load carrier

1, oil tanker 61, passenger-cargo 5, refrigerated cargo 1, roll-on/roll-off cargo 11 (1997 est.)

Airports: 3,291 (1997 est.)

Airports—with paved runways:

total: 502

over 3,047 m: 5

2,438 to 3,047 m: 19

1,524 to 2,437 m: 130

914 to 1,523 m: 319

under 914 m: 29 (1997 est.)

Airports—with unpaved runways:

total: 2,789

1,524 to 2,437 m: 76

914 to 1,523 m: 1,324

under 914 m: 1,389 (1997 est.)

Top Agricultural Products (20)

Coffee, soybeans, wheat, rice, corn, sugarcane, cocoa, citrus; beef.

MANUFACTURING SECTOR

GDP & Manufacturing Summary (21)

Detailed value added figures are listed by both International Standard Industry Code (ISIC) and product title.

	1980	1985	1990	1994
GDP ($-1990 mil.)[1]	273,079	295,835	327,129	360,879
Per capita ($-1990)[1]	2,252	2,191	2,203	2,268
Manufacturing share (%) (current prices)[1]	31.1	30.0	23.0	NA
Manufacturing				
Value added ($-1990 mil.)[1]	75,491	72,703	74,263	*82,231*
Industrial production index	100	107	109	*121*
Value added ($ mil.)	71,700	77,082	85,189	154,425
Gross output ($ mil.)	189,076	174,341	175,803	*285,569*
Employment (000)	5,562	5,501	4,688	4,698
Profitability (% of gross output)				
Intermediate input (%)	62	56	52	*46*
Wages and salaries inc. supplements (%)	10	9	*11*	*12*
Gross operating surplus	28	*36*	*37*	*42*

	1980	1985	1990	1994
Productivity ($)				
Gross output per worker	33,993	31,692	37,131	60,670
Value added per worker	12,891	14,012	17,992	34,853
Average wage (inc. supplements)	3,400	2,756	4,230	7,072
Value added ($ mil.)				
311/2 Food products	7,996	9,259	8,687	19,394
313 Beverages	1,375	958	1,388	2,313
314 Tobacco products	495	587	726	1,940
321 Textiles	4,860	4,586	3,862	7,101
322 Wearing apparel	2,307	2,639	3,816	4,408
323 Leather and fur products	309	464	584	1,155
324 Footwear	985	1,353	1,957	2,359
331 Wood and wood products	1,903	1,220	951	1,158
332 Furniture and fixtures	1,087	949	843	1,130
341 Paper and paper products	2,238	2,260	2,556	5,282
342 Printing and publishing	1,901	1,496	2,305	3,400
351 Industrial chemicals	3,428	5,379	6,346	10,907
352 Other chemical products	3,544	7,296	9,025	15,655
353 Petroleum refineries	3,075	2,058	2,265	3,910
354 Miscellaneous petroleum and coal products	1,216	612	594	966
355 Rubber products	941	1,420	1,059	1,770
356 Plastic products	1,994	1,742	1,847	3,387
361 Pottery, china and earthenware	200	844	249	537
362 Glass and glass products	558	525	466	1,036
369 Other non-metal mineral products	3,447	1,941	2,553	5,675
371 Iron and steel	4,128	4,927	5,198	8,833
372 Non-ferrous metals	1,115	1,564	1,496	2,564
381 Metal products	3,599	3,063	3,711	6,081
382 Non-electrical machinery	7,171	7,092	8,355	11,600
383 Electrical machinery	4,536	5,831	6,341	12,329
384 Transport equipment	5,625	4,954	5,652	15,994
385 Professional and scientific equipment	453	910	861	1,310
390 Other manufacturing industries	1,216	1,154	1,497	2,230

FINANCE, ECONOMICS, & TRADE

Economic Indicators (22)

National product: GDP—purchasing power parity—$1.04 trillion (1997 est.)

National product real growth rate: 3% (1997)

National product per capita: $6,300 (1997 est.)

Inflation rate—consumer price index: 4.8% (1997)

Exchange Rates (24)

Exchange rates:

R$ per US$1

January 1998	1.120
1997	1.078
1996	1.005
1995	0.918
1994	0.639

CR$ per US$1

January 1994	390.845
1993	88.449

Top Import Origins (25)

$61.4 billion (f.o.b., 1997) Data are for 1996.

Origins	%
European Union	26
United States	22
Argentina	13
Japan	5

Top Export Destinations (26)

$53 billion (f.o.b., 1997). Data are for 1996.

Destinations	%
European Union	.28
Latin America	.23
United States	.20
Argentina	.12

Economic Aid (27)

Recipient: ODA, $107 million (1993).

Import Export Commodities (28)

Import Commodities	Export Commodities
Crude oil	Iron ore
Capital goods	Soybean bran
Chemical products	Orange juice
Foodstuffs	Footwear
Coal	Coffee
	Motor vehicle parts

Balance of Payments (23)

	1990	1992	1993	1994	1995
Exports of goods (f.o.b.)	31,408	35,793	39,630	44,120	46,506
Imports of goods (f.o.b.)	−20,661	−20,554	−25,301	−33,241	−49,663
Trade balance	10,747	15,239	14,329	10,861	−3,157
Services - debits	−20,288	−16,545	−21,185	−21,547	−28,192
Services - credits	4,919	5,206	5,273	7,110	9,592
Private transfers (net)	798	2,202	1,620	2,391	3,663
Government transfers (net)	1	−13	−17	32	−42
Overall balance	−3,823	6,089	20	−1,153	−18,136

BRITISH VIRGIN ISLANDS

CAPITAL: Road Town.

FLAG: The flag of the British Virgin Islands is blue with the flag of the United Kingdom in the upper hoist-side quadrant and the Virgin Islander coat of arms centered in the outer half of the flag; the coat of arms depicts a woman flanked on either side by a vertical column of six oil lamps above a scroll bearing the Latin word *vigilate* (Be Watchful).

ANTHEM: God Save the Queen.

MONETARY UNIT: United States dollars are used.

WEIGHTS AND MEASURES: The imperial system is used.

HOLIDAYS: New Year's Day; Commonwealth Day, early March; Good Friday; Easter Sunday and Monday; Whitmonday; the Queen's Official Birthday; Territory Day, 1 July; Summer Festival Days, early August; St. Ursula's Day, 21 October; the Prince of Wales's Birthday, 14 November; Christmas Day; and Boxing Day, 26 December.

TIME: 8 AM = noon GMT.

LOCATION AND SIZE: The British Virgin Islands consist of some 50 Caribbean islands and islets, totaling 153 sq. km (59 sq. mi.), at about 18°30′N and 64°30′W. The islands lie north of Leeward Islands and adjacent to the U.S. Virgin Islands, and between the Caribbean Sea and the North Atlantic Ocean, east of Puerto Rico.

CLIMATE: The climate is pleasantly subtropical, with the humidity moderated by trade winds. Temperatures average 29°C (84°F) in the summer and 27°C (80°F) in the winter. A 4°C (10°F) drop in temperature can be expected in the evening. The average annual rainfall is 40 inches (102 cm).

INTRODUCTORY SURVEY

RECENT HISTORY

Arawak Indians and the warlike Caribs were the first occupants of the string of islands Christopher Columbus named Santa Ursula y las Once Mil Virgenes ("St. Ursula and the Eleven Thousand Virgins"). However, the Spanish killed or expelled the natives. Pirates and buccaneers used the islands; the Dutch held them for a time. However, English planters took over the islands now known as the British Virgin Islands in 1666. They imported slaves to labor in sugar plantations. Today, about 90% of the island's 19,156 inhabitants (July 1999 estimate) are black.

For several hundred years, the British Virgin Islands were an indistinct portion of the Leeward Islands. In 1956, the Colony of the Leeward Islands was defederated, and the approximately fifty islands of the British Virgin Islands were established as a separate colony. The general form of the island's government was established in 1967. The constitution was established in 1977.

GOVERNMENT

The British Virgin Islands is a self-governing overseas territory of the United Kingdom. As such, the head of state is the British monarch, who is represented on the islands by an appointed governor. The government of the British Virgin Islands includes an executive branch which is headed by the chief minister. The Executive Council serves as a cabinet, led by the chief minister. Members of the

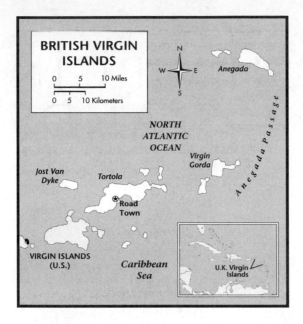

BRITISH VIRGIN ISLANDS

NORTH ATLANTIC OCEAN

Anegada

Anegada Passage

Jost Van Dyke

Tortola

Road Town

Virgin Gorda

VIRGIN ISLANDS (U.S.)

Caribbean Sea

U.K. Virgin Islands

Executive Council are appointed by the governor from the elected Legislative Council.

A unicameral legislature called the Legislative Council is elected for five year terms. Eligible voters are all legal residents over the age of eighteen. There are thirteen seats in the Legislative Council. One member is elected from each of the nine electoral districts; four members are elected at-large.

International relations and security are the responsibility of the United Kingdom. However, the British Virgin Island's government participates as an observer in several international organizations such as Caricom, the IOC, OECS, and UNESCO.

Judiciary

The judicial branch of the government is independent. The Eastern Caribbean Supreme Court is comprised of the High Court of Justice and the Court of Appeal, the Magistrate's Court, Juvenile Court, and Court of Summary Jurisdiction. One of the judges of the Supreme Court is a resident of the islands and presides over the High Court. The legal system is based upon English common law.

Political Parties

There are basically four political parties in the British Virgin Islands: The United Party, the Virgin Islands Party, the Concerned Citizens Movement, and the Independent People's Movement.

DEFENSE

Defense is the responsibility of the United Kingdom. There is a small police force, but no permanent military garrison.

ECONOMIC AFFAIRS

The British Virgin Islands is located in an ideal climate, subtropical but outside the normal hurricane zone. Consequently, the sparkling beaches, coral reefs, and tropical vegetation make the islands a natural tourist destination. With over 400,000 visitors annually, tourism is the largest income producer in the country—nearly half of the island's total income. Off shore banking services and corporate registrations have been encouraged, and by 1997, some 250,000 companies were registered.

While 20% of the land is arable, the quality of the soil is poor and agriculture is not a large segment of the economy. Livestock raising is the major agricultural activity. Bananas, sugarcane, citrus fruits, coconuts, mangoes, and various root crops are raised and harvested. Most agricultural products are consumed in the islands and not exported.

Some light industry has developed on the islands. These include concrete block production and construction, alcoholic beverages (mostly rum), and paint. Many small concerns produce handicrafts for sale within the tourist industry. Fishing is a growth industry and fresh fish is exported. There are five radio stations and one broadcast television station on the islands.

Exports include rum, fresh fish, fruits, animals, gravel and sand. Imports include building materials, automobiles, foodstuffs, and machinery. The country enjoys a negative balance of payments with 1996 figures showing $24 million in exports and $121.5 million in imports. The cash infusion from tourism, corporate registrations, and remittances from migrated workers makes up the difference.

Public Finance

Tied closely with the U.S. Virgin Islands economically, the currency of the British Virgin Islands is the U.S. dollar. Government revenues are raised via taxes, corporate registration fees, and tourist fees and taxes. The government spent $115.5 million with $121.5 million in revenues in 1997. Economic aid of $2.6 million was received in 1995.

Income

The British Virgin Islands enjoys a better economy than many of its Caribbean neighbors. The per capita income of the islands was estimated in 1997 at $10,000. Gross Domestic Product was estimated in 1997 at $183 million.

Industry

Light industries are established on the islands, including distilleries for alcoholic beverages, a concrete block factory, boat building, and handicrafts. Fishing is a growth industry. Tourism, off shore banking services and corporate registrations are the greatest contributors to national income.

Banking and Finance

Local banking services as well as large off shore banking services are present.

Economic Development

The three economic growth areas for the British Virgin Islands are tourism, corporate registrations, and fishing. A comprehensive insurance law was enacted in 1994 to attract international businesses to the country. The law provided a blanket of confidentiality and provided regulated statutory gateways for the investigation of criminal offenses.

SOCIAL WELFARE

The government is not heavily involved in social welfare programs.

Healthcare

Healthcare in the islands is improving as noticed by a reduction in infant mortality from about 79 deaths per 1,000 live births in 1960 to just over 19 in 1996. There are about 250 hospital beds available in the islands and a physician for every 1,000 residents.

Housing

On the whole, housing is adequate.

EDUCATION

Education is provided by the state from ages five to fifteen, and it is compulsory until age thirteen. The are twenty primary schools and three high schools in the islands. Scholarships are available from the government for those wishing to attend higher education facilities in the United States or the United Kingdom. Some additional education is available at other Caribbean locations. Virtually all adults in the islands are literate.

1999 KEY EVENTS TIMELINE

February

- Major Caribbean regattas, including the British Virgin Islands Spring Regatta, jointly create the Caribbean Big Boat Series (CBBS).

March

- Britain decides to offer full citizenship to residents in its overseas territories. The move is seen as way to stop tax evasion.

April

- The 28th Annual British Virgin Islands Spring Regatta is held.

May

- Ralph O'Neal is sworn in as chief minister, after his Virgin Islands Party retains its 13-year hold on power, winning seven of 13 legislative seats.

June

- The British Virgin Islands joins several other Caribbean nations to create the Association of Caribbean Heads of Prisons. The group is expected to address many complaints about Caribbean prisons, which have been criticized by prominent human rights organizations.

August

- Delegates from the Commonwealth Parliamentary Association visit BVI.

- The European Union will help fund community college culinary arts program.

September

- The government raises the minimum wage, both for workers and high school students.

October

- BVI chief minister Ralph O'Neal considers repealing an immigration order banning ''hippies'' and Rastafarians from the islands.

- Trade in endangered turtles, corals and iguanas is being openly carried out in British overseas territories, even though it is banned under international law.

- The BVI says it will conduct a census in 2001 in conjunction with the rest of the Caribbean Community.

- The British Virgin Islands ranks among the top 10 destinations in the "Paradise Found" category of a *National Geographic Traveler* overview of the world's travel attractions.

November

- Hurricane Lenny, with winds as high as 145 miles per hour, hits the British Virgin Islands and neighboring islands in the Caribbean. High winds and the resulting high tides cause extensive damage to homes, boats, and public buildings along the shore.

ANALYSIS OF EVENTS: 1999

BUSINESS AND THE ECONOMY

A minimum wage increase to four dollars an hour took effect at the beginning of September, the first such increase since 1994. (Wage minimums for high school students were kept at three dollars.) The wage increase was recommended by the Labor Advisory Committee following a study of various occupations and workplaces. The next review of the minimum wage is set for 2001.

Early in the year, the BVI Electricity Corporation received the go-ahead for the next phase in its major facility upgrade project. The government guaranteed loan repayment on nearly $20 million for development construction including new generators, a double circuit transmission line, new cables, and a desalination plant that would use waste heat from existing and new generators. The plant is scheduled for completion by the end of 2001. Further infrastructure improvements were authorized when the government approved borrowing to finance the Beef Island Airport Project.

The British Virgin Islands were only one of numerous locales that figured in the bizarre escapades of U.S. financier Martin Frankel, which came to an end in September. Frankel was captured and arrested in Germany in connection with the disappearance of hundreds of millions of dollars in insurance money as well as close to $2 billion belonging to a fraudulent Catholic charity. Frankel had registered the charity, called the St. Francis of Assisi Foundation, in the British Virgin Islands when he established it in 1998.

Tourism remained a major force in the territory's economy. Drawn by the colorful scenery of its mountainous islands, tourists came to enjoy the features of its fine resorts and participate in a variety of water sports, including swimming, diving, snorkeling, sailing, and yachting. The islands were particularly popular with skin divers thanks to their species diversity, healthy coral reefs, and high degree of underwater visibility.

GOVERNMENT AND POLITICS

In March, Britain offered United Kingdom citizenship to all its island territories, including the British Virgin Islands (BVI). (BVI is comprised of forty-six islands, eleven of which are inhabited.) In return, the British government asked the territories to prosecute tax evasion and other financial irregularities, and bring its laws on capital punishment, flogging, and homosexuality into line with British and European standards. More than 19,000 people who live in the British Virgin Islands will be affected.

In general elections held May 17 the Virgin Islands Party (VIP), which had governed the British Virgin Islands for the past thirteen years, retained power by a narrow margin, winning seven of the thirteen seats on the Legislative Council. Major opposition came from the newly formed New Democratic Party (NDP), supported mostly by businesspersons and professionals, which made an impressive showing, winning five seats in its first electoral contest. The VIP managed to stay in power by narrowly winning the sixth district, where incumbent Omar Hodge withstood a strong challenged by NDP candidate Elvis Harrigan, and won by only 14 votes. The remaining seat went to the Concerned Citizen Movement (CCM). Altogether twenty candidates competed for a total of nine seats from specific districts and four at-large seats. No incidents were reported either during the hotly contested campaign or on election day. Ralph O'Neal, leader of the Virgin Islands Party, was expected to form a new government at the official request of Governor Frank Savage.

A delegation from the Commonwealth Parliamentary Association (CPA) visited the British Virgin Islands for five days in August, holding talks with top officials, including the governor and chief minister, and touring the islands of Virgin Gorda and Tortola. Delegates praised the BVI for its political stability and economic prosperity, singling out its effective promotion and regulation of offshore business, which was cited as a model for other Caribbean jurisdictions.

In June the British Virgin Islands participated in the establishment of the Association of Caribbean Heads of Prisons, a group formed to address long-standing complaints by Amnesty International and other human rights groups about Caribbean prisons, which were known for overcrowding and substandard conditions. The association hoped to bring prisons in the region up to minimum United Nations standards by identifying problems within area prison systems and notifying the governments involved. Other nations represented were Anguilla, Barbados, Guyana, Trinidad and Tobago, Turks and Caicos, and St. Kitts and Nevis.

CULTURE AND SOCIETY

In the British Virgin Islands, it is commonly known as the "Rasta Law." In legal terms, it is known as the Immigration and Passport Order, Prohibited Class of Persons. Passed in 1980, the "Rasta Law" prevented entry into the territory by people who were deemed to be Rastafarians and hippies. Islanders passed the law during a crime wave that was blamed on Rastafarian visitors. The law has come under fire in recent years, and in October, the Legislative Council voted on a motion to ask chief minister Ralph O'Neal to revoke it. O'Neal has opposed the motion, arguing the laws were intended to keep out criminals.

But critics said the law has been abused. Some respected international figures, including a NAACP lawyer from Washington, D.C., and the movie actor Morgan Freeman were unfairly singled out by the law, which has been widely criticized outside the British Virgin Islands. Opposition leaders said "Rasta Laws" violate human rights and continue to embarrass the British Virgin Islands.

In February, three major Caribbean regattas, including the British Virgin Islands Spring Regatta and its counterparts on St. Maarten and Antigua, jointly created the Caribbean Big Boat Series (CBBS) with the goal of encouraging competition by larger "big boat" fleets. The British Virgin Islands regatta held its 28th annual event between April 9 and 11. The Champion Yacht award went to Jersey Devils, skippered by a 17-year-old from St. Croix. The third-place winner, from the British Virgin Islands, was Rushin Rowlette.

Through a program launched jointly by the British Virgin Islands government and the European Development Fund of the European Union, 1 million euros were earmarked for the establishment of a Culinary Arts Centre at the H. Lavity Stoutt Community College. The center would train students in food preparation and service with the goal of providing both the BVI and the regional job market with qualified food service industry professionals.

DIRECTORY

CENTRAL GOVERNMENT

Head of State

Governor
Francis Joseph Savage, Office of the Governor, Road Town, Tortola, British Virgin Islands
PHONE: (284) 4942345
FAX: (284) 4945790

Chief Minister
Ralph T. O'Neal, Office of the Chief Minister, Central Administration Building, Road Town, Tortola, British Virgin Islands
PHONE: (284) 4943701
FAX: (284) 4946413
E-MAIL: pscmo@bvigovernment.org

Ministers

Minister of Finance
Ministry of Finance
E-MAIL: chiefminister@bvigovernment.org

Minister of Communications and Works
Ministry of Communications
E-MAIL: mcw@bvigovernment.org

Minister of Health, Welfare, Education, and Culture
Ministry of Health, Welfare, Education, and Culture
E-MAIL: eparsons@bvigovernment.org

POLITICAL ORGANIZATIONS

United Party (UP)

NAME: Conrad Maduro

Virgin Islands Party

NAME: Ralph T. O'Neal

Concerned Citizens Movement

NAME: E. Walwyn Brewley

Independent People's Movement
NAME: Omar Hodge and Allen O'Neal

JUDICIAL SYSTEM
Eastern Caribbean Supreme Court
E-MAIL: supremecourt@bvigovernment.org

FURTHER READING
Articles
"British Plan for Colonies Revives Independence Debate for Some." Associated Press, 5 April 1999.

"British Virgin Islands Chief Minister to Decide on 'Hippie' Ban." Associated Press, 6 October 1999.

"British Virgin Islands Leader Takes Oath, Continues Party's 13-Year Rule." Associated Press, 20 May 1999.

"Doing What the Islands Do Best." *The New York Times*, 24 October 1999, p. TR10.

Linskey, Tom. "If This is Anegada, This Must Be Race Two." *Sail* (March 1999): 94.

"*National Geographic Traveler* Names the Must-Spots of a Lifetime." Associated Press, 1 October 1999.

"Regional Caribbean Women Seen as Still Disadvantaged." *The Miami Herald*, 11 October 1999.

"Regional Supreme Court Plans Delayed for Discussion." *The Miami Herald*, 18 October 1999.

Books
Maurer, Bill. *Recharting the Caribbean: Land, Law, and Citizenship in the British Virgin Islands*. Ann Arbor: University of Michigan Press, 1997.

Internet
Caribbean Week. Available Online @ http://www.cweek.com (November 1, 1999).

BRITISH VIRGIN ISLANDS: STATISTICAL DATA

For sources and notes see "Sources of Statistics" in the front of each volume.

GEOGRAPHY

Geography (1)

Area:

Total: 150 sq km.

Land: 150 sq km.

Water: 0 sq km.

Note: includes the island of Anegada.

Area—comparative: about 0.9 times the size of Washington, DC.

Land boundaries: 0 km.

Coastline: 80 km.

Climate: subtropical; humid; temperatures moderated by trade winds.

Terrain: coral islands relatively flat; volcanic islands steep, hilly.

Natural resources: NEGL.

Land use:

Arable land: 20%

Permanent crops: 7%

Permanent pastures: 33%

Forests and woodland: 7%

Other: 33% (1993 est.).

HUMAN FACTORS

Demographics (2A)

	1990	1995	1998	2000	2010	2020	2030	2040	2050
Population	NA	17.7	18.7	19.6	24.1	27.9	30.5	31.8	31.8
Net migration rate (per 1,000 population)	NA	NA	NA	NA	NA	NA	NA	NA	NA
Births	NA	NA	NA	NA	NA	NA	NA	NA	NA
Deaths	NA	NA	NA	NA	NA	NA	NA	NA	NA
Life expectancy - males	NA	79.6	74.2	74.5	76.0	77.1	78.0	78.7	79.2
Life expectancy - females	NA	70.0	75.7	76.1	77.9	79.4	80.7	81.8	82.7
Birth rate (per 1,000)	NA	16.3	16.1	15.8	14.6	12.0	11.1	10.7	9.7
Death rate (per 1,000)	NA	4.8	4.8	4.6	4.8	5.8	7.8	10.1	11.7
Women of reproductive age (15-49 yrs.)	NA	5.4	5.8	6.1	6.9	7.0	7.2	6.8	6.7
of which are currently married	NA	NA	NA	NA	NA	NA	NA	NA	NA
Fertility rate	NA	1.7	1.7	1.7	1.7	1.7	1.7	1.7	1.7

Except as noted, values for vital statistics are in thousands; life expectancy is in years.

Ethnic Division (6)

Black 90%

White, Asian . . . .

Religions (7)

Protestant 86%

Methodist 45%

Anglican 21%

Church of God 7%

Seventh-Day Adventist 5%

Baptist 4%

Jehovah's Witnesses .2%

Other 2%

Roman Catholic 6%

None 2%

Other 6% (1981)

Languages (8)

English (official).

EDUCATION

Educational Attainment (10)

Age group (1991) . . . . .25+

Total population 8,986

Highest level attained (%)

No schooling 0.7

First level

Not completed 43.2

Completed . . . . .NA

Entered second level

S-1 . . . . .34.8

S-2 . . . . .6.4

Postsecondary 13.6

GOVERNMENT & LAW

Political Parties (12)

Legislative Council	No. of seats
Virgin Islands Party (VIP) 6	
Concerned Citizens Movement (CCM) 2	
United Party (UP) 2	
Independents 3	

Government Budget (13B)

Revenues . . . .$77.1 million

Expenditures . . . .$76.4 million

Capital expenditures . . . . .NA

Data for FY93/94. NA stands for not available.

Military Affairs (14A)

Defense is the responsibility of the UK.

LABOR FORCE

Labor Force (16)

Total 4,911 (1980).

Unemployment Rate (17)

3% (1995).

PRODUCTION SECTOR

Electric Energy (18)

Capacity . . . . .13,000 kW (1995)

Production . . . . .42 million kWh (1995)

Consumption per capita . . . . .3,224 kWh (1995)

Transportation (19)

Highways:

total: 113 km (1995 est.)

paved: NA km

unpaved: NA km

Merchant marine: none (1995 est.)

Airports: 3 (1997 est.)

Airports—with paved runways:

total: 2

914 to 1,523 m: 1

under 914 m: 1 (1997 est.)

Airports—with unpaved runways:

total: 1

914 to 1,523 m: 1 (1997 est.)

Top Agricultural Products (20)

Fruits, vegetables; livestock, poultry; fish.

FINANCE, ECONOMICS, & TRADE

Economic Indicators (22)

National product: GDP—purchasing power parity— $144 million (1996 est.)

National product real growth rate: 4.5% (1996 est.)

National product per capita: $11,000 (1996 est.)

Inflation rate—consumer price index: 2.5% (1990 est.)

Exchange Rates (24)

Exchange rates: US currency is used.

Top Import Origins (25)

$11.5 million (c.i.f., 1988).

Origins	%
Virgin Islands (US)	NA
Puerto Rico	NA
United States	NA

NA stands for not available.

Top Export Destinations (26)

$3.4 million (f.o.b., 1990).

Destinations	%
Virgin Islands (US)	NA
Puerto Rico	NA
United States	NA

NA stands for not available.

Economic Aid (27)

$NA. NA stands for not available.

Import Export Commodities (28)

Import Commodities	Export Commodities
Building materials	Rum
Automobiles	Fresh fish
Foodstuffs	Fruits
Machinery	Animals; gravel
	Sand

BRUNEI DARUSSALAM

CAPITAL: Bandar Seri Begawan.

FLAG: On a yellow field extend three diagonal stripes of white and black, with the state emblem centered in red.

ANTHEM: National Anthem, beginning *Ya Allah lanjutkan usia* ("God bless His Highness with a long life").

MONETARY UNIT: The Brunei dollar (B $, or ringgit) of 100 cents is valued at par with, and is interchangeable with, the Singapore dollar. There are coins of 1, 5, 10, 20, and 50 cents, and notes of 1, 5, 10, 50, 100, 500, 1,000, and 10,000 Brunei dollars. B $1 = US $0.7035; (or US $1 = B $1.4214).

WEIGHTS AND MEASURES: Imperial weights and measures are in common use, as are certain local units, but a change to the metric system is slowly proceeding.

HOLIDAYS: New Year's Day, 1 January; National Day, 23 February; Anniversary of the Royal Brunei Armed Forces, 31 May; Sultan's Birthday, 15 July. Movable holidays include the Chinese New Year and various Muslim holy days.

TIME: 8 PM = noon GMT.

LOCATION AND SIZE: Brunei occupies 5,770 square kilometers (2,228 square miles) on the northwestern coast of the island of Borneo. Comparatively, Brunei is slightly larger than the state of Delaware. It comprises two small areas separated by the Limbang River Valley, part of the Malaysian State of Sarawak. Brunei's total boundary length is 542 kilometers (337 miles). Brunei's capital city, Bandar Seri Begawan, is located in the northern part of the country.

CLIMATE: The country has a tropical climate, with temperatures ranging from 23° to 32°C (73°–89°F). Humidity is high—about 80% all year round—and annual rainfall varies from about 275 centimeters (110 inches) along the coast to more than 500 centimeters (200 inches) in the interior.

Nation of Brunei, Abode of Peace
Negara Brunei Darussalam

INTRODUCTORY SURVEY

RECENT HISTORY

In 1888, Brunei became a British protectorate. By a 1959 agreement, Brunei was recognized as fully self-governing, with Britain retaining responsibility for defense and foreign affairs. Brunei's first elections in 1962 were won by militant nationalists who revolted against the sultan. Since then, the Sultan's government has ruled by decree under a national state of emergency. In 1967, Sultan Omar abdicated in favor of his son, Muda Hassanal Bolkiah.

During the 1970s, Brunei's oil wealth made it the richest state in Southeast Asia. On 1 January 1984, the country attained full independence and membership in the British Commonwealth. During that year, Brunei joined both the Association of South-East Asian Nations (ASEAN) and the United Nations. In 1985, the Brunei National Democratic Party (BNDP) was formed, but the government restricted its operation and, in 1988, arrested its top two leaders. Since that year, the state has emphasized a religious ideology called *Melayu Islam Beraja* (MIB). In 1991, the import of alcohol and the public celebration of Christmas were banned.

His Majesty Sultan Haji Hassanal Bolkiah Mu'izzaddin Waddaulah celebrated 25 years on the throne in October 1992. In 1997, *Fortune* magazine's estimate of the Sultan's personal wealth, $38 billion, indicated that he may be the richest man in the world. Brunei, along with the People's Republic of China, Vietnam, Malaysia, Taiwan, and the

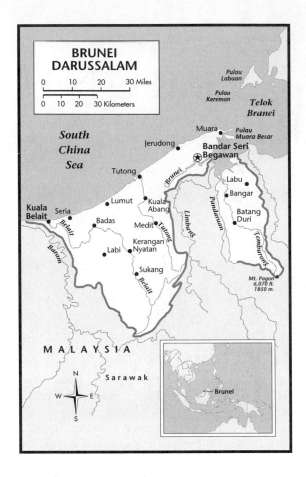

Philippines, is engaged in a regional dispute over claims to the Spratly Islands, situated in the South China Seas. The islands are militarily important and may have large oil reserves.

GOVERNMENT

Brunei is an independent Islamic sultanate. The 1959 constitution gives supreme executive authority to the sultan and provides for four Constitutional Councils to assist him. In 1992, the Sultan clearly stated his commitment to preserving Brunei's political system based on the concept of *Melayu Islam Beraja* (MIB), or Malay Islam Monarchy. Brunei has four administrative districts. An elected Legislative Council is being considered as part of constitutional reform, but any elections are unlikely for several years.

Judiciary

There are five levels of courts, with the High Court at the top. Decisions of the High Court can be taken to the Court of Appeal. The Supreme Court consists of the High Court and the Court of Appeal.

Political Parties

In 1988, political parties were banned and many of their leaders arrested. At that time, the political parties were the Brunei National Democratic Party (BNDP), the Brunei National United Party (BNUP), and the Brunei National Solidarity Party (BNSP).

DEFENSE

The Royal Brunei Armed Forces in 1995 consisted of an army of 3,900 men and women, a navy of 700, and an air force of 400. Brunei spent $268 million for defense in 1995.

ECONOMIC AFFAIRS

Brunei's economy depends almost entirely on oil and gas resources. The country's oil reserves are estimated to last another 20–25 years.

Public Finance

Brunei continues to maintain large surpluses in its annual budgets. The largest single items of expenditure were defense, education, and public works; taxes and royalties from the oil industry are by far the leading sources of government income. The 1991–96 National Development Plan allocates some B$5.5 billion for economic diversifion. The U.S. CIA estimates that, in 1995, government revenues totaled approximately $2.1 billion and expenditures $2.1 billion, including capital expenditures of $427 million.

Income

In 1998, the gross domestic product (GDP) was $5.4 billion in current dollars, or about $17,000 per person.

Industry

Industry depends almost entirely on oil and natural gas production. The small manufacturing section includes construction products, sawmills, and brick and tile factories.

Banking and Finance

The banking industry is controlled by the Association of Banks, in liaison with the government. In 1993, there were seven banks with thirty-three branches operating in Brunei.

Economic Development

The development plan for 1986–90 envisioned expenditures of B$16.2 billion, of which B$2.6 billion was slated for new projects. The plan's main objective was to diversify the economy in order to prepare for the time when oil and gas reserves will run out. Thus, it emphasized development of the agricultural sector to lessen the country's reliance on imported foods. Industrial development projects focused on light industries, but also included plants for the production of cement and precast concrete. Service industries were encouraged, especially banking and finance, in the hope of developing Brunei into an international financial center. The establishment of a development bank also ranked high on the government's agenda. The Sixth National Development Plan (1991–95) was allocated a budget of B$5.5 billion to stimulate growth of the private sector, and to promote human resources and industrial development. The largest budget allocation was for social services (29.3%), with equal percentages for public utilities and transport and communications (20% each), 10% allocated to trade and industry, and about 7% to security forces. The two main traditional employers are the government, which absorbs about half the work force, and Brunei Shell Petroleum. Development efforts for a non-oil, non-state sector and the potential for increasing foreign investment are limited by the small domestic market, a shortage of skilled manpower, and relatively high labor and transport costs.

SOCIAL WELFARE

The state provides pensions for the old and disabled, and financial aid for those living in poverty. A major social change in recent years has been the increasing influence of Islam as a way of life. Women are denied equal status with men in many areas, and citizenship is passed on through males only.

Healthcare

Medical personnel in 1991 included 197 physicians. Life expectancy is estimated at 76 years. In 1990, 96% of the population had access to health care services. There is still some risk of filariasis and tuberculosis.

Housing

Development plans for 1986–90 included a public housing program, and government allocations for housing development totaled an estimated $46 million in 1985.

EDUCATION

In 1994, there were 158 primary schools, with 42,270 pupils and 2,772 teachers. Secondary schools had 28,851 students and 2,413 teachers. An estimated 11.8% of adults were illiterate. Brunei has a university and institutes of education and technology.

1999 KEY EVENTS TIMELINE

July

- The Sultan of Brunei leads *Forbes'* list of the net worth of "Kings, Queens, and Dictators" with an estimated $30 billion in wealth. According to a United Nations study, the net worth of the Bill Gates family, the Sultan of Brunei, and the Walton family (the three wealthiest families in the world) is higher than the combined gross domestic product of the forty-three poorest nations in the world.

August

- Man-made fires in the east Malaysian states of Sabah and Sarawak threaten the Southeast Asian Games (SEA) in Brunei. Smog prevention becomes a priority in Malaysia, and the government steps up enforcement on open burning. Slash and burn fires by small farmers and plantation owners rekindle fear of the 1997 smoke pollution crisis that caused health problems throughout the region.

- Sultan Haj Hassanal Bolkiah of Brunei hosts a two day visit of Joseph Estrada of the Philippines to discuss trade and the possibility of a bilateral agreement concerning such issues as migratory labor.

September

- Sultan Haj Hassanal Bolkiah confers with Morocco's King Mohammed on bi-lateral relations.

November

- Indonesian President Abdurraham Wahid visits the Sultan of Brunei as part of his tour of the Association of South East Asian Nations (ASEAN).

- At an informal meeting in Manila, Philippines, six members of the Association of Southeast Asian Nations (ASEAN)—Brunei, Indonesia, Malaysia, Philippines, Singapore, and Thailand—agree to establish a free-trade zone by eliminating duties on most goods traded in the region by 2010. The remaining four newer and less-developed nation members—Cambodia, Laos, Myanmar (Burma), and Vietnam—will eliminate duties by 2015. Rice will be excluded from trade agreements, however.

December

• Brunei hosts the World Grand Prix badminton finals. The International Badminton Federation (IBF) has chosen Brunei as the venue for the annual badminton finals until 2001.

ANALYSIS OF EVENTS: 1999

BUSINESS AND THE ECONOMY

Brunei is located on the north coast of Malaysia jutting out into the South China Sea. Among non-European and non-North American nations, Brunei is relatively wealthy. Its per capita GDP in 1998 was $17,000. The economy is supported mainly by revenues from the petroleum sector which accounted for over half of Brunei's Gross Domestic Product (GDP).

Brunei is the third largest oil producer in Southeast Asia. It is the fourth-largest producer of liquefied natural gas in the world. In the past this has normally guaranteed a brisk pace of economic life and low unemployment. (The unemployment rate stood at 4.8 percent in 1994.) But in the late 1990s the Asian structural crisis slowed Brunei's economy as it did that of its trading partners. In 1998 the growth rate for Brunei was 1 percent. Fluctuating oil prices also weakened the economy. Thus, the Asian financial crisis and the lower world oil prices combined to slow economic growth for Brunei in 1999. The country continued to pursue foreign investment and to give new companies tax advantages. Some signs pointed to an early end to the economic doldrums in Brunei. In case the hard times were to hang on, Brunei's ruling elite had already deployed an extensive social welfare system.

The Brunei government made efforts to diversify the economy with agriculture, forestry, fishing, and banking. There are typically labor shortages in almost all job categories. One-third of the work force is foreign labor. However, immigrant labor is tightly monitored for fear that Bruneian society would be disrupted. The government owns a cattle farm in Australia which supplies the country's beef. Most of Brunei's food is imported.

GOVERNMENT AND POLITICS

Brunei is ruled by the Sultan of Brunei. He is one of the wealthiest men in the world. His wealth is estimated at $30 billion. Brunei is not a democracy. There is no suffrage for anybody in the society. Brunei's legal system is based on English common law, although Islamic Shari'a law also has a role to play in this multi-cultural society.

In 1999 Brunei made a concerted effort to enhance its international profile. Through the year 2001 it will be hosting three international events: the Southeast Asian Games, the APEC 2000 summit, and the World Grand Prix badminton finals. The Sultan of Brunei was also developing relations with other leaders in the region. In September he conferred with Morocco's King Mohammed on bilateral relations. In November the Indonesian President Abdurraham Wahid visited the Sultan of Brunei as part of his tour of the Association of South East Asian Nations (ASEAN).

Sultan Haj Hassanal Bolkiah of Brunei also hosted a two-day visit of President Joseph Estrada of the Philippines to discuss trade and the possibility of a bilateral agreement concerning issues relating to labor shortages and guest workers. The two discuss the creation of a Philippines-Brunei Joint Commission for Bilateral Cooperation. President Estrada planned to amend the Philippine constitution to allow for greater foreign investment in order to create more jobs in the Philippines.

CULTURE AND SOCIETY

Brunei's population was estimated in July 1999 to be 322,982. Life expectancy at birth for the total populations was 71.84 years. The infant mortality rate for 1999 was 22.83 deaths per 1,000 live births. The fertility rate for 1999 was estimated at 3.33 children born per woman. The government provided all medical services, free education, and subsidizes food, fuel and housing. Education in Brunei begins in preschool and nine years of elementary school are compulsary. Most college students attend institutions abroad. The literacy rate of the total population is 88.2 percent.

Ethnic groups in Brunei are Malay (64%), Chinese (20%), and other (16%). The official religion is Muslim, but Buddhism, Christianity and indigenous beliefs are also practiced. The official language is Malay, but English is used in business. Chinese, Iban and numerous native dialects are spoken.

DIRECTORY

CENTRAL GOVERNMENT

Head of State

Sultan and Prime Minister
Hassanal Bolkiah, Office of the Prime Minister,
Bandar Seri Begawan 1000, Brunei
PHONE: +673 (2) 229988
FAX: +673 (2) 241717
E-MAIL: PRO@jpm.gov.bn

Ministers

Minister of Health
Abdul Aziz bin Umar, Ministry of Health,
Bandar Seri, Begawan 3910, Brunei
PHONE: +673 (2) 381640
FAX: +673 (2) 381980

Minister of Communication
Zakaria bin Sulaiman, Ministry of
Communication, Bandar Seri, Begawan 3510,
Brunei
PHONE: +673 (2) 381064
FAX: +673 (2) 383636

Minister of Culture, Youth and Sports
Hussain bin Mohamed Yusof, Ministry of
Culture, Youth and Sports, Bandar Seri,
Begawan 8110, Brunei
PHONE: +673 (2) 240585
FAX: +673 (2) 236282

Minister of Development
Ismail bin Damit, Ministry of Development,
Bandar Seri, Begawan 3510, Brunei
PHONE: +673 (2) 383911
FAX: +673 (2) 380033

Minister of Finance
Bolkiah Hassanal, Ministry of Finance, Bandar
Seri, Begawan 8710, Brunei
PHONE: +673 (2) 234501
FAX: +673 (2) 241829

Minister of Foreign Affairs
Mohamed Bolkiah, Ministry of Foreign Affairs,
Bandar Seri, Begawan 2710, Brunei
PHONE: +673 (2) 261177
FAX: +673 (2) 262904

Minister of Defense
Hassanal Bolkiah, Ministry of Defense, Bandar
Seri, Begawan 3510, Brunei
PHONE: +673 (2) 330130
FAX: +673 (2) 382110

POLITICAL ORGANIZATIONS

Political Parties were banned in 1988.

DIPLOMATIC REPRESENTATION

Embassies in Brunei

Australia
4th Floor, Teck Guan Plaza, Bandar Seri
Begawan 2085, Brunei
PHONE: +673 229435
FAX: +673 221652

Indonesia
EDR 4303, Lot 4498 KG, Bandar Seri Begawan,
Brunei
PHONE: +673 330180

New Zealand
35a Seri Lambak Shopping Centre, Bandar Seri
Begawan 1927, Brunei
PHONE: +673 331010
FAX: +673 331612

United Kingdom
3rd Floor, Hong Kong Bank Chambers, Jalan
Pemancha/Sultan, P.O. Box 2197, Bandar Seri
Begawan, Brunei
PHONE: +673 (2) 222231
FAX: +673 (2) 226002

United States
3rd Floor, Teck Guan Plaza, Jalan Sultan,
Bandar Seri Begawan PSC 470, Brunei
PHONE: +673 (2) 229670
FAX: +673 (2) 225293

JUDICIAL SYSTEM

Supreme Court

Court of Appeal

High Court

FURTHER READING

Books

Brunei Darussalam in Profile. Government of
Brunei Darussalam, 1992.

Bartholomew, James. *The Richest Man in the
World: The Sultan of Brunei.* London:
Penguin Group, 1990.

Chalfont, Lord Alun. *By God's Will: A Portrait
of the Sultan of Brunei.* London: Weidenfeld
and Nicolson, 1989.

Cleary, Mark and Shuang Yann Wong. *Oil,
Economic Development and Diversification in*

Brunei Darussalam. New York: St. Martin's Press, 1994.

Leake, David, Jr. *Brunei: The Modern Southeast-Asian Islamic Sultanate.* Jefferson, N.C.: McFarland and Company, 1989.

Krausse, Sylvia C. Engelen. *Brunei.* Oxford: Santa Barbara, CA: Clio, 1988.

Major, John S. *The Land and People of Malaysia and Brunei.* New York: HarperCollins, 1991.

Pigafetta, Antonio. *Magellan's Voyage.* Trans. and ed. by R. A. Skelton. New Haven: Yale University Press, 1969.

Schelander, Bjorn. *Brunei: Abode of Peace.* Honolulu: Center for Southeast Asian Studies, School of Hawaiian, Asian and Pacific Studies, University of Hawaii, 1998.

Singh, D.S. Ranjit. *Brunei 1839-1983: The Problems of Political Survival.* London: Oxford University Press, 1984.

Tyler, Rodney. *Brunei Darussalam: the Making of a Modern Nation.* Bandar Seri Begawan: R. Tyler, 1996.

Vreeland, N., et al. *Malaysia, a country study.* Area Handbook Series. Fourth edition. Washington, D.C.: Department of the Army. 1984.

BRUNEI: STATISTICAL DATA

For sources and notes see "Sources of Statistics" in the front of each volume.

GEOGRAPHY

Geography (1)

Area:

Total: 5,770 sq km.

Land: 5,270 sq km.

Water: 500 sq km.

Area   comparative: slightly smaller than Delaware.

Land boundaries:

Total: 381 km.

Border countries: Malaysia 381 km.

Coastline: 161 km.

Climate: tropical; hot, humid, rainy.

Terrain: flat coastal plain rises to mountains in east; hilly lowland in west.

Natural resources: petroleum, natural gas, timber.

Land use:

Arable land: 1%

Permanent crops: 1%

Permanent pastures: 1%

Forests and woodland: 85%

Other: 12% (1993 est.).

HUMAN FACTORS

Ethnic Division (6)

Malay 64%

Chinese 20%

Other 16%

Religions (7)

Muslim (official) 63%

Buddhism 14%

Christian 8%

Indigenous beliefs and other 15% (1981)

HUMAN FACTORS

Demographics (2A)

	1990	1995	1998	2000	2010	2020	2030	2040	2050
Population	254.0	292.3	315.3	330.7	409.6	490.1	568.2	641.8	704.4
Net migration rate (per 1,000 population)	NA	NA	NA	NA	NA	NA	NA	NA	NA
Births	NA	NA	NA	NA	NA	NA	NA	NA	NA
Deaths	NA	NA	NA	NA	NA	NA	NA	NA	NA
Life expectancy - males	68.7	69.7	70.2	70.5	72.1	73.5	74.7	75.7	76.6
Life expectancy - females	72.3	72.9	73.3	73.6	74.8	75.9	76.9	77.9	78.7
Birth rate (per 1,000)	27.7	25.8	24.9	24.5	22.8	21.2	19.8	18.2	15.8
Death rate (per 1,000)	5.0	5.1	5.2	5.3	5.8	6.5	7.4	7.9	7.9
Women of reproductive age (15-49 yrs.)	62.5	73.9	79.8	83.4	98.8	116.5	134.6	151.6	168.1
of which are currently married	NA	NA	NA	NA	NA	NA	NA	NA	NA
Fertility rate	3.5	3.4	3.3	3.3	3.1	3.0	2.8	2.5	2.2

Except as noted, values for vital statistics are in thousands; life expectancy is in years.

Languages (8)

Malay (official), English, Chinese.

EDUCATION

Educational Attainment (10)

Age group (1981) . . . . .25+

Total population 75,283

Highest level attained (%)

No schooling 32.1

First level

Not completed 28.3

Completed . . . . .NA

Entered second level

S-1 . . . . .30.1

S-2 . . . . .NA

Postsecondary 9.4

Literacy Rates (11A)

In thousands and percent[1]	1990	1995	2000	2010
Illiterate population (15+ yrs.)	24	22	20	14
Literacy rate - total adult pop. (%)	85.1	88.2	90.8	94.9
Literacy rate - males (%)	90.5	92.6	94.3	96.8
Literacy rate - females (%)	79.0	83.4	86.9	92.9

GOVERNMENT & LAW

Political Parties (12)

The country is ruled by a traditional Islamic monarch. There are no elections.

Government Budget (13B)

Revenues . . . .$2.5 billion

Expenditures . . . .$2.6 billion

Capital expenditures . . . .$768 million

Data for 1995 est.

Crime (15)

Crime rate (for 1997)

Crimes reported 3,250

Total persons convicted 1,300

Crimes per 100,000 population 1,100

Persons responsible for offenses

Total number of suspects 2,750

Total number of female suspects 125

Total number of juvenile suspects 225

LABOR FORCE

Labor Force (16)

Total 144,000; includes foreign workers and military personnel. Data for 1995 est.

Unemployment Rate (17)

4.8% (1994 est.)

PRODUCTION SECTOR

Electric Energy (18)

Capacity . . . . .646,000 kW (1997 est.)

Production . . . . .1.26 billion kWh (1995)

Consumption per capita . . . . .4,311 kWh (1995)

Transportation (19)

Highways:

total: 1,150 km

paved: 399 km

unpaved: 751 km (1996 est.)

Waterways: 209 km; navigable by craft drawing less than 1.2 m

Pipelines: crude oil 135 km; petroleum products 418 km; natural gas 920 km

Merchant marine:

total: 7 liquefied gas tankers (1,000 GRT or over) totaling 348,476 GRT/340,635 DWT (1997 est.)

Airports: 2 (1997 est.)

Airports—with paved runways:

total: 1

over 3,047 m: 1 (1997 est.)

Airports—with unpaved runways:

total: 1

914 to 1,523 m: 1 (1997 est.)

Top Agricultural Products (20)

Rice, cassava (tapioca), bananas; water buffalo.

GOVERNMENT & LAW

Military Affairs (14B)

	1990	1991	1992	1993	1994	1995
Military expenditures						
Current dollars (mil.)	333	NA	436	NA	340	269
1995 constant dollars (mil.)	382	NA	469	NA	348	269
Armed forces (000)	4	4	4	4	4	5
Gross national product (GNP)						
Current dollars (mil.)	3,980	4,290	4,362	4,297	4,304	4,500[e]
1995 constant dollars (mil.)	4,574	4,741	4,692	4,502	4,412	4,500[e]
Central government expenditures (CGE)						
1995 constant dollars (mil.)	1,897	NA	NA	2,359	NA	NA
People (mil.)	.3	.3	.3	.3	.3	.3
Military expenditure as % of GNP	8.4	NA	10.0	NA	7.9	6.0
Military expenditure as % of CGE	20.1	NA	NA	NA	NA	NA
Military expenditure per capita (1995 $)	1,505	NA	1,742	NA	1,224	919
Armed forces per 1,000 people (soldiers)	16.7	17.0	14.9	14.4	14.1	17.1
GNP per capita (1995 $)	18,010	18,120	17,420	16,260	15,500	15,400
Arms imports[6]						
Current dollars (mil.)	10	0	0	0	0	5
1995 constant dollars (mil.)	11	0	0	0	0	5
Arms exports[6]						
Current dollars (mil.)	0	0	0	0	0	0
1995 constant dollars (mil.)	0	0	0	0	0	0
Total imports[7]						
Current dollars (mil.)	1,019	1,084	NA	1,200[e]	1,800[e]	NA
1995 constant dollars (mil.)	1,171	1,198	NA	1,258[e]	1,845[e]	NA
Total exports[7]						
Current dollars (mil.)	2,226	2,480	2,496[e]	2,373[e]	2,400[e]	NA
1995 constant dollars (mil.)	2,558	2,470	2,685[e]	2,488[e]	2,460[e]	NA
Arms as percent of total imports[8]	1.0	0	NA	0	0	NA
Arms as percent of total exports[8]	0	0	0	0	0	NA

MANUFACTURING SECTOR

GDP & Manufacturing Summary (21)

	1980	1985	1990	1992	1993	1994
Gross Domestic Product						
Millions of 1990 dollars	4,248	3,526	3,596	3,690	3,542	3,648
Growth rate in percent	−7.00	−1.49	2.74	−1.00	−4.00	3.00
Per capita (in 1990 dollars)	22,011.1	15,603.1	13,991.9	13,716.0	12,927.1	13,029.6
Manufacturing Value Added						
Millions of 1990 dollars	430	254	323	239	*224*	*228*
Growth rate in percent	−8.35	−5.42	5.31	−4.56	*−6.30*	*1.93*
Manufacturing share in percent of current prices	11.7	10.0	8.8	7.7	NA	NA

FINANCE, ECONOMICS, & TRADE

Economic Indicators (22)

National product: GDP—purchasing power parity—$5.4 billion (1997 est.)

National product real growth rate: 3.5% (1997 est.)

National product per capita: $18,000 (1997 est.)

Inflation rate—consumer price index: 2% (1997 est.)

Exchange Rates (24)

Exchange rates:

Bruneian dollars (B$) per US$1

January 1998	1.7533
1997	1.4848
1996	1.4100
1995	1.4174
1994	1.5274
1993	1.6158

The Bruneian dollar is at par with the Singapore dollar.

Top Import Origins (25)

$2.65 billion (c.i.f., 1996 est.). Data are for 1994 est.

Origins	%
Singapore	29
United Kingdom	19
United States	13
Malaysia	9%
Japan	5%

Top Export Destinations (26)

$2.62 billion (f.o.b., 1996 est.). Data are for 1996 est.

Destinations	%
ASEAN	31
Japan	27
South Korea	26
United Kingdom	NA
Taiwan	NA

NA stands for not available.

Economic Aid (27)

$NA. NA stands for not available.

Import Export Commodities (28)

Import Commodities	Export Commodities
Machinery and transport equipment	Crude oil
Manufactured goods	Liquefied natural gas
Food	Petroleum products
Chemicals	

BULGARIA

Republic of Bulgaria
Republika Bulgaria

INTRODUCTORY SURVEY

RECENT HISTORY

In September 1946, the Bulgarian people voted to replace the monarchy with the People's Republic of Bulgaria. A new constitution in 1947 gave the government control of industry, banking, public utilities, and agriculture. Each program was modeled on the system of the USSR, a powerful communist country at that time.

The Bulgarian government remained steadfastly loyal to the Soviet Union. However, in the late 1980s and early 1990s, the radical changes that the leader of the Soviet Union, Mikhail Gorbachev, was introducing encouraged reformist elements within the Bulgarian Communist Party. The reformists eventually won the day and Bulgaria's first non-Communist government since World War II was elected in October 1991. The new government undertook an ambitious program of economic and political transformation.

However, Bulgaria's economy continued to deteriorate, and political and economic problems persist. In 1996, the economy had deteriorated so badly that the country replaced Albania as the poorest in Europe. In 1996 elections, the Union of Democratic Forces party won presidential elections, and in 1997 the parliamentary elections were won by its allies. The government is currently instituting a broad program of economic reform.

GOVERNMENT

The Constitution of July 1991 provides for a presidential-parliamentary form of republican government.

The president, who is chief of state, is popularly elected. The president chooses the prime minister, who is then confirmed by the National Assembly. In practice, the president sets the overall direction of policy. The prime minister and his cabinet, presently fourteen people, are responsible for putting that policy to work. The legislative

branch of government is the National Assembly, with 240 seats.

Judiciary

As of 1996, Bulgaria had a system of regional courts and a constitutional court. Judges are appointed by the Supreme Judicial Council. The twelve judges on the Constitutional Court are appointed to nine-year terms by the National Assembly.

The Constitutional Court handles review of legislation and resolves issues of competency in other branches of government and impeachments. The judiciary is independent of the legislative and executive branches.

Political Parties

The former Communist Party, renamed the Bulgarian Socialist Party (BSP) in 1990, did surprisingly well in the 1991 elections, gaining 53% of the vote. By 1992, their support had dropped to 33%, making them a minority party by four parliamentary seats. The largest vote-getter in 1992 was the Union of Democratic Forces (UDF), an umbrella group of opposition forces.

The third party, the Movement for Rights and Freedoms (MRF), primarily represents the interests of Bulgaria's large Turkish minority (about 11% of the population).

Right-wing parties include the Bulgarian National Radical Party, the Defense of National Interests, and the Revival Movement.

Presidential elections in 1996 saw the election of the UDF's candidate, Peter Stoyanov. Parliamentary elections were held in 1997, with 137 seats being won by the UDF, making it the majority party.

DEFENSE

In 1995, the strength of the armed forces was estimated at 103,500 men, including 70,000 draftees. It consists of ground, naval, and air elements. The army numbered 51,600, the navy 6,100, and the air force 20,100, with some 259 combat aircraft.

ECONOMIC AFFAIRS

Until 1990, the country had a centrally planned economy, along Soviet lines. Its sequence of five-year economic plans, beginning in 1949, emphasized industrial production. The Bulgarian economy was greatly influenced by the breakup of the Soviet Union because it relied on the Soviet Union and other CMEA (Council for Mutual Economic Assistance) countries for essential imports and as the major markets for its exports.

Bulgaria began an economic reform program supported by the IBRD (International Bank for Reconstruction and Development) and IMF (International Monetary Fund). However, the economy remained largely state controlled. Following years of rampant corruption, the inflation rate in early 1997 was 300%, and Bulgaria had become the poorest country in Europe with average monthly wages at $30. After widespread street protests in that year, a new government was elected that instituted harsh economic reforms.

Public Finance

An annual budget for all levels of government, becoming effective on 1 January, is voted by the National Assembly, after having been prepared by the Ministry of Finance. The disintegration of the communist system in November 1989 and the subsequent collapse of the Soviet trade bloc caused severe economic disruption, pushing the government's budget deficit to 8.5% of GDP in 1990 (not including interest payments on commercial foreign debt). By the end of 1993, the budget deficit totaled $894 million, due to a 25% drop in tax collections.

The U.S. CIA estimates that, in 1995, government revenues totaled approximately $3.8 billion and expenditures $4.4 billion. External debt totaled $10.4 billion, approximately 64% of which was financed abroad.

By 1996, the government was spending two-thirds of its budget on domestic and foreign interest payments, leaving little left for essential services. Schools went without heat and hospitals ran out of medical supplies. In an effort to bring the economy under control, Bulgaria's parliament approved a budget in June 1997 adhering to IMF imposed restraints.

Income

The gross national product (GNP) is approximately $10.1 billion, or $1,230 per capita. For the period 1985–95 the average inflation rate was 45.3%, resulting in a decline in per capita gross national product of 2.2%.

Industry

In the postwar period, the communist regime emphasized an industrial program that resulted in a large increase in the metalworking and chemical industries. Official statistics indicate that industrial output grew by 1,100% between 1956 and 1980.

In the early 1990s, industry suffered from the break-up of the Soviet Union. Between 1993 and 1995, however, industrial production had recovered. It accounted for 29.3% of gross domestic product in 1995.

Banking and Finance

All banks were nationalized in 1947 in accord with Soviet banking policies. Until 1969, the Bulgarian National Bank (BNB) was the chief banking institution handling deposits of state and local governments and national enterprises. It was the bank of issue and was authorized to credit enterprises with funds for facilities and activities not covered by the capital investment plan. In 1969, it was renamed the Bulgarian Central bank and remained the bank of issue.

When Bulgaria achieved independence in 1991, a two-tier banking system was formed. The Bulgarian National Bank became the country's central bank. In 1996, the Bulgarian National Bank, lacking reserves, virtually gave up attempts to stabilize the exchange rate and contain inflation.

The First Bulgarian Stock Exchange was established in Sofia on 8 November, 1991 as a joint stock company with capital of Lv10,000,000 divided into 10,000 shares of Lv1,000 each. The exchange currently trades mainly in unlisted securities.

Economic Development

The economy was almost entirely nationalized or cooperatively owned until 1990, and operated on the basis of state plans. In 1971, productive enterprises were grouped into more than sixty state concerns responsible for almost all nonagricultural production.

In the 1990s, the post-Communist government began a program of privatization and reform of the nation's economy. It rescheduled the foreign debt, abolished price controls, and became a member of the IMF and IBRD. The reforms, however, were not embraced by the Socialist government that took power in 1994, and by 1996 the economy was in a tailspin. The new government that took power in 1997 seems much stronger in its efforts at reform.

SOCIAL WELFARE

Social insurance is administered by the trade unions and is comprehensive. A state employee qualifies for sickness benefits after three months of employment. Disability pensions range from 40% to 75% of previous earnings. Benefits also include old-age and survivors' pensions.

Due to the severe economic problems of 1996–97, pensions and other benefits are paid at the minimum levels allowed and do not ensure a minimum standard of living.

Special benefits include a grant upon birth of a child and monthly family allowances for children. The amounts increase with the number of children. Paid maternity leave is 100% of earnings for 4–6 months, depending on the number of other children.

Although women have equal rights under the constitution, they have not had the same employment opportunities as men.

Healthcare

The Ministry of Health is the controlling agency for the health system in Bulgaria. Medical care has never been well funded, and the shift from a centrally planned to a private enterprise system made matters worse. Doctors continue to receive low wages and operate inadequate and outdated machinery. Patients on the whole receive minimal health services.

In 1990, there were 28,497 doctors. As of 1998, there were about 3.5 doctors per 1,000 people. In 1990, there were 90,000 hospital beds (10 beds per 1,000 people).

More people die from strokes in Bulgaria than anywhere else in Europe, and circulatory diseases account for almost 60% of deaths. Smoking is on the increase; alcohol consumption is high; physical activity is low; and obesity is common. Bulgarians have a high intake of fats, sugars, and salt. One out of eight people has high blood pressure. Life expectancy averages 71 years.

Housing

Although housing construction during 1976–85 averaged about 60,000 units per year, the housing shortage continues, especially in the larger cities. This is due to the influx into urban areas of new workers.

In 1991, there were 3.4 million dwelling units in the country, 24% more than in 1975. The number of new houses built plummeted from 62,926 in 1988 to 19,423 in 1991.

EDUCATION

Illiteracy has been decreasing steadily. The government claims that literacy is universal, but Western sources estimate 2% illiteracy. Education is free and compulsory for eight years between the ages of seven and fifteen. In 1994, there were 2,758 primary level schools with 58,201 teachers and 825,984 students. At the secondary level, there were 31,305 teachers and 371,102 students, 212,401 of them in vocational courses.

There are over thirty higher education institutions, including four universities. The most important is the University of Sofia, founded in 1888.

1999 KEY EVENTS TIMELINE

March

- NATO begins its air war against Serbia in response to Yugoslav ''ethnic cleansing'' of ethnic Albanians in the Serbian province of Kosovo.

April

- Bulgaria grants permission for Turkish military aircraft to fly over Bulgarian airspace en route to Serbia.

- An errant NATO missile lands in the outskirts of Sofia causing damage to an apartment building.

May

- United States Secretary of State Madeline Albright travels to Bulgaria.

July

- The Bulgarian Family Planning Association launches the ''cool condom'' program.

September

- The Bulgarian government destroys the mausoleum of Georgi Dimitrov, the country's first communist leader.

November

- The European Union announces that it will increase grants to Bulgaria during the period 2000-2003, and will consider the country's application for EU membership. Bulgaria must first close outdated nuclear reactors and improve the structure of the economy.

- U.S. president Bill Clinton visits Bulgaria to mark the tenth anniversary of the end of communism.

December

- The Council of Europe expresses concern over large-scale corruption as Bulgaria's industries are privatized.

ANALYSIS OF EVENTS: 1999

BUSINESS AND THE ECONOMY

In domestic policy, the UDF's main emphasis was economic reform. The UDF continued its policy of divestment and the promotion of membership in the European Union (EU). Bulgaria currently holds associate membership. While many of the austerity measures were unpopular, the government persisted in its efforts and remains much more powerful than its former communist opponents.

In a major move, the government entered the New Year with the lev (Bulgarian currency) pegged to the euro at a 1,955.83:1 rate. Inflation held at around one percent. In another sudden move, the government stamped out the widespread music piracy trade.

Yet critics continue to point to the low standard of living and the slow pace of reform in Bulgaria, particularly divestment of government enterprises. By any measure, Bulgaria has a long way to go toward catching up with the former communist states of Central Europe, let alone EU members. Nonetheless, the progress made by Bulgaria over the previous two years (since the country's banking system collapsed) is an impressive accomplishment.

GOVERNMENT AND POLITICS

Nineteen ninety-nine was another year of full-speed-ahead reform pursued by the center-right government of Prime Minister Ivan Kostov. Bulgaria also followed a strongly pro-Western and reformist domestic program with the support of president and fellow reformer Petar Stoyanov. By year's end, these policies had contributed greatly to Bulgaria's standing as a stable country in the region.

The unabashedly pro-Western stance of the government was in evidence as soon as the NATO air strikes against Serbia began in late March. Although the overwhelming majority of Bulgarians opposed the conflict (as was the case in neighboring Greece and Macedonia), the Bulgarian government supported NATO's action wholeheartedly and even went to the length of permitting Turkish warplanes to fly over Bulgaria on their way to targets in Serbia. As one headline summed up this policy, the pro-NATO policy was, indeed, a "brave gamble" for Bulgaria. Not only did nearly all Bulgarians oppose the war, Bulgaria itself suffered from the continuation of hostilities. Errant NATO missiles struck suburban Sofia; the bombing of Serbia cut off Bulgaria from the Danube River, its primary trading route; and expected economic growth declined by over half from five to two percent.

In the final analysis, however, Bulgaria's gamble paid off. NATO's recognition of Bulgarian support for the war effort bodes well for Bulgaria's desire to be included in a subsequent expansion of the Atlantic Alliance. The United States also extended much needed economic assistance.

Following the end of hostilities, Stoyanov and Kostov continued their pro-Western reform-minded diplomacy. In the spring, Bulgaria reached agreement with Macedonia on its language. Prior to this settlement, Bulgaria considered Macedonian to be a western Bulgarian dialect thereby negating a claim to a distinct Macedonian national identity. Stoyanov and Kostov also reached agreement with Albania on an oil pipeline which is to run from the Bulgarian Black Sea port of Bourgas to Albania's Adriatic port of Vlore.

Domestically, the reformist Union of Democratic Forces (UDF) maintained its support during municipal elections in October. A symbol of the reformist spirit of the UDF was the previous month's destruction of the mausoleum of Bulgaria's first Communist dictator, Georgi Dimitrov.

CULTURE AND SOCIETY

Bulgarian society remains deeply affected by the country's recent history of economic and political instability. A major recent phenomenon has been the development of crime syndicates that are comprised of former members of the communist security service. These organizations profit from their questionable business ventures, particularly with government firms, that invariably leave their collaborators broke. After less than a decade in existence, their power already threatens the establishment of a constitutional authority.

Private initiatives in birth control and safe sex aimed at young people stressed the importance of condoms. In July, the Bulgarian Family Planning Association introduced a "Cool Condom" program while in September the BBC began airing its television program "Sexwise" in eleven countries, including Bulgaria. In another field, the city of Plovdiv opened a two-month cultural festival in late May. In October, the Bulgarian documentary, "The Unwanted," a story of three women (two Turks, one Bulgarian) in the ethnically heterogeneous border region of the Eastern Rhodope Mountains, won second prize at the Religion Today International Festival in Italy.

DIRECTORY

CENTRAL GOVERNMENT

Head of State

President
Petar Stoyanov

Prime Minister
Ivan Kostov, Office of the Prime Minister

Ministers

Deputy Prime Minister and Minister of Industry
Alexander Boshkov, Ministry of Industry

Deputy Prime Minister and Minister of Regional and Urban Development
Evgeniy Bakardjiev, Ministry of Regional and Urban Development

Deputy Prime Minister and Minister of Education and Science
Vesselin Metodiev, Ministry of Education and Science

Minister of State Administration
Mario Tagarinski, Ministry of State Administration, 1 Doundukov Blvd., BG-1149 Sofia, Bulgaria
PHONE: +359 9810118; 8872079
FAX: +359 9802028
E-MAIL: R.Kinkina@bulgaria.govrn.bg

Minister of the Interior
Bogomil Bonev, Ministry of the Interior, 23 Gurko Str., BG-1000 Sofia
PHONE: +359 98222014
FAX: +359 9877967
E-MAIL: spvo@mvr.bg/

Minister of Defense
Gueorgui Ananiev, Ministry of Defense, Information and Public Relations Office, 3, Vassil Levski Str., BG-1000 Sofia
PHONE: +359 9885885
FAX: +359 873228

Minister of Culture
Emma Moskova, Ministry of Culture, 17, Alexander Stamboliiski Blvd., BG-1000 Sofia, Bulgaria
PHONE: +359 9805384
FAX: +359 9818145
E-MAIL: press.culture@newsmail.bta.bg

Minister of Environment and Waters
Evdokia Maneva, Ministry of Environment and Waters, 67 William Gladstone Str., BG-1000 Sofia, Bulgaria
PHONE: +359 9811385
FAX: +359 9885913
E-MAIL: veselinovaz@moew.government.bg

Minister of Labor and Social Policy
Ivan Neikov, Ministry of Labor and Social Policy, 2, Triaditza Str., BG-1000 Sofia, Bulgaria
PHONE: +359 873394
FAX: +359 9861318
E-MAIL: varshi@mlsp.government.bg

Minister of Finance
Mouravei Radev, Ministry of Finance, 102, Georgi Rakovski Str., BG-1000 Sofia, Bulgaria
PHONE: +359 98592020
FAX: +359 870581
E-MAIL: O.Raeva@minfin.govrn.bg

Minister of Foreign Affairs

Nadezhda Mihailova, Ministry of Foreign
Affairs, 2, Alexander Jendov Str., BG-1113
Sofia, Bulgaria
PHONE: +359 737997
FAX: +359 703041
E-MAIL: mfainf@mb.bia-bg

Minister of Health

Peter Boyadjiev, Ministry of Health, 5, St.
Nedelia Sq., BG-1000 Sofia, Bulgaria
PHONE: +359 9811830
FAX: +359 9811830
E-MAIL: mzpress@mbox.infotel.bg

Minister of Trade and Tourism

Vasil Gotsev, Ministry of Trade and Tourism, 12
Kniaz Alexander Batenberg Str., BG-1000 Sofia,
Bulgaria
PHONE: +359 9870696
FAX: +359 9819953
E-MAIL: mttpress@tradel.net

Minister of Justice and European Legal Integration

Ventsislav Vurbanovasil, Ministry of Justice and
European Legal Integration, 1, Slavianska Str.,
BG-1000 Sofia, Bulgaria
PHONE: +359 9819157
FAX: +359 9819157
E-MAIL: mjeli.press@melsity.com

Minister of Agriculture, Forestry and Agrarian Reform

Wilhelm Kraus, Ministry of Agriculture, Forestry
and Agrarian Reform, 55, Hristo Botev Blvd.,
BG-1000 Sofia, Bulgaria
PHONE: +359 9809927
FAX: +359 9806256

Minister of Industry

Alexander Boshkov, Ministry of Industry, 8,
Slavianska Str., BG-1000 Sofia, Bulgaria
PHONE: +359 9885532
FAX: +359 9802690
E-MAIL: vlambrinova@mi.government.bg

Minister of Transport

Valentina Luleva, Ministry of Transport, 9,
Levski Str., BG-1000 Sofia, Bulgaria
PHONE: +359 9885329
FAX: +359 9885329

Minister of Education and Science

Gemma Barruh, Ministry of Education and
Science, 2, Doundukov Blvd., BG-1000 Sofia,
Bulgaria
PHONE: +359 9805384

FAX: +359 9818145

Minister of Regional and Urban Development

Ministry of Regional and Urban Development,
17-19, Kiril and Metodii Str., BG-1000 Sofia,
Bulgaria
PHONE: +359 9882954
FAX: +359 9875856

POLITICAL ORGANIZATIONS

Social Democratic Party of Bulgaria (BSDP)

TITLE: Chairman
NAME: Petar Dertliev

United Democratic Forces (ODS)

NAME: Ivan Kostov

Alliance for Social Democracy (OSD)

NAME: Chavdar Kyranov

Union of Democratic Forces (SDS)

NAME: Ivan Kostov

Movement for Rights and Freedom

NAME: Ahmed Dogan

Bulgarian Socialist Party (BSP)

NAME: Georgi Parvanov

Union for National Salvation (UNS)

NAME: Ahmed Dogan

Bulgarian Agrarian People's Union (PU)

NAME: Anastasia Dimitrova-Mozer

People's Union

NAME: Stefan Savov

Bulgarian Agrarian People's Union (BZNS)

NAME: Georgi Pinchev

Democratic Party (DP)

NAME: Stefan Savov

Bulgarian Business Block (BBB)

NAME: George Gantchev

New Pro-European Left (Euro Left)

TITLE: Chair
NAME: Alexander Tomov

Labour Block

NAME: Krastyu Petkov

Social Democratic Party

NAME: Blagoy Dimitrov

New Social Democratic Party

NAME: Vassil Mikhailov

Confederation of Independent Trade Unions of Bulgaria

TITLE: President
NAME: Zhelyazko Khristov

Podkrepa Confederation of Labor

TITLE: President
NAME: Konstantin Trenchev

Bulgarian Democratic Center

NAME: Nikola Petkov

DIPLOMATIC REPRESENTATION

Embassies in Bulgaria

Albania

10, Krakra Street, Sofia, Bulgaria
PHONE: +359 441110

Argentina

131, Evlogi Georgiev Blvd., Sofia, Bulgaria
PHONE: +359 443821

Austria

4, Shipka Street, Sofia, Bulgaria
PHONE: +359 803572

Belgium

1, Velchova Zavera Square, Sofia, Bulgaria
PHONE: +359 651062

Brazil

19, Joliot Curie Street, Sofia, Bulgaria
PHONE: +359 443655

China

5-7 Henn. Barbusse Street, Sofia, Bulgaria
PHONE: +359 722127

Columbia

17 Vassil Aprilov Street, Sofia, Bulgaria
PHONE: +359 446177

Croatia

3, Vassil Levski Blvd., Sofia, Bulgaria
PHONE: +359 880470

Cuba

1, Konstantin Shtarkelov Street, Sofia, Bulgaria
PHONE: +359 720996

France

29, Oborishte Street, Sofia, Bulgaria
PHONE: +359 441171

Germany

25, Joliot Curie Street, Sofia, Bulgaria
PHONE: +359 650451

Japan

14, Lyulyakova Gradira Street, Sofia, Bulgaria
PHONE: +359 723984

Macedonia

17, Joliot Curie Street, Sofia, Bulgaria
PHONE: +359 701003

Poland

46, Khan Kroum Street, Sofia, Bulgaria
PHONE: +359 885182

South Africa

3, Vassil Aprilov Street, Sofia, Bulgaria
PHONE: +359 442916

United Kingdom

38, Vassil Levski Blvd., BG-1000 Sofia, Bulgaria
PHONE: +359 9801220
FAX: +359 9801229
E-MAIL: britembsof@mbox.cit.bg

United States

1, Saborna Street, Sofia, Bulgaria
PHONE: +359 884801

JUDICIAL SYSTEM

Constitutional Court

Supreme Court of Cassation

Supreme Administrative Court

FURTHER READING

Articles

Jones, Colin. "Westward Leaning (Bulgaria Attempts to Align Itself with the West)." *The Banker* 149 (June 1999): 43+.

"Political Dynamite." *Time International* 154 (September 6, 1999): 20.

"The Tortoise and the Hare: Romania and Bulgaria." *The Economist* (August 7, 1999): 40.

Books

Bell, John D., ed. *Bulgaria in Transition: Politics, Economics, Society, and Culture after Communism.* Boulder, CO: Westview Press, 1998.

Crampton, R. J. *A Concise History of Bulgaria.* New York: Cambridge University Press, 1997.

Jones, Derek C. and Jeffrey Miller, eds. *The Bulgarian Economy: Lessons from Reform during Early Transition.* Brookfield, Vt.: Ashgate, 1997.

Internet

Balkan Info-Bulgaria. Available Online @ http://www.b-info.com/places/Bulgaria/news/ (November 3, 1999).

Bulgaria.Com. Available Online @ http://www.bulgaria.com (November 3, 1999).

BULGARIA:
STATISTICAL DATA

For sources and notes see "Sources of Statistics" in the front of each volume.

GEOGRAPHY

Geography (1)

Area:

Total: 110,910 sq km.

Land: 110,550 sq km.

Water: 360 sq km.

Area—comparative: slightly larger than Tennessee.

Land boundaries:

Total: 1,808 km.

Border countries: Greece 494 km, The Former Yugoslav Republic of Macedonia 148 km, Romania 608 km,

Serbia and Montenegro 318 km (all with Serbia), Turkey 240 km.

Coastline: 354 km.

Climate: temperate; cold, damp winters; hot, dry summers.

Terrain: mostly mountains with lowlands in north and southeast.

Natural resources: bauxite, copper, lead, zinc, coal, timber, arable land.

Land use:

Arable land: 37%

Permanent crops: 2%

Permanent pastures: 16%

Forests and woodland: 35%

Other: 10% (1993 est.).

HUMAN FACTORS

Demographics (2A)

	1990	1995	1998	2000	2010	2020	2030	2040	2050
Population	NA	8,399.0	8,240.4	8,155.8	7,903.8	7,514.9	7,066.2	6,531.5	5,904.9
Net migration rate (per 1,000 population)	NA	NA	NA	NA	NA	NA	NA	NA	NA
Births	NA	NA	NA	NA	NA	NA	NA	NA	NA
Deaths	NA	NA	NA	NA	NA	NA	NA	NA	NA
Life expectancy - males	NA	67.4	68.4	69.1	72.0	74.4	76.3	77.7	78.8
Life expectancy - females	NA	74.8	75.7	76.3	78.9	81.0	82.6	83.9	84.9
Birth rate (per 1,000)	NA	8.6	8.1	9.3	9.5	7.3	7.2	6.1	5.7
Death rate (per 1,000)	NA	13.7	13.2	13.2	13.1	13.1	13.9	15.2	16.7
Women of reproductive age (15-49 yrs.)	NA	2,050.8	2,022.4	1,992.9	1,849.2	1,665.5	1,436.2	1,189.0	1,069.5
of which are currently married	NA	NA	NA	NA	NA	NA	NA	NA	NA
Fertility rate	NA	1.2	1.1	1.3	1.5	1.4	1.4	1.3	1.3

Except as noted, values for vital statistics are in thousands; life expectancy is in years.

Health Personnel (3)

Total health expenditure as a percentage of GDP, 1990-1997[a]

Public sector 3.5

Private sector 1.4

Total[b] 6.7

Health expenditure per capita in U.S. dollars, 1990-1997[a]

Purchasing power parity 287

Total 68

Availability of health care facilities per 100,000 people

Hospital beds 1990-1997[a] 1060

Doctors 1993[c] 333

Nurses 1993[c] 652

Health Indicators (4)

Life expectancy at birth

1980 71

1997 71

Daily per capita supply of calories (1996) 2,756

Total fertility rate births per woman (1997) 1.1

Maternal mortality ratio per 100,000 live births (1990-97) . . . . .20[b]

Safe water % of population with access (1995) . . . .

Sanitation % of population with access (1995) . . . .

Consumption of iodized salt % of households (1992-98)[a] . . . .

Smoking prevalence

Male % of adults (1985-95)[a] 49

Female % of adults (1985-95)[a] 17

Tuberculosis incidence per 100,000 people (1997) 43

Adult HIV prevalence % of population ages 15-49 (1997) 0.01

Infants and Malnutrition (5)

Under-5 mortality rate (1997) 19

% of infants with low birthweight (1990-97) 6

Births attended by skilled health staff % of total[a] . . .99

% fully immunized (1995-97)

TB 97

DPT 94

Polio 96

Measles 93

Prevalence of child malnutrition under age 5 (1992-97)[b] . . . . .NA

Ethnic Division (6)

Bulgarian 85.3%

Turk 8.5%

Gypsy 2.6%

Macedonian 2.5%

Armenian 0.3%

Russian 0.2%

Other 0.6%

Religions (7)

Bulgarian Orthodox 85%

Muslim 13%

Jewish 0.8%

Roman Catholic 0.5%

Uniate Catholic 0.2%

Protestant, Gregorian Armenian and other 0.5%

Languages (8)

Bulgarian, secondary languages closely correspond to ethnic breakdown

EDUCATION

Public Education Expenditures (9)

Public expenditure on education (% of GNP)

1980 . . . . .4.5

1996 . . . . .3.3

Expenditure per student

Primary % of GNP per capita

1980 . . . . .17.5

1996 . . . . .31.9

Secondary % of GNP per capita

1980 . . . .

1996 . . . .

Tertiary % of GNP per capita

1980 . . . . .51.3

1996 . . . . .18.0

Expenditure on teaching materials

Primary % of total for level (1996) . . . .

Secondary % of total for level (1996) . . . .

Primary pupil-teacher ratio per teacher (1996) 17

Duration of primary education years (1995) 4

Educational Attainment (10)

Age group (1992)[22] . . . . .25+

Total population 5,649,672

Highest level attained (%)

No schooling 4.7

First level

Not completed 12.5

Completed 31.9

Entered second level

S-1 ....35.7

S-2 ....NA

Postsecondary 15.0

Literacy Rates (11B)

Adult literacy rate

1980

Male ....-

Female ....-

1995

Male 99

Female 98

GOVERNMENT & LAW

Political Parties (12)

National Assembly	No. of seats
Union of Democratic Forces (UDF) 137	
Bulgarian Socialist Party (BSP) 58	
Alliance for National Salvation (ANS) 19	
Euro-left 14	
Bulgarian Business Bloc (BBB) 12	

Military Affairs (14B)

	1990	1991	1992	1993	1994	1995
Military expenditures						
Current dollars (mil.)	3,887	1,464	1,196	1,040	982	1,073
1995 constant dollars (mil.)	4,467	1,618	1,286	1,090	1,007	1,073
Armed forces (000)	129	107	99	52	80	86
Gross national product (GNP)						
Current dollars (mil.)	45,290	36,900	36,910	35,960	36,900	37,670
1995 constant dollars (mil.)	52,050	40,780	39,700	37,700	37,830	37,670
Central government expenditures (CGE)						
1995 constant dollars (mil.)	NA	NA	16,280	17,510	16,480	17,050
People (mil.)	9.0	8.9	8.9	8.5	8.5	8.6
Military expenditure as % of GNP	8.6	4.0	3.2	2.6	2.7	2.8
Military expenditure as % of CGE	NA	NA	7.9	6.2	6.1	6.3
Military expenditure per capita (1995 $)	498	181	145	128	118	125
Armed forces per 1,000 people (soldiers)	14.4	12.0	11.2	6.1	9.4	10.0
GNP per capita (1995 $)	5,805	4,574	4,476	4,438	4,435	4,394
Arms imports[6]						
Current dollars (mil.)	675	0	0	5	0	0
1995 constant dollars (mil.)	776	0	0	5	0	0
Arms exports[6]						
Current dollars (mil.)	80	110	120	80	60	150
1995 constant dollars (mil.)	92	122	129	84	62	150
Total imports[7]						
Current dollars (mil.)	9,600	2,800[e]	4,346[e]	5,059	4,377	5,252
1995 constant dollars (mil.)	11,030	3,094[e]	4,675[e]	5,304	4,487	5,252
Total exports[7]						
Current dollars (mil.)	8,400	3,500[e]	3,600[e]	3,738	4,226	5,391
1995 constant dollars (mil.)	9,654	3,868[e]	3,872[e]	3,919	4,332	5,391
Arms as percent of total imports[8]	7.0	0	0	.1	0	0
Arms as percent of total exports[8]	1.0	3.1	3.3	2.1	1.4	2.8

Government Budget (13A)

Year: 1997

Total Expenditures: 5,733.2 Millions of Leva

Expenditures as a percentage of the total by function:

General public services and public order 10.59

Defense 8.03

Education 5.65

Health 5.70

Social Security and Welfare 27.08

Housing and community amenities 43

Recreational, cultural, and religious affairs 1.09

Fuel and energy 3.21

Agriculture, forestry, fishing, and hunting 2.55

Mining, manufacturing, and construction 41

Transportation and communication 2.91

Other economic affairs and services 7.21

Crime (15)

Crime rate (for 1997)

Crimes reported 241,800

Total persons convicted 116,500

Crimes per 100,000 population 2,900

Persons responsible for offenses

Total number of suspects 113,500

Total number of female suspects 11,000

Total number of juvenile suspects 14,900

LABOR FORCE

Labor Force (16)

Total (million) 3.57

Industry 41%

Agriculture 18%

Other 41%

Data for 1996 est. Percent distribution for 1992.

Unemployment Rate (17)

14% (1997 est.).

PRODUCTION SECTOR

Electric Energy (18)

Capacity . . . . .12.087 million kW (1995)

Production . . . . .41.449 billion kWh (1995)

Consumption per capita . . . . .4,821 kWh (1995)

Transportation (19)

Highways:

total: 36,720 km

paved: 33,746 km (including 314 km of expressways)

unpaved: 2,974 km (1996 est.)

Waterways: 470 km (1987)

Pipelines: crude oil 193 km; petroleum products 525 km; natural gas 1,400 km (1992)

Merchant marine:

total: 94 ships (1,000 GRT or over) totaling 1,027,117 GRT/1,541,266 DWT ships by type: bulk 45, cargo 23, chemical tanker 4, container 2, oil tanker 9, passenger-cargo 1, railcar carrier 2, refrigerated cargo 1, roll-on/roll-off cargo 6, short-sea passenger 1 (1997 est.)

Airports: 34 (1997 est.)

Airports—with paved runways:

total: 34

over 3,047 m: 1

2,438 to 3,047 m: 14

1,524 to 2,437 m: 9

under 914 m: 10 (1997 est.)

Top Agricultural Products (20)

Grain, oilseed, vegetables, fruits, tobacco; livestock.

MANUFACTURING SECTOR

GDP & Manufacturing Summary (21)

Detailed value added figures are listed by both International Standard Industry Code (ISIC) and product title.

	1980	1985	1990	1994
GDP ($-1990 mil.)[1]	16,571	19,885	18,543	15,544
Per capita ($-1990)[1]	1,870	2,219	2,062	1,763
Manufacturing share (%) (current prices)[1]	46.0	54.0	44.0	*42.8*
Manufacturing				
Value added ($-1990 mil.)[1]	5,715	8,153	8,166	*5,883*
Industrial production index	100	125	124	*84*
Value added ($ mil.)	11,771	20,759	10,227	5,889
Gross output ($ mil.)	*25,818*	*44,413*	21,453	7,835
Employment (000)	1,260	1,316	1,374	744
Profitability (% of gross output)				
Intermediate input (%)	*54*	*53*	52	25

	1980	1985	1990	1994
Wages and salaries inc. supplements (%)	8	7	10	9
Gross operating surplus	38	39	38	66
Productivity ($)				
Gross output per worker	21,221	35,355	16,252	11,262
Value added per worker	9,675	16,525	7,748	8,464
Average wage (inc. supplements)	1,737	2,649	1,693	1,195
Value added ($ mil.)				
311/2 Food products	1,870	3,093	1,429	392
313 Beverages	308	504	230	133
314 Tobacco products	426	627	260	125
321 Textiles	904	1,421	760	240
322 Wearing apparel	517	967	518	141
323 Leather and fur products	84	179	91	31
324 Footwear	156	332	169	97
331 Wood and wood products	248	384	142	68
332 Furniture and fixtures	233	365	137	56
341 Paper and paper products	119	186	84	47
342 Printing and publishing	83	146	86	76
351 Industrial chemicals	404	671	264	1,945
352 Other chemical products	291	585	292	224
353 Petroleum refineries	NA	NA	NA	

	1980	1985	1990	1994
354 Miscellaneous petroleum and coal products	126	179	93	61
355 Rubber products	227	350	134	44
356 Plastic products	110	234	123	46
361 Pottery, china and earthenware	45	63	38	37
362 Glass and glass products	121	178	109	87
369 Other non-metal mineral products	469	685	242	92
371 Iron and steel	447	636	285	712
372 Non-ferrous metals	189	342	105	145
381 Metal products	484	946	529	211
382 Non-electrical machinery	1,614	2,850	1,407	227
383 Electrical machinery	743	1,585	968	192
384 Transport equipment	567	1,194	714	197
385 Professional and scientific equipment	49	88	43	7
390 Other manufacturing industries	937	1,967	974	257

FINANCE, ECONOMICS, & TRADE

Economic Indicators (22)

National product: GDP—purchasing power parity—$35.6 billion (1997 est.)

National product real growth rate: -7.4% (1997 est.)

National product per capita: $4,100 (1997 est.)

Inflation rate—consumer price index: 1% (1998 est.)

Balance of Payments (23)

	1990	1992	1994	1995	1996
Exports of goods (f.o.b.)	6,113	3,956	3,935	5,345	4,890
Imports of goods (f.o.b.)	−7,427	−4,169	−3,952	−5,224	−4,703
Trade balance	−1,314	−212	−17	121	188
Services - debits	−1,478	−1,386	−1,523	−1,860	−1,823
Services - credits	957	1,195	1,342	1,581	1,547
Private transfers (net)	125	40	164	117	67
Government transfers (net)	NA	3	3	15	37
Overall balance	−1,710	−360	−31	−26	16

Exchange Rates (24)

Exchange rates:

Leva (Lv) per US$1

1997	1,740
1996	483.4
1995	70.7
1994	54.2
1993	27.1

Top Import Origins (25)

$4.5 billion (f.o.b., 1997 est.). Data are for 1995.

Origins	%
OECD	45.5
European Union	38.1
CIS and Central/Eastern Europe	41.1
Arab countries	1.8
Other	11.6

Top Export Destinations (26)

$4.9 billion (f.o.b., 1997). Data are for 1995.

Destinations	%
OECD 50.0% (EU 37.2%); CIS and Central and Eastern Europe 32.4%; Arab countries 5.8%; Other	11.8

Economic Aid (27)

NA. NA stands for not available.

Import Export Commodities (28)

Import Commodities	Export Commodities
Fuels	Machinery and equipment 15.2%; agriculture and food 18.9%; textiles and apparel 14.8%; metals
Minerals	
And raw materials 40.7%; machinery and equipment 18.4%; textiles and apparel 11.6%; agricultural products 7.5%; metals and ores 5.2%; chemicals and plastics 12.2%; other 4.4%	Minerals
	And fuels 26.5%; chemicals and plastics 20%; other 4.6%

BURKINA FASO

Republic of Burkina Faso
Burkina Faso Jamahiriya

INTRODUCTORY SURVEY

RECENT HISTORY

Until the end of the nineteenth century, the history of Burkina Faso is the history of the empire-building Mossi. When the first known European arrivals occurred, late in the nineteenth century, internal fighting made the Mossi prey to the invaders. The Mossi accepted French domination as a form of protection from their hostile neighbors.

In 1919, the French created a separate colony called Upper Volta (now Burkina Faso). In 1932, Upper Volta's territory was divided among Niger, French Sudan (now Mali), and Côte d'Ivoire. Throughout the colonial period, the traditional political structure of the Mossi was unchanged, and the *moro naba* (ruler) of Ouagadougou was regarded by the French as the emperor of the Mossi.

In 1958, Upper Volta's territorial assembly voted to make the country a self-governed state within the French Community. The republic achieved independence on 5 August 1960. Maurice Yaméogo, leader of the Volta Democratic Union, became president, and his government banned all opposition parties. In 1965, a single election list was offered to the people, and the opposition—joined by civil servants, trade unionists, and students—started riots. Yaméogo was replaced as president in January 1966 by Lieutenant Colonel (later General) Sangoulé Lamizana, a former army chief of staff. He suspended the 1960 constitution, dissolved the National Assembly, and formed a military-civilian cabinet.

During the 1970s and early 1980s, Upper Volta suffered from severe political unrest, with military takeovers in 1980, 1982, and 1983, and 1987. In 1984, the nation was renamed Burkina Faso, meaning roughly "Land of Upright Men."

After the coup of 1987, Captain Blaise Compaoré became chief of the governments. Under his government, political parties were legalized.

GOVERNMENT

A new constitution, establishing the Fourth Republic, was adopted on 2 June 1991 and called for an Assembly of People's Deputies with 107 seats. Captain Blaise Compaoré is Chief of State and Head of Government and he chairs a Council of Ministers.

Judiciary

At the top of the judicial system are the courts of appeal at Ouagadougou and Bobo-Dioulasso. District courts deal with cases involving civil, criminal, and commercial law. In the villages, tra-

ditional courts apply customary law in cases involving divorce and inheritance.

Political Parties

Political parties were banned from 1980 until 1992. The Compaoré government legalized parties before holding elections on 24 May 1992, when Compaoré's party, the Popular Democratic Organization—Worker's Movement (ODP-MT) gained seventy-eight seats. The National Convention of Progressive Patriots—Social Democratic Party (CNPP-PSD) won twelve seats, and the African Democratic Assembly (ADA) won 6. Eight other parties are represented in the Assembly of People's Deputies.

DEFENSE

In 1995, Burkina Faso had an army of 5,600 personnel. The army consisted of five small infantry regiments, one airborne regiment, one artillery battalion, one tank battalion, and one engineering battalion. The 200-member air force had 18 combat aircraft. Paramilitary forces totaled 1,750, and

45,000 men and women serve in a ''people's militia.'' The country spent $68 million on defense in 1995.

ECONOMIC AFFAIRS

Burkina Faso is an agricultural country where about 85% of the labor force produces food, mostly for domestic consumption. Food staples—millet, sorghum, maize and rice—are the main crops. Cotton is the principal export crop.

Public Finance

Burkina Faso's revenue sources are limited, and the country depends heavily on subsidies from France. Over 40% of government income is derived from customs duties. Personnel expenses account for over 40% of outlays. Budget deficits averaging 13% of GDP during 1986–90 added significantly to the debt service burden.

The U.S. CIA estimates that, in 1993, government revenues totaled approximately $483 million and expenditures $548 million, including capital expenditures of $189 million. External debt totaled $1 billion.

Income

Burkina Faso's gross national product (GNP) is about $2.6 million at current prices, or about $240 per person. For the period 1985–95 the average inflation rate was 2.5%, resulting in a slight decline (less than one percent) in GNP.

Industry

Industry accounts for 15% of Burkina's gross domestic product (GDP). The principal centers for economic activity are Bobo-Dioulasso, Ouagadougou, Banfora, and Koudougou. These cities are on the rail line to Abidjan, Côte d'Ivoire.

Banking and Securities

In 1959, the Central Bank of West African States (Banque Centrale des États de l'Afrique de l'Ouest—BCEAO) succeeded the Currency Board of French West Africa and Togo as the bank of issue for the former French West African territories. In 1962, it was reorganized as the joint note-issue bank of Benin (then Dahomey), Côte d'Ivoire, Mauritania (which withdrew in 1973), Niger, Senegal, Togo, and Burkina Faso (then Upper Volta). BCEAO notes, known as CFA francs, are guaranteed by France without limitation.

Economic Development

Development of the agricultural sector and of infrastructure have been the priorities established by Burkina's recent development plans. The 1991–95 plan estimated that 75% of the CFA Fr508 billion investment total would be allocated to agriculture. A 1995–97 plan, developed with support by the IMF, included a goal of 5% real annual growth in GDP, with inflation controlled to a maximum of 3% per year.

SOCIAL WELFARE

The very nature of tribal organization in Burkina Faso carries with it a type of social welfare. The basic needs of the individual are cared for by the group. Workers outside the tribal system normally receive 20% of average monthly earnings after retirement at age 55.

Healthcare

In 1992, there were three hospital beds per 10,000 inhabitants. Average life expectancy is estimated at 46 years. About 70% of the population has access to health care.

Housing

Many African people, especially the Mossi, live in round huts with cone-shaped straw roofs or in rectangular huts with flat roofs. Urban centers consist primarily of French colonial architecture. There are severe housing shortages in most cities.

EDUCATION

Though education is listed as compulsory for all children aged 6 to 15, attendance is not enforced. Only 32% of children are enrolled in primary schools and 7% in secondary schools. All public education is free. The language of instruction is French. Primary education lasts for six years and secondary for seven years. The Center for Higher Education was established in 1969, and in 1974 it became the University of Ouagadougou. In 1995, adult literacy was estimated at 19%.

1999 KEY EVENTS TIMELINE

January

- The fall-out from Norbert Zongo's death on December 13, 1998, begins with a wave of public anger sweeping the country. Zongo was an investigative journalist, and the managing editor of the *Indépendent*. The Paris-based *Reporteurs sans Frontières* (RSF) concludes that Zongo and his colleagues had almost certainly been assassinated. The RSF report criticizes the police for failing to secure evidence and gather testimony from witnesses.

- Two three-day rallies are organized that practically shut down the country in reaction to Zongo's death.

- An electricity worker in Bobo-Dioulasso, the country's second largest city, dies of injuries inflicted by the police. In retaliation, the electric union, Sonabel, cuts power to the entire country.

- The MBDHP, the Burkinabé main human rights organization, and other leaders meet with Prime Minister Kader Desiré Oudraogo to establish the independent investigation committee (CEI) that will look into the Zongo affair.

- President Compaoré shuffles his cabinet. Five members lose their positions, and nine more are added.

- A public administration raise comes into effect that will give public sector workers between 5% and 10% higher salaries.

February

- Ouagadougou hosts the 16th biennial African film festival, FESPACO. Over the past three decades, FESPACO becomes Africa's premier film festival. Compaoré is booed at the festival by a mostly young audience.

- The CEI begins to take testimony.

- The MBDHP issues figures showing that at least 100 people have died since 1989 in suspicious and unresolved deaths.

- Several hundred intellectuals attempt to march on the presidential palace to present a protest manifesto. They are stopped by a contingent of riot police under the direction of the Minister of Territorial Administration.

- The Group of February 14, a coalition of nine opposition parties, celebrates its first anniversary by participating in anti-government demonstrations.

- An extraordinary meeting of the Council of Ministers is called to discuss holding a special election.

- Air Burkina begins flights between Ouagadougou and Accra.

March

- Eight youth associations organize ''Fespaco Death Day,'' in memory of Norbert Zongo.

Demonstrators march peacefully through the capital to Zongo's grave while most people go about business as usual. Most schools and the University of Ouagadougou remained closed.

- Michel Camdessus, managing director of the IMF, visits Ouagadougou and praises the results achieved by the government's structural adjustment program. He cites Burkina as an example for many African countries.

- It is revealed that criminal charges were filed earlier this year against François Compaoré in connection with the death of his brother's driver. The court however, declared itself incompetent to hear the case. At least 47 groups affiliated with the MBDHP are constituted.

- A two-day mini summit of the OAU to discuss conflict in Africa is cancelled because too few African leaders agree to attend.

- A minimum wage increase is adopted, bringing it to about $46.50 a month.

- Charles Josselin, French Minister of Cooperation, visits Ouagadougou for three days of meetings.

April

- Hundreds of women's associations march in protest of the government's abuse of basic human rights.

May

- An independent commission reports that independent journalist Norbert Zongo was the victim of a political killing.

June

- A general strike is organized involving unions belonging to the sugar, cement, and other federations. Dismissal warnings are issued to 47 workers of a cement company, and shop stewards are dismissed from the sugar company.

July

- Foreign affairs ministers of member countries of the Islamic Conference (OCI) meet in Ouagadougou.

- The European Union gives Burkina two grants worth some $37 million for its education and agriculture sectors.

- Soldiers demonstrate for the reinstatement of their housing allowances. The government promises rapid measures to resolve the crisis.

August

- A group of opposition parties, unions, and human rights activists, the Collectif, calls upon the government to end its culture of impunity.

- For the second time in less than two months, workers stage a general strike.

- A *conseil de sages* (committee of elders) submits a report to the president, suggesting that a truth and reconciliation committee be established to find a way out of the country's current crisis. It also suggests that a government of national unity be formed.

- Roch Marc Christian Kaboré is elected general secretary of the ruling party, the Congress for Democracy and Progress, at the end of its scheduled party convention in Ouagadougou.

September

- September rains continue to be evenly distributed across the country, presaging good harvests.

October

- Burkina is among five West African countries having achieved the largest reductions in undernourishment worldwide in the 1990s according to the FAO.

- President Compaore reshuffles his government, appointing a number of new ministers, and creating new positions for two moderate members of the opposition. The main opposition shuns his efforts to form a full national unity government.

December

- Thousands of demonstrators march in the capital, Ouagodougou, calling for investigations into the murder of journalist Norbert Zongo a year ago, and asking for the resignation of President Blaise Compaore. An independent inquiry into Zongo's death named members of the presidential guard as suspects. Many believe Zongo was murdered because he was investigating the details of a murder of a government employee.

ANALYSIS OF EVENTS: 1999

BUSINESS AND THE ECONOMY

The unsettling political climate in 1999 did not have as much impact on the economy as might have been expected. Real GDP grew by 6.2% in 1998, and remained strong in 1999 thanks in part to abundant rains and favorable weather conditions for agriculture. Unfortunately, inflation also climbed to 5.1%.

The government continues to privatize. In 1998 it divested itself of its sugar company, and made good progress in 1999 with privatizing telecommunications. The government also divested some shares in the national railway that runs from Ouagadougou to Abidjan. Of the 42 state enterprises selected for sale, 21 were privatized. By the end of March, the sales and fiscal revenue derived from state enterprises had netted some $18 million.

1999 was a record year for cotton production, the country's main export, and a good year for cereal production. The harvest of seed cotton reached approximately 419,000 tons, exceeding 1998's 334,000 tons, and marking the fifth consecutive year of strong growth. The majority of cotton growers are now organized into a professional farmers' association and benefit from a number of incentives including higher producer prices, cheaper credits, and a more regular supply of inputs. Burkina Faso is expected to have a 108,000-ton surplus in cereals thanks to good rains. These mainstays of the Burkina economy will be bolstered by gold production, which the government predicts will triple in 2000.

The political fallout from the Zongo affair did not completely spare the economy. Major donors such as Denmark, Austria, and France made it clear that they were concerned about human rights, and urged the government to resolve the death of Norbert Zongo. Nevertheless, these nations signed long-term aid agreements with the government which are expected to stand, given a resolution of the Zongo case.

GOVERNMENT AND POLITICS

The year began on an uneasy note in the wake of the suspicious death of independent journalist Norbert Zongo. Zongo's body was found along with three others in his car on December 13, 1998, in Sapouy, about 100 kilometers from the capital. The bodies were burned and bullet holes were found in the car, leaving little doubt that the deaths were not accidental. A public outcry forced President Blaise Compaoré to establish an independent commission to investigate. Signs that Zongo's death was a political assassination then forced him to compose a committee of elders to investigate unpunished political crimes since independence in 1960.

The demonstrations, riots, strikes, "villes mortes," and power black-outs sparked by Norbert Zongo's death were signs that his murder was probably the proverbial straw that broke the camel's back. Blaise Compaoré came to power with the coup assassination of Thomas Sankara in 1987. Since 1989, over 100 people are believed to have died at the hands of the police, or in politically motivated killings that are never solved. The January 1998 killing of Compaoré's brother's driver, for example, was unsolved. Speculation is that Zongo was investigating the driver's death, and getting too close to the truth. Furthermore, Compaoré's inner circle, certain members of his ruling party (CDP), and the presidential guard are suspected of having supplied arms to Sierra Leonean RUF rebels in return for payment in diamonds. If true, it would be all the more embarrassing for Compaoré, who was OAU head at the time.

The independent commission arrested three presidential guards in connection with the driver's death, but no arrests were made in the Zongo case. The elder's council recommended a government of national unity as a way out of the crisis. Some members of the CDP, fearing for their own safety, took to arming militias, while others called for immediate parliamentary elections. "The Collectif," as the coalition of opposition parties, unions, and human rights groups is called, demanded that Compaoré's brother, François, and six guards suspected in the killing, be arrested and stand trial. They also demanded the immediate and complete reform of the justice system.

Clearly, the matter superseded the ability of the ruling party to contain the problem, and even if resolved transparently, it will likely change the face of Burkina's government, and its "culture of impunity" in this land of upright people.

CULTURE AND SOCIETY

Burkina is perhaps best known for Fespaco (Festival Pan-africaine du Cinéma â Ouagadougou) held every other year, alternating with the Carthage festival. The idea germinated in 1969 when a few visionaries gathered in Ougadougou to screen African films. A few years later the first festival was held. At the time, two French companies monopolized film distribution for the entire Francophone African market. A decision to nationalize cinemas gave Africans more control over the industry, while the quality and popularity of African films was such that thousands of film aficionados began to flock to this formerly unknown part of the world. In 1991, a Burkinabé, Idrissa Ouédraogo, won the main prize for his film, *Tilai*. This year's grand prize went to *Pièces d'Indentité* from Kinshasa.

The festivities this year opened to Alpha Blondy's concert in a 60,000-seat stadium. His social critique was not lost on the audience, which booed and hissed President Compaoré who, in a case of bad timing, had to follow Blondy. The unwelcome greeting for Compaoré was uncustomary for Burkinabé, but it demonstrated the depth of dissatisfaction with the politics of his government.

The glamour of world-class cinema cannot hide the low standard of living most Burkinabé live with daily. Only 7% of the population enjoy access to electricity, though the government expects to increase this number to 15% by 2000 through its electrification program. Solar energy projects are underway in several regional capitals, which in this sunny part of the world may speed up the process and offer sustainable, clean energy.

DIRECTORY

CENTRAL GOVERNMENT
Head of State

President
Blaise Compaoré, Office of the President, BP 7030, Ouagadougou 03, Burkina Faso
PHONE: +226 306630
FAX: +226 314926

Prime Minister
Kadré Dèsiré Ouédraogo, Office of the Prime Minister, BP 7027, Ouagadougou 03, Burkina Faso
PHONE: +226 324889
FAX: +226 314761

Ministers

Minister of Agriculture
Issa Martin Bikienga, Ministry of Agriculture, BP 7005, Ouagadougou 03, Burkina Faso
PHONE: +226 324963

Minister of Environment and Water

Bognessan Arsène, Ministry of Environment and
Water, 565, rue Agostino Neto, Secteur 4,
Koulouba, Ouagadougou 03, Burkina Faso
PHONE: +226 324074
FAX: +226 307039
E-MAIL: diallo@ouaga.orstom.bf

Minister of Foreign Affairs

Youssouf Ouédraogo, Ministry of Foreign
Affairs, BP 7038, Ouagadougou 03, Burkina
Faso
PHONE: +226 324974
FAX: +226 308792

Minister of Economy and Finance

Tertius Zongo, Ministry of Economy and
Finance, 395 Avenue Ho Chi Minh 01, BP 7008
Ouagadougou 01, Burkina Faso
PHONE: +226 324211
FAX: +226 312715
E-MAIL: +226 312715

Minister of Defense

Albert D. Millogo, Ministry of Defense, BP 496,
Ouagadougou 01, Burkina Faso
PHONE: +226 307214
FAX: +226 313610

Minister of Justice

Boureima Badini, Ministry of Justice, BP 526,
Ouagadougou 01, Burkina Faso
PHONE: +226 324833

Minister of Territorial Administration and Security

Yéro Boly, Ministry of Territorial Administration
and Security, BP 7034, Ouagadougou 03,
Burkina Faso
PHONE: +226 324783
FAX: +226 308417

Minister of Commerce, Industry, and Crafts

Abdoulaye Abdoulkader Cissé, Ministry of
Commerce, Industry, and Crafts, BP 514,
Ouagadougou 01, Burkina Faso
PHONE: +226 324786
FAX: +226 324828

Minister of Energy and Mines

Elie Ouédraogo, Ministry of Energy and Mines,
BP 644, Ouagadougou 01, Burkina Faso
PHONE: +226 318429
FAX: +226 318430

Minister of Higher Education and Scientific Research

Christophe Dabiré, Ministry of Higher Education
and Scientific Research, BP 7047, Ouagadougou
03, Burkina Faso
PHONE: +226 324868

Minister of Basic Education and Mass Literacy

Baworo Seydou Sanou, Ministry of Basic
Education and Mass Literacy, BP 7032,
Ouagadougou 03, Burkina Faso
PHONE: +226 324870
FAX: +226 308086

Minister of Infrastructure, Housing, and Urban Planning

Hyppolite Lingani, Ministry of Infrastructure,
Housing, and Urban Planning, BP 7011,
Ouagadougou 03, Burkina Faso
PHONE: +226 324954
FAX: +226 318408

Minister of Civil Service and Institutional Development

Paramanga Ernest Yonli, Ministry of Civil
Service and Institutional Development, BP 7006,
Ouagadougou 03, Burkina Faso
PHONE: +226 324010

Minister of Employment, Labor, and Social Security

Sané Mohamed Topan, Ministry of Employment,
Labor, and Social Security, BP 7016,
Ouagadougou 03, Burkina Faso
PHONE: +226 300960
FAX: +226 318801

Minister of Regional Integration

Bernadette Sanou, Ministry of Regional
Integration, BP 06, Ouagadougou 01, Burkina
Faso
PHONE: +226 324833
FAX: +226 314190

Minister of Parliamentary Relations

Cyril Goungounga, Ministry of Parlimentary
Relations, BP 2079, Ouagadougou 01, Burkina
Faso
PHONE: +226 302744
FAX: +226 307894

Minister of Culture and Arts

Mahamoudou Ouédraogo, Ministry of Culture
and Arts, BP 7045, Ouagadougou 03, Burkina
Faso
PHONE: +226 324886
FAX: +226 315599

Minister of Health
Alain Ludovic Tou, Ministry of Health, BP 7009, Ouagadougou 03, Burkina Faso
PHONE: +226 324171

Minister of Youth and Sports
Emile Kaboré, Ministry of Youth and Sports, BP 7035, Ouagadougou 03, Burkina Faso
PHONE: +226 324786

Minister of Transportation and Tourism
Bédouma Alain Yoda, Ministry of Transportation and Tourism, BP 7048, Ouagadougou 03, Burkina Faso
PHONE: +226 306211

Minister of Social and Family Affairs
Nayabtigungou Congo Kaboré, Ministry of Social and Family Affairs, BP 515, Ouagadougou 01, Burkina Faso
PHONE: +226 306875
FAX: +226 316737

Minister of Animal Resources
Alassane Séré, Ministry of Animal Resources, BP 7026, Ouagadougou 03, Burkina Faso
PHONE: +226 324651
FAX: +226 318475

Minister for the Promotion of Women
Gisèle Guigma, Ministry for the Promotion of Women

Minister of State
Ram Ouédraogo, Ministry of State

Minister of Missions to the President
Pierre Joseph Emmanuel Tapsoba, Ministry of Missions to the President, BP 7030, Ouagadougou 03, Burkina Faso
PHONE: +226 306630
FAX: +226 314926

Minister of Communication
Théodore Kilimité Hien, Ministry of Communication, BP 7045, Ouagadougou 03, Burkina Faso
PHONE: +226 324886
FAX: +226 315599

POLITICAL ORGANIZATIONS

Congrès pour la Démocratie et le Progrès (Congress for Democracy and Progress)

NAME: Din Salif Sawadago
E-MAIL: cdp@cenatrin.bf

Parti pour la Démocratie et le Progrès (Party for Democracy and Progress)

NAME: Joseph Ki-zerbo

Rassemblement démocratique africain (African Democratic Rally)

NAME: Gerard Kango Ouedraogo

Alliance pour la démocratie et la féderation (Alliance for Democracy and Federation)

NAME: Herman Yameogo

DIPLOMATIC REPRESENTATION
Embassies in Burkina Faso

Algeria
BP 3893, Ouagadougou 01, Burkina Faso
PHONE: +226 306401

Belgium
BP 6829, Ouagadougou 01, Burkina Faso
PHONE: +226 332059

Canada
BP 548, Ouagadougou 01, Burkina Faso
PHONE: +226 311894
FAX: +226 311800

China
BP 5563, Ouagadougou 01, Burkina Faso
PHONE: +226 316195
FAX: +226 316197

Côte d'Ivoire
BP 20, Ouagadougou 01, Burkina Faso
PHONE: +226 318228
FAX: +226 318230

Cuba
BP 9155, Ouagadougou 01, Burkina Faso
PHONE: +226 306491

Denmark
BP 1760, Ouagadougou 01, Burkina Faso
PHONE: +226 313192
FAX: +226 313189

Egypt
BP 7042, Ouagadougou 01, Burkina Faso
PHONE: +226 306637

France
BP 504, Ouagadougou 01, Burkina Faso
PHONE: +226 306774
FAX: +226 314166

Germany

BP 600, Ouagadougou 01, Burkina Faso
PHONE: +226 306731
FAX: +226 313991

Ghana

BP 212, Ouagadougou 01, Burkina Faso
PHONE: +226 307635

India

BP 6648, Ouagadougou 01, Burkina Faso
PHONE: +226 312354

Iran

BP 1342, Ouagadougou 01, Burkina Faso
PHONE: +226 307707
FAX: | 226 311626

Italy

BP 3432, Ouagadougou 01, Burkina Faso
PHONE: +226 308694
FAX: +226 310477

Libya

BP 1601, Ouagadougou 01, Burkina Faso
PHONE: +226 306753
FAX: +226 313470

Mali

BP 1911, Ouagadougou 01, Burkina Faso
PHONE: +226 381922

Nigeria

BP 132, Ouagadougou 01, Burkina Faso
PHONE: +226 306667

Netherlands

BP 1302, Ouagadougou 01, Burkina Faso
PHONE: +226 316846
FAX: +226 307695

Spain

BP 23, Ouagadougou 01, Burkina Faso
PHONE: +226 306160

United States

BP 35, Ouagadougou 01, Burkina Faso
PHONE: +226 306723
FAX: +226 312368
TITLE: Ambassador
NAME: Sharon P. Wilkinson

JUDICIAL SYSTEM

Supreme Court

BP 586, Ouagadougou 01, Burkina Faso
PHONE: +226 313609; 313613
FAX: +226 310271

FURTHER READING

Books

Crowder, Michael. *West Africa Under Colonial Rule*. Evanston, Illinois: Northwestern University Press, 1968.

Crowther, Geoff, ed. "Burkina Faso." In *Africa on a Shoestring*. Berkeley, California: Lonely Planet, 1989.

Foltz, William Jay. *From French West Africa to the Mali Federation*. New Haven: Yale University Press, 1965.

Glaze, Anita. *Art and Death in a Senufo Village*. Bloomington, IN: Indiana University Press, 1981.

Guirma, Frederic. *Princess of the Full Moon*. Trans. John Garrett. New York: Macmillan, 1970.

Le Vine, Victor T. "The Coups in Upper Volta, Dahomey, and the Central African Republic." In *Protest and Power in Black Africa*, ed., Robert I. Rotberg and Ali A. Mazrui. New York: Oxford University Press, 1970.

McFarland, Daniel Miles, and Lawrence A. Rupley. *Historical Dictionary of Burkina Faso*. Second Edition. African Historical Dictionaries, No. 74. Lanham, Md.: The Scarecrow Press, 1998.

Robinson, Pearl. "Sahelian Regional Development in a Changing World Order." *Journal of African Studies*, 11, 4: 175–181, 1984–85.

———. "Grassroots Legitimation of Military Governance in Burkina Faso and Niger: The Core Contradictions." In *Governance and Politics in Africa*, ed., Goran Hyden and Michael Bratton, 1992.

Sankara, Thomas. *Women's Liberation and the African Freedom Struggle*. London: Pathfinder, 1990.

Schmidt, Nancy J. "Publications on African Film: Focus on Burkina Faso and Nigeria." In *African Book Publishing Record*. London, 16, 3: 153–156, 1990.

Skinner, Elliot Percival. *The Mossi of the Upper Volta: The Political Development of a Sudanese People*. Stanford, California: Stanford University Press, 1964.

Wilks, Ivor. "The Mossi and Akan States." In *History of West Africa*. Third Edition. Edited by J.F.A. Ajayi and Michael Crowder. Harlow, U.K.: Longman, 1985.

Zahan, Dominique. ''The Mossi Kingdoms.'' In *West African Kingdoms in the Nineteenth Century*. ed., Daryll Forde and P.M. Kaberry. Oxford: Oxford University Press, 1967.

Internet

Africaonline. Available Online @ http://www.africaonline.com (October 28, 1999).

Africa News Online. Available Online @ http://www.africanews.org/west/stories/1999_feat1.html (October 28, 1999).

Integrated Regional Information Network (IRIN). Available Online @ http://www.reliefweb.int/IRIN (October 28, 1999).

BURKINA FASO: STATISTICAL DATA

For sources and notes see "Sources of Statistics" in the front of each volume.

GEOGRAPHY

Geography (1)

Area:

Total: 274,200 sq km.

Land: 273,800 sq km.

Water: 400 sq km.

Area—comparative: slightly larger than Colorado.

Land boundaries:

Total: 3,192 km.

Border countries: Benin 306 km, Ghana 548 km, Cote d'Ivoire 584 km, Mali 1,000 km, Niger 628 km, Togo 126 km.

Coastline: 0 km (landlocked).

Climate: tropical; warm, dry winters; hot, wet summers.

Terrain: mostly flat to dissected, undulating plains; hills in west and southeast.

Natural resources: manganese, limestone, marble; small deposits of gold, antimony, copper, nickel, bauxite, lead, phosphates, zinc, silver.

Land use:

Arable land: 13%

Permanent crops: 0%

Permanent pastures: 22%

Forests and woodland: 50%

Other: 15% (1993 est.).

HUMAN FACTORS

Demographics (2A)

	1990	1995	1998	2000	2010	2020	2030	2040	2050
Population	9,024.3	10,375.3	11,266.4	11,892.0	15,371.1	19,239.5	23,711.1	29,135.9	34,956.2
Net migration rate (per 1,000 population)	NA	NA	NA	NA	NA	NA	NA	NA	NA
Births	NA	NA	NA	NA	NA	NA	NA	NA	NA
Deaths	NA	NA	NA	NA	NA	NA	NA	NA	NA
Life expectancy - males	47.9	46.7	45.4	44.6	45.1	48.6	57.9	67.3	70.8
Life expectancy - females	47.6	46.9	46.8	46.8	46.1	50.1	61.7	73.3	77.2
Birth rate (per 1,000)	49.8	47.7	46.2	45.5	40.4	34.8	29.4	24.6	21.0
Death rate (per 1,000)	18.9	18.0	17.6	17.5	16.3	13.7	8.5	4.8	4.4
Women of reproductive age (15-49 yrs.)	2,026.1	2,309.9	2,501.7	2,644.9	3,522.0	4,678.9	6,179.7	7,918.4	9,513.8
of which are currently married	NA	NA	NA	NA	NA	NA	NA	NA	NA
Fertility rate	7.2	6.9	6.6	6.5	5.4	4.3	3.4	2.8	2.5

Except as noted, values for vital statistics are in thousands; life expectancy is in years.

Health Personnel (3)

Total health expenditure as a percentage of GDP, 1990-1997[a]

Public sector 4.7

Private sector 3.2

Total[b] 5.5

Health expenditure per capita in U.S. dollars, 1990-1997[a]

Purchasing power parity 49

Total 17

Availability of health care facilities per 100,000 people

Hospital beds 1990-1997[a] 30

Doctors 1993[c] . . . . .NA

Nurses 1993[c] . . . . .NA

Health Indicators (4)

Life expectancy at birth

1980 44

1997 44

Daily per capita supply of calories (1996) 2,137

Total fertility rate births per woman (1997) 6.6

Maternal mortality ratio per 100,000 live births (1990-97) . . . . .930[c]

Safe water % of population with access (1995) . . . .

Sanitation % of population with access (1995) . . . .

Consumption of iodized salt % of households (1992-98)[a] 23

Smoking prevalence

Male % of adults (1985-95)[a] . . . .

Female % of adults (1985-95)[a] . . . .

Tuberculosis incidence per 100,000 people (1997) 155

Adult HIV prevalence % of population ages 15-49 (1997) 7.17

Infants and Malnutrition (5)

Under-5 mortality rate (1997) 169

% of infants with low birthweight (1990-97) 21

Births attended by skilled health staff % of total[a] . . .41

% fully immunized (1995-97)

TB 46

DPT 28

Polio 28

Measles 33

Prevalence of child malnutrition under age 5 (1992-97)[b] 33

Ethnic Division (6)

Mossi about 24%; Gurunsi, Senufo, Lobi, Bobo, Mande, Fulani.

Religions (7)

Indigenous beliefs 40%

Muslim 50%

Christian 10%

Christian is mainly Roman Catholic.

Languages (8)

French (official), tribal languages belonging to Sudanic family, spoken by 90% of the population.

EDUCATION

Public Education Expenditures (9)

Public expenditure on education (% of GNP)

1980 . . . . .2.2

1996 . . . . .1.5

Expenditure per student

Primary % of GNP per capita

1980 . . . . .23.1

1996 . . . . .21.2[1]

Secondary % of GNP per capita

1980 . . . . .87.3[1]

1996 . . . .

Tertiary % of GNP per capita

1980 . . . . .2,960.8

1996 . . . .

Expenditure on teaching materials

Primary % of total for level (1996) 0.8

Secondary % of total for level (1996) . . . .

Primary pupil-teacher ratio per teacher (1996) . . . . .51[1]

Duration of primary education years (1995) 6

Literacy Rates (11A)

In thousands and percent[1]	1990	1995	2000	2010
Illiterate population (15+ yrs.)	4,207	4,597	4,993	5,853
Literacy rate - total adult pop. (%)	16.3	19.2	22.6	31.0
Literacy rate - males (%)	25.6	29.5	33.9	43.6
Literacy rate - females (%)	7.2	9.2	11.7	18.7

GOVERNMENT & LAW

Political Parties (12)

National Assembly	No. of seats
Congress for Democracy and Progress (CDP)	101
Democracy and Progress (PDP)	6
African Democratic Assembly (RDA)	2
Alliance for Democracy and Federation (ADF)	2

Government Budget (13A)

Year: 1992

Total Expenditures: 134,828 Millions of Francs

Expenditures as a percentage of the total by function:

General public services and public order	7.80
Defense	13.96
Education	17.33
Health	6.90
Social Security and Welfare	-
Housing and community amenities	79
Recreational, cultural, and religious affairs	86
Fuel and energy	-
Agriculture, forestry, fishing, and hunting	4.99
Mining, manufacturing, and construction	3.01
Transportation and communication	2.18
Other economic affairs and services	1.00

Military Affairs (14B)

	1990	1991	1992	1993	1994	1995
Military expenditures						
Current dollars (mil.)	53	49	49	46	65[e]	68[e]
1995 constant dollars (mil.)	61	54	53	48	67[e]	68[e]
Armed forces (000)	10	10	9	9	9	9
Gross national product (GNP)						
Current dollars (mil.)	1,720	1,953	2,057	2,089	2,159	2,310
1995 constant dollars (mil.)	1,977	2,158	2,213	2,190	2,213	2,310
Central government expenditures (CGE)						
1995 constant dollars (mil.)	297	NA	378	401[e]	NA	NA
People (mil.)	9.0	9.3	9.6	9.8	10.1	10.4
Military expenditure as % of GNP	3.1	2.5	2.4	2.2	3.0	2.9
Military expenditure as % of CGE	20.4	NA	14.0	12.0	NA	NA
Military expenditure per capita (1995 $)	7	6	6	5	7	7
Armed forces per 1,000 people (soldiers)	1.1	1.1	.9	.9	.9	.9
GNP per capita (1995 $)	219	232	232	223	219	223
Arms imports[6]						
Current dollars (mil.)	20	0	5	10	5	0
1995 constant dollars (mil.)	23	0	5	10	5	0
Arms exports[6]						
Current dollars (mil.)	0	0	0	0	0	0
1995 constant dollars (mil.)	0	0	0	0	0	0
Total imports[7]						
Current dollars (mil.)	536	600	545	554	390	549
1995 constant dollars (mil.)	616	663	586	581	400	549
Total exports[7]						
Current dollars (mil.)	152	954	897	798	349	536
1995 constant dollars (mil.)	175	1,054	965	837	358	536
Arms as percent of total imports[8]	3.7	0	.9	1.8	1.3	0
Arms as percent of total exports[8]	0	0	0	0	0	0

Crime (15)

Crime rate (for 1997)

Crimes reported 825

Total persons convicted .825

Crimes per 100,000 population 8

Persons responsible for offenses

Total number of suspects 1,100

Total number of female suspects . . . . .NA

Total number of juvenile suspects . . . . .NA

LABOR FORCE

Labor Force (16)

Agriculture 80%

Industry 15%

Commerce, services, and government 5%

Unemployment Rate (17)

Rate not available.

PRODUCTION SECTOR

Electric Energy (18)

Capacity . . . . .78,000 kW (1995)

Production . . . . .220 million kWh (1995)

Consumption per capita . . . . .21 kWh (1995)

Transportation (19)

Highways:

total: 12,506 km

paved: 2,001 km

unpaved: 10,505 km (1995 est.)

Airports: 33 (1997 est.)

Airports—with paved runways:

total: 2

over 3,047 m: 1

2,438 to 3,047 m: 1 (1997 est.)

Airports—with unpaved runways:

total: 31

1,524 to 2,437 m: 3

914 to 1,523 m: 14

under 914 m: 14 (1997 est.)

Top Agricultural Products (20)

Peanuts, shea nuts, sesame, cotton, sorghum, millet, corn, rice; livestock.

MANUFACTURING SECTOR

GDP & Manufacturing Summary (21)

Detailed value added figures are listed by both International Standard Industry Code (ISIC) and product title.

	1980	1985	1990	1994
GDP ($-1990 mil.)[1]	1,718	1,915	2,165	2,255
Per capita ($-1990)[1]	247	243	241	224
Manufacturing share (%) (current prices)[1]	12.2	11.9	13.2	NA
Manufacturing				
Value added ($-1990 mil.)[1]	231	235	258	287
Industrial production index	100	110	130	136
Value added ($ mil.)	144	120	201	131
Gross output ($ mil.)	391	318	596	420
Employment (000)	8	9	10	10
Profitability (% of gross output)				
Intermediate input (%)	63	62	66	69
Wages and salaries inc. supplements (%)	8	7	8	8
Gross operating surplus	28	31	26	24
Productivity ($)				
Gross output per worker	47,326	36,048	62,714	41,717
Value added per worker	17,465	13,637	21,189	13,073
Average wage (inc. supplements)	4,021	2,637	5,028	3,257
Value added ($ mil.)				
311/2 Food products	55	56	95	63
313 Beverages	29	20	33	21
314 Tobacco products	1	1	2	1
321 Textiles	20	18	29	19
322 Wearing apparel	2	2	3	2
323 Leather and fur products	2	1	3	2
324 Footwear	3	3	5	4
331 Wood and wood products	—	—	—	—
332 Furniture and fixtures	2	1	2	2
341 Paper and paper products	—	—	—	—

Value added ($ mil.)	1980	1985	1990	1994
342 Printing and publishing	1	*1*	2	*1*
351 Industrial chemicals	1	*1*	*1*	*1*
352 Other chemical products	—	—	—	—
353 Petroleum refineries	—	—	—	—
354 Miscellaneous petroleum and coal products	—	—	—	—
355 Rubber products	4	2	3	*1*
356 Plastic products	2	*1*	*1*	*1*
361 Pottery, china and earthenware	—	—	—	—
362 Glass and glass products	—	—	—	—
369 Other non-metal mineral products	—	—	—	—
371 Iron and steel	*1*	*1*	*1*	*1*
372 Non-ferrous metals	—	—	—	—
381 Metal products	1	—	*1*	—
382 Non-electrical machinery	1	—	—	—
383 Electrical machinery	1	—	*1*	*1*
384 Transport equipment	3	*1*	3	2
385 Professional and scientific equipment	—	—	—	—
390 Other manufacturing industries	12	9	13	8

FINANCE, ECONOMICS, & TRADE

Economic Indicators (22)

National product: GDP—purchasing power parity—$10.3 billion (1997 est.)

National product real growth rate: 6% (1997 est.)

National product per capita: $950 (1997 est.)

Inflation rate—consumer price index: 3% (1996 est.)

Exchange Rates (24)

Exchange rates:

CFA francs (CFAF) per US$1

January 1998	.608.36
1997	.583.67
1996	.511.55
1995	.499.15
1994	.555.20
1993	.283.16

Beginning 12 January 1994 the CFA franc was devalued to CFAF 100 per French franc from CFAF 50 at which it had been fixed since 1948

Top Import Origins (25)

$500 million. (f.o.b., 1995 est.).

Origins	%
Cote d'Ivoire	NA
France	NA
Togo	NA
Nigeria	NA

NA stands for not available.

Balance of Payments (23)

	1990	1991	1992	1993	1994
Exports of goods (f.o.b.)	280	269	237	226	216
Imports of goods (f.o.b.)	−542	−490	−459	−469	−344
Trade balance	−262	−221	−222	−243	−129
Services - debits	−233	−269	−227	−238	−176
Services - credits	86	85	86	86	65
Private transfers (net)	105	98	112	102	70
Government transfers (net)	227	217	227	221	186
Overall balance	−77	−91	−23	−71	15

Top Export Destinations (26)

$298 million (f.o.b., 1995 est.).

Destinations	%
Cote d'Ivoire	NA
France	NA
Italy	NA
Mali	NA

NA stands for not available.

Economic Aid (27)

Recipient: ODA, $NA. NA stands for not available.

Import Export Commodities (28)

Import Commodities	Export Commodities
Machinery	Cotton
Food products	Animal products
Petroleum	Gold

BURUNDI

Republic of Burundi
République du Burundi
Republika yu Burundi

INTRODUCTORY SURVEY

RECENT HISTORY

On 1 July 1962, Burundi became an independent kingdom headed by Mwami (King) Mwambutsa IV. He was removed from office in July 1966 and was replaced in September by his heir, Mwami Ntare V. On 29 November 1966, Mwami Ntare V in turn was overthrown by a military takeover headed by Premier Michel Micombero, and Burundi was declared a republic with Micombero as president. In 1969 and 1972, the Micombero government was threatened by Hutu-led takeover attempts, the second of which resulted in widespread civil war and 100,000 deaths. The Hutu are a tribal group in Burundi. By the end of 1973, however, the government was fully in control.

On 1 November 1976, President Micombero was stripped of all powers by a military takeover led by Colonel Jean-Baptiste Bagaza. Bagaza was then named president. The new government, like the old one, was dominated by the Tutsi tribes. A new constitution was adopted in 1981, and a National Assembly was elected in 1982. Bagaza was reelected unopposed to a new five-year term in 1984, but in September 1987, he was overthrown by the military while he was attending a conference in Canada. Major Pierre Buyoyo became president.

Between 5,000 and 25,000 Hutu were massacred in an eruption of ethnic violence in 1988. Afterward, Major Buyoyo agreed to the restoration of multiparty politics in 1991. A new constitution was approved in March 1992. In the elections of June

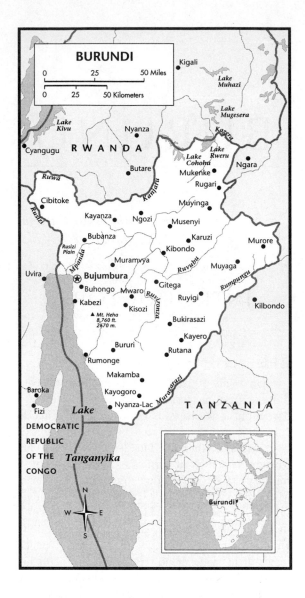

BURUNDI

0   25   50 Miles

0   25   50 Kilometers

Rwanda's airport. Two members of his cabinet also died in the attack.

Sylvestre Ntibantunganya was elected president following the deaths and was able to maintain relative calm, at least in comparison to neighboring Rwanda, which saw genocidal violence. However, Burundi did suffer significant social unrest and violence.

In 1996, Major Pierre Buyoya seized power in a coup. Violence continued and in September 1996, Archbishop Joachim Ruhuma was assassinated. Many of Burundi's African neighbors cut their ties with the country, demanding a return to democratic rule. On 1 January 1998, rebels attacked a village near the country's main airport and killed some 300 people.

GOVERNMENT

A new constitution which recognized "democracy, human rights and development" was adopted on 13 March 1992. It provides for a directly elected president, a prime minister, and an eighty-one-seat National Assembly. In July 1996, however, a military coup overthrew the government and imposed a "transition period" on the Assembly, essentially taking away its powers.

Judiciary

Traditionally, the judicial system has been based on German and French models. The coup in 1996, however, ended the 1992 constitution and replaced it with a transitional decree, which is still in force. The decree calls for an independent judiciary, but in practice the judicial system operates to serve the military leaders.

Political Parties

Until 1993, Burundi's Party for Unity and National Progress (UPRONA) controlled the country. But in the 1993 elections, President Ndadaye's party, the Burundi Democratic Front (FRODEBU) received 72% of the vote and sixty-five of parliament's eighty-one seats. UPRONA won the remaining seats with 21% of the ballots cast.

DEFENSE

In 1995, Burundi had an army with about 18,500 soldiers. The troops include two infantry battalions, a battalion of commandos, and a battalion of paratroopers. The naval force had 50 members and 3 patrol boats. The air force had 100 members with three counterinsurgency aircraft and 14 support aircraft and helicopters. The 1994 de-

1993, Buyoyo was defeated by Melchior Ndadaye, a Hutu. Ndadaye's government included nine Tutsis (one of whom was the prime minister) among the twenty-three ministers. However, on 21 October 1993, Burundi's first elected president—also its first Hutu president—and several cabinet members were assassinated by Tutsi soldiers in an unsuccessful military takeover attempt. In the resulting violence, as many as 100,000 people may have been killed.

In February 1994, Ndadaye's successor, Cyprien Ntaryamira, was inaugurated. But his liberal government was unable to restore order. In an effort to negotiate peace, he went to Tanzania for meetings. On his flight home, the plane in which he was returning with Rwanda's President Habyarimana was shot down near Kigali,

fense budget was $47 million, or 3.7% of gross national product (GNP).

ECONOMIC AFFAIRS

Burundi's economy is based on agriculture and livestock, with over 80% of the population engaged in subsistence agriculture. Bananas, plantains, sweet potatoes, and manioc are Burundi's staple crops, followed by beans, taro, and maize. Coffee and tea are the main export crops.

Public Finance

Government expenditures have generally exceeded reserves. The fiscal deficit (excluding grants) during 1986–92 averaged 12.3% of GDP. The U.S. CIA estimates that, in 1994, government revenues totaled approximately $318 million and expenditures $326 million, including capital expenditures of $150 million. External debt totaled $1.05 billion.

Income

In 1997, Burundi's gross national product (GNP) was $935 million at current prices, or $140 per person. For the period 1985–95 the average inflation rate was 6.1%, resulting in decline in per capita GNP of just over one percent.

Industry

Industrial activities are mostly concentrated in Bujumbura. The industrial sector primarily transforms agricultural and forestry products into finished products. The future of industrial development is largely linked to the development of electric power and transportation, as well as improved commercial relations with neighboring countries.

Banking and Finance

Until the Democratic Republic of Congo (formerly Zaire) became independent in 1960, the monetary and banking systems of Ruanda-Urundi were integrated with those of the Congo. Thereafter, Ruanda-Urundi had its own monetary structure and central bank. Shortly after the UN-sponsored Addis Ababa conference of July 1962, Rwanda and Burundi entered into an economic agreement providing for a continuation of the monetary union. After the breakup of the economic union in December 1963, Burundi's banking operations were transacted through the Bank of the Kingdom of Burundi, which in 1967 became the Bank of the Republic of Burundi, the central bank and bank of issue.

Economic Development

Burundi began a complete review of economic and financial policy with the help of the UN in 1986, when a reform of the currency and the first of a series of devaluations occurred.

Burundi depends on foreign assistance for both development programs and current operations. Diversification of its export base and financial stability are key goals.

SOCIAL WELFARE

Under the tribal system, the individual's basic welfare needs have traditionally been the responsibility of the group. Even now, the family remains the most important social welfare institution. There are social centers for women and youth. Missions help to look after orphans and the aged. For the relatively small number of wage earners, a government social security system insures against accidents and occupational diseases and provides pensions.

Terrible human rights abuses have occurred during the ethnic conflicts between the majority Hutu and minority Tutsi peoples. According to Amnesty International, more than 100,000 people were killed between October 1993 and December 1995.

Healthcare

Since the beginning of inter-tribal violence in 1993, approximately 683,000 people have fled their homes for neighboring countries, rural villages or towns where sanitation is poor and health care nearly non-existent. In 1997, nearly 50,000 new cases of louse-born typhus have been reported, the largest number in fifty years.

Many of Burundi's people do not eat enough animal protein and fat, so almost all diseases associated with malnutrition are found in Burundi. In 1993, 80% of the population had access to health care. In 1995, the infant mortality rate was 98 per 1,000 live births. Average life expectancy is estimated at 47 years.

Housing

The basic type of housing in the rural areas is the hut, most commonly beehive shaped, made of strips of wood woven around poles (wattle). Formerly, roofs were made of thatch, but they are now more likely to be covered with tin since thatch has become scarce. The huts are generally not grouped into villages but are organized in groups on a family basis.

EDUCATION

Education is compulsory for children between the ages of 7 and 13. Primary education lasts for six years and secondary education for seven. Only about 4% of the eligible young people attend secondary or technical schools. The University of Burundi in Bujumbura (founded in 1960) is the country's only institution of higher learning.

1999 KEY EVENTS TIMELINE

January

- At a summit in Tanzania, leaders of several East African nations vote to suspend the economic sanctions imposed on Burundi in 1996 when Mayor General Pierre Buyoya overthrew the government.

May

- The Supreme Court condemns five people to death and convicts twenty-three others for the killing of Melchior Ndadaye, Burundi's first democratically elected president, in 1993.

June

- Burundi peace talks begin in Arusha, Tanzania, with former Tanzanian president Julius Nyerere serving as mediator.

August

- On August 10, thousands of civilians flee a slum area on the outskirts of Burundi's capital after Hutu rebels attack the market of Kanyosha, killing at least one soldier before fleeing into the surrounding hills with the army in pursuit.

- On August 13, Burundian villagers accuse the Tutsi-dominated army of killing 147 Hutu civilians to avenge the Hutu rebel attack on the market of Kanyosha; however, the army blames the rebels for the killings.

- The United States asks the government of Burundi to allow independent investigations of reports that the army killed civilians on the southern outskirts of the capital.

- United Nations Secretary-General Kofi Annan condemns the killing of civilians in Burundi by rebels and government troops and calls for an end to all attacks.

- Colonel Gabriel Gunungu, governor of the southern province of Makamba, reports that at least 30 civilians have been killed in three separate attacks in recent days.

- On August 28, Hutu rebels attack Bujumbura in brutal overnight raids, murdering 38 civilians before battling the army in a fight that killed another 20 people; the government issues a statement that the weekend attack has undermined the country's fragile peace process.

September

- The government adds two hours to the existing night curfew in response to the weekend rebel attack on the capital.

- The European Union condemns the August 28 killing of civilians by rebels and urges national reconciliation in Burundi.

- Burundi's Defense Minister Colonel Alfred Nkurunziza tells the army to consider journalists as enemies if they enter a province close to the capital where the military is fighting ethnic Hutu rebels; French press group Reporters sans Frontieres condemns the statement as a "call to murder."

- Talks in Arusha, Tanzania, to end Burundi's civil war resume despite the absence of mediator Julius Nyerere, the former Tanzanian president, who is hospitalized in London; however, the round of negotiations ends with no sign of a draft peace agreement that delegates say they hope to ratify by December.

- The army and rebels engage in a fresh round of fighting: ten are killed in the Mutanga area of eastern Bujumbura; twelve are killed in Kayogoro village in the province of Makamba; eight are killed, four wounded in the village of Munyika in the southern Rutana province.

- President Pierre Buyoya denies, after weekend talks with Rwandan counterpart Pasteur Bizimungu, that Rwanda sent troops to help counter an upsurge in rebel guerilla attacks.

- Some thirty Roman Catholic civilians are murdered while praying in a church outside Bujumbura.

- Burundi qualifies as one of the heavily indebted countries eligible for U.S. debt relief.

October

- As a counter-insurgency tactic to deny Hutu rebels food and support from the local population, the Burundian army forcibly resettles almost 260,000 civilians into camps in the hills around Bujumbura; the government appeals to aid agencies to help provide food, medical care and shelter as living conditions are poor and disease runs rampant.

- Burundi's Foreign Minister Severin Ntahomvukiye calls Hutu rebels to join in upcoming peace talks to be held in Tanzania.

- Burundi qualifies for export credits extended by the U.S. Agriculture Department.

- Prices of Burundi coffee slide at auction due to low demand and global oversupply.

December

- Nelson Mandela mediates peace talks in Burundi, raising hopes of reconciliation in central Africa.

- In late December, the Tutsi-controlled government rounds up 350,000 Hutus and restricts them to camps in the hills outside the capital.

ANALYSIS OF EVENTS: 1999

BUSINESS AND THE ECONOMY

After three years of economic sanctions against Burundi, East African nations met and voted to lift the sanctions. As one of the world's most heavily indebted nations, Burundi also qualified for debt relief from the United States. The economy of Burundi continued to flounder, however, with income from coffee exports declining because of lower world demand and global oversupply, and ongoing civil unrest and violent conflict between Hutu and Tutsi factions undermining the development of enterprise and commerce.

GOVERNMENT AND POLITICS

The government struggled to impose curfews and other regulations aimed at curbing attacks by rebels and warring ethnic factions. The efforts were largely unsuccessful, however, as the country continued to be ravaged by violent civil unrest. Thousands of refugees are homeless or living in makeshift camps, while malnutrition and disease overwhelm them. Instability in neighboring Democratic Republic of the Congo has caused governments of nations in the region, including Burundi, Rwanda, and Uganda, to send troops to support Congolese Tutsi in their attempts to restore security to border regions.

CULTURE AND SOCIETY

The brutality of the civil war in Burundi underlies all activities of daily life. International organizations estimated that 120,000 Burundian Hutus who had fled the country for the Democratic Republic of the Congo since 1996 have been forced to return to Burundi. Burundian Hutu refugees continued to look for a safe place to flee, traveling to neighboring Tanzania where conditions are somewhat more stable. In 1999, an estimated 260,000 Burundian Hutus were living in camps in Tanzania under the auspices of the United Nations Office of the High Commissioner for Refugees (UNHCR).

DIRECTORY

CENTRAL GOVERNMENT

Head of State

President
Pierre Buyoya, Office of the President,
Bujumbura, Burundi
PHONE: +257 226063
FAX: +257 227490

Premier Vice President
Frédéric Bamvuginyumvira, Office of the Vice President
PHONE: +257 3363
FAX: +257 2264424

Deuxieme Vice President
Mathias Sinamenye, Office of the Vice President
PHONE: +257 3363
FAX: +257 2264424

Ministers

Minister of Commerce, Industry, and Tourism
Nestor Nyabenda, Ministry of Commerce, Industry, and Tourism, Départment du commerce extérieur, Bujumbura, Burundi
PHONE: +257 225019
FAX: +257 225595

Minister of Finance
Astère Girukwigomba, Ministry of Finance, Bujumbura, Burundi
PHONE: +257 223988
FAX: +257 223827

Minister for External Relations and Co-operation

Sévérin Ntahomvukiye, Ministry for External Relations and Co-operation

Minister of the Interior and Public Security

Ascension Twagiramungu, Ministry of the Interior and Public Security
PHONE: +257 224242
FAX: +257 2223904

Minister of Defense

Alfred Nkurunziza, Ministry of Defense
PHONE: +257 224611; 225686
FAX: +257 217507

Minister of Development and Reconstruction

Léon Nimbona, Ministry of Development and Reconstruction
PHONE: +257 225394
FAX: +257 224193

Minister of Education

Prosper Mpawenayo, Ministry of Education
PHONE: +257 224407
FAX: +257 228477

Minister of Communication du Gouvernement

Luc Rukingama, Ministry of Communication
PHONE: +257 224666
FAX: +257 216318

Minister of Public Health

Juma Mohamed Kariburyo, Ministry of Public Health
PHONE: +257 226020
FAX: +257 229196

Minister of Labour, Civil Service and Vocational

Emmanuel Tungamwese, Ministry of Labour, Civil Service and Vocational Training

Minister of Communal Development

Gaspard Ntirampeba, Ministry of Communal Development
PHONE: +257 225267
FAX: +257 224678

Minister of Justice

Térence Sinunguruza, Ministry of Justice
PHONE: +257 225934
FAX: +257 222148

Minister of Tranports, Posts and Communications

Colonel Epitace Bayaganakandi, Ministry of Tranports, Posts and Communications
PHONE: +257 223100
FAX: +257 219324

Minister of Women and Social Affairs

Romaine Ndorimana, Ministry of Women and Social Affairs
PHONE: +257 223331
FAX: +257 216102

Minister of Youth and Sports

Gérard Nyamwiza, Ministry of Youth and Sports
PHONE: +257 222135
FAX: +257 226231

Minister of Agriculture

Salvator Ntihabose, Ministry of Agriculture
PHONE: +257 222087
FAX: +257 222873

Minister for Human Rights, Institutional Reforms and Relations

Eugène Nindorera, Ministry for Human Rights, Institutional Reforms and Relations
PHONE: +257 213682
FAX: +257 213847

Minister for the Peace Process

Ambroise Niyonsaba, Ministry for the Peace Process
PHONE: +257 226063; 219460
FAX: +257 219459

Minister of Public Works

Denis Nshimirimana, Ministry of Public Works
PHONE: +257 226841
FAX: +257 226840

Minister of Energy and Mines

Bernard Barandereka, Ministry of Energy and Mines
PHONE: +257 225909
FAX: +257 223337

Minster of Reintegration and Resettlement of Displaced and Repatriated People

Pascal Nkunrunziza, Minstry of Reintegration and Resettlement of Displaced and Repatriated People
PHONE: +257 212596
FAX: +257 218201

POLITICAL ORGANIZATIONS

Uprona Party

NAME: Antoine Nduwayo

Frodebu Party

NAME: Sylvestre Ntibantunganya

DIPLOMATIC REPRESENTATION

Embassies in Burundi

United States

BP 1720, Avenue des Etats-Unis, Bujumbura, Burundi
PHONE: +257 223454
FAX: +257 222926
TITLE: Ambassador
NAME: Morris N. Hughes, Jr.

JUDICIAL SYSTEM

Supreme Court

FURTHER READING

Articles

Bigg, Matthew. "Burundi Rebel Killings Hit Buyoya's Hopes." Reuters, 30 August 1999.

"Burundi Army Forcibly Resettles 260,000 into Camps." Reuters, 1 October 1999.

Cravero-Kristofferson, Kathleen and Marie Diamond. "Burundi: What Sanctions Meant on the Ground." *UN Chronicle* 36 (Spring 1999): 88 (2).

Denyer, Simon. "Congo War Bounces Back to Haunt Burundi." Reuters, 10 October 1999.

Denyer, Simon. "Burundians Caught in Cauldron of Civil War." Reuters, 15 September 1999.

Misser, Francois. "Lifting of Embargo Gives Life to Economy." *African Business* 244 (June 1999): 36 (2).

Books

Eggers, Ellen K. *Historical Dictionary of Burundi.* 2nd ed. Lanham, Md.: Scarecrow Press, 1997.

Lemarchand, Reni. *Burundi: Ethnocide as Discourse and Practice.* Washington, D.C.: Woodrow Wilson Center Press; New York: Cambridge University Press, 1994.

Nyankanzi, Edward L. *Genocide: Rwanda and Burundi.* Rochester, Vt.: Schenkman Books, 1998.

Internet

Africa News Online. Available Online @ http: // www.africanews.org/ (November 30, 1999).

World Full Coverage. Available Online @ http: //fullcoverage.yahoo.com/Full_Coverage/ World/Burundi (November 30, 1999).

BURUNDI: STATISTICAL DATA

For sources and notes see "Sources of Statistics" in the front of each volume.

GEOGRAPHY

Geography (1)

Area:

Total: 27,830 sq km.

Land: 25,650 sq km.

Water: 2,180 sq km.

Area—comparative: slightly smaller than Maryland.

Land boundaries:

Total: 974 km.

Border countries: Democratic Republic of the Congo 233 km, Rwanda 290 km, Tanzania 451 km.

Coastline: 0 km (landlocked).

Climate: equatorial; high plateau with considerable altitude variation (772 m to 2,760 m); average annual temperature varies with altitude from 23 to 17 degrees centigrade but is generally moderate as the average altitude is about 1,700 m; average annual rainfall is about 150 cm; wet seasons from February to May and September to November, and dry seasons from June to August and December to January.

Terrain: hilly and mountainous, dropping to a plateau in east, some plains.

Natural resources: nickel, uranium, rare earth oxides, peat, cobalt, copper, platinum (not yet exploited), vanadium.

Land use:

Arable land: 44%

Permanent crops: 9%

Permanent pastures: 36%

Forests and woodland: 3%

Other: 8% (1993 est.).

HUMAN FACTORS

Demographics (2A)

	1990	1995	1998	2000	2010	2020	2030	2040	2050
Population	5,284.7	5,339.0	5,537.4	5,930.8	7,539.3	9,431.9	11,621.9	14,344.6	17,303.8
Net migration rate (per 1,000 population)	NA	NA	NA	NA	NA	NA	NA	NA	NA
Births	NA	NA	NA	NA	NA	NA	NA	NA	NA
Deaths	NA	NA	NA	NA	NA	NA	NA	NA	NA
Life expectancy - males	45.7	44.6	43.8	43.3	43.7	47.3	57.3	67.2	70.9
Life expectancy - females	48.0	47.3	47.4	47.4	46.9	50.9	62.6	74.3	78.3
Birth rate (per 1,000)	47.3	43.4	41.6	41.0	39.6	35.0	29.7	25.4	21.2
Death rate (per 1,000)	19.3	18.0	17.4	17.1	16.4	14.0	8.6	4.9	4.3
Women of reproductive age (15-49 yrs.)	1,188.3	1,185.8	1,255.6	1,368.4	1,786.2	2,282.4	3,038.0	3,897.6	4,724.5
of which are currently married	NA	NA	NA	NA	NA	NA	NA	NA	NA
Fertility rate	6.9	6.6	6.4	6.3	5.3	4.3	3.5	2.9	2.5

Except as noted, values for vital statistics are in thousands; life expectancy is in years.

Health Personnel (3)

Total health expenditure as a percentage of GDP, 1990-1997[a]

Public sector 1.0

Private sector ....NA

Total[b] ....NA

Health expenditure per capita in U.S. dollars, 1990-1997[a]

Purchasing power parity ....NA

Total ....NA

Availability of health care facilities per 100,000 people

Hospital beds 1990-1997[a] 70

Doctors 1993[c] 6

Nurses 1993[c] 17

Health Indicators (4)

Life expectancy at birth

1980 47

1997 42

Daily per capita supply of calories (1996) 1,708

Total fertility rate births per woman (1997) 6.3

Maternal mortality ratio per 100,000 live births (1990-97) ....1,300[c]

Safe water % of population with access (1995) 58

Sanitation % of population with access (1995) 48

Consumption of iodized salt % of households (1992-98)[a] 80

Smoking prevalence

Male % of adults (1985-95)[a] ....

Female % of adults (1985-95)[a] ....

Tuberculosis incidence per 100,000 people (1997) 252

Adult HIV prevalence % of population ages 15-49 (1997) 8.30

Infants and Malnutrition (5)

Under-5 mortality rate (1997) 176

% of infants with low birthweight (1990-97) ......NA

Births attended by skilled health staff % of total[a] ...24

% fully immunized (1995-97)

TB 71

DPT 60

Polio 60

Measles 50

Prevalence of child malnutrition under age 5 (1992-97)[b] 38

Ethnic Division (6)

Hutu (Bantu) 85%

Tutsi (Hamitic) 14%

Twa (Pygmy) 1%

Europeans 3,000

South Asians 2,000

Religions (7)

Christian 67%

Roman Catholic 62%

Protestant 5%

Indigenous beliefs 32%

Muslim 1%

Languages (8)

Kirundi (official), French (official), Swahili (along Lake Tanganyika and in the Bujumbura area).

EDUCATION

Public Education Expenditures (9)

Public expenditure on education (% of GNP)

1980 ....3.4[1]

1996 ....3.1

Expenditure per student

Primary % of GNP per capita

1980 ....

1996 ....18.6[1]

Secondary % of GNP per capita

1980 ....222.1[1]

1996 ....

Tertiary % of GNP per capita

1980 ....1,479.0[1]

1996 ....

Expenditure on teaching materials

Primary % of total for level (1996) ....

Secondary % of total for level (1996) ....

Primary pupil-teacher ratio per teacher (1996) .....50[1]

Duration of primary education years (1995) 6

Educational Attainment (10)

Age group (1990) ....25+

Total population 1,897,323

Highest level attained (%)

No schooling 75.4

First level

Not completed 19.9

Completed ....NA

Entered second level

S-1 ....2.5

S-2 ....NA

Postsecondary 0.6

Literacy Rates (11A)

In thousands and percent[1]	1990	1995	2000	2010
Illiterate population (15+ yrs.)	2,062	2,221	2,399	2,794
Literacy rate - total adult pop. (%)	31.3	35.3	39.8	49.1
Literacy rate - males (%)	45.3	49.3	53.4	61.1
Literacy rate - females (%)	18.5	22.5	27.2	37.7

GOVERNMENT & LAW

Political Parties (12)

National Assembly	% of seats
Democratic Front (FRODEBU) 71.0	
Unity for National Progress (UPRONA) 21.4	

Military Affairs (14B)

	1990	1991	1992	1993	1994	1995
Military expenditures						
Current dollars (mil.)	24	27	31[e]	32[e]	35[e]	46
1995 constant dollars (mil.)	28	29	33[e]	33[e]	36[e]	46
Armed forces (000)	12	12	7	7	17	22
Gross national product (GNP)						
Current dollars (mil.)	998	1,096	1,154	1,112	1,061	1,050
1995 constant dollars (mil.)	1,147	11,211	1,241	1,166	1,087	1,050
Central government expenditures (CGE)						
1995 constant dollars (mil.)	206	211	243	240	188	186
People (mil.)	5.6	5.8	5.9	6.1	6.2	5.9
Military expenditure as % of GNP	2.4	2.4	2.7	2.8	3.3	4.4
Military expenditure as % of CGE	13.6	13.9	13.7	13.8	19.4	24.8
Military expenditure per capita (1995 $)	5	5	6	5	6	8
Armed forces per 1,000 people (soldiers)	2.1	2.1	1.2	1.2	2.7	3.7
GNP per capita (1995 $)	204	209	210	192	174	177
Arms imports[6]						
Current dollars (mil.)	5	10	0	10	5	0
1995 constant dollars (mil.)	6	11	0	10	5	0
Arms exports[6]						
Current dollars (mil.)	0	0	0	0	0	0
1995 constant dollars (mil.)	0	0	0	0	0	0
Total imports[7]						
Current dollars (mil.)	231	248	221	204	224	234
1995 constant dollars (mil.)	265	274	238	214	230	234
Total exports[7]						
Current dollars (mil.)	75	90	72	68	108	106
1995 constant dollars (mil.)	86	99	77	71	111	106
Arms as percent of total imports[8]	2.2	4.0	0	4.9	2.2	0
Arms as percent of total exports[8]	0	0	0	0	0	0

Government Budget (13A)

Year: 1997

Total Expenditures: 80,800 Millions of Francs

Expenditures as a percentage of the total by function:

General public services and public order 24.12

Defense 26.11

Education 13.87

Health 2.58

Social Security and Welfare 5.84

Housing and community amenities . . . .-

Recreational, cultural, and religious affairs 41

Fuel and energy . . . .

Agriculture, forestry, fishing, and hunting . . . .

Mining, manufacturing, and construction . . . .

Transportation and communication . . . .

Other economic affairs and services . . . .

LABOR FORCE

Labor Force (16)

Total (million) 1.9

Agriculture 93.0%

Government 4.0%

Industry and commerce 1.5%

Services 1.5%

Data for 1983 est.

Unemployment Rate (17)

Rate not available.

PRODUCTION SECTOR

Electric Energy (18)

Capacity . . . . .43,000 kW (1995)

Production . . . . .158 million kWh (1995)

Consumption per capita . . . . .32 kWh (1995)

Imports some electricity from Democratic Republic of the Congo.

Transportation (19)

Highways:

total: 14,480 km

paved: 1,028 km

unpaved: 13,452 km (1995 est.)

Waterways: Lake Tanganyika

Airports: 4 (1997 est.)

Airports—with paved runways:

total: 1

over 3,047 m: 1 (1997 est.)

Airports—with unpaved runways:

total: 3

914 to 1,523 m: 2

under 914 m: 1 (1997 est.)

Top Agricultural Products (20)

Coffee, cotton, tea, corn, sorghum, sweet potatoes, bananas, manioc (tapioca); meat, milk, hides.

MANUFACTURING SECTOR

GDP & Manufacturing Summary (21)

Detailed value added figures are listed by both International Standard Industry Code (ISIC) and product title.

	1980	1985	1990	1994
GDP ($-1990 mil.)[1]	762	968	1,148	969
Per capita ($-1990)[1]	184	204	209	156
Manufacturing share (%) (current prices)[1]	9.0	13.2	16.8	13.4
Manufacturing				
Value added ($-1990 mil.)[1]	75	142	189	167
Industrial production index	100	142	174	188
Value added ($ mil.)	56	94	105	94
Gross output ($ mil.)	95	190	209	172
Employment (000)	3	5	7	8
Profitability (% of gross output)				
Intermediate input (%)	41	51	50	45
Wages and salaries inc. supplements (%)	9	8	10	12
Gross operating surplus	51	41	40	43
Productivity ($)				
Gross output per worker	27,639	38,404	31,820	22,221
Value added per worker	16,370	19,249	16,048	12,368
Average wage (inc. supplements)	2,357	3,169	3,303	2,742
Value added ($ mil.)				
311/2 Food products	30	51	59	53
313 Beverages	11	20	23	20
314 Tobacco products	3	5	5	5

	1980	1985	1990	1994
321 Textiles	2	9	9	8
322 Wearing apparel	3	1	1	1
323 Leather and fur products	1	—	—	—
324 Footwear	—	—	—	—
331 Wood and wood products	—	—	1	1
332 Furniture and fixtures	—	—	1	1
341 Paper and paper products	—	—	—	—
342 Printing and publishing	1	1	1	1
351 Industrial chemicals	1	1	—	—
352 Other chemical products	—	1	1	1
353 Petroleum refineries	—	—	—	—
354 Miscellaneous petroleum and coal products	—	—	—	—
355 Rubber products	—	—	—	—
356 Plastic products	—	1	—	—
361 Pottery, china and earthenware	—	—	—	—
362 Glass and glass products	—	—	—	—
369 Other non-metal mineral products	1	2	2	1
371 Iron and steel	—	—	—	—
372 Non-ferrous metals	—	—	—	—
381 Metal products	2	3	2	2
382 Non-electrical machinery	—	—	—	—
383 Electrical machinery	—	—	—	—
384 Transport equipment	—	—	—	—
385 Professional and scientific equipment	—	—	—	—
390 Other manufacturing industries	—	—	1	1

FINANCE, ECONOMICS, & TRADE

Economic Indicators (22)

National product: GDP—purchasing power parity—$4 billion (1997 est.)

National product real growth rate: 4.4% (1997 est.)

National product per capita: $660 (1997 est.)

Inflation rate—consumer price index: 26% (1996 est.)

Exchange Rates (24)

Exchange rates:

Burundi francs (FBu) per US$1

January 1998	412.59
1997	352.35
1996	302.75
1995	249.76
1994	252.66
1993	242.78

Balance of Payments (23)

	1990	1992	1993	1994	1995
Exports of goods (f.o.b.)	73	77	74	81	113
Imports of goods (f.o.b.)	−189	−182	−173	−173	−176
Trade balance	−116	−105	−99	−92	−63
Services - debits	−152	−165	−138	−115	−122
Services - credits	25	32	25	23	27
Private transfers (net)	11	14	19	22	15
Government transfers (net)	164	165	163	144	136
Overall balance	−69	−60	−29	−18	−7

Top Import Origins (25)

$127 million (c.i.f., 1996)

Origins	%
European Union	.47
Asia	.25
United States	.6

Top Export Destinations (26)

$40 million (f.o.b., 1996).

Destinations	%
European Union	.60
United States	.7
Asia	.1

Economic Aid (27)

Recipient: ODA, $NA. NA stands for not available.

Import Export Commodities (28)

Import Commodities	Export Commodities
Capital goods 26%	Coffee 81%
Petroleum products	Tea
Foodstuffs	Cotton
Consumer goods	Hides

CAMBODIA

Kingdom of Cambodia
Preahreacheanachakr Kampuchea

INTRODUCTORY SURVEY

RECENT HISTORY

In 1863, the king of Cambodia placed the country under French protection. The French combined Cambodia, Laos, and Vietnam to form French Indochina. The French ruled this protectorate until the end of World War II (1939–45).

Cambodia became a constitutional monarchy on 6 May 1947 and was officially granted independence within the French Union on 9 November 1949. On 17 October 1953, Prince Norodom Sihanouk, who had ascended the throne in 1941, was granted full military control of his country by France. During the next fifteen years, Sihanouk sought to keep Cambodia neutral in the deepening conflict that was taking place between neighboring Vietnam and the United States. This proved increasingly difficult, however, as the National Liberation Front (also known as the Vietcong) used Cambodian border areas as bases from which to launch attacks on the Republic of Vietnam (RVN, or South Vietnam). In 1969, the United States launched an undeclared air war against these guerrilla sanctuaries.

On 18 March 1970, Marshal Lon Nol, prime minister and army chief, overthrew the chief of state, Prince Sihanouk; the coup ended 1,168 years of rule by Khmer monarchs. Meanwhile, U.S. President Richard M. Nixon announced that 30,000 United States and 40,000 RVN troops would invade Cambodia. Their object was to destroy North Vietnamese strongholds in Cambodia.

In October 1970, the Lon Nol government in Phnom Penh abolished the monarchy and changed Cambodia's name to the Khmer Republic. Lon Nol was elected president of the republic. However, the communist military rebels known as Khmer Rouge continued their fight and eventually took control of the government in January 1976. They renamed the country Democratic Kampuchea (DK). Communist leader Pol Pot was named prime minister.

Pol Pot's government plunged the country into near-total isolation from other countries of the

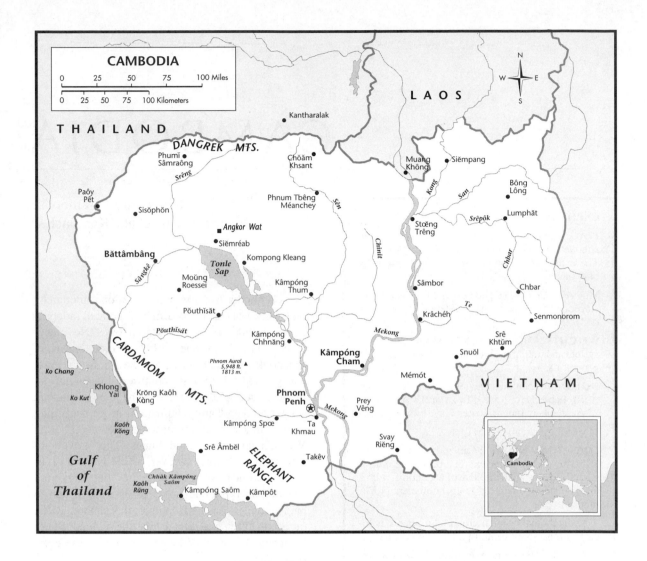

world. Currency was abolished, religion almost erased, education suspended, and families divided. An estimated 2–3 million people died of starvation, exhaustion, disease, or massacre under the Pol Pot regime.

In December 1978, Vietnam invaded Cambodia with a force of more than 100,000 troops. They took control of the country and installed a pro-Vietnamese government. Khmer Rouge rebels fled to the jungles and began a guerilla war against the new government. The following years saw further fighting and competition for political power.

Finally, on 23 October 1991, an end to thirteen years of war in Cambodia was achieved. In 1993, the first multiparty election in more than twenty years was held. A 120-member national assembly was elected and a new constitution was ratified,

with the former Prince Sihanouk becoming Cambodia's constitutional monarch.

On 11 June 1994, the Khmer Rouge announced it had formed its own government with headquarters in northern Cambodia. In response, the National Assembly voted to outlaw the Khmer Rouge. The country would remain in turmoil for the next few years.

By 1997, the Khmer Rouge was diminished to a few hundred rebels who retreated into northern Cambodia. In July 1998, Hun Sen's Cambodian People's Party won the majority in parliamentary elections, defeating the royalist party.

On December 4, 1998, the surviving Khmer Rouge reached an agreement with the government whereby they would lay down their arms and accept the authority of the government of Phnom Phen. In return the government promised them their own land, housing, food, and integration into the Cambodian armed forces.

GOVERNMENT

On 23 October 1991, a UN peace accord was signed by Cambodia's political factions; the agreement provided for elections with proportional representation. The country was divided into twenty provinces. In 1993, a National Assembly was elected and a new constitution was ratified. The monarchy was reestablished and commitments to liberal democracy, the rule of law, and women's rights were included.

Prince Norodom Sihanouk ratified the constitution and again became King of Cambodia. The new government began capturing Khmer Rouge strongholds and driving its members into Thailand. In 1997, what was left of the UN-imposed government fell apart as Hun Sen staged a coup to consolidate power within his wing of the government. In the parliamentary elections of July 1998, Prince Ranariddh lost his bid to become prime minister to then-prime minister Hun Sen.

Judiciary

The 1993 constitution provides legal guarantees such as presumption of innocence until proven guilty and also guarantees an independent judiciary. The structure of the new judicial system will be defined by laws yet to be enacted.

Political Parties

The main political parties include FUNCINPEC (National Front for an Independent, Neutral, Peaceful and Cooperative Cambodia), Prince Ranariddh's main political organization formed in 1981; the Cambodia People's Party; and the Buddhist Liberal Democratic Party.

DEFENSE

Because of the ongoing civil war, military figures for Cambodia are unreliable. The Cambodian government reports a regular army of 36,000, an air force of 500, and a navy of 1,200. Another 270,000 Khmer and minorities make up provincial and village militia.

ECONOMIC AFFAIRS

Twenty years of civil war placed heavy economic burdens on Cambodia. Serious damage to industry and agriculture required massive rehabilitation and reconstruction. Over half of basic transport and communications facilities were destroyed.

Since 1989, Cambodia has passed legislation to restore the right to own and inherit property, free prices, and open up the country to increased trade and foreign investment.

In the early 1990s, Cambodia remained mainly agricultural with more than 85% of workers employed in farm work. Inexpensive, unskilled Cambodian labor is plentiful, but there is a severe shortage of educated and trained personnel. In addition, the nation still must overcome corruption and mismanagement, and the widening gap between the urban rich and the rural poor.

Cambodia remains a major shipping source for illegal drugs, especially heroin. It is also becoming a large producer of marijuana.

Cambodia has significant natural resources (including timber, rubber, gems, and oil and natural gas) and beautiful scenery that could support a tourism industry. Growth of industries built on these natural resources depends on the government's ability to sustain peace.

Public Finance

From 1989–91, the public deficit nearly tripled as a result of falling revenue collection. As assistance from the Soviet bloc ceased after 1990, monetary expansion soared to cover the deficit. By the middle of 1992, with hyperinflation imminent, the government began a series of stabilization efforts to halt the fiscal deterioration.

Income

In 1997, Cambodia's gross national product (GNP) was $3.2 billion at current prices, or $300 per person. For the period 1985–95 the average inflation rate was 70.5%.

Industry

Industrial activity has traditionally centered on the processing of agricultural and forestry products and on the small-scale manufacture of consumer goods. Rice milling has been the main food-processing industry. Industrial expansion came to a virtual halt in 1970 with the outbreak of war. The Pol Pot government placed all industries under state control in 1975. By late 1985, there were a reported 60 government-run factories producing household goods, textiles, soft drinks, pharmaceutical products, and other light consumer goods.

Major industries include rice milling, fishing, wood and timber products, cement, and gem mining. Cambodia has significant mineral deposits of gold, silver, iron, copper, marble, limestone, and phosphate.

Banking and Finance

All banking institutions were nationalized by the Sihanouk government on 1 July 1964. The National Bank of Cambodia, a semi-autonomous government agency functioning as the sole currency authority, was charged with central banking responsibilities, including the control of credit. The decision by then Premier Lon Nol to permit foreign banks to do business in the country in early 1970 was a factor leading to his break with Prince Sihanouk and to the latter's overthrow in March 1970.

In April 1975, the Pol Pot government assumed control of the National Bank, and virtually all banking operations in Kampuchea were liquidated. The PRK government reintroduced a money economy, and by 1983 the National Bank of Cambodia and a Foreign Trade Bank had been established. In 1991, the government created a state commercial bank to take over the commercial banking operations of the national bank.

There is no securities trading in Cambodia.

Economic Development

In 1991, at the Tokyo Conference on the Rehabilitation and Reconstruction of Cambodia, $880 million in assistance was pledged to Cambodia by donor countries and multilateral institutions. An additional $80 million in aid was pledged by the Asian Development Bank, and the World Bank planned a $75-million assistance program. Under Sam Rainsy, Minister of Finance and Economy, the national assembly passed a budget and new Financial Structure Laws effective 1 January 1994. The new government's aim is to establish central control of the economy while striking out at the corrupt practices of the current system. About 48% of the budget is made up of international assistance; there are no land or income taxes with tax revenues providing only 6% of GDP, and customs duties provide 54% of total revenue. Estimates are that underground trade is equal to official trade and thus a further drain on state revenue. The new law requires that all state revenues "be sent to the national treasury totally, directly, and immediately." Development in Cambodia is inextricably linked to the government's ability to maintain peace. Investment, job creation, infrastructure improvements, and vocational education are FUNCINPEC's approach both to economic development and undermining the Khmer Rouge.

SOCIAL WELFARE

During the Pol Pot period, the social fabric of the country was severely damaged. Overall social conditions in Cambodia remain among the worst in southeast Asia. Political violence peaked in the period before the UN-sponsored elections of May 1993 and then fell sharply. After 1997, however, violence was increasing and social conditions were again deteriorating. Cambodia's constitution provides equal rights for women in such areas as work and marriage.

Healthcare

Life expectancy in Cambodia is estimated at 54 years. The infant mortality rate in 1995 was 108 per 1,000 live births. Dysentery, malaria, tuberculosis, trachoma, and yaws are widespread. The 1970s era of war and upheaval aggravated many health problems. Malnutrition became widespread among the millions driven from their homes. In 1994, only 13% of the population had access to safe water (compared to 36% in 1991) and a mere 14% had adequate sanitation.

During the war, landmines may have inflicted more wounds than any other weapon. Cambodia today has the world's highest percentage of physically disabled persons.

Housing

Cambodia's housing traditionally compared favorably with that of other countries in Southeast Asia. The most common type of dwelling consists of one or more rooms raised on mangrove piles some 3 meters (10 feet) above the ground.

EDUCATION

Most of the educated class had been killed by 1979. Only 50 of 725 university instructors and 307 of 2,300 secondary-school teachers survived. In the 1990s, education was gradually recovering. Adult literacy was estimated to be 65% in 1993. Total school enrollment increased from about 1 million in 1979 to more than 1.7 million in 1985, and the number of teachers more than doubled, from 21,000 to 46,500. All schooling is public, and six years of primary education (ages 6–12) are compulsory. Most students continue their higher education at foreign universities.

1999 KEY EVENTS TIMELINE

January

• Prime Minister Hun Sen decides to try Khmer Rouge leaders Khieu Samphan and Nuon Chea, who had defected in December, after international pressure to bring them to justice intensified.

February

• Hun Sen consults the South African government about its post-apartheid Truth and Reconciliation Commission as a possible model for holding Khmer Rouge leaders accountable for their deeds.

• Japan announces resumption of loans to Cambodia, which had been suspended for thirty years.

March

• A Taiwanese company, Formosa Plastics, pledges to clean up its massive dump of toxic waste near the coastal city of Sihanoukville.

• Opposition leader Sam Rainsy, citing corruption, asks international lenders to refuse aid to the Cambodian government.

• Hun Sen seeks $1.3 billion in aid at a World Bank meeting.

• Khmer Rouge leader Ta Mok is captured by the government, which plans its own trial for the Khmer Rouge, rejecting calls for a UN genocide tribunal.

April

• Hun Sen proposes a local trial with foreign judges and prosecutors participating, rather than an international tribunal, for the Khmer Rouge leaders.

• The Cambodian government announces wage increases for civil servants, most of whom have been earning under $20 a month.

May

• Cambodia becomes the 10th member of the Association of South East Asian Nations (ASEAN).

• Notorious Khmer Rouge prison warden Duch confesses his crimes in an interview, and is then arrested and charged with murder.

June

• Nuon Paet, a Khmer Rouge commander, is convicted of the 1994 murder of three foreign tourists.

• During a visit by Vietnamese Communist Party officials, Vietnam and Cambodia agree to end border disputes.

July

• Cambodian movie star Piseth Pilika is murdered, a crime linked to police and political corruption in the capital, Phnom Penh.

• Phnom Penh's gambling casinos are shut down and those in other areas are restricted to foreigners only.

August

• Cambodia's parliament allows detention without trial for Khmer Rouge genocide suspects. Sam Rainsy leads a protest march demanding a United Nations tribunal for the Khmer Rouge.

• Two Cambodian human rights activists are accused of inciting riots over the Sihanoukville toxic waste scandal; charges are dropped.

• King Norodom Sihanouk and Princess Bopha Devi, the Minister of Culture, speak out on the need to safeguard Cambodia's archeological sites.

September

• A scandal exposes the non-governmental organization Cambodian Mine Action Center's misuse of landmine-clearing funds.

• Khmer Rouge officials Ta Mok and Duch are formally charged with genocide.

• Following a meeting with UN Secretary-General Kofi Annan, Prime Minister Hun Sen pledges that genocide trials of Khmer Rouge leaders will not be delayed.

November

• At an informal meeting in Manila, Philippines, six members of the Association of Southeast Asian Nations (ASEAN)—Brunei, Indonesia, Malaysia, Philippines, Singapore, and Thailand—agree to establish a free-trade zone by eliminating duties on most goods traded in the region by 2010. The remaining four newer and less-developed nation members—Cambodia, Laos, Myanmar (Burma), and Vietnam—will eliminate duties by 2015. Rice will be excluded from trade agreements, however.

ANALYSIS OF EVENTS: 1999

BUSINESS AND THE ECONOMY

Cambodia's economy, hit hard by Asia's economic crisis and Prime Minister Hun Sen's coup d'etat of 1997, began to recover by mid-1999. Its currency remained stable, and international lending agencies were considering major aid packages, contingent on frequent monitoring. Japan announced the resumption of aid to Cambodia, and assistance projects were initiated by China. Foreign investment remained weak, however, falling some 20% despite some new Japanese and South Korean ventures. Tourism was promising, with new direct flights from Bangkok and Hong Kong and a 50% increase in visitors, although airport and railway infrastructure desperately needed improvement. The garment industry remained a major source of foreign exchange, despite some labor unrest.

Logging was a lucrative source of illicit money, particularly for the Cambodian military. The World Bank and environmental groups made dire predictions of the total deforestation of Cambodia within a few years if the timber trade continued uncontrolled. Smuggling of goods, including narcotics, to and from neighboring countries remained rife in 1999. The government proposed the sale of part of its telephone system to a private firm, a potentially controversial move due to charges of government profiteering. Cambodia's agriculture remained important but the industry is in need of land reform laws and the development of agro-industries such as palm oil and rubber processing. The first Cambodian tapioca factory, a joint venture with a Thai firm opened, with plans to export the product to South Korea.

GOVERNMENT AND POLITICS

In 1999, the need to hold the surviving Khmer Rouge leaders accountable for the 1975–79 genocide in which an estimated two million Cambodians died, dominated the news. As the entire Khmer Rouge top echelon (minus Pol Pot, who died in 1998) was taken into custody in 1999, international pressure increased for their trial and punishment. The United Nations called for an international genocide tribunal, with the support of four members of the Security Council. The fifth, China, supported Cambodian Prime Minister Hun Sen's wishes for a Cambodian trial. Hun Sen was willing to compromise to the extent of allowing foreign judges and prosecutors to participate, and to give assurances that the trial would not be delayed. This did not allay suspicions that local courts would hold mere show trials shadowed by the threat of renewed warfare with remaining Khmer Rouge troops.

At peace for the first time since the early 1970s, Cambodia's government pledged reductions in the size of its military and police, cutting military spending and corruption. Thousands of "phantom soldiers" who existed only on paper were to be cut from army payrolls. Cambodia's admittance in May as the tenth member of the Association of South East Asian Nations (ASEAN), delayed by Hun Sen's 1997 coup d'etat, earned Cambodia new respectability and the opportunity to participate in regional policy conferences.

The opposition, led by Sam Rainsy, continued to push for reforms and accountability. An investigation conducted by two Cambodian human rights groups and the international organization Human Rights Watch, concluded that Cambodian courts were lax in holding soldiers and others accountable for acts violating human rights. Controversy continued over the clean-up of some 3,000 tons of toxic waste deposited in the port city of Sihanoukville by a Taiwanese company. Human rights activists who had been arrested for protesting the toxic dumping were released, and the government banned future import of toxic waste.

CULTURE AND SOCIETY

Cambodia's first national census in 36 years revealed a population count of 11.4 million. The census also enumerated severe social underdevelopment, such as an illiteracy rate of one-third of all adults, and a lack of safe drinking water or electricity for most Cambodians. Cambodia's population was growing at 2.5% per year, according to the census. The government stated that it would use the census findings to establish population policy for Cambodia.

The health care system remained dependent on foreign assistance. UNICEF cited high rates of child malnutrition and infant mortality in Cambodia, and the spread of HIV/AIDS, malaria and other infectious diseases remained virtually unchecked.

Flash floods in August destroyed the homes of thousands of people in central-southern Cambodia. The need to clear land mines from the countryside remained a high priority, although a well-regarded non-government organization involved in the de-mining work was rocked by a corruption scandal.

Public dismay over the murder of beloved Cambodian movie actress Piseth Pilika, in Cambodia's capital, Phnom Penh, spotlighted rampant violent crime and police corruption. In an effort to clean up Phnom Penh's image, the city's gambling casinos were shut down and the remaining ones, at least 125 miles out, were declared open for foreigners only.

The royal families of Cambodia and Thailand decried the looting and smuggling of treasures from Cambodia's famous archeological sites. In 1999, archeologists excavated a burial site from 2,500 years ago, in southern Cambodia.

DIRECTORY

CENTRAL GOVERNMENT

Head of State

King
Norodom Sihanouk, Monarch

President of the National Assembly
Prince Norodom Ranariddh, Office of the President of the National Assembly

Prime Minister
Hun Sen, Office of the Prime Minister

Ministers

Deputy Prime Minister
Sar Kheng, Office of the Deputy Prime Minister

Deputy Prime Minister
Tol Lah, Office of the Deputy Prime Minister

Minister in the Council of Ministers
Sok An, Office of the Council of Ministers

Minister of Agriculture, Forestry and Fishing
Chhea Song, Ministry of Agriculture, Forestry and Fishing, Norodom Blvd., Phnom Penh, Cambodia
PHONE: +855 (23) 427320
FAX: +855 (23) 427320

Minister of Commerce
Cham Prasit, Ministry of Commerce, Norodom Blvd., Phnom Penh, Cambodia
PHONE: +855 (23) 723775

FAX: +855 (23) 426396

Minister of Culture and Fine Arts
Norodom Bopha Devi, Ministry of Culture and Fine Arts, Monivong Blvd., Phnom Penh, Cambodia
PHONE: +855 (23) 362647

Minister of Economy and Finance
Keat Chhon, Ministry of Economy and Finance, Daun Penh Street, Phnom Penh, Cambodia
PHONE: +855 (23) 722863
FAX: +855 (23) 427798

Minister of Education, Youth, and Sports
Tok Lah, Ministry of Education, Youth and Sports, Norodom Blvd., Phnom Penh, Cambodia
PHONE: +855 (23) 360233
FAX: +855 (23) 426791

Minister of Environment
Mok Maret, Ministry of Environment, Sihanouk Blvd., Phnom Penh, Cambodia
PHONE: +855 (23) 426814
FAX: +855 (23) 427844

Minister of Foreign Affairs and International Cooperation
Hor Namhong, Ministry of Foreign Affaires and International Cooperation, Sihanouk Blvd., Phnom Penh, Cambodia
PHONE: +855 (23) 426122
FAX: +855 (23) 426144

Minister of Health
Hong Sun Huot, Ministry of Health, #128 Kampuchea Krom, Phnom Penh, Cambodia
PHONE: +855 (23) 426841
FAX: +855 (23) 426841

Minister of Industry, Mines, and Energy
Suy Sem, Ministry of Industry, Mines and Energy, Norodom Blvd., Phnom Penh, Cambodia
PHONE: +855 (23) 723077
FAX: +855 (23) 427840

Minister of Information and Press
Lu Lay Sreng, Ministry of Information and Press, Monivong Blvd., Phnom Penh, Cambodia
PHONE: +855 (23) 426059
FAX: +855 (23) 426059

Co-Ministers of Interior
Sar Kheng, Yu Hokkri, Ministry of Interior, Norodom Blvd., Phnom Penh, Cambodia
PHONE: +855 (23) 724237

Minister of Justice
Uk Vithun, Ministry of Justice, Sothearos Blvd., Phnom Penh, Cambodia

PHONE: +855 (23) 360421

Co-Ministers of National Defense
Tie Banh, Sisowath Sirirath, Ministry of
National Defense, Pochentong Blvd., Phnom
Penh, Cambodia
PHONE: +855 (23) 366170
FAX: +855 (23) 366169

Minister of Planning
Chhay Than, Ministry of Planning, #386
Monivong Blvd., Phnom Penh, Cambodia
PHONE: +855 (23) 362307

Minister of Posts and Telecommunications
So Khun, Ministry of Post and
Telecommunications, Preah Ang Eng/Preah Ang
Non, Phnom Penh, Cambodia
PHONE: +855 (23) 722823

Minister of Public Works and Transportation
Khy Tainglim, Ministry of Public Works,
Khsattreiani Kossomak Street, Phnom Penh,
Cambodia
PHONE: +855 (23) 420813; 752113
FAX: +855 (23) 427862

**Minister of Relations with Parliament and
Inspection**
Khun Hang, Ministry of Relations with
Parliament and Inspection

Minister of Religious Affairs
Chea Savoeun, Ministry of Religious Affairs,
Sisowath Blvd., Phnom Penh, Cambodia
PHONE: +855 (23) 725699; 722699

Minister of Rural Development
Chhim Siekleng, Ministry of Rural Development,
Czechoslovakia Blvd./Pochentong Blvd., Phnom
Penh, Cambodia
PHONE: +855 (23) 722425; 426814

**Minister of Social Affairs, Labor, Vocational
Training, and Youth Rehabilitation**
Itsam-Heng, Ministry of Social Welfare, Labor
and Veterans, #68 Norodom Blvd., Phnom
Penh, Cambodia
PHONE: +855 (23) 725191
FAX: +855 (23) 427322

Minister of Tourism
Veng Sereyvuth, Ministry of Tourism, #3
Monivong Blvd., Phnom Penh, Cambodia
PHONE: +855 (23) 213911
FAX: +855 (23) 426107; 426364

Minister of Urbanization and Construction
Im Chhunlim, Ministry of Urbanization and
Construction

Minister of Water Resources and Meteorology
Lim Kean-Hao, Ministry of Water Resources
and Meteorology

**Minister of Women's Affairs and War
Veterans**
Mu Sochua, Ministry of Women's Affairs
PHONE: +855 (23) 366412

POLITICAL ORGANIZATIONS

FUNCINPEC (National United Front for an Independent, Neutral, Peaceful, and Cooperative Cambodia)

11 Moha Vithei Preah Monivong, Sankat Srah
Chak, Khan Daun Penh, Phnom Penh, Cambodia
PHONE: +855 (23) 217768; 428863; 428869
FAX: +855 (23) 426471
E-MAIL: funcinpec@funcinpec.org
NAME: King Norodom Ranariddh

Kanakpak Pracheachon Kampuchea (Cambodian Pracheachon Party or Cambodian People's Party)

NAME: Chea Sim
E-MAIL: cpp@cppusa.net

Sam Rangsi Party (SRP)

14A, Keo Chea Street, Phnom Penh, Cambodia
E-MAIL: Masavang@datagraphic.fr
NAME: Sam Rangsi

Kanakpak Preachethippatai Serei Niyum Preah Pothasasna-BLP (Buddhist Liberal Party)

NAME: Ieng Mouly

Populist Party

NAME: Ung Huot

Khmer Citizen Party (KCP)

NAME: Nguon Soeur

National Liberation Movement of Cambodia

Pheakki Kampuchea Prachea Thippatai (Party for a Democratic Cambodia)

Molinaka

NAME: Prom Neakareach

DIPLOMATIC REPRESENTATION

Embassies in Cambodia

Australia
Villa 11R, V Senei Vannavaut, Oum (St. 254),
Daun Penh District, Phnom Penh, Cambodia
PHONE: +855 (23) 2326001

Bulgaria
227 Norodom Blvd., Phnom Penh, Cambodia
PHONE: +855 (23) 723181
FAX: +855 (23) 426491

Brunei Darussalam
237 Street 51, Phnom Penh, Cambodia
PHONE: +855 (23) 211457
FAX: +855 (23) 211456

Cuba
98 Street 214, Phnom Penh, Cambodia
PHONE: +855 (23) 368610
FAX: +855 (23) 217428

Germany
No. 76-78, St. 214, Phnom Penh, Cambodia
PHONE: +855 (23) 426381
FAX: +855 (23) 427746

Indonesia
90 Norodom Blvd., Phnom Penh, Cambodia
PHONE: +855 (23) 217934; 216148; 216623
FAX: +855 (23) 217566; 217947

Japan
No. 75, Norodom Blvd., Phnom Penh, Cambodia
PHONE: +855 (23) 427161; 427162
FAX: +855 (23) 426162

Laos
No. 15-17, Mao Tse Tung Blvd., Phnom Penh,
Cambodia
PHONE: +855 (23) 426441
FAX: +855 (23) 427454

Malaysia
11 Street 51, Phnom Penh, Cambodia
PHONE: +855 (23) 216176
FAX: +855 (23) 216004

Malta
10 Street 370, Phnom Penh, Cambodia
PHONE: +855 (23) 368184
FAX: +855 (23) 368184

Myanmar
181 Norodom Blvd., Phnom Penh, Cambodia
PHONE: +855 (23) 213664
FAX: +855 (23) 213665

Russia
213 Sothearos Boulevard, Phnom Penh,
Cambodia

Singapore
92 Norodom Blvd., Phnom Penh, Cambodia
PHONE: +855 (23) 360855

Thailand
4 Monivong Blvd., Phnom Penh, Cambodia
PHONE: +855 (23) 363870
FAX: +855 (23) 810860

United Kingdom
No. 27-29 St. 75, Phnom Penh, Cambodia
PHONE: +855 (23) 427124
FAX: +855 (23) 427125

United States
27 Street 240, Phnom Penh, Cambodia
PHONE: +855 (23) 216436; 216438; 216807
FAX: +855 (23) 216437
TITLE: Ambassador
NAME: Kenneth M. Quinn

Vietnam
No. 436 Monivong Blvd., Phnom Penh,
Cambodia
PHONE: +855 (23) 725481
FAX: +855 (23) 427385

JUDICIAL SYSTEM

Supreme Council of the Magistracy

FURTHER READING

Articles

Gluck, Caroline. ''Hunger's Silent Victims:
Cambodia Turns Its Attention to Child
Malnutrition Rates that Are Even Worse Than
North Korea's.'' *Time International* 153 (May
17, 1999): 20.

''Helping the Other Guys. (International Donors
Try to Change Cambodia's Politics).'' *The
Economist* (February 27, 1999): 39.

''Wooden Soldiers: Cambodia makes a show of
cracking down on illegal logging but may be
trying to save more than trees.'' *Time
International* (April 19, 1999): 36.

Books

Chandler, David P. *Brother Number One: A
Political Biography of Pol Pot.* Boulder CO:
Westview Press, 1999.

Curtis, Grant. *Cambodia Reborn?: The Transition to Democracy and Development.* Washington DC: Brookings Institution, 1998.

Impunity in Cambodia: How Human Rights Offenders Escape Justice. New York: Human Rights Watch Report, 1999.

Kamm, Henry. *Cambodia: Report from a Stricken Land.* New York: Arcade Publishing, 1998.

Toxic Justice: Human Rights, Justice and Toxic Waste in Cambodia. New York: Human Rights Watch Report, 1999.

Internet

Cambodian Online. Available Online @ http://www.cambodian-online.com (November 3, 1999.

Royal Embassy of Cambodia, Washington, D.C. Available Online @ http://www.embassy.org/cambodia/ (November 3, 1999.

CAMBODIA: STATISTICAL DATA

For sources and notes see "Sources of Statistics" in the front of each volume.

GEOGRAPHY

Geography (1)

Area:

Total: 181,040 sq km.

Land: 176,520 sq km.

Water: 4,520 sq km.

Area—comparative: slightly smaller than Oklahoma.

Land boundaries:

Total: 2,572 km.

Border countries: Laos 541 km, Thailand 803 km, Vietnam 1,228 km.

Coastline: 443 km

Climate: tropical; rainy, monsoon season (May to November); dry season (December to April); little seasonal temperature variation.

Terrain: mostly low, flat plains; mountains in southwest and north.

Natural resources: timber, gemstones, some iron ore, manganese, phosphates, hydropower potential.

Land use:

Arable land: 13%

Permanent crops: 0%

Permanent pastures: 11%

Forests and woodland: 66%

Other: 10% (1993 est.).

HUMAN FACTORS

Demographics (2A)

	1990	1995	1998	2000	2010	2020	2030	2040	2050
Population	8,717.0	10,490.9	11,339.6	11,918.9	15,180.2	19,163.6	23,893.3	29,304.4	35,065.1
Net migration rate (per 1,000 population)	NA	NA	NA	NA	NA	NA	NA	NA	NA
Births	NA	NA	NA	NA	NA	NA	NA	NA	NA
Deaths	NA	NA	NA	NA	NA	NA	NA	NA	NA
Life expectancy - males	45.9	46.1	46.6	47.0	50.9	53.9	61.2	68.4	71.4
Life expectancy - females	49.0	48.4	49.4	50.1	54.8	57.9	65.6	73.3	76.4
Birth rate (per 1,000)	46.7	44.3	41.6	40.7	36.7	33.8	29.3	25.0	21.7
Death rate (per 1,000)	17.8	17.5	16.5	15.9	12.8	11.2	8.0	5.6	5.3
Women of reproductive age (15-49 yrs.)	2,270.5	2,520.8	2,704.5	2,838.6	3,678.5	4,640.6	6,033.4	7,557.1	9,109.1
of which are currently married	NA	NA	NA	NA	NA	NA	NA	NA	NA
Fertility rate	5.8	5.8	5.8	5.8	5.2	4.6	3.9	3.3	2.8

Except as noted, values for vital statistics are in thousands; life expectancy is in years.

Health Personnel (3)

Total health expenditure as a percentage of GDP, 1990-1997[a]

Public sector 0.7

Private sector 6.5

Total[b] 7.2

Health expenditure per capita in U.S. dollars, 1990-1997[a]

Purchasing power parity . . . . .NA

Total 18

Availability of health care facilities per 100,000 people

Hospital beds 1990-1997[a] 210

Doctors 1993[c] 58

Nurses 1993[c] 136

Health Indicators (4)

Life expectancy at birth

1980 39

1997 54

Daily per capita supply of calories (1996) 1,947

Total fertility rate births per woman (1997) 4.6

Maternal mortality ratio per 100,000 live births (1990-97) . . . . .900[c]

Safe water % of population with access (1995) 13

Sanitation % of population with access (1995) . . . .

Consumption of iodized salt % of households (1992-98)[a] 7

Smoking prevalence

Male % of adults (1985-95)[a] 70

Female % of adults (1985-95)[a] 10

Tuberculosis incidence per 100,000 people (1997) 529

Adult HIV prevalence % of population ages 15-49 (1997) 2.40

Infants and Malnutrition (5)

Under-5 mortality rate (1997) 167

% of infants with low birthweight (1990-97) . . . . . .NA

Births attended by skilled health staff % of total[a] . . .31

% fully immunized (1995-97)

TB 82

DPT 70

Polio 70

Measles 68

Prevalence of child malnutrition under age 5 (1992-97)[b] 38

Ethnic Division (6)

Khmer 90%

Vietnamese 5%

Chinese 1%

Other 4%

Religions (7)

Theravada Buddhism 95%

Other 5%

Languages (8)

Khmer (official), French.

EDUCATION

Public Education Expenditures (9)

Public expenditure on education (% of GNP)

1980 . . . .

1996 . . . . .2.9

Expenditure per student

Primary % of GNP per capita

1980 . . . .

1996 . . . .

Secondary % of GNP per capita

1980 . . . .

1996 . . . .

Tertiary % of GNP per capita

1980 . . . .

1996 . . . .

Expenditure on teaching materials

Primary % of total for level (1996) . . . .

Secondary % of total for level (1996) . . . .

Primary pupil-teacher ratio per teacher (1996) 44

Duration of primary education years (1995) 5

Educational Attainment (10)

Age group (1993) . . . . .5+

Total population 8,664,920

Highest level attained (%)

No schooling 30.5

First level

Not completed 47.0

Completed . . . . .NA

Entered second level

S-1 . . . . .16.2

S-2 . . . . .4.1

Postsecondary 1.0

Literacy Rates (11B)

Adult literacy rate

1980

Male 74x

Female 23x

1995

Male 80x

Female 53x

GOVERNMENT & LAW

Political Parties (12)

National Assembly	No. of seats
National United Front (FUNCINPEC) 58	
Cambodian People's Party (CPP) 51	
Buddhist Liberal Democratic Party (BLDP) 10	
Movement Pour La Liberation Nationale Khmere (MOLINAKA), ...1	

The May 1993 elections were for the Constituent Assembly which became the National Assembly after the new constitution was promulgated in September 1993.

Military Affairs (14B)

	1990	1991	1992	1993	1994	1995
Military expenditures						
Current dollars (mil.)	NA	71	108	80	NA	90
1995 constant dollars (mil.)	NA	78	116	84	NA	90
Armed forces (000)	112	112	135	102	70	90
Gross national product (GNP)						
Current dollars (mil.)	1,803	2,018	2,218	2,369	2,520	2,925
1995 constant dollars (mil.)	2,072	2,230	2,386	2,484	2,583	2,925
Central government expenditures (CGE)						
1995 constant dollars (mil.)	NA	NA	NA	NA	355	NA
People (mil.)	8.7	9.0	9.4	9.9	10.3	10.6
Military expenditure as % of GNP	NA	3.5	4.9	3.4	NA	3.1
Military expenditure as % of CGE	NA	NA	NA	NA	NA	NA
Military expenditure per capita (1995 $)	NA	9	12	8	NA	9
Armed forces per 1,000 people (soldiers)	12.8	12.4	14.3	10.3	6.8	8.5
GNP per capita (1994 $)	237	247	253	251	252	277
Arms imports[6]						
Current dollars (mil.)	330	40	0	10	10	20
1995 constant dollars (mil.)	379	44	0	10	10	20
Arms exports[6]						
Current dollars (mil.)	0	0	0	0	0	0
1995 constant dollars (mil.)	0	0	0	0	0	0
Total imports[7]						
Current dollars (mil.)	111	100[e]	138	223	427	631
1995 constant dollars (mil.)	127	110[e]	149	223	438	631
Total exports[7]						
Current dollars (mil.)	53	145[e]	213	181	167	241
1995 constant dollars (mil.)	61	160[e]	229	190	171	241
Arms as percent of total imports[8]	298.4	40.1	0	4.5	2.3	3.2
Arms as percent of total exports[8]	0	0	0	0	0	0

Government Budget (13B)

Revenues . . . .$261 million

Expenditures . . . .$496 million

  Capital expenditures . . . . .NA

Data for 1995 est. NA stands for not available.

LABOR FORCE

Labor Force (16)

Agriculture 80%.

Unemployment Rate (17)

Rate not available.

PRODUCTION SECTOR

Electric Energy (18)

Capacity . . . . .35,000 kW (1995)

Production . . . . .190 million kWh (1995)

Consumption per capita . . . . .18 kWh (1995)

Transportation (19)

Highways:

total: 35,769 km

paved: 4,165 km

unpaved: 31,604 km (1997 est.)

Waterways: 3,700 km navigable all year to craft drawing 0.6 m; 282 km navigable to craft drawing 1.8 m

Merchant marine:

total: 87 ships (1,000 GRT or over) totaling 390,566 GRT/556,743 DWT ships by type: bulk 10, cargo 66, container 2, livestock carrier 2, oil tankers 3, refrigerated cargo 1, roll-on/roll-off cargo 3 note: a flag of convenience registry; includes ships of 7 countries: Aruba 1, Cyprus 8, Egypt 1, South Korea 1, Malta 1, Panama 1, Russia 5 (1997 est.)

Airports: 20 (1997 est.)

Airports—with paved runways:

total: 7

2,438 to 3,047 m: 2

1,524 to 2,437 m: 2

914 to 1,523 m: 3 (1997 est.)

Airports—with unpaved runways:

total: 13

1,524 to 2,437 m: 3

914 to 1,523 m: 10 (1997 est.)

Top Agricultural Products (20)

Rice, rubber, corn, vegetables.

FINANCE, ECONOMICS, & TRADE

Economic Indicators (22)

National product: GDP—purchasing power parity—$7.7 billion (1997 est.)

National product real growth rate: 1.5% (1997 est.)

National product per capita: $715 (1997 est.)

Inflation rate—consumer price index: 9.5% (1997 est.)

Exchange Rates (24)

Exchange rates:

Riels (CR) per US$1

  January 1998 . . . . .3,537.0

  1997 . . . . .2,946.3

  1996 . . . . .2,624.1

  1995 . . . . .2,450.8

  1994 . . . . .2,545.3

  1993 . . . . .2,689.0

Balance of Payments (23)

	1992	1993	1994	1995	1996
Exports of goods (f.o.b.)	265	284	490	855	644
Imports of goods (f.o.b.)	−443	−471	−744	−1,187	−1,072
Trade balance	−179	−187	−255	−332	−428
Services - debits	−84	−137	−189	−255	−279
Services - credits	50	64	57	124	175
Private transfers (net)	9	9	20	20	20
Government transfers (net)	111	147	210	257	215
Overall balance	−93	−104	−157	−186	−298

Top Import Origins (25)

$1 billion (1996 est.)

Origins	%
Singapore	NA
Vietnam	NA
Japan	NA
Australia	NA
Hong Kong	NA
Indonesia	NA

NA stands for not available.

Top Export Destinations (26)

$615 million (1996 est.).

Destinations	%
Singapore	NA
Japan	NA
Thailand	NA

Hong Kong	NA
Indonesia	NA
Malaysia	NA
United States	NA

NA stands for not available.

Economic Aid (27)

Recipient: ODA, $NA. Note: international donors pledged a total of $1.8 billion in 1995 and 1996. NA stands for not available.

Import Export Commodities (28)

Import Commodities	Export Commodities
Cigarettes	Timber
Construction materials	Garments
Petroleum products	Rubber
Machinery	Soybeans
Motor vehicles	Sesame

CAMEROON

Republic of Cameroon
République du Cameroun

INTRODUCTORY SURVEY

CAPITAL: Yaoundé.

FLAG: The flag is a tricolor of green, red, and yellow vertical stripes with one gold star imprinted in the center of the red stripe.

ANTHEM: The national anthem begins "O Cameroun, berceau de nos ancêtres" ("O Cameroon, cradle of our ancestors").

MONETARY UNIT: The Communauté Financière Africaine franc (CFA Fr) is a paper currency. There are coins of 1, 2, 5, 10, 25, 50, 100, and 500 CFA francs, and notes of 50, 100, 500, 1,000, 5,000, and 10,000 CFA francs. CFA Fr1 = $0.00196 (or $1 = CFA Fr510.65).

WEIGHTS AND MEASURES: The metric system is the legal standard.

HOLIDAYS: New Year's Day, 1 January; Youth Day, 11 February; Labor Day, 1 May; National Day, 20 May; Christmas, 25 December. Movable religious holidays include Ascension, Good Friday, Easter Monday, End of Ramadan (Djoulde Soumae), and Festival of the Lamb ('Id al-Kabir or Djoulde Laihadji).

TIME: 1 PM = noon GMT.

LOCATION AND SIZE: Situated in West Africa, Cameroon, shaped like an elongated triangle, contains an area of 475,440 square kilometers (183,568 square miles), extending 1,206 kilometers (749 miles) north–south and 717 kilometers (446 miles) east–west. Comparatively, the area occupied by Cameroon is slightly larger than the state of California. Cameroon's capital city, Yaoundé, is located in the southern part of the country.

CLIMATE: The southern and northern regions of the country are two distinct climatic areas. In the south there are two dry seasons, December to February, and July to September. The northern part of the country has a more comfortable climate. The temperature ranges from 22°C to 29°C (72°F– 84°F) along the coast. The dry season in the north is from October to April.

RECENT HISTORY

After the defeat of the Germans in World War II (1939–45), France granted French Cameroon representation in the French National Assembly. An elected territorial assembly was instituted, and political parties were recognized. Immediately, many political parties began to emerge. Only one, the Union of Cameroon Peoples (Union des Populations du Cameroun–UPC), had effective organization. The UPC demanded immediate reunification of the British Cameroons and French Cameroon, and eventual independence. From 1955 until 1971, the UPC carried out a campaign of sabotage, violence, and terror.

A proposal to unify British Cameroons and French Cameroon was ratified by popular referendum on 20 May 1972; the vote was reportedly 99.97% in favor of unification. A new constitution went into effect on 2 June, and the country was renamed the United Republic of Cameroon. Ahmadou Ahidjo became president of the republic. Running unopposed, he was reelected for a fourth five-year term on 5 April 1975. In June, by constitutional amendment, the office of prime minister was created, and Paul Biya was appointed to the post.

Ahidjo, reelected unopposed, began his fifth five-year term as president in May 1980. In November 1982, he resigned and was succeeded by Biya. However, Biya's own presidential guard turned against him and attempted to overthrow the government in April. The plot failed and the rebel-

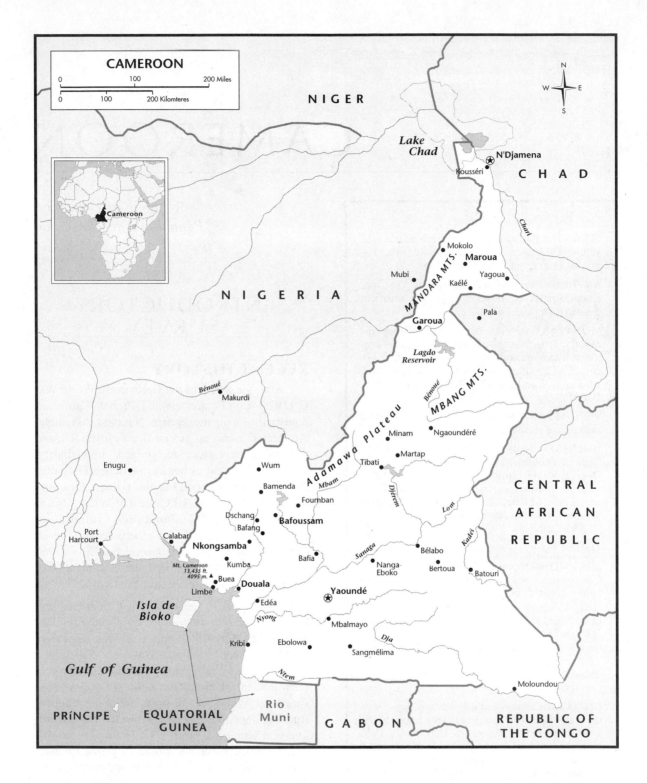

CAMEROON

lion was stamped out by the army. In retaliation, forty-six of the plotters were executed. A state of emergency was declared, and remained in effect for over five years.

Late in 1984, the name of the country was changed to the Republic of Cameroon. Democratic reforms were begun in 1990, but political power remains firmly in the hands of President Biya.

Biya was reelected on 11 October 1992 in elections that were disputed by international observers. The constitution places few checks on the power of the president. Consequently, the Biya government is widely unpopular. The government is weak, and the opposition is divided. In 1995, Biya was reelected to the post of leader of his party, effectively retaining for him control of the government. The National Assembly has passed laws meant to bring the country more democracy, but the measures have not been acted upon.

GOVERNMENT

Under the 1972 constitution, as amended in 1984, Cameroon is a republic headed by a president who is elected by universal suffrage to successive five-year terms. The president appoints the ministers and vice-ministers and can dismiss them. He is also the head of the armed forces and can make the laws. The legislative branch comprises a National Assembly of 180 members. Reforms passed by the Assembly in 1995, including calling for the creation of a directly elected Senate and presidential term limits, have not been acted upon.

Judiciary

The legal system includes magistrates' courts in the provinces and a fifteen-member High Court of Justice, appointed by the National Assembly. The Supreme Court gives final judgment on appeals from the judgments of the provincial courts of appeal. A Court of Impeachment has the right to try the president for high treason and cabinet ministers for conspiracy against the security of the state. The State Security Court, established in 1990, hears cases involving internal or external state security. Despite constitutional reform calling for an independent judiciary, the Cameroonian judiciary is still under the control of the government.

Political Parties

The Cameroon National Union (Union Nationale Camerounaise–UNC) was Cameroon's sole legal political party until opposition parties were legalized in 1990. In 1985, it was renamed the Cameroon People's Democratic Movement (CPDM or Rassemblement Démocratique du Peuple Camerounaise–RDPC). In 1995, sixteen opposition parties formed a loose alliance to work for democratic reforms.

DEFENSE

Cameroon's armed forces totaled 22,100 in 1995. The army had 11,500 personnel, the navy had 1,300 personnel, and the air force had 300 personnel. Paramilitary police forces totaled 9,000. In 1994, Cameroon spent $158 million (1.9% of gross national product or GNP) on defense.

ECONOMIC AFFAIRS

Cameroon has seen its economy suffer since the mid-1980s. The causes of this were the simultaneous sharp declines in petroleum, coffee, and cacao prices and the rise of the U.S. dollar relative to the French franc.

However, Cameroon's economy retains a number of fundamental strong points. It is based on a diversified and self-sufficient agriculture supplemented by substantial petroleum production and a sizable manufacturing sector.

Public Finance

Cameroon relies heavily on customs duties and direct taxes as sources of government revenue. Most of Cameroon's oil revenues do not appear in the national budget and are maintained in secret accounts abroad.

The U.S. CIA estimates that, in 1995, government revenues totaled approximately $2.6 billion and expenditures $2.3 billion, including capital expenditures of $226 million. External debt totaled $6.6 billion, approximately 83% of which was financed abroad.

Income

In 1998, Cameroon's gross national product (GNP) was $8.7 billion at current prices, or $610 per person.

Industry

Since independence, Cameroon has had a favorable attitude toward industry. The government, once a large shareholder in many industries, now advocates increased privatization. Manufacturing accounted for 23% of gross domestic product (GDP) in 1994. Between 1994 and 1996, the government reported an overall 2.8% increase in industrial production.

Banking and Finance

The bank of issue is the Bank of the Central African States (Banque des États de l'Afrique Central—BEAC), which replaced the Central Bank of the State of Equatorial Africa and Cameroon in November 1972. The government's Exchange Control Office controls all financial transactions effected between Cameroon and foreign territories. The Cameroonian Development Bank, an 82% government-owned institution established in 1961, provides financial and technical assistance to development projects. The National Fund for Rural Development grants loans to farmers and artisans.

There are also commercial banks, a savings bank, and a postal bank. Informal savings and loan systems known as tontines take the place of banks for many tribal members, with repayment enforced by social pressure.

There is no securities exchange in Cameroon.

Economic Development

The government has initiated several efforts since 1989 to reduce its role in the economy and to promote private sector development. Price controls were lifted in 1994 with the exception of pharmaceuticals, petroleum products, and goods and services produced by public monopolies.

A prominent feature in Cameroon's economic development strategy is the Industrial Free Zone (IFZ), which covers the entire country. Manufacturing and service industries authorized to operate under the program pay no duties on imported inputs, require no licenses, and are exempt from customs control. An IFZ firm must produce goods or services that are 80% export-bound and that are not environmentally destructive.

SOCIAL WELFARE

Social centers concern themselves with child care, hygiene, and juvenile delinquency, and they maintain kindergartens, orphanages, and classes in homemaking. There are no welfare services covering the whole population. However, a 1969 law established an employees' old-age, invalid, and survivors' pension plan, financed by employee and employer contributions. Benefits are also paid for occupational diseases and accidents. The Public Health Service is supposed to provide free medical, surgical, and pharmaceutical services to those unable to pay.

The government has perpetrated serious human rights abuses in recent years, including political and extrajudicial murders. Arbitrary arrest and physical abuse of prisoners is common. In June 1995, a member of a local human rights organization was arrested and beaten for investigating claims of human rights abuses.

Healthcare

Many missionaries maintain health and leprosy centers. The government is pursuing a vigorous policy of public health improvement, with considerable success in reducing sleeping sickness, leprosy, and other diseases.

The need for modernization is urgent, with many clinics using outdated equipment, some of which was imported illegally from Nigeria. In 1993, there was only one physician per 12,001 people, and one nursing professional per 1,690 people. In 1992, only 41% of the population had access to health care services. Between 1990 and 1995, 1.4% of gross domestic product (GDP) went to health care services. Fourteen percent of all children under five were malnourished. Life expectancy is 56 years.

Housing

Differences in climate, building materials, and patterns of living have resulted in a variety of traditional structures in rural areas. There is a housing shortage, and many people live in thatched hovels of mud and wood, with no running water or modern facilities.

EDUCATION

Education is free in state schools and compulsory between ages 6 and 13. Most secondary schools have been made bilingual, with instruction in both French and English. Working alongside the public schools are the missionary schools, which have been extremely important in the history of Cameroonian education. Children go through six years of primary schooling followed by three years of secondary at the first stage and two years at the second. Adult literacy rate is about 63%.

At Yaoundé University (founded in 1962) and other equivalent institutions, there were 31,360 students and 761 instructors in 1990.

1999 KEY EVENTS TIMELINE

January

- President Biya expresses his concerns about the probity and transparency of Cameroon's judicial system.

February

- France prepares to supply heavy military equipment, spare parts, and office equipment for use by security forces in Cameroon.

March

- The European Union and the governments of Cameroon and Chad sign a grant agreement for CFA 72 billion to fund the building of a road linking Ngaoundere, the northern terminus of the railway to Moundou in southern Chad.

- The United Nations World Food Program grants 18,000 tons in food aid worth about $8.6 million for school children in the northern and eastern provinces of Cameroon.

- Mt. Cameroon erupts for the sixth time since 1902. Several hundred people are evacuated from their villages.

- The International Court of Justice (ICJ) in the Hague declares inadmissible Nigeria's request for an interpretation of the judgement of June 11, 1998, concerning the Land and Maritime Boundary between Cameron and Nigeria.

April

- French general Jean-Francois Roux announces plans to support three new military training centers for the air force, the gendarmerie, and the police.

- The Mt. Cameroon eruption has left some 247 people homeless. Cameroonian authorities begin to distribute gas masks to villagers living around the mountain.

- Cameroon launches a long-term health development program to 2008.

- The Agence Francaise de Developpement (AFD) approves a $40 million loan to the government for partial funding of the country's structural adjustment program during 1998/99 fiscal year (July-June).

- The EU and Cameroon sign a convention for the disbursement of a CFA 64 billion grant for the construction of a road linking Beroua to Garoua Boulai on the border with The Central African Republic.

- One of Cameroon's most prominent elder statesmen, John Ngu Foncha, dies.

- The main opposition party, the Social Democratic Front (SDF), holds its fifth congress in Yaounde.

- Justice Minister Laurent Esso declares that the judicial system has become thoroughly corrupt.

- The heads of police of eight Central African countries hold their second general assembly in Yaounde to focus on armed robbery, ex-rebels, illicit arms flows, and crossborder crime and banditry.

May

- General Abubakar of Nigeria meets with President Biya for talks in Yaounde where they pledge to try to resolve their differences by peaceful means.

- External Affairs Minister, Augustin Kontchou Koumegni, visits Equatorial Guinea to look for an equitable solution to their dispute over oil resources in undemarcated areas of the Gulf of Guinea.

- Troops for the infantry and commando battalion in Koutaba, Western Province, are deployed in Bui and Bamenda, the provincial capital of the Northwest Province.

- Scientists give the green light for the return of evacuees of the Mt. Cameroon eruption.

June

- The United Nations International Children's Emergency Fund (UNICEF) and the government sign a five-year co-operation agreement aimed at reducing infant mortality by 50%.

July

- Equatorial Guinea files application at the International Court of Justice for permission to intervene in the land and maritime boundary dispute between Nigeria and Cameroon, presently before the court.

August

- Registration of refugees gets underway.

- Volcanic activity around Lake Nyos reported. A crisis committee orders urgent action on lake.

September

- Water shortages in Yaounde due to a damaged pipeline pose health problems. Water rationing is announced.

- The International Monetary Fund approves a third ESAF loan.

- Floods claim about 20 lives.

October

- Amnesty International criticizes the trial of alleged secessionists.

- Flooding occurs along the River Benue.

- The International Center Against Censorship accuses the government of systematically violating human rights, ranging from illegitimate detention to torture and deaths in custody.

- A task force is established to clean up volcanic lakes Nyos and Monoum. In 1986, Lake Nyos gases killed nearly 1,700 people.

November

- The U.N. Human Rights Committee says it is concerned by lack of freedom of expression in Cameroon, according to the committee's chairperson, Cecelia Medina Quiroga.

December

- The first meeting of the Interparliamentary Commission of the Economic and Monetary Community of Central Africa (CEMAC), of which Cameroon is a member, takes place.

- Prime Minister Peter Mafany Musonge announces a plan to introduce better management and business practices in accounting for projects that receive international funding, especially from the World Bank.

ANALYSIS OF EVENTS: 1999

BUSINESS AND THE ECONOMY

Prospects for economic growth in 1999 were good based on a recovery in oil prices and other export commodities, and further progress in economic reforms. An increase in real Gross Domestic Product was expected from 4.4% in 1998–99 to 4.9% in 1999–2000. The CFA franc is expected to remain weak, which should benefit exports. Cameroon's current account deficit is expected to fall slightly in 1998–99 to $219 million before increasing to $296 million in 1999–2000, which is in line with International Monetary Fund targets. It was at 2.4% of GDP in 1997–98 despite a difficult external environment.

In March, the National Assembly passed a bill authorizing the creation of a bank deposit guarantee fund for members of CEMAC, which was intended to restore confidence in the banking sector. In early April, the government indicated that the country's 37 toll roads will be privatized. The signing of an open-skies initiative with CEMAC states should make air travel more competitive, and the construction of new roads to CAR, Chad, and Equatorial Guinea should improve regional trade. Based on this performance and outlook, the IMF approved Cameroon's third ESAF loan in April.

On the downside, the World Trade Organization ruling in the banana trade wars hurt ACP countries including Cameroon. Cameroon has an EU market quota of 162,000 tons, or 19% of the ACP share. Cameroon's banana industry will find it difficult to compete with "dollar" bananas from Central and South America. A regional environmental protection initiative will decrease timber exports, which contributed about 7% of the GDP in 1998.

The imminent construction of the Chad-Cameroon oil pipeline by the Cameroon Oil Transportation Company (COTCO) should give Cameroon an economic boost. In 1999, the project was on hold pending the resolution of environmental concerns and the World Bank's approval. The $1 billion project involves drilling 300 wells in the south of Chad, and the laying of a 1,050 kilometer buried pipeline to the port of Kribi on the Atlantic coast. Because the pipeline will pass through rainforest and pygmy settlements, a $3.5 million endowment is being proposed for the preservation of the Campo national park and forest areas.

GOVERNMENT AND POLITICS

President Biya's hold on power seems to be less threatened by the opposition than his own government's inability to abide by the country's laws. Early in the year Biya expressed his concerns about the probity and transparency of Cameroon's judicial system. Soon after, Justice Minister Laurent Esso declared that the judicial system had become thoroughly corrupt.

In April, one of Cameroon's most prominent elder statesmen, John Ngu Foncha, died. Ngu Foncha was a long-time proponent of federalism, and a fly in the ointment of the government's unitary policies. The main opposition party, the Social Democratic Front (SDF) also held its fifth congress in Yaounde. While John Nfru Ndi was re-elected, the Bamileke ethnic group—the strongest Francophone supporters of this mainly Anglophone party—lost most of their positions on the National Executive Committee. This development could hurt the party both in its desire to be a truly national party, and in funding from the Bamileke region. The SDF claims to have won the 1997 elections.

Internationally, Cameroon gained the upper hand in its dispute with Nigeria over the Bakassi peninsula and maritime boundaries. The International Court of Justice (ICJ) in the Hague, declared inadmissible Nigeria's request for an interpretation of the judgement of June 11, 1998, concerning the Land and Maritime Boundary between Cameroon and Nigeria. General Abubakar of Nigeria met with

President Biya for talks in Yaounde where they pledged to try to resolve their differences by peaceful means. External Affairs Minister, Augustin Kontchou Koumegni, visited Equatorial Guinea to look for an equitable solution to their dispute over oil resources in the Gulf of Guinea. In the meantime, Equatorial Guinea filed an application at the International Court of Justice for permission to intervene in the land and maritime boundary dispute between Nigeria and Cameroon, presently before the court.

CULTURE AND SOCIETY

Environmental challenges dominated the scene in Cameroon in 1999. In March, Mt. Cameroon erupted for the sixth time since 1902. The lava flows and gases forced hundreds from their homes, while some plantations were destroyed, and key roads blocked. In August, volcanic activity broke out around Lake Nyos, where an emission of poisonous gases in 1988 killed nearly 1,700 people and thousands of cattle. A crisis committee ordered urgent action on cleaning up the lake. In September the bursting of a water pipeline 50 kilometers south of Yaounde forced its residents to ration water, and presented sanitation hazards to the city's 1.2 million residents. In October, flooding on the Benue River forced evacuations of hundreds of people, killing as many as 20.

The year also highlighted challenges to social cohesion and basic civil rights. The United Nations Committee on human rights criticized the state's power to seize and confiscate publications, which amounts to censorship. Amnesty International criticized the trial of 65 alleged secessionists, more than half of whom were convicted by a military tribunal. Amnesty said the trial was flawed because many of the defendants were tortured during interrogation and some died as a result. Those convicted were English-speakers from Northwest and Southwest Provinces, perhaps members of Southern Cameroon's National Council (SCNC), which supports independence for the two minority provinces. The issue is far from resolved. Troops from the infantry and commando battalion in Koutaba, Western Province, were deployed in Bui and Bamenda, the provincial capital of the Northwest Province to calm the population.

DIRECTORY

CENTRAL GOVERNMENT
Head of State
President
Paul Biya, Office of the President

Ministers
Prime Minister
Peter M. Musonge, Office of the Prime Minister
PHONE: +237 238005
FAX: +237 235735
E-MAIL: spm@spm.gov.cm.

Minister of Tourism
Mbafou Claude Joseph, Ministry of Tourism
PHONE: +237 224411; 222137
FAX: +237 221295
E-MAIL: mintour@camnet.cm

Minister of Youth and Sports
Owono Joseph, Ministry of Youth and Sports

Minister of Industrial and Commercial Development
Bouba Maigari, Ministry of Industrial and Commercial Development
PHONE: +237 232388
FAX: +237 222704
E-MAIL: mindic@camnet.cm

Minister of Economy and Finance
Akame Mfoumou Edouard, Ministry of Economy and Finance, B.P. 13750, Yaoundé, Cameroon
FAX: +237 232099

Minister of Posts and Telecommunications
Mounchipou Seidou, Ministry of Posts and Telecommunications

Minister of Defense
Amadou Ali, Ministry of Defense

Minister of External Relations
Kontchou Kouemegni Augustin, Ministry of External Relations

Minister of Culture
Oyono Ferdinand-Leopold, Ministry of Culture

Minister of Education
Étoundi Charles, Ministry of Education

Minister of Justice
Esso Laurent, Ministry of Justice

Minister of Territorial Administration
Ename Ename Samson, Ministry of Territorial Administration

Minister of Scientific and Technical Research
Hogbe Nlend Henri, Ministry of Scientific and Technical Research

Minister of Public Health
Monekesso Godlieb, Ministry of Public Health

Minister of Agriculture
Perevet Zacharie, Ministry of Agriculture

Minister of Environment and Forestry
Naah Ondoua Sylvestre, Ministry of Environment and Forestry

Minister of Town Planning and Housing
Hele Pierre, Ministry of Town Planning and Housing

Minister of City Affairs
Zanga Antoine, Ministry of City Affairs

Minister of Social Affairs
Fouda Madeleine, Ministry of Social Affairs

Minister of Higher Education
Atangana Mebara Jean-Marie, Ministry of Higher Education

Minister of Public Service and Administrative Reform
Sali Dairou, Ministry of Public Service and Administrative Reform

Minister of Communication
Ze Nguele Rene, Ministry of Communication

Minister of Women Affairs
Yaou Aissatou, Ministry of Women Affairs

Minister of Public Investments and Regional Planning
Ndioro Justin, Ministry of Public Investments and Regional Planning

Minister of Public Works
Étah Jerome, Ministry of Public Works

Minister of Transport
Tsanga Abanda Joseph, Ministry of Transport

Minister of Employment, Labour, and Social Welfare
Ondoua Pius, Ministry of Employment, Labour, and Social Welfare

Minister of Mines, Water Resources and Energy
Mbele Yves, Ministry of Mines, Water Resources and Energy

Minister of Animal Breeding, Fisheries, and Animal Industries
Hamadjoda Adjoudji, Ministry of Animal Breeding, Fisheries, and Animal Industries

POLITICAL ORGANIZATIONS

Front Sociale-Démocratique (Social Democratic Front)

P.O. Box 490, Bamenda, Cameroon
PHONE: +237 363949
FAX: +237 362991
E-MAIL: info@sdfparty.org
TITLE: Leader
NAME: John Fru Ndi

Rassemblement démocratique du Peuple Camerounais-RDPC (Cameroon People's Democratic Movement)

TITLE: President
NAME: Paul Biya

Union Démocratique du Cameroun-UDC (Cameroonian Democratic Union)

NAME: Adamou Ndam Njoya

Union Nationale pour la Démocratie et le Progrès-UNDP (National Union for Democracy and Progress)

TITLE: Chairman
NAME: Maigari Bello Bouba

DIPLOMATIC REPRESENTATION

Embassies in Cameroon

France
Plateau Atémengué, B.P. 1631, Yaoundé, Cameroon
PHONE: +237 230463
TITLE: Ambassador
NAME: Phillipe Selz

Israel
P.O. Box 5934, Yaoundé, Cameroon
PHONE: +237 201644; 211291
FAX: +237 210823

Italy
Quartier Bastos, Yaoundé, Cameroon
PHONE: +237 212198; 203376
FAX: +237 215250

United Kingdom
Avenue Winston Churchill, Yaoundé B.P. 547, Cameroon
PHONE: +237 220545; 220796
FAX: +237 220148
TITLE: High Commissioner
NAME: Peter Boon

United States
Rue Nachtigal, B.P. 817, Yaoundé, Cameroon
TITLE: Ambassador
NAME: Charles Twining

JUDICIAL SYSTEM
Supreme Court

FURTHER READING
Books

Africa on File. New York: 1995 Facts on File, 1995.

Monga, Celestin. *The Anthropology of Anger: Civil Society and Democracy in Africa*. N.p., 1996.

Internet

Africaonline. Available Online @ http://www.africaonline.com (October 28, 1999).

Africa News Online. Available Online @ http://www.africanews.org/west/stories/1999_feat1.html (October 28, 1999).

Integrated Regional Information Network (IRIN). Available Online @ http://www.reliefweb.int/IRIN (October 28, 1999).

CAMEROON:
STATISTICAL DATA

For sources and notes see "Sources of Statistics" in the front of each volume.

GEOGRAPHY

Geography (1)

Area:

Total: 475,440 sq km.

Land: 469,440 sq km.

Water: 6,000 sq km.

Area—comparative: slightly larger than California.

Land boundaries:

Total: 4,591 km.

Border countries: Central African Republic 797 km, Chad 1,094 km, Republic of the Congo 523 km, Equatorial Guinea 189 km, Gabon 298 km, Nigeria 1,690 km.

Coastline: 402 km.

Climate: varies with terrain, from tropical along coast to semiarid and hot in north.

Terrain: diverse, with coastal plain in southwest, dissected plateau in center, mountains in west, plains in north.

Natural resources: petroleum, bauxite, iron ore, timber, hydropower potential.

Land use:

Arable land: 13%

Permanent crops: 2%

Permanent pastures: 4%

Forests and woodland: 78%

Other: 3% (1993 est.).

HUMAN FACTORS

Demographics (2A)

	1990	1995	1998	2000	2010	2020	2030	2040	2050
Population	11,894.0	13,799.9	15,029.4	15,891.5	20,631.5	26,059.0	32,483.8	40,237.1	48,605.8
Net migration rate (per 1,000 population)	NA	NA	NA	NA	NA	NA	NA	NA	NA
Births	NA	NA	NA	NA	NA	NA	NA	NA	NA
Deaths	NA	NA	NA	NA	NA	NA	NA	NA	NA
Life expectancy - males	51.1	50.4	49.9	49.6	48.1	51.3	59.9	68.4	71.7
Life expectancy - females	54.7	53.3	53.0	52.8	51.6	55.1	64.5	73.9	77.4
Birth rate (per 1,000)	44.3	42.9	42.1	41.6	38.7	34.5	30.0	25.5	21.7
Death rate (per 1,000)	13.9	14.0	14.0	13.9	14.1	12.2	8.1	5.0	4.5
Women of reproductive age (15-49 yrs.)	2,582.2	3,002.9	3,287.0	3,490.9	4,692.4	6,277.1	8,350.5	10,744.1	13,094.1
of which are currently married	NA	NA	NA	NA	NA	NA	NA	NA	NA
Fertility rate	6.3	6.1	5.9	5.7	5.0	4.2	3.5	3.0	2.6

Except as noted, values for vital statistics are in thousands; life expectancy is in years.

Health Personnel (3)

Total health expenditure as a percentage of GDP, 1990-1997[a]

Public sector 1.0

Private sector 0.4

Total[b] 1.4

Health expenditure per capita in U.S. dollars, 1990-1997[a]

Purchasing power parity 24

Total 7

Availability of health care facilities per 100,000 people

Hospital beds 1990-1997[a] 260

Doctors 1993[c] 7

Nurses 1993[c] . . . . .NA

Health Indicators (4)

Life expectancy at birth

1980 50

1997 57

Daily per capita supply of calories (1996) 2,175

Total fertility rate births per woman (1997) 5.3

Maternal mortality ratio per 100,000 live births (1990-97) . . . . .550[c]

Safe water % of population with access (1995) 41

Sanitation % of population with access (1995) 40

Consumption of iodized salt % of households (1992-98)[a] 86

Smoking prevalence

Male % of adults (1985-95)[a] . . . .

Female % of adults (1985-95)[a] . . . .

Tuberculosis incidence per 100,000 people (1997) 133

Adult HIV prevalence % of population ages 15-49 (1997) 4.89

Infants and Malnutrition (5)

Under-5 mortality rate (1997) 99

% of infants with low birthweight (1990-97) 13

Births attended by skilled health staff % of total[a] . . .58

% fully immunized (1995-97)

TB 53

DPT 44

Polio 47

Measles 43

Prevalence of child malnutrition under age 5 (1992-97)[b] . . . . .NA

Ethnic Division (6)

Cameroon Highlanders .31%

Equatorial Bantu 19%

Kirdi 11%

Fulani 10%

Northwestern Bantu 8%

Eastern Nigritic 7%

Other African 13%

Non-African . . . .<1%

Religions (7)

Indigenous beliefs 51%

Christian 33%

Muslim 16%

Languages (8)

24 major African language groups, English (official), French (official).

EDUCATION

Public Education Expenditures (9)

Public expenditure on education (% of GNP)

1980 . . . . .3.6

1996 . . . . .2.9[1]

Expenditure per student

Primary % of GNP per capita

1980 . . . . .11.0[1]

1996 . . . .

Secondary % of GNP per capita

1980 . . . .

1996 . . . .

Tertiary % of GNP per capita

1980 . . . . .400.2[1]

1996 . . . .

Expenditure on teaching materials

Primary % of total for level (1996) . . . .

Secondary % of total for level (1996) . . . .

Primary pupil-teacher ratio per teacher (1996) . . . .

Duration of primary education years (1995) 6

Literacy Rates (11A)

In thousands and percent[1]	1990	1995	2000	2010
Illiterate population (15+ yrs.)	2,741	2,712	2,660	2,473
Literacy rate - total adult pop. (%)	57.0	63.4	69.2	79.0

In thousands and percent[1]	1990	1995	2000	2010
Literacy rate - males (%)	70.1	75.0	79.3	86.1
Literacy rate - females (%)	44.4	52.1	59.4	72.0

GOVERNMENT & LAW

Political Parties (12)

National Assembly	No. of seats
Cameroon People's Democratic Movement (CPDM) . . .109	
Social Democratic Front (SDF) 43	
National Union for Democracy and Progress (UNDP) 13	

Cameroonian Democratic Union (UDC) 5

Union of Cameroonian Populations (UPC) 1

Movement for the Defense of the Republic (MDR) . . .1

Movement for the Youth of Cameroon (MLJC) 1

7 contested seats will be filled in an election at a time to be set by the Supreme Court. The constitution calls for an upper chamber for the legislature, to be called Senate, which the government says will be established in 1998.

Government Budget (13A)

Year: 1995

Total Expenditures: 525.27 Billions of Francs

Expenditures as a percentage of the total by function:

General public services and public order 22.10

Continued on next page.

Military Affairs (14B)

	1990	1991	1992	1993	1994	1995
Military expenditures						
Current dollars (mil.)	140	125	129	150	147	NA
1995 constant dollars (mil.)	161	138	139	158	150	NA
Armed forces (000)	23	24	12	12	12	22[e]
Gross national product (GNP)						
Current dollars (mil.)	8,529	8,159	8,006	8,056	7,599	8,051
1995 constant dollars (mil.)	9,802	9,016	8,612	8,446	7,790	8,051
Central government expenditures (CGE)						
1995 constant dollars (mil.)	2,211	2,108	1,689	1,546	NA	NA
People (mil.)	11.9	12.3	12.7	13.1	13.4	13.9
Military expenditure as % of GNP	1.6	1.5	1.6	1.9	1.9	NA
Military expenditure as % of CGE	7.3	6.5	8.2	10.2	NA	NA
Military expenditure per capita (1995 $)	13	11	11	12	11	NA
Armed forces per 1,000 people (soldiers)	1.9	2.0	.9	.9	.9	1.6
GNP per capita (1995 $)	823	734	680	647	579	581
Arms imports[6]						
Current dollars (mil.)	10	0	0	0	5	10
1995 constant dollars (mil.)	11	0	0	0	5	10
Arms exports[6]						
Current dollars (mil.)	0	0	0	0	0	0
1995 constant dollars (mil.)	0	0	0	0	0	0
Total imports[7]						
Current dollars (mil.)	1,400	1,173	1,163	1,102	1,083	1,241
1995 constant dollars (mil.)	1,609	1,296	1,251	1,155	1,110	1,241
Total exports[7]						
Current dollars (mil.)	2,002	1,834	1,840	1,883	1,486	2,040
1995 constant dollars (mil.)	2,301	2,027	1,979	1,974	1,523	2,040
Arms as percent of total imports[8]	.7	0	0	0	.5	.8
Arms as percent of total exports[8]	0	0	0	0	0	0

Government Budget (13A) (cont.)

Defense 12.24

Education 14.62

Health 4.17

Social Security and Welfare 74

Housing and community amenities 1.64

Recreational, cultural, and religious affairs 1.98

Fuel and energy 48

Agriculture, forestry, fishing, and hunting 4.16

Mining, manufacturing, and construction 58

Transportation and communication 5.33

Other economic affairs and services 1.24

Crime (15)

Crime rate (for 1997)

Crimes reported 8,800

Total persons convicted . . . . .NA

Crimes per 100,000 population 73

Persons responsible for offenses

Total number of suspects 9,300

Total number of female suspects 650

Total number of juvenile suspects 625

LABOR FORCE

Unemployment Rate (17)

Rate not available.

PRODUCTION SECTOR

Electric Energy (18)

Capacity . . . . .627,000 kW (1995)

Production . . . . .2.715 billion kWh (1995)

Consumption per capita . . . . .201 kWh (1995)

Transportation (19)

Highways:

total: 34,300 km

paved: 4,288 km

unpaved: 30,012 km (1995 est.)

Waterways: 2,090 km; of decreasing importance

Merchant marine:

total: 2 cargo ships (1,000 GRT or over) totaling 24,122 GRT/33,509 DWT (1996 est.)

Airports: 52 (1997 est.)

Airports—with paved runways:

total: 11

over 3,047 m: 2

2,438 to 3,047 m: 4

1,524 to 2,437 m: 3

914 to 1,523 m: 1

under 914 m: 1 (1997 est.)

Airports—with unpaved runways:

total: 41

1,524 to 2,437 m: 8

914 to 1,523 m: 19

under 914 m: 14 (1997 est.)

Top Agricultural Products (20)

Coffee, cocoa, cotton, rubber, bananas, oilseed, grains, root starches; livestock; timber.

MANUFACTURING SECTOR

GDP & Manufacturing Summary (21)

Detailed value added figures are listed by both International Standard Industry Code (ISIC) and product title.

	1980	1985	1990	1994
GDP ($-1990 mil.)[1]	9,332	14,036	12,735	10,195
Per capita ($-1990)[1]	1,078	1,408	1,105	792
Manufacturing share (%) (current prices)[1]	9.2	11.4	14.2	13.1
Manufacturing				
Value added ($-1990 mil.)[1]	689	1,437	1,781	*1,437*
Industrial production index	100	151	175	*144*
Value added ($ mil.)	*692*	*702*	*826*	470
Gross output ($ mil.)	*1,708*	*1,480*	*2,530*	1,333
Employment (000)	*51*	*67*	50	50
Profitability (% of gross output)				
Intermediate input (%)	*60*	*53*	67	65
Wages and salaries inc. supplements (%)	*14*	*15*	*15*	12
Gross operating surplus	*26*	*32*	*18*	*23*
Productivity ($)				
Gross output per worker	*33,434*	*22,199*	50,106	26,897
Value added per worker	*13,583*	*10,398*	16,357	9,490
Average wage (inc. supplements)	*4,794*	*3,261*	7,281	*3,332*

	1980	1985	1990	1994
Value added ($ mil.)				
311/2 Food products	*187*	*135*	185	54
313 Beverages	*183*	*195*	294	89
314 Tobacco products	*24*	*26*	23	5
321 Textiles	*36*	*51*	104	36
322 Wearing apparel	*10*	*9*	−9	1
323 Leather and fur products	*7*	*3*	*1*	—
324 Footwear	*10*	*5*	*7*	*1*
331 Wood and wood products	*30*	*63*	84	*77*
332 Furniture and fixtures	*13*	*16*	3	3
341 Paper and paper products	*17*	*7*	11	7
342 Printing and publishing	*20*	*8*	6	3
351 Industrial chemicals	*10*	*18*	17	9
352 Other chemical products	*12*	*21*	21	7
353 Petroleum refineries	—	*10*	*114*	*32*
354 Miscellaneous petroleum and coal products	—	—	—	—
355 Rubber products	*2*	*3*	2	*4*
356 Plastic products	*16*	*20*	24	*66*
361 Pottery, china and earthenware	*6*	*5*	8	*3*
362 Glass and glass products	*4*	*4*	6	2
369 Other non-metal mineral products	*12*	*10*	16	7
371 Iron and steel	*24*	*35*	38	*38*
372 Non-ferrous metals	*19*	*23*	15	*15*

	1980	1985	1990	1994
381 Metal products	*13*	*11*	*37*	*3*
382 Non-electrical machinery	*18*	*11*	*11*	*1*
383 Electrical machinery	*4*	*3*	*9*	*3*
384 Transport equipment	*3*	*6*	*3*	—
385 Professional and scientific equipment	—	—	—	—
390 Other manufacturing industries	*11*	*5*	*6*	*5*

FINANCE, ECONOMICS, & TRADE

Economic Indicators (22)

National product: GDP—purchasing power parity—$30.9 billion (1997 est.)

National product real growth rate: 5% (1997 est.)

National product per capita: $2,100 (1997 est.)

Inflation rate—consumer price index: 3% (1997 est.)

Exchange Rates (24)

Exchange rates:

CFA francs (CFAF) per US$1

January 1998	608.36
1997	583.67
1996	511.55
1995	499.15
1994	555.20
1993	283.16

Beginning 12 January 1994, the CFA franc was devalued to CFAF 100 per French franc from CFAF 50 at which it had been fixed since 1948

Balance of Payments (23)

	1990	1992	1993	1994	1995
Exports of goods (f.o.b.)	2,125	1,934	1,508	1,454	1,736
Imports of goods (f.o.b.)	−1,430	−1,041	−1,005	−1,052	−1,109
Trade balance	695	893	502	402	627
Services - debits	−1,611	−1,731	−1,411	−830	−923
Services - credits	390	449	408	351	317
Private transfers (net)	−52	−94	−81	−34	12
Government transfers (net)	26	118	69	55	58
Overall balance	−551	−366	−512	−56	90

Top Import Origins (25)

$1.5 billion (f.o.b., 1996).

Origins	%
European Union (France)	.40
African countries	.NA
United States	.7

NA stands for not available.

Top Export Destinations (26)

$1.9 billion (f.o.b., 1996).

Destinations	%
European Union (particularly France, Italy, and Spain) about	.60
African countries	.NA
Korea	.NA
Taiwan	.NA
China	.NA

NA stands for not available.

Economic Aid (27)

France signed two loan agreements totaling $55 million in September 1997 and the Paris Club agreed in October 1997 to reduce the official debt by 50% and to reschedule it on favorable terms with a consolidation of payments due through 2000.

Import Export Commodities (28)

Import Commodities	Export Commodities
Machines and electrical equipment	Crude oil and petroleum products
Food	Lumber
Consumer goods	Cocoa beans
Transport equipment	Aluminum
Petroleum products	Coffee
	Cotton

CANADA

INTRODUCTORY SURVEY

RECENT HISTORY

Canada was vitally important in World War II (1939–45). More than one million Canadians took part in the Allied war effort, and over 32,000 were killed. The nation emerged from the war with enhanced prestige, concerned with world affairs and fully committed to the Atlantic alliance.

Domestically, a far-reaching postwar development was the resurgence in the 1960s of French Canadian separatism. Although administrative reforms—including the establishment of French as Quebec's official language in 1974—helped meet the demands of cultural nationalists, separatism continued to be an important force in Canadian politics. In the 1976 provincial elections, the separatist Parti Québécois came to power in Quebec, and its leader, Premier René Lévesque, proposed that Quebec become politically independent from Canada. However, his proposal was defeated, 59.5% to 40.5%, in a 1980 referendum.

Meanwhile, other provinces had their own grievances, especially over oil revenues. The failure of Newfoundland and the federal government to agree on development and revenue sharing stalled the exploitation of the vast Hibernia offshore oil and gas field in the early 1980s.

In the 1980s, Liberal Prime Minister Pierre Elliott Trudeau worked for "patriation" of the constitution (revoking the British North America Act so that Canada could reclaim authority over its own constitution from the United Kingdom). The

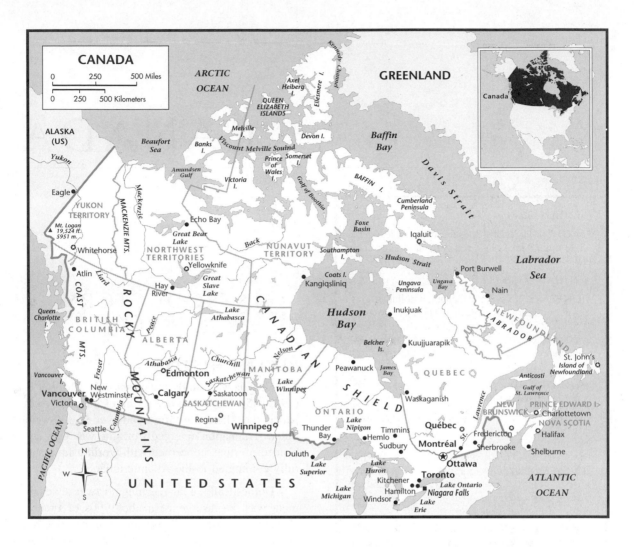

Constitution Act, passed in December 1981 and proclaimed by Queen Elizabeth II on 17 April 1982, thus replaced the British North America Act as the basic document of Canadian government. However, Quebec, New Brunswick, and Manitoba failed to ratify it due to inter-provincial tensions and other problems.

Canada joined with the United States and Mexico to negotiate the North American Free Trade Agreement (NAFTA), which was built upon the United States–Canada Free Trade Agreement (FTA). The three nations came to an agreement in August 1992 and signed the text on 17 December 1992. NAFTA, which seeks to create a single common market of 370 million consumers, was implemented in 1994.

In 1992, the Inuit approved an agreement with the federal government of Canada to create a homeland by dividing the Northwest Territories in half in 1999. This would create a new semi-autonomous region called Nunavit Territory. In 1998, the federal government signed a treaty with the Nisga'a tribe of British Columbia, marking the first time in Canada's history that a tribe was given the right to govern itself.

The province of Quebec has also historically claimed special status within the federal system and has several times threatened to secede from the union. In 1995, secession was put to a referendum. In the end, voters decided by small margin to remain a part of Canada. It is expected that another referendum will be held soon. In August 1998, Canada's supreme court ruled that Quebec does not have the right to secede on its own, and that the rest of Canada would also have to approve if Quebec voted to secede.

GOVERNMENT

Canada is a federation of ten provinces and two northern territories. On 1 April 1999, the

Northwest Territories was scheduled to split into two separate territories, creating a total of three Canadian territories. In 1982, the British North America Act of 1867 (which effectively served, together with a series of subsequent British statutes, as Canada's constitution) was superseded by the Constitution Act (or Canada Act). Its principal innovations are the Charter of Rights and Freedoms and the provision for amendment.

Under the Constitution Act, the British sovereign remains sovereign of Canada and head of state; for the most part, the personal participation of Queen Elizabeth II in the function of the crown for Canada is reserved for such occasions as a royal visit. The queen's personal representative in the federal government is the governor-general, appointed by the crown on the advice of the prime minister of Canada.

The federal Parliament is made up of the House of Commons and the Senate. A new House of Commons, with 301 members as of 1997, is elected at least once every five years. The leader of the party that wins the largest number of seats in a House of Commons becomes prime minister and is asked to form the government. The governor-in-council (cabinet) is chosen by the prime minister.

The 104 members of the Senate, or upper house, are appointed for life, or until age 75, by the governor-general on the nomination of the prime minister, with equality of representation for regional divisions. In October 1992, Canadian voters declined a constitutional amendment that would have made the Senate an elected body.

Judiciary

Civil and criminal courts exist on county, district, and superior levels. The Supreme Court in Ottawa has appeals, civil, and criminal jurisdiction throughout Canada; its chief justice and eight associate justices are appointed by the governor-general. The Federal Court of Canada (formerly the Exchequer Court) hears cases having to do with taxation, claims involving the federal government, copyrights, and admiralty (maritime) law. The death penalty in Canada was abolished in 1976; that decision was upheld in a vote by the House of Commons in June 1987.

Political Parties

Throughout most of the twentieth century, national unity has been the primary aim of every Canadian government: leaders of both the English-speaking majority and the French-speaking minority have cooperated to develop a united Canada to which differences arising from national origin were subordinate. Canadian nationalism has been fueled partially by reaction against being too closely identified with either the United Kingdom or the United States. In the 1970s, this unity was challenged by a growing demand for French Canadian autonomy.

The Liberal Party (LP), which held office from 1935 to 1957 and again (except for part of 1979) from 1968 to 1984, traditionally emphasized trade and cultural relationships with the United States, while its principal rival, the Progressive Conservative Party (PC), which held power from 1957 to 1968, and from May to December 1979, stresses Canada's relationships with the United Kingdom. In economic policy, the Liberals generally champion free trade, whereas the Conservatives favor a degree of government protection.

The New Democratic Party (NDP) is a labor-oriented party formed in 1961 by the merger of The Cooperative Commonwealth Federation (CCF) and the Canadian Labour Congress.

Brian Mulroney became prime minister following a landslide PC victory in the September 1984 elections. In 1993, the PC fell from power, primarily due to one of the worst Canadian recessions in nearly sixty years and the failure of the PC government to implement constitutional reforms.

Brian Mulroney resigned, and was succeeded by Kim Campbell, Canada's first woman prime minister. The Liberal party soundly defeated the PC in the October 1993 election and named Jean Chrétien as the new prime minister. Chrétien called for new elections in 1997, which resulted in the Liberal Party losing twenty-two seats. A new party, the Reform Party, led by Robert Manning, won most of the seats the Liberals lost.

DEFENSE

All service in the armed forces is voluntary. Total forces as of 1995 were 70,500; there were 23,350 reserves. The Land Forces had 21,500 troops in 1995; the Maritime Forces had 9,500; and the air force had a strength of 16,400, with eight fighter squadrons (some 300 aircraft).

The Royal Canadian Mounted Police (RCMP) is a civil force maintained by the federal government, originally to police federal territories. However, all the provinces except Ontario and Quebec, which have their own police forces, have entered into contracts with the "mounties" to enforce provincial laws.

ECONOMIC AFFAIRS

The Canadian economy is the seventh largest among the western industrialized nations. The postwar period has seen a steady shift from the production of goods toward increased emphasis on services. Although no longer the foremost sector of the economy, agriculture is of major importance to the economy. Canada accounts for approximately 20% of the world's wheat trade. Canada is also the world's leading producer of newsprint and ranks among the leaders in other forestry products.

Differences in prosperity among the provinces increased during the 1980s, with the central provinces relatively robust, the western provinces suffering declines in growth because of lower prices for oil and other natural resources, and the Atlantic provinces depressed. By the second quarter of 1990, the economy had begun to decline, affected by a recession and the central bank's monetary policy. Recovery began in the second half of 1991, although the early 1990s were marked by continuing unemployment. The economy grew by 4.1% in 1994, by 2.35% in 1995, and by 2.7% in 1996. Unemployment remained high at 9.7% in 1996, but this was a drop from 11.2% in 1993.

Public Finance

By far the largest item of expenditure of the federal government is for social services, including universal pension plans, old-age security, veterans benefits, unemployment insurance, family and youth allowances, and assistance to disabled, handicapped, unemployed, and other needy persons.

Through the early 1970s, federal budgets remained relatively in balance, fluctuating between small surpluses and small deficits. Since then, however, the budget has been in continuous and growing deficit. The federal government made some progress in slowing down the growth of the public debt after 1984, reducing the annual federal deficit from C$38.3 billion in fiscal 1985 to C$28.1 billion in fiscal 1991. Government options to reduce the deficit are constrained by the high level of nondiscretionary spending in the federal budget.

The U.S. CIA estimates that, in 1995, government revenues totaled approximately U.S.$90.4 billion and expenditures U.S.$114.1 billion. External debt totaled U.S.$233 billion.

Income

In 1996, Canada's gross national product (GNP) was $73.7 billion at current prices, or $19,020 per person. For the period 1985–95 the average inflation rate was 2.9%, resulting in a real growth rate in GNP of 0.4% per person.

Industry

The leading industrial areas are foods and beverages, transport equipment, petroleum and coal products, paper and paper products, primary metals, chemicals, fabricated metals, electrical products, and wood products. The value added in industrial production in 1994 amounted to c $81.4 billion.

Of the total manufacturing output, about half is concentrated in Ontario, which not only is the center of Canadian industry but also has the greatest industrial diversification. Quebec ranks second in manufacturing production, accounting for more than 25% of the value of Canadian manufactured goods. British Columbia ranks third.

Banking and Finance

The Bank of Canada, which was established in 1934, is a government-owned institution that regulates the total volume of currency and credit through changes in the cash reserves of eight domestic (at the end of 1994) chartered banks and fifty-four foreign bank subsidiaries. The Bank of Canada also acts as the government's fiscal agent, manages the public debt, and has the sole right to issue paper money for circulation in Canada. It is empowered to buy and sell securities on the open market, to fix minimum rates at which it will make advances, and to buy and sell bullion and foreign exchange.

The Federal Business Development Bank, established as the Industrial Development Bank in 1944 as a subsidiary of the Bank of Canada, has operated as a separate entity since 1974. It does not engage in the business of deposit banking but supplements the activities of the chartered banks and other agencies by supplying medium- and long-range capital for small enterprises.

The Toronto Stock Exchange was founded in 1852 and incorporated in 1878; the Standard Stock and Mining Exchange, incorporated in 1908, merged with it in 1934. Its members have branch offices in principal Canadian cities and in some U.S. financial centers.

The Montréal Stock Exchange was incorporated in 1874. In 1974, it merged with the Canadian

Stock Exchange, which was organized in 1926 as the Montréal Curb Market.

Economic Development

Canada has a free-enterprise economy. However, the government has intervened in times of economic crisis and to accomplish specific social or economic goals.

A recurrent problem for Canada has been the dominant position of U.S. corporations and investors. Attempts to limit U.S. influence have included tightened tax policies, the Foreign Investment Review Act, and, in 1980, the National Energy Program (NEP), which aimed at reducing foreign ownership of Canada's oil and gas industry, principally through assisting Canadian companies to take over foreign holdings.

SOCIAL WELFARE

Welfare needs are met by federal, provincial, and municipal governments as well as by voluntary agencies. Federal programs include family allowances, old-age security, and earning-related disability and survivors' pensions. In general, families with children under 16 (and youths aged 16 or 17 who attend school full time), regardless of means, are eligible for small monthly allowances, which decline as family income increases.

Persons aged 65 and over receive monthly pensions, supplemented in some provinces on a means-test basis. Under federal-provincial programs, monthly allowances are paid to needy persons aged 65 to 69, and to needy persons aged 18 or over who are blind or totally and permanently disabled.

Liberalization of divorce and abortion laws since the 1960s, coupled with the increased participation of women in the labor force, have brought significant changes to Canadian family life. Since 1968, the crude divorce rate (per 100,000 population) has risen by more than 400%.

Women participate fully in the Canadian labor force, including business and the professions, although government reports show that their average earnings are still less than those of men. A report published in 1995 showed that women on average earn 72 cents for each dollar earned by men.

Healthcare

Canada adopted a national health insurance scheme in 1971. It is administered regionally, with each province running a public insurance plan and the government contributing about 40% of the cost.

Access to health care and cost containment is good, but there are strains on the budget, increased by the demands of an aging population.

Diseases of the heart and arteries account for more than 40% of all deaths, and cancer accounts for just under one-third; the proportion of deaths from causes related to old age is rising. Accidents are the leading cause of death in childhood and among young adult males, and rank high for other population groups. Life expectancy is estimated at 79 years.

Housing

There were slightly more than 10 million occupied private dwellings in Canada in 1991. Housing starts were estimated at just over 156,000 during 1991, a 14% drop from 1990 due to the recession. Single homes are the most common type of dwelling, although their relative numbers have gradually fallen in favor of multiple dwellings.

EDUCATION

Practically the entire adult population is literate. The age limits of compulsory school attendance are roughly from age 6 to age 15. Primary school lasts for eight years, and secondary or high school another three to five years. In 1993, primary schools numbered 12,344. There were 158,059 teachers and 2.4 million students in primary schools. The same year, secondary schools had 168,027 teachers and 2.5 million students.

Each province is responsible for its own system of education. While the systems differ in some details, the general plan is the same for all provinces except Quebec, which has two parallel systems: one mainly for Roman Catholics and speakers of French, the other primarily for non-Catholics and speakers of English.

During 1996 there were sixty-nine degree-granting colleges and universities in Canada. In 1993, full-time enrollment in all higher level institutions, colleges and universities was 2 million.

1999 KEY EVENTS TIMELINE

January

- A British Columbia Supreme Court judge rules that a federal law governing possession of child pornography violates privacy.

• Federal and provincial governments approve a $1.5 billion Agricultural Income Disaster Assistance program.

March

• Canadian Airlines executives seek financial support for sagging business.

April

• Government establishes Nunavut, a new territory in northern Canada.

• Canadian hockey star Wayne Gretzky announces his retirement from the National Hockey League.

June

• Canadian pop star Sarah McLachlan announces plans for the final Lilith Fair tour.

July

• The United Nations Development Program lists Canada as the leading country in overall human development.

• eBay founder Jeff Skoll declared the fifth-richest Canadian.

August

• Organizers of Open Ice conference in Toronto discuss improvements to the game of ice hockey.

September

• A Supreme Court ruling causes hostile relations between native and non-native fishermen.

• Canada launches Aboriginal Peoples Television Network.

October

• Canadian economist Robert A. Mundell wins the Nobel Prize for economic sciences.

November

• Canada's federal government reveals it is headed toward an annual budget surplus of roughly $30 billion ($20 billion in U.S. currency) within the next five years.

• A lockout of 2,700 port workers in Vancouver halts shipments and raises the prospect of disruption of trade across Canada.

December

• Prime Minister Jean Chrétien introduces a measure that would increase Parliament's power over provincial independence movements. The bill is designed to set rules for future Québec separatist movements.

ANALYSIS OF EVENTS: 1999

BUSINESS AND THE ECONOMY

The Canadian airline industry became the center of controversy in 1999 when the two of the country's airlines engaged in a hostile takeover battle. When debt-ridden Canadian Airlines sought financial support from Onex Corp., a Toronto buyout firm, Gerry Schwartz, the founder and CEO, suggested a merger with Montreal-based Air Canada. With the help of U.S. carrier American Airlines and Germany's Lufthansa, Schwartz proposed to purchase both airlines and consolidate them under the Star Alliance. Air Canada reacted by suing Schwartz, who, in turn, filed a suit against Air Canada. Fearing the loss of thousands of jobs, unions threatened a nationwide airline strike.

A July issue of Canadian Business magazine declared eBay founder Jeff Skoll the fifth-richest Canadian. Described as the "Silicon billionaire," the 34-year-old has acquired more than $3 million since the auction Web site began in 1995.

A Canadian retail tradition came to an end when T. Eaton Company, the 130-year-old department store chain, filed for bankruptcy in August. Sears Canada, the Toronto division of U.S. retailer Sears, Roebuck and Co., offered to purchase a portion of the business for approximately $41 million.

GOVERNMENT AND POLITICS

Conservative groups and the Canadian media attacked British Columbia Supreme Court judge Duncan Shaw's January ruling that the federal law against possession of child pornography violated privacy and freedom of expression. The judge received death threats and was placed under police protection.

In February, Canada's federal and provincial governments approved a $1.5 billion Agricultural Income Disaster Assistance program which allots aid to farmers who show a profit margin 70 percent below that of the three preceding years.

On April 1 the Canadian government established a new territory in northern Canada, covering 850,000 square miles. Known as Nunavut, the territory is home to 25,000 citizens, 85 percent of whom are Inuit, and half of whom are under 25.

A September Supreme Court of Canada ruling to acquit a native of fishing without a license and out of season resulted in hostility and violence. Fearing that native fishermen would impose on their livelihood, non-native fishermen destroyed natives' lobster traps in Miramichi Bay and set fire to a native sacred site. Natives responded by blocking access to a seaside wharf in New Brunswick. Fisheries Minister Herb Dhaliwal traveled to the Atlantic provinces to work out an agreement between the two groups.

CULTURE AND SOCIETY

Canadian politicians often promote their country as the best place to live, and for the past six years, a U.N. agency has agreed. The United Nations Development Program again selected Canada as the leading country in overall human development. Canada ranked above 174 other countries in areas such as health, education, and standard of living.

Ice hockey star Wayne Gretzky ended his 20-year career in New York City in April. The Brantford, Ontario, native led four National Hockey League teams to the Stanley Cup championship and acquired 61 league records.

In June pop star and festival founder Sarah McLachlan announced her third and final Lilith Fair tour. The all-female music festival received international acclaim as a showcase for both established and rising artists.

In August representatives of the Canadian Ice Hockey Association, coaches, and players held a three-day Open Ice conference in Toronto to discuss ways to improve Canada's national sport. Organizers addressed topics such as new training methods and growing violence in the sport.

Native peoples of Canada declared the September launch of the Aboriginal Peoples Television Network a historic event. Network executives announced that the Winnipeg-based channel would appear in basic cable packages and would feature programs in English, French, and several native languages. Management predicted that the network would attract seven million subscribers within two years.

Columbia University professor Robert A. Mundell won the Nobel Prize for economic sciences in October. Economists praised the Canadian's studies of exchange rates and their effects on monetary policies.

DIRECTORY

CENTRAL GOVERNMENT
Head of State

Queen
Elizabeth II, Monarch, The Visitor's Office, Buckingham Palace, London SW1A 1AA England
PHONE: +44 (0171) 8391377
FAX: +44 (0171) 9309625

Governor General and Commander in Chief
Adrienne Clarkson, Rideau Hall, 1 Sussex Drive, Ottawa, Ontario K1A 0A1, Canada
FAX: +(613) 9981664
E-MAIL: info@gg.ca

Prime Minister
Jean Chrétien, Office of the Prime Minister, 24 Sussex Drive, Ottawa, ON K1M 1M8, Canada
E-MAIL: pm@pm.gc.ca

Ministers

Deputy Prime Minister
Herb Gray, Office of the Deputy Prime Minister

Minister of Agriculture
Lyle VanClief, Ministry of Agriculture and Agri-Food Canada, Sir John Carling Building, Room 914, 930 Carling Avenue, Ottawa, Ontario K1A 0C5 Canada
PHONE: +(613) 7591101
FAX: +(613) 7591040

Minister of Canadian Heritage
Sheila Copps, Ministry of Canadian Heritage, 15 Eddy Street, Hull, Quebec K1A 0M5, Canada
PHONE: +(819) 9970055
E-MAIL: min_copps@pch.gc.ca

Minister of Citizenship and Immigration
Elinor Caplan, Ministry of Citizenship and Immigration
E-MAIL: caplie@parl.gc.ca

Minister of Defense
Arthur Eggleton, Ministry of Defense

Minister of Environment
David Anderson, Ministry of Environment

Minister of Finance
Paul Martin, Ministry of Finance

Minister of Fisheries and Oceans
Herb Dhaliwal, Ministry of Fisheries and Oceans

Minister of Foreign Affairs
Lloyd Axworthy, Ministry of Foreign Affairs

Minister of Health
Allan Rock, Ministry of Health

Minister of Human Resources Development
Stewart Jane, Ministry of Human Resources Development

Minister of Indian Affairs and Northern Development
Robert Nault, Ministry of Indian Affairs and Northern Development

Minister of Industry
John Manley, Ministry of Industry

Minister of Intergovernmental Affairs
Stephane Dion, Ministry of Intergovernmental Affairs

Minister of International Cooperation and the Francophonie
Maria Minna, Ministry of International Cooperation and the Francophonie

Minister of International Trade
Pierre Pettigrew, Ministry of International Trade

Minister of Justice and Attorney General
Anne McLellan, Ministry of Justice and Attorney General

Minister of Labor
Claudette Bradshaw, Ministry of Labor

Minister of National Revenue
Martin Cauchon, Ministry of National Revenue

Minister of Natural Resources and Wheat Board
Ralph Goodale, Ministry of Natural Resources and Wheat Board

Minister of Public Works and Government Services
Alfonso Gagliano, Ministry of Public Works and Government Services

Minister of Transport
David Collenette, Ministry of Transport

POLITICAL ORGANIZATIONS

Abolitionist Party
Box 9534, Ottawa, Ontario K1G 3V1, Canada

Bloc Québécois
Pièce 533-S, Édifice du Centre, Ottawa, ON K1A OA6, Canada
PHONE: +(613) 9472495

Communist Party of Canada
National Office, 396 Cooper St., Suite 405, Ottawa, ON K2P 2H7, Canada
PHONE: +(613) 5656446
FAX: +(613) 5658787
E-MAIL: office@cpcml.ca
TITLE: National Leader
NAME: Sandra Smith

Liberal Party of Canada
National Office, 81 Metcalfe Street, Suite 400, Ottawa, Ontario K1P 6M8, Canada
PHONE: +(613) 2370740
FAX: +(613) 2357208
TITLE: Leader
NAME: Jean Chretien

New Democratic Party
TITLE: Leader of Canada's NDP
NAME: Alexa McDonough

New Socialist
P.O. Box 167, 253 College Street, Toronto, Ontario M5T 1R5, Canada
PHONE: +(416) 9693209
E-MAIL: newsoc@web.net

Progressive Conservative Party of Canada
501-275 Slater, Ottawa, Ontario K1P 5H9, Canada
PHONE: +(613) 2386111
FAX: +(613) 2387429
E-MAIL: Pfinfo@pcparty.ca

Socialist Party of Canada
P.O. Box 4280, Victoria, BC V8X 3X8, Canada
PHONE: +(603) 6767417
E-MAIL: spc@iname.com

DIPLOMATIC REPRESENTATION
Embassies in Canada

Angola
75 Albert Street, Suite #900, Ottawa, Ontario K1P 5E7, Canada
PHONE: +(613) 2341152

FAX: +(613) 2341179
E-MAIL: info@angolan.org

Argentina
2000 Peel, Suite 710, Montreal, Quebec H3A 2W5, Canada
PHONE: +(514) 8426582
FAX: +(514) 8425797

Austria
Consulat Général d'Autriche à Montréal, Section Commerciale, 1010 ouest, Rue Sherbrooke, Suite 1410, Montreal, PQ H3A 2R7 Canada
PHONE: +(514) 8493708
FAX: +(514) 8499577
E-MAIL: atc_mtr@istar.ca

Burkina Faso
48, Chemin Range, Ottawa, Ontario K1N 8J4, Canada
PHONE: +(613) 2384796
FAX: +(613) 2383812

Chile
1801-2 Bloor St. West, Toronto, Ontario M4W 3E2, Canada
PHONE: +(416) 9240176
FAX: +(416) 9242627
E-MAIL: mskoknic@prochile.org

People's Republic of China
515 St. Patrick Street, Ottawa, Ontario K1N 5H3, Canada
PHONE: +(613) 7893434
FAX: +(613) 7891911

Columbia
360 Albert Street, Suite 1002, Ottawa, Ontario K1R 7X7, Canada
PHONE: +(613) 2303761
FAX: +(613) 2304416

Denmark
151 Bloor Street West, Suite 310, Toronto, Ontario M5S 1S4, Canada
PHONE: +(416) 9625661
FAX: +(416) 9623668
E-MAIL: danish@tradecomm.com

Ecuador
50 O'Connor St., Suite 131, Ottawa, Ontario K1P 6L2, Canada
PHONE: +(613) 5638206
FAX: +(613) 2355776

Ethiopia
#210-151 Slater Street, Ottawa, Ontario K1P 5H3, Canada
PHONE: +(613) 2356637

FAX: +(613) 2354638
E-MAIL: infoethi@magi.com

Finland
55 Metcalfe Street, Suite 850, Ottawa, Ontario K1P 6L5, Canada
PHONE: +(613) 2362389
FAX: +(613) 2381474
E-MAIL: finembott@synapse.net

France
42 Promenade Sussex, Ottawa, Ontario K1M 2C9, Canada
PHONE: +(613) 7891795
FAX: +(613) 5623704

Germany
1 Waverly Street, Ottawa, Ontario K2P 0T8, Canada
PHONE: +(613) 2321101
FAX: +(613) 5949330

Greece
1170 Place du Frere Andre, Suite 300, Montreal, Quebec H3B 3C6, Canada
PHONE: +(514) 8752119
FAX: +(514) 8758781

Hungary
299 Waverly Street, Ottawa, Ontario K2P 0V9, Canada
PHONE: +(613) 2302717
FAX: +(613) 2307560

India
10 Springfield Road, Ottawa, Ontario K1M 1C9, Canada
PHONE: +(613) 7443751
FAX: +(613) 7440913

Indonesia
55 Parkdale Avenue, Ottawa, Ontario K1Y 1E5, Canada
PHONE: +(613) 7241100
FAX: +(613) 7241105

Iran
245 Metcalfe St., Ottawa, Ontario K2P 2K2, Canada
PHONE: +(613) 2354726
FAX: +(613) 2325712

Israel
50 O'Connor Street, Suite 1005, Ottawa, Ontario K1P 6L2, Canada
PHONE: +(613) 5676450
FAX: +(613) 2378865

Italy
275 Slater Street, 21st Floor, Ottawa, Ontario
K1P 5H9, Canada
PHONE: +(613) 2322401
FAX: +(613) 2331484

Japan
255 Sussex Drive, Ottawa, Ontario K1N 9E6,
Canada
PHONE: +(613) 2418541
FAX: +(613) 2417415

Kenya
415 Laurier Avenue East, Ottawa, Ontario K1N
6R4, Canada
PHONE: +(613) 5631773
FAX: +(613) 2336599

Latvia
112 Kent Street, Tower B, Suite 208, Ottawa,
Ontario K1P 5P2, Canada
PHONE: +(613) 2386014
FAX: +(613) 2387044

Lebanon
640 Lyon Street, Ottawa, Ontario K1S 3Z5,
Canada
PHONE: +(613) 2365825
FAX: +(613) 2321609

Mexico
Commerce Court West, 199 Bay Street, Suite
4440, Toronto, Ontario M5L 1E9, Canada
PHONE: +(416) 3682875
FAX: +(416) 3688342

Norway
Royal Bank Centre, 90 Sparks Street, Suite 532,
Ottawa, Ontario K1P 5B4, Canada
PHONE: +(613) 2386571
FAX: +(613) 2382765
E-MAIL: nor-emb-ott@intranet.ca

Pakistan
PHONE: +(514) 8452297
FAX: +(514) 8451354

Paraguay
151 Slater Street, Suite 401, Ottawa, Ontario
K1P 5H3, Canada
PHONE: +(613) 5671283
FAX: +(613) 5671679

Poland
443 Daly Avenue, Ottawa, Ontario K1P 6H3,
Canada
PHONE: +(613) 7890468
FAX: +(613) 7891289

Slovakia
50 Rideau Terrace, Ottawa, Ontario K1M 2A1,
Canada
PHONE: +(613) 7494442
FAX: +(613) 7494989
E-MAIL: slovakemb@sprint.ca.

South Africa
15 Sussex Drive, Ottawa, Ontario K1M 1M8,
Canada
PHONE: +(613) 7440330
FAX: +(613) 7411639

Sri Lanka
333 Laurier Ave. West, Suite 1204, Ottawa,
Ontario K1P 1C1, Canada
PHONE: +(613) 2338449
FAX: +(613) 2388448

Sweden
377 Dalhousie Street, Ottawa, Ontario K1N 9N8,
Canada
PHONE: +(613) 2418553
FAX: +(613) 2412277
E-MAIL: info@sweden-suede-can.org

Thailand
180 Island Park Drive, Ottawa, Ontario K1Y
0A2, Canada
PHONE: +(613) 7224444
FAX: +(613) 7226624

United Kingdom
British Trade and Investment Office, 777 Bay
Street, Suite 2800, Toronto, Ontario M5G 2G2,
Canada
PHONE: +(416) 5931290
FAX: +(416) 5931229

Uruguay
130 Albert Street, Suite 1905, Ottawa, Ontario
K1P 5G4, Canada
PHONE: +(613) 2342727; 2342727; 2342937
FAX: +(613) 2334670

Venezuela
32 Range Road, Ottawa, Ontario K1N 8J4,
Canada
PHONE: +(613) 2355151
FAX: +(613) 2353205
E-MAIL: embavene@travet-net.com

Zimbabwe
332 Somerset Street West, Ottawa, Ontario K2P
0J9, Canada
PHONE: +(613) 2374388
FAX: +(613) 5638269
E-MAIL: zim.highcomm@sympatico.ca

JUDICIAL SYSTEM
Supreme Court

Supreme Court of Canada, Kent and Wellington
Streets, Ottawa, Ontario K1A 0J1, Canada
PHONE: +(613) 9954330
FAX: +(613) 9963063
E-MAIL: reception@scc-csc.gc.ca

Federal Court
Tax Courts
Provincial Courts
Superior Courts

FURTHER READING
Articles

Banks, Brian. "The Silicon Billionaire."
Canadian Business (July 30, 1999): 26+.

Clark, Andrew. "An Electronic Meeting Place:
The New Channel Will Celebrate All Aspects
of Aboriginal Culture." *Maclean's*
(September 6, 1999): 60.

Crary, David. "Kid Porn Ruling Riles Canada:
British Columbia Judge Rules It's Not a
Crime to Possess Explicit Material." *Detroit
News*, 27 January 1999, p. A13.

Deacon, James. "The Great One." *Maclean's*
(April 26, 1999): 16+.

Deacon, James, et al. "No Quick Fix: Canadians
Say Their Hockey System Has Problems. Can
the Open Ice Summit Provide the Answers?"
Maclean's (August 30, 1999): 42.

Elliott, Ian. "Canadian Politicians Agree on
Details of Farm Aid Program." *Feedstuffs*
(March 8, 1999): 1+.

Loof, Susanna. "Canadian Wins Nobel for
Economics." *Associated Press*, 13 October
1999.

"News and Grooves." *Detroit News*, 7 June
1999, p. E1.

Noble, Kimberley, et al. "Air Gerry: Financier
Gerry Schwartz Unveils an Audacious
Proposal For One National Airline."
Maclean's (September 6, 1999): 42.

"Nunavut of the Above." *The Economist*
(March 27, 1999): 40.

Pearlstein, Steven. "Canada's Fight Over
Flight." *Washington Post*, 28 September
1999, p. E1.

Pritchard, Timothy. "Eaton's Bankruptcy Plan."
New York Times, 13 October 1999, p. 4.

Regan, Tom. "When Stores Lose the Stuff
Dreams Are Made Of: A Victim of the
Changing Face of Retailing, Canada's Home-
Grown Store." *Christian Science Monitor*
(September 2, 1999): 8.

Schwartz, Stephen. "The Americas: Magazine
Content Rules Are No Favor to Canadians."
Wall Street Journal, 7 May 1999, p. A19.

"Sears, Roebuck and Co.: Accord Is Reached to
Buy Additional Eaton's Stores." *Wall Street
Journal*, 5 October 1999, p. A12.

"UN Gives Canada Top Spot." *Maclean's* (July
12, 1999): 30.

Walker, Ruth. "Choppy Seas for Canada After
Fishing Case: Violence Has Escalated This
Week Following a Court Ruling That Allows
Natives to Fish Year-Round." *Christian
Science Monitor* (October 7, 1999): 1.

CANADA: STATISTICAL DATA

For sources and notes see "Sources of Statistics" in the front of each volume.

GEOGRAPHY

Geography (1)

Area:

Total: 9,976,140 sq km.

Land: 9,220,970 sq km.

Water: 755,170 sq km.

Area—comparative: slightly larger than US.

Land boundaries:

Total: 8,893 km.

Border countries: US 8,893 km (includes 2,477 km with Alaska).

Coastline: 243,791 km.

Climate: varies from temperate in south to subarctic and arctic in north.

Terrain: mostly plains with mountains in west and lowlands in southeast.

Natural resources: nickel, zinc, copper, gold, lead, molybdenum, potash, silver, fish, timber, wildlife, coal, petroleum, natural gas.

Land use:

Arable land: 5%

Permanent crops: 0%

Permanent pastures: 3%

Forests and woodland: 54%

Other: 38% (1993 est.).

HUMAN FACTORS

Demographics (2A)

	1990	1995	1998	2000	2010	2020	2030	2040	2050
Population	NA	29,619.0	30,675.4	31,330.3	34,279.0	36,896.8	38,840.4	39,906.3	40,490.7
Net migration rate (per 1,000 population)	NA	NA	NA	NA	NA	NA	NA	NA	NA
Births	NA	NA	NA	NA	NA	NA	NA	NA	NA
Deaths	NA	NA	NA	NA	NA	NA	NA	NA	NA
Life expectancy - males	NA	75.1	75.9	76.4	77.8	78.9	79.6	80.0	80.4
Life expectancy - females	NA	82.2	82.6	82.9	83.7	84.2	84.7	85.1	85.5
Birth rate (per 1,000)	NA	12.9	12.1	11.6	10.8	10.4	9.6	9.4	9.4
Death rate (per 1,000)	NA	7.2	7.3	7.3	8.0	8.9	10.6	12.1	12.6
Women of reproductive age (15-49 yrs.)	NA	7,886.1	8,036.6	8,118.2	8,244.6	8,121.4	8,254.5	8,288.3	8,234.2
of which are currently married	NA	NA	NA	NA	NA	NA	NA	NA	NA
Fertility rate	NA	1.7	1.6	1.6	1.6	1.6	1.6	1.6	1.6

Except as noted, values for vital statistics are in thousands; life expectancy is in years.

Health Personnel (3)

Total health expenditure as a percentage of GDP, 1990-1997[a]

Public sector 6.3

Private sector 2.9

Total[b] 9.2

Health expenditure per capita in U.S. dollars, 1990-1997[a]

Purchasing power parity 2,112

Total 1,829

Availability of health care facilities per 100,000 people

Hospital beds 1990-1997[a] 510

Doctors 1993[c] 221

Nurses 1993[c] 958

Health Indicators (4)

Life expectancy at birth

1980 75

1997 79

Daily per capita supply of calories (1996) 3,056

Total fertility rate births per woman (1997) 1.6

Maternal mortality ratio per 100,000 live births (1990-97) . . . . .6[c]

Safe water % of population with access (1995) 99

Sanitation % of population with access (1995) 95

Consumption of iodized salt % of households (1992-98)[a] . . . .

Smoking prevalence

Male % of adults (1985-95)[a] 31

Female % of adults (1985-95)[a] 29

Tuberculosis incidence per 100,000 people (1997) 7

Adult HIV prevalence % of population ages 15-49 (1997) 0.33

Infants and Malnutrition (5)

Under-5 mortality rate (1997) 7

% of infants with low birthweight (1990-97) 6

Births attended by skilled health staff % of total[a] . . .NA

% fully immunized (1995-97)

TB . . . . .NA

DPT 93%

Polio 89%

Measles 98%

Prevalence of child malnutrition under age 5 (1992-97)[b] . . . . .NA

Ethnic Division (6)

British Isles origin 40%

French origin 27%

Other European 20%

Amerindian 1.5%

Other, mostly Asian 11.5%

Religions (7)

Roman Catholic 45%

United Church 12%

Anglican 8%

Other 35% (1991)

Languages (8)

English (official), French (official).

EDUCATION

Public Education Expenditures (9)

Public expenditure on education (% of GNP)

1980 . . . . .6.9

1996 . . . . .7.0[1]

Expenditure per student

Primary % of GNP per capita

1980 . . . .

1996 . . . .

Secondary % of GNP per capita

1980 . . . . .48.5[1]

1996 . . . . .51.0[1]

Tertiary % of GNP per capita

1980 . . . . .39.1

1996 . . . . .40.5[1]

Expenditure on teaching materials

Primary % of total for level (1996) . . . .

Secondary % of total for level (1996) . . . .

Primary pupil-teacher ratio per teacher (1996) . . . . .16[1]

Duration of primary education years (1995) 6

Educational Attainment (10)

Age group (1991) . . . . .25+

Total population .17,471,920

Highest level attained (%)

No schooling 1.0

First level

Not completed 4.0

Completed 11.7

Entered second level

S-1 ....34.3

S-2 ....27.7

Postsecondary 21.4

GOVERNMENT & LAW

Political Parties (12)

House of Commons	% of seats
Liberal Party	.38
Reform Party	.19
Tories	.19

Bloc Quebecois 11

New Democratic Party 11

Other 2

Government Budget (13A)

Year: 1994

Total Expenditures: 181,947 Millions of Dollars

Expenditures as a percentage of the total by function:

General public services and public order 10.68

Defense 5.81

Education 2.89

Health 4.89

Social Security and Welfare 39.79

Military Affairs (14B)

	1990	1991	1992	1993	1994	1995
Military expenditures						
Current dollars (mil.)	9,187	8,866	9,177	9,438	9,408	9,077
1995 constant dollars (mil.)	10,560	9,797	9,871	9,895	9,644	9,077
Armed forces (000)	87	89	82	76	75	70
Gross national product (GNP)						
Current dollars (mil.)	435,700	446,100	459,900	483,300	516,500	541,800[e]
1995 constant dollars (mil.)	500,700	492,900	494,700	506,700	529,500	541,800[e]
Central government expenditures (CGE)						
1995 constant dollars (mil.)	125,100	127,600	131,100	133,200	134,900	NA
People (mil.)	26.6	27.0	27.4	27.8	28.2	28.5
Military expenditure as % of GNP	2.1	2.0	2.0	2.0	1.8	1.7
Military expenditure as % of CGE	8.4	7.7	7.5	7.4	7.1	NA
Military expenditure per capita (1995 $)	397	363	360	356	342	318
Armed forces per 1,000 people (soldiers)	3.3	3.2	3.0	2.7	2.7	2.5
GNP per capita (1994 $)	18,810	18,250	18,050	18,220	18,790	19,000
Arms imports[6]						
Current dollars (mil.)	190	330	430	220	270	210
1995 constant dollars (mil.)	218	365	463	231	277	210
Arms exports[6]						
Current dollars (mil.)	625	575	1,200	750	270	280
1995 constant dollars (mil.)	718	635	1,291	786	277	280
Total imports[7]						
Current dollars (mil.)	123,200	124,800	129,300	139,000	155,100	168,400
1995 constant dollars (mil.)	141,600	137,900	139,000	145,800	159,000	168,400
Total exports[7]						
Current dollars (mil.)	127,600	127,200	134,400	145,200	165,400	192,200
1995 constant dollars (mil.)	146,700	140,500	144,600	152,200	169,500	192,200
Arms as percent of total imports[8]	.2	.3	.3	.2	.2	.1
Arms as percent of total exports[8]	.5	.5	.9	.5	.2	.1

Government Budget (13A)

Housing and community amenities 1.02

Recreational, cultural, and religious affairs 46

Fuel and energy 08

Agriculture, forestry, fishing, and hunting 1.56

Mining, manufacturing, and construction 68

Transportation and communication 2.98

Other economic affairs and services 3.49

Crime (15)

Crime rate (for 1997)

Crimes reported .2,632,100

Total persons convicted 953,600

Crimes per 100,000 population 8,700

Persons responsible for offenses

Total number of suspects 546,800

Total number of female suspects 101,500

Total number of juvenile suspects 121,400

LABOR FORCE

Labor Force (16)

Total (million) 15.3

Services 75%

Manufacturing 16%

Agriculture 3%

Construction 5%

Other 1%

Data for 1997.

Unemployment Rate (17)

8.6% (December 1997)

PRODUCTION SECTOR

Electric Energy (18)

Capacity . . . . .113.645 million kW (1995)

Production . . . . .532.64 billion kWh (1995)

Consumption per capita . . . . .17,448 kWh (1995)

Transportation (19)

Highways:

total: 1.021 million km

paved: 358,371 km (including 19,000 km of expressways)

unpaved: 662,629 km (1995 est.)

Waterways: 3,000 km, including Saint Lawrence Seaway

Pipelines: crude and refined oil 23,564 km; natural gas 74,980 km

Merchant marine:

total: 57 ships (1,000 GRT or over) totaling 638,267 GRT/902,923 DWT ships by type: bulk 10, cargo 9, chemical tanker 4, oil tanker 16, passenger 2, passenger-cargo 1, railcar carrier 2, roll-on/roll-off cargo 7, short-sea passenger 5, specialized tanker 1 note: does not include ships used exclusively in the Great Lakes (1997 est.)

Airports: 1,393 (1997 est.)

Airports—with paved runways:

total: 515

over 3,047 m: 17

2,438 to 3,047 m: 16

1,524 to 2,437 m: 149

914 to 1,523 m: 240

under 914 m: 93 (1997 est.)

Airports—with unpaved runways:

total: 878

1,524 to 2,437 m: 73

914 to 1,523 m: 350

under 914 m: 455 (1997 est.)

Top Agricultural Products (20)

Wheat, barley, oilseed, tobacco, fruits, vegetables; dairy products; forest products; commercial fisheries provide annual catch of 1.5 million metric tons, of which 75% is exported.

MANUFACTURING SECTOR

GDP & Manufacturing Summary (21)

Detailed value added figures are listed by both International Standard Industry Code (ISIC) and product title.

	1980	1985	1990	1994
GDP ($-1990 mil.)[1]	429,917	496,034	569,433	602,557
Per capita ($-1990)[1]	17,481	19,121	20,490	20,677
Manufacturing share (%) (current prices)[1]	19.5	19.0	17.7	NA
Manufacturing				
Value added ($-1990 mil.)[1]	74,712	85,669	90,399	94,853
Industrial production index	100	111	121	129

	1980	1985	1990	1994
Value added ($ mil.)	59,803	74,209	112,195	100,322
Gross output ($ mil.)	167,211	211,017	295,448	286,933
Employment (000)	1,853	1,765	1,867	1,655
Profitability (% of gross output)				
Intermediate input (%)	64	65	62	65
Wages and salaries inc. supplements (%)	17	16	17	16
Gross operating surplus	19	19	21	19
Productivity ($)				
Gross output per worker	89,995	119,306	158,104	166,552
Value added per worker	32,187	41,957	60,039	58,465
Average wage (inc. supplements)	15,296	19,168	27,543	26,916
Value added ($ mil.)				
311/2 Food products	6,142	8,001	12,701	11,740
313 Beverages	1,660	2,189	2,948	3,131
314 Tobacco products	479	608	977	894
321 Textiles	2,130	2,152	2,974	2,679
322 Wearing apparel	1,694	1,933	2,828	2,083
323 Leather and fur products	154	154	163	105
324 Footwear	299	344	334	264
331 Wood and wood products	2,968	3,236	4,465	5,941
332 Furniture and fixtures	1,044	1,332	2,245	1,763
341 Paper and paper products	5,714	5,410	8,750	6,118
342 Printing and publishing	3,054	4,517	7,671	6,359
351 Industrial chemicals	2,164	2,570	4,808	3,596
352 Other chemical products	2,421	3,755	6,256	5,855
353 Petroleum refineries	1,531	1,867	2,271	1,654
354 Miscellaneous petroleum and coal products	111	132	291	236
355 Rubber products	873	1,069	1,397	1,583
356 Plastic products	873	1,654	2,897	2,945
361 Pottery, china and earthenware	43	29	69	43
362 Glass and glass products	385	578	643	503
369 Other non-metal mineral products	1,497	1,713	2,803	2,002
371 Iron and steel	2,652	2,906	3,231	3,222
372 Non-ferrous metals	2,190	2,284	3,222	2,674
381 Metal products	4,414	4,363	6,454	4,622
382 Non-electrical machinery	3,952	4,912	7,576	6,794
383 Electrical machinery	3,849	4,531	7,465	6,435
384 Transport equipment	5,911	10,088	14,124	14,824
385 Professional and scientific equipment	667	659	926	820
390 Other manufacturing industries	932	1,223	1,706	1,437

FINANCE, ECONOMICS, & TRADE

Balance of Payments (23)

	1990	1992	1994	1995	1996
Exports of goods (f.o.b.)	130,328	135,153	166,788	193,085	205,799
Imports of goods (f.o.b.)	−120,815	−127,772	−152,682	−168,443	−175,737
Trade balance	9,513	7,381	14,106	24,643	30,062
Services - debits	−62,755	−59,793	−67,402	−75,060	−75,192
Services - credits	34,281	32,198	38,814	45,125	47,620
Private transfers (net)	−42	56	187	312	249
Government transfers (net)	−594	−856	−431	−325	69
Overall balance	−19,597	−21,014	−14,725	−5,305	2,809

Economic Indicators (22)

National product: GDP—purchasing power parity—$658 billion (1997 est.)

National product real growth rate: 3.5% (1997 est.)

National product per capita: $21,700 (1997 est.)

Inflation rate—consumer price index: 1.8% (1997)

Exchange Rates (24)

Exchange rates:

Canadian dollars (Can$) per US$1.

January 1998	1.4408
1997	1.3846
1996	1.3635
1995	1.37241
1994	1.3656
1993	1.2901

Top Import Origins (25)

$194.4 billion (c.i.f., 1997).

Origins	%
United States	NA
Japan	NA
United Kingdom	NA
Germany	NA
France	NA
Mexico	NA
Taiwan	NA
South Korea	NA

NA stands for not available.

Top Export Destinations (26)

$208.6 billion (f.o.b., 1997).

Destinations	%
United States	NA
Japan	NA
United Kingdom	NA
Germany	NA
South Korea	NA
Netherlands	NA
China	NA

NA stands for not available.

Economic Aid (27)

Donor: ODA, $1.6 billion (1995). Note: ODA and OOF commitments, $10.1 billion (1986-91).

Import Export Commodities (28)

Import Commodities	Export Commodities
Crude oil	Wood pulp
Chemicals	Timber
Motor vehicles and parts	Crude petroleum
Durable consumer goods	Machinery
Computers; telecommunications equipment and parts	Natural gas
	Aluminum
Newsprint	Motor vehicles and parts
	Telecommunications equipment

CAPE VERDE

Republic of Cape Verde
República de Cabo Verde

INTRODUCTORY SURVEY

RECENT HISTORY

After the 1974 military coup in Portugal, an independence agreement was signed leading to the establishment of the independent Republic of Cape Verde on 5 July 1975. Cape Verde and Guinea-Bissau—where Luis de Almeida Cabral, a Cape Verdean, was president—were supposed to work toward unification. But a military coup in Guinea-Bissau toppled Cabral in November 1980. Diplomatic relations with Guinea-Bissau, severed at the time of the coup, were resumed in June 1982.

In 1990, after fifteen years of single-party rule by the African Party for the Independence of Cape Verde (PAICV), the constitution was amended to legalize opposition groups. In 1995, legislative elections were held, and the PAICV held onto power. In 1996, Antonio Mascarenhas was re-elected as president, in the second presidential ballot since the constitutional reforms in 1990.

GOVERNMENT

The constitution was amended on 28 September 1990 to legalize opposition parties and revised again in 1992. The People's Assembly now has 72 members and the president is elected directly by popular vote.

Judiciary

In the preindependence period, Cape Verde was subject to Portuguese civil and criminal codes. The 1992 constitution provided for the creation of an independent judiciary. The Supreme Tribunal of

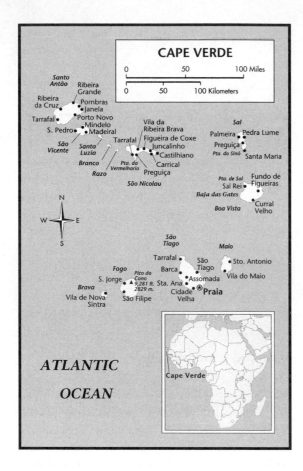

CAPE VERDE

0   50   100 Miles

0   50   100 Kilometers

Santo Antão
Ribeira da Cruz
Ribeira Grande
Pombras
Janela
Porto Novo
Tarrafal
Mindelo
S. Pedro
Madeiral
São Vicente
Santa Luzia
Branco
Pta. da Vermelharia
Razo

Vila da Ribeira Brava
Tarrafal
Figueira de Coxe
Juncalinho
Castilhiano
Carrical
Preguiça
São Nicolau

Sal
Palmeira
Pedra Lume
Preguiça
Pta. do Sinó
Santa Maria

Pta. de Sol
Sal Rei
Baja das Gates
Boa Vista

Fundo de Figueiras
Curral Velho

São Tiago
Tarrafal
São Tiago
Barca
Assomada
Sta. Ana
Cidade Velha
Fogo
Pico do Cano
9,281 ft.
2829 m.
S. Jorge
Brava
Vila de Nova Sintra
São Filipe

Maio
Sto. Antonio
Vila do Maio
Praia

N W E S

ATLANTIC

OCEAN

Cape Verde

Justice has five members. The Ministry of Justice and Labor appoints local judges. Criminal defendants are presumed innocent and have the right to council, to public, nonjury trial, and to appeal.

Political Parties

The African Party for the Independence of Cape Verde (Partido Africano da Independência do Cabo Verde–PAICV) was the sole legal political party from 1975 until 1990. On 28 September 1990, the constitution was amended to legalize opposition parties. In the legislative elections of 1995, the opposition party, Movement for Democracy (MPD), won 50 of the 72 seats in the assembly.

DEFENSE

The Popular Revolutionary Armed Forces numbered 1,300 in 1993. Of these, 1,000 were in a two-battalion people's militia with Russian arms. The navy numbered 200, and the air force numbered about 100.

ECONOMIC AFFAIRS

Agriculture, forestry, and fishing are the leading economic activities of the people of Cape Verde. Cape Verde is drought-prone, and less than 10% of food requirements are met by local producers. Perhaps Cape Verde's most important asset is its strategic economic location, which makes it an important refueling location for international air and ocean traffic. Eleven percent of gross domestic product in 1993 came from money sent from Cape Verdeans abroad.

Public Finance

The U.S. CIA estimates that, in 1993, government revenues totaled approximately $174 million and expenditures $235 million, including capital expenditures of $165 million. External debt totaled $156 million.

Income

In 1997, Cape Verde's gross national product (GNP) was $436.8 million at current prices, or about $1,060 per person. For the period 1985–95 the average inflation rate was 7.2%, resulting in a real growth rate in GNP of 2.1% per person.

Industry

The manufacturing sector employs about 1,700 Cape Verdeans and contributes five percent to gross domestic product. Cape Verde manufactures frozen and canned fish, tobacco, bread and biscuits, soft drinks, and clothing. Germany has sponsored the expansion of a butane gas factory.

Banking and Finance

The Bank of Cape Verde is the central bank and also acts as a commercial bank. The main savings institution is the National Solidarity Fund. Other official banking institutions are the National Development Fund and the Cape Verde Institute, which handles foreign aid.

Economic Development

The development plan adopted in 1992 seeks to transform Cape Verde into an open-market style economy. The development priorities include the promotion of the service-sector industries such as tourism, fishing, maritime services, and transhipping. In 1994, the government announced a five-year plan to develop the fishing industry, focusing mostly on lobster and tuna. A free-trade port is projected, and legislation permitting, the development of offshore banking is planned.

SOCIAL WELFARE

Social welfare services are being expanded by the government with United Nations assistance. As of 1995, old age pension, disability, sickness, maternity, and work injury benefits were in place for employed persons. The constitution bans sex discrimination, although social discrimination and violence against women have been reported. In 1995, there were two women among the ministers of government.

Healthcare

Malnutrition (aggravated by the prolonged drought), influenza, and malaria are major health problems in Cape Verde. There is less than one doctor per 1,000 persons. Average life expectancy is 66 years. There was a cholera epidemic in 1995.

Housing

Housing on the islands varies greatly, from the elegant, Mediterranean-style homes of Europeans and middle-class Cape Verdeans, to the simple timber and mud-block houses of peasants. Almost all housing units are one-floor dwellings.

EDUCATION

Primary education is compulsory and lasts for six years. This is followed by three years of general secondary education. The literacy rate was estimated at 72% in 1993. That year, primary schools enrolled 78,173 students. Secondary and technical schools had 14,097 students, a dramatic increase from 1980s enrollment of 3,341.

1999 KEY EVENTS TIMELINE

April

- Prime Minister Carlos Veiga, who is in poor health, announces that he will retire as leader of the Movimento Para a Democracia at the party congress in February 2000.

May

- The World Bank approves financing U.S.$22.1 million to support the government's efforts to improve the living standards of the poor, and to develop a technically and financially sustainable education and training system.

- Vice-Prime Minister António Gualberto do Rosário announces his intention to succeed Carlos Veiga as head of the MPD and Prime Minister in party elections next year.

August

- Eighteen people die on Sao Vicente island in Cape Verde's worst air crash, due to bad weather.

- The Foreign Minister of Cape Verde, Jose Luis Jesus, is appointed judge at the international court of the law of the sea and is replaced by Rui Figueiredo Soares.

September

- Prime Minister Carlos Veiga makes an official visit to the United States.

November

- The World Bank approves U.S.$3 million equivalent in credit from the International Development Association (IDA), the World Bank's lending arm for the poorest countries for the Second Public Sector Reform and Capacity Building Project in Cape Verde.

December

- The government reports that gross domestic product (GDP) is expected to reach $540 million for the year, with inflation at an estimated three percent compared to 10 percent in 1991. Privatization of main industries is expected to be completed by the end of the year, with all planned privatization completed by early in 2002.

ANALYSIS OF EVENTS: 1999

BUSINESS AND THE ECONOMY

Cape Verde's ten islands suffer from cyclical drought and the lack of arable land. Despite these restraints, the ruling political party in Cape Verde, Movimento para a Democracia (MPD) (Movement for Democracy) has been successful in reducing government direct ownership of enterprises. The nation is progressing toward full convertibility of its currency through direct ties to the Portuguese escudo (thus providing the potential for greater trade with the European Union) and in attracting foreign investment in its fisheries sector, tourism, and light industry. Fisheries remains a sector where investment opportunities are wide open, with only one-third of its resources being exploited. The government's success has been rewarded by foreign donors. However, the trade deficit continues to widen, hampered by the country's very minimal export sector.

Cape Verde's unemployment rate is an unchanging 26 percent, and about 40 percent of the population lives in poverty. Fourteen percent of the country's 400,000 people live in absolute poverty, predominantly among the illiterate and female-headed households.

For the last 200 years, with the decline in the shipping and whaling industry, Cape Verdeans have engaged in significant out-migration, particularly to the northeastern United States, where it is estimated that 400,000 to 500,000 Cape Verdean immigrants live. Since the country's independence in 1975, about 2,000 Cape Verdeans every year have received permanent residence status in the United States. Foreign remittances are an important source of income for the poverty-stricken islands. More than half of the population is rural.

Scarce water supplies and arable land limits farming. The water problem can also hamper the development of tourism. The cities of Praia and Mindelo use desalination for much of their water supply, but the plants are powered by imported oil thus making reliance on this process a very expensive proposition for this impoverished nation.

GOVERNMENT AND POLITICS

The Movement for Democracy (MPD) holds the presidency, the prime ministership under Carlos Veiga, and an absolute majority in the National Assembly. The announcement in April of Mr. Veiga's decision to resign has awakened competition within the party to succeed him. The favorite is Vice-Prime Minister António Gualberto do Rosário, the former Minister of Economic Coordination, a position in which he received good marks from foreign donors. However, Jacinto Santos, the MPD Mayor of Praia, has also announced his intention to seek the office. Support for the previously ruling party, the socialist-oriented Party for African Independence–Cape Verde, which brought the nation to independence in 1975 and ruled it until 1991, remains strong. The two parties have clearly competing visions for the direction of the country. Cape Verde's young democracy, controlled since 1991 by the MPD, seems to be vigorous and extends to its diaspora communities where the same political lines and tensions are felt.

CULTURE AND SOCIETY

Though economically poor in the export sector, Cape Verde does have one well-known and successful export—its music. Several Cape Verdean solo artists and groups have successful tours each year in the United States, Portugal, Holland, and France, as well as success with recording sales. Its music draws many tourists each year. In August, Mindelo hosts a well-attended music festival, drawing the return of many of its exiled musicians.

A new social issue facing the nation comes from the U.S. government's change in immigration laws in 1996. Foreign residents convicted of a felony now face deportation, and hundreds of young, ethnic Cape Verdeans have been deported back to Cape Verde. These young people, many convicted of serious and violent felonies, for the most part left their homeland as young children. Their Portuguese and Crioulo relatives are poor or non-existent, they have little family support in the islands, and are arriving in lands where the high unemployment rate and relatively crime-free lifestyle means that their criminal past makes it highly unlikely that they will receive employment. They began to fill the Cape Verdean prisons and create real dispute between the two governments as well as between Cape Verdeans and their fellow citizens in the diaspora.

The government has had success in its education programs, achieving almost full enrollment for primary school age children. However, in the past few years social indicators, such as access to immunization for young children and to sanitation, have been declining. Credits in 1991 from foreign donors seek to reverse this decline, support the expanding education system and assist the government in its continuing modernization of civil services.

DIRECTORY

CENTRAL GOVERNMENT
Head of State

President
Antonio Mascarenhas Monteiro, Office of the President, PO Box 100, Praia, Santiago, Cape Verde
PHONE: +238 616555
FAX: +238 614356

Prime Minister

Carlos Whanon de Carvalho Veiga, Office of the Prime Minister, Praia, Santiago, Cape Verde
PHONE: +238 610513
FAX: +238 613099

Vice Prime Minister

Antonio Gualberto do Rosario, Office of the Vice Prime Minister

Ministers

Minister of the Presidency of the Council of Ministers

Rui Figueiredo Soares, Ministry of the Presidency of the Council of Ministers

Minister of Agriculture, Food, Environment, and Food Safety

Jose Antonio Pinto Monteiro, Ministry of Agriculture, Food, Environment, and Food Safety

Minister of Defense

Ulpio Napoleao Fernandes, Ministry of Defense

Ministry of Education, Science, Youth, and Sport

Jose Luis Livramento Monteiro de Brito, Ministry of Education, Science, Youth, and Sport

Minister of Employment, Training, and Social Integration

Orlanda Maria Duarte Santos Ferreira, Ministry of Employment, Training, and Social Integration

Minister of Finance

Jose Ulysses Correia Silva, Ministry of Finance

Minister of Foreign Affairs and Communities

Jose Luis Jesus, Ministry of Foreign Affairs and Communities

Minister of Health

Joao Baptista Medina, Ministry of Health

Minister of Infrastructure and Housing

Antonio Joaquim Rocha Fernandes, Ministry of Infrastructure and Housing

Minister of Justice and Internal Administration

Simao Rodrigues Monteiro, Ministry of Justice and Internal Administration

Minister of Tourism, Transport, and Sea

Maria Helena Semedo, Ministry of Tourism, Transport, and Sea
PHONE: +238 615778
FAX: +238 611770

Ministry of Trade, Industry, and Energy

Alexandre Dias Monteiro, Ministry of Trade, Industry, and Energy

POLITICAL ORGANIZATIONS

Movement for Democracy (MPD)

TITLE: President
NAME: Carlos Veiga

African Party for Independence of Cape Verde (PAICV)

TITLE: Chairman
NAME: Pedro Verona Rodrigues Pires

Party for Democratic Convergence (PCD)

TITLE: President
NAME: Eurico Monterio

Party of Work and Solidarity (PTS)

TITLE: President
NAME: Oresimo Silveria

JUDICIAL SYSTEM

Supremo Tribunal da Justica

Praca Plato, Alexandre de Albuquerque, PO Box 117, Praia Cape Verde
PHONE: +238 612369; 615808; 615810
FAX: +238 611751

FURTHER READING

Articles

"Cape Verde." *Africa Confidential* (July 22, 1999).

"Cape Verde deepens Public Sector Reform." M2 Presswire, 24 November 1999.

"Cape Verde for Adventure." *New York Times*, 12 March 1999.

"Cape Verdeans in N.E." *Boston Globe*, 5 September 1999.

"A Homeland, But Not Home." *Boston Globe*, 6 September 1999.

"Sida Bridges the Gap." *African Business* (July–August, 1999).

"Travel: An Island Green with Energy." *The Independent (London)*, 22 May 1999.

"Where History Stopped By." *New York Times*, 7 March 1999.

"World Bank Approves U.S.$22.1 million in financing for the Republic of Cape Verde." M2 Presswire, 26 May 1999.

Internet

BBC World Service, BBC News Online.
   Available Online @ http://
   news2.thls.bbc.co.uk/ (December 4, 1999).

*Embassy of the Republic of Cape Verde in the
   United States.* Available Online @ http://
   www.capeverdeusembassy.org/ (December 4,
   1999).

CAPE VERDE: STATISTICAL DATA

For sources and notes see "Sources of Statistics" in the front of each volume.

GEOGRAPHY

Geography (1)

Area:

Total: 4,030 sq km.

Land: 4,030 sq km.

Water: 0 sq km.

Area—comparative: slightly larger than Rhode Island.

Land boundaries: 0 km.

Coastline: 965 km.

Climate: temperate; warm, dry summer; precipitation meager and very erratic.

Terrain: steep, rugged, rocky, volcanic.

Natural resources: salt, basalt rock, pozzuolana (a siliceous volcanic ash used to produce hydraulic cement), limestone, kaolin, fish.

Land use:

Arable land: 11%

Permanent crops: 0%

Permanent pastures: 6%

Forests and woodland: 0%

Other: 83% (1993 est.).

HUMAN FACTORS

Demographics (2A)

	1990	1995	1998	2000	2010	2020	2030	2040	2050
Population	349.4	381.5	399.9	411.5	463.8	512.0	546.0	557.0	545.0
Net migration rate (per 1,000 population)	NA	NA	NA	NA	NA	NA	NA	NA	NA
Births	NA	NA	NA	NA	NA	NA	NA	NA	NA
Deaths	NA	NA	NA	NA	NA	NA	NA	NA	NA
Life expectancy - males	63.4	65.9	67.2	68.1	71.9	74.7	76.7	78.2	79.1
Life expectancy - females	69.9	72.5	73.9	74.8	78.6	81.4	83.3	84.6	85.4
Birth rate (per 1,000)	42.0	37.6	34.5	32.5	26.9	23.0	17.9	15.1	12.7
Death rate (per 1,000)	9.4	7.9	7.0	6.5	5.3	4.7	4.6	6.1	7.9
Women of reproductive age (15-49 yrs.)	75.5	82.3	88.5	93.0	113.0	124.4	136.6	134.2	117.8
of which are currently married	18.0	NA	NA	NA	NA	NA	NA	NA	NA
Fertility rate	5.9	5.4	5.1	4.8	3.7	2.9	2.4	2.2	2.1

Except as noted, values for vital statistics are in thousands; life expectancy is in years.

Infants and Malnutrition (5)

Under-5 mortality rate (1997) 73
% of infants with low birthweight (1990-97) 9
Births attended by skilled health staff % of total[a] . . .NA
% fully immunized (1995-97)
  TB 80
  DPT 78
  Polio 77
  Measles 82
Prevalence of child malnutrition under age 5
  (1992-97)[b] . . . . .NA

Ethnic Division (6)

Creole (mulatto) 71%
African 28%
European 1%

Religions (7)

Roman Catholicism fused with indigenous beliefs.

Languages (8)

Portuguese, Crioulo, a blend of Portuguese and West
African words.

EDUCATION

Literacy Rates (11A)

In thousands and percent[1]	1990	1995	2000	2010
Illiterate population (15+ yrs.)	70	64	61	53
Literacy rate - total adult pop. (%)	62.9	71.6	76.9	85.3
Literacy rate - males (%)	74.8	81.4	85.0	90.4
Literacy rate - females (%)	53.3	63.8	70.2	80.8

GOVERNMENT & LAW

Military Affairs (14B)

	1990	1991	1992	1993	1994	1995
Military expenditures						
Current dollars (mil.)	NA	3	3	3	4	4
1995 constant dollars (mil.)	NA	4	4	4	4	4
Armed forces (000)	1	1	1	1	1	1
Gross national product (GNP)						
Current dollars (mil.)	248	269	316	333	356	382
1995 constant dollars (mil.)	285	298	340	349	364	382
Central government expenditures (CGE)						
1995 constant dollars (mil.)	NA	137	NA	268	NA	NA
People (mil.)	.4	.4	.4	.4	.4	.4
Military expenditure as % of GNP	NA	1.3	1.1	1.0	1.0	1.0
Military expenditure as % of CGE	NA	2.8	NA	1.3	NA	NA
Military expenditure per capita (1995 $)	NA	10	9	9	9	9
Armed forces per 1,000 people (soldiers)	2.7	2.6	2.5	2.4	2.4	2.3
GNP per capita (1995 $)	760	771	854	850	861	875
Arms imports[6]						
Current dollars (mil.)	5	0	0	0	0	0
1995 constant dollars (mil.)	6	0	0	0	0	0
Arms exports[6]						
Current dollars (mil.)	0	0	0	0	0	0
1995 constant dollars (mil.)	0	0	0	0	0	0
Total imports[7]						
Current dollars (mil.)	136	147	180	189[e]	209[e]	NA
1995 constant dollars (mil.)	136	162	194	198[e]	214[e]	NA
Total exports[7]						
Current dollars (mil.)	6	6	5	4	5	NA
1995 constant dollars (mil.)	7	7	5	4	5	NA
Arms as percent of total imports[8]	3.7	0	0	0	0	NA
Arms as percent of total exports[8]	0	0	0	0	0	NA

Political Parties (12)

National Assembly	% of seats
Movement for Democracy (MPD) 59	
African Party for Independence of Cape Verde (PAICV) 28	
Party for Democratic Convergence (PCD) 6	

Government Budget (13B)

Revenues . . . .$188 million
Expenditures . . . .$228 million
    Capital expenditures . . . .$116 million

Data for 1996.

LABOR FORCE

Unemployment Rate (17)

NA %

PRODUCTION SECTOR

Electric Energy (18)

Capacity . . . . .7,000 kW (1995)
Production . . . . .40 million kWh (1995)
Consumption per capita . . . . .92 kWh (1995)

Transportation (19)

Highways:

total: 1,100 km

paved: 858 km

unpaved: 242 km (1995 est.)

Merchant marine:

total: 4 (1,000 GRT or over) totaling 9,620 GRT/13,920
DWT ships by type: cargo 3, chemical tanker 1 (1997 est.)

Airports: 6 (1997 est.)

Airports—with paved runways:

total: 6

over 3,047 m: 1

914 to 1,523 m: 5 (1997 est.)

Top Agricultural Products (20)

Bananas, corn, beans, sweet potatoes, sugarcane, coffee, peanuts; fish.

FINANCE, ECONOMICS, & TRADE

Economic Indicators (22)

National product: GDP—purchasing power parity—$538 million (1997 est.)

National product real growth rate: 4.5% (1997 est.)

National product per capita: $1,370 (1997 est.)

Inflation rate—consumer price index: 6.2% (1996)

Exchange Rates (24)

Exchange rates:

Cape Verdean escudos (CVEsc) per US$1	
December 1997	.95.400
1997	.93.177
1996	.82.591
1995	.76.853
1994	.81.891
1993	.80.427

MANUFACTURING SECTOR

GDP & Manufacturing Summary (21)

	1980	1985	1990	1992	1993	1994
Gross Domestic Product						
Millions of 1990 dollars	209	283	368	401	417	436
Growth rate in percent	3.32	8.54	3.70	3.37	4.02	4.60
Per capita (in million 1990 dollars)	723.5	912.8	1,079.8	1,112.8	1,126.3	1,144.1
Manufacturing Value Added						
Millions of 1990 dollars	12	18	21	24	26	27
Growth rate in percent	7.14	36.12	6.21	6.53	6.43	6.38
Manufacturing share in percent of current prices	4.8	5.8	6.1	6.2	5.8	NA

Top Import Origins (25)

$237 million (f.o.b., 1996 est.)

Origins	%
Portugal	.41
Netherlands	NA
France	NA
Spain	NA
United States	NA

NA stands for not available.

Top Export Destinations (26)

$12.8 million (f.o.b., 1996 est.).

Destinations	%
Portugal	NA
Spain	NA

France	NA
United Kingdom	NA

NA stands for not available.

Economic Aid (27)

Recipient: ODA, $70 million (1995).

Import Export Commodities (28)

Import Commodities	Export Commodities
Foodstuffs	Shoes
Consumer goods	Garments
Industrial products	Fish
Transport equipment	Bananas
Fuels	Hides

Balance of Payments (23)

	1990	1992	1993	1994	1995
Exports of goods (f.o.b.)	6	4	4	5	8
Imports of goods (f.o.b.)	−119	−173	−152	−195	−232
Trade balance	−114	−169	−148	−190	−224
Services - debits	−37	−31	−37	−40	−62
Services - credits	61	59	49	60	78
Private transfers (net)	52	70	71	81	100
Government transfers (net)	26	67	54	60	69
Overall balance	−12	−4	−11	−29	−39

CAYMAN ISLANDS

CAPITAL: George Town.

FLAG: The flag of the Cayman Islands is blue with the flag of the United Kingdom in the upper hoist-side quadrant and the Caymanian coat of arms on a white disk centered on the outer half of the flag; the coat of arms includes a pineapple and turtle above a shield with three stars (representing the three islands) and a scroll at the bottom bearing the motto, "He hath founded it upon the seas".

ANTHEM: *Beloved Isle Cayman.*

MONETARY UNIT: 1 Caymanian dollar (CI $) = 100 cents.

WEIGHTS AND MEASURES: The imperial system is used with some exceptions.

HOLIDAYS: New Year's Day; Ash Wednesday; Good Friday; Easter Monday; Discovery Day, 19 May; Queen's Birthday, observed in June; Constitution Day, in July; Remembrance Day, in November; Christmas Day; Boxing Day, 26 December.

TIME: 7 AM = noon GMT.

LOCATION AND SIZE: The three low-lying Cayman Islands—Grand Cayman, Little Cayman, and Cayman Brac, with a total area of 262 sq. km (101 sq. mi.)—are situated between 79°44′ and 81°27′W and 19°15′ and 19°45′N, about 290 km (180 mi.) WNW of Jamaica, of which they were formerly a dependency. Grand Cayman, flat, rockbound, and protected by coral reefs, is about 32 km (20 mi.) long and 6 to 11 km (4–7 mi.) broad; George Town, on Grand Cayman, is the capital and chief town. The other two islands are about 145 km (90 mi.) to the NE.

CLIMATE: Prevailing northeast winds moderate the Cayman Islands' climate. Average temperature in the relatively dry winter (November to April) is 24°C (75°F), and temperatures in the summer (May to October) stay between 26°C and 29°C (79°F and 84°F). Very little rain falls from May through October, the islands' "rainy season".

INTRODUCTORY SURVEY

RECENT HISTORY

The three islands of the Cayman Islands were initially discovered by Christopher Columbus, but the islands were inhabited only briefly until the English attached the islands to their Jamaican colony. The Cayman Islands were always a part of Jamaica until the independence movement for Jamaica was successful in 1959. Caymanians wanted to remain a British territory, and they did.

Positioned between Jamaica and Cuba, the islands are conveniently located for persons fleeing Fidel Castro's rule. They are also strategically positioned between Cuba and Central America, and have had some problems with drug smuggling and money laundering.

GOVERNMENT

The government of the islands was established in a constitution of 1959 which has been revised twice since, in 1972 and 1992. As a British territory, the head of state is the British monarch as represented on the islands by an appointed governor. The executive branch of government also includes a seven member Executive Council. In the Executive Council are four members elected by the Legislative Assembly and three appointed by the governor.

The Legislative Assembly is a unicameral body of eighteen, with fifteen elected to four year terms by popular vote. Suffrage is granted to all British citizens over the age of 18. The Legislative Assembly's other three seats serve by appointment.

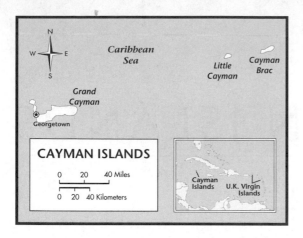

As an overseas British territory, the Cayman Islands are autonomous in local matters but have no international agreements or representation, where they are subject to the government of the United Kingdom. They do, however, participate as an observer in several international organizations such as Caricom and the IOC.

Administration of the islands is accomplished via eight districts: Creek, Eastern, Midland, South Town, Spot Bay, Stake Bay, West End, and Western. The capital is seated at George Town.

Judiciary

English common law forms the basis for the legal system in the islands. The courts are headed by a Grand Court and the Cayman Islands Court of Appeal.

Political Parties

There are no formally organized political parties. In the 1996 elections, however, nine seats in the Legislative Assembly were captured by an organization who called themselves the National Team.

DEFENSE

There are no defense forces in the Cayman Islands, as they depend on the United Kingdom for defense from external threats. There is a local police organization called the Royal Cayman Islands Police Force.

ECONOMIC AFFAIRS

As is the case in several Caribbean island nations, the Cayman Islands enjoy great subtropical weather, clean beaches, and are a natural tourist draw. Tourism accounts for nearly three quarters of the islands' gross income, with more than 1.2 million visitors in 1997, mostly from North America. The second most important element of the Cayman Islands' economy is as a burgeoning offshore finance center. With no direct taxation, more than 40,000 companies were registered in the Cayman Islands in 1997. Nearly 600 bank and trust companies controlled assets exceeding $500 billion and a stock exchange was opened in 1997. The islands are also an opportunity to register ships under the flag of convenience concept, again aided by low taxes and favorable laws. In 1997, 76 ships of greater than 1,000 GRT or over were registered.

With virtually no arable land and a small land mass, agriculture is not viable in the Cayman Islands. Some locally grown foodstuffs are available, particularly citrus fruits, bananas, mangoes, plantains, coconuts, sweet potatoes, yams, and tomatoes. Some livestock is raised. However, between 80 and 90 percent of the islands' food and commodities need to be imported.

Originally named Las Tortugas by Columbus because of the large number of great sea turtles that live in the area, raising and farming of turtles is an important industry. The government runs a turtle farm. There is some export of turtle meat and shells, although restrictions on trade of endangered species has impacted this trade. Some fishing, particularly of sharks, and the gathering of sponges also provides some employment and export potential.

There are no other major industries in the Cayman Islands. Unemployment is very low and is due to the heavy tourism and banking industries. Virtually all food, construction materials, fuel, machinery, and manufactured items must be imported. Trading partners are the United State, Trinidad and Tobago, the United Kingdom, the Netherlands Antilles, and Japan. In 1998, there were five radio stations and no local television.

Public Finance

The unit of exchange in the Cayman Islands is the Caymanian dollar. The government spent $248.9 million in 1997 on revenues of $265.2 million. This favorable ratio disguises a huge balance of payment deficit (imports of $379.4 million in 1996 vs. exports of $2.65 million) and the country held about $70 million in external debt in that year.

Income

Gross Domestic Product in 1997 was estimated by the CIA at $930 million and was showing a real growth rate of 5.5%. This represents a per capita value of $24,500, one of the world's better per capita incomes. Unemployment was low in 1996, and unemployment is not considered a major problem in the islands.

Industry

The principal industries in the Cayman Islands are tourism, followed by banking, insurance and finance, and corporate and ship registries. Local industries of construction, fishing and turtle farming, and furniture provide employment. Handicrafts for tourist consumption, especially the making of jewelry from black coral, is an established industry throughout the islands.

Banking and Finance

Banking and financial matters are handled by the government via the many banks registered on the islands.

Economic Development

Maintaining and building the tourist industry is a number one priority of the government. Some significant public investment continues in this area. The offshore banking industry also enjoys priority. The government maintains the turtle farm and continues to control this rare natural resource.

SOCIAL WELFARE

Caymanians enjoy a relatively high standard of living. The government provides adequate social services. Unemployment is low. Health care is provided. Community organizations provide art exhibits and theater.

Healthcare

The Health Services Department of the Cayman Islands provides health care. There are two hospitals, one each on Grand Cayman and Cayman Brac islands. Incidence of tropical disease is low. Life expectancy is 77.1 years.

Housing

Housing is adequate and private.

EDUCATION

Education is compulsory for children between the ages of 5 and 15, and is provided at government expense. While there are some religious schools, the government schools are the main source of education, including three secondary schools and the International College of the Cayman Islands.

1999 KEY EVENTS TIMELINE

January

- The Cayman Islands Monetary Authority issues a letter to financial institutions and managers urging compliance with its Y2K readiness campaign.

March

- The British government sends a letter to all overseas territories asking them to legalize homosexuality.

April

- The Cayman Islands government announces its opposition to legalizing homosexuality in spite of request by British government.

- The United Nations announces it will conduct a review of the Cayman Islands' financial operations.

May

- Peter John Smith replaces John Owen as governor.

August

- Former Cayman banker John Mathewson is sentenced in the U.S. for money laundering activities.

- Federal investigators with the U.S. government state that a Guardian bank probe could lead to an investigation of as many as 1,500 suspected tax evaders in U.S.

October

- The Cayman Islands conducts its first census in a decade.

ANALYSIS OF EVENTS: 1999

BUSINESS AND THE ECONOMY

By 1999 the offshore banking industry begun three decades earlier had turned the Cayman Islands into the world's fifth-largest banking center, with 590 banks and over $500 billion in deposits. Factors contributing to the success of the financial sector were its strict confidentiality and a no-tax policy. However, since the 1970s the Cayman banks had operated under a cloud of suspicion over money laundering and tax evasion by depositors, most of them Americans.

In August 1999 a former Cayman Islands banker, John Mathewson, was sentenced by a U.S. court in connection with operations at Guardian Bank and Trust, which he had headed from the 1986 until it was closed down by the Cayman Islands government a decade later. Since Mathewson's arrest in 1996 he had cooperated fully with U.S. authorities, releasing an unprecedented amount of information from extensive computerized files he kept on his bank's depositors and on the "shelf corporations" that served as conduits for their deposits—information authorities believed could result in as many as 1,500 investigations and potentially yield as much as $300 million in taxes and penalties. By mid-1999 over a dozen persons had already been indicted or convicted in several U.S. jurisdictions, and Mathewson, in exchange for his cooperation, received a light sentence in a New Jersey court.

Although the Cayman Islands government officially applauded the prosecution of Mathewson and claimed credit for liquidating his bank, it had refused to cooperate in decoding the banker's encrypted computer data, a task that had required expert assistance and taken 18 months, and in fact gone to court in the U.S. in an unsuccessful attempt to block the use of the data by prosecutors. Because of the enormous amount of detail revealed not only about individual depositors but also about the workings of the banking system on the Cayman Islands, it was thought that the Guardian case might put a substantial dent in the islands' banking industry.

In addition to banking, tourism was a major sector in the Cayman Islands' economy. Following a major decline in the recessionary period of the early 1990s, tourism revenues had risen sharply in recent years. Tourism accounted for a about one-third of employment on the islands and some 70 percent of their GDP.

The islands also had a substantial shipping registry and were home to nearly 500 captive insurance companies.

GOVERNMENT AND POLITICS

In 1999 the Cayman Islands, a direct dependency of the United Kingdom, was governed under its 1972 constitution, as amended in 1992. The National Team had been returned to office as the islands' ruling party in the last general election, held in November 1992, but with a reduced majority. It held nine seats in the 15-member Legislative Assembly, the Democratic Alliance held two, Team Cayman held one, and independents held the remaining three. The next elections were scheduled for 2000. The ministers of a five-member Executive Council created in 1994 advised the governor on administrative issues. In May, Peter John Smith became the Cayman Islands' seventh governor since 1962.

With the millions of dollars handled by the Caymans' flourishing offshore banking industry and participation in global trade and commerce, one of the government's chief concerns in 1999 was addressing the Y2K problem, and comprehensive planning was in place, encompassing the islands' energy, water, communications, transportation, and health sectors, as well as their business community. Contingency plans to deal with any mishaps were slated for completion by mid-1999. In January the Cayman Islands Monetary Authority (CIMA), which supervises some 3,000 licensed financial entities, issued a letter to all banks, insurance companies, and other financial service providers urging them to adopt Y2K compliance as a top priority for the year.

In October, the government began collecting data for its first official census in ten years. Beyond simply ascertaining population size, the census was an attempt to provide a comprehensive picture of the islands' diverse inhabitants and included questions about nationality, languages, employment, and religion.

CULTURE AND SOCIETY

In 1999 efforts continued to document the islands' history over the past three centuries, spearheaded by the Cayman Islands National Archive. The Pedro St. James plantation site, the islands' first national historic landmark, was in its first full year of operation, welcoming visitors in a special visitor center and theater opened the previous December, where they could view a half-hour video describing the islands' history. The house, newly restored to reflect its original late-18th- and early-19th-century architecture, was located in the center of a 7.5-acre heritage park on the southern coast of Grand Cayman.

Looking to the future, the Cayman Islands Health Services Department reviewed and updated its plans to deal with any Y2K emergencies, an operation led by a special Y2K planning team headquartered in the recently completed Cayman Islands Hospital. Due to the large number of visitors expected over the new year's holiday, added personnel would be on duty December 31 and January 1.

Rebuffing a request the British government had issued the previous month, the government of the Cayman Islands announced in April that it opposed legalizing homosexuality.

DIRECTORY

CENTRAL GOVERNMENT

Head of State

Queen
Elizabeth II, Monarch

Governor
Peter John Smith, Governor's Office

Ministers

Minister of Tourism, Commerce, Transport and Works
Thomas C. Jefferson, Ministry of Tourism, Commerce, Transport and Works

Minister of Education, Aviation and Planning
Truman M. Bodden, Ministry of Education, Aviation and Planning

Minister of Community Affairs, Sports, Women's and Youth Affairs and Culture
Julianna O'Connor Connolly, Ministry of Community Affairs, Sports, Women's and Youth Affairs and Culture

Minister of Agriculture, Communications, Environment, and Natural Resources
John B. McLean, Ministry of Agriculture, Communications, Environment, and Natural Resources

Minister of Health, Social Welfare, Drug Abuse Prevention and Rehabilitation
Anthony S. Eden, Ministry of Health, Social Welfare, Drug Abuse Prevention and Rehabilitation

POLITICAL ORGANIZATIONS

No formal political parties.

DIPLOMATIC REPRESENTATION

None (Overseas territory of the United Kingdom)

JUDICIAL SYSTEM

Grand Court

Cayman Islands Court of Appeal

FURTHER READING
Articles

"Caymans Bank Investigation Focuses on Unlikely Targets." *The New York Times*, 4 August 1999, p. B5.

"Caymans History, with a Video." *The New York Times*, 7 February 1999, p. TR3.

"In Plea Deal, a Banker Outlines Money Laundering in Caymans." *The New York Times*, 3 August 1999, p. A1.

"Murky World of Offshore Banking Emerges in U.S. Tax-Fraud Probe." *The Wall Street Journal*, 3 August 1999, p. A18.

Roberts, Sally. "Still Hot, Cayman Islands Nears the 500 Milestone." *Business Insurance* 12 April 1999: 22.

Internet

Caribbean Week. Available Online @ http://www.cweek.com (November 1, 1999).

CAYMAN ISLANDS: STATISTICAL DATA

For sources and notes see "Sources of Statistics" in the front of each volume.

GEOGRAPHY

Geography (1)

Area:

Total: 260 sq km.

Land: 260 sq km.

Water: 0 sq km.

Area—comparative: 1.5 times the size of Washington, DC.

Land boundaries: 0 km.

Coastline: 160 km.

Climate: tropical marine; warm, rainy summers (May to October) and cool, relatively dry winters (November to April).

Terrain: low-lying limestone base surrounded by coral reefs.

Natural resources: fish, climate and beaches that foster tourism.

Land use:

Arable land: 0%

Permanent crops: 0%

Permanent pastures: 8%

Forests and woodland: 23%

Other: 69% (1993 est.).

HUMAN FACTORS

Demographics (2B)

Population (July 1998 est.) 37,716

Age structure:

   0-14 years . . . . .NA

   15-64 years . . . . .NA

   65 years and over . . . . .NA

Population growth rate (1998 est.) 4.22%

Birth rate, 1998 est. (births/1,000 population) 13.95

Death rate, 1998 est.

   (deaths/1,000 population) 4.98

Net migration rate, 1998 est.

   (migrant(s)/1,000 population) 33.2

Life expectancy at birth (years):

   Total population 77.1

   Male . . . . .75.37 years

   Female (1998 est.) . . . . .78.81 years

Total fertility rate, 1998 est.

   (children born/woman) .1.34

Major destination for Cubans trying to migrate to the US

Ethnic Division (6)

Mixed 40%

White 20%

Black 20%

Expatriates of various ethnic groups 20%

Religions (7)

United Church (Presbyterian and Congregational), Anglican, Baptist, Roman Catholic, Church of God, other Protestant denominations

Languages (8)

English.

EDUCATION

Educational Attainment (10)

Age group (1989) . . . . .25+

Total population 15,270

Highest level attained (%)

   No schooling 0

   First level

      Not completed 45.4

      Completed . . . . .NA

Educational Attainment (10)

Entered second level

S-1 . . . . .40.6

S-2 . . . . .NA

Postsecondary 14.2

GOVERNMENT & LAW

Political Parties (12)

Legislative Assembly	No. of seats
National Team coalition	.9
Independents	.6

Government Budget (13B)

Revenues . . . .$141.5 million

Expenditures . . . .$160.7 million

Capital expenditures . . . . .NA

Data for 1991. NA stands for not available.

Military Affairs (14A)

Defense is the responsibility of the UK.

LABOR FORCE

Labor Force (16)

Total 8,061

Service workers 18.7%

Clerical 18.6%

Construction 12.5%

Finance and Investment 6.7%

Directors and business managers 5.9%

Data for 1979.

Unemployment Rate (17)

7% (1992)

PRODUCTION SECTOR

Electric Energy (18)

Capacity . . . . .75,000 kW (1995)

Production . . . . .230 million kWh (1995)

Consumption per capita . . . . .6,929 kWh (1995)

Transportation (19)

Highways:

total: 406 km

paved: 304 km

unpaved: 102 km

Merchant marine:

total: 54 ships (1,000 GRT or over) totaling 751,113 GRT/1,139,958 DWT ships by type: bulk 4, cargo 8, chemical tanker 4, container 5, oil tanker 6, refrigerated cargo 18, roll-on/roll-off cargo 7, specialized tanker 1, vehicle carrier 1 note: a flag of convenience registry; includes ships from 10 countries: Greece 11, US 8, UK 5, Cyprus 1, Finland 1, India 1, Japan 1, Norway 1, Sweden 1, and Switzerland 1 (1997 est.)

Airports: 3 (1997 est.)

Airports—with paved runways:

total: 2

1,524 to 2,437 m: 2 (1997 est.)

Airports—with unpaved runways:

total: 1

914 to 1,523 m: 1 (1997 est.)

Top Agricultural Products (20)

Vegetables, fruit; livestock; turtle farming.

FINANCE, ECONOMICS, & TRADE

Economic Indicators (22)

National product: GDP—purchasing power parity— $860 million (1996 est.)

National product real growth rate: 4.5% (1996 est.)

National product per capita: $23,800 (1996 est.)

Inflation rate—consumer price index: 2.1% (1996 est.)

Exchange Rates (24)

Exchange rates:

Caymanian dollars (CI$) per US$1

3 November 1995 . . . . .0.83

22 November 1993 . . . . .0.85

Top Import Origins (25)

$333 million (c.i.f., 1995 est.)

Origins	%
United States	.NA
Trinidad and Tobago	.NA
United Kingdom	.NA
Netherlands Antilles	.NA
Japan	.NA

NA stands for not available.

Top Export Destinations (26)

$3.4 million (f.o.b., 1995 est.).

Destinations	%
mostly US . . . . .NA	

NA stands for not available.

Economic Aid (27)

Recipient: ODA, $NA. NA stands for not available.

Import Export Commodities (28)

Import Commodities	Export Commodities
Foodstuffs	Turtle products
Manufactured goods	Manufactured consumer goods

CENTRAL AFRICAN REPUBLIC

République Centrafricaine

CAPITAL: Bangui.

FLAG: The national flag consists of four horizontal stripes (blue, white, green, and yellow) divided at the center by a vertical red stripe. In the upper left corner is a yellow five-pointed star.

ANTHEM: *La Renaissance (Rebirth).*

MONETARY UNIT: The Communauté Financière Africaine franc (CFA Fr) is a paper currency. There are coins of 1, 2, 5, 10, 25, 50, 100, and 500 CFA francs, and notes of 50, 100, 500, 1,000, 5,000, and 10,000 CFA francs. CFA Fr1 = $0.00196 (or $1 = CFA Fr510.65).

WEIGHTS AND MEASURES: The metric system is the legal standard.

HOLIDAYS: New Year's Day, 1 January; Anniversary of President Boganda's Death, 29 March; Labor Day, 1 May; National Day of Prayer, 30 June; Independence Day, 13 August; Assumption, 15 August; All Saints' Day, 1 November; Proclamation of the Republic, 28 November; National Day, 1 December; and Christmas, 25 December. Movable religious holidays include Easter Monday, Ascension, Pentecost Monday.

TIME: 1 PM = noon GMT.

LOCATION AND SIZE: Located in Central Africa, entirely within the tropical zone and entirely landlocked, the Central African Republic has an area of 622,980 square kilometers (240,535 square miles). Comparatively, the area occupied by Central African Republic (CAR) is slightly smaller than the state of Texas. The Central African Republic's capital city, Bangui, is located in the southwestern part of the country.

CLIMATE: The climate is tropical, with abundant rainfall of about 180 centimeters (70 inches) annually in the south, decreasing to about 80 centimeters (31.5 inches) in the extreme northeast. Floods are common. Temperatures at Bangui have an average daily minimum and maximum range from 21°C (70°F) to 32°F (90°F).

INTRODUCTORY SURVEY

RECENT HISTORY

In a referendum on 28 September 1958, Ubangi-Shari voted to become an autonomous republic within the French community. The Central African Republic was proclaimed on 1 December 1958, with Barthélémy Boganda as president. In 1961, the constitution was amended to establish a presidential government with a single-party system.

On 1 January 1966, a military coup d'etat led by Colonel (later Field Marshal) Jean-Bédel Bokassa abolished the constitution and dissolved the National Assembly. Bokassa, who became president in 1968 and president for life in 1972, proclaimed himself emperor of the newly formed Central African Empire on 4 December 1976. On 20 September 1979, David Dacko, with French support, led a bloodless coup that overthrew Bokassa while he was out of the country. The republic was restored, and Bokassa, who took refuge in Côte d'Ivoire and France, was sentenced to death in absentia for various crimes, including cannibalism.

A new constitution allowing free political activity was approved by referendum in February 1981. A month later, Dacko was elected, but he was overthrown on 1 September 1981 by a military coup. Free elections were not held again until 19 September 1993, when citizens elected Ange-Felix Patasse president.

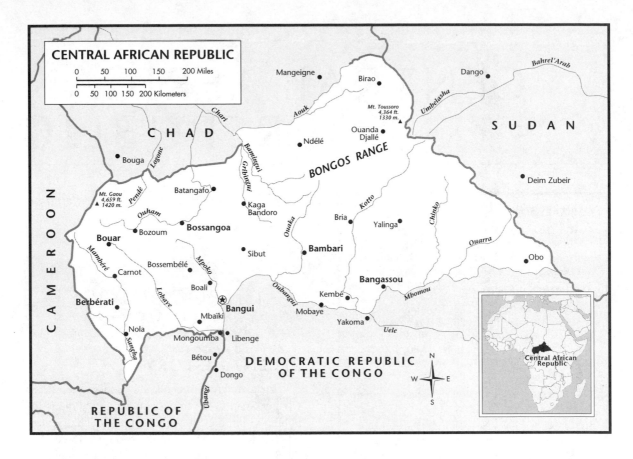

The transition from military to elected government has gone smoothly, although the economy has faltered. The human rights picture has improved, yet the security forces still exercise arbitrary power. In 1993, the military engaged in two brief mutinies, and in 1996, 200 soldiers briefly rebelled over non-payment of salaries. There was further unrest in the country that year, and in June the government was reorganized to give more power to the prime minister, decreasing the power of the president.

GOVERNMENT

After a 1992 election was invalidated by the Supreme Court, new elections were conducted successfully in September 1993. For the 1993 elections, the National Assembly was enlarged to eighty-five members. Ange-Felix Patasse was elected president, and a graceful transition to multi-party democracy took place. The new coalition government is headed by the MLPC and includes members of three other parties. Constitutional reforms in 1995 and 1996 created a stronger prime minister, a constitutional court, and created regional assemblies.

Judiciary

The 1994 constitution reorganized the judiciary, which consists of regular and military courts. The constitutional court's judges are appointed by the president. Criminal defendants are presumed innocent and have the right to counsel, to public trial and to confront witnesses. Trials are public and frequently broadcast on national media.

Political Parties

In 1991, opposition parties were legalized, and on 19 September 1993, new elections led to President André Kolingba's defeat. His old rival, Ange-Felix Patasse, became president and the MLPC (Mouvement pour la Libération du Peuple Centrafricain) gained thirty-three of the eighty-five seats in the National Assembly.

DEFENSE

The army, numbering about 2,500 in 1995, consisted of seven battalions. The 150-man air force had 21 noncombatant aircraft and helicopters. The government spent $24 million on defense in 1995, or 1.9% of gross domestic product (GDP).

ECONOMIC AFFAIRS

The Central African Republic has a basically agricultural economy (85% of the workforce is engaged in agriculture, producing 50% of the gross domestic product) supplemented by the export of diamonds. Coffee, cotton, and timber lead the list of agricultural exports.

Public Finance

The Central African Republic and the IMF have worked together since 1980 to attempt to better manage the economy. The 1980 austerity plan focused on stabilizing budget and foreign deficits by concentrating on agricultural production. The 1982 Recovery Plan, also conducted within IMF frameworks, led to a formal structural adjustment plan in 1987. A second structural adjustment plan was agreed to in 1990. Goals of the IMF-sponsored program were a reduction of the number of government employees and their salaries, price-policy reforms, and privatization of the parastatal sector.

Income

In 1997, Central African Republic's gross national product (GNP) was $1 billion at current prices, or $300 per capita. For the period 1985–95 the average inflation rate was 3.7%, resulting in a decline in the GNP of 2.0% per person.

Industry

Industry contributes about 14% of gross domestic product (GDP). Textile and leather manufacturing are the leading industries. All cotton produced in the country is ginned locally. Refined sugar and palm oil are also produced, as are soap and cigarettes.

Banking and Finance

In November 1972, a new central bank, the Bank of the Central African States (Banque des États de l'Afrique Central-BEAC), replaced the existing Central Bank of the States of Equatorial Africa and Cameroon, which had been controlled by French interests. This move was designed to strengthen the monetary solidarity and sovereignty of the Central African Republic and other member African nations, which would now control part of their foreign exchange and monetary policies.

Economic Development

Development expenditures are financed almost exclusively by foreign donors. The World Bank extended a $30 million loan in 1986. As of 1993, the estimated external debt was $904.3 million.

In 1986, the government began a structural adjustment program (SAP) to improve agricultural production, to encourage early retirement among government workers, and to privatize government enterprises. Phase two of this program began in 1988, and phase three in 1990.

SOCIAL WELFARE

Since 1 July 1956, family allowances have been paid to all salaried workers. Contributions are made by employers at a fixed percentage of the employee's wage. There are other programs for salaried workers, but only a small percentage of the workforce is eligible since most people work in agriculture. The constitution mandates that women have equal treatment, but they sometimes suffer severe discrimination. The forest forager people, a minority group, also experience discrimination.

Healthcare

Mobile medical crews treat local epidemic diseases, conduct vaccination and inoculation campaigns, and enforce local health regulations. The most common diseases are bilharziasis, leprosy, malaria, tuberculosis, and yaws. The average life expectancy in 1995 was 49 years. In 1990, there were 113 doctors, or 1 for every 25,930 people.

Housing

The Central African Real Estate Investments Society makes small loans for the repair of existing houses and larger loans for new construction. Fourteen percent of the urban and 11% of the rural population have access to a safe water supply.

EDUCATION

Education is provided free in government-financed schools. Education is compulsory between ages 6 and 14. Primary education lasts for six years; secondary lasts for seven years (four plus three). Adult illiteracy was about 40% in 1995 (males, 31.5%; females, 47.6%).

Specialized institutions include two agricultural colleges, a national college of the performing and plastic arts, and the University of Bangui, founded in 1969. In 1991, enrollment in these institutions was 3,783.

1999 KEY EVENTS TIMELINE

January

- Members of the opposition coalition, formed by the winners of 55 of the 109 National Assembly seats after the December 1998 election, walked out of the opening session of the National Assembly. They were protesting the defection of one coalition member.

- President Ange-Félix Patasse appoints a member of his own party, Central African People's Liberation Movement (MLPC), to replace the prime minister.

- Despite a boycott by the opposition, the MLPC deputies and their allies elect Luc-Appolanaire Dondon-Konamabaye as Speaker of the National Assembly.

- Thousands of refugees from neighboring Congo have been flooding across the border into the Central African Republic to escape fighting in the region, immigration authorities said.

February

- The United Nations Security Council decides to maintain UN peacekeepers in the Central African Republic until November, but said it wants the mission to end after that.

July

- The Constitutional Court publishes the list of candidates for president. Among the ten candidates running for office are current President Ange-Félix Patasse and former presidents André Kolingba and David Dacko.

August

- In response to pressure from international financial aid organizations, an independent electoral commission is established on August 9. Opposition parties demand that presidential elections scheduled for August 29 be postponed until September 12.

- The government postpones presidential elections for two weeks, saying electoral lists and voter registration cards are not ready.

September

- All nine opposition candidates reject election results in advance, accusing incumbent president Patasse and his supporters of staging an electoral coup d'etat.

- Elections for a new president are largely trouble-free despite charges of voter fraud and fears of political bloodshed.

October

- Official results give President Ange-Felix Patasse a second term in the September election. His supporters celebrate in the streets of the capital.

- Nine opposition candidates charge that the presidential election, in which President Ange-Felix Patasse was reelected, was rigged and that Patasse intimidated voters into supporting his candidacy. The opposition candidates further demand that the election be nullified.

- Prime Minister Anice-Georges Dologuele resigns following the reelection of Patasse, but Patasse is expected to reappoint him.

December

- Kofi Annan, secretary-general of the United Nations, submits a proposal to the Security Council to send a mission to CAR. The mission would be installed by February 2000 when the UN peacekeeping forces withdraw.

- On December 28, President Patasse announces plans to curb freedom of the press as of January 1, 2000, citing the role of the press in inciting rebellion.

ANALYSIS OF EVENTS: 1999

BUSINESS AND THE ECONOMY

In July, the International Monetary Fund loaned the Central African Republic $11 million to fund unpaid government salaries and continue economic reforms that were launched in 1998, saying the country was showing some positive signs of recovery. The government owed about nine months of unpaid salaries to 20,000 civil servants and army soldiers. The government was also behind in payments of grants for students and retirement benefits for pensioners.

International observers, including the United Nations, told the government that only political stability will encourage economic development, which would increase employment and government revenue. While the country is considered to be rich in resources—such as diamonds, gold and lumber—more than 60 percent of the population lives in poverty.

GOVERNMENT AND POLITICS

On September 19, over half of the 1.7 million registered voters participated in the presidential elections. After years of political instability, the vote was supposed to be the final step to bring peace to the Central African Republic, whose people have been under the protection of United Nations peace troops since 1998.

President Ange-Felix Patasse was reelected with 51.6 percent of the votes, defeating nine other candidates. His nearest challenger was Andre Kolingba, who earned 19.3 percent, and David Dacko, with 11.1 percent.

The national crisis began in 1996, when unpaid soldiers began to mutiny. The Central African Republic had already been plagued by serious social and economic problems, and the mutinies aggravated the situation. Hundreds of people lost their lives, and the fighting displaced tens of thousands. Widespread looting destroyed small businesses and factories in the capital. A United Nations peace mission arrived in 1998, and attempted to re-establish order. In November and December of 1998, the U.N. monitored legislative elections for the 109-seat National Assembly. Opposition parties won 55 seats and captured the majority in the Assembly by one seat. The UN considered the elections to be generally free and fair.

On January 4, 1999, the coalition of opposition parties walked out of the opening Assembly session to protest the loss of its majority. Opponents claimed the Central African People's Liberation Movement (MLPC) bribed Dieudonné Koudoufara so he would defect and give Patasse control of the assembly. Patasse formed a new government, and chose a fellow party member, Anicet Georges Dologuele, as prime minister.

Following the presidential elections, U.N. Secretary-General Kofi Annan said he hoped the government and opposition would find ways to work together in a "spirit of national reconciliation, toward the consolidation of peace and development in the country."

In October, the U.N. Security Council extended the peace mission until February 15, 2000, and agreed to examine conditions for a U.N. presence beyond the withdrawal date. The continued presence of U.N. peacekeepers would ease the nation's transition from conflict to peace building, and give the government more time to restructure the armed forces, Annan said. Annan acknowledged that the political situation remained tense, and opponents and the government remained at odds.

CULTURE AND SOCIETY

In the Central African Republic, humanitarian aid organizations say, each employed person supports about 20 family or community members. The government has not been able to pay salaries, and many people are down to eating one meal per day, observers in the Central African Republic told IRIN, a U.N. information network. People were weaker and more susceptible to disease. A recent UNICEF survey showed that over 79 percent of children under five years of age were anemic. Malaria, and diarrhea also had increased among children.

"There are at least 30 people a day being buried in just the official cemeteries of Bangui, whereas it was 16 to 20 people two years ago," IRIN was told by its sources. The situation in the interior of the country was reportedly worse.

According to government figures, about 63 percent of the population lives in poverty, and only 45 percent has access to adequate health facilities. Most villagers have no access to clean drinking water. Chronic malnutrition affects about one-quarter of children.

DIRECTORY

CENTRAL GOVERNMENT
Head of State

President
Ange-Félix Patassé, Office of the President

Prime Minister
Anicet Georges Dologuele

Ministers

Minister of Agriculture
Charles Massi, Ministry of Agriculture

Minister of Communications
Thierry Ignifolo Vanden-Boss, Ministry of Communications

Minister of Economy, Planning, and International Cooperation
Christophe Bremaidou, Ministry of Economy, Planning, and International Cooperation

Minister of Environment
Joseph Yomba, Ministry of Environment

Minister of Family and Social Affairs
Eliane Mokodopo, Ministry of Family and Social Affairs

Minister of Finance and Budget
Anicet Georges Doleguele, Ministry of Finance and Budget

Minister of Foreign Affairs
Jean Mette-Yapende, Ministry of Foreign Affairs

Minister of Higher Education and Research
Theophile Touba, Ministry of Higher Education and Research

Minister of Housing and Urban Development
Clement Belibanga, Ministry of Housing and Urban Development

Minister of Human Rights, Culture, and National Reconciliation
Laurent Gomina Pampali, Ministry of Human Rights, Culture, and National Reconciliation

Minister of Industry and Commerce
Simon Bongolape, Ministry of Industry and Commerce

Minister of Interior and Security
Francois Ndjadder-Bedaya, Ministry of Interior and Security

Minister of Justice
Marcel Metefara, Ministry of Justice

Minister of Mines
Joseph Agbo, Ministry of Mines

Minister of National Defense
Pascal Kado, Ministry of National Defense

Minister of National Education
Albert Mberio, Ministry of National Education

Minister of Parliamentary Relations
Charles Armel Doubane, Ministry of Parliamentary Relations

Minister of Posts and Telecommunications
Michel Bindo, Ministry of Posts and Telecommunications

Minister of Public Function
Jean-Claude Ngouandjia, Ministry of Public Function

Minister of Public Health
Fernand Djemgbo, Ministry of Public Health

Minister of Public Works
Jackson Mazette, Ministry of Public Works

Minister of Tourism, Arts, and Culture
Gaston Beina Gbandi, Ministry of Tourism, Arts, and Culture

Minister of Transport
Andre Gombacko, Ministry of Transport

Minister of Youth and Sports
Bertin Bea, Ministry of Youth and Sports

POLITICAL ORGANIZATIONS

Alliance pour la Démocratie et le Progrès-ADP (Alliance for Democracy and Progress)

NAME: Tchapka Brede

Rassemblement Démocratique Centrafricain-RDC (Central African Democratic Assembly)

NAME: André Kolingba

Forum Civique-FC (Civic Forum)

NAME: General Timothee Malendoma

Parti Libéral Démocratique-PLD (Liberal Democratic Party)

NAME: Nestor Kombo-Naguemon

Mouvement pour la Démocratie et le Développement-MDD (Movement for Democracy and Development)

NAME: David Dacko

Mouvement pour la Libération du Peuple-MLPC (Movement for the Liberation of the Central African People)

NAME: Ange-Félix Patassé

Parti de l'Unité Nationale-PUN (National Unity Party)

Front Patriotique pour le Progress-FPP (Patriotic Front for Progress)

NAME: Abel Goumba

Parti Social Democratique-PSD (Social Democratic Party)

NAME: Enoch Derant Lakoué

DIPLOMATIC REPRESENTATION

Embassies in Central African Republic

United States
B.P. 924, Bangui, Central African Republic
PHONE: +236 610200
TITLE: Ambassador
NAME: Mosina H. Jordan

JUDICIAL SYSTEM

Supreme Court

Constitutional Court

FURTHER READING

Articles

"Central African Republic Holds Peaceful Vote Amid Violence Fears." Associated Press, 19 September 1999.

"Central African Republic Postpones Presidential Vote." Associated Press, 12 September 1999.

"Congo Refugees Flood into Central African Republic." Associated Press, 5 January 1999.

"Dancing with the Devil." *House Beautiful* January 1999: 16.

"Patasse Wins Presidential Ballot in Central African Republic." Associated Press, 2 October 1999.

"Security Council Extends Mission in Central African Republic." Associated Press, 27 February 1999.

Internet

Africa News Online. Available Online @ http://www.africanews.org/west/stories/1999_feat1.html (October 28, 1999).

Africaonline. Available Online @ http://www.africaonline.com (October 28, 1999).

Integrated Regional Information Network (IRIN). Available Online @ http://www.reliefweb.int/IRIN (October 28, 1999).

CENTRAL AFRICAN REPUBLIC: STATISTICAL DATA

For sources and notes see "Sources of Statistics" in the front of each volume.

GEOGRAPHY

Geography (1)

Area:

Total: 622,980 sq km.

Land: 622,980 sq km.

Water: 0 sq km.

Area—comparative: slightly smaller than Texas.

Land boundaries:

Total: 5,203 km.

Border countries: Cameroon 797 km, Chad 1,197 km, Democratic Republic of the Congo 1,577 km, Republic of the Congo 467 km, Sudan 1,165 km.

Coastline: 0 km (landlocked).

Climate: tropical; hot, dry winters; mild to hot, wet summers.

Terrain: vast, flat to rolling, monotonous plateau; scattered hills in northeast and southwest.

Natural resources: diamonds, uranium, timber, gold, oil.

Land use:

Arable land: 3%

Permanent crops: 0%

Permanent pastures: 5%

Forests and woodland: 75%

Other: 17% (1993 est.).

HUMAN FACTORS

Demographics (2A)

	1990	1995	1998	2000	2010	2020	2030	2040	2050
Population	2,797.7	3,182.9	3,375.8	3,515.7	4,314.5	5,132.7	5,981.0	6,943.4	7,915.3
Net migration rate (per 1,000 population)	NA	NA	NA	NA	NA	NA	NA	NA	NA
Births	NA	NA	NA	NA	NA	NA	NA	NA	NA
Deaths	NA	NA	NA	NA	NA	NA	NA	NA	NA
Life expectancy - males	43.3	44.0	45.0	45.7	48.5	51.8	60.3	68.8	72.1
Life expectancy - females	46.0	47.5	48.7	49.5	53.4	56.9	66.2	75.6	79.1
Birth rate (per 1,000)	43.0	40.2	38.7	37.9	33.3	28.2	23.9	20.4	17.5
Death rate (per 1,000)	18.9	17.7	16.7	16.2	14.1	12.4	8.8	6.0	5.8
Women of reproductive age (15-49 yrs.)	651.8	733.9	783.1	821.0	1,057.5	1,330.5	1,633.1	1,908.8	2,122.1
of which are currently married	NA	NA	NA	NA	NA	NA	NA	NA	NA
Fertility rate	5.7	5.4	5.1	4.9	4.1	3.3	2.7	2.4	2.2

Except as noted, values for vital statistics are in thousands; life expectancy is in years.

Health Personnel (3)

Total health expenditure as a percentage of GDP, 1990-1997[a]

Public sector 2.0

Private sector . . . . .NA

Total[b] . . . . .NA

Health expenditure per capita in U.S. dollars, 1990-1997[a]

Purchasing power parity . . . . .NA

Total . . . . .NA

Availability of health care facilities per 100,000 people

Hospital beds 1990-1997[a] 90

Doctors 1993[c] 6

Nurses 1993[c] 45

Health Indicators (4)

Life expectancy at birth

1980 46

1997 45

Daily per capita supply of calories (1996) 1,938

Total fertility rate births per woman (1997) 4.9

Maternal mortality ratio per 100,000 live births (1990-97) . . . . .700[d]

Safe water % of population with access (1995) 23

Sanitation % of population with access (1995) 45

Consumption of iodized salt % of households (1992-98)[a] 65

Smoking prevalence

Male % of adults (1985-95)[a] . . . .

Female % of adults (1985-95)[a] . . . .

Tuberculosis incidence per 100,000 people (1997) 237

Adult HIV prevalence % of population ages 15-49 (1997) 10.77

Infants and Malnutrition (5)

Under-5 mortality rate (1997) 173

% of infants with low birthweight (1990-97) 15

Births attended by skilled health staff % of total[a] . . .46

% fully immunized (1995-97)

TB 94

DPT 53

Polio 51

Measles 46

Prevalence of child malnutrition under age 5 (1992-97)[b] 23

Ethnic Division (6)

Baya 34%

Banda 27%

Sara 10%

Mandjia 21%

Mboum 4%

M'Baka 4%

Europeans 6,500

Europeans include 3,600 French.

Religions (7)

Indigenous beliefs 24%

Protestant 25%

Roman Catholic 25%

Muslim 15%

Other 11%

Note: animistic beliefs and practices strongly influence the Christian majority.

Languages (8)

French (official), Sangho (lingua franca and national language), Arabic, Hunsa, Swahili.

EDUCATION

Public Education Expenditures (9)

Public expenditure on education (% of GNP)

1980 . . . .

1996 . . . .

Expenditure per student

Primary % of GNP per capita

1980 . . . . .22.0

1996 . . . .

Secondary % of GNP per capita

1980 . . . .

1996 . . . .

Tertiary % of GNP per capita

1980 . . . . .939.5

1996 . . . .

Expenditure on teaching materials

Primary % of total for level (1996) . . . .

Secondary % of total for level (1996) . . . .

Primary pupil-teacher ratio per teacher (1996) . . . .

Duration of primary education years (1995) 6

Educational Attainment (10)

Age group (1988) . . . . .25+
Total population 920,929
Highest level attained (%)
  No schooling 70.7
  First level
    Not completed 19.5
    Completed . . . . .NA
  Entered second level
    S-1 . . . . .7.3
    S-2 . . . . .NA
  Postsecondary 2.0

Literacy Rates (11A)

In thousands and percent[1]	1990	1995	2000	2010
Illiterate population (15+ yrs.)	841	760	671	489
Literacy rate - total adult pop. (%)	49.9	60.0	68.7	82.4
Literacy rate - males (%)	59.6	68.5	75.9	87.4
Literacy rate - females (%)	41.2	52.4	62.1	77.8

GOVERNMENT & LAW

Military Affairs (14B)

	1990	1991	1992	1993	1994	1995
Military expenditures						
Current dollars (mil.)	16	NA	21e	24e	NA	NA
1995 constant dollars (mil.)	18	NA	22e	25e	NA	NA
Armed forces (000)	4	4	7	7	5	5
Gross national product (GNP)						
Current dollars (mil.)	965	981	976	949	1,106	1,115
1995 constant dollars (mil.)	1,109	1,084	1,050	995	1,134	1,115
Central government expenditures (CGE)						
1995 constant dollars (mil.)	NA	270e	NA	NA	NA	NA
People (mil.)	2.8	2.9	3.0	3.1	3.1	3.2
Military expenditure as % of GNP	1.6	NA	2.1	2.5	NA	NA
Military expenditure as % of CGE	NA	NA	NA	NA	NA	NA
Military expenditure per capita (1995 $)	6	NA	8	8	NA	NA
Armed forces per 1,000 people (soldiers)	1.4	1.4	2.4	2.3	1.6	1.5
GNP per capita (1994 $)	395	376	354	325	360	347
Arms imports[6]						
Current dollars (mil.)	0	0	0	0	0	0
1995 constant dollars (mil.)	0	0	0	0	0	0
Arms exports[6]						
Current dollars (mil.)	0	0	0	0	0	0
1995 constant dollars (mil.)	0	0	0	0	0	0
Total imports[7]						
Current dollars (mil.)	154	93	145	126	142	189
1995 constant dollars (mil.)	177	103	156	132	146	189
Total exports[7]						
Current dollars (mil.)	120	47	107	110	150	187
1995 constant dollars (mil.)	138	52	115	115	154	187
Arms as percent of total imports[8]	0	0	0	0	0	0
Arms as percent of total exports[8]	0	0	0	0	0	0

Political Parties (12)

National Assembly	No. of seats
Movement for the Liberation of the Central African People (MLPC)	34
African Democratic Assembly (RDC)	13
Liberal Democratic Party (PLD)	7
Patriotic Front for Progress (FPP)	7
Alliance for Democracy and Progress (ADP)	6
Social Democratic Party (PSD)	3
National Convention (CN)	3
Democratic Movement for the Renaissance and Evolution of Central Africa (MDREC)	1
Central African Republican Party (PRC)	1
Civic Forum (FC)	1
Social Evolution Movement of Black Africa (MESAN)	1
Independents supporting David Dacko	6
Other independents	2

Government Budget (13B)

Revenues . . . .$638 million

Expenditures . . . .$1.9 billion

   Capital expenditures . . . .$888 million

Data for 1994 est.

LABOR FORCE

Unemployment Rate (17)

6% (1993)

PRODUCTION SECTOR

Electric Energy (18)

Capacity . . . . .43,000 kW (1995)

Production . . . . .100 million kWh (1995)

Consumption per capita . . . . .31 kWh (1995)

Transportation (19)

Highways:

total: 23,810 km

paved: 429 km

unpaved: 23,381 km (1995 est.)

Waterways: 800 km; traditional trade carried on by means of shallow-draft dugouts; Oubangui is the most important river

Airports: 52 (1997 est.)

Airports—with paved runways:

total: 3

2,438 to 3,047 m: 1

1,524 to 2,437 m: 2 (1997 est.)

Airports—with unpaved runways:

total: 49

2,438 to 3,047 m: 1

1,524 to 2,437 m: 10

914 to 1,523 m: 23

under 914 m: 15 (1997 est.)

Top Agricultural Products (20)

Cotton, coffee, tobacco, manioc (tapioca), yams, millet, corn, bananas; timber.

MANUFACTURING SECTOR

GDP & Manufacturing Summary (21)

Detailed value added figures are listed by both International Standard Industry Code (ISIC) and product title.

	1980	1985	1990	1994
GDP: $-1990 mil.)[1]	1,136	1,222	1,296	1,323
Per capita ($-1990)[1]	491	471	443	409
Manufacturing share (%) (current prices)[1]	8.8	7.1	6.8	NA
Manufacturing				
Value added ($-1990 mil.)[1]	67	78	89	98
Industrial production index	100	100	117	129
Value added ($ mil.)	35	33	62	26
Gross output ($ mil.)	98	108	165	67
Employment (000)	6	8	5	5
Profitability (% of gross output)				
Intermediate input (%)	64	70	62	61
Wages and salaries inc. supplements (%)	16	18	15	15
Gross operating surplus	19	12	22	24
Productivity ($)				
Gross output per worker	16,613	13,857	30,521	14,000
Value added per worker	5,935	4,156	11,454	5,644
Average wage (inc. supplements)	2,703	2,428	4,654	2,050

	1980	1985	1990	1994
Value added ($ mil.)				
311/2 Food products	5	8	15	8
313 Beverages	3	4	8	4
314 Tobacco products	4	6	13	7
321 Textiles	5	—	3	1
322 Wearing apparel	1	—	—	—
323 Leather and fur products	—	—	—	—
324 Footwear	—	—	—	—
331 Wood and wood products	11	8	12	2
332 Furniture and fixtures	—	1	1	—
341 Paper and paper products	—	—	—	—
342 Printing and publishing	1	2	3	—
351 Industrial chemicals	1	1	1	1
352 Other chemical products	2	1	3	2
353 Petroleum refineries	—	—	—	—
354 Miscellaneous petroleum and coal products	—	—	—	—
355 Rubber products	—	—	—	—
356 Plastic products	—	—	—	—
361 Pottery, china and earthenware	—	—	—	—
362 Glass and glass products	—	—	—	—
369 Other non-metal mineral products	—	—	—	—
371 Iron and steel	—	—	—	—
372 Non-ferrous metals	—	—	—	—
381 Metal products	1	—	—	—
382 Non-electrical machinery	—	—	—	—
383 Electrical machinery	—	—	—	—
384 Transport equipment	2	1	1	1
385 Professional and scientific equipment	—	—	—	—
390 Other manufacturing industries	—	1	1	—

FINANCE, ECONOMICS, & TRADE

Economic Indicators (22)

National product: GDP—purchasing power parity—$3.3 billion (1997 est.)

National product real growth rate: NA%

National product per capita: $1,000 (1997 est.)

Inflation rate—consumer price index: 4% (1996 est.)

Exchange Rates (24)

Exchange rates:

CFA francs (CFAF) per US$1

January 1998	608.36
1997	583.67
1996	511.55
1995	499.15
1994	555.20
1993	283.16

Beginning 12 January 1994, the CFA franc was devalued to CFAF 100 per French franc from CFAF 50 at which it had been fixed since 1948.

Balance of Payments (23)

	1990	1991	1992	1993	1994
Exports of goods (f.o.b.)	151	126	116	133	146
Imports of goods (f.o.b.)	−242	−179	−189	−158	−131
Trade balance	−91	−53	−73	−26	15
Services - debits	−191	−156	−175	−155	−137
Services - credits	70	56	52	54	33
Private transfers (net)	−23	−22	−27	−31	−25
Government transfers (net)	146	113	141	145	88
Overall balance	−89	−62	−83	−13	−25

Top Import Origins (25)

$174 million (f.o.b., 1995).

Origins	%
France	.37
other EU countries	.NA
Japan	.24
Algeria	.NA
Cameroon	.NA
Namibia	.NA

NA stands for not available.

Top Export Destinations (26)

$171 million (f.o.b., 1995).

Destinations	%
France	.16
Belgium-Luxembourg	.40.1
Italy	.NA
Japan	.NA
United States	.NA
Spain	.NA

Iran	.NA
Democratic Republic of the Congo	.NA
Republic of the Congo	.NA

NA stands for not available.

Economic Aid (27)

Recipient: ODA, $NA; traditional budget subsidies from France. NA stands for not available.

Import Export Commodities (28)

Import Commodities	Export Commodities
Food	Diamonds
Textiles	Timber
Petroleum products	Cotton
Machinery	Coffee
Electrical equipment	Tobacco
Motor vehicles	
Chemicals	
Pharmaceuticals	
Consumer goods	
Industrial products	

CHAD

Republic of Chad
République du Tchad

INTRODUCTORY SURVEY

RECENT HISTORY

After 1945, Chad became one of the territories of French Equatorial Africa in the French Union, and in the referendum of 28 September 1958, the territory of Chad voted to become an autonomous republic within the French Community. On 11 August 1960, Chad achieved full independence, with François (later Ngarta) Tombalbaye as head of state and prime minister. On 4 April 1962, a new constitution was proclaimed and a new government formed, with Tombalbaye as president.

After 1965, there was full-scale rebellion in the Muslim north country. In 1973, Libya provided a major source of covert aid for the rebels. Libya also occupied and annexed the Aozou Strip in northern Chad. However, in 1994, the World Court granted administration of the Aozou Strip to Chad.

In April 1975, Tombalbaye's fifteen-year rule ended with his assassination in an army coup. General Félix Malloum became the new president. Four years later, after sustained opposition from the Muslim north, Malloum resigned and fled the country. Hissène Habré, leader of the Armed Forces of the North (Forces Armées du Nord–FAN) became defense minister and Goukouni Oueddei interior minister in a coalition government.

Fighting between FAN and government forces broke out in March 1980, and Habré was dismissed from the cabinet in April. Following Libyan military intervention on Oueddi's behalf, Habré's forces fled to eastern Chad and the Sudan. When

CHAD

Aozou Strip
The World Court, in
February of 1994, granted
administration of
the Aozou Strip to Chad.

Habré reoccupied the capital in June 1982, Oueddei fled to Algeria, and Habré declared himself president of Chad on 19 October 1982.

By early 1983, the Habré regime, with the help of French forces, had extended its control to southern Chad. However, they were meeting increasing difficulties in the north from ousted president Oueddei, who had formed a rival government there. In early 1984, Chad was effectively divided, and there were growing fears that Libya was moving to annex northern Chad. A November 1984 agreement between France and Libya called for both countries to withdraw their forces from Chad, but although France complied, Libya failed to carry out the agreement. French troops returned in 1985 to help drive back an enemy offensive, and Libya agreed to a cease-fire, effective 11 September.

The Habré regime fell after a three-week campaign in late 1990 by guerrillas loyal to an ex-army commander, Indriss Déby. A Sovereign National Conference that lasted from January to April 1993 confirmed Déby as chief of state, established a new transitional government, elected fifty-seven counselors to a Higher Transitional Council (a quasi-legislative body), and adopted the Transitional Charter, an interim constitution. In 1995, opposition political forces formed the Political Parties Concentration (CPP), which, joining with France and other Western nations, began calling for changes in the administration of the Transitional Council.

GOVERNMENT

In early 1993, a three-month conference (Sovereign National Conference) established a fifty-seven-member Higher Transitional Council. A new constitution was released in 1994. It provides for an elected president, a bicameral legislature, and a constitutional court.

Judiciary

In most rural areas where there is no access to formal judicial institutions, sultans and chiefs preside over customary courts. Their decisions may be appealed to ordinary courts. Civil unrest and prolonged war have led to the deterioration of the official judicial system.

Political Parties

After the Déby coup, his Patriotic Salvation Movement (MPS) took over from the National Union for Independence and Revolution (Union Nationale pour l'Indépendence et la Révolution–UNIR). Parties were legalized in 1992, and eventually twenty-eight registered with the authorities.

DEFENSE

In 1995, Chad's armed forces totaled about 30,350 men, all but 350 (air force) in the army. Chad spent $34 million, or 2.7% of gross national product (GNP), on defense.

ECONOMIC AFFAIRS

Water-resource limitations are the critical factor influencing the Chadian economy. Much of the country is desert—suitable only for very limited agriculture and livestock production—while the remainder is threatened by periodic drought.

Despite these conditions, agriculture is Chad's primary sector, comprising 48% of gross domestic product (GDP). Cotton is a principal export commodity, but the sector has suffered considerably from a variety of ills.

Public Finance

The military accounts for about 35% of expenditures, and more than half the sum is outside the budget, raised by "voluntary" contributions. Customs duties are the principal revenue source. Increased military and civil servant outlays contribute to the fiscal deficit.

Chad began working with the IMF in the preparation of the 1986 budget, which sought to limit the deficit. In return for help in covering the shortfall, Chad agreed to raise taxes and to lower spending on subsidies and the civil service. Consequently, a structural adjustment program covering 1987 to 1990 was funded by the IMF. However, the 1992 austerity budget precipitated civil disorder. The U.S. CIA estimates that, in 1993, government revenues totaled approximately $120 million and expenditures $363 million, including capital expenditures of $104 million. External debt totaled $757 million, approximately 85% of which was financed abroad.

Income

In 1997, Chad's gross national product (GNP) was $240 per person. For the period 1985–95 the average inflation rate was a negative 3.1%, resulting in a real growth rate in GNP of 0.5% per person.

Industry

Because it lacks power and adequate transportation, Chad is industrially one of the least developed countries in Africa. Industry accounts for only about 18% of gross domestic product (GDP). Cotton processing is the largest activity, though reduced in scope by the reorganization of the cotton industry in 1986 and competition from Nigeria.

Banking and Finance

In November 1972, a new central bank, the Bank of the Central African States (Banque des États de l'Afrique Centrale–BEAC), was established, replacing the Central Bank of the States of Equatorial Africa and Cameroon as the bank of issue. All banking offices closed in 1979 and 1980 when N'Djamena was the scene of heavy fighting in the civil war. The BEAC re-opened in 1981 along with the Development Bank of Chad (BDT). Only the International Bank for Commerce and Industry in Chad (BICIT) had failed to reopen by late 1987, leaving Chad with only three banks plus the central bank.

Economic Development

Foremost among governmental objectives are the expansion and improvement of the transportation network, the expansion and diversification of agriculture, and the attainment of food self-sufficiency. Following the 1994 devaluation of the CFA franc, Chad undertook an IMF-designed economic stabilization plan that included budget reform, the freezing of wage increases, and the introduction of social programs to limit the impact of inflation on the population.

SOCIAL WELFARE

Social services in Chad have been largely disrupted by warfare. Legislation calls for family allowances to be paid to all salaried workers. Political violence, both by the government and by opposition and separatist groups, continues.

Healthcare

In 1993, there was one physician per 30,030 people, and health care was available to only 26% of the population. In 1994, only 29% of the population had access to safe drinking water.

The most common diseases are schistosomiasis, leprosy, malaria, spinal meningitis, tuberculosis, and yaws, as well as malnutrition. The average life expectancy in 1993 was estimated at 48 years, and the overall death rate was 18 per 1,000.

Housing

Forty thousand buildings and homes were destroyed during the civil war. According to the latest available figures for 1980–88, the total housing stock numbered 700,000, with 7.2 people per dwelling.

EDUCATION

The educational system is patterned on the French system, and the language of instruction is French. Education is compulsory between ages 6 and 14, but it is not enforced. Primary education lasts for six years followed by secondary education which lasts for another seven years.

In 1971, the University of Chad was officially opened in N'Djamena. About 3,000 students are enrolled at all higher level institutions in Chad.

1999 KEY EVENTS TIMELINE

February

- Chad receives up to 50,000 refugees from Sudan fleeing ethnic clashes over land and water in Sudan's Western Darfur state.

April

- Chad's president signs a mediation agreement between the Democratic Republic of the Congo's Kabila and Ugandan President Yoweri Museveni in Sirte, Libya, which is to lead to the withdrawl

of foreign forces, including over 2,000 Chadian military.

August

- The World Food Programme dispatches over 2,500 tons of food for 53,000 Chadians to alleviate famine conditions following poor harvests in the country.

September

- Chadian dancers perform with troupes from 19 other African countries in Tripoli, Libya, in celebration of Gaddafi's tenure in office.

November

- Chad is elected to membership of the executive board at the 30th session of the United Nations Education Science and Culture Organisation (UNESCO).

- Royal Dutch Shell and Elf inform Chad's government they are withdrawing from the Chad-Cameroon Petroleum Development and Pipeline (PDP) project. Thousands of citizens march in the streets of Chad's capital to voice their concern. Exxon, the third transnational corporation involved in the project, confirms its continued backing.

- Chad's President Idriss Deby holds talks with Libyan President Moammar Gaddafi in Benghazi, Libya, on armed conflicts in Africa, the progress of the Community of Sahel-Saharan States (COMESSA), and the Syrte Declaration on the setting up of an African union adopted in September at the end of an Organisation of African Unity summit held in Syrte, Libya.

- The Movement for Democracy and Justice, a rebel group fighting the government in the north, claims to have captured the area around Aozou in the Tibesti mountains.

December

- The United States government terminates the family reunion program for Chad and five other African countries.

- President Idriss Deby of Chad appoints his close aide Nagoum Yamassoum to replace Nassour Ouado as prime minister. Nassour Ouado resigned after two years in office.

ANALYSIS OF EVENTS: 1999

BUSINESS AND THE ECONOMY

Chad ranks consistently as one of the poorest countries in the world and has joined with other highly-indebted nations to press the International Monetary Fund (IMF) for a greater say in the poverty-reduction plans that it imposes. The IMF received increasing criticism from a growing number of organizations and countries regarding its structural adjustment policies in 1999, which hit the budgets of social welfare programs of developing nations very hard.

One of the most controversial development projects in Africa remains uncertain at the close of 1999. Originally involving three international companies—Exxon, Elf and Royal Dutch Shell—and strong support from the people of Chad, Elf and Shell removed their backing for the project in November. If completed, the World Bank expects the Petroleum Development and Pipeline Project (PDP) to generate about US$2.5 billion in royalties, tax revenue and dividends for Chad over its 25-year life span. The project involves the extraction and movement of an estimated one billion barrels of oil in the Doba basin of south-western Chad through a 650 mile pipeline to the Kribi port in Cameroon.

Critics of the project—several hundred NGOs, environmental groups, and human rights groups—have numerous complaints. They cite neighboring Nigeria's difficulties with oil exports, list environmental degradation, corruption, loss of agricultural land and conflict between communities over oil revenues when the national government is not stable as issues that need to be clearly addressed in the planning stage before the project proceeds.

In June, Esso presented a 12-volume environmental study in support of the project. The U.N. Development Program came back in favor of the project in August. The World Bank, in attempting to ward off the Nigerian difficulties, imposed prerequisites for oversight and use of the revenues in order for Cameroon and Chad to receive the loans requested to complete the pipeline and gave its formal backing to the project in October. How the World Bank will react to the withdrawal of Elf and Shell was unclear.

Like other Sahelian African countries, Chad had benefited from a good cotton price on the world market. However, at the end of 1999, Sahelian-exporting countries were hit very hard by falling prices. Until this year, cotton production and the price it garnered on the world market had been one of the few bright spots in Chad's economy.

GOVERNMENT AND POLITICS

Since October 1998 and continuing throughout 1999, the government has been plagued by a rebellion in the northern region of Tibesti. One of the leaders of the rebel group—the Movement for Democracy and Justice (MDJT)—is Youssouf Togoimi, who had been Minister of Defense in Deby's government. In July the movement claimed that they would enter the capital by the end of the year; fighting in November, in which the government finally acknowledged casualties, seemed to make their claims seem more valid. The government is currently negotiating with the rebels.

In addition to the military engagements with northern rebels, Chad's government is also supporting Kabila of the Democratic Republic of the Congo with military forces. Reports indicate that Libya is providing some of the financing for Chad's participation in the DRC.

In September, Chad negotiated a cooperation agreement with Sudan. Some of the issues covered in this accord were smuggling, cross-border banditry, refugees, and border demarcation. Also included in the agreement was the formation of a committee to meet with Chadian refugees in Sudan and Sudanian refugees in Chad to encourage them to return to their respective countries. The UNHCR estimates that there are 25,000 Chadian refugees in Cameroon, Central African Republic and Sudan and approximately the same number of Sudanese refugees in Chad, with the latest group seeking refuge from ethnic violence in Southern Darfur Province at the beginning of the year. The UNHCR will be assisting in the repatriation.

CULTURE AND SOCIETY

The World Bank rates Chad as the second poorest nation in the world. Its per capita income is only $100; life expectancy is 50 years, and only about one quarter of the Chadian population of 7,000,000 has access to safe drinking water. Its illiteracy rate is 50% for men, 65% for women, and primary school enrollment is 28%. These stark health and educational figures paint a grim picture for Chad's ability to gain the foreign investment backing the government needs to raise the economic level of its population. In August the people in 11 of the 14 provinces in the country were hit with flooding; thousands of homes were destroyed, 165,000 hectares of farmland went under water and thousands of head of livestock were lost in the disaster. The international community responded with food donations.

The World Bank also pointed out that Chad is one of the African Sahelian countries that nearly excludes girls from formal education, where on average 80 percent of girls are never enrolled. The World Bank's report cites a widespread parental belief in Chad that schooling pushes girls to prostitution and rebellion against both their parents and their husbands. Thus, bride wealth payments for new brides are reduced proportionally to their level of education. A family's need for the labor of school-age girls added to the school fees, uniforms and transportation along with cultural norms of early marriage, initiation ceremonies, bride price and Islamic conservatism in rural areas (not the case in urban areas) work against the education of girls.

DIRECTORY

CENTRAL GOVERNMENT

Head of State

President
Idriss Déby, Office of the President

Prime Minister
Nagoum Yamassoum, Office of the Prime Minister

Ministers

Minister of State
Mahamat Saleh Ahmat, Ministry of State

Minister of Foreign Affairs
Mahamat Saleh Annadif, Ministry of Foreign Affairs

Minister of Mines, Energy and Oil
Abdoulaye Lamana, Ministry of Mines, Energy and Oil

Minister of Finances and Economy
Bichara Chérif Daoussa, Ministry of Finances and Economy

Minister of National Defense and Reinsertion
Oumar Kadjallami Boukar, Ministry of National Defense and Reinsertion

Minister of Interior Security and Decentralization
Oumarou Djibrillah, Ministry of Interior Security and Decentralization

Minister of Justice, Holder of the Seal
Mahamat Limane, Ministry of Justice

Minister of Agriculture
Mohktar Moussa, Ministry of Agriculture

Minister of Livestock
Mahamat Nouri, Ministry of Livestock

Minister of Public Health
Younouss Kedella, Ministry of Public Health

Minister of Higher Education and Scientific Research
Adoum Goudja, Ministry of Higher Education and Scientific Research

Minister of Basic and Secondary Education
Abderahim Breme Hamid, Ministry of Basic and Secondary Education

Minister of Industrial and Commercial Development, and Handicrafts
Djitangar Djibangar, Ministry of Industrial and Commercial Development, and Handicrafts

Minister of Communication, Delegate to the Parliament, Spokesman of the Government
Moussa Dago, Ministry of Communication

Minister of Social Action and Family
Agnes Alafi, Ministry of Social Action and Family

Minister of Environment and Water
Pascal Yoadimnadji, Ministry of Environment and Water

Minister of Touristic Development
Sékimbaye Bessane, Ministry of Touristic Development

Minister of Public Service, Labor, Employment Promotion and Modernization
Mahamoud Hissene Mahamoud, Ministry of Public Service, Labor, Employment Promotion and Modernization

Minister of Public Works, Transportation, Housing and Urban Development
Ahmat Lamine, Ministry of Public Works, Transportation, Housing and Urban Development

Minister of Planning and Territorial
Development
Mahamat Ali Hassan, Ministry of Planning and
Territorial Development

Minister of Posts and Telecommunications
Salibou Garba, Ministry of Posts and
Telecommunications

Minister of Culture, Youth and Sport
Promotion
Nagoum Yamassoum, Ministry of Culture,
Youth and Sport Promotion

POLITICAL ORGANIZATIONS
Mouvement Patriotique du Salue-MPS (Patriotic Salvation Movement)
TITLE: Chairman
NAME: Maldom Bada Abbas

Union Nationale pour la Démocratie et Renouveau-UNDR (National Union for Democracy and Renewal)
TITLE: Leader
NAME: Saleh Kebzabo

Union pour Réenouvea et la Démocratie-URD (Union for Renewal and Democracy)
TITLE: Leader
NAME: Wadal Abdelkader Kamouqué

Rally for Democracy and Progress (RDP)
TITLE: Leader
NAME: Lal Mahamat Choua

DIPLOMATIC REPRESENTATION
Embassies in Chad
France
Rue du Lieutenant-Franjoux, BP 431
N'Djamena, Chad
PHONE: +235 512575

United States
Avenue Felkix Eboue, N'Djamena, B.P. 413,
Chad
PHONE: +235 517009; 519052; 519233
FAX: +235 515654
TITLE: Ambassador
NAME: David C. Halstead

JUDICIAL SYSTEM
Supreme Court
Court of Appeal
Criminal Courts
Magistrate Courts

FURTHER READING
Internet
Africa News Online. Available Online @ http://www.africanews.org/south/mozambique (November 25, 1999).

Chad Embassy. Available Online @ http://www.chadembassy.org/ (December 3, 1999).

Durbin, Andrea. "In Focus: World Bank's Private Sector Agenda." *Friends of the Earth.* Available Online @ http://www.igc.org/infocus/briefs/vol3/v3n40bank.html (December 1, 1999).

ExxonMobil. Chad Cameroon Development Project. Available Online @ http://www.exxon.com/essochad/ (December 1, 1999).

Horta, Korinna. "Questions Concerning The World Bank and Chad/Cameroon Oil and Pipeline Project." *Environmental Defense Fund.* Available Online @ http://www.chadembassy.org/ (December 3, 1999).

Integrated Regional Information Network, United Nations Office for the Coordination of Humanitarian Affairs. Available Online @ http://www.reliefweb.int/IRIN/archive/chad.htm (November 25, 1999).

CHAD: STATISTICAL DATA

For sources and notes see "Sources of Statistics" in the front of each volume.

GEOGRAPHY

Geography (1)

Area:

Total: 1.284 million sq km.

Land: 1,259,200 sq km.

Water: 24,800 sq km.

Area—comparative: slightly more than three times the size of California.

Land boundaries:

Total: 5,968 km.

Border countries: Cameroon 1,094 km, Central African Republic 1,197 km, Libya 1,055 km, Niger 1,175 km, Nigeria 87 km, Sudan 1,360 km.

Coastline: 0 km (landlocked).

Climate: tropical in south, desert in north.

Terrain: broad, arid plains in center, desert in north, mountains in northwest, lowlands in south.

Natural resources: petroleum (unexploited but exploration under way), uranium, natron, kaolin, fish (Lake Chad).

Land use:

Arable land: 3%

Permanent crops: 0%

Permanent pastures: 36%

Forests and woodland: 26%

Other: 35% (1993 est.).

HUMAN FACTORS

Demographics (2A)

	1990	1995	1998	2000	2010	2020	2030	2040	2050
Population	5,888.6	6,784.5	7,359.5	7,760.3	10,054.7	12,830.6	15,950.9	19,230.6	22,503.9
Net migration rate (per 1,000 population)	NA	NA	NA	NA	NA	NA	NA	NA	NA
Births	NA	NA	NA	NA	NA	NA	NA	NA	NA
Deaths	NA	NA	NA	NA	NA	NA	NA	NA	NA
Life expectancy - males	43.3	44.9	45.8	46.5	49.7	53.1	56.5	59.8	62.9
Life expectancy - females	47.9	49.7	50.7	51.5	55.2	58.9	62.5	66.0	69.2
Birth rate (per 1,000)	44.8	44.6	43.5	42.8	38.9	34.6	29.8	25.5	22.1
Death rate (per 1,000)	18.9	17.7	16.9	16.3	13.6	11.4	9.6	8.4	7.8
Women of reproductive age (15-49 yrs.)	1,371.3	1,569.6	1,700.1	1,794.7	2,384.8	3,167.2	4,107.3	5,125.1	6,072.2
of which are currently married	NA	NA	NA	NA	NA	NA	NA	NA	NA
Fertility rate	5.9	5.9	5.7	5.6	5.0	4.3	3.6	3.0	2.6

Except as noted, values for vital statistics are in thousands; life expectancy is in years.

Health Personnel (3)

Total health expenditure as a percentage of GDP, 1990-1997[a]

Public sector 1.6

Private sector 0.1

Total[b] 2.7

Health expenditure per capita in U.S. dollars, 1990-1997[a]

Purchasing power parity 33

Total 6

Availability of health care facilities per 100,000 people

Hospital beds 1990-1997[a] 70

Doctors 1993[c] 2

Nurses 1993[c] 6

Health Indicators (4)

Life expectancy at birth

1980 42

1997 49

Daily per capita supply of calories (1996) 1,972

Total fertility rate births per woman (1997) 6.5

Maternal mortality ratio per 100,000 live births (1990-97) . . . . .840[d]

Safe water % of population with access (1995) 24

Sanitation % of population with access (1995) 21

Consumption of iodized salt % of households (1992-98)[a] 55

Smoking prevalence

Male % of adults (1985-95)[a] . . . .

Female % of adults (1985-95)[a] . . . .

Tuberculosis incidence per 100,000 people (1997) 205

Adult HIV prevalence % of population ages 15-49 (1997) 2.72

Infants and Malnutrition (5)

Under-5 mortality rate (1997) 198

% of infants with low birthweight (1990-97) . . . . . .NA

Births attended by skilled health staff % of total[a] . . .15

% fully immunized (1995-97)

TB 36

DPT 16

Polio 15

Measles 17

Prevalence of child malnutrition under age 5 (1992-97)[b] 39

Ethnic Division (6)

Muslims (Arabs, Toubou, Hadjerai, Fulbe, Kotoko, Kanembou, Baguirmi, Boulala, Zaghawa, and Maba), non-Muslims (Sara, Ngambaye, Mbaye, Goulaye, Moundang, Moussei, Massa), non-indigenous 150,000 (of whom 1,000 are French).

Religions (7)

Muslim 50%

Christian 25%

Indigenous beliefs 25%

Indigenous beliefs are mostly animism.

Languages (8)

French (official), Arabic (official), Sara and Sango (in south), more than 100 different languages and dialects.

EDUCATION

Public Education Expenditures (9)

Public expenditure on education (% of GNP)

1980 . . . .

1996 . . . . .2.4[1]

Expenditure per student

Primary % of GNP per capita

1980 . . . .

1996 . . . . .9.0

Secondary % of GNP per capita

1980 . . . .

1996 . . . .

Tertiary % of GNP per capita

1980 . . . .

1996 . . . .

Expenditure on teaching materials

Primary % of total for level (1996) . . . .

Secondary % of total for level (1996) . . . .

Primary pupil-teacher ratio per teacher (1996) 67

Duration of primary education years (1995) 6

Literacy Rates (11A)

In thousands and percent[1]	1990	1995	2000	2010
Illiterate population (15+ yrs.)	1,804	1,868	1,939	1,988
Literacy rate - total adult pop. (%)	42.7	48.1	53.5	63.6
Literacy rate - males (%)	57.1	62.1	66.9	75.0
Literacy rate - females (%)	29.0	34.7	40.7	52.7

GOVERNMENT & LAW

Political Parties (12)

National Assembly	No. of seats
Patriotic Salvation Movement (MPS)	.65
Union for Renewal and Democracy (URD)	.29
National Union for Development and Renewal (UNDR)	.15
Rally for Democracy and Progress (RDP)	.3
Others	.13

In mid-1996 Chad had about 60 political parties, of which these are the most prominent in the new National Assembly.

Government Budget (13B)

Revenues	.$198 million
Expenditures	.$218 million
Capital expenditures	.$146 million

Data for 1998 est.

LABOR FORCE

Labor Force (16)

Agriculture 85% (subsistence farming, herding, and fishing).

Unemployment Rate (17)

Rate not available.

Military Affairs (14B)

	1990	1991	1992	1993	1994	1995
Military expenditures						
Current dollars (mil.)	NA	49[e]	26[e]	NA	33	34
1995 constant dollars (mil.)	NA	54[e]	28[e]	NA	34	34
Armed forces (000)	50	50	30[e]	30	30	30
Gross national product (GNP)						
Current dollars (mil.)	838	922	967	976	1,038	1,117
1995 constant dollars (mil.)	963	1,019	1,040	1,024	1,064	1,117
Central government expenditures (CGE)						
1995 constant dollars (mil.)	313	327	291[9]	NA	NA	NA
People (mil.)	5.9	6.0	6.2	6.4	6.6	6.8
Military expenditure as % of GNP	NA	5.3	2.7	NA	3.2	3.1
Military expenditure as % of CGE	NA	16.6	9.7	NA	NA	NA
Military expenditure per capita (1995 $)	NA	9	5	NA	5	5
Armed forces per 1,000 people (soldiers)	8.5	8.3	4.8	4.7	4.6	4.4
GNP per capita (1994 $)	164	169	167	160	161	165
Arms imports[6]						
Current dollars (mil.)	50	10	10	5	40	10
1995 constant dollars (mil.)	57	11	11	5	41	10
Arms exports[6]						
Current dollars (mil.)	0	0	0	0	0	0
1995 constant dollars (mil.)	0	0	0	0	0	0
Total imports[7]						
Current dollars (mil.)	286	250	243	201	177	220
1995 constant dollars (mil.)	329	276	261	211	181	220
Total exports[7]						
Current dollars (mil.)	188	194	182	132	148	252
1995 constant dollars (mil.)	216	214	196	138	152	252
Arms as percent of total imports[8]	17.5	4.0	4.1	2.5	22.6	4.5
Arms as percent of total exports[8]	0	0	0	0	0	0

PRODUCTION SECTOR

Electric Energy (18)

Capacity . . . . .29,000 kW (1995)

Production . . . . .80 million kWh (1995)

Consumption per capita . . . . .14 kWh (1995)

Transportation (19)

Highways:

total: 32,700 km

paved: 262 km

unpaved: 32,438 km (1995 est.)

Waterways: 2,000 km navigable

Airports: 53 (1997 est.)

Airports—with paved runways:

total: 6

over 3,047 m: 1

2,438 to 3,047 m: 2

1,524 to 2,437 m: 2

under 914 m: 1 (1997 est.)

Airports—with unpaved runways:

total: 47

1,524 to 2,437 m: 16

914 to 1,523 m: 21

under 914 m: 10 (1997 est.)

Top Agricultural Products (20)

Cotton, sorghum, millet, peanuts, rice, potatoes, manioc (tapioca); cattle, sheep, goats, camels.

FINANCE, ECONOMICS, & TRADE

Economic Indicators (22)

National product: GDP—purchasing power parity—$4.3 billion (1997 est.)

National product real growth rate: 5.5% (1997 est.)

National product per capita: $600 (1997 est.)

Inflation rate—consumer price index: 15% (1997 est.)

Exchange Rates (24)

Exchange rates:

CFA Francs (CFAF) per US$1

January 1998	.608.36
1997	.583.67
1996	.511.55
1995	.499.15
1994	.555.20
1993	.283.16

Beginning 12 January 1994 the CFA franc was devalued to CFAF 100 per French franc from CFAF 50 at which it had been fixed since 1948.

Top Import Origins (25)

$301 million (f.o.b., 1996 est.)

Origins	%
Singapore	.NA
Vietnam	.NA
Japan	.NA
Australia	.NA
Hong Kong	.NA
Indonesia	.NA

NA stands for not available.

MANUFACTURING SECTOR

GDP & Manufacturing Summary (21)

	1980	1985	1990	1992	1993	1994
Gross Domestic Product						
Millions of 1990 dollars	722	1,107	1,213	1,197	1,162	1,246
Growth rate in percent	−7.40	21.90	−2.70	0.32	−2.90	7.20
Per capita (in 1990 dollars)	161.4	220.6	218.4	204.7	193.3	201.5
Manufacturing Value Added						
Millions of 1990 dollars	125	239	174	161	156	*166*
Growth rate in percent	−12.00	−6.65	−38.84	−6.59	−3.04	*6.40*
Manufacturing share in percent of current prices	22.9	11.1	15.4	11.1	14.1	*13.4*

FINANCE, ECONOMICS, & TRADE

Top Export Destinations (26)

$259 million (f.o.b., 1996 est.).

Destinations	%
Portugal	.30
Germany	.18
South Africa	.16
France	.7

Economic Aid (27)

Recipient: $125 million committed by Taiwan (August 1997); $30 million committed by African Development Bank.

Import Export Commodities (28)

Import Commodities	Export Commodities
Machinery and transportation equipment 39%	Cotton
	Cattle
Industrial goods 20%	Textiles
Petroleum products 13%	
Foodstuffs 9%; textiles;	

Balance of Payments (23)

	1990	1991	1992	1993	1994
Exports of goods (f.o.b.)	230	194	182	152	135
Imports of goods (f.o.b.)	−260	−250	−243	−215	−212
Trade balance	−29	−56	−61	−64	−77
Services - debits	−252	−219	−239	−251	−212
Services - credits	44	40	44	51	60
Private transfers (net)	205	182	199	176	199
Government transfers (net)	−13	−12	−29	−29	−8
Overall balance	−46	−66	−86	117	−38

CHILE

Republic of Chile
República de Chile

INTRODUCTORY SURVEY

RECENT HISTORY

After World War II, Chile, an example of stability by Latin American standards for so long, seethed with tension. Its pursuit of industrialization between the world wars had led to increasing social problems as the cities had many unemployable rural workers. As the cost of living soared, riots and strikes broke out throughout the country.

The 1952 election brought 75-year-old former president Carlos Ibáñez del Campo back to power. Despite his reputation as an authoritarian and his connection with Argentina's leader Juan Perón, Ibáñez ruled democratically until 1958.

A devastating earthquake and tidal wave in 1960 cut drastically into the programs of newly elected president Jorge Alessandri Rodríguez, and his government was unable to regain momentum. In September 1964, Eduardo Frei Montalva, candidate of the new Christian Democratic Party, was elected by an absolute majority.

The Frei government implemented educational reform, land reform, and a program to give Chile majority ownership of its copper mines. Under Frei, Chile became a cornerstone of the Alliance for Progress, a harsh critic of communism, and a leading exponent of Christian democracy. However, the Frei administration was not able to control the chronic inflation that has plagued Chile for more than eighty years.

The 1970 presidential election was won by socialist Senator Salvador Allende. The victory

CHILE

0   200   400 Miles

0   200   400 Kilometers

BOLIVIA

PACIFIC
OCEAN

PARAGUAY

Arica
Iquique
Atacama
Loa
Calama
Antofagasta
Desert

Mt. Ojos
del Salado
22,572 ft.
6880 m.

Isla San Ambrosio
Isla San Felix

Copiapó
Copiapó

La Serena

ARGENTINA

San Felipe
Mt. Tupungato
22,310 ft.
6800 m.
Viña del Mar
Valparaíso
Santiago
Rancagua
Talca
Maule

Isla
Juan Fernández

MOUNTAINS

Concepción
Chillán
Lebu
Bío-Bío
Valdivia
Toltén
Osorno
Puerto Montt

Sala y
Gómez

Isla de Pascua
(Easter I.)

Vaihú

Ancud
Isla Grande
de Chiloé

Archipélago
de los
Chonos

ANDES

Negro

Chubut

Mt. San Valentin
13,314 ft.
4038 m.

Península
Taitao

Chile

Estrecho de
Magallanes

TIERRA DEL
FUEGO

Punta Arenas

Cabo de
Hornos

On 11 September 1973, the Allende government was violently overthrown. Allende himself was assassinated—officially reported as a suicide. A four-man junta (military group) headed by General Augusto Pinochet Ugarte seized power, dissolved Congress, and banned all political activities. At least 2,500 (and possibly as many as 10,000) people were killed during and immediately after the coup (takeover). The military declared a state of siege, and assumed dictatorial powers.

During its sixteen years in power, the military attempted to return the Chilean economy to private ownership. However, while doing so it tried to maintain dictatorial control of the population, which was continually placed under ever-renewed states of siege.

Although forced to operate in secret, an opposition still emerged. The Catholic Church had become increasingly critical of the Pinochet regime, and when Pope John Paul II visited Chile in 1987, he brought accusations of torture and other human rights abuses. Finally, in 1988, Pinochet called for an election to determine whether he should remain president for another eight years. He was soundly defeated. Pinochet continued to serve as the head of Chile's military until 1998.

In 1989, new elections were held. Christian Democrat Patricio Aylwin, running as the candidate of a seventeen-party Concert of Parties for Democracy was elected and assumed office in 1990. Although Aylwin had some difficult times, he completed his term, and Chilean economic performance improved. In the elections of December 1993, voters gave the Christian Democratic Party candidate, Eduardo Frei Ruiz-Tagle, an impressive 58% of the vote.

Frei has continued the economic policies of his predecessor, and by 1997, the country had achieved fourteen consecutive years of economic growth. Its commitment to democratic, representative government appears secure and stable.

GOVERNMENT

The 1980 constitution, as amended in 1989, provides for a strong executive with a four-year term. The president has the authority to proclaim a state of emergency for up to twenty days. He can dissolve Congress and call for new elections once per term. The president can also introduce legislation. There is a two-chamber National Congress, consisting of a 120-member Chamber of Deputies and a 46-member Senate. The constitution also

was unique in that for the first time in the Western Hemisphere, a Marxist candidate took office by means of a free election. Allende called for a socialist economy, a new, leftist constitution, and full diplomatic and trade relations with Cuba, China, and other communist countries.

After an initial rise in employment and prosperity, the economy began to lag. In June 1973, against a backdrop of strikes and street brawls, a failed coup attempt was staged by a rightist army contingent.

provides for an independent judiciary, headed by a seventeen-member Supreme Court.

Judiciary

The judiciary remains subject to criticism for inefficiency and lack of independence. Reforms passed in 1991 (the *cumplido* laws), however, transferred some of the jurisdiction of the military tribunals to the civilian courts.

Political Parties

The re-emergence of political parties in the aftermath of Pinochet has been dramatic. The ruling Concert of Parties for Democracy includes four major parties: the Christian Democrats (PDC), the Party for Democracy (PPD), the Radical Party (PR), and the Socialist Party (PS). The opposition from the right comes from the Independent Democratic Union (UDI) and the National Renewal (RN), which controlled the Senate until 1993. The Chilean Communist Party (PCCh) and the Allende Leftist Democratic Movement (MIDA) remain active, although they lack any representation in Congress.

DEFENSE

Chilean males between the ages of 14 and 49 are eligible for military service, but only about 15,000 are called up from a pool of over 100,000 each year. The army had 51,700 personnel in 1995, the navy 24,000, and the air force 14,000 regulars and 1,000 conscripts (draftees). After their active service, Chilean men serve in the reserve (estimated at 50,000 active in 1995). Defense expenditures were $1.9 billion in 1995, or about 3.6% of gross domestic product (GDP).

ECONOMIC AFFAIRS

The Chilean economy is strongly oriented toward commerce and industry, although minerals, chiefly copper and iron ore, provide most of the country's foreign exchange earnings. Chile's leading industries process local raw materials; they include metallurgy, petroleum products, textiles— both wool and synthetics—and paper products. Chilean agriculture, dwarfed in value by mining and manufacturing, supports less than one-sixth of the population. Fertile land is limited, and livestock raising is the main rural enterprise.

In the 1990s, the Chilean economy completed a decade of strong and sustained expansion. The most active areas were construction, trade, and services, while agriculture and fishing showed the slowest growth. Unemployment was 6.6% in 1996.

Public Finance

Chile experienced budget deficits from the early 1960s through the mid-1970s. Expenditures grew steadily with the expansion of public-sector participation in social welfare and economic activities and with increasing government investment in development projects; the resulting deficits were covered by Central Bank loans and foreign borrowing. Budgetary surpluses were recorded from 1975 through 1981, after which the pattern reverted to deficits. From 1985 to 1993, Chile reduced its external debt by $11.3 billion through debt-equity conversions. In 1994, interest on the debt was equivalent to 4.4% of current revenue.

The U.S. CIA estimates that, in 1995, government revenues totaled approximately $17 billion and expenditures $17 billion. External debt totaled $21.1 billion.

Income

In 1998, Chile's gross national product (GNP) was $71.3 billion at current prices, or $4,810 per person. For the period 1985–95 the average inflation rate was 17.9%, resulting in a real growth rate in GNP of 6.1% per person.

Industry

Chile ranks among the most highly industrialized Latin American countries. Key industries include textiles, automobiles, chemicals, rubber products, steel, cement, and consumer goods.

Output of selected industrial products in 1995 included refined copper, 1.5 million tons; crude steel, 1.0 million tons; ferroalloys, 19,500 tons; and cement, 2.9 million tons. Chile produced 46.9 million barrels of refined petroleum products in 1995, including 18.5 million barrels of distillate fuel oil and 13.5 million barrels of gasoline.

Banking and Finance

During the Allende period, almost all private banks were taken over by the government, mainly through the purchase of stock. The military government reversed its predecessor's policy, and now the financial market is essentially private. In 1985, Chile had, in addition to the Central Bank, 18 domestic banks and 7 finance societies.

As of 1992, Central Bank foreign assets stood at p5,238.5 billion. Commercial bank reserves amounted to p528.6 billion; time, savings and foreign currency deposits, p4,596.7 billion; and demand deposits, p456.7 billion. The total money supply, as measured by M2, was p5,838 billion.

Securities trading has been traditionally inhibited by the Chilean investors' preference for real estate investment. Chronic inflation also has had a disruptive effect upon stock exchange transactions. There is free sale of securities, the largest groups of which are in mining, banking, textile, agricultural, metallurgical, and insurance stocks. All corporations with more than 100 shareholders must register with a stock exchange.

In 1995, 284 companies were listed on the Bolsa de Comercio de Santiago, (BCS), which was founded in 1893.

Economic Development

Chile has established two free trade zones: the Free Zone of Iquique (ZOFRI) in the northern tip (Region I), and the Free Zone of Punta Arenas (PARANEZON) in the southern tip (Region XII). Chile has been negotiating for admission into NAFTA since 1994, but the process has been stalled by the United States Congress. Chile also has become a member of the South American Mercosur free-trade bloc. Through its concentration on value-added exports and increased foreign direct investment, Chile has become one of Latin America's most developed nations.

SOCIAL WELFARE

Prior to the 1973 coup, Chile had built one of the most comprehensive social welfare systems in the world, with over fifty separate agencies participating in programs. Following the military's takeover of power in 1973, many of the welfare benefits were stopped temporarily, and regulations lapsed. From 1974 to 1981, the junta (military officers holding state powers) remodeled the welfare system along the lines of private enterprise.

Social security covers all members of the work force and their dependents. The system includes pensions, family allowances, medical care, sickness benefits, and unemployment compensation.

A 1989 law removed many restrictions on women, although some legal distinctions exist, and divorce is illegal. It has been estimated that one in four Chilean women have been subject to domestic abuse.

Healthcare

As of 1993, Chile's budget for the public health sector increased for the fourth consecutive year. In 1995, 97% of the population had access to health care services.

An estimated 15% of Chileans in the early 1980s, including 10% of children under the age of five, fell below the minimum nutritional requirements established by the UN Food and Agriculture Organization (FAO). Protein deficiency among the general population has induced an abnormally high rate of congenital mental handicap. However, Chile has made excellent progress in raising health standards: the infant mortality rate declined from 147 per 1,000 live births in 1948 to 12 in 1994. Average life expectancy in 1993 was 75 years.

Housing

In 1991, the total housing stock numbered 3.3 million. The number of new dwellings completed jumped from 88,000 in 1991 to 106,000 in 1992.

EDUCATION

The adult illiteracy rate, estimated at 50% in 1920, had been reduced to 5% by 1995, according to UNESCO.

All state schools provide free education. An eight-year primary and four-year secondary program, with increased emphasis on vocational instruction at the secondary level, was introduced. In 1994, enrollment in secondary and professional schools was 664,498 (general: 387,272 and vocational: 277,226).

The University of Chile (founded as Universidad Real de San Felipe in 1738) and the University of Santiago de Chile are national universities with branches in other cities. Higher educational enrollment was approximately 342,788 in 1995.

1999 KEY EVENTS TIMELINE

January

- Former Chilean dictator General Augusto Pinochet said he is resigned to dying in Britain. British police arrested Pinochet on October 16, 1998 at a London hospital where he was recovering from back surgery. Spanish authorities filed the extradition warrant for alleged torture and murder during 1973–90 dictatorship.

April

- Chilean journalist Alejandra Matus publishes a highly critical book about the Chilean Supreme Court. She is forced to leave the country after the former president of the court stops her book's distribution.

- Raul Silva Henriquez, a vocal opponent of Pinochet's rule and defender of the oppressed, dies on April 9. He was 91.

July

- The United States releases 5,800 formerly classified documents about the 1973 military coup. The documents are released to the National Archives, and are to be posted on the Internet. Chilean authorities welcome the release of the documents, as do human rights lawyers who expect to use the information against Pinochet.

- Socialist Ricardo Lagos is the frontrunner in Chile's presidential elections. He insists Socialists have become Social Democrats.

August

- Blind protesters walk for three days to the Chilean Congress to demand jobs.

- The government expects to have its first fiscal deficit in 13 years and Chile faces a recession.

September

- Heavy snow and torrential rains end the longest drought on record this century. Three Chileans die in the storms.

- Chile expects four percent growth in final quarter, which may be enough to pull the nation out of its worst recession in 20 years.

- Gustavo Leigh, the former head of the Chilean Air Force, and one of the original members of the four-man military junta led by Pinochet, dies of vascular problems. He was 79.

October

- The U.S. Central Intelligence Agency could have played a pivotal role in the death of U.S. journalist Charles Horman, according to formerly classified documents released by the government. Horman, whose life was the subject of the 1982 film "Missing," was murdered by the Chilean military after the September 11, 1973 coup.

- The Chilean Supreme Court considers an Italian extradition request for former secret police commander Manuel Contreras, who is serving a sentence in Chile for planning an assassination in Washington D.C. In the Italian case, Contreras was sentenced in absentia to 20 years for planning the assassination of a former Chilean president living in Rome.

- A London court ruled that Pinochet may be extradited to Spain to stand trial on one charge of conspiracy to torture and 34 charges of torturing individual Chileans. The decision can be appealed.

November

- Joaquin Lavin, presidential candidate of Chile's right-wing parties, appeals to poor voters, and polls show him almost tied with the Concertacion's candidate, Ricardo Lagos.

- Chile's central bank declares an end to 12 months of recession.

- Chile's business community is angry about government plans to push labor law reforms through parliament before the December 12th presidential elections.

December

- Businesses welcome the Chilean senate's rejection of a labor reform bill that promised collective bargaining for an extra 2.5 million workers.

- Ricardo Lagos, candidate for president of the ruling Socialist-Christian Democratic coalition, is disappointed in the results of the December 12 first round of voting. He faces Joaquin Lavin, candidate of the conservative coalition, in the January 16, 2000 runoff.

ANALYSIS OF EVENTS: 1999

BUSINESS AND THE ECONOMY

The December 1999 presidential elections have been muddled by an unexpected dip in the economy. Ever since the right-wing coup against Chile's socialist government in 1973, Chile has set the standard for creating a business-friendly climate for foreign investors. The result was a generally expansive economy from the mid-1970s through the 1990s. Chile faced its first serious recession in 1999. The real gross domestic product fell 2.8 percent in the last quarter of 1998, and was expected to shrink by another 2.8 percent in the first quarter of 1999.

Chilean economists blamed a dip in world copper prices and a decrease in tax collections. By June, unemployment reached almost 11 percent, with 620,000 people out of work. Frei's government announced that it would spend $90 million to create about 64,000 jobs between September and December. The government also planned to sell its water utilities and rights to operate state-owned ports. In August, it raised $300 million in three port auctions.

By September, forecasts were slightly more positive. Chile's finance minister Eduardo Aninat said the country would rise from its worst recession in 20 years, and grow by 4 percent in the last quarter of 1999. Yet, Chile was expected to end 1999 with a growth rate of around 0 percent. The International Monetary Fund predicted a 0.4 percent contraction for the year.

GOVERNMENT AND POLITICS

As much as some Chileans may have wanted to forget the past, events in 1999 would not let them. The arrest of former dictator Augusto Pinochet in England in October 1998, at the request of Spanish authorities, reminded the world of the brutal excesses of the 1973–90 dictatorship, when thousands of Chileans were arrested, tortured and murdered. Other European nations sought to extradite Pinochet, who had been untouchable in his own country. In mid-1999, the United States released 5,800 formerly classified documents on Pinochet and his government. And a key document released in October showed the Central Intelligence Agency may have played a prominent role in the murder of a U.S. journalist during the first days of the coup.

Some of the general's most notorious subordinates faced charges in Chile and abroad. One of them was Manuel Contreras, who planned and ordered assassinations in Washington D.C. and Italy. In Chile, judges found a loophole in the 1978 amnesty law, which covered crimes between 1973 and 1978. Chilean judges said "disappearances" were equivalent to kidnappings, and were not covered under amnesty. Prominent former military leaders were arrested, leading to serious conflict between the armed forces and the civilian government of President Eduardo Frei.

In England, Pinochet insisted he had nothing to do with the tortures and killings. It was not possible

to keep on eye on all of his underlings, he said. Pinochet also declared that Spain, whose human rights record remains tarnished from the days of the Spanish Civil War (1936–39), had no right to interfere in Chilean affairs. But Spanish authorities said Pinochet was directly responsible for crimes committed against Chileans as well as some Spanish citizens living in Chile at the time. Under international law, this could force Pinochet to face a Spanish judge. Pinochet and his foes spent most of 1999 arguing in British court. The international community and nervous former dictators followed the case closely. International law was being redefined, according to law experts.

In October, Spanish authorities claimed partial victory when a London court ruled Pinochet could be extradited to Spain to stand trial on one charge of conspiracy to torture and 34 charges of torturing individual Chileans. Pinochet's lawyers were expected to appeal. In Chile reaction was mixed. Chileans of both the right and the left have slowly adjusted to Pinochet's forced absence. But even without him, the nation remained highly polarized by one of its most controversial figures. The right, especially the right upper class, staunchly supported him. The mood of the Chilean middle class was harder to gauge. Many worried what the Spanish extradition request would do to Chilean—or to any country's—national sovereignty. Frei and Pinochet's supporters in the military agreed on one thing: Pinochet's arrest had violated Chilean sovereignty.

A dictator for 17 years, Pinochet remained leader of the armed forces after giving up power in 1990. When he retired from the military in 1998, he became a senator for life, and enjoyed unwavering support from the armed forces. Until his arrest, the military was untouchable. Not so now. Military leaders, threatened by Supreme Court actions, are talking directly to human rights lawyers, a remarkable development. The military has admitted that victims' families have a right to know what happened. That could mean recovering the bodies of the "disappeared."

Chile weathered the storm and a return to military rule seemed quite unlikely. Presidential elections were scheduled for December 1999, and to the consternation of the right, the socialist Ricardo Lagos was a leading candidate. To leftists, Lagos is really a centrist. Lagos has distanced himself from former President Salvador Allende, the Marxist leader who died during the 1973 coup. Lagos is a member of the *Concertación*, the center-left coalition that has held power since the country's return to democracy in 1990. The right has never managed more than 30 percent in elections, and the Pinochet case is not likely to help their cause. Although he runs as a conservative, Joaquin Lavin, a popular mayor of the wealthy Las Condes Santiago suburb, has distanced himself from the harsh politics of the right. Lavin has softened his image by visiting some of the poorest neighborhoods and spending the night with some of the families he meets. But political observers do not believe he has a chance against the popular Lagos.

CULTURE AND SOCIETY

In August, President Eduardo Frei promised the government would give more than $275 million in economic aid to the indigenous Mapuche of southern Chile. The money would be used to build roads and bilingual schools, write off debts, and give scholarship to Mapuche children. For the Mapuches, ostracized by most Chileans, it was a step in the right direction. There are about 1 million Mapuches living in Chile, a country of 15 million people. Most Mapuches live in their traditional homeland, and in recent years, they have become more vocal about their rights.

In April, a Supreme Court judge stopped the distribution of a book by Chilean journalist Alejandra Matus, citing state security concerns. The investigative "Black Book of Chilean Justice" took a highly critical look at the Supreme Court, accusing its members of nepotism, abuse of power, and unprofessional behavior, among many other charges. Matus asserts the court was incapable of defending human rights and stopping military violations during the dictatorship of 1973–90.

Matus fled the country to avoid arrest while a small press run of 3,000 books languished in storage. Judge Servando Jordán, a prominent subject of the book, stopped its distribution. The Chilean newspaper La Tercera posted the book at a U.S. Internet site to circumvent Chilean law. Within a week, the site posted more than 90,000 hits. Hundreds of emails praised the newspaper for publishing the book.

The death of Chilean cardinal Raul Silva Henriquez on April 9 saddened many Chileans. The priest was one of the most visible defenders of Pinochet's victims. He often took positions that displeased the military dictatorship as well as the Vatican, which declined to condemn the regime publicly. While not a supporter of liberation ideology, Silva Henriquez championed the people's rights during the period of military rule. From his pulpit, he called for an end to the dictatorship and set up a network to help victims. In time he became a major player in the country's transition to democracy, and many Chileans urged him to seek the presidency.

DIRECTORY

CENTRAL GOVERNMENT

Head of State

President
Eduardo Frei Ruiz-Tagle, Office of the President, Palacio de la Moneda, Santiago, Chile
PHONE: +56 (2) 6904362; 6904921
FAX: +56 (2) 6904020
E-MAIL: webmaster@presidencia.cl

Ministers

Minister of Justice
María Soledad Alvear, Ministry of Justice, Morandé 107, Clasificador 69, Santiago, Chile
PHONE: +56 (2) 6743100
E-MAIL: minju@reuna.cl

Minister of Agriculture
Angel Sartori Arellano, Ministry of Agriculture
E-MAIL: webmaster@minagri.gob.cl

Minister of the Interior
Raúl Troncoso Castillo, Ministry of the Interior, Palacio de La Moneda, Santiago, Chile
PHONE: +56 (2) 6904000
FAX: +56 (2) 6990394

Minister of Public Works
Jaime Toha, Ministry of Public Works
E-MAIL: webmaste@mop.cl

Minister of Public Domains
Sergio Galilea Ocón, Ministry of Public Domains, Juan Antonio Rios 6, Santiago, Chile
PHONE: +56 (2) 6339305
FAX: +56 (2) 6339316
E-MAIL: consultas@mbienes.cl

Minister of the Economy
Jorge Leiva Lavalle, Ministry of the Economy, Teatinos 120, Piso 10, Santiago, Chile
PHONE: +56 (2) 6725522
FAX: +56 (2) 6966305

Minister of Education
José Pablo Arellano Marín, Ministry of
Education
E-MAIL: info@neruda.mineduc.cl.

Minister of Finance
Eduardo Aninat Ureta, Ministry of Finance
E-MAIL: webmaster@minhda.cl

Minister of Planning and Development
Germán Quintana, Ministry of Planning and
Development, Ahumada 48, Piso 4, 6500748
Santiago, Chile
PHONE: +56 (2) 6751400
E-MAIL: info@mideplan.cl

Minister of Foreign Relations
Juan Gabriel Valdes Soublette, Ministry of
Foreign Relations, Bandera N° 52, Piso 5,
Santiago, Chile
PHONE: +56 (2) 6983502; 6710396
FAX: +56 (2) 6971909
E-MAIL: difrol2@minrel.cl

Minister of Health
Alex Figueroa, Ministry of Health

POLITICAL ORGANIZATIONS

Partido Demócrata Cristiano (DC)

TITLE: Presidente
NAME: Enrique Krauss

Partido por la Democracia (PPD)

TITLE: Presidente
NAME: Sergio Bitar

Partido Radical Socialdemócrata

TITLE: Presidente
NAME: Anselmo Sule

Partido Renovación Nacional (RN)

TITLE: Presidente
NAME: Alberto Espina

Partido Socialista de Chile (PS)

TITLE: Presidente
NAME: Camilo Escalona

Partido Unión de Centro Centro Progresista (UCCP)

TITLE: Presidente
NAME: Alfredo García-Huidobro

Partido Unión Demócrata Independiente (UDI)

TITLE: Presidente
NAME: Pablo Longueira

DIPLOMATIC REPRESENTATION

Embassies in Chile

Argentina
Miraflores 285, Santiago, Chile
PHONE: +56 6331076; 6331078; 6380890
FAX: +56 6393321
TITLE: Ministro Consejero
NAME: Horacio Wamba

Australia
Gertrudis Eche-ique N° 420, Casilla 33, Correo
10, Las Condes, Santiago, Chile
PHONE: +56 2285065; 2285172
FAX: +56 2064261; 2081707; 2080328
E-MAIL: austemb@entelchile.net
TITLE: Embajadora Extraordinaria y
Plenipotenciaria
NAME: Susan Tanner

Bolivia
Avda Santa Maria 2796, Santiago, Chile
PHONE: +56 (2) 2328180
FAX: +56 (2) 2329839

Brazil
Mac-Iver 225, Piso 15, Edificio Banco Exterior,
Casilla 1110, Chile
PHONE: +56 (2) 6398867
FAX: +56 (2) 6336848
E-MAIL: cobrachi@ctc-mundo.net

Canada
Nueva Tajamar 481, Piso 12, Edificio World
Trade Center, Torre norte, Santiago, Chile
PHONE: +56 (2) 3629660
FAX: +56 (2) 3629663
E-MAIL: stago@dfait-maeci.gc.ca
TITLE: Ambassador
NAME: Lawrence D. Lederman

China
Av. Pedro De Valdivia 550, CP 3417,
Providencia
PHONE: +56 2339880
FAX: +56 2341129; 3352755
TITLE: Embajador Extraordinario y
Plenipotenciario
NAME: Zhang Shaying

COLOR FLAGS, SEALS AND REGIONAL MAPS

Color seals for Guadeloupe, Martinique and Serbia are not available at this time.

Afghanistan	Albania	Algeria	American Samoa	Andorra
Angola	Anguilla	Antigua and Barbuda	Argentina	Armenia
Aruba	Australia	Austria	Azerbaijan	Bahamas, The
Bahrain	Bangladesh	Barbados	Belarus	Belgium
Belize	Benin	Bermuda	Bhutan	Bolivia
Bosnia and Herzegovina	Botswana	Brazil	British Virgin Islands	Brunei

Bulgaria

Burkina Faso

Burundi

Cambodia

Cameroon

Canada

Cape Verde

Cayman Islands

Central African Republic

Chad

Chile

China

Christmas Island

Colombia

Comoros

Congo, Democratic
Republic of the

Congo, Republic of the

Cook Islands

Costa Rica

Cote d'Ivoire

Croatia

Cuba

Cyprus

Czech Republic

Denmark

Djibouti

Dominica

Dominican Republic

Ecuador

Egypt

El Salvador

Equatorial Guinea

Eritrea

Estonia

Ethiopia

Falkland Islands

Faroe Islands

Fiji

Finland

France

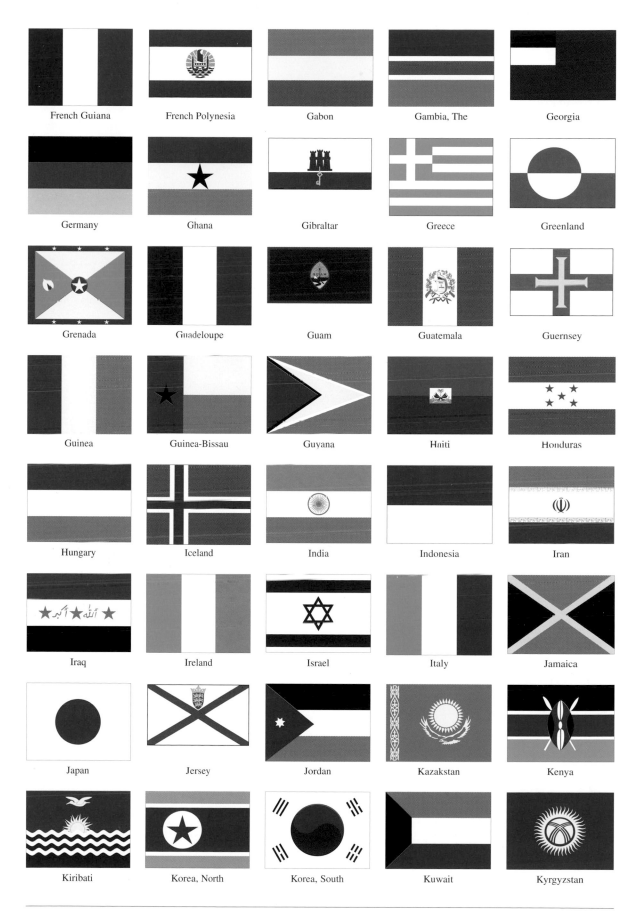

French Guiana	French Polynesia	Gabon	Gambia, The	Georgia
Germany	Ghana	Gibraltar	Greece	Greenland
Grenada	Guadeloupe	Guam	Guatemala	Guernsey
Guinea	Guinea-Bissau	Guyana	Haiti	Honduras
Hungary	Iceland	India	Indonesia	Iran
Iraq	Ireland	Israel	Italy	Jamaica
Japan	Jersey	Jordan	Kazakstan	Kenya
Kiribati	Korea, North	Korea, South	Kuwait	Kyrgyzstan

Laos

Latvia

Lebanon

Lesotho

Liberia

Libya

Liechtenstein

Lithuania

Luxembourg

Macau

Macedonia

Madagascar

Malawi

Malaysia

Maldives

Mali

Malta

Man, Isle of

Marshall Islands

Martinique

Mauritania

Mauritius

Mayotte

Mexico

Micronesia, Federated States of

Midway Islands

Moldova

Monaco

Mongolia

Montenegro

Montserrat

Morocco

Mozambique

Myanmar

Namibia

Nauru

Nepal

Netherlands

Netherlands Antilles

New Caledonia

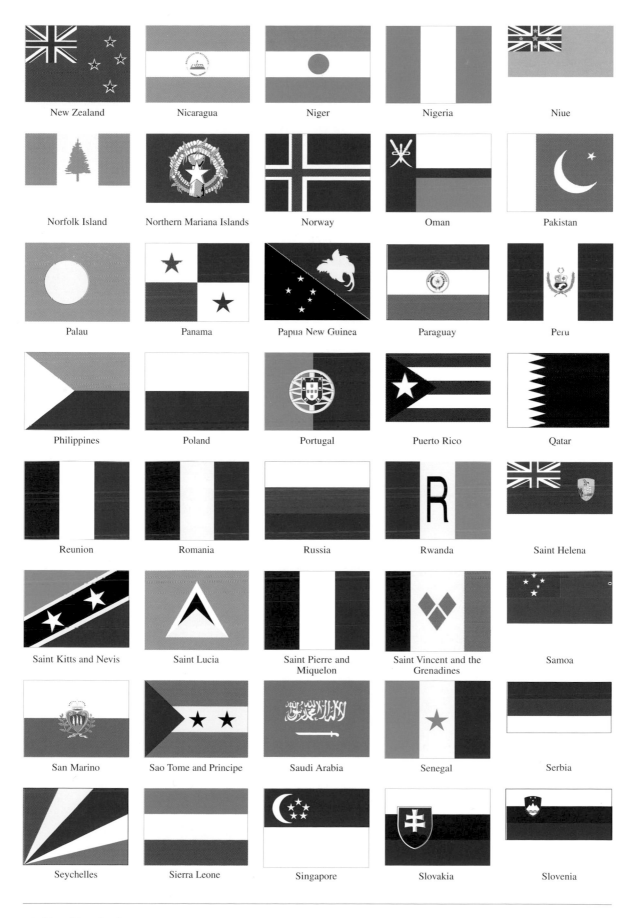

New Zealand

Nicaragua

Niger

Nigeria

Niue

Norfolk Island

Northern Mariana Islands

Norway

Oman

Pakistan

Palau

Panama

Papua New Guinea

Paraguay

Peru

Philippines

Poland

Portugal

Puerto Rico

Qatar

Reunion

Romania

Russia

Rwanda

Saint Helena

Saint Kitts and Nevis

Saint Lucia

Saint Pierre and Miquelon

Saint Vincent and the Grenadines

Samoa

San Marino

Sao Tome and Principe

Saudi Arabia

Senegal

Serbia

Seychelles

Sierra Leone

Singapore

Slovakia

Slovenia

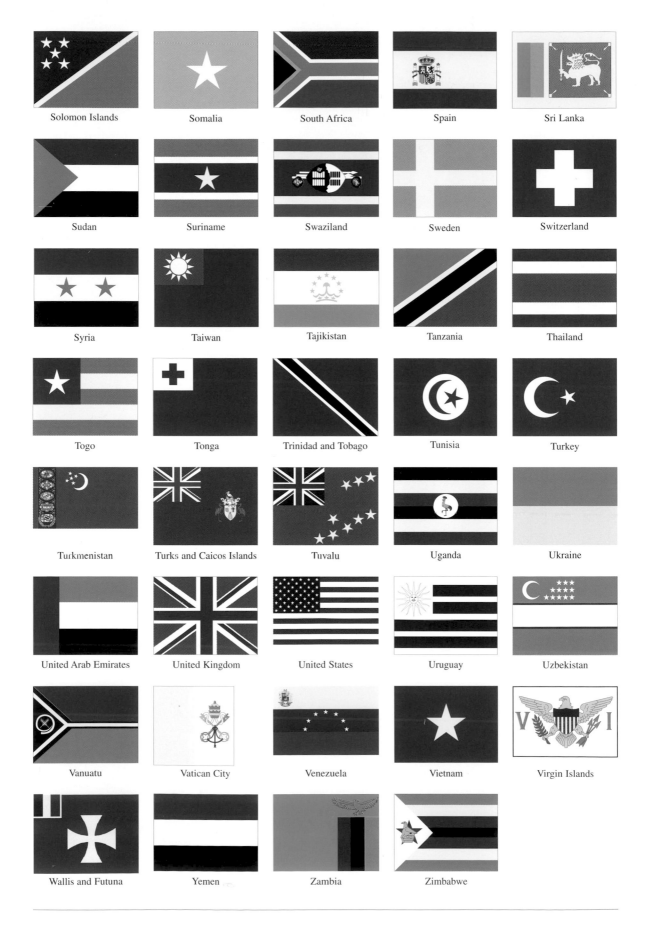

Solomon Islands	Somalia	South Africa	Spain	Sri Lanka
Sudan	Suriname	Swaziland	Sweden	Switzerland
Syria	Taiwan	Tajikistan	Tanzania	Thailand
Togo	Tonga	Trinidad and Tobago	Tunisia	Turkey
Turkmenistan	Turks and Caicos Islands	Tuvalu	Uganda	Ukraine
United Arab Emirates	United Kingdom	United States	Uruguay	Uzbekistan
Vanuatu	Vatican City	Venezuela	Vietnam	Virgin Islands
Wallis and Futuna	Yemen	Zambia	Zimbabwe	

Afghanistan

Albania

Algeria

American Samoa

Andorra

Angola

Anguilla

Antigua and Barbuda

Argentina

Armenia

Aruba

Australia

Austria

Azerbaijan

Bahamas, The

Bahrain

Bangladesh

Barbados

Belarus

Belgium

Belize

Benin

Bermuda

Bhutan

Bolivia

Bosnia and Herzegovina

Botswana

Brazil

British Virgin Islands

Brunei

Bulgaria

Burkina Faso

Burundi

Cambodia

Cameroon

Canada

Cape Verde

Cayman Islands

Central African Republic

Chad

Chile

China

Christmas Island

Columbia

Comoros

Congo, Democratic Republic of the

Congo, Republic of the

Cook Islands

Costa Rica

Cote d'Ivoire

Croatia

Cuba

Cyprus

Czech Republic

Denmark

Djibouti

Dominica

Dominican Republic

Ecuador

Egypt

El Salvador

Equatorial Guinea

Eritrea

Estonia

Ethiopia

Falkland Islands

Faroe Islands

Fiji

Finland

France

French Guiana

French Polynesia

Gabon

Gambia, The

Georgia

Germany

Ghana

Gibraltar

Greece

Greenland

Grenada

Guam

Guatemala

Guernsey

Guinea

Guinea-Bissau

Guyana

Haiti

Honduras

Hungary

Iceland

India

Indonesia

Iran

Iraq

Ireland

Israel

Italy

Jamaica

Japan

Jersey

Jordan

Kazakstan

Kenya

Kiribati

Korea, North

Korea, South

Kuwait

Kyrgyzstan

Laos

Latvia

Lebanon

Lesotho

Liberia

Libya

Liechtenstein

Lithuania

Luxembourg

Macau

Macedonia

Madagascar	Malawi	Malaysia	Maldives	Mali
Malta	Man, Isle of	Marshall Islands	Mauritania	Mauritius
Mayotte	Mexico	Micronesia, Federated States of	Midway Islands	Moldova
Monaco	Mongolia	Montenegro	Montserrat	Morocco
Mozambique	Myanmar	Namibia	Nauru	Nepal
Netherlands	Netherlands Antilles	New Caledonia	New Zealand	Nicaragua
Niger	Nigeria	Niue	Norfolk Island	Northern Mariana Islands
Norway	Oman	Pakistan	Palau	Panama

Papua New Guinea

Paraguay

Peru

Philippines

Poland

Portugal

Puerto Rico

Qatar

Reunion

Romania

Russia

Rwanda

Saint Helena

Saint Kitts and Nevis

Saint Lucia

Saint Pierre and Miquelon

Saint Vincent and the Grenadines

Samoa

San Marino

Sao Tome and Principe

Saudi Arabia

Senegal

Scychelles

Sierra Leone

Singapore

Slovakia

Slovenia

Solomon Islands

Somalia

South Africa

Spain

Sri Lanka

Sudan

Suriname

Swaziland

Sweden

Switzerland

Syria

Taiwan

Tajikistan

Tanzania

Thailand

Togo

Tonga

Trinidad and Tobago

Tunisia

Turkey

Turkmenistan

Turks and Caicos Islands

Tuvalu

Uganda

Ukraine

United Arab Emirates

United Kingdom

United States

Uruguay

Uzbekistan

Vanuatu

Vatican City

Venezuela

Vietnam

Virgin Islands

Wallis and Futuna

Yemen

Zambia

Zimbabwe

EUROPE

0   200   400 Miles

0   200   400 Kilometers

RUSSIA

0   250   500 Miles

0   250   500 Kilometers

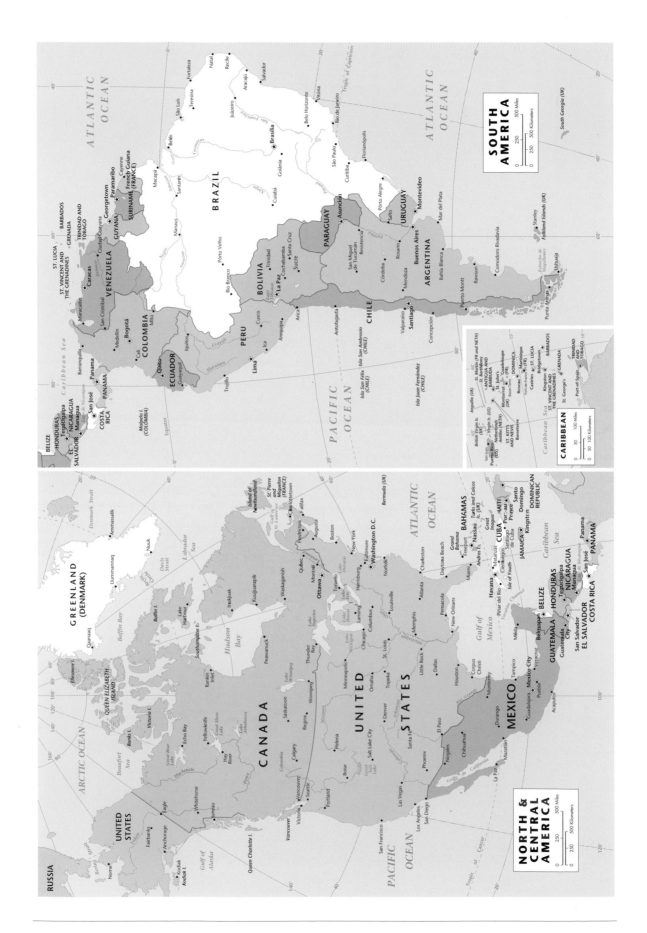

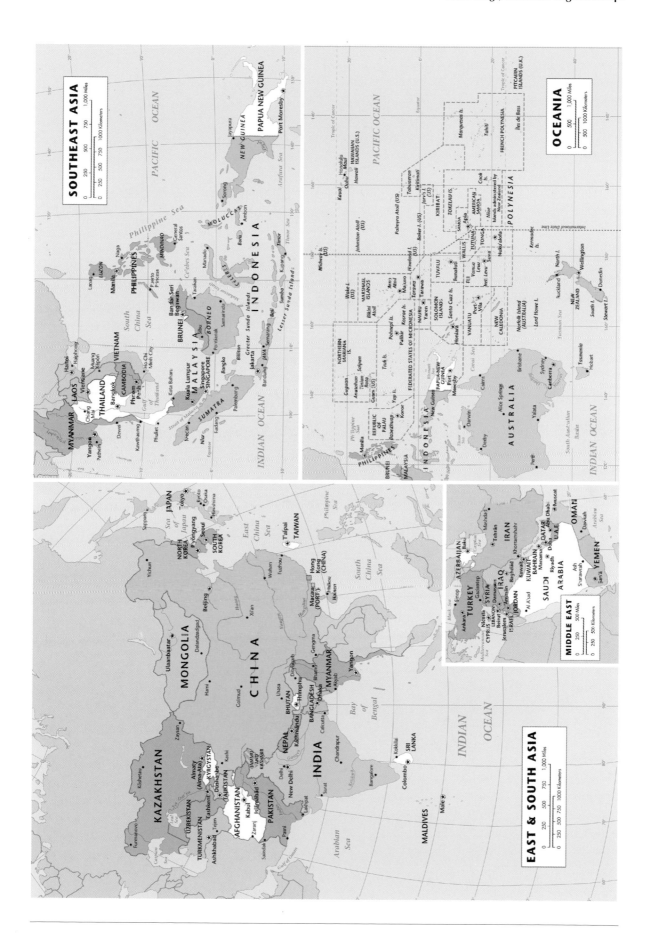

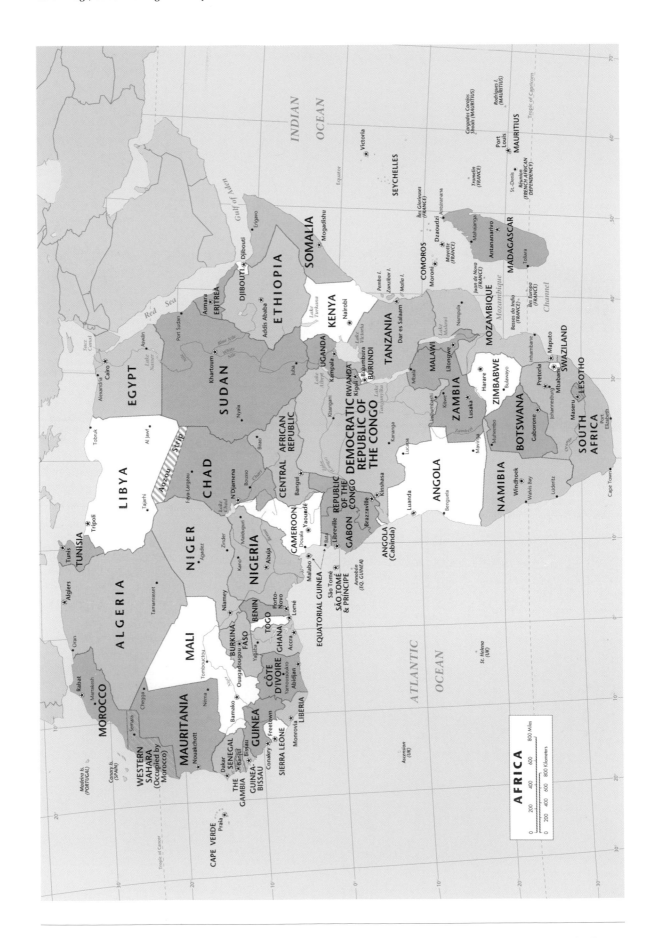

Colombia

Av. Presidente Errazuriz 3943, Las Condes,
1262, Correo Central, Santiago, Chile
PHONE: +56 2061318; 2061314; 2061999
FAX: +56 2080712
E-MAIL: emcolchi@entelchile.net
TITLE: Embajador Extraordinario y
Plenipotenciario
NAME: Samuel Eduardo Salazar Echeverri

Cuba

Los Leones 1346, Providencia, Chile
PHONE: +56 2745021; 2745263; 2745135
FAX: +56 2745708
E-MAIL: emcuchil@ctcinternet.cl
TITLE: Aramis Fuente Hernandez
NAME: Embajador Extraordinario y
Plenipotenciario

Denmark

Jacques Cazotte 5531, Vitacura 13430, Sucursal
21, Santiago, Chile
PHONE: +56 2185949
FAX: +56 2181736
E-MAIL: dkemba@entelchile.net
TITLE: Embajador Extraordinario y
Plenipotenciario
NAME: Bent Kiilerich

Ecuador

Providencia N° 1979, Piso 5, CP 16007, Correo
9, Providencia, Chile
PHONE: +56 2312015; 2315073
FAX: +56 2325833
E-MAIL: eecuador@ctc-mundo.net
TITLE: Embajador Extraordinario y
Plenipotenciario
NAME: Jaime Marchan Romero

Egypt

Roberto del Rio N° 1871, CP 9904, Correo
Central, Providencia, Chile
PHONE: +56 2748881; 2746334
FAX: +56 2746334
TITLE: Embajador Extraordinario y
Plenipotenciario
NAME: Taher A. Khalifa

France

PHONE: +56 2251030
FAX: +56 2741353
E-MAIL: ambafran@ia.cl
TITLE: Embajador Extraordinario y
Plenipotenciario
NAME: Jean-Michel Gaussot

Germany

Agustinas 785, Pisos 7 y 8, Santiago, Chile
PHONE: +56 6335031
FAX: +56 6336119
TITLE: Ministro Consejero
NAME: Alexander Muhlen

Greece

Isidora Goyenechea 3162, Of. 902, El Golf,
Chile
PHONE: +56 2311244; 2311245
FAX: +56 2311246
TITLE: Embajador Extraordinario y
Plenipotenciario
NAME: Dimitrios Manolopoulos

India

PHONE: +56 2352005; 2352633
FAX: +56 2359607
E-MAIL: embindia@entelchile.net
TITLE: Embajador Extraordinario y
Plenipotenciario
NAME: Ram Mohan

Indonesia

Av. Nueva Costanera N° 3318, Vitacura, CP 20-
D, Santiago
PHONE: +56 2076266
FAX: +56 2079901
E-MAIL: kbristgo@entelchile.net
TITLE: Embajador Extraordinario y
Plenipotenciario
NAME: Herijanto Soeprapto

Israel

San Sebastian 2812, Piso 5, Las Condes, CP
1224, Santiago, Chile
PHONE: +56 7500500
FAX: +56 7500555
E-MAIL: eisrael@rdc.cl
TITLE: Embajador Extraordinario y
Plenipotenciario
NAME: Ori Noy

Japan

Av. Ricardo Lyon 520, CP 124, Correo 35,
Providencia, Chile
PHONE: +56 2321807
FAX: +56 2321812
TITLE: Embajador Extraordinario y
Plenipotenciario
NAME: Yubun Narita

Mexico

PHONE: +56 2066148
FAX: +56 2066146; 2066147

TITLE: Embajador Extraordinario y Plenipotenciario
NAME: Otto Granados Roldan

New Zealand
PHONE: +56 2909802; 2909821; 2909825; 2909830
FAX: +56 2072333
E-MAIL: nzembsgo@ctcreuna.cl
TITLE: Embajador Extraordinario y Plenipotenciario
NAME: David Grant McKee

Pakistan
PHONE: +56 7751294
FAX: +56 7761186
TITLE: Embajador Extraordinario y Plenipotenciario
NAME: Zafar Habibi

Paraguay
PHONE: +56 6395112; 639464; 6392599
FAX: +56 6334426
E-MAIL: epychemb@chilesat.net
TITLE: Embajador Extraordinario y Plenipotenciario
NAME: Carlos Villagra Marsal

Peru
Av. Andres Bello 1751, CP 16277, Santiago 9, Chile
PHONE: +56 2356451; 2352356
FAX: +56 2358139; 2352053
E-MAIL: embstgo@entelchile.net
TITLE: Embajador Extraordinario y Plenipotenciario
NAME: Jorge Colunge Villacorta

Russia
Calle Cristobal Colon 4152, Las Condes, Santiago, Chile
PHONE: +56 2083413; 2061386
FAX: +56 2061386
E-MAIL: embrusia@mcl.cl

Spain
Av. Andres Bello N° 1895, Providencia, Chile
PHONE: +56 2352754; 2352755; 2352761
FAX: +56 2361547
TITLE: Embajador Extraordinario y Plenipotenciario
NAME: Juan Manuel Egea Iba-ez

United Kingdom
Av. El Bosque Norte 0125, CP 72-D, Chile
PHONE: +56 3704100
FAX: +56 3704140

TITLE: Embajador Extraordinario y Plenipotenciario
NAME: Glynne D. Evans

United States
Andres Bello 2800 Codina Building, Agustinas 1343, APO AA 34033, Santiago, Chile
PHONE: +56 (2) 2322600
FAX: +56 (2) 3303710
TITLE: Ambassador
NAME: John O'Leary

Uruguay
Av. Pedro De Valdivia 711, CP 2638, Correo 21, Providencia, Chile
PHONE: +56 2047988; 2744066
FAX: +56 2047772
E-MAIL: urusgo@uruguay.cl
TITLE: Embajador Extraordinario y Plenipotenciario
NAME: Juan B. Oddone Silveira

Venezuela
Bustos 2021, Providencia, Santiago, Chile
PHONE: +56 2250021
FAX: +56 2099117
E-MAIL: emvenchi@entelchile.net
TITLE: Embajador Extraordinario y Plenipotenciario
NAME: Alberto Müller Rojas

JUDICIAL SYSTEM
Supreme Court
Courts of Appeal

FURTHER READING
Articles
''The Americas Shift toward Private Health Care. Chile Leads the Way.'' *The Economist* (May 8, 1999): 27.

''Chile: After the Pinochet Ruling.'' *The Economist* (March 27, 1999): 38.

''Chile: Dropping Out.'' *The Economist* (May 1, 1999): 34.

''Chile is the Place to Watch.'' *Newsweek International* (June 14, 1999): 4.

''Chile's Right in the Shadow of an Embarrassing Old General.'' *The Economist* (August 14, 1999): 28.

''Chilean Court Give Enap OK for Pipeline.'' *The Oil Daily* (March 5, 1999).

''Goodbye Copper, Hello Recession.'' *Business Week* (March 29, 1999): 3.

"Judges of the Past: Pinochet's Arrest Carries National Consequences." *The Economist* (June 26, 1999): 40.

"A New Twist to an Old Tale: Mapuche Indian Resistance." *The Economist* (September 4, 1999): 40.

"The Pinochet Affair: Blackwashing Allende." *The Economist* (January 30, 1999): 34.

"The Politics of Pinochet: Chile's Right Hopes the Pinochet Affair will Split its Governing Coalition." *The Economist* (December 19, 1998): 45.

"Raul Silva Henriquez, Defender of the Oppressed, Dead." *The Economist* (April 17, 1999): 93.

"Socialist is Front-Runner in the Race to Lead Chile." *The Seattle Times*, 1 July 1999.

"Top Pinochet Aides Stay Back in Chile for Fear of Arrest." *The Seattle Times*, 23 April 1999.

CHILE: STATISTICAL DATA

For sources and notes see "Sources of Statistics" in the front of each volume.

GEOGRAPHY

Geography (1)

Area:

Total: 756,950 sq km.

Land: 748,800 sq km.

Water: 8,150 sq km.

Note: includes Easter Island (Isla de Pascua) and Isla Sala y Gomez.

Area—comparative: slightly smaller than twice the size of Montana.

Land boundaries:

Total: 6,171 km.

Border countries: Argentina 5,150 km, Bolivia 861 km, Peru 160 km.

Coastline: 6,435 km.

Climate: temperate; desert in north; cool and damp in south.

Terrain: low coastal mountains; fertile central valley; rugged Andes in east.

Natural resources: copper, timber, iron ore, nitrates, precious metals, molybdenum.

Land use:

Arable land: 5%

Permanent crops: 0%

Permanent pastures: 18%

Forests and woodland: 22%

Other: 55% (1993 est.).

HUMAN FACTORS

Demographics (2A)

	1990	1995	1998	2000	2010	2020	2030	2040	2050
Population	13,127.8	14,205.4	14,787.8	15,155.5	16,796.4	18,159.2	19,077.1	19,489.4	19,453.0
Net migration rate (per 1,000 population)	NA	NA	NA	NA	NA	NA	NA	NA	NA
Births	NA	NA	NA	NA	NA	NA	NA	NA	NA
Deaths	78.4	NA	NA	NA	NA	NA	NA	NA	NA
Life expectancy - males	69.1	71.1	72.0	72.7	74.9	76.6	77.8	78.7	79.4
Life expectancy - females	75.9	77.7	78.5	79.0	81.1	82.6	83.8	84.7	85.3
Birth rate (per 1,000)	23.4	19.7	18.3	17.4	14.9	13.2	11.6	10.6	9.9
Death rate (per 1,000)	6.1	5.7	5.6	5.5	5.9	6.8	8.1	9.7	11.0
Women of reproductive age (15-49 yrs.)	3,485.2	3,733.9	3,890.2	3,976.3	4,369.2	4,469.4	4,501.6	4,329.6	4,048.2
of which are currently married	NA	NA	NA	NA	NA	NA	NA	NA	NA
Fertility rate	2.7	2.4	2.3	2.2	1.9	1.8	1.8	1.7	1.7

Except as noted, values for vital statistics are in thousands; life expectancy is in years.

Health Personnel (3)

Total health expenditure as a percentage of GDP, 1990-1997[a]

Public sector 2.3

Private sector 3.7

Total[b] 7.9

Health expenditure per capita in U.S. dollars, 1990-1997[a]

Purchasing power parity 783

Total 295

Availability of health care facilities per 100,000 people

Hospital beds 1990-1997[a] 320

Doctors 1993[c] 108

Nurses 1993[c] 42

Health Indicators (4)

Life expectancy at birth

1980 69

1997 75

Daily per capita supply of calories (1996) 2,810

Total fertility rate births per woman (1997) 2.4

Maternal mortality ratio per 100,000 live births (1990-97) ....65[b]

Safe water % of population with access (1995) 91

Sanitation % of population with access (1995) 81

Consumption of iodized salt % of households (1992-98)[a] ....

Smoking prevalence

Male % of adults (1985-95)[a] 38

Female % of adults (1985-95)[a] 25

Tuberculosis incidence per 100,000 people (1997) 29

Adult HIV prevalence % of population ages 15-49 (1997) 0.20

Infants and Malnutrition (5)

Under-5 mortality rate (1997) 13

% of infants with low birthweight (1990-97) 5

Births attended by skilled health staff % of total[a] ...99

% fully immunized (1995-97)

TB 98

DPT 91

Polio 91

Measles 92

Prevalence of child malnutrition under age 5 (1992-97)[b] 1

Ethnic Division (6)

White and white-Amerindian 95%

Amerindian 3%

Other 2%

Religions (7)

Roman Catholic 89%

Protestant 11%

Languages (8)

Spanish.

EDUCATION

Public Education Expenditures (9)

Public expenditure on education (% of GNP)

1980 ....4.6

1996 ....3.1

Expenditure per student

Primary % of GNP per capita

1980 ....9.5

1996 ....10.1

Secondary % of GNP per capita

1980 ....16.7[1]

1996 ....10.8

Tertiary % of GNP per capita

1980 ....111.2

1996 ....18.8

Expenditure on teaching materials

Primary % of total for level (1996) 0.0

Secondary % of total for level (1996) ....

Primary pupil-teacher ratio per teacher (1996) 30

Duration of primary education years (1995) 8

Educational Attainment (10)

Age group (1992) ....25+

Total population ....NA

Highest level attained (%)

No schooling 5.8

First level

Not completed 48.0

Completed ....NA

Entered second level

S-1 ....33.9

S-2 ....NA

Postsecondary 12.3

Literacy Rates (11A)

In thousands and percent[1]	1990	1995	2000	2010
Illiterate population (15+ yrs.)	546	485	437	326
Literacy rate - total adult pop. (%)	94.1	95.2	96.0	97.5
Literacy rate - males (%)	94.4	95.4	96.2	97.6
Literacy rate - females (%)	93.8	95.0	95.8	97.4

GOVERNMENT & LAW

Political Parties (12)

Chamber of Deputies—	% of seats
Coalition of Parties for Democracy	.50.55
Union for the Progress of Chile	.36.23

Government Budget (13A)

Year: 1997

Total Expenditures: 6,695.35 Billions of Pesos

Expenditures as a percentage of the total by function:

General public services and public order 9.63

Military Affairs (14B)

	1990	1991	1992	1993	1994	1995
Military expenditures						
Current dollars (mil.)[3]	1,154e	1,232e	1,133	1,771	1,832	2,243
1995 constant dollars (mil.)[3]	1,327e	1,362e	1,218	1,857	1,877	2,243
Armed forces (000)	95	90	92	92	102	102
Gross national product (GNP)						
Current dollars (mil.)	35,500	39,700	45,450	50,270	53,210	59,060
1995 constant dollars (mil.)	40,790	43,870	48,890	52,700	54,540	59,060
Central government expenditures (CGE)						
1995 constant dollars (mil.)	8,625	9,717	10,410	11,310	11,520	12,820
People (mil.)	13.1	13.3	13.6	13.8	14.0	14.2
Military expenditure as % of GNP	3.3	3.1	2.5	3.5	3.4	3.8
Military expenditure as % of CGE	15.4	14.0	11.7	16.4	16.3	17.5
Military expenditure per capita (1995 $)	101	102	90	135	134	158
Armed forces per 1,000 people (soldiers)	7.2	6.7	6.8	6.7	7.3	7.2
GNP per capita (1995 $)	3,109	3,289	3,607	3,829	3,906	4,173
Arms imports[6]						
Current dollars (mil.)	60	60	90	30	110	380
1995 constant dollars (mil.)	69	66	97	31	113	380
Arms exports[6]						
Current dollars (mil.)	20	0	5	10	0	0
1995 constant dollars (mil.)	23	0	5	10	0	0
Total imports[7]						
Current dollars (mil.)	7,678	8,094	10,130	11,120	11,820	15,910
1995 constant dollars (mil.)	8,824	8,944	10,900	11,660	12,120	15,910
Total exports[7]						
Current dollars (mil.)	8,310	8,942	10,010	9,199	11,600	16,040
1995 constant dollars (mil.)	9,550	9,881	10,760	9,644	11,890	16,040
Arms as percent of total imports[8]	.8	.7	.9	.3	.9	2.4
Arms as percent of total exports[8]	.2	0	0	.1	0	0

Government Budget (13A)

Defense 8.43

Education 15.98

Health 12.05

Social Security and Welfare 33.42

Housing and community amenities 5.25

Recreational, cultural, and religious affairs . . . . -

Fuel and energy . . . .

Agriculture, forestry, fishing, and hunting . . . .

Mining, manufacturing, and construction . . . .

Transportation and communication . . . .

Other economic affairs and services . . . .

Crime (15)

Crime rate (for 1994)

Crimes reported .1,229,300

Total persons convicted 24,510

Crimes per 100,000 population 8,784

Persons responsible for offenses

Total number of suspects 701,291

Total number of female suspects 49,360

Total number of juvenile suspects 6,065

LABOR FORCE

Labor Force (16)

Total (million) 5.7

Services 38.3%

Industry and commerce .33.8%

Agriculture, forestry, and fishing 19.2%

Mining 2.3%

Construction 6.4%

Data for 1997 est. Percent distribution for 1990. Services
includes government 12%.

Unemployment Rate (17)

6.1% (1997)

PRODUCTION SECTOR

Electric Energy (18)

Capacity . . . . .5.504 million kW (1995)

Production . . . . .24.5 billion kWh (1995)

Consumption per capita . . . . .1,730 kWh (1995)

Transportation (19)

Highways:

total: 79,800 km

paved: 11,012 km

unpaved: 68,788 km (1996 est.)

Waterways: 725 km

Pipelines: crude oil 755 km; petroleum products 785
km; natural gas 320 km

Merchant marine:

total: 39 ships (1,000 GRT or over) totaling 473,173
GRT/770,619 DWT ships by type: bulk 12, cargo 9,
chemical tanker 4, container 2, liquefied gas tanker 1,
oil tanker 4, passenger 2, roll-on/roll-off cargo 3,
vehicle carrier 2 (1997 est.)

Airports: 380 (1997 est.)

Airports—with paved runways:

total: 52

over 3,047 m: 5

2,438 to 3,047 m: 5

1,524 to 2,437 m: 18

914 to 1,523 m: 18

under 914 m: 6 (1997 est.)

Airports—with unpaved runways:

total: 328

over 3,047 m: 1

2,438 to 3,047 m: 4

1,524 to 2,437 m: 15

914 to 1,523 m: 74

under 914 m: 234 (1997 est.)

Top Agricultural Products (20)

Wheat, corn, grapes, beans, sugar beets, potatoes, fruit;
beef, poultry, wool; timber; 1991 fish catch of 6.6
million metric tons.

MANUFACTURING SECTOR

GDP & Manufacturing Summary (21)

Detailed value added figures are listed by both International
Standard Industry Code (ISIC) and product title.

	1980	1985	1990	1994
GDP ($-1990 mil.)[1]	23,413	22,550	30,387	39,626
Per capita ($-1990)[1]	2,101	1,867	2,310	2,822
Manufacturing share (%) (current prices)[1]	14.7	16.2	18.6	NA
Manufacturing				
Value added ($-1990 mil.)[1]	4,209	3,933	5,359	6,736
Industrial production index	100	100	128	159
Value added ($ mil.)	4,991	4,713	8,757	*13,022*
Gross output ($ mil.)	10,790	10,477	21,215	*30,237*

	1980	1985	1990	1994
Employment (000)	206	185	298	*337*
Profitability (% of gross output)				
Intermediate input (%)	54	55	59	*57*
Wages and salaries inc. supplements (%)	*9*	6	7	*8*
Gross operating surplus	*38*	39	34	*35*
Productivity ($)				
Gross output per worker	51,994	56,380	70,919	*89,485*
Value added per worker	24,050	25,363	29,274	*38,542*
Average wage (inc. supplements)	*4,444*	3,499	4,861	*7,419*
Value added ($ mil.)				
311/2 Food products	827	805	1,543	*2,725*
313 Beverages	289	177	374	*671*
314 Tobacco products	214	205	303	*488*
321 Textiles	234	162	333	*360*
322 Wearing apparel	111	83	163	*314*
323 Leather and fur products	22	18	37	*43*
324 Footwear	77	51	121	*184*
331 Wood and wood products	153	143	270	*467*
332 Furniture and fixtures	37	14	53	*97*
341 Paper and paper products	281	278	561	*782*
342 Printing and publishing	182	104	224	*420*
351 Industrial chemicals	55	94	247	*412*
352 Other chemical products	324	289	617	*1,037*
353 Petroleum refineries	184	277	480	*937*
354 Miscellaneous petroleum and coal products	27	47	69	*105*
355 Rubber products	60	48	72	*134*
356 Plastic products	50	63	178	*350*
361 Pottery, china and earthenware	14	9	9	*28*
362 Glass and glass products	38	27	51	*89*
369 Other non-metal mineral products	146	115	218	*535*
371 Iron and steel	188	226	284	*331*
372 Non-ferrous metals	965	1,175	1,716	*1,265*
381 Metal products	181	130	366	*527*
382 Non-electrical machinery	96	50	168	*230*
383 Electrical machinery	90	61	125	*195*
384 Transport equipment	127	50	153	*255*
385 Professional and scientific equipment	5	4	9	*21*
390 Other manufacturing industries	13	7	14	*20*

FINANCE, ECONOMICS, & TRADE

Economic Indicators (22)

National product: GDP—purchasing power parity—$168.5 billion (1997 est.)

National product real growth rate: 7.1% (1997 est.)

National product per capita: $11,600 (1997 est.)

Inflation rate—consumer price index: 6% (1997)

Balance of Payments (23)

	1992	1993	1994	1995	1996
Exports of goods (f.o.b.)	10,008	9,199	11,604	16,137	15,353
Imports of goods (f.o.b.)	−9,238	−10,181	−10,880	−14,657	−16,499
Trade balance	770	−982	724	1,480	−1,146
Services - debits	−4,780	−4,559	−5,071	−5,631	−6,298
Services - credits	2,880	3,098	3,346	3,984	4,051
Private transfers (net)	362	315	311	280	400
Government transfers (net)	68	56	46	29	72
Overall balance	−700	−2,072	−644	142	−2,921

Exchange Rates (24)

Exchange rates:

Chilean pesos (Ch$) per US$1

January 1998	.452.60
1997	.419.30
1996	.412.27
1995	.396.78
1994	.420.08
1993	.404.35

Top Import Origins (25)

$18.2 billion (f.o.b., 1997) Data are for 1995 est.

Origins	%
European Union	.18
United States	.25
Asia	.16
Latin America	.26

Top Export Destinations (26)

$16.9 billion (f.o.b., 1997) Data are for 1995 est.

Destinations	%
European Union	.25
United States	.15
Asia	.34
Latin America	.20

Economic Aid (27)

Recipient: ODA, $50.3 million (1996 est.).

Import Export Commodities (28)

Import Commodities	Export Commodities
Capital goods 25.2%	Copper 37%
Spare parts 24.8%	Other metals and minerals 8.2%
Raw materials 15.4%	
Petroleum 10%	Wood products 7.1%
Foodstuffs 5.7%	Fish and fishmeal 9.8%
	Fruits 8.4%

CHINA

People's Republic of China
Zhonghua Renmin Gongheguo

CAPITAL: Beijing (Peking).

FLAG: The flag is red with five gold stars in the upper left quadrant; one large star is near the hoist and four smaller ones are arranged in an arc to the right.

ANTHEM: *March of the Volunteers.*

MONETARY UNIT: The renminbi, or "people's money," denominated in yuan (Y), is equivalent to 10 jiao or 100 fen. There are coins of 1, 2, and 5 fen, 1, 2, and 5 jiao, and 1 yuan, and notes of 1, 2, and 5 fen, 1, 2, and 5 jiao, and 1, 2, 5, 10, 50, and 100 yuan. Y1 = $0.1125 (or $1 = Y8.0).

WEIGHTS AND MEASURES: The metric system is the legal standard, but some Chinese units remain in common use.

HOLIDAYS: New Year's Day, 1 January; Spring Festival (Chinese New Year), from the 1st to the 3d day of the first moon of the lunar calendar, usually in February; International Women's Day, 8 March; May Day, 1 May; Army Day, 1 August; Teachers' Day, 9 September; and National Day, 1–2 October.

TIME: 8 pm = noon GMT.

LOCATION AND SIZE: China is the third-largest country in the world and the largest nation in Asia. It claims an area of 9.6 million square kilometers (3.7 million square miles), including Taiwan, which the PRC claims as a province. The country has a coastline of 14,500 kilometers (9,009 miles). China's territory includes several large islands, the most important of which is Hainan, off the south coast. China's total boundary length is 36,643 kilometers (22,769 miles). Beijing, is located in the northeastern part of the country.

CLIMATE: Although most of China lies within the temperate zone, climate varies greatly with topography. Minimum winter temperatures range from −27°C (−17°F) to 16°C (61°F).

Rain falls mostly in summer. Precipitation is heaviest in the south and southeast, with Guangzhou receiving more than 200 centimeters (80 inches), and diminishes to about 60 centimeters (25 inches) in north and northeast China, and to less than 10 centimeters (4 inches) in the northwest.

INTRODUCTORY SURVEY

RECENT HISTORY

After a long civil war, the People's Republic of China (PRC) was declared on 1 October 1949. The communists, under the leadership of Mao Zedong, were in power. The government pursued rapid programs of industrialization and socialization, including, in 1958–59, the Great Leap Forward, a crash program designed to quickly improve China's economy. The results were disastrous, resulting in shortages of food and raw materials, and starvation among the population. The Soviet Union (which broke into 15 republics in 1991) had supplied advisors to the Chinese government, and was held responsible for much of the failure. This and other matters of contention led to the 1960 Sino-Soviet split.

In 1966, Mao again steered the country onto the revolutionary path with the Great Proletarian Cultural Revolution, one of the most dramatic and turbulent periods in modern Chinese history. It continued until Mao's death in 1976, but the stormiest years were from 1966 to 1969. During those years, cities witnessed fighting between factions, accompanied by attacks on bureaucrats, intellectuals, scientists and technicians, and anyone known to have overseas connections. Amid the rising conflict, the party structure collapsed in major cities. Estimates place the number of dead as a direct result of Cultural Revolution at 400,000.

On the international front, the PRC and the United States had a strained relationship. The United States had supported the Nationalists

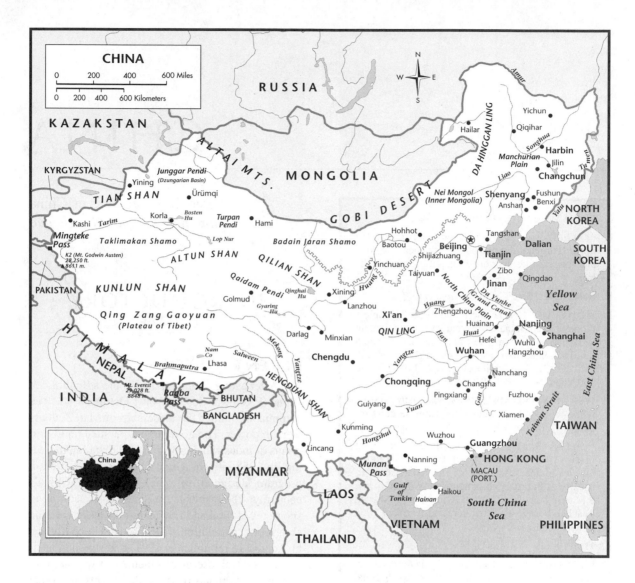

CHINA

against the Communist revolution, fought Chinese troops during the Korean War, and refused to acknowledge the large communist nation. However, President Richard M. Nixon journeyed to China in 1972 for an unprecedented state visit, and the two countries took major steps toward normalizing relations. Full diplomatic relations were established by 1979.

Mao Zedong died on 9 September 1976. The next long-term Chinese leader was Deng Xiaoping, who initiated more reforms and modernizations beginning in the countryside and spreading to urban areas. They were very effective. By the mid-1980s China began to move away from a socialist system of central planning to a market economy. At the same time, it began to open its economy to the outside world and encourage foreign investment.

Until 1989, economic reforms were accompanied by relatively greater openness in intellectual spheres. However, student pro-democracy demonstrations began in the mid-1980s, and economic problems, including inflation of up to 35% in major cities, led to major disagreements within the government. This led to a slowdown in reforms.

A student demonstration in Beijing in the spring of 1989 drew over a million people and garnered much public support. The government declared martial law and sent troops to clear Beijing's Tiananmen Square, where demonstrators were camped. In the early hours of 4 June armed troops, armored personnel carriers, and tanks, firing on demonstrators and bystanders, entered the square. Firing continued for several days and estimates of the total number killed range from 200 to 3,000. The events of 4 June sparked protests across the country, and thousands were arrested as the movement was suppressed.

The city of Hong Kong, long a British protectorate and economic tiger, returned to Chinese control on 1 July 1997. China, a communist state, agreed to allow Hong Kong to maintain its political, economic, and judicial systems. As the time for the handover drew near, however, tensions rose on both sides as the Chinese began to dismantle the few democratic institutions the British had put in place. When Hong Kong did return to Chinese control, the feared anti-democratic crackdown did not occur. China established its own legislature, and appointed a chief executive to oversee the city.

Deng Xiaoping died in 1997 and was succeeded by Jiang Zemin. Under Jiang relations with the United States improved. He visited the United States in 1997, and U.S. President Bill Clinton traveled to China in 1998. The two discussed trade and nuclear non-proliferation issues, as well as China's questionable human rights record.

GOVERNMENT

On 4 December 1982, China adopted its fourth constitution since 1949, succeeding those of 1954, 1975, and 1978. In theory, the highest organ of state power is the National People's Congress (NPC), in which legislative power is vested. The constitution stipulates, however, that the Congress is to function under the direction of the Chinese Communist Party.

The PRC consists of 23 provinces, or *sheng*, of which Taiwan is claimed as the twenty-third; five autonomous regions (*zizhiqu*), and three centrally administered municipalities (*zhixiashi*).

Judiciary

China's legal system, instituted after the establishment of the PRC in 1949, is largely based on that of the former Soviet Union. The highest judicial body is the Supreme People's Court which supervises the administration of justice in the basic people's courts.

In 1996, the National People's Congress passed legal reform legislation, recognizing that lawyers represent their clients and not the state. It allowed lawyers to set up private practices. In 1997, reforms allowed suspects to retain an attorney after being questioned by the police; attorneys were given the right to conduct limited investigations, call defense witnesses, and argue in an open court. Until these reforms, defendants were not presumed innocent.

Political Parties

The Chinese Communist Party (CCP) has been the ruling political organization in China since 1949. Eight other minor parties have existed since 1949 as members of a United Front, but their existence has been purely a formality. The Communist Party plays a decisive role in formulating and implementing government policies.

After the death of longtime leader Deng Xiaoping in February 1997, the leadership of the CCP, and, thus of China, was fought over among a small group of rulers. At the 15th Communist Party Congress in 1997, Jiang Zemin, a hardliner many people blame for the Tiananmen massacre of 1989, was elected as party leader.

DEFENSE

The Chinese military has focused its efforts on becoming a strong land-based power with the capability of launching defense operations beyond its coastal borders. In 1996, China engaged in military maneuvers in the waters of Taiwan, an island it considers a rogue province. In response, the United States sent two aircraft battle groups to the area in a show of support for Taiwan, but the Chinese military completed its maneuvers before returning to the mainland.

China retains a sizeable nuclear arsenal but has dedicated itself to nuclear non-proliferation by signing the Non-Proliferation Treaty, issuing detailed regulations for nuclear export control in 1997, and setting up regulations for control over nuclear-related dual-use items in 1998.

ECONOMIC AFFAIRS

After the commune reforms of the 1980s and the government's move to make a transition from a fully centrally planned economy to a mixed free-market and socialist economy, the business landscape in China changed. The goal was for all urban businesses to become responsible for their own profits and losses and for national and local government to give up direct control over business and take a regulatory and supervisory position. Pay would be based on productivity; government subsidies would be abolished; wages and prices would find their own level; and private enterprise would be encouraged.

These reforms were remarkably successful, leading to much higher rates of industrial and general economic growth than previously expected. Real gross national product (GNP) grew by an average of 9.6% annually between 1979–88, reaching over 11% in 1988. From 1991–95 economic growth accelerated, averaging more than 10% annually, giving China one of the fastest growing economies in the world. In 1997, China regained control over Hong Kong, one of the richest, most economically productive centers of capitalism in the world, and Party leader Jiang Zemin announced that China would begin a major privatization plan over the next few years. The privatization measures are part of China's 13-year effort to gain entry into the World Trade Organization (WTO). It has also reduced import tariffs in a continuing effort to align its market with the WTO membership standards.

Public Finance

The annual state budget is prepared by the Ministry of Finance and approved by the National People's Congress. A new system of allocating revenues and expenditures between local and national levels of government was implemented in 1980. It fixed for a five-year period the proportion of local income to be paid to the central government and (except for emergency appropriations for floods and other such disasters) the level of subsidies to be provided by the central government, as well as the proportion of local income to be retained by local governments. Autonomous regions receive proportionately greater state subsidies than the provinces and centrally administered municipalities, and they are entitled to keep all revenues from local industrial and commercial taxes.

During the early 1990s, the Chinese consolidated budget deficit was growing at a rapidly increasing rate. The 1998 annual budget deficit was 4% of gross domestic product (GDP), while government revenues were at 12.8%. External debt for 1998 was estimated at $159 billion.

Income

According to World Bank estimates, in 1998 the growth rate of China's gross national product (GNP) was 7%, with a rate of 6.2% per capita. The average annual GNP growth rate was 7.4%.

Industry

China's primary state industries include coal, iron, steel, machine building, armaments, textiles, and light industrial products. The country's automobile and electric power generation industries are growing quickly, helped by economic growth in many cities. The estimated industrial annual growth rate for 1998 was 9.2%. Manufacturing experienced an 8.9% annual growth rate for 1998, and the services industry grew up 7.6%.

Banking and Finance

The nation's central bank is the People's Bank of China (PBC). Commercial operations are handled by the Industrial and Commercial Bank, and specialized agencies, such as the Agricultural Bank of China and the State General Administration of Exchange Control, handle other services.

The People's Construction Bank makes payments for capital construction according to state plans and budgets. The Bank of China (BOC) handles foreign exchange and international settlements for the PBC. The BOC is charged with financing China's foreign trade and acquiring and channeling into appropriate areas the foreign capital needed for imports of industrial equipment and other items for modernization.

Economic Development

China's experiment with special economic zones (SEZs), begun in 1993, has been a success, generating high volumes of foreign investment and economic growth. Growth for 1997 was 8.9%; for 1998 it was 7.9% and estimated growth for 1999 was 7%.

China survived the Asian Financial Crisis of 1997–98 without serious damage to its economy and played a stabilizing role in the crisis by refusing to devalue its currency. It was not unaffected by the economic turmoil, however, and has experienced a decrease in exports and foreign direct investment.

SOCIAL WELFARE

China's estimated population is over 1.2 billion. Population policies and family planning measures have been in place since the mid-1970s, when the government began efforts to reign in population growth. Incentives exist to maintain a one-child family, with penalties for families having over two children without first receiving special permission.

Since 1950, the situation of women has improved due to legislation guaranteeing equal pay for equal work. In 1993, the government continued to condemn and took steps to curb traditional abuse of women, including their abduction and sale for wives or prostitutes, abuse of female children, and female infanticide.

Human rights abuses continue to be a problem in China. Arbitrary arrest and lengthy detention, forced confessions, torture and the mistreatment of prisoners are all serious problems. Prison conditions are poor and China does not allow any independent monitoring of its prisons. The government does not tolerate any political dissent, and is especially virulent in its suppression of separatist movements.

Healthcare

China has made significant improvements in health care since 1948, with 90% of the population covered by 1975, but the program began to slow in the 1980s and disparities in health care grew rapidly between coastal and rural areas. By the late 1990s the poorest quarter of China's rural population experienced an infant mortality rate 3.5 times greater than that of city dwellers. In addition, the official number of HIV infections in 1997 was 8,000. To help China address its health care issues the World Bank granted it a $10 million loan. The cost of China's health care improvements is estimated at $140 million.

Housing

China has an acute shortage of housing, attributable not only to the large annual increases in population (over 10 million a year) that must be accommodated, but also to the long-standing policy of directing investment funds into heavy industry rather than into housing and other social amenities.

It has, however, begun to privatize the housing industry. State owned housing units, generally provided to employees for little or no rent, are now being made available for purchase by residents. The government has also established a tax incentive to encourage buyers and may open special housing banks in many cities.

EDUCATION

After the Cultural Revolution, during which formal education ceased for most students, education in China was reoriented in 1978 under the Four Modernizations policy, and universal primary education by 1990 became the main target

In June 1999 the National Education Conference was created for the task of improving China's education system. These improvement measures include maintaining and universalizing the compulsory nine year education, especially in rural areas, by 2000, and increasing education expenditures as a percentage of GDP.

Among the largest and most prestigious institutions are Beijing University and Qinghua University, both in Beijing.

1999 KEY EVENTS TIMELINE

January

- A Hong Kong court voids a law restricting immigration by mainland Chinese.

February

- United States Secretary of State Madeleine Albright visits China as part of Far East tour.

March

- The New York Times reports the theft of U.S. nuclear secrets by a spy working for the Chinese.
- The U.S. Department of Energy fires Wen Ho Lee, a Chinese scientist, due to suspicions of espionage.

April

- The grassroots religious cult Falun Gong holds a mass demonstration in Beijing.
- Chinese prime minister Zhu Rongji meets with President Clinton in Washington, D.C.

May

- NATO pilots mistakenly bomb the Chinese embassy in Belgrade during the Kosovo crisis.
- China breaks off trade talks following the embassy bombing, despite an official apology from the United States.
- The U.S. Congress issues a report on Chinese weapons espionage activities.

June

- The tenth anniversary of the Tienanmen Square massacre passes quietly in China, but is marked in Hong Kong.
- North Korean officials make the highest-level diplomatic visit to China in eight years.

July

- Taiwan declares a more independent stance in its relations with the People's Republic.

- China conducts military exercises in response to a shift in Taiwan policy.

- The Chinese women's soccer team loses the World Cup championship match to the U.S. team.

- The Chinese government outlaws the Falun Gong religious cult.

- The U.S. Congress votes to renew China's most-favored-nation trade status.

August

- China protests a proposed $550 million U.S. arms sale to Taiwan.

September

- China prepares for a gala 50th celebration of the founding of the People's Republic.

- A 9,000-year-old flute is discovered in the Yellow River Valley; it is the oldest working musical instrument ever found.

- President Clinton meets with Chinese premier Jiang Zemin in New Zealand.

November

- China and the United States sign a trade deal, paving the way for China's entry into the World Trade Organization.

- China's space program conducts its first successful launch and recovery of a craft designed to carry astronauts; *Shen Zhou* (meaning Divine or Magical Vessel) was launched from Gansu province and circled the earth 14 times before safely landing 21 hours later in Inner Mongolia.

- At least 119 people die and more than 160 are missing after a Chinese passenger ferry carrying more than 300 people catches fire and capsizes in a storm near Yantai on the Shandong peninsula.

December

- Two prominent members of an outlawed opposition party charged with subversion are tried as part of a government campaign to squash dissent.

- The World Bank reviews its lending policies to China.

ANALYSIS OF EVENTS: 1999

BUSINESS AND THE ECONOMY

The dominating economic issue for China in 1999 was the country's continued progress toward admission to the World Trade Organization (WTO). Although Chinese Premier Zhu Rongji and U.S. President Bill Clinton did not conclude the hoped-for trade agreement in April that would have paved the way for WTO status for China, President Clinton held further trade talks in New Zealand with President Jiang Zemin in September. Indications were that China could expect admittance to the 134-member trade group as early as January 2000. China's trade prospects were also bolstered when the U.S. Congress approved the renewal of its most-favored-nation trade status in July, guaranteeing continued low tariffs for Chinese exports to the U.S.

Although 1999 marked the fiftieth anniversary of Communist China, many observers noted that the country had, increasingly, evolved into "capitalist China" with the rapid development of its free-market sector. In the decade since Tienanmen Square, its leaders had maintained their authoritarian grip on the nation but at the same time implemented economic reforms at a rapid rate. China attracted approximately $200 billion in foreign investment over the course of the decade, and the private sector was thought to account for as much as one-third of the nation's economy by 1999. In addition, the government had taken steps to privatize such sectors as health care and housing.

As it turned out, however, free-market reforms did not necessarily guarantee an overall strong economy. As the year drew to a close, devaluation of the country's currency—the yuan—looked increasingly likely in the near future. China's consumers were saving rather than spending, and weak consumer demand for domestically produced goods had combined with overproduction to produce serious deflation. Retail prices continued the decline begun the previous year. Other recessionary developments included rising unemployment, falling wages, and a declining trade surplus.

GOVERNMENT AND POLITICS

As the People's Republic of China reached the tenth anniversary of the massacre of pro-democracy demonstrators in Tienanmen Square, repression by its government once again received international attention. This time the government's target was Falun Gong, a religious cult combining elements of Buddhism, Taoism, and the Chinese martial arts. Since its inception in 1992, the group had attracted millions of members, and in April 1999 as many as 20,000 held a mass, peaceful demonstration outside government headquarters in Beijing. China's rulers called this gathering the most serious threat to the nation's political stability since the pro-democracy demonstrations of 1989. The prospect of a religious group organized well enough to muster such a large crowd outside the residential compound of the nation's leaders was considered enough of a threat to get the group outlawed by July.

In international affairs, China's relationship with the United States was tested on several fronts in 1999. In March, Wen Ho Lee, a Chinese computer scientist working in the U.S., was fired from his position at the Los Alamos National Laboratory for allegedly stealing nuclear secrets for the People's Republic. Two months later, China was the injured party when NATO war planes accidentally bombed its embassy in Belgrade during the crisis in Kosovo, killing three persons and injuring twenty more. The incident provoked the strongest wave of anti-American feeling in China since China and the United States established diplomatic ties over twenty years ago. Both President Clinton and NATO Secretary General Javier Solana apologized for the attack, as China demanded an international investigation into the incident and financial reparations.

Further complicating relations between China and the United States was a July statement by Taiwan's president that challenged China's official view of the island as a "renegade province," proposing, instead, that relations between the two countries be carried out on a "special state-to-state basis." In response, China held civilian mobilization exercises near Taiwan later in the month. Meanwhile, relations with China's Communist neighbor, North Korea, were enjoying a thaw. North Korea's second-highest-ranking political leader, President Yong Nam, paid a state visit to China in June, becoming the highest-ranking North Korean official to visit China since 1991.

As October approached, the mainland Chinese prepared to celebrate their republic's fiftieth anniversary with gala festivities in Beijing. The city underwent improvements that cost an estimated $13 billion, including the construction of new bank and military buildings, hotel renovations, road and public transit modernization, and the addition of a new airport terminal.

CULTURE AND SOCIETY

China's rich cultural legacy—and the history of music itself—was extended further into the past with the discovery in Henan Province of a tiny flute. The flute, which was carved from the wing bone of a crane and whose age was estimated at 9,000 years, is the oldest functional musical instrument ever found anywhere. It provided an important glimpse of a neolithic people who flourished in northern China between 7000 and 5700 B.C. and were among the first to make the transition from cave dwelling to agricultural village life.

After playing many close matches in the past, the Chinese and U.S. women's soccer teams met in the Women's World Cup championship games in Pasadena, California, where the United States won the championship in a game decided by penalty kicks. The match was attended by the largest crowd ever to watch a women's sporting event.

The Chinese government's campaign against the Falun Gong cult drew attention to the growing role of religion in contemporary Chinese life, and to the uneasiness with which it is regarded by China's government, which outlawed the cult after April's mass demonstration in the nation's capital. In addition to non-traditional religious groups like Falun Gong, millions of Chinese subscribe to the mainstream religions of Buddhism, Islam, and Christianity. Many consider the growth of religious faith a consequence of popular disillusionment with Communist rule since the late 1950s. It is also seen as a sign of a quest for the sense of unity and belonging that is being lost as China's formerly monolithic public sector recedes in the face of growing privatization and commercialization.

DIRECTORY

CENTRAL GOVERNMENT
Head of State

President
Jiang Zemin, Office of the President

Vice President
Hu Jintao, Office of the Vice President

Premier
Zhu Rongji, Office of the Premier

Ministers

Minister of Agriculture
Chen Yaobang, Ministry of Agriculture, 11 Nongzhanguan Nanli, Chaoyang District, Beijing 100020, People's Republic of China
PHONE: +86 64193366

Minister of Communications
Huang Zhendong, Ministry of Communications, 11 Jianguomennei Dajie, Beijing 100736, People's Republic of China
PHONE: +86 65292114

Minister of Construction
Yu Zhengsheng, Ministry of Construction, 9 Sanlihe Road, Beijing 100835, People's Republic of China
PHONE: +86 68394114

Minister of Finance
Xiang Huaicheng, Ministry of Finance, 3 Nansanxiang, Sanlihe, Xidan District, Beijing 100820, People's Republic of China
PHONE: +86 68551888
FAX: +86 68533635

Minister of Foreign Trade and Economic Cooperation
Shi Guangsheng, Ministry of Foreign Trade and Economic Cooperation, 2 Dongchang'anjie, Beijing 100731, People's Republic of China
PHONE: +86 65198114.
FAX: +86 64198912

Minister of Information Industry
Wu Jichuan, Ministry of Information Industry, 13 Xichang'anjie, Beijing 100804, People's Republic of China
PHONE: +86 66014249.
FAX: +86 62016362

Minister of State Development Planning Commission
Zeng Peiyan, Ministry of State Development Planning Commission, 38 Yuetannanjie, Xicheng District, Beijing 100824, People's Republic of China
PHONE: +86 68502114
FAX: +86 68512929

Minister of State Economic and Trade Commission
Sheng Huaren, Ministry of State Economic and Trade Commission, 26 Xuanwumen Xidajie, Beijing 100053, People's Republic of China

PHONE: +86 63192298
FAX: +86 63045326

Minister of Railways
Fu Zhihuan, Ministry of Railways, 10 Fuxinglu, Haidian District, Beijing 100844, People's Republic of China
PHONE: +86 63240114
FAX: +86 63242150

POLITICAL ORGANIZATIONS

China Association for Promoting Democracy
TITLE: Chairwoman
NAME: Lei Jieqiong

China Democratic League
TITLE: Chairman
NAME: Fei Xiaotong

China Democratic National Construction Association
TITLE: Chairman
NAME: Sun Qimeng

China Revolutionary Committee of the Kuomintang
TITLE: Chairman
NAME: Li Peiyao

China Zhi Gong Dang
TITLE: Chairman
NAME: Dong Yinchu

Chinese Peasants' and Workers' Democratic Party
TITLE: Chairman
NAME: Lu Jiaxi

Communist Party of China
TITLE: General Secretary
NAME: Jiang Zemin

Jiu San Society
TITLE: Chairman
NAME: Wu Jieping

Taiwan Democratic Self-government League
TITLE: Chairman
NAME: Cai Zimin

DIPLOMATIC REPRESENTATION

Embassies in China

Afghanistan
8 Dongzhimenwai Da Jie, Sanlitun, Beijing 100600, People's Republic of China
PHONE: +86 65321582

Albania
28 Guanghua Lu, Jianguomenwai, Beijing 100600, People's Republic of China
PHONE: +86 65321120

Algeria
7 Sanlitun Lu, Beijing 100600, People's Republic of China
PHONE: +86 65321231

Angola
1-13-1 Tayuan Diplomatic Office Bldg., Jianguomenwai, Beijing 100600, People's Republic of China
PHONE: +86 65326968

Argentina
11 Dongwu Jie, Sanlitun, Beijing 100600, People's Republic of China
PHONE: +86 65322090; 65322142

Australia
21 Dongzhimenwai Da Jie, Sanlitun, Beijing 100600, People's Republic of China
PHONE: +86 65322331

Austria
5 Xiushui Nan Jie, Jianguomenwai, Beijing 100600, People's Republic of China, China
PHONE: +86 65322061

Azerbaijan
2-10-2 Tayuan Diplomatic Ofc. Bldg., Jianguomenwai, Beijing 100600, People's Republic of China
PHONE: +86 65324614

Bahrain
2-9-1 Tayuan Diplomatic Ofc. Bldg., Jianguomenwai, Beijing 100600, People's Republic of China
PHONE: +86 65325025

Bangladesh
42 Guanghua Lu, Jianguomenwai, Beijing 100600, People's Republic of China
PHONE: +86 65322521; 65323706

Belarus
2-10-1 Tayuan Diplomatic Ofc. Bldg., Jianguomenwai, Beijing 100600, People's Republic of China
PHONE: +86 65326426

Belgium
6 Sanlitun Lu, Beijing 100600, People's Republic of China
PHONE: +86 65321736; 65322782

Benin
38 Guanghua Lu, Jianguomenwai, Beijing 100600, People's Republic of China
PHONE: +86 65322741; 65323122

Bolivia
2-3-2 Tayuan Diplomatic Ofc. Bldg., Beijing 100600, People's Republic of China
PHONE: +86 65324370; 65323074

Botswana
1-8-1 Tayuan Diplomatic Ofc. Bldg., Jianguomenwai, Beijing 100600, People's Republic of China
PHONE: +86 65325751

Brazil
27 Guanghua Lu, Jianguomenwai, Beijing 100600, People's Republic of China
PHONE: +86 65322881; 65323883; 65322902

Brunei Darussalam
1-91 Sanlitun Ofc. Bldg., Beijing 100600, People's Republic of China
PHONE: +86 65324094

Bulgaria
4 Xiushui Bei Jie, Jianguomenwai, Beijing 100600, People's Republic of China
PHONE: +86 65321946; 65321916

Burkina Faso
9 Sanlitun Liu Jie, Beijing 100600, People's Republic of China
PHONE: +86 65322550; 65322798

Burundi
25 Guanghua Lu, Jianguomenwai, Beijing 100600, People's Republic of China
PHONE: +86 65322328

Cambodia
9 Dongzhimenwai Da Jie, Beijing 100600, People's Republic of China
PHONE: +86 65321889

Cameroon
7 Dongwu Jie, Sanlitun, Beijing 100600, People's Republic of China

PHONE: +86 65321828; 65322119

Canada
19 Dongzhimenwai Da Jie, Chaoyangqu, Beijing 100600, People's Republic of China
PHONE: +86 65323536

Central African Republic
1 Dongsan Jie, Sanlitun, Beijing 100600, People's Republic of China
PHONE: +86 65321789

Chad
21 Guanghua Lu, Jianguomenwai, Beijing 100600, People's Republic of China
PHONE: +86 65321295; 65324830

Chile
1 Dongsi Jie, Sanlitun, Beijing 100600, People's Republic of China
PHONE: +86 65321591; 65322074

Columbia
34 Guanghua Lu Jianguomenwai, Beijing 100600
PHONE: +86 65323377; 65321713

Congo
7 Dongsi Jie, Sanlitun, Beijing 100600, People's Republic of China
PHONE: +86 65321658

Côte d'Ivoire
9 Beixiao Jie, Sanlitun, Beijing 100600, People's Republic of China
PHONE: +86 65321223; 65323192

Croatia
2-1-31 Sanlitun, Diplomatic Apartments, Beijing 100600, People's Republic of China
PHONE: +86 65326241; 65326256

Cuba
1 Xiushui Nan Jie, Jianguomenwai, Beijing 100600, People's Republic of China
PHONE: +86 65321714; 65322349; 65326656

Cyprus
2-13-2 Tayuan Diplomatic Ofc. Bldg., Beijing 100600, People's Republic of China
PHONE: +86 65325057

Czech Republic
Ritan Lu, Jianguomenwai, Beijing 100600, People's Republic of China
PHONE: +86 65321531; 65326902

Denmark
Dongwu Jie, Sanlitun, Beijing 100600, People's Republic of China
PHONE: +86 65322431; 65322432

E-MAIL: ambadan@public.bta.net.cn

Ecuador
11-2-1 Jianguomenwai, Beijing 100600, People's Republic of China
PHONE: +86 65323158; 65323849

Egypt
2 Ritan Dong Lu, Jianguomenwai, Beijing 100600, People's Republic of China
PHONE: +86 65321825; 65321880

Equtorial Guinea
2 Dongsi Jie, Sanlitun, Beijing 100600, People's Republic of China
PHONE: +86 65323679

Eritrea
1-4-2 Tayuan Diplomatic Ofc. Bldg., Jianguomenwai, Beijing 100600, People's Republic of China
PHONE: +86 65326534

Ethiopia
3 Xiushui Nan Jie, Jianguomenwai, Beijing 100600, People's Republic of China
PHONE: +86 65321782

Finland
Kerry Centre, South Tower, Level 26, Guanghua 1, Beijing 100020, People's Republic of China
PHONE: +86 85298541
FAX: +86 85298547
E-MAIL: finemb@public3.bta.net.cn

France
3 Dongsan Jie, Sanlitun, Beijing 100600, People's Republic of China
PHONE: +86 65321274

Gabon
36 Guanghua Lu, Jianguomenwai, Beijing 100600, People's Republic of China
PHONE: +86 65322810; 65323824

Germany
5 Dongzhimenwai Da Jie, Sanlitun, Beijing 100600, People's Republic of China
PHONE: +86 65322161; 65321181

Ghana
8 Sanlitun Lu, Beijing 100600, People's Republic of China
PHONE: +86 65321319; 65321544

Greece
19 Guanghua Lu, Jianguomenwai, Beijing 100600, People's Republic of China
PHONE: +86 65321317; 65321391; 65321588

Guinea
2 Xiliu Jie, Sanlitun, Beijing 100600, People's
Republic of China
PHONE: +86 65323649

Guyana
1 Xiushui Dong Jie, Jianguomenwai, Beijing
100600, People's Republic of China
PHONE: +86 65321337

Hungary
10 Dongzhimenwai Da Jie, Sanlitun, Beijing
100600, People's Republic of China
PHONE: +86 65321431

Iceland
3-2-11 Tayuan Diplomatic Ofc. Bldg.,
Jianguomenwai, Beijing 100600, People's
Republic of China
PHONE: +86 65326881

India
1 Ritan Dong Lu, Jianguomenwai, Beijing
100600, People's Republic of China
PHONE: +86 65321908; 65321856

Indonesia
Ofc. Bldg. B, Sanlitun, Beijing 100600, People's
Republic of China
PHONE: +86 65325489; 65325484

Iran
13 Dongliu Jie, Sanlitun, Beijing 100600,
People's Republic of China
PHONE: +86 65322040

Iraq
25 Xiushui Bei Jie, Jianguomenwai, Beijing
100600, People's Republic of China
PHONE: +86 65323385; 65321873

Ireland
3 Ritan Dong Lu, Jianguomenwai, Beijing
100600, People's Republic of China
PHONE: +86 65322691; 65322914

Israel
Rm. 405, West Wing Ofc., 1 Jianguomenwai Da
Jie, Beijing 100004, People's Republic of China
PHONE: 65050328; 65052970

Italy
2 Donger Jie, Sanlitun, Beijing 100600, People's
Republic of China
PHONE: +86 65322131

Japan
7 Ritan Lu, Jianguomenwai, Beijing 100600,
People's Republic of China
PHONE: +86 65322361; 65322121

Jordan
5 Dongliu Jie, Sanlitun, Beijing 100600,
People's Republic of China
PHONE: +86 65323906; 65323283

Kazakhstan
9 Dongliujie, Sanlitun, Beijing 100600, People's
Republic of China
PHONE: +86 65326182; 65326541

Kenya
4 Xiliu Jie, Sanlitun, Beijing 100600, People's
Republic of China
PHONE: +86 65323381; 65322473

North Korea
Ritan Bei Lu, Jianguomenwai, Beijing 100600,
People's Republic of China
PHONE: +86 65321186; 65321154

South Korea
4/F, China World Tower, 1 Jianguomenwai Da
Jie, Beijing 100004, People's Republic of China
PHONE: 65052608

Kuwait
23 Guanghua Lu, Jianguomenwai, Beijing
100600, People's Republic of China
PHONE: +86 65322216; 65322182

Kyrgyzstan
2-4-1 Tayuan Diplomatic Ofc. Bldg., Beijing
100600, People's Republic of China
PHONE: +86 65326458

Laos
11 Dongsi Jie, Sanlitun, Beijing 100600,
People's Republic of China
PHONE: +86 65321224

Lebanon
51 Dongliu Jie, Sanlitun, Beijing 100600,
People's Republic of China
PHONE: +86 65322197; 65323281; 65321560

Lesotho
2-3-13 Sanlitun, Diplomatic Compound, Beijing
100600, People's Republic of China
PHONE: +86 65326842

Libya
3 Dongliu Jie, Sanlitun, Beijing 100600,
People's Republic of China
PHONE: +86 65323666

Lithuania
8-2-12 Tayuan Diplomatic Ofc. Bldg.,
Jianguomenwai, Beijing 100600, People's
Republic of China
PHONE: +86 65324421

Luxembourg
21 Neiwubu Jie, Beijing 100600, People's
Republic of China
PHONE: 65135937

Macedonia
5-2-22 Sanlitun Diplomatic Apartments, Beijing
100600, People's Republic of China
PHONE: +86 65326282

Madagascar
3 Sanlitun Dong Jie, Beijing 100600, People's
Republic of China
PHONE: +86 65321353

Malaysia
13 Dongzhimenwai Da Jie, Beijing 100600,
People's Republic of China
PHONE: +86 65322531

Mali
8 Dongsi Jie, Sanlitun, Beijing 100600, People's
Republic of China
PHONE: +86 65321704; 65321687; 65321618

Malta
2-1-22 Tayuan Diplomatic Ofc. Bldg., Beijing
100600, People's Republic of China
PHONE: +86 65323114

Marshall Islands
2-14-1 Tayuan Diplomatic Ofc. Bldg.,
Jianguomenwai, Beijing 100600, People's
Republic of China
PHONE: +86 65325819; 65325904

Mauritania
9 Dongsan Jie, Sanlitun, Beijing 100600,
People's Republic of China
PHONE: +86 65321346; 65321703; 65321685

Mexico
5 Dongwu Jie, Sanlitun, Beijing 100600,
People's Republic of China
PHONE: +86 65322574; 65322070

Mongolia
2 Xiushui Bei Jie, Jianguomenwai, Beijing
100600, People's Republic of China
PHONE: +86 65321203

Morocco
16 Sanlitun Lu, Beijing 100600, People's
Republic of China
PHONE: +86 65321796; 65321483; 65321453

Mozambique
1-7-1 Tayuan Diplomatic Ofc. Bldg., Beijing
100600, People's Republic of China
PHONE: +86 65323664; 65323578

Myanmar
6 Dongzhimenwai Da Jie, Chaoyangqu, Beijing
100600, People's Republic of China
PHONE: +86 65321584; 65321425; 65321488

Namibia
1-13-2 Tayuan Diplomatic Ofc. Bldg.,
Jianguomenwai, Beijing 100600, People's
Republic of China
PHONE: +86 65324810

Nepal
1 Xiliu Jie, Sanlitun, Beijing 100600, People's
Republic of China
PHONE: +86 65321795

Netherlands
4 Liangmahe Nan Lu, Beijing 100600, People's
Republic of China
PHONE: +86 65321131

New Zealand
1 Donger Jie, Ritan Lu, Chaoyangqu, Beijing
100600, People's Republic of China
PHONE: +86 65322731

Nicaragua
2-12-2 Tayuan Diplomatic Ofc. Bldg., Beijing
100600, People's Republic of China
PHONE: +86 65323014

Niger
11 Dongliu Jie, Sanlitun, Beijing 100600,
People's Republic of China
PHONE: +86 65322768

Nigeria
2 Donhwu Jie, Sanlitun, Beijing 100600,
People's Republic of China
PHONE: +86 65323631

Norway
1 Dongyi Jie, Sanlitun, Beijing 100600, People's
Republic of China
PHONE: +86 65322261; 65321329

Oman
6 Liangmahe Nan Lu, Sanlitun, Beijing 100600,
People's Republic of China
PHONE: +86 65323276; 65323692

Pakistan
1 Dongzhimenwai Da Jie, Sanlitun, Beijing
100600, People's Republic of China
PHONE: +86 65322504; 65322695; 65326660

Palestine
2 Dongsan Jie, Sanlitun, Beijing 100600,
People's Republic of China
PHONE: +86 65321361; 65323241

Papua New Guinea
2-11-2 Tayuan Diplomatic Ofc. Bldg., Beijing
100600, People's Republic of China
PHONE: +86 65324312

Peru
2-82 Sanlitun Diplomatic Ofc. Bldg., Beijing
100600, People's Republic of China
PHONE: +86 65324658; 65323719

Philippines
23 Xiushui Bei Jie, Jianguomenwai, Beijing
100600, People's Republic of China
PHONE: +86 65322794; 65321872; 65322518

Poland
1 Ritan Lu, Jianguomenwai, Beijing 100600,
People's Republic of China
PHONE: +86 65321235

Portugal
2-15 Tayuan Diplomatic Ofc. Bldg., Beijing
100600, People's Republic of China
PHONE: +86 65323497; 65323242

Qatar
1-9-2 Tayuan Diplomatic Ofc. Bldg., Beijing
100600, People's Republic of China
PHONE: +86 65322231

Romania
Ritan Lu, Donger Jie, Beijing 100600, People's
Republic of China
PHONE: +86 65323442; 65323255

Russia
4 Dongzhimenbei Zhong Jie, Beijing 100600,
People's Republic of China
PHONE: +86 65322051; 65321381

Rwanda
30 Xiushui Bei Jie, Jianguomenwai, Beijing
100600, People's Republic of China
PHONE: +86 65322193; 65321762

Saudi Arabia
1 Sanlitun Beixiao Jie, Beijing 100600, People's
Republic of China
PHONE: +86 65324825; 65325325

Senegal
1 Dongyi Jie, Ritan Lu, Jianguomenwai, Beijing
100600, People's Republic of China
PHONE: +86 65322593; 65322576

Sierra Leone
7 Dongzhimenwai Da Jie, Sanlitun, Beijing
100600, People's Republic of China
PHONE: +86 65321222; 65322174

Singapore
1 Xiushui Bei Jie, Jianguomenwai, Beijing
100600, People's Republic of China
PHONE: +86 65323926; 65323143

Slovakia
Ritan Lu, Jianguomenwai, Beijing 100600,
People's Republic of China
PHONE: +86 65321531

Slovenia
3-53 Jianguomenwai, Beijing 100600, People's
Republic of China
PHONE: +86 65326356

Somali
2 Sanlitun Lu, Beijing 100600, People's
Republic of China
PHONE: +86 65321752

Spain
9 Sanlitun Lu, Beijing 100600, People's
Republic of China
PHONE: +86 65321986; 65323728

Sri Lanka
3 Jianhua Lu, Jianguomenwai, Beijing 100600,
People's Republic of China
PHONE: +86 65321861

Sudan
1 Donger Jie, Sanlitun, Beijing 100600, People's
Republic of China
PHONE: +86 65323715; 65322205

Sweden
3 Dongzhimenwai Da Jie, Beijing 100600,
People's Republic of China
PHONE: +86 65323331

Switzerland
3 Dongwu Jie, Sanlitun, Beijing 100600,
People's Republic of China
PHONE: +86 65322736

Syria
6 Dongsi Jie, Sanlitun, Beijing 100600, People's
Republic of China
PHONE: +86 65321372; 65321347

Tanzania
8 Liangmahe Nan Lu, Sanlitun, Beijing 100600,
People's Republic of China
PHONE: +86 65321491; 65321719

Thailand
40 Guanghua Lu, Jianguomenwai, Beijing
100600, People's Republic of China
PHONE: +86 65321903; 65323955

Togo
11 Dongzhimenwai Da Jie, Beijing 100600, People's Republic of China
PHONE: +86 65322202; 65322444

Tunisia
1 Sanlitun Dong Jie, Beijing 100600, People's Republic of China
PHONE: +86 65322435

Turkey
9 Dongwu Jie, Sanlitun, Beijing 100600, People's Republic of China
PHONE: +86 65322347; 65322184; 65323846; 65322650

Turkmenistan
1-15-2 Tayuan Diplomatic Compound, Beijing 100600, People's Republic of China
PHONE: +86 65326975

Uganda
5 Dong Jie, Sanlitun, Beijing 100600, People's Republic of China
PHONE: +86 65321708

Ukraine
11 Dongliu Jie, Sanlitun, Beijing 100600, People's Republic of China
PHONE: +86 65326359

United Arab Emirates
1-9-1 Tayuan Diplomatic Ofc. Bldg., Beijing 100600, People's Republic of China
PHONE: +86 65322112

United Kingdom
11 Guanghua Lu, Jianguomenwai, Beijing 100600, People's Republic of China
PHONE: +86 65321961; 65321930; 65321937

United States
3 Xiushui Bei Jie, Jianguomenwai, Beijing 100600, People's Republic of China
PHONE: +86 65323831

Uruguay
2-7-2 Tayuan Diplomatic Ofc. Bldg., Beijing 100600, People's Republic of China
PHONE: +86 65324445; 65324413

Uzbekistan
2-1-92 Tayuan Diplomatic Compound, Beijing 100600, People's Republic of China
PHONE: +86 65326854

Venezuela
14 Sanlitun Lu, Beijing 100600, People's Republic of China
PHONE: +86 65321295

Vietnam
32 Guanghua Lu, Jianguomenwai, Beijing 100600, People's Republic of China
PHONE: +86 65321155; 65325415

Yemen
5 Dongsan Jie, Sanlitun, Beijing 100600, People's Republic of China
PHONE: +86 65321558

Zaire
6 Dongwu Jie, Sanlitun, Beijing 100600, People's Republic of China
PHONE: +86 65321995; 65322713

Zambia
5 Dongsi Jie, Sanlitun, Beijing 100600, People's Republic of China
PHONE: +86 65321554; 65321778; 65322058

Zimbabwe
7 Dongsan Jie, Sanlitun, Beijing 100600, People's Republic of China
PHONE: +86 65323665; 65323397; 65323795; 65323964

JUDICIAL SYSTEM
Supreme People's Court

FURTHER READING
Articles

"After 9,000 Years, Oldest Playable Flute is Heard Again." *The New York Times*, 28 September 1999, p. D2.

"As China turns 50, a Duel of Stability and Reform." *The New York Times*, 1 October 1999, p. A1.

"The Birthday Party." *The Economist* (September 25, 1999): 50.

"China and America: A Summer Thaw?" *The Economist* (September 11, 1999): 47.

"China, at 50, on a Long March to Modernity." *U.S. News and World Report* (October 4, 1999): 35.

"China Celebrates 50 Years of Communism." *The Christian Science Monitor* (October 1, 1999): 1.

"China's New Revolution." *Business Week*, (September 27, 1999): 74.

"Clinton and Jiang Heal Rift and Set New Trade Course." *The New York Times*, 12 September 1999, p. 1N.

"In China, Decades of Economic Reform Have Helped Knit Vast Nation Together." *The*

Wall Street Journal, 16 September 1999, p. 26A.

''Inside China's Search for its Soul.'' *Time* (October 4, 1999): 69.

''The Real Enemy Within.'' *The Economist* (May 1, 1999): 39.

''Steady as She Slows.'' *The Economist* (September 11, 1999): 48.

''Taiwan's High-Stakes Game.'' *The Economist* (August 21, 1999).

''Why the Exercisers Exercise China's Party.'' *The Economist* (July 31, 1999): 32.

Books

Twohey, Michael. *Authority and Welfare in China: Modern Debates in Historical Perspective.* New York: St. Martin's Press, 1999.

Winckler, Edwin A., ed. *Transition from Communism in China: Institutional and Comparative Analyses.* Boulder, Colo.: Lynne Reinner Publishers, 1999.

CHINA: STATISTICAL DATA

For sources and notes see "Sources of Statistics" in the front of each volume.

GEOGRAPHY

Geography (1)
Area:

Total: 9,596,960 sq km.

Land: 9,326,410 sq km.

Water: 270,550 sq km.

Area—comparative: slightly smaller than the US.

Land boundaries:

Total: 22,143.34 km.

Border countries: Afghanistan 76 km, Bhutan 470 km, India 3,380 km, Kazakstan 1,533 km, North Korea 1,416 km, Kyrgyzstan 858 km, Laos 423 km, Macau 0.34 km, Mongolia 4,673 km, Myanmar 2,185 km, Nepal 1,236 km, Pakistan 523 km, Russia (northeast) 3,605 km, Russia (northwest) 40 km, Tajikistan 414 km, Vietnam 1,281 km.

Continued on next page.

HUMAN FACTORS

Demographics (2A)

	1990	1995	1998	2000	2010	2020	2030	2040	2050
Population	1,138,894.6	1,203,383.1	1,236,914.7	1,256,167.7	1,334,485.5	1,397,433.5	1,406,655.3	1,384,560.4	1,322,434.9
Net migration rate (per 1,000 population)	NA	NA	NA	NA	NA	NA	NA	NA	NA
Births	NA	NA	NA	NA	NA	NA	NA	NA	NA
Deaths	NA	NA	NA	NA	NA	NA	NA	NA	NA
Life expectancy - males	66.9	67.6	68.3	68.8	71.0	72.2	73.6	74.8	75.9
Life expectancy - females	68.5	69.8	71.1	71.9	75.5	77.6	79.2	80.6	81.7
Birth rate (per 1,000)	21.2	17.1	15.7	14.5	13.9	11.3	9.8	10.0	8.8
Death rate (per 1,000)	7.3	7.0	7.0	7.0	7.4	8.5	10.2	12.5	14.6
Women of reproductive age (15-49 yrs.)	306,441.1	327,285.2	337,795.5	342,295.9	361,684.2	331,043.9	310,159.0	281,229.9	258,784.0
of which are currently married	965,555.9	NA	NA	NA	NA	NA	NA	NA	NA
Fertility rate	2.2	1.8	1.8	1.8	1.8	1.8	1.7	1.7	1.7

Except as noted, values for vital statistics are in thousands; life expectancy is in years.

GEOGRAPHY

Geography (1) (cont.)

Coastline: 14,500 km.

Climate: extremely diverse; tropical in south to subarctic in north.

Terrain: mostly mountains, high plateaus, deserts in west; plains, deltas, and hills in east.

Natural resources: coal, iron ore, petroleum, mercury, tin, tungsten, antimony, manganese, molybdenum, vanadium, magnetite, aluminum, lead, zinc, uranium, hydropower potential (world's largest).

Land use:

Arable land: 10%

Permanent crops: 0%

Permanent pastures: 43%

Forests and woodland: 14%

Other: 33% (1993 est.).

HUMAN FACTORS

Health Personnel (3)

Total health expenditure as a percentage of GDP, 1990-1997[a]

Public sector 2.1

Private sector 1.8

Total[b] 3.8

Health expenditure per capita in U.S. dollars, 1990-1997[a]

Purchasing power parity 90

Total 19

Availability of health care facilities per 100,000 people

Hospital beds 1990-1997[a] 240

Doctors 1993[c] 115

Nurses 1993[c] 88

Health Indicators (4)

Life expectancy at birth

1980 67

1997 70

Daily per capita supply of calories (1996) 2,844

Total fertility rate births per woman (1997) 1.9

Maternal mortality ratio per 100,000 live births (1990-97) . . . . .95[e]

Safe water % of population with access (1995) 83

Sanitation % of population with access (1995) . . . .

Consumption of iodized salt % of households (1992-98)[a] 83

Smoking prevalence

Male % of adults (1985-95)[a] 61

Female % of adults (1985-95)[a] 7

Tuberculosis incidence per 100,000 people (1997) 113

Adult HIV prevalence % of population ages 15-49 (1997) 0.06

Infants and Malnutrition (5)

Under-5 mortality rate (1997) 47

% of infants with low birthweight (1990-97) 9

Births attended by skilled health staff % of total[a] . . .85

% fully immunized (1995-97)

TB 96

DPT 96

Polio 97

Measles 96

Prevalence of child malnutrition under age 5 (1992-97)[b] 16

Ethnic Division (6)

Han Chinese 91.9%; Zhuang, Uygur, Hui, Yi, Tibetan, Miao, Manchu, Mongol, Buyi, Korean, and other nationalities 8.1%.

Religions (7)

Daoism (Taoism), Buddhism, Muslim 2%-3%, Christian 1% (est.). Officially atheist, but traditionally pragmatic and eclectic.

Languages (8)

Standard Chinese or Mandarin (Putonghua, based on the Beijing dialect), Yue (Cantonese), Wu (Shanghaiese), Minbei (Fuzhou), Minnan (Hokkien-Taiwanese), Xiang, Gan, Hakka dialects, minority languages.

EDUCATION

Public Education Expenditures (9)

Public expenditure on education (% of GNP)

1980 . . . . .2.5

1996 . . . . .2.3

Expenditure per student

Primary % of GNP per capita

1980 . . . . .3.8

1996 . . . . .6.5

Public Education Expenditures (9) (cont.)

Secondary % of GNP per capita

1980 . . . .

1996 . . . . .15.0[1]

Tertiary % of GNP per capita

1980 . . . . .245.4

1996 . . . . .65.9

Expenditure on teaching materials

Primary % of total for level (1996) . . . .

Secondary % of total for level (1996) . . . .

Primary pupil-teacher ratio per teacher (1996) 24

Duration of primary education years (1995) 5

Educational Attainment (10)

Age group (1990)[16] . . . . .25+

Total population .571,589,800

Highest level attained (%)

No schooling 29.3

First level

Not completed 34.3

Completed . . . . .NA

Entered second level

S-1 . . . . .34.4

S-2 . . . . .NA

Postsecondary 2.0

Literacy Rates (11A)

In thousands and percent[1]	1990	1995	2000	2010
Illiterate population (15+ yrs.)	181,609	166,173	143,458	96,730
Literacy rate - total adult pop. (%)	77.8	81.5	85.0	91.1
Literacy rate - males (%)	87.0	89.9	92.3	95.9
Literacy rate - females (%)	68.1	72.7	77.4	86.1

GOVERNMENT & LAW

Political Parties (12)

Legislative branch is the unicameral National People's Congress (2,979 seats members elected by municipal, regional, and provincial people's congresses to serve five-year terms).

Government Budget (13B)

Revenues . . . . .NA

Expenditures . . . . .NA

Capital expenditures . . . . .NA

NA stands for not available.

Crime (15)

Crime rate (for 1997)

Crimes reported 1,613,600

Total persons convicted 1,172,100

Crimes per 100,000 population 125

Persons responsible for offenses

Total number of suspects .NA

Total number of female suspects 5

Total number of juvenile suspects 51

LABOR FORCE

Labor Force (16)

Total (million) 623.9

Agriculture and forestry .53%

Industry and commerce .26%

Construction and mining 7%

Social services 4%

Other 10%

Data for 1995. Percent distribution for 1995.

Unemployment Rate (17)

Officially 4% in urban areas; probably 8%-10%; substantial unemployment and underemployment in rural areas (1997 est.)

PRODUCTION SECTOR

Electric Energy (18)

Capacity . . . . .250 million kW (1997 est.)

Production . . . . .1.135 trillion kWh (1997 est.)

Consumption per capita . . . . . . .1,100 kWh (1997 est.)

Transportation (19)

Highways:

total: 1.18 million km

paved: 241,300 km

unpaved: 938,700 km (1998 est.)

Transportation (19) (cont.)

Waterways: 138,600 km; about 110,600 km navigable

Pipelines: crude oil 9,070 km; petroleum products 560 km; natural gas 9,383 km (1998)

Merchant marine:

total: 1,708 ships (1,000 GRT or over) totaling 16,139,185 GRT/24,154,260 DWT

Airports: 206 (1996 est.)

Airports—with paved runways:

total: 192

over 3,047 m: 18

2,438 to 3,047 m: 65

1,524 to 2,437 m: 90

914 to 1,523 m: 13

under 914 m: 6 (1996 est.)

Airports—with unpaved runways:

total: 14

1,524 to 2,437 m: 8

914 to 1,523 m: 5

under 914 m: 1 (1996 est.)

GOVERNMENT & LAW

Military Affairs (14B)

	1990	1991	1992	1993	1994	1995
Military expenditures						
Current dollars (mil.)	48,440	48,210	51,500	53,780	57,040	63,510
1995 constant dollars (mil.)	55,660	53,270	55,390	56,390	58,470	63,510
Armed forces (000)	3,500	3,200	3,160	3,031	2,930	2,930
Gross national product (GNP)						
Current dollars (bil.)	1,382,000	1,583,000	1,855,000	2,156,000	2,461,000	2,759,000
1995 constant dollars (bil.)	1,588,000	1,749,000	1,995,000	2,260,000	2,523,000	2,759,000
Central government expenditures (CGE)						
1995 constant dollars (mil.)	295,600	307,800	328,600	346,700	325,400	343,900
People (mil.)	1133.7	1148.1	1161.1	1173.6	1185.9	1198.1
Military expenditure as % of GNP	3.5	3.0	2.8	2.5	2.3	2.3
Military expenditure as % of CGE	18.8	17.3	16.9	16.3	18.0	18.5
Military expenditure per capita (1995 $)	49	46	48	48	49	53
Armed forces per 1,000 people (soldiers)	3.1	2.8	2.7	2.6	2.5	2.4
GNP per capita (1994 $)	1,401	1,523	1,718	1,926	2,127	2,303
Arms imports[6]						
Current dollars (mil.)	300	300	1,300	575	260	725
1995 constant dollars (mil.)	345	332	1,398	603	267	725
Arms exports[6]						
Current dollars (mil.)	2,000	1,400	1,100	1,100	725	625
1995 constant dollars (mil.)	2,298	1,547	1,183	1,153	743	625
Total imports[7]						
Current dollars (mil.)	53,340	63,790	80,580	103,100	115,700	129,100
1995 constant dollars (mil.)	61,310	70,490	86,680	108,100	118,600	129,100
Total exports[7]						
Current dollars (mil.)	61,270	71,910	84,940	90,970	121,000	148,800
1995 constant dollars (mil.)	70,410	79,460	91,360	95,370	1,241,000	148,800
Arms as percent of total imports[8]	.6	.5	1.6	.6	.2	.6
Arms as percent of total exports[8]	3.3	1.9	1.3	1.2	.6	.4

Top Agricultural Products (20)

Rice, wheat, potatoes, sorghum, peanuts, tea, millet, barley, cotton, other fibers, oilseed; pork and other livestock products; fish.

MANUFACTURING SECTOR

GDP & Manufacturing Summary (21)

Detailed value added figures are listed by both International Standard Industry Code (ISIC) and product title.

	1980	1985	1990	1994
GDP				
($-1990 mil.)[1]	165,378	265,369	388,125	596,060
Per capita ($-1990)[1]	169	253	342	502
Manufacturing share (%) (current prices)[1]	41.0	37.2	33.6	30.7
Manufacturing				
Value added ($-1990 mil.)[1]	52,672	84,816	130,329	237,818
Industrial production index	NA	NA	NA	NA
Value added ($ mil.)	88,577	78,380	90,259	139,031
Gross output ($ mil.)	232,460	246,331	349,604	451,906
Employment (000)	24,390	39,957	52,627	61,931
Profitability (% of gross output)				
Intermediate input (%)	62	68	74	69
Wages and salaries inc. supplements (%)	6	5	5	5
Gross operating surplus	32	27	21	26
Productivity ($)				
Gross output per worker	9,531	6,017	6,643	7,297
Value added per worker	3,632	1,946	1,715	2,245
Average wage (inc. supplements)	548	286	317	340

Value added ($ mil.)

	1980	1985	1990	1994
311/2 Food products	3,764	3,433	4,489	7,149
313 Beverages	1,587	1,696	2,414	3,834
314 Tobacco products	3,545	3,999	6,220	6,410
321 Textiles	13,409	8,587	10,299	12,964
322 Wearing apparel	1,866	1,716	2,109	4,120
323 Leather and fur products	911	747	944	2,347
324 Footwear				
331 Wood and wood products	751	591	502	1,155
332 Furniture and fixtures	653	514	455	682
341 Paper and paper products	1,929	1,532	1,949	2,226
342 Printing and publishing	1,042	960	1,036	1,443
351 Industrial chemicals	7,125	5,584	8,459	6,595
352 Other chemical products	2,924	2,292	3,372	2,603
353 Petroleum refineries	4,223	3,676	2,714	4,686
354 Miscellaneous petroleum and coal products	154	183	208	352
355 Rubber products	2,175	1,593	1,603	1,605
356 Plastic products	1,256	1,317	1,736	2,572
361 Pottery, china and earthenware	439	431	504	1,025
362 Glass and glass products	838	822	705	1,386
369 Other non-metal mineral products	4,425	4,340	4,524	10,931
371 Iron and steel	6,538	5,810	6,571	14,972
372 Non-ferrous metals	1,868	1,730	2,050	3,057
381 Metal products	4,861	2,582	2,946	5,106
382 Non-electrical machinery	13,418	10,941	10,116	15,425
383 Electrical machinery	3,216	6,458	7,445	13,746
384 Transport equipment	3,013	4,134	3,918	8,764
385 Professional and scientific equipment	810	1,021	843	1,499
390 Other manufacturing industries	1,838	1,691	2,125	2,378

FINANCE, ECONOMICS, & TRADE

Economic Indicators (22)

National product: GDP—purchasing power parity—$4.25 trillion (1997 estimate as extrapolated from World Bank estimate for 1995 with use of official Chinese growth figures for 1996-97; the result may overstate China's GDP by as much as 25%)

National product real growth rate: 8.8% (1997 est.)

National product per capita: $3,460 (1997 est.)

Inflation rate—consumer price index: 2.8% (1997 est.)

Exchange Rates (24)

Exchange rates:

Yuan (¥) per US$1

December 1997	8.2796
1997	8.2898
1996	8.3142
1995	8.3514
1994	8.6187
1993	5.7620

Beginning 1 January 1994, the People's Bank of China quotes the midpoint rate against the US dollar based on the previous day's prevailing rate in the interbank foreign exchange market

Top Import Origins (25)

$142.4 billion (c.i.f., 1997) Data are for 1997.

Origins	%
Japan	NA
Taiwan	NA
United States	NA
South Korea	NA
Hong Kong	NA
Germany	NA
Singapore	NA

NA stands for not available.

Top Export Destinations (26)

$182.7 billion (f.o.b., 1997) Data are for 1997.

Destinations	%
Hong Kong	NA
United States	NA
Japan	NA
South Korea	NA
Germany	NA
Netherlands	NA

NA stands for not available.

Economic Aid (27)

Recipient: ODA, $1.977 billion (1993).

Balance of Payments (23)

	1992	1993	1994	1995	1996
Exports of goods (f.o.b.)	69,568	75,659	102,561	128,110	151,077
Imports of goods (f.o.b.)	−64,385	−86,313	−95,271	−110,060	−131,542
Trade balance	5,183	−10,654	7,290	18,050	19,535
Services - debits	−14,781	−17,710	−23,074	−42,188	−42,340
Services - credits	14,844	15,583	22,357	24,321	27,919
Private transfers (net)	351	289	−501	625	301
Government transfers (net)	804	883	836	810	1,828
Overall balance	6,401	−11,609	6,908	1,618	7,243

FINANCE, ECONOMICS, & TRADE

Import Export Commodities (28)

Import Commodities	Export Commodities
Mechanical appliances	Electrical machinery
Electrical machinery	Clothing
Mineral fuels	Footwear
Plastics	Toys
Iron and steel	Mineral fuels
Fabrics	Leather
Cotton and yarn	Plastics
	Fabrics

CHRISTMAS ISLAND

CAPITAL: The Settlement.

FLAG: The flag of Australia is used.

ANTHEM: Advance Australia Fair.

MONETARY UNIT: 1 Australian dollar ($A) = 100 cents.

WEIGHTS AND MEASURES: Metric system is used.

HOLIDAYS: New Year's Day, 1 January; Australia Day, end of January; Good Friday; Easter Monday; Anzac Day, 25 April; Queen's Birthday, Mid-June; Christmas Day, 25 December; and Boxing Day, 26 December.

TIME: 6 PM = noon GMT.

LOCATION AND SIZE: Situated at 10°30'S and 105°40'E in the Indian Ocean, directly south of the western tip of Java, Christmas Island is 2,623 km (1,630 mi.) northwest of Perth and has an area of about 135 sq km (52 sq mi.).

CLIMATE: The climate is tropical, and temperatures average 27°C (81°F) throughout the year. The rainy season runs from December to April (monsoon season), during which the island may get up to 287 cm (113 inches) of rain.

INTRODUCTORY SURVEY

RECENT HISTORY

British and Dutch navigators first sighted Christmas Island in the seventh century. Captain William Myrors of the British East India Ship Company named the island on Christmas Day of 1643. Isolation and a rugged coastline deterred settlement. In 1887 the men of the *HMS Egeria* collected rock samples which were analyzed by Dr. John Murray of Britain and found to be nearly pure phosphate. Dr. Murray advised the British Admiralty to annex Christmas Island, which they did on June 6, 1888. George Clunies-Ross established the

first settlement at Flying Fish Cove and in 1891 the British government offered both Clunies-Ross and Dr. Murray a joint ninety-nine year lease to extract the phosphate and cut timber. The lease was transferred in 1897 to the Christmas Island Phosphate Company largely owned by the two former lessees. Two hundred Chinese laborers were initially brought onto the island to work the mines. The first shipment of phosphate left the island in 1900.

For administrative purposes Christmas Island was incorporated with the Straits Settlements, now Singapore and part of Malaysia, in 1900. The phosphate mine continued profitable operations until World War II when Japanese occupied the island from 1942 to 1945. For a short period following the war, the island became a dependent colony of Singapore.

In 1948 the mining was taken over by the Australian and New Zealand governments in partnership. From 1949 to 1958 a large expansion program led to recruitment of workers from Cocos Islands, Malaysia, and Singapore. Bringing their families, these workers established the first permanent population on the island. Christmas Island remained a Crown colony until its transfer to Australia in 1958. The Australian government appointed an Official Representative to the territory until 1968 when new legislation provided for an Administrator. Unionization of the mine workers into the Union of Christmas Island Workers brought dramatic improvement in living and working conditions in the 1970s.

Also in the 1970s conflict between conservation and mining interests lead to the appointment of a Government Conservator from the Australian National Park and Wildlife Service. In 1980 a national

CHRISTMAS ISLAND

0   2   4 Miles

0   2   4 Kilometers

INDIAN OCEAN

⊛ The Settlement

airfield

INDIAN OCEAN

Christmas I. — Ashmore & Cartier Is.

Cocos Is.

Coral Sea Islands Territory

Islands administered by Australia

AUSTRALIA

Norfolk I.

Heard & McDonald Is.

Macquarie I.

park covering 63% of the island was established in 1980 in the Egeria Point area.

As deposits of phosphates began to be exhausted the Australian government in 1984 created Christmas Island Services Corporation. The Corporation sought to ease the phosphate company's responsibilities by taking over infrastructure services such as housing and lighting. The Corporation, placed under the Christmas Island Assembly, comprised of nine members first elected in 1985. Australian citizenship and social services were extended to the island's residents. Effects of drought and falling phosphate prices led to the mine closure in December of 1987. However, the mine was opened under private operation in 1992. Also, in 1992 the Christmas Island Shire Council superseded the corporation and assembly.

With hopes of economic diversification, a multi-million dollar casino opened in 1993. It enjoyed some success, but lost its license in 1998 and was forced to close until a new owner could be found.

GOVERNMENT

Christmas Island is administered as an external territory of Australia. The island has no administrative divisions. The chief of state is the British monarch, represented by the governor-general of Australia. The senior government representative on the island is the administrator, appointed by the Australian governor-general, and responsible to the Minister of Regional Services, Territories and Local Government.

The legislative branch is the unicameral Christmas Island Shire Council with nine seats, popularly elected for one year terms. The Shire provides local government services and manages tourism and economic development.

Judiciary

Christmas Island's judicial system includes the Supreme Court, District Court, Magistrate's Court, and Children's Court. The territory's legal system experienced major changes with passage of the Territories Law Reform Bill of 1992. Commonwealth and state laws, which apply in the state of Western Australia, also apply to Christmas Island. However, some of those laws have been repealed because of the island territory's unique status.

Political Parties

No political parties exist on Christmas Island.

DEFENSE

The Australian military provides defense protection to Christmas Island. The Australian and United States military are in close alliance through a 1951 Australian, New Zealand, and United States security treaty (ANZUS).

ECONOMIC AFFAIRS

Historically, Christmas Island's economy has been based almost entirely on the mining of phosphate for shipment primarily to Australia and New Zealand. In 1984 approximately 463,000 metric tons of phosphate were exported to Australia, 332,000 tons to New Zealand, and 341,000 tons to other countries. However, reserves were projected to be sufficient only until the mid-1990s. The Australian government closed the mine in 1987 claiming it no longer economically viable. The mine was reopened under strict environmental controls by private investors in 1990. A total of 220,000 metric tons of phosphate were produced in 1995. Employing 100 people, activities consisted mostly of the removal of stockpiles.

In an effort to develop an alternative economic base, the government encourages tourism. The National Park has been expanded to cover 70% of the island, which is rich in unique flora and fauna. A multi-million dollar hotel and casino development owned mostly by Chinese and Indonesian interests and employing 100 people opened in 1993. In 1994 revenue from the complex totaled $A 500 million. However, a decision by Ansett Australia to discontinue its twice-weekly air service to the island in 1997 dealt a blow to the tourism sector.

Although nearing depletion, the chief export at the end of the twentieth century remains phosphate shipped to Australia and New Zealand. Most consumer goods must be imported, the principal supplier being Australia. The territory's exports in 1996/97 totaled $A 4 million while its imports from Australia cost $A 17 million.

Public Finance

The government primarily receives its revenues from local income taxes, its duty-free status, and the Australian government. The Australian government invested approximately $A 32 million in the development of Christmas Island's infrastructure between 1992 and 1997.

Industry

Extraction and export of rock phosphate is the chief industry. Private sector development of tourism is encouraged by the government including the opening of a multi-million dollar casino in 1993.

Banking and Finance

Australian currency is the only legal tender in the territory. The Bank of New South Wales provides full banking facilities to island residents including currency exchange.

SOCIAL WELFARE

The Australian government extends its national social security, health, and education benefits to the island.

Healthcare

A ten-bed hospital provides medical and dental care. In 1994 health personnel included two doctors, a visiting dentist, and a pharmacist.

Housing

Most residents live in the areas of Settlement and Flying Fish Cove. Dwellings are mostly detached houses, unit-style accommodations, or prefabricated dwellings.

EDUCATION

In 1995 Christmas Island had a district school with fifty pre-primary, 369 primary, and seventy-three secondary level students. Primary and secondary course work is based on Australian curriculum.

1999 KEY EVENTS TIMELINE

August

- The Asia Pacific Space Centre company makes an environmental impact statement for its proposed Christmas Island launch facility available for public review.

October

- The tender period for offers to buy Christmas Island's Resort Casino complex, in receivership since its license was revoked in 1998, ends.

- The public review and commenting period for Asia Pacific Space Centre's environmental impact statement ends.

ANALYSIS OF EVENTS: 1999

BUSINESS AND THE ECONOMY

With Christmas Island's supply of phosphates dwindling, there has been a push throughout the late 1980s and 1990s to develop new industries on the island. While 1999 saw little actual change in Christmas Island's economy, this was made up for by rampant speculation about its future. Major changes in tourism and industry seem poised to bring many new inhabitants, tourists, and jobs to Christmas Island in 2000.

Christmas Island's Casino Resort complex, which opened in 1993, was a major source of jobs and tourism on the island, until its license was revoked in 1998 and it was placed in receivership. The Australian government took offers for the casino through October 1999, and it is expected that a new owner will be named and operations resume in 2000. This will come none-to-soon for Christmas Island. The resort employed over three hundred people, out of a population of about 2,000 islanders. By some estimates as many as a fifth of the island's population has left to find new employment since the resort shut down.

Also in the works in 1999 were plans by the Asian Pacific Space Centre company to build a satellite launching facility at the uninhabited southern end of Christmas Island. Christmas Island is seen as an excellent launch site because it is within easy reach of Indonesia and Singapore to the north, yet it has thousands of miles of open ocean to the east and south (the directions that launches would head in). The Asian Pacific Space Centre claims that several hundred jobs would be created during the construction and operation of the facility, many of them open to current inhabitants of the island.

Construction on the launch site is slated to begin in 2000, and launches in 2002. There is some concern, however, that the facility would harm the unique environment and species of Christmas Island. In its 1999 environmental impact statement, the Asian Pacific Space Centre claimed that there would be a negligible impact on the environment, primarily because the site will be built on abandoned phosphate mines where little native wildlife is present. The Australian government was still assessing the environmental risks of the proposal at the end of 1999.

CULTURE AND SOCIETY

In November and December, the rainy season saw the annual migration of Christmas Island's red crab population. The red crab is perhaps the most famous inhabitant of Christmas Island; their annual migration is often called a natural wonder and helps draw tourists to the island. For most of the year the red crabs dwell in the inland rainforests, feeding on the vegetation there. But every year the crabs, over one hundred million of them, swarm down to the beaches to mate and release their eggs into the ocean. During the height of these annual migrations travel can slow to a crawl, as many roads are closed because they are literally covered in red crabs.

DIRECTORY

CENTRAL GOVERNMENT

Christmas Island is a territory of Australia. An Administrator oversees its management. Government ministries, political organizations, and diplomatic representation are directly connected with those of Australia.

Head of State

Queen
Elizabeth II, Monarch

Administrator
William Taylor, Office of the Administrator
PHONE: +672 91647901
E-MAIL: wtaylor@ciadmin.iocomm.com.au

JUDICIAL SYSTEM

Supreme Court

FURTHER READING

Internet

APSC Environmental Impact Statement - Executive Summary. Available Online @ http://www.apsc.com.au/XSum/ (February 8, 2000).

Christmas Island Tourism Association. Available Online @ http://www.christmas.net.au/ (November 2, 1999).

CHRISTMAS ISLAND: STATISTICAL DATA

For sources and notes see "Sources of Statistics" in the front of each volume.

GEOGRAPHY

Geography (1)

Area:

Total: 135 sq km.

Land: 135 sq km.

Water: 0 sq km.

Area—comparative: about 0.7 times the size of Washington, DC.

Land boundaries: 0 km.

Coastline. 138.9 km.

Climate: tropical; heat and humidity moderated by trade winds.

Terrain: steep cliffs along coast rise abruptly to central plateau.

Natural resources: phosphate.

Land use:

Arable land: NA%

Permanent crops: NA%

Permanent pastures: NA%

Forests and woodland: NA%

Other: 100% (1993 est.).

HUMAN FACTORS

Demographics (2B)

Population (July 1998 est.) 2,195

Age structure:

   0-14 years . . . . .NA

   15-64 years . . . . .NA

   65 years and over . . . . .NA

Population growth rate (1998 est.) 7.77%

Birth rate (births/1,000 population) . . . . .NA

Death rate (deaths/1,000 population) . . . . .NA

Net migration rate (migrant(s)/1,000 population) . . .NA

Infant mortality rate (deaths/1,000 live births) . . . . .NA

Life expectancy at birth:

   Total population . . . . .NA

   Male . . . . .NA

   Female . . . . .NA

Total fertility rate (children born/woman) . . . . .NA

Ethnic Division (6)

Chinese 61%

Malay 25%

European 11%

Other 3%

Religions (7)

Buddhist 55%

Christian 15%

Muslim 10%

Other 20% (1991)

Languages (8)

English.

GOVERNMENT & LAW

Political Parties (12)

Legislative branch is a unicameral Christmas Island Shire Council (9 seats; members elected by popular vote to serve one-year terms). All members are independents.

Government Budget (13B)

Revenues . . . . .NA

Expenditures . . . . .NA

   Capital expenditures . . . . .NA

NA stands for not available.

Military Affairs (14A)

Defense is the responsibility of Australia.

LABOR FORCE

Labor Force (16)

Total not available. Tourism 400 people, mining 100 people.

Unemployment Rate (17)

Rate not available.

PRODUCTION SECTOR

Electric Energy (18)

No data available.

Transportation (19)

Highways:

total: NA km

paved: NA km

unpaved: NA km

Merchant marine: none

Airports: 1 (1997 est.)

Airports—with paved runways:

total: 1

1,524 to 2,437 m: 1 (1997 est.)

Top Agricultural Products (20)

NA.

FINANCE, ECONOMICS, & TRADE

Economic Indicators (22)

No data available.

Exchange Rates (24)

Exchange rates:

Australian dollars ($A) per US$1

January 1998	1.5281
1997	1.3439
1996	1.2773
1995	1.3486
1994	1.3667
1993	1.4704

Economic Aid (27)

None.

Import Export Commodities (28)

Import Commodities	Export Commodities
Consumer goods	Phosphate

COLOMBIA

Republic of Colombia
República de Colombia

CAPITAL: Bogotá.

FLAG: The national flag consists of three horizontal stripes; the yellow upper stripe is twice as wide as each of the other two, which are blue and red.

ANTHEM: *Himno Nacional*

MONETARY UNIT: The Colombian peso (C $) of 100 centavos is a paper currency. There are coins of 10, 20, and 50 centavos and of 1, 2, 5, 10, 20, and 50 pesos, and notes of 100, 200, 500, 1,000, 2,000, 5,000 and 10,000 pesos. Commemorative gold coins of various denominations also have been minted. C $1 = US $0.00101 (or US $1 = C $987.65).

WEIGHTS AND MEASURES: The metric system is the official standard, but Spanish units are also used.

HOLIDAYS: New Year's Day, 1 January; Epiphany, 6 January; St. Joseph's Day, 19 March; Labor Day, 1 May; Day of St. Peter and St. Paul, 29 June; Independence Day, 20 July; Battle of Boyacá, 7 August; Assumption, 15 August; Columbus Day, 12 October; All Saints' Day, 1 November; Independence of Cartagena, 11 November; Immaculate Conception, 8 December; Christmas, 25 December. Movable religious holidays include Holy Thursday, Good Friday, Holy Saturday, Ascension, Sacred Heart, and Corpus Christi. In addition there are six official commemorative days.

TIME: 7 AM = noon GMT.

LOCATION AND SIZE: Colombia is the only South American country with both Caribbean and Pacific coastlines. It has a total area of 1,138,910 square kilometers (439,736 square miles). Colombia's total boundary length is 10,657 kilometers (6,596 miles). Bogotá is located in the center of the country.

CLIMATE: Colombia is a tropical country where the main variations in climate are due to altitude. At sea level the mean annual temperature is 24°C to 27°C (75–81°F). Average temperatures are lower in the mountains. Bogotá (altitude 2,598 meters/8,525 feet) averages 14°C (57°F) year-round. Rainfall is heaviest on the west coast and in the Andes.

INTRODUCTORY SURVEY

RECENT HISTORY

During World War II (1939–45), which Colombia entered on the side of the Allies, social and political divisions within the country intensified. The postwar period was marked by growing social unrest and riots in the capital and in the countryside. An extended and bloody period of rural disorder (La Violencia) claimed 150,000 to 200,000 lives between 1947 and 1958.

The disorder in the country led to a military coup in 1953 that brought General Gustavo Rojas Pinilla to power. Initially, Rojas enjoyed wide popular support, partly for his success in reducing the ongoing violence (La Violencia). When he did not promptly restore democratic government, however, he was overthrown in 1957 by the military with the backing of both political parties. After his overthrow, a provisional government took office.

In 1957, the liberals and the conservatives formed a coalition government that lasted for sixteen years. This arrangement, called the National Front, provided for a free election to be held in 1958. The parties would then alternate in power for four-year terms until 1974. In August 1974, with the inauguration of the liberal Alfonso López Michelsen as president, Colombia returned to a two-party system for presidential and congressional elections.

However, Colombia was plagued by political violence, including numerous kidnappings and political murders by both left- and right-wing organi-

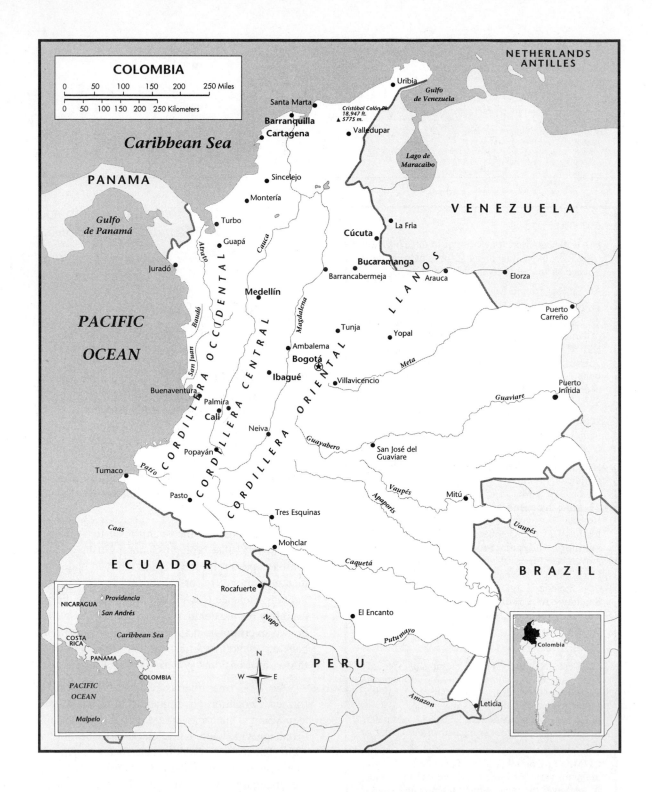

zations. The country also became increasingly plagued by drug traffickers. In 1990, two presidential candidates were assassinated by drug lords intent on intimidating the government from pursuing anti-drug policies. However, the government responded by announcing a new hard-line policy against both the drug traffickers and the anti-government guerrillas.

In 1991 a new constitution was created that included a number of reforms aimed at increasing the democratization of Colombia's elite-controlled political system. In the 1994 elections, Colombians once again chose a liberal government. The elections were marked by widespread political violence and the newly elected president, Ernesto Samper, soon found himself charged with accepting campaign contributions from known drug traffickers. Colombia's political violence, driven by the huge profits to be made in the drug business, continues to be a major problem.

In 1998, Andrés Pastrana was elected president, and he planned to start peace talks with armed rebels who have attacked police and military bases in recent years.

GOVERNMENT

Colombia is a republic, organized democratically under the current constitution of 1991. The Congress consists of a Chamber of Representatives and a Senate. Members of both are elected directly for four-year terms. In 1990, there were 163 representatives and 102 senators. The chief executive is granted the power to declare a state of emergency during times of economic and social stress. Under such a declaration, the president may rule by decree for a period of not longer than ninety days in any one year.

Judiciary

The Supreme Court in Bogotá comprises twenty-four magistrates selected for lifetime terms by justices already in office. The Supreme Court reviews state and municipality laws, frames bills to be submitted to Congress, and proposes reforms. It presides over impeachment trials.

There is a superior court of three or more judges in each of the judicial districts and a number of municipal courts. There are also special labor courts. In criminal cases, the judge chooses a five-member jury; jury duty is obligatory. There is no capital punishment; the maximum penalty for crimes is twenty years in prison.

Political Parties

For many years, the Colombian constitution allowed only two political parties, the Liberal and the Conservative, to participate in the national government.

The Liberal Party (Partido Liberal-PL) supports religious toleration and a positive response to the social and economic demands of the masses. Liberals have been far more successful in elections than the conservatives, having won all but one election since 1974, and they continue to enjoy majority support in both houses.

The policy of the Conservative Party (Partido Conservador Social-PCS) has been characterized by close cooperation with the Roman Catholic Church, a lack of tolerance for non-Roman Catholic religious beliefs, maintenance of class privileges, and highly centralized government.

Recent changes allow for more parties, and several have emerged. The Colombian Communist Party (Partido Communista de Colombia-PCC) is a traditional, Moscow-oriented party. In 1991, the M-19 (which stands for the April 19 Movement) gave up its armed struggle against the government, which it had been waging since 1970, and entered candidates in the 1990 elections. Currently, M-19 is part of a coalition of leftist parties called the Democratic Alliance M-19.

The 1994 elections saw Ernesto Samper of the Liberal Party elected president. Following that vote, the Liberal Party held fifty-nine seats in the Senate and eighty-nine seats in the House. In 1998, Andrés Pastrana of the Conservative Party was elected president, with the largest margin of victory in Colombia's history.

DEFENSE

Colombia's total armed forces amount to 146,300 personnel. All adult males (ages 18–30) are required by the constitution to serve, if called, for one or two years.

In 1995, the army consisted of 120,000 personnel, the air force numbered 7,300 personnel, and the navy had 18,000 personnel.

ECONOMIC AFFAIRS

Despite the gradual expansion of manufacturing, Colombia's economy remains basically agricultural. Coffee is by far the most important crop: its share of total exports ranged from about 40% to 65% of the annual total between 1964 and 1986.

In 1995, growth was up to 5.3% but had fallen to 2% in 1996. Growth was strongest in mining, oil and construction. In 1996, however, the economy hit a stumbling block when U.S. president Bill Clinton decertified Colombia as a country that fully cooperates with U.S. drug policy. Besides enraging the Colombian people, this move made it difficult for U.S. companies to invest in Colombia.

Public Finance

Considerable sums are spent to stimulate the development of industry, and higher than normal military expenditures have been necessitated by the continuing and disruptive guerrilla activity. By the early 1990s, reforms in the public sector had greatly improved the efficiency of public expenditures; the deficit of the nonfinancial sector fell from 0.6% of GDP in 1990 to 0.2% in 1991.

Disbursed and outstanding debt in 1991 totaled $17.5 billion, or 49% of GDP. In 1991, external public debt amounted to $16,703 million, with foreign debt equivalent to 39.9% of GDP (down from 43.3% in 1988).

Income

In 1998, Colombia's gross national product (GNP) was $106 billion, or about $2,600 per person. For the period 1985–95 the average inflation rate was 25.2%, resulting in a real growth rate in GNP of 2.8% per person.

Industry

Industry accounted for 27% of gross domestic product (GDP) in 1995. Colombia is almost self-sufficient in consumer products, which represent about half of total industrial production.

High growth rates have been recorded in many export-oriented industries in recent years. In 1995, coal and oil derivatives, mining and hydrocarbons grew by 17.4%. The rest of the industrial economy, however, has been sluggish due to a series of factors including poor infrastructure, labor difficulties and civil unrest.

Banking and Finance

Under a 1975 law, banks must be at least 51% Colombian-owned. The government supervises the banking system by means of a special governmental body, the Superintendency of Banks.

The Bank of Bogotá, founded in 1879, was the first Colombian credit establishment. The Bank of the Republic was established in 1923 as the semiofficial central bank.

The Banco de la República (the central bank) eased monetary policy in the fourth quarter of 1996 in a bid to slow the reevaluation of the peso, reduce interest rates, and accommodate the seasonal increase in demand for money in the final quarter.

The Bogotá Stock Exchange, organized in 1928, is the largest official stock exchange in the country.

Economic Development

In 1990, President Cesar Gaviria instituted a new national system of economic liberalization known domestically as ''opertura,'' or opening.

The system called for greatly increased international investment, lowering trade barriers, and massive state sell-offs. These began in earnest in the early 1990s as the government sold off seaports, airports, power plants, telecommunications networks, banks—even roads.

In addition to these measures, the government has aggressively pursued the creation of regional trading blocs and has come out in recent years as a major voice in support of a hemispheric free trade area. As of 1996, Colombia was a member of ANCOM, LAIA, a bilateral free-trade pact with Chile and the G-3. These liberalizations have secured Colombia as a steady reliable regional market.

SOCIAL WELFARE

Social security coverage extends to salaried and self-employed people alike. The government, employers, and employees pay for the program, which includes disability, old age, and death benefits as well as coverage of nonoccupational illnesses, maternity, and job-related accidents. A comprehensive medical program was implemented in 1995 and coverage is gradually being extended to all Colombians regardless of their contributions.

The Colombian Institute of Social Security administers other programs, including severance pay, pensions, vacation benefits, group life insurance, job training, transportation and clothing subsidies, educational benefits for families, and a scholarship fund. The Family Welfare Institute coordinates an estimated 1,000 public and private charities involved in caring for children and destitute families.

There is still discrimination against women, especially in rural areas. They earn 30–40% less than men for doing similar work and occupy few of the top positions in government.

Human rights abuses have declined in recent years, but reports of extra-judicial killings and disappearances continue. Prison conditions are harsh, but international monitoring is allowed by the government.

Healthcare

Health standards have improved greatly since the 1950s, but malaria is still prevalent up to 1,100 meters (3,500 feet) in altitude, and many Colombians suffer from intestinal parasites. Malnutrition, formerly a very serious problem, with nutritional goiter, anemia, scurvy, and pellagra frequent, had become less severe by the early 1980s. Average life expectancy is 70 years.

According to a study made between 1994–95, 87% of the population had access to health care services, and 96% had access to safe water.

Housing

Colombia's housing shortage is largely a result of the rapid growth of the urban population. With the annual urban population growth rate at over 3%, the housing deficit was estimated to be around 800,000 units and is expanding annually. Total housing units numbered 6.9 million in 1992; roughly 67% were owner occupied and 24% were rented.

EDUCATION

Education is free and compulsory for five years in Colombia. Illiteracy is declining, having dropped from an estimated 90% at the end of the nineteenth century to an estimated 9% in 1995. By law, Colombia must spend at least 10% of its annual budget on education. Although schooling is compulsory for children in the 7–11 age group, dropout rates are high at the primary level, particularly in rural areas, where the students frequently live at considerable distances from their schools.

In 1994, there were 588,322, students enrolled in higher education in Colombia. The National University in Bogotá, founded in 1572, is one of the oldest in the Western Hemisphere.

1999 KEY EVENTS TIMELINE

January

- President Andrés Pastrana opens peace talks with leftist Revolutionary Armed Forces of Colombia (FARC) guerrillas in the southern town of San Vicente del Caguán.

- FARC suspends the peace talks because of killings by right-wing paramilitaries.

- The worst earthquake in a century ravages the west-central cities of Pereira and Armenia, among others.

February

- A drug-smuggling ring is uncovered within the Colombian air force.

March

- The first videotaped cattle auction is held in Medellin; ranchers can now do business without venturing into Colombia's rebel-held countryside.

- Nobel-winning novelist Gabriel Garcia Marquez buys and overhauls the Colombian newsweekly, *Cambio*.

- Marianella Maal Paccini, Miss Colombia 1999, is a finalist in the Coral Way Lions Club Gala to benefit earthquake victims in Colombia's coffee region.

- A spokesman for the leftist rebel Revolutionary Armed Forces of Colombia says the group is responsible for the killings of three American researchers.

- The 39th International Film Festival of Cartagena is held.

April

- Environmental officials plead with religious leaders to encourage alternatives for Colombian Lent and Easter traditions so that the country's biodiversity will stop being damaged.

- Defense minister Rodrigo Lloreda announces plans to alter the military penal system, resulting in the armed forces facing civilian justice.

- Air traffic controllers in Colombia begin preparations for guiding airplanes via radio reports and paper charts, as a way to address concern that "Y2K" problems in their computerized radar systems will not be solved in time.

- Peace commissioner Victor Ricardo meets with FARC leaders, hoping to restart the peace talks.

May

- The Museum of Modern Art in Bogotá opens an unsettling exhibition entitled, "Art and Violence in Colombia Since 1948."

- President Pastrana meets with FARC leader Manuel "Sureshot" Marulanda in the forest of the demilitarized zone to talk about peace.

- Colombian parliament senator Piedad Cordoba de Castro is abducted.

- Defense Minister Rodrigo Lloreda resigns from office, saying that the Colombian government has made "too many concessions" to the FARC rebels.

- The National Liberation Army (ELN), a smaller leftist group, seizes 143 worshippers during a church mass in the city of Cali.

June

- A bill is defeated in a committee of Colombia's Congress that would have given President Pastrana powers to grant political concessions.

- The International Poetry Festival is held in Medellin.

- Hurt by a continued economic decline Colombia devalues its national currency by ten percent.

July

- The Clinton administration's top anti-drug official asks the United States to make $1 billion in emergency assistance available to the Colombian government to increase its efforts to combat drug trafficking.

- Peace talks between Colombia's government and the FARC are postponed indefinitely.

- President Pastrana, in his independence day speech, tells the Colombian people that the government is ready for either war or peace, indicating he is losing patience with the FARC.

August

- U.S. Undersecretary of State Thomas Pickering visits Bogotá to show support for President Pastrana's stalled peace process and reject calls for military aid to fight drug trafficking.

- In final medal standings at the Pan American Games in Winnipeg, Manitoba, Colombia places seventh out of 42 competing countries.

- Television comedian and unofficial peacemaker Jaime Garzon is assassinated.

September

- President Pastrana travels to the United States to meet with President Clinton to appeal for an increase in American military aid to help Colombia's army fight the left-wing guerrillas.

- Marco Londono, mayor of Vista Hermosa, is gunned down.

- Nobel writer Gabriel Garcia Marquez lets it be known that he has been quietly acting as a mediator in talks between the United States and Colombia on how to suppress Colombia's drug and civil wars.

- Rookie Colombian racecar driver Juan Pablo Montoya is dominating the CART circuit, a 20-race series held mainly in the United States.

October

- A pair of U'wa Tribe twins are returned to their tribe after an eight-month-long custody battle with the Colombian government.

- Orlando Sanchez Christancho, a key suspect in a Colombian drug smuggling organization, is arrested in south Florida.

- The "No Mas" grassroots peace movement—around 15 million people—turns out for marches across Colombia as the government and rebels once again began peace talks.

- Colombia's Maria Luisa Calle places fourth in the 25km race of the world track championships held in Berlin.

November

- Colombia's Congress postpones debating a bill aimed at reducing the country's fiscal deficit, placing a huge strain on the government's timetable for implementing its structural reform program.

- A car bomb in Bogota kills six people.

- In spite of the October peace negotiations between the government and the FARC, the largest left-wing guerilla group in Colombia, FARC launches its biggest offensive since July, attacking 14 towns, killing eight policemen and a navy marine, and blowing up several electricity pylons.

- Colombian drug lord Pablo Escobar's widow and son are arrested in Argentina on suspicion of laundering drug money and falsifying documents.

- A Colombian police chief announces that sharply increasing amounts of cocaine are entering Europe as ties grow between drug cartels and the Russian mafia.

- President Andres Pastrana's government extradites a Colombian accused of heroin trafficking by the United States to face trial (with a pledge that at least 41 other alleged traffickers may follow) in hopes that alliance with the United States will save Colombia from its economic problems and looming civil war.

1999 ANALYSIS OF EVENTS

BUSINESS AND THE ECONOMY

The worst earthquake in a century—registering 6.0 on the Richter scale—hit the town of Armenia in the west-central, mountainous province of Quindio on January 25, killing around 2,000 people. The city's infrastructure was in ruins and complaints from residents grew as rescue equipment and relief supplies were slow in coming. The cost of the disaster is enormous as the quake struck a major coffee-growing region—a mainstay of the economy. Coffee brings in about $2 billion a year in foreign currency. The country began looking for both international emergency relief and lending, to help rebuild the damaged area.

A deepening recession hit Colombia in 1999, shrinking the economy by nearly five percent in the first quarter of the year. This was a record decline. May and June brought heavy selling pressure on Colombia's currency. The government spent $275 million buying pesos and reducing the number of them in circulation in an attempt to shield the peso's value. An emergency decree was then ordered on June 28 which devalued Colombia's national currency by ten percent by decreasing the range in which the country trades. In the past Colombia has had modestly stable economic growth due to its exports of coffee and oil, not to mention illegal earnings from the international sale of drugs. But the political unrest in the country between the government, the left-wing guerrillas, and the right-wing paramilitary has destabilized the economy and worried foreign investors. As a result, foreign investment in Colombia's three main stock markets has dropped significantly.

As the country struggled to deal with Year 2000 compliance, air traffic controllers began brushing up on more primitive practices of doing flight technology. They prepared for guiding airplanes via radio reports and paper charts instead of by computerized radar, in case any computer problems are not solved by the arrival of the new year.

GOVERNMENT AND POLITICS

Violence and unrest continued to mark Colombia in 1999. Though President Andrés Pastrana made plans to open peace talks with leftist Revolutionary Armed Forces of Colombia (FARC) guerrillas in January, the talks were continually suspended. Assassinations, kidnappings, and other forms of violence continued to be prevalent. Members of the United Self-Defense Forces of Colombia, a right-wing paramilitary alliance, executed more than 140 people during the month of January alone. The general populace of Colombia became increasingly impatient with the continuation of the 35-year-long civil war. A grassroots peace movement—called "No Mas" ("No More")—urged civilians to turn out to march in cities across Colombia as the government and rebels finally met again in late October to talk peace.

In May President Pastrana went so far as to meet with FARC leader Manuel "Sureshot" Marulanda deep in the demilitarized zone to talk about peace. The zone, comprised of five municipalities and home to 90,000 civilians, has been under FARC control since late 1998. The decision to let FARC keep control of the zone indefinitely—or at least through the duration of the peace talks—not only upset the residents of the area but caused Defense Minister Rodrigo Lloreda to resign. Lloreda and others believe that the Colombian government has made too many concessions to the FARC rebels.

A smaller leftist group, the National Liberation Army (ELN), is another key player. In April the group hijacked a plane and kidnapped the passengers and crew, and in May they seized worshippers during a church mass in the city of Cali, all as a show of their increasing intolerance with the lack of progress in their own peace plan.

The tie-in with illegal drug trafficking played a role as well. The United States continued to have an interest in the war against Colombian cocaine arriving on U.S. soil for sale. In July the Clinton administration's top anti-drug official recommended that the United States make $1 billion in emergency assistance available to the Colombian government to increase its efforts to combat drug trafficking. However, in August U.S. Undersecretary of State Thomas Pickering visited Bogotá to show support for President Pastrana's stalled peace process and reject calls for military aid to fight drug trafficking. Further, in September, Pastrana traveled to the United States to meet with President Clinton to appeal for an increase in American military aid to help Colombia's army fight the left-wing guerrillas. The line between funding for anti-drug efforts and aid for the fight against the rebels has become increasingly blurred.

CULTURE AND SOCIETY

Colombia's U'wa Amerindians were in the news in 1999. Early in the year the tribe continued protests against Occidental Petroleum that had been underway since 1997. The company has been drilling for oil on land that is sacred to the U'wa. In March three American human rights workers working with the U'wa to defend their land were killed. In October a months-long custody battle ended in favor of a U'wa couple who had given their twins to a clinic when they were born in February. Twins are considered bad luck to the U'wa, who typically abandon them as a result. The 8,000-member tribe felt the pressure of the negative publicity in this case, and decided to ask for the children to be returned. Only after tribal leaders promised that the twins would not be hurt—thereby making an exception to their traditions—did the government decide to return them to their parents.

In March the first videotaped cattle auction was held in Medellin. The gatherings allow ranchers to do business and socialize without venturing into Colombia's rebel-held countryside. Cattle ranchers have become targets for leftist rebels, who kidnap them and demand a high ransom in attempts to fund their cause. Some cattlemen pay the rebels to leave them alone. Additionally, the meetings save ranchers money, as they can avoid the high costs of transporting the cows to various auctions. The popularity of the auctions continues to grow, and they have since taken place in four other cities across Colombia.

As Lent and Easter neared, environmental officials pleaded with religious leaders to encourage alternatives for traditional Colombian celebrations that have been threatening the country's biodiversity. Along the Caribbean coast, reptile meat and eggs are delicacies during this season, but large numbers of endangered species are being killed—and their habitats being destroyed—as hunters collect the items. Additionally, the rare wax palm tree is endangered as its use during Palm Sunday processions increases. There is resistance to the ecological pleas as clerics defend church traditions and call them an inconsequential concern for Colombians. They insist that deforestation and the illegal trade of wild animals—both increasing problems—are much more distressing to Colombia's environment.

Though the country continues to focus on civil unrest, the arts in Colombia continued to flourish. In May the Museum of Modern Art in Bogotá opened an exhibition entitled ''Art and Violence in Colombia Since 1948.'' The show comprised about 150 pieces of work by 50 Colombian artists. The show speaks to the various demonstrations of the violence that is tearing the country apart. The show drew in more than 60,000 visitors in the first three months of its run, prompting museum officials to pursue opening the display in more Colombian cities. Additionally, offers have come in from France and Spain to host the exhibit.

In Colombian sports, weightlifter R. Berrío Hernández moved up in the medal standings at the Pan American Games in Winnipeg, Manitoba, Canada, in August. Berrío Hernández had won the silver medal in the 136-pound class when it was discovered that Cuban weightlifter and gold-medalist William Vargas Trujillo had tested positive for steroid use. Vargas's disqualification made Berrío Hernández the gold-medal winner. In the overall final medal standings, Colombia placed seventh out of 42 competing countries. In racing news, rookie Colombian racecar driver Juan Pablo Montoya dominated the CART circuit, a 20-race series held mainly in the United States. In the world of track and field, Colombia's Maria Luisa Calle placed fourth in the 25-kilometer race at the world track championships in Berlin, Germany, on October 24.

DIRECTORY

CENTRAL GOVERNMENT

Head of State

Presidente

Andres Pastrana Arango, Office of the President, Casa de Narino, Carrera 8a. 7–26, Santa Fe de Bogotá, Colombia
PHONE: +57 (1) 2483300
E-MAIL: pastrana@presidencia.gov.co

Ministers

Minister of Agriculture

Ministry of Agriculture, Av. Jiménez # 7–65, Santa Fe de Bogotá, Colombia
PHONE: +57 (1) 3341199
FAX: +57 (1) 2841775
E-MAIL: minagric@colomsat.net.co

Minister of Communications

Ministry of Communications, Cr. 7 y 8 con Calle 12 A y 13, Bogotá, Colombia
PHONE: +57 (1) 2866911

FAX: +57 (1) 3366401
E-MAIL: sistemas@mincomunicaciones.gov.co

Minister of Culture
Ministry of Culture, Calle 8 # 6–97, Bogotá, Colombia
PHONE: +57 (1) 3424100
FAX: +57 (1) 3421721

Minister of Defense
Ministry of Defense, Av. El Dorado CAN Cr. 52, Bogotá, Colombia
PHONE: +57 (1) 2220499
FAX: +57 (1) 2221874

Minister of Education
Ministry of Education, CAN, Bogotá, Colombia
PHONE: +57 (1) 2222800
FAX: +57 (1) 2224578
E-MAIL: ciudad01@mineducacion.gov.co

Minister of Economic Development
Ministry of Economic Development, Cr. 13 # 28–01 5th Floor, Bogotá, Colombia
PHONE: +57 (1) 3200077
FAX: +57 (1) 2874737

Minister of the Environment
Ministry of the Environment, Calle 37 # 8–40, Bogotá, Colombia
PHONE: +57 (1) 2886877
FAX: +57 (1) 2889892

Minister of Finance
Ministry of Finance, Cr. 8 # 6–64, Bogotá, Colombia
PHONE: +57 (1) 2861504
FAX: +57 (1) 2834024

Minister of Health
Ministry of Health, Cr. 13 # 32–76, Bogotá, Colombia
PHONE: +57 (1) 3365066
FAX: +57 (1) 3360296
E-MAIL: wmaster@bogota.minsalud.gov.co

Minister of Foreign Relations
Ministry of Foreign Relations, Calle 10 # 5–51, Bogotá, Colombia
PHONE: +57 (1) 3429967
FAX: +57 (1) 3416777

Minister of Passports
Ministry of Passports, Calle 100 # 17 A–25, Bogotá, Colombia
PHONE: +57 (1) 6107574

Minister of Visas and Immigration
Ministry of Visas and Immigration, Calle 98 # 17 A–34, Bogotá, Colombia
PHONE: +57 (1) 6106345
FAX: +57 (1) 2575784

Minister of the Interior
Ministry of the Interior, Palacio Echeverry, Bogotá, Colombia
PHONE: +57 (1) 2829069
FAX: +57 (1) 2815884
E-MAIL: sistint@sinpro.gov.co

Minister of Foreign Trade
Ministry of Foreign Trade, Calle 28 # 13 A–15, Bogotá, Colombia
PHONE: +57 (1) 3363690
FAX: +57 (1) 3349908

Minister of Justice
Ministry of Justice, Av. Jiménez # 8–89, Bogotá, Colombia
PHONE: +57 (1) 2860211
FAX: +57 (1) 2816384
E-MAIL:
admin_web@alcaraban.minjusticia.gov.co

Minister of Labor and Social Security
Ministry of Labor and Social Security, Cr. 7 # 34–50, Bogotá, Colombia
PHONE: +57 (1) 2858362
FAX: +57 (1) 2857091

Minister of Mining and Energy
Ministry of Mining and Energy, Av El Dorado CAN, Bogotá, Colombia
PHONE: +57 (1) 2224555
FAX: +57 (1) 2223651
E-MAIL: minas1@col-online.com

Minister of Transportation
Ministry of Transportation, Av. El Dorado CAN, Bogotá, Colombia
PHONE: +57 (1) 2224411
FAX: +57 (1) 2221647
E-MAIL: mtransp1@sinpro.gov.co

POLITICAL ORGANIZATIONS
Democracia Cristiana (Christian Democracy)

Avda 42, No. 18–08, Apdo. 25867, Santa Fe de Bogotá, Colombia
PHONE: +57 (1) 2856639
NAME: Juan A. Polo Figueroa

Movimiento Unitario Metapolítico-MUM

Calle 13, No. 68d–40, Santa Fe de Bogotá, DC
PHONE: +57 (1) 2921330
FAX: +57 (1) 2925502
NAME: Regina Betancourt de Liska

Partido Liberal-PL (Liberal Party)

Avda Jiménez, No. 8–56, Santa Fe de Bogotá,
DC
NAME: Ernesto Samper Pizano

Partido Social Conservador Colombiano-PSC (Colombian Social Conservative Party)

Avda 22, No. 37–09, Santa Fe de Bogotá, DC
PHONE: +57 (1) 2681189
FAX: +57 (1) 2695354
NAME: Misael Pastrana Borrero

Partido Comunista Colombiano (PCC)

Calle 18a, No. 14–56, Apdo Aéreo 2523, Santa
Fe de Bogotá, DC
PHONE: +57 (1) 3341946
FAX: +57 (1) 2818259

DIPLOMATIC REPRESENTATION

Embassies in Colombia

Argentina
Av. 40 A # 13–09 16th Floor, Bogotá,
Colombia
PHONE: +57 (1) 2880900
FAX: +57 (1) 2888868

Brazil
Calle 93 # 14–20 8th Floor, Bogotá, Colombia
PHONE: +57 (1) 2184402
FAX: +57 (1) 2180800

Canada
Calle 76 # 11–52, Bogotá, Colombia
PHONE: +57 (1) 3131355
FAX: +57 (1) 3133071

Chile
Calle 100 # 11 B–44, Bogotá, Colombia
PHONE: +57 (1) 2147990
FAX: +57 (1) 6193863
E-MAIL: trauco.colomsat.net.co:80/cicc /
cicc@colomsat.net.co / echileco@colomsat.net.co

China
Calle 71 No.2A–41, Santa fe de Bogata,
Colombia
PHONE: +57 (1) 2115411
FAX: +57 (1) 2178985

Ecuador
Calle 89 # 13–07, Bogotá, Colombia
PHONE: +57 (1) 6350322
FAX: +57 (1) 2579799

France
Cr. 11 # 93–12, Bogotá, Colombia
PHONE: +57 (1) 6183255
FAX: +57 (1) 6185023

Germany
Cr. 4 # 72–35 6th Floor, Bogotá, Colombia
PHONE: +57 (1) 3484040
FAX: +57 (1) 2104256

Greece
Greek Consulate, Cr. 11 # 7–88, Bogotá,
Colombia
PHONE: +57 (1) 2557403

Indonesia
Carrera 9, No. 76–27, Santa Fe De Bogota,
Colombia
PHONE: +57 (1) 2176738; 2175993; 3103363
FAX: +57 (1) 2103507

Israel
Calle 35 # 7–25 14th Floor, Bogotá, Colombia
PHONE: +57 (1) 2320764
FAX: +57 (1) 2877783
E-MAIL: embisrae@latino.net.co

Italy
Ufficio di Bogotà, Calle 100 n° 8A–55 Of. 417,
Edificio World Trade Center–Torre C, Santa fè
de Bogotà, Colombia
PHONE: +57 (1) 6211438; 6211349; 6211015
FAX: +57 (1) 6211448
E-MAIL: icebogot@cable.net.co

Nicaragua
Carretera 19, No. 106–91, Urbanización Santa
Barbara, Santafé de Bogotá D.C., Colombia
PHONE: +57 (1) 6128777; 6198963; 6198934
FAX: +57 (1) 6120201; 2157911
TITLE: Minister Consultant with Consulars
Affaires
NAME: Micaela de los A. Gómez P.

Japan
Cr. 7 # 71–21 Torre B 11th Floor, Bogotá,
Colombia

PHONE: +57 (1) 3175001
FAX: +57 (1) 3174989
E-MAIL: embjapon@colomsat.net.co

Korea
Calle 94 # 9–39, Bogotá, Colombia
PHONE: +57 (1) 6167200
FAX: +57 (1) 6100338

Mexico
Calle 82 # 9–25, Bogotá, Colombia
PHONE: +57 (1) 6104070
FAX: +57 (1) 2185999

Panama
Calle 92 # 7–70, Bogotá, Colombia
PHONE: +57 (1) 2575067
FAX: +57 (1) 2575068

Peru
Cr. 10 # 93–48, Bogotá, Colombia
PHONE: +57 (1) 2364298
FAX: +57 (1) 2573753

Spain
Calle 92 # 12–68, Bogotá, Colombia
PHONE: +57 (1) 6181288
FAX: +57 (1) 6107443

Taiwan
Trade Office, Cr. 7 # 79–75 Of. 502, Bogotá, Colombia
PHONE: +57 (1) 2354713
FAX: +57 (1) 3145237
E-MAIL: econtai@inter.net.co

United Kingdom
Cr. 9 # 76–49 9th Floor, Bogotá, Colombia
PHONE: +57 (1) 3176690
FAX: +57 (1) 3176523
E-MAIL: embajad1@latino.net.co

United States
Carrera 45 # 22D–45, Santa fe de Bogotá, D.C., Colombia
PHONE: +57 (1) 3150811
FAX: +57 (1) 3152197

Venezuela
Calle 33 # 6–94, 10th Floor, Bogotá, Colombia
PHONE: +57 (1) 2852286
FAX: +57 (1) 2857372

JUDICIAL SYSTEM
Corte Suprema de Justicia (Criminal law)

Corte Constitucional (Constitutional Law)

FURTHER READING
Government Publications
Background Notes: Colombia, January 1999. Released by the Bureau of Western Hemisphere Affairs, U.S. Department of State.

Articles
"Alleged Colombian Drug Trafficker Nabbed in U.S." Reuters, 24 October 1999.

"Colombia at War." *Current History* (March 1999): 111+.

"Colombia Calls for Arms from Uncle Sam." *The Economist* (September 25, 1999): 37+.

"Colombia Talks Peace in the Long Shadow of War." *The Economist* (January 9, 1999): 31+.

"Colombia's Defense Minister Quits Over Concession to Rebels." *The New York Times*, 27 May 1999.

"Colombia's Easter Environment." *The Economist* (April 3, 1999): 32.

"Colombia's Latest Horror." *The Economist* (January 30, 1999): 33.

"Colombia's Trembling Peace." *The Economist* (June 12, 1999): 31+.

"Colombian Mayor Assassinated—Eighth this Year." Agence France Press, 19 September 1999.

"Colombians Dream of Peace." *The Economist* (May 15, 1999): 37+.

"Killing Americans." *The Economist* (March 13, 1999): 46+.

Kotler, Jared. "Colombian Peace Movement Growing." Associated Press, 22 October 1999.

"Messages of War." *The Economist* (May 29, 1999): 32+.

"The Month in Review, January 1999." *Current History* (March 1999): 140.

"The Month in Review, March 1999." *Current History* (May 1999): 237+.

"Peace in Colombia? This Year, Next Year, Sometime . . ." *The Economist* (April 10, 1999): 31+.

"Policy, Which Policy?" *The Economist* (February 20, 1999): 34.

Rohter, Larry. "Colombia Devalues the Peso by 10 Percent." *The New York Times*, 29 June 1999.

———. "In the Trauma of Barbarity, Art Speaks Out." *The New York Times*, 17 October 1999.

———. "Violence Erupts as Colombia Learns What Was Lost in Quake, and What Remains." *The New York Times*, 28 January 1999.

Rohter, Larry with Christopher S. Wren. "U.S. to Consider $1 Billion More for Colombia Drug War." *The New York Times*, 17 July 1999.

"Should Blind Justice also be Faceless?" *The Economist* (April 24, 1999): 32+.

"Supermodel Angst." *The Economist* (July 3, 1999): 30.

"Warpaths." *The Economist* (July 24, 1999): 34.

COLOMBIA: STATISTICAL DATA

For sources and notes see "Sources of Statistics" in the front of each volume.

GEOGRAPHY

Geography (1)

Area:

Total: 1,138,910 sq km.

Land: 1,038,700 sq km.

Water: 100,210 sq km.

Note: includes Isla de Malpelo, Roncador Cay, Serrana Bank, and Serranilla Bank.

Area—comparative: slightly less than three times the size of Montana.

Land boundaries:

Total: 7,408 km.

Border countries: Brazil 1,643 km, Ecuador 590 km, Panama 225 km, Peru 2,900 km, Venezuela 2,050 km.

Coastline: 3,208 km (Caribbean Sea 1,760 km, North Pacific Ocean 1,448 km).

Climate: tropical along coast and eastern plains; cooler in highlands.

Terrain: flat coastal lowlands, central highlands, high Andes Mountains, eastern lowland plains.

Natural resources: petroleum, natural gas, coal, iron ore, nickel, gold, copper, emeralds.

Land use:

Arable land: 4%

Permanent crops: 1%

Permanent pastures: 39%

Forests and woodland: 48%

Other: 8% (1993 est.).

HUMAN FACTORS

Demographics (2A)

	1990	1995	1998	2000	2010	2020	2030	2040	2050
Population	32,984.8	36,396.5	38,580.9	40,036.9	47,284.9	54,626.1	61,805.5	68,109.7	73,348.8
Net migration rate (per 1,000 population)	NA	NA	NA	NA	NA	NA	NA	NA	NA
Births	NA	NA	NA	NA	NA	NA	NA	NA	NA
Deaths	NA	NA	NA	NA	NA	NA	NA	NA	NA
Life expectancy - males	64.7	65.0	66.2	66.9	70.3	72.9	75.0	76.6	77.8
Life expectancy - females	71.5	72.9	74.1	75.0	78.3	80.9	82.7	84.1	85.0
Birth rate (per 1,000)	26.0	26.3	24.9	24.0	20.8	19.0	17.2	15.6	14.5
Death rate (per 1,000)	6.0	6.0	5.7	5.5	5.2	5.3	6.0	7.1	8.0
Women of reproductive age (15-49 yrs.)	9,012.6	9,974.2	10,532.5	10,911.8	12,586.2	13,859.2	15,191.9	16,408.7	17,167.7
of which are currently married	NA	6.6	NA	NA	NA	NA	NA	NA	NA
Fertility rate	2.9	3.0	2.9	2.8	2.6	2.5	2.3	2.2	2.1

Except as noted, values for vital statistics are in thousands; life expectancy is in years.

Health Personnel (3)

Total health expenditure as a percentage of GDP, 1990-1997[a]

Public sector 2.9

Private sector 4.4

Total[b] 7.4

Health expenditure per capita in U.S. dollars, 1990-1997[a]

Purchasing power parity 477

Total 140

Availability of health care facilities per 100,000 people

Hospital beds 1990-1997[a] 130

Doctors 1993[c] 105

Nurses 1993[c] 49

Health Indicators (4)

Life expectancy at birth

1980 66

1997 70

Daily per capita supply of calories (1996) 2,800

Total fertility rate births per woman (1997) 2.8

Maternal mortality ratio per 100,000 live births (1990-97) . . . . .100[c]

Safe water % of population with access (1995) 75

Sanitation % of population with access (1995) 59

Consumption of iodized salt % of households (1992-98)[a] 92

Smoking prevalence

Male % of adults (1985-95)[a] 35

Female % of adults (1985-95)[a] 19

Tuberculosis incidence per 100,000 people (1997) 55

Adult HIV prevalence % of population ages 15-49 (1997) 0.36

Infants and Malnutrition (5)

Under-5 mortality rate (1997) 30

% of infants with low birthweight (1990-97) 9

Births attended by skilled health staff % of total[a] . . .85

% fully immunized (1995-97)

TB 98

DPT 84

Polio 85

Measles 76

Prevalence of child malnutrition under age 5 (1992-97)[b] 8

Ethnic Division (6)

Mestizo 58%

White 20%

Mulatto 14%

Black 4%

Mixed black-Amerindian .3%

Amerindian 1%

Religions (7)

Roman Catholic 95%

Languages (8)

Spanish.

EDUCATION

Public Education Expenditures (9)

Public expenditure on education (% of GNP)

1980 . . . . .2.4

1996 . . . . .4.4

Expenditure per student

Primary % of GNP per capita

1980 . . . . .6.6

1996 . . . . .10.4

Secondary % of GNP per capita

1980 . . . .

1996 . . . . .11.4[1]

Tertiary % of GNP per capita

1980 . . . . .56.0

1996 . . . . .37.4

Expenditure on teaching materials

Primary % of total for level (1996) . . . .

Secondary % of total for level (1996) . . . .

Primary pupil-teacher ratio per teacher (1996) 25

Duration of primary education years (1995) 5

Educational Attainment (10)

Age group (1993) . . . . .25+

Total population 15,088,203

Highest level attained (%)

No schooling 11.9

First level

Not completed 27.3

Completed 18.3

Entered second level

S-1 . . . . .13.3

S-2 . . . . .16.7

Postsecondary 10.4

Literacy Rates (11A)

In thousands and percent[1]	1990	1995	2000	2010
Illiterate population (15+ yrs.)	2,164	2,046	1,944	1,628
Literacy rate - total adult pop. (%)	89.6	91.3	92.6	94.8
Literacy rate - males (%)	89.8	91.2	92.4	94.4
Literacy rate - females (%)	89.5	91.4	92.8	95.3

GOVERNMENT & LAW

Political Parties (12)

House of Representatives	No. of seats
Liberal Party	.89
Conservatives	.53
Democratic Alliance M-19 (AD/M-19)	.2
Other	.17

Military Affairs (14B)

	1990	1991	1992	1993	1994	1995
Military expenditures						
Current dollars (mil.)	1,225	1,466	1,377	1,629	1,302	2,000
1995 constant dollars (mil.)	1,408	1,620	1,481	1,708	1,335	2,000
Armed forces (000)	110	110	139	139	146	146
Gross national product (GNP)						
Current dollars (mil.)	52,170	55,700	60,280	65,030	71,260	76,270
1995 constant dollars (mil.)	59,960	61,550	64,840	68,170	73,050	76,270
Central government expenditures (CGE)						
1995 constant dollars (mil.)	7,573	7,440	10,620	10,810	11,340	12,370[e]
People (mil.)	33.0	33.6	34.3	34.9	35.6	36.2
Military expenditure as % of GNP	2.3	2.6	2.3	2.5	1.8	2.6
Military expenditure as % of CGE	18.6	21.8	13.9	15.8	11.8	16.2
Military expenditure per capita (1995 $)	43	48	43	49	38	55
Armed forces per 1,000 people (soldiers)	3.3	3.3	4.1	4.0	4.1	4.0
GNP per capita (1994 $)	1,818	1,830	1,891	1,951	2,053	2,107
Arms imports[6]						
Current dollars (mil.)	90	210	100	50	40	60
1995 constant dollars (mil.)	103	232	108	52	41	60
Arms exports[6]						
Current dollars (mil.)	0	0	0	0	0	0
1995 constant dollars (mil.)	0	0	0	0	0	0
Total imports[7]						
Current dollars (mil.)	5,590	4,906	6,516	9,832	11,880	13,850
1995 constant dollars (mil.)	6,424	5,421	7,009	10,310	12,180	13,580
Total exports[7]						
Current dollars (mil.)	6,766	7,232	6,917	7,116	8,399	9,764
1995 constant dollars (mil.)	7,776	7,991	7,440	7,460	8,610	9,764
Arms as percent of total imports[8]	1.6	4.3	4.5	.5	.3	.4

Government Budget (13A)

Year: 1993

Total Expenditures: 6,309.4 Billions of Pesos

Expenditures as a percentage of the total by function:

General public services and public order 29.42

Defense 8.68

Education 19.02

Health 5.41

Social Security and Welfare 7.82

Housing and community amenities 1.40

Recreational, cultural, and religious affairs 48

Fuel and energy 1.71

Agriculture, forestry, fishing, and hunting 3.96

Mining, manufacturing, and construction 36

Transportation and communication 6.49

Other economic affairs and services 3.48

Crime (15)

Crime rate (for 1997)

Crimes reported 231,900

Total persons convicted .NA

Crimes per 100,000 population 575

Persons responsible for offenses

Total number of suspects 114,500

Total number of female suspects 9,150

Total number of juvenile suspects 9,150

LABOR FORCE

Labor Force (16)

Total (million) 16.8

Services 46%

Agriculture 30%

Industry 24%

Data for 1997 est. Percent distribution for 1990.

Unemployment Rate (17)

12.2% (1997 est.)

PRODUCTION SECTOR

Electric Energy (18)

Capacity . . . . .10.781 million kW (1995)

Production . . . . .47 billion kWh (1995)

Consumption per capita . . . . .1,307 kWh (1995)

Transportation (19)

Highways:

total: 107,000 km

paved: 12,733 km

unpaved: 94,267 km (1996 est.)

Waterways: 14,300 km, navigable by river boats

Pipelines: crude oil 3,585 km; petroleum products 1,350 km; natural gas 830 km; natural gas liquids 125 km

Merchant marine:

total: 19 ships (1,000 GRT or over) totaling 70,775 GRT/94,677 DWT ships by type: bulk 5, cargo 8, container 1, multi-function large load carrier 2, oil tanker 3 (1997 est.)

Airports: 1,136 (1997 est.)

Airports—with paved runways:

total: 86

over 3,047 m: 2

2,438 to 3,047 m: 10

1,524 to 2,437 m: 36

914 to 1,523 m: 31

under 914 m: 7 (1997 est.)

Airports—with unpaved runways:

total: 1,050

2,438 to 3,047 m: 1

1,524 to 2,437 m: 65

914 to 1,523 m: 348

under 914 m: 636 (1997 est.)

Top Agricultural Products (20)

Coffee, cut flowers, bananas, rice, tobacco, corn, sugarcane, cocoa beans, oilseed, vegetables; forest products; shrimp farming.

MANUFACTURING SECTOR

GDP & Manufacturing Summary (21)

Detailed value added figures are listed by both International Standard Industry Code (ISIC) and product title.

	1980	1985	1990	1994
GDP ($-1990 mil.)[1]	28,799	32,184	40,274	47,572
Per capita ($-1990)[1]	1,086	1,092	1,247	1,377
Manufacturing share (%) (current prices)[1]	23.3	21.4	19.9	*17.7*
Manufacturing				
Value added ($-1990 mil.)	6,010	6,365	8,034	*9,427*
Industrial production index	100	108	130	144
Value added ($ mil.)	7,131	6,711	7,882	*10,846*
Gross output ($ mil.)	16,453	16,823	20,601	*25,882*
Employment (000)	508	440	489	*616*

	1980	1985	1990	1994
Profitability (% of gross output)				
Intermediate input (%)	57	60	62	58
Wages and salaries inc. supplements (%)	8	7	6	7
Gross operating surplus	35	33	33	35
Productivity ($)				
Gross output per worker	31,860	37,635	41,526	38,235
Value added per worker	13,809	15,012	15,887	16,022
Average wage (inc. supplements)	2,583	2,709	2,359	2,972
Value added ($ mil.)				
311/2 Food products	951	1,166	1,306	2,068
313 Beverages	1,021	1,032	928	1,175
314 Tobacco products	160	224	173	54
321 Textiles	803	619	816	761
322 Wearing apparel	241	206	221	387
323 Leather and fur products	59	47	66	75
324 Footwear	50	54	100	133
331 Wood and wood products	50	46	54	81
332 Furniture and fixtures	34	29	38	47
341 Paper and paper products	227	274	301	410
342 Printing and publishing	185	180	213	339
351 Industrial chemicals	303	405	522	692
352 Other chemical products	419	457	597	981
353 Petroleum refineries	773	90	151	290
354 Miscellaneous petroleum and coal products	17	28	34	54
355 Rubber products	117	138	131	180
356 Plastic products	141	169	223	384
361 Pottery, china and earthenware	44	46	60	107
362 Glass and glass products	76	92	113	138
369 Other non-metal mineral products	232	264	338	513
371 Iron and steel	217	205	281	445
372 Non-ferrous metals	34	36	56	53
381 Metal products	260	242	279	347
382 Non-electrical machinery	120	114	124	187
383 Electrical machinery	244	211	271	353
384 Transport equipment	256	221	332	412
385 Professional and scientific equipment	26	38	70	76
390 Other manufacturing industries	72	78	84	104

FINANCE, ECONOMICS, & TRADE

Economic Indicators (22)

National product: GDP—purchasing power parity—$231.1 billion (1997 est.)

National product real growth rate: 3.1% (1997 est.)

National product per capita: $6,200 (1997 est.)

Inflation rate—consumer price index: 17.7% (1997 est.)

Balance of Payments (23)

	1992	1993	1994	1995	1996
Exports of goods (f.o.b.)	7,263	7,429	8,748	10,222	10,651
Imports of goods (f.o.b.)	−6,029	−9,086	−11,040	−12,921	−12,784
Trade balance	1,234	−1,657	−2,292	−2,699	−2,133
Services - debits	−4,499	−4,665	−5,817	−6,901	−7,977
Services - credits	2,432	3,081	4,133	4,821	4,825
Private transfers (net)	−14	—	—	—	—
Government transfers (net)	1,747	1,138	862	679	532
Overall balance	900	−2,102	−3,114	−4,101	−4,753

Exchange Rates (24)

Exchange rates:

Colombian pesos (Col$) per US$1

February 1998	.1345.0
1997	.1,140.96
1996	.1,036.69
1995	.912.83
1994	.844.84
1993	.863.06

Top Import Origins (25)

$13.5 billion (c.i.f., 1997 est.) Data are for 1992.

Origins	%
United States	.36
EC	.18
Brazil	.4
Venezuela	.6.5
Japan	.8.7

Top Export Destinations (26)

$11.4 billion (f.o.b., 1997 est.) Data are for 1992.

Destinations	%
United States	.39
EC	.25.7
Japan	.2.9
Venezuela	.8.5

Economic Aid (27)

Recipient: ODA, $30 million (1993).

Import Export Commodities (28)

Import Commodities	Export Commodities
Industrial equipment	Petroleum
Transportation equipment	Coffee
Consumer goods	Coal
Chemicals	Bananas
Paper products	Fresh cut flowers

COMOROS

Federal Islamic Republic of the
Comoros
Jumhuriyat al-Qumur al-Ittihadiyah al-Islamiyah

INTRODUCTORY SURVEY

RECENT HISTORY

In World War II (1939–45), the Comoros were occupied by a British force and turned over to the Free French. The Comoros were granted administrative autonomy within the Republic of France on 9 May 1946, acquiring overseas territorial status, and on 22 December 1961 achieved internal autonomy under special statute.

In a referendum held on 22 December 1974, a large majority on the islands, except Mayotte, voted in favor of independence. On 6 July 1975, the Comoros legislature unilaterally declared independence for all four islands, including Mayotte. The UN General Assembly backed the Comorian claim to Mayotte despite French opposition. Nonetheless, Mayotte remained French.

Considerable domestic turmoil accompanied the birth of the new nation. The first Comorian government held power only a month before it was overthrown on 3 August 1975 with the aid of foreign white mercenaries. On 13 May 1978, 'Ali Soilih, who had led the 1975 military coup and had become head of state in January 1976, was overthrown by mercenaries led by Bob Denard, who reinstalled the nation's first president, Ahmad 'Abdallah. 'Abdallah ruled until he was assassinated in November 1989, when Said Mohamed Djohar, head of the Supreme Court, was appointed interim president.

A French peacekeeping force enabled the government to lift political restrictions and conduct a

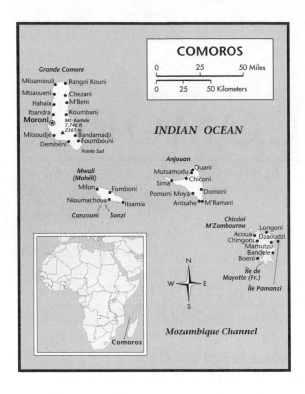

presidential election. On 11 March 1990, Djohar won a runoff with 55% of the vote. Subsequently, his coalition government survived three coup attempts.

In the controversial December 1993 legislative elections, supporters of Djohar won twenty-four of the forty-two seats in the assembly. Members of the opposition parties contested the validity of both the election results and the choice of Djohar's son-in-law as president of the assembly on 7 January. On 17 January, the main opposition parties agreed to coordinate their actions in a Forum for National Recovery (FRN).

Djohar's government grew increasingly authoritarian, and in September 1995, Bob Denard, a former leader of the government, staged a coup that resulted in the arrest of President Djohar and the creation of a transitional government. France was displeased with this turn of events and landed a military party that overthrew Denard's transitional government and prepared the way for elections. These elections were held in 1996 and were won by Mohammed Taki Abdulkarim.

GOVERNMENT

A new constitution was adopted in June 1992. The president and forty-two-member Federal Assembly are elected by universal suffrage for four- and five-year terms, respectively. It also provides

for a fifteen-member Senate to be chosen by an electoral college for a term of six years. The post of prime minister is held by a member of the majority party in the assembly.

Judiciary

The Supreme Court resolves constitutional questions, supervises presidential elections, and arbitrates (judged by an impartial person) any case in which the government is accused of malpractice. The Supreme Court also reviews decisions of the lower courts, including the Superior Court of Appeals at Moroni. Amendments to the constitution passed in 1996 provide for a number of safeguards, including the equality of all citizens before the law. It does not mention the right to counsel, however.

Political Parties

In February 1982, the Comorian Union for Progress (Union Comorienne pour le Progrés—UCP) was established as the only legal party. Despite earlier assurances of a free ballot, few opposition candidates were allowed to run, and dissidents were subject to intimidation and imprisonment.

On 10 September 1993, the UCP merged with the Union for Democracy and Decentralization (UNDC), the largest party in the assembly. Djohar hastily created his own party, the RDR, to contest the December 1993 elections. The two leading parties in the assembly after the 1996 elections were the National Rally for Development and the National Front for Justice).

DEFENSE

There is a small French-trained army of almost 1,000 men. A 300-man presidential guard is run by European mercenaries.

ECONOMIC AFFAIRS

The economy of the Comoros is agriculture-based, dependent on trade and foreign assistance. Mineral resources are few; there is little industry. Tourism, however, increased considerably in the 1990s as a result of promotion by South African interests. Comoros is the world's second largest producer of vanilla and the world's leading producer of ylang-ylang, an oil used in perfumes.

Public Finance

From 1986 to 1989, the budget deficit (excluding grants) averaged 26% of GDP. The deficit was subsidized by foreign grants and loans, chiefly from France. The Comoros government and the IMF agreed in 1990 to a structural adjustment program covering 1991 to 1993. The program provides $135 million and proposes a plan whereby the government diversifies its exports, reduces public expenditures, and privatizes its parastatal sector.

The CIA estimates that, in 1996, government revenues totaled approximately $83 million and expenditures $92 million, including capital expenditures of $32 million. External debt totaled about $160 million.

Income

In 1998, Comoros's gross national product (GNP) was $196 million, or about $370 per person. For the period 1985–95 the average inflation rate was 4.0%.

Industry

There are various small-scale industries, mostly for processing the islands' agricultural products. Comoros has twenty sawmills, a soap factory, a soft drink plant, and metal-working shops.

Banking and Finance

The Central Bank of the Comoros was established in 1981. The Banque Pour l'Industrie et le Commerce, is the main commercial bank; the French Commercial Bank is also represented. The Banque de Développement des Comores is half state owned. There are no securities exchanges. The exchange rate as of 17 January 1997 was Co Fr405.3 to the dollar.

Economic Development

Development projects in the late 1980s and early 1990s focused on the agricultural sector, hydroelectric development, fishing, and start-up investment funds for small and intermediate enterprises. In addition, the European Development Funds provided resources for the redevelopment of the port at Moroni.

SOCIAL WELFARE

Women occupy a subservient position in this extremely traditional society but retain some strength from the matrilineal social structure. Although the government regards the fertility rate as too high, no major population control programs have been launched. Human rights abuses have been reported since 1995.

Healthcare

In 1996, there were six main hospitals, ten secondary hospitals and medical centers, and four maternity clinics. Lack of animal protein is a seri-ous problem. In addition, a large percentage of the adult population suffers from malaria, and there is a high incidence of tuberculosis and leprosy. Average life expectancy is 59 years.

Housing

Over 65% of all housing units are straw huts with roofs of cocoa leaves, and 25% are made of durable materials including stone, brick, or concrete.

EDUCATION

Primary education lasts for six years followed by seven years of secondary education. There is a teacher training college near Moroni, and two technical schools. Higher level institutions had 229 students in 1992. About 43% of the population aged 15 or over was illiterate in 1995.

1999 KEY EVENTS TIMELINE

April

- The Organization of African Unity (OAU) sponsors talks to resolve dilemma posed by separatist movements on Anjouan and Moheli.

- A military coup led by army chief of staff Colonel Azali Assoumani overthrows government.

May

- Colonel Azali names a new cabinet and appoints himself president, prime minister, and defense minister.

- French mercenary Bob Denard goes on trial in Paris for the 1989 assassination of former Comoros president Ahmed 'Abdallah.

June

- U.S. suspends military aid following coup in April.

December

- Leaders in Africa threaten separatists on the island of Anjouan, urging them to sign an agreement aimed at keeping the island nation intact.

ANALYSIS OF EVENTS: 1999

GOVERNMENT AND POLITICS

Unresolved tensions surrounding the 1997 secession of the island of Anjouan (the second largest island, also known as Nzwani) and the secessionist movement on Moheli (Mwali) came to a head in 1999, leading to a military coup. In addition to having created instability on the national level, Anjouan's secessionist rulers themselves were divided over the fate of the island, with one faction favoring union with France and another favoring total independence. On April 23, representatives of Anjouan refused to sign an agreement drawn up by the Organization of African Unity (OAU) that proposed to reunify the country under a new central administration with increased autonomy for Grand Comore, Anjouan, and Moheli. (The status of Mayotte, the fourth of the Comoros islands, had been in dispute throughout the 1990s. Both the Federal Islamic Republic of the Comoros, and France officially claimed Mayotte, but France administered it, and its de facto status was that of a French possession.)

The following week, the ongoing violence on Anjouan escalated and spread to Grand Comore and the capital city of Moroni. On April 30, Colonel Azali Assoumani, army chief of staff, led a bloodless coup that deposed interim President Mohamed Tadjidine Ben Said Massounde and the government of Prime Minister Abbas Djoussouf. Early in May, Colonel Azali moved to form a new government, appointing a twelve-member military-civilian cabinet and having himself sworn in as president (he also appointed himself prime minister and defense minister). In spite of appeals by former government leaders for Azali to step down, the military leader insisted that he would remain in power until Anjouan accepted the terms of the OAU agreement, after which elections would be scheduled.

In Paris, the French mercenary Bob Denard, who had been involved in political intrigues in several of France's former African colonies and had been a major player in Comorian politics for a number of years, went on trial for the 1989 murder of former Comorian president Ahmed 'Abdallah. Denard had earlier helped bring 'Abdallah to power. Prosecutors were seeking a sentence of twelve to fifteen years for the seventy-year-old Denard.

In June the United States suspended military aid to Comoros to protest the military takeover of the country. There was no interruption of other types of assistance.

As of September, no agreement had been reached between the central government and the separatists on Anjouan.

BUSINESS AND THE ECONOMY

Comoros remained one of the world's poorest and least developed countries. The islands had few natural resources, scarce land, and a rapidly expanding population, and market demand for its major exports, ylang-ylang (an oil used in perfumes) and vanilla, had dropped throughout the decade. The country's economic plight was exacerbated by government instability and corruption, an uneducated workforce, unsound agricultural practices, and inadequate communication and transportation networks. Unemployment was high, and the country was heavily dependent on foreign aid, most of which came from France, which was also its major trading partner (Comoros had a large negative trade balance).

Agriculture was the dominant economic sector, accounting for roughly 40 percent of the nation's GDP and employed about 80 percent of its labor force. However, subsistence agriculture on the islands did not produce enough food to feed the population, and Comoros was obliged to import about half its food. Besides ylang-ylang and vanilla, other major crops included cloves, copra, and cassava (tapioca).

There was a modest-sized tourist industry, which the government was attempting to expand by supporting new hotel construction and marketing to tour promoters from South Africa and other countries.

The Comorian franc was pegged to the French franc.

CULTURE AND SOCIETY

Living standards in Comoros were low due to the country's weak economy (but they were markedly higher on French-administered Mayotte). Over one-quarter of the total population (estimated at 562,723 as of July) lived in urban areas. Conflicts among the people of Comoros tended to be based on inter-island rivalries rather than on ethnic divisions. Some 86 percent of the population was Sunni Muslim, and virtually all the rest were Roman Catholic. The average life expectancy was roughly sixty years, and the birth rate was 40.29 births per 1,000 population. Almost half the population was under the age of fourteen.

One of the major areas that had suffered from government budget cuts was education, and many teachers had taught for extended periods without pay. The country's literacy rate ranked among the world's lowest (about 64 percent for males and 50 percent for females), and there was a serious shortage of doctors, teachers, and other professionals.

The government was trying to improve education and health services and lower the rate of population growth.

DIRECTORY

CENTRAL GOVERNMENT

Head of State

Prime Minister
Abbas Djoussouf

President
Azali Assoumani, Office of the President

Ministers

Minister of Finance, Budget, Economy, Commerce, and Investments
Said Said Hamadi, Ministry of Finance, Budget, Economy, Commerce, and Investments

Minister of Foreign Affairs and Cooperation
Salim Hadj Himidi, Ministry of Foreign Affairs and Cooperation

Minister of Francophony, Culture, Industry, and Information
Issamidine Adaine, Ministry of Francophony, Culture, Industry, and Information

Minister of Justice, Public Function, Employment, Professional Training, Administration Decentralization, and Constitution
Mohamed Abdou Madi, Ministry of Justice, Public Function, Employment, Professional Training, Administration Decentralization, and Constitution

Minister of National Education, Public Health, Youth, and Sports
Sultan Chouzour, Ministry of National Education, Public Health, Youth, and Sports

Minister of Production, Fisheries, Environment, and Craft
Mahamoud Ahmed Abdallah, Ministry of Production, Fisheries, Environment, and Craft

Minister of Regional Planning, Urbanism, Lodging, Transportation, Tourism, Posts and Telecommunications
Ali Toihir Mohamed, Ministry of Regional Planning, Urbanism, Lodging, Transportation, Tourism, Posts and Telecommunications

POLITICAL ORGANIZATIONS

Parti Republicain des Comores (Republican Party of Comoros)

TITLE: President
NAME: Mohamed Said Abdallah Mchangama
E-MAIL: mchangama@snpt.km

Forum pour le Redressement National (Forum for National Renewal)

Front National pour la Justice (National Front for Justice)

Rassemblement National pour la Developpement (National Rally for Development)

NAME: Mohamed Taki Abdulkarim

Rally for Democracy and Renewal

Union for Democracy and Decentralization

NAME: Mohamed Taki Halidi Ibraham

JUDICIAL SYSTEM

Supreme Court

FURTHER READING

Articles

"Comoros: Coup Leader Holds Talks." *The New York Times* (May 4, 1999): A14.

"Comoro Islands: U.S. Cuts Arms Aid." *The New York Times* (June 11, 1999): A6.

"Comoros: Mercenary on Trial." *The New York Times* (May 5, 1999): A8.

Books

Ottenheimer, Martin. *Historical Dictionary of the Comoro Islands.* Metuchen, N.J.: Scarecrow Press, 1994.

Weinberg, Samantha. *Last of the Pirates: The Search for Bob Denard.* New York: Pantheon Books, 1994.

Internet

ArabNet. Comoros Islands. Available Online @ http://www.arab.net/comoros/comoros_contents.html (November 11, 1999).

CIA World Factbook 1999. Available Online @ http://www.odci.gov/cia/publications/factbook/cn.html (November 11, 1999).

Comoro Islands. Available Online @ http://www.ksu.edu/sasw/comoros/comoros.html (November 11, 1999).

COMOROS: STATISTICAL DATA

For sources and notes see "Sources of Statistics" in the front of each volume.

GEOGRAPHY

Geography (1)

Area:

Total: 2,170 sq km.

Land: 2,170 sq km.

Water: 0 sq km.

Area—comparative: slightly more than 12 times the size of Washington, DC.

Land boundaries: 0 km.

Coastline: 340 km.

Climate: tropical marine; rainy season (November to May).

Terrain: volcanic islands, interiors vary from steep mountains to low hills.

Natural resources: NEGL.

Land use:

Arable land: 35%

Permanent crops: 10%

Permanent pastures: 7%

Forests and woodland: 18%

Other: 30% (1993 est.).

HUMAN FACTORS

Infants and Malnutrition (5)

Under-5 mortality rate (1997) 93

% of infants with low birthweight (1990-97) 8

Births attended by skilled health staff % of total[a] . . .NA

% fully immunized (1995-97)

  TB 55

  DPT 48

HUMAN FACTORS

Demographics (2A)

	1990	1995	1998	2000	2010	2020	2030	2040	2050
Population	429.0	497.3	545.5	580.5	781.8	1,022.5	1,309.5	1,626.5	1,953.3
Net migration rate (per 1,000 population)	NA	NA	NA	NA	NA	NA	NA	NA	NA
Births	NA	NA	NA	NA	NA	NA	NA	NA	NA
Deaths	NA	NA	NA	NA	NA	NA	NA	NA	NA
Life expectancy - males	54.5	56.7	57.9	58.8	62.9	66.6	69.7	72.3	74.4
Life expectancy - females	58.5	61.3	62.8	63.9	68.8	73.1	76.6	79.3	81.4
Birth rate (per 1,000)	40.2	41.2	40.5	40.1	34.8	31.1	28.0	24.3	21.5
Death rate (per 1,000)	11.9	10.4	9.5	8.9	6.6	5.3	4.6	4.4	4.7
Women of reproductive age (15-49 yrs.)	101.2	121.3	131.6	139.2	187.4	254.7	326.7	416.0	503.9
of which are currently married	NA	NA	NA	NA	NA	NA	NA	NA	NA
Fertility rate	5.7	5.6	5.5	5.4	4.8	4.1	3.5	3.1	2.7

Except as noted, values for vital statistics are in thousands; life expectancy is in years.

Polio .... .48

Measles .... .49

Prevalence of child malnutrition under age 5
(1992-97)[b] .... .NA

Ethnic Division (6)

Antalote, Cafre, Makoa, Oimatsaha, Sakalava.

Religions (7)

Sunni Muslim .... .86%

Roman Catholic .... .14%

Languages (8)

Arabic (official), French (official), Comoran (a blend of
Swahili and Arabic).

EDUCATION

Literacy Rates (11A)

In thousands and percent[1]	1990	1995	2000	2010
Illiterate population (15+ yrs.)	128	143	160	202
Literacy rate - total adult pop. (%)	54.4	57.3	60.3	65.8
Literacy rate - males (%)	61.8	64.2	66.4	71.0
Literacy rate - females (%)	47.0	50.4	53.9	60.6

GOVERNMENT & LAW

Political Parties (12)

Federal Assembly	No. of seats
Rassemblement National pour le Development (RND) .... .39	
RND candidate running as independent 1	
Front National pour la Justice (FNJ) 3	

Under a new constitution ratified in October 1996, a two party
system was established; President Mohamed Taki Abdulkarim
called for all parties to dissolve and join him in creating the
RND; the constitution stipulates that only parties that win six
seats in the Federal Assembly (two from each island) are
permitted to be in opposition, but if no party accomplishes that
the second most successful party will be in opposition; in the
elections of December 1996 the FNJ appeared to qualify as
opposition.

Government Budget (13B)

Revenues ....$55 million

Expenditures ....$71 million

Capital expenditures ....$15 million

Data for 1995 est.

Military Affairs (14A)

Availability of manpower

Males age 15-49 (1998 est.) .... .129,095

Fit for military service

Males (1998 est.) .... .76,991

Total expenditures (1994 est.) ....$3 million

Expenditures as % of GDP .... .NA

NA stands for not available.

LABOR FORCE

Labor Force (16)

Total .... .144,500

Agriculture .... .80%

Government 3%

Data for 1996 est.

Unemployment Rate (17)

20% (1996 est.)

PRODUCTION SECTOR

Electric Energy (18)

Capacity .... .9,750 kW (1996)

Production .... .31 million kWh (1996)

Consumption per capita .... .38 kWh (1996)

Transportation (19)

Highways:

total: 880 km

paved: 673 km

unpaved: 207 km (1996 est.)

Merchant marine: none

Airports: 4 (1997 est.)

Airports—with paved runways:

total: 4

2,438 to 3,047 m: 1

914 to 1,523 m: 3 (1997 est.)

Top Agricultural Products (20)

Vanilla, cloves, perfume essences, copra, coconuts,
bananas, cassava (tapioca).

FINANCE, ECONOMICS, & TRADE

Economic Indicators (22)

National product: GDP—purchasing power parity— $400 million (1997 est.)

National product real growth rate: 3.5% (1997 est.)

National product per capita: $685 (1997 est.)

Inflation rate—consumer price index: 3.5% (1996 est.)

Exchange Rates (24)

Exchange rates:

Comoran francs (CF) per US$1

January 1998	.456.27
1997	.437.75
1996	.383.66
1995	.374.36
1994	.416.40
1993	.283.16

Beginning 12 January 1994, the Comoran franc was devalued to 75 per French franc from 50 per French franc at which it had been fixed since 1948

Top Import Origins (25)

$70 million (f.o.b., 1996 est.)

Origins	%
France	.60
South Africa	.10
Kenya	.5
Singapore	.4

Top Export Destinations (26)

$11.4 million (f.o.b., 1996 est.).

Destinations	%
France	.54
Germany	.18
United States	.18

Economic Aid (27)

Recipient: ODA, $NA. NA stands for not available.

Import Export Commodities (28)

Import Commodities	Export Commodities
Rice and other foodstuffs	Vanilla
Consumer goods; petroleum products	Ylang-ylang
	Cloves
Cement	Perfume oil
Transport equipment	Copra

Balance of Payments (23)

	1991	1992	1993	1994	1995
Exports of goods (f.o.b.)	24	21	22	11	11
Imports of goods (f.o.b.)	−54	−58	−50	−45	−54
Trade balance	−29	−37	−28	−34	−42
Services - debits	−49	−53	−51	−48	−52
Services - credits	28	30	34	31	38
Private transfers (net)	37	40	44	35	29
Government transfers (net)	4	5	11	9	9
Overall balance	−10	−14	10	−7	−19

CONGO, DEMOCRATIC REPUBLIC OF THE

Democratic Republic of the Congo
République Democratique du Congo

INTRODUCTORY SURVEY

RECENT HISTORY

The rise of nationalism in the various African territories following World War II (1939–45) seemed to have bypassed the Belgian Congo, which remained without self-government (except for a few large cities) until 1959. The Congolese demanded independence and rioted, first in Léopoldville (now Kinshasa) and then elsewhere. At first, the Belgian government proposed gradual progress toward self-rule in the colony, but as the independence movement persisted and grew, Belgium agreed to grant the Congo its independence in mid-1960 and to continue economic and other aid after independence.

The newly independent Republic of the Congo was inaugurated on 30 June 1960, with Joseph Kasavubu as its first head of state and Patrice Lumumba its first premier. It was immediately confronted by massive economic, political, and social problems. A week after independence, the armed forces mutinied (rebelled), as separatist movements and intertribal conflict threatened to split the country.

A major blow to the new republic was the secession of the mineral-rich southwest province, announced on 11 July 1960 by Moïse Tshombe, head of the provincial government. The central government was crippled by the loss of revenues from its richest province and by the departure of Belgian civil servants, doctors, teachers, and technicians. Faced with the threatened collapse of a new nation, the UN responded with what grew into

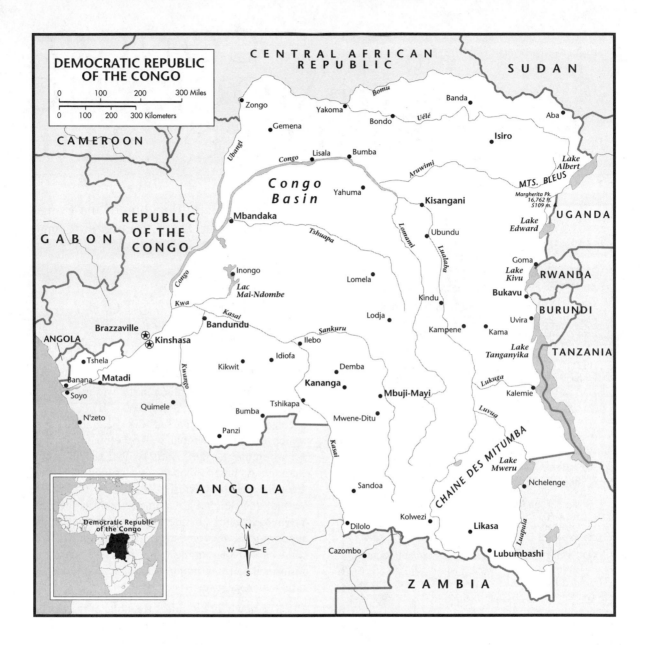

a program of massive assistance—financial, military, administrative, and technical.

In September 1960, Kasavubu and Lumumba each attempted to remove the other from the government. Finally, Kasavubu, with the help of army chief of staff Colonel Joseph-Désiré Mobutu, took Lumumba prisoner and turned him over to the authorities in the province that had seceded. They put Lumumba to death early in 1961.

In September 1961, UN Secretary-General Dag Hammarskjöld flew to the Congo, where he boarded a plane for Northern Rhodesia (now Zambia) to meet with Moise Tshombe, head of the government of Katanga, the seceded province. The plane crashed, killing him and all others on board. UN troops eventually resorted to broad-scale military operations to disarm the Katanga forces throughout the province. Tshombe capitulated, and the secession of Katanga was ended on 14 January 1963.

A new series of rebellions soon began. However, UN troops were withdrawn on 30 June 1964. The self-exiled Tshombe was recalled and offered the position of prime minister. Rebel-held Stanleyville (now Kisangani) was recaptured in November 1964.

On 13 October 1965, Tshombe was removed from office by Kasavubu, who attempted to replace him with Evariste Kimba, also from Katanga. When Kimba was not endorsed by the parliament, General Mobutu, commander-in-chief of the Congolese National Army, seized power in a coup d'état on 24 November 1965 and assumed the presidency. Tshombe's hopes for a comeback were dashed when he was kidnapped in June 1967 and imprisoned in Algeria, where he died two years later.

The country was officially transformed into a one-party state in 1970. In 1971, the name of the country was changed from Congo to Zaire. Mobutu was elected without opposition to a new seven-year term as president in 1977, but he continued to face opposition, both external and internal. In 1982, Mobutu resumed diplomatic ties with Israel, which had been broken in 1974; five Arab nations quickly cut ties with Zaire, and $350 million in promised Arab aid to Zaire was blocked. In 1983, Zaire sent 2,700 troops to Chad to aid the government against Libyan-backed rebels; they were withdrawn in 1984. Mobutu was reelected ''unopposed'' to a new seven-year presidential term in July 1984.

For their support of U.S. positions throughout the cold war, Zaire, and in particular Mobutu, were handsomely rewarded. Mobutu was said to be the wealthiest person in Africa. However, widely publicized human rights violations in the late 1980s put Mobutu on the defensive.

In September 1991, he was forced to call a National Conference of some 2,800 delegates to draft a new constitution. It often failed to arrive at a consensus, and when it did, Mobutu thwarted its decisions. In November 1991, Mobutu split the coalition known as the Sacred Union by naming Nguza Karl-I-Bond of the Union of Federalists and Independent Republicans (UFERI) as prime minister. Nguza closed the National Conference in February 1992. On 14 August 1992, the Conference elected Etienne Tshisekedi of the Union for Democracy and Social Progress (UDPS) as prime minister of a transitional government.

Mobutu, who countered by forming a new government under his control and dismissing Tshisekedi in December 1992, controlled the army, the central bank, and the police. The High Council of the Republic, the interim legislature, continued to recognize Tshisekedi as did Zaire's principal economic partners abroad.

Two parallel governments attempted to rule Zaire. One controlled the country's wealth and the media, the other had a popular following and professed support from Western governments.

In 1993, Mobutu's Bank of Zaire introduced new currency on three occasions, but it soon became worthless. Merchants would not accept it, and riots broke out when soldiers could not spend their pay. Anarchy, corruption, uncontrolled violence, and poverty now prevail. Government authority dissolved, leaving the country to pillaging soldiers and roaming gangs. The southwest province of Shaba (formerly Katanga) had declared its autonomy. AIDS was rampant.

In 1995, a new outbreak of the Ebola virus (a contagious deadly disease that cannot be treated and may kill as many as 90% of those infected by it) was reported, which caused 250 deaths.

The civil strife in neighboring Rwanda in 1994–95 forced over 1 million people to flee into Zaire. Many of the refugees were Rwandan Hutus who had participated in the genocide against the Tutsis. The refugees quickly became a great strain on the region's resources, and Zaire's government stepped up the efforts to return them to Rwanda in August 1995. When the Zairian government began to expel Hutu refugees, many were afraid of being imprisoned or killed by Rwanda's Tutsi-led government.

In October 1996, the government of the Zairian province of South Kivu began a crackdown not only against Rwandan refugees but against a group of Rwandans who had lived in Zaire for over a century. As a result, the Rwandans began a rebellion. By November, the provincial government had been overthrown, and the major cities of the province had come under rebel control. At this point, Laurent Désiré Kabila emerged as a leader of the rebellion, and he shifted its focus from protecting Rwandans to organizing a rebellion against the Zairian government itself. The rebels' influence grew throughout eastern Zaire, and soon included many Zairians of different ethnicities.

During the first few months of the rebellion, President Mobuto had been out of the country. In December 1996, Mobuto returned and reorganized the army command. In January 1997, the army launched an attack against the rebels, but it was soundly defeated and the rebels gained territory. The rebels had gained control of most of the western provinces by February 1997 and were threatening to overrun the whole country unless Mobuto stepped down. Peace talks failed, and the rebels gained control over Lubumbashi (the second largest city) and the diamond-rich province of Kasai.

As the rebels closed in on Kinshasa in May 1997, South African president Nelson Mandela hosted talks between Kabila and Mobuto aboard a South African ship. As rebel forces drew ever closer, Mobuto gave up any hope of retaining power, and he fled to his northern hometown and then abroad. Kabila's forces entered Kinshasa to a hero's welcome. Kabila announced that the country's name would go back to the one it had used between 1960 and 1970, the Democratic Republic of the Congo.

Kabila, however, soon proved to be a suspicious hero. Kabila himself and most of his top associates are Tutsis and were connected with the mass killings of Rwandan Hutu refugees in the eastern provinces they had controlled since late 1996. Kabila refused to cooperate with UN investigators who were looking into the alleged abuses. Kabila's support plummeted during his first year in power, as he alienated many of those who had helped him to power. In July 1998, a new group of rebels opposed to Kabila captured three eastern towns, while forces sympathetic with the rebels fought with Kabila's forces in Kinshasa. As of the spring of 1999, the civil war remained a stalemate with Mr. Kabila in control of most of the interior, including the rich southeastern Katanga province, while rebel forces and their foreign allies control much of the border regions of the country.

GOVERNMENT

With the overthrow of the Mobutu government in 1997, there was a great deal of uncertainty over the structure of the new government. As of September 1997, President Kabila had named several associates to ministry-level posts but had given little indication of how he intended to structure the new government. He repeatedly has promised to restore democracy.

Judiciary

The courts include courts of first hearing, appeals courts, a Supreme Court, and the Court of State Security. Many disputes are settled at the local level by administrative officials or traditional authorities.

Political Parties

In 1970, General Mobuto established a single-party system, with the sole legal party the ruling MPR (Popular Movement of the Revolution). The chairman of the MPR automatically holds the office of head of state; party and state are effectively one, and every citizen is automatically a member of the MPR.

The constitution was amended to permit party activity in April 1990. The most important among the new parties combined to form a coalition known as the Sacred Union. These include the Union for Democracy and Social Progress (UDPS), the Union of Federalists and Independent Republicans (UFERI), the Unified Lumumbist Party (PALU), and the Social Democratic Christian Party (PDSC).

As of 1997, the future of political parties in the DROC was uncertain. President Kabila outlawed all political parties until at least 1999, when elections are to be held. Until then, Kabila's Alliance of Democratic Forces for the Liberation of Congo rules alone.

DEFENSE

In 1995, the Zairian army had 25,000 personnel. The navy had 1,300 personnel; and the air force, 1,800 personnel. In 1995, Zaire spent $125 million on defense, probably equal to about 1–1.5% of the gross domestic product (GDP).

ECONOMIC AFFAIRS

The DROC has a wealth of natural resources that should provide the foundation for a stable economy. However, in September 1991, mutinous military troops looted all major urban centers, practically bringing the economy to a standstill. A large government deficit, primarily to pay salaries for the military and civil servants, was financed by printing currency. Severe inflation and economic collapse followed. Many multinational businesses have left the country.

Public Finance

Public finance from the late 1970s to the mid-1980s was characterized by uncontrolled spending, poor tax collection, and large deficits, often covered by creating new money. Expenditures are almost entirely current. The state-owned copper mining company typically has generated one-third of the government's revenue.

The U.S. Central Intelligence Agency estimates that, in 1996, government revenues totaled approximately $479 million and expenditures $479 million. External debt totaled $11.3 billion.

Income

In 1998, the former Zaire had a gross national product (GNP) of $5.3 billion, or about $110 per person. For the period 1985–95, the average annual real growth rate of the GNP per person was −8.5%.

Industry

Much of the DROC's industry involves the processing of agricultural products (sugar, flour) and mineral-bearing ore (copper, zinc, petroleum, cement). The production of consumer goods (beer, soft drinks, textiles) plays a leading role in the sector as well.

Banking and Finance

The Bank of Zaire serves as the country's central bank and bank of issue. At the end of 1994, money supply, as measured by M2, was NZ 584 billion. At that time, total foreign reserves, excluding gold, amounted to $102.69 million. An indication of the deterioration of economic life was a strong disinclination by the public to keep money in banks. There are no securities exchanges in the DROC.

Economic Development

Development expenditures are usually made year by year, and despite occasional, vaguely conceived three-year plans, little progress has been made over the years. The development horizon in the DROC appears limitless in each of its principal sectors. Since 1992, however, any semblance of economic planning and development management has evaporated. The currency is out of control, and change for the better seems unlikely until the political situation stabilizes.

SOCIAL WELFARE

Social security is handled by the National Social Security Institute. In addition to pension funds, the institute administers compensation for accidents and illness; old age, disability, and death benefits; and family allowances. The Department of Social Affairs administers a number of welfare agencies. They offer vocational training for unemployed youths, adult education programs, and a number of activities for women. However, the Roman Catholic Church still provides most of the nation's welfare and social programs.

A married woman must have her husband's permission to open a bank account, take a job, get a passport, or rent or sell real estate.

Healthcare

Medical personnel in 1990 included 2,469 physicians. In 1993, only 59% of the population had access to health care services.

Diseases include malaria, trypanosomiasis, onchocerciasis, schistosomiasis, tuberculosis, measles, leprosy, dysentery, typhoid, and hookworm; AIDS has also been recognized, and in 1987, tests indicated that 9% of babies were born with the virus. In 1994, 3.7% of all adults in Zaire were infected with HIV, the virus that causes AIDS. Malnutrition is a serious health problem, especially among children. Average life expectancy was 53 years.

Housing

The massive migration to the cities that began after independence led to a fourfold increase in the population of Kinshasa, creating a massive housing problem that is still far from solved. Tens of thousands of squatters are crowded into squalid shantytowns on the outskirts of the capital. Unable to come up with adequate alternatives, the government began extending basic utilities to the new settlements. As of 1984, 52% of housing units were traditional one-room adobe, straw, or mud structures, and 45% were modern houses of durable or semi-durable material containing one or more rooms.

EDUCATION

Education is compulsory between ages 6 and 12. Primary-school enrollment rose to 4.9 million in 1993. The development of secondary education has also been dramatic: the number of secondary-school students rose from 38,000 in 1960–61 to 1.3 million in 1993. In 1995, adult illiteracy was 33%.

The National University of Zaire is organized into three separate campuses located in Kinshasa, Lubumbashi, and Kisangani.

1999 KEY EVENTS TIMELINE

January

- Wall Street, Kinshasa's black marketeer money-changing district, is closed down by the government in an effort to bring the exchange rate closer to that of the new Congo franc.

- Three hundred Congolese troops enter the Central African Republic (CAR) to halt advancing rebels who recently seized the border town of Zongo.

- Rebels claimed to have killed 400 Hutu militia, but deny allegations of killing about 500 civilians.

February

- Peace talks reportedly on course in Lusaka.

- President Clinton's envoy, Howard Wolpe, holds meetings on a five-week African tour to find ways to end the six-month-old crisis.

March

- A government reshuffling takes place.

- The economy is considered marginally better in rebel-held areas.

- Gecamines cancels its contracts with all its marketing agents and grants exclusive rights to MRG, a London-based trader. Mitsui refuses to allow Gecamines agents access to their warehouses to verify Cobalt stocks, insisting that Cobalt has already been paid for under its contract.

April

- Kabila dissolves the ruling Alliance des forces démocratiques pour la libération du Congo-Zaire (AFDL) and replaces it with grass-roots structures, the comités du pouvoir populaire (CPP).

- Zambian President, Frederick Chiluba, arranges talks between Laurent Kabila and the rebels.

- Kabila and President Yoweri Museveni of Uganda, sign a cease-fire brokered by Colonel Muammar Gaddafi. The presidents of Chad and Eritrea are also in attendance at the mini-summit.

May

- The rebel movement, Rassemblement Congolais pour la Démocratie (RCD), splits into two factions with Ilunga claiming that Wamba dia Wamba no longer controls significant forces.

- Shooting breaks out between sides of allied Ugandan and Rwandan forces in Kisangani, leaving several dead.

June

- The Environment ministers of the Republic of Congo and the DC meet in Kinshasa to harmonize their views on the African Timber Organization.

- Warring parties meet in Lusaka to finalize a cease-fire formula that can lay the ground rules for a United Nations peacekeeping force.

- Peace talks begin in Lusaka with participation from all countries involved in the conflict except Rwanda.

- The DC health minister condemns female genital mutilation.

- Mayi-Mayi rebels in the east carry out anti-Tutsi Banyamulengi attacks.

- Rwanda-backed RCD forces advance on the Mbuji Mayi diamond center in Kasai Orientale.

- The UN High Commissioner for Refugees, Sadako Ogata, visits Kinshasa and several refugee sites in DC.

- The franc congolais formally replaces the nouveau zaire, which as of June 30 is no longer legal tender.

July

- Foreign ministers of the DC and Rwanda meet to discuss their differences under mediation by President Mbeki of South Africa.

- All nations involved in the war sign a peace accord in Lusaka. However, the rebel force, RCD, owing to factional infighting, refuses to sign.

- The DC sues Uganda in the World Court for illegally occupying its territory.

- Fighting over land erupts between the Hema ethnic group and the Lendu people in the Ituri region, in the area of Djugu, near Bunia.

August

- Rebel leader Jean-Pierre Bemba of the Movement for the Liberation of Congo (MLC) signs the cease-fire agreement of July 10.

- The government signs an agreement with the trade union umbrella of the civil service to end a general strike for pay increases and payment for arrears.

- The UN announces its plan to deploy peacekeepers in the DC.

- More than 1,300 rebels in Katanga surrender to government and military authorities.

- A peace march commemorating the first anniversary of the war is hijacked by thousands of unarmed government soldiers and members of the CPPs.

September

- A second polio immunization round is held.

- A national debate is scheduled to take place in 30 days.

- A contingent of 22 UN military observers arrives in Kinshasa.

October

- Kofi Annan recommends to the UN Security Council that it extend until January 15, 2000 the mandate of a few dozen UN liaison officers in the DC, and authorize a 500-member UN peace-keeper observer mission.

- Accusations of cease fire violations are rife.

- Regional ministers seek faster UN deployment, while Kofi Annan urges all sides to abide by the truce.

- The RCD-Goma rebel movement reshuffles, reducing its "administrative departments" from 24 to 16. The top figures remain the same.

- France calls for a regional peace conference, which the Netherlands supports.

- Kabila sends a personal message of peace to Museveni, containing an invitation for talks regarding implementation of the Lusaka accord.

November

- The UN estimates that some 6,000 people died by the end of the first year of the Congo conflict, many of them civilians.

- The Joint Military Commission (JMC) partitions the country into four operational zones covering territory controlled by both the government and the rebels. Each zone will be chaired by a military officer from a neutral African state.

- Initial three-month mandate for UN observer mission expires November 6.

- After weeks of conflict between the Congolese government and Congolese rebels, a full-scale fight breaks out at Gbadolite in northern Congo. Two leaders of separate rebel factions, Jean-Pierre Bemba and Ernest Wamba dia Wamba, cite government violations and declare the Lukasa ceasefire, signed in July and August, to be void.

December

- Superstitious citizens blame Congolese children for country's problems, and accuse them of witchcraft, subjecting "possessed" children to painful exorcisms.

ANALYSIS OF EVENTS: 1999

BUSINESS AND THE ECONOMY

Since the war began in August 1998, the government has depreciated the franc four times to keep up with inflation. Its macroeconomic policies have not worked, and have consisted mainly in cracking down on exchange bureaus. In March, the economy was considered marginally better in rebel-held areas gauged by the difference in black market exchange rates. The franc congolais was 3.6 to one U.S. dollar in rebel areas, and 8.2 to one in government areas. However, in the east, purchasing power was very low and few people were coming to towns to do business. Frequent Mayi-Mayi attacks, fear of Interahamwe guerrillas, and the RCD rebels brought commerce to a standstill, and the fear was indeed warranted. The Catholic Church reported that up to 100 civilians, mostly women market vendors, were massacred by RCD rebels in South Kivu on October 23.

Going into November, the government was struggling to find the foreign exchange it needed to pay for food and fuel imports. Its main exports, located in rebel-held areas, might be expected to revive if the peace holds. However, the severe absence of foreign exchange will cause recurrent fuel shortages, a steady depreciation of the franc, and feed inflation since most goods are imported. The government also faced a possible uprising from civil servants angry over low salaries.

GOVERNMENT AND POLITICS

Thirty-nine years after Patrice Lumumba invited U.N. peacekeepers to save Katanga, the U.N. "casques bleus" returned to Congo again—this time as unwanted guests—to oversee the implementation of the July Lusaka peace accord. All parties, except for two rebel groups, signed the accord July 10. The RCD, which split apart in May, appended its signature by the end of July, and the MLC of Jean-Pierre Bemba signed in August. The subsequent arrival of a handful of U.N. observers from MONUC, resented and restricted in movement by the government, are expected to be joined by 500 more, although at least 10,000 peacekeepers will be necessary for adequate oversight.

The split in the RCD reflected the growing distance between Uganda and Rwanda. Rwanda's stated military objectives have been two-fold: protection from and retaliation against Interahamwe (Hutu) rebels seeking refuge in the DC. Rwanda has sought to accomplish these objectives by extending its sphere of influence in Kivu. Both Uganda and Rwanda have been motivated by control of land, timber, diamonds and other resources, as have Zimbabwe and other nations. By the time of the cease-fire, Rwanda was backing RCD—Goma, Ilunga's forces, while Uganda aligned with Bemba's MLC. Ernest Wamba dia Wamba appeared to be the loser in the realignment, and unless he receives backing from Uganda, his rival RCD faction in Kisangani no longer represents a significant threat. Most DC civilians regard Uganda and Rwanda as aggressors, and remain hostile toward the RCD rebels, the Interahamwe, and other rebels groups.

Kabila's government enjoys little credibility. He is president, minister of defense, and holds the power of the executive, legislature, and the military. Opposition parties are technically illegal, while civil society organizations exercise a weak voice in public affairs at best. To shore up its image abroad, the government has retained the services of Cohen and Woods International, a public relations firm. Finance Minister Mawapanga Mwana Nanga recently met with former Assistant Secretary of State for Africa, Herman Cohen, partner in Cohen and Woods.

In early November, fighting between Bemba's forces and government troops was reported in Equateur, and troop movements on various sides prompted U.S. concern over violations of the accord. Building a stable peace will require significant changes in attitudes and relationships. The Interahamwe and Mayi-Mayi rebels were not involved in the Lusaka negotiations. Although relations have improved between Kabila and Museveni, Kabila considers Rwanda and Uganda aggressors, and he refuses to negotiate with rebels as equals. Rwandan President Paul Kagame would like to secure a buffer zone in eastern Kivu for protection against Interahamwe and Mayi-Mayi forces. However, many Congolese living in eastern Kivu view Tutsi relocation with

great suspicion, and will resist their settlement in the area.

CULTURE AND SOCIETY

With major portions of the country at war, under rebel control, or occupied by refugees, Congolese civilians struggled just to survive and to make a living. Given at least five separate rebel factions, and two opposing sets of governmental military forces, it was difficult to tell who was on whose side. The government bombed civilians in Kisangani, Ulvira, and Goma, and carried out more than 100 public executions. In August, the government sabotaged a peace march organized by civil society associations. Over the year, it arrested journalists, political leaders, and human rights activists for no apparent reason. Some 6,000 children were estimated in military service. Thousands of Congolese civilians have died directly and indirectly from the conflict.

Massacres, murders, rapes, and other atrocities whether random, or systematic, underscore the lawlessness and deep divisions within Congolese society, and the absence of enforcement and mediating institutions. The Tutsi residents in eastern Kivu, the Banyamulenge, want a federated state for their protection. The fighting in the northeast between Hema and Lendu peoples over land, which has claimed thousands of lives and displaced more than 100,000 people, is presently beyond the control of state and civil authorities. Thousands of civil servants routinely go to work in hopes of receiving back wages. Health, education, and other social infrastructure functions at a fraction of its capacity.

Perhaps because of this dismal reality, Congolese found ways to distract themselves. The Kinshasa music scene continued to be productive, despite the death of the leader of Empire Bakuba, one of the country's consistently popular bands. Kofi Olimede gave major concerts in Paris, and Dafao went to Washington to play. The Fespaco (Festival Pan-africaine du Cinéma â Ouagadougou) grand prize this February went to Pièces d'Indentité from Kinshasa. Another film shown there, Mobutu, roi du Zaïre, by Thierry Michel, depicted the life and times of the former dictator, who for 32 years enriched himself while impoverishing the country he ruled.

DIRECTORY

CENTRAL GOVERNMENT

Head of State

President
Laurent-Désiré Kabila, Office of the President

Ministers

Minister of Internal Affairs
Kakudji Gautan, Ministry of Internal Affairs

Minister of Oil and Presidential Affairs
Pierre-Victor Mpoyo, Ministry of Oil and
Presidential Affairs

**Minister of Foreign Affairs and International
Cooperation**
Yerodia Abdoulaye Ndombasi, Ministry of
Foreign Affairs and International Cooperation

Minister of Planning and Commerce
Badimayi Dilembu Mulumba, Ministry of
Planning and Commerce, 4155, avenue des
Coteaux, Kinshasa, Democratic Republic of
Congo
PHONE: +243 31332; 32843

Minister of Justice
Mwenze Kongolo, Ministry of Justice, 228,
avenue de Lemura, Kinshasa, Democratic
Republic of Congo
PHONE: +243 32432; 32433

Minister of Finance
Mawapanga Mwana Nanga, Ministry of Finance,
boulevard du 30 Juin, BP 12997, Kinshasa,
Democratic Republic of Congo
PHONE: +243 (12) 31197

Minister of Economy and Industry
Bemba Saolona, Ministry of Economy and
Industry

Minister of Public Work
Yagi Sitolo, Ministry of Public Work

Minister of Post and Telecommunications
Prosper Kibuey, Ministry of Post and
Telecommunications, 4484, avenue des Huileries,
Kinshasa, Democratic Republic of Congo
PHONE: +243 23878; 24580

Minister of Reconstruction
Denis Kalume Numbi, Ministry of
Reconstruction

**Minister of Transportation and
Communication**
Babandoa Etoa Odette, Ministry of
Transportation and Communication

Minister of Agriculture
Kitanga Eshima Musebo Etienne, Ministry of
Agriculture

Minister of Environment, Fishing and Forest
Bishikwabo Tshubaka, Ministry of Environment,
Fishing and Forest

Minister of Energy
Babi Mbayi, Ministry of Energy

Minister of Education
Kamara Rwakakara, Ministry of Education

Minister of Human Rights
Léonard She Okitundu, Ministry of Human
Rights

Minister of Culture and Art
Juliana Lumumba, Ministry of Culture and Art

Minister of Information and Tourism
Didier Mumengi, Ministry of Information and
Tourism

Minister of Labor and Social Welfare
Paul Kapita Shabangi, Ministry of Labor and
Social Welfare

Minister of Mining
Frédéric Kibassa Maliba, Ministry of Mining,
239, avenue de la Justice, Kinshasa, Democratic
Republic of Congo
PHONE: +243 30104; 31462

Minister of Health and Social Affairs
Jean-Baptiste Sondji, Ministry of Health and
Social Affairs, boulevard du 30 Juin, Kinshasa,
Democratic Republic of Congo
PHONE: +243 30147; 31750

POLITICAL ORGANIZATIONS

Alliance of Democratic Forces for the Liberation of Congo-Zaire (AFDL)

NAME: Laurent-Désirée Kabila

Popular Movement of the Revolution (MPR)

Union for the Republic (UPR)

Union for Democracy and Social Progress (UDPS)

NAME: Etienne Tshisekedi wa Mulumba, 12eme
rue, Kinshasa, Democratic Republic of Congo
E-MAIL: udps@globalserve.net

Congolese Rally for Democracy (RCD)

NAME: Ernest Wamba dia Wamba

Democratic Social Christian Party (PDSC)

NAME: Andre Bo-Boliko

Union of Federalists and Independent Republicans (UFERI)

NAME: Gabriel Kyungu wa Kumwunzu

Unified Lumumbast Party (PALU)

NAME: Antoine Gizenga

Rally for a New Society (RNS)

BP 10238, Kinshasa 1, Democratic Republic of Congo
E-MAIL: rnscongo@freewwweb.com
TITLE: President
NAME: Alafuele M. Kalala

DIPLOMATIC REPRESENTATION

Embassies in the Democratic Republic of Congo

United States
310 avenue des Aviateurs, Kinshasa, Democratic Republic of Congo
PHONE: +243 (12) 2153335

JUDICIAL SYSTEM

Supreme Court

FURTHER READING

Articles

"Congo: Wall Street Raided." *The Economist* 350 (January 23, 1999): 42.

"High Treason Charged in Congolese Tin Case." *American Metal Market* 107, 195 (October 8, 1999): 2.

Whitelaw, Kevin. "Struggling to Deliver on Promises of Peace." *U.S. News and World Report* 127, 10 (September 13, 1999): 32.

Books

Africa on File. New York: Facts on File, 1995.

Hochschild, Adam. *King Leopold's Ghost: A Story of Greed, Terror, and Heroism in Colonial Africa.* Boston: Houghton Mifflin, 1998.

Lumumba-Kasongo, Tukumbi. *The Dynamics of Economic and Political Relations Between Africa and Foreign Powers: A Study in International Relations.* Westport, CT: Praeger, 1999.

Young, Crawford, and Thomas Turner. *The Rise and Fall of the Zairian State.* Madison: The University of Wisconsin Press, 1995.

Internet

Africaonline. Available Online @ http://www.africaonline.com. (October 28, 1999).

Africa News Online. Available Online @ http://www.africanews.org/west/stories/1999_feat1.html. (October 28, 1999).

Integrated Regional Information Network (IRIN). Available Online @ http://www.reliefweb.int/IRIN. (October 28, 1999).

CONGO, DEMOCRATIC REPUBLIC OF THE: STATISTICAL DATA

For sources and notes see "Sources of Statistics" in the front of each volume.

GEOGRAPHY

Geography (1)

Area:

Total: 2,345,410 sq km.

Land: 2,267,600 sq km.

Water: 77,810 sq km.

Area—comparative: slightly less than one-fourth the size of US.

Land boundaries:

Total: 10,271 km.

Border countries: Angola 2,511 km, Burundi 233 km, Central African Republic 1,577 km, Republic of the Congo 2,410 km, Rwanda 217 km, Sudan 628 km, Uganda 765 km, Zambia 1,930 km.

Coastline: 37 km.

Climate: tropical; hot and humid in equatorial river basin; cooler and drier in southern highlands; cooler and wetter in eastern highlands; north of Equator - wet season April to October, dry season December to February; south of Equator - wet season November to March, dry season April to October.

Terrain: vast central basin is a low-lying plateau; mountains in east.

Natural resources: cobalt, copper, cadmium, petroleum, industrial and gem diamonds, gold, silver, zinc, manganese, tin, germanium, uranium, radium, bauxite, iron ore, coal, hydropower potential, timber.

Land use:

Arable land: 3%

Permanent crops: 0%

Permanent pastures: 7%

Forests and woodland: 77%

Other: 13% (1993 est.).

HUMAN FACTORS

Demographics (2A)

	1990	1995	1998	2000	2010	2020	2030	2040	2050
Population	37,977.8	45,755.6	49,000.5	51,987.8	70,276.4	92,851.9	119,815.1	151,214.5	184,455.8
Net migration rate (per 1,000 population)	NA	NA	NA	NA	NA	NA	NA	NA	NA
Births	NA	NA	NA	NA	NA	NA	NA	NA	NA
Deaths	NA	NA	NA	NA	NA	NA	NA	NA	NA
Life expectancy - males	46.8	47.2	47.3	47.3	49.7	52.7	60.0	67.4	70.4
Life expectancy - females	49.7	50.6	51.4	51.9	54.2	57.5	66.0	74.5	77.8
Birth rate (per 1,000)	48.6	48.4	46.8	46.0	42.1	37.3	31.8	26.5	22.3
Death rate (per 1,000)	16.6	15.8	15.2	14.8	12.6	10.7	7.2	4.7	4.4
Women of reproductive age (15-49 yrs.)	8,488.0	10,167.6	10,789.3	11,443.9	15,912.5	22,177.9	30,362.5	40,214.3	49,999.4
of which are currently married	NA	NA	NA	NA	NA	NA	NA	NA	NA
Fertility rate	6.7	6.7	6.5	6.4	5.6	4.7	3.8	3.1	2.6

Except as noted, values for vital statistics are in thousands; life expectancy is in years.

Ethnic Division (6)

Over 200 African ethnic groups of which the majority are Bantu; the four largest tribes—Mongo Luba, Kongo (all Bantu), and the Mangbetu-Azande (Hamitic) Make up about 45% of the population.

Religions (7)

Roman Catholic 50%

Protestant 20%

Kimbanguist 10%

Muslim 10%

Syncretic sects, trad. beliefs 10%

Languages (8)

French (official), Lingala (a lingua franca trade language), Kingwana (a dialect of Kiswahili or Swahili), Kikongo, Tshiluba.

EDUCATION

Educational Attainment (10)

Age group (1984) . . . . .25+

Total population 10,439,400

Highest level attained (%)

No schooling 52.4

First level

Not completed 30.3

Completed . . . . .NA

Entered second level

S-1 . . . . .14.6

S-2 . . . . .NA

Postsecondary 1.3

GOVERNMENT & LAW

Political Parties (12)

Legislative activity has been suspended pending the establishment of Kabila's promised constitutional reforms.

Government Budget (13B)

Revenues . . . .$269 million

Expenditures . . . .$244 million

Capital expenditures . . . .$24 million

Data for 1996 est.

LABOR FORCE

Labor Force (16)

Total (million) 14.51

Agriculture 65%

Industry 16%

Services 19%

Data for 1993 est. Percent distribution for 1991 est.

Unemployment Rate (17)

Rate not available.

PRODUCTION SECTOR

Electric Energy (18)

Capacity . . . . .2.831 million kW (1995)

Production . . . . .5.22 billion kWh (1995)

Consumption per capita . . . . .95 kWh (1995)

Transportation (19)

Highways:

total: 145,000 km

paved: 2,500 km

unpaved: 142,500 km (1993 est.)

Waterways: 15,000 km including the Congo, its tributaries, and unconnected lakes

Pipelines: petroleum products 390 km

Merchant marine: none

Airports: 234 (1997 est.)

Airports—with paved runways:

total: 24

over 3,047 m: 4

2,438 to 3,047 m: 3

1,524 to 2,437 m: 15

914 to 1,523 m: 2 (1997 est.)

Airports—with unpaved runways:

total: 210

1,524 to 2,437 m: 20

914 to 1,523 m: 96

under 914 m: 94 (1997 est.)

Top Agricultural Products (20)

Coffee, sugar, palm oil, rubber, tea, quinine, cassava (tapioca), palm oil, bananas, root crops, corn, fruits; wood products.

GOVERNMENT & LAW

Military Affairs (14B)

	1990	1991	1992	1993	1994	1995
Military expenditures						
Current dollars (mil.)	NA	NA	239	500	36	17
1995 constant dollars (mil.)	NA	NA	257	524	37	17
Armed forces (000)	55	60	55	55	53	49
Gross national product (GNP)						
Current dollars (mil.)	7,567	7,140	6,429	5,556	5,216	5,190
1995 constant dollars (mil.)	8,697	7,889	6,915	5,824	5,346	5,190
Central government expenditures (CGE)						
1995 constant dollars (mil.)	1,866	2,202	1,602	2,058	294	468
People (mil.)	37.8	39.1	40.2	41.4	42.7	45.4
Military expenditure as % of GNP	NA	NA	3.7	9.0	.7	.3
Military expenditure as % of CGE	NA	NA	16.1	25.5	12.6	3.7
Military expenditure per capita (1995 $)	NA	NA	6	13	1	0
Armed forces per 1,000 people (soldiers)	1.5	1.5	1.4	1.3	1.2	1.1
GNP per capita (1994 $)	230	202	172	141	125	114
Arms imports[6]						
Current dollars (mil.)	70	20	0	10	0	0
1995 constant dollars (mil.)	80	22	0	10	0	0
Arms exports[6]						
Current dollars (mil.)	0	0	0	0	0	0
1995 constant dollars (mil.)	0	0	0	0	0	0
Total imports[7]						
Current dollars (mil.)	886	710	420	372	382	397
1995 constant dollars (mil.)	1,018	785	452	390	392	397
Total exports[7]						
Current dollars (mil.)	999	830	426	368	419	438
1995 constant dollars (mil.)	1,148	917	458	386	430	438
Arms as percent of total imports[8]	7.9	2.8	0	2.7	0	0
Arms as percent of total exports[8]	0	0	0	0	0	0

Previously Zaire.

FINANCE, ECONOMICS, & TRADE

Economic Indicators (22)

National product: GDP—purchasing power parity— $18 billion (1996 est.)

National product real growth rate: 1.5% (1996 est.)

National product per capita: $400 (1996 est.)

Inflation rate—consumer price index: NA

Exchange Rates (24)

Exchange rates:

New zaires (Z) per US$1

January 1998	115,000
October 1996	83,764
1995	7,024
1994	1,194
1993	.3

On 22 October 1993 the new zaire, equal to 3,000,000 old zaires, was introduced.

Balance of Payments (23)

	1992	1993	1994	1995	1996
Exports of goods (f.o.b.)	1,179	1,119	959	1,175	1,487
Imports of goods (f.o.b.)	−438	−500	−613	−650	−1,424
Trade balance	740	619	346	524	63
Services - debits	−1,117	−1,230	−1,287	−1,180	−1,168
Services - credits	79	68	69	79	100
Private transfers (net)	45	43	107	36	16
Government transfers (net)	−63	−52	−28	−33	−46
Overall balance	−316	−553	−793	−573	−1,034

Top Import Origins (25)

$1.1 billion (c.i.f., 1996 est.)

Origins	%
Belgium	NA
South Africa	NA
United States	NA
France	NA
Germany	NA
Italy	NA
Japan	NA
United Kingdom	NA

NA stands for not available.

Top Export Destinations (26)

$1.9 billion (f.o.b., 1996 est.).

Destinations	%
Belgium	NA
United States	NA
France	NA
Germany	NA
Italy	NA
United Kingdom	NA
Japan	NA
South Africa	NA

NA stands for not available.

Economic Aid (27)

Recipient: ODA, $NA. NA stands for not available.

Import Export Commodities (28)

Import Commodities	Export Commodities
Consumer goods	Diamonds
Foodstuffs	Copper
Mining and other machinery	Coffee
	Cobalt
Transport equipment	Crude oil
Fuels	

CONGO, REPUBLIC OF THE

Republic of the Congo
République du Congo

CAPITAL: Brazzaville.

FLAG: The flag consists of a green triangular section at the hoist and a red triangular section at the fly, separated by a diagonal gold bar.

ANTHEM: *The Congolaise.*

MONETARY UNIT: The Communauté Financière Africaine franc (CFA Fr) is a paper currency, tied to the French franc at the rate of CFA Fr50 = Fr1. There are coins of 1, 2, 5, 10, 25, 50, 100, and 500 CFA francs and notes of 50, 100, 500, 1,000, 5,000, and 10,000 CFA francs. CFA Fr1 = $0.0096 (or $1 = CFA Fr510.65).

WEIGHTS AND MEASURES: The metric system is the legal standard.

HOLIDAYS: New Year's Day, 1 January; Labor Day, 1 May; Three Glorious Days, 13–15 August (including Independence Day, 15 August); Christmas Day, 25 December. Movable religious holidays include Good Friday and Easter Monday.

TIME: 1 PM = noon GMT.

LOCATION AND SIZE: Lying astride the Equator, the Republic of the Congo (ROC) contains an area of about 342,000 square kilometers (132,000 square miles). Comparatively, the area occupied by the ROC is slightly smaller than the state of Montana. The ROC's capital city, Brazzaville, is located in the southeastern part of the country.

CLIMATE: The ROC has a tropical climate characterized by high humidity and heat. There are two wet and two dry seasons. Annual rainfall varies from 105 centimeters (41 inches) at Pointe-Noire, in the southwest, to 185 centimeters (73 inches) at Impfondo, in the northeast.

INTRODUCTORY SURVEY

RECENT HISTORY

By 1910, Gabon, Middle Congo, and Ubangi-Shari (including Chad) constituted French Equatorial Africa, all under a governor general at Brazzaville. In World War II (1939–45), French Equatorial Africa joined the Free French movement and the Allied war effort against the Axis powers.

After the war, France promised reforms in French Africa. These reforms eventually led to independence, and on 28 November 1958, the Republic of the Congo was proclaimed. A constitution was adopted the following year, and Fulbert Youlou was elected prime minister and president. Youlou resigned in 1963, following antigovernment rioting. The military took control of the government, and Alphonse Massamba-Debat was installed as an interim president. He was subsequently elected to a five-year term. In 1964, relations were established with the former Soviet Union and China, and Massamba-Debat then announced the establishment of a "scientific Socialist state" with one-party control.

However, political stability proved difficult to achieve. Between 1968 and 1979, the ROC had four different presidents, one of whom—Marien Ngouabi—survived seven coup attempts in seven years in office. On 5 February 1979, Denis Sassou-Nguesso became president. He was to hold power for twelve years. During his tenure, a twenty-year treaty of friendship and cooperation was signed with the former Soviet Union.

In 1990, a conference of the ruling party agreed to abandon its Marxist ideology and its monopoly of power. Sassou-Nguesso was stripped of his powers the following year, and in 1992, a multiparty government with Pascal Lissouba as president was elected. Strikes, violent civil unrest, and a changing coalition of opposition parties have threatened the new regime. Despite mediation by the Organization of African Unity (OAU) and new

elections in 1993, fighting continued into 1994 as armed forces loyal to Lissouba battled independent partisan militias.

The Lissouba regime was never able to impose order on the country and forces loyal to the former leader Sassou-Nguesso continued to fight the government. In June 1997, civil war began in Brazzaville, killing hundreds over a span of four months. France sent 1,250 soldiers to restore order. Brazzaville was looted and reduced to ruins.

GOVERNMENT

On 15 March 1992, voters approved a new constitution that provided for a mixed presidential-parliamentary form of government after the French model. Executive authority is vested in a directly elected president, who appoints the prime minister and cabinet. There is also a sixty-member Senate.

Judiciary

Judicial bodies include a Supreme Court (appointed by the president), a court of appeals, a criminal court, regional and magistrate's courts, labor courts, and courts of common law, where local chiefs apply traditional laws and customs. The constitution provides for an independent judiciary, but in practice the judicial system is highly influenced by political leaders and has been nearly destroyed by the civil war.

Political Parties

The 1991 National Conference led to an interim government and multiparty elections in 1992. Continual shifts in parties and in coalitions of parties have taken place since. The Pan-African Union for Social Development (UPADS) was the largest in the National Assembly as civil society deteriorated in the face of continued civil war.

DEFENSE

In 1995, the ROC had an army of 8,000 personnel, a navy of 800, and an air force of 1,200.

ECONOMIC AFFAIRS

The ROC's economy is built on its petroleum resources, transport services, and agriculture. After several prosperous years in the early 1980s, the price of oil declined and cast the Congolese economy into the financial turmoil that has yet to stabilize. Continued political instability and a violent civil war have brought most economic production to a standstill.

Public Finance

In the late 1980s and early 1990s, weak oil prices and a massive public sector combined to drive up Congo's debt. Civil service salaries absorbed over half of the government's 1995 budget. The budget deficit rose form 5.5% of GDP in 1985 to 14% in 1991 and was estimated at $240 million in 1995. In 1995, total external debt was approximately $5 billion with service on the debt amounting to 155% of revenues annually, one of the highest ratios in the world. Also in 1995, Congo reached an agreement with the IMF and World Bank that would help alleviate some of its debt burden.

Income

In 1998, the ROC's gross national product (GNP) was $1.92 billion at current prices, or about $690 per person.

Industry

The largest industries are food processing, including beverages and tobacco, followed by chemicals and petroleum products, woodworking, metalworking and electrical industries, nonmetallic mineral products, paper and cardboard, and textiles.

Banking and Finance

The bank of issue is the Bank of the Central African States (BEAC), which serves all the members of the UDEAC. The National Development Bank of the Congo extends loans for economic development. The Congo has a 13% share in UDEAC's development bank.

There is no securities market in the Congo.

Economic Development

France is the leading foreign donor country (about $400 million between 1960 and 1985). France for a time reduced its participation (1985–89), but raised it to record levels in 1990 ($230 million). China and the former Soviet Union also provided substantial aid in the past. Between 1946 and 1986, Congo also received $107.7 million from the European Economic Community, $111.7 million from the World Bank, $74 million from International Development Agency, and $93.7 million from the African Development Bank.

SOCIAL WELFARE

Since 1 July 1956, family allowances have been paid to all salaried workers. Contributions are made by employers at a fixed percentage of the employee's wage. Other payments include a pension scheme, prenatal allowances, and a lump sum payable at the birth of each of the first three children. Human rights abuses have long been a problem in the ROC. The long, violent civil war has considerably damaged the society.

Healthcare

In 1992, 83% of the population had access to health care services. A local disease control service conducts vaccination and inoculation campaigns. All medicine, antibiotic, and vaccine imports must be authorized by the Ministry of Health. From 1991 to 1996, only 38% of inhabitants had access to safe water. The average life expectancy is 51 years.

Housing

As of 1984, 88.3% of all housing units were private houses.

EDUCATION

All private schools were taken over by the government in 1965. Education is compulsory between the ages of 6 and 16. Primary schooling lasts for six years and secondary for seven years. The National University, which opened in Brazzaville in 1971, was later renamed Marien Ngouabi University. Higher level institutions had 656 teachers and 13,086 students in 1992.

1999 KEY EVENTS TIMELINE

January

- Republic of Congo President Denis Sassou-Nguesso orders assaults on Ninja rebels south of Brazzaville, killing several hundred and wounding many others.

- President Sassou-Nguesso appoints Lekounzon Iti Osetoumba as Minister of Defense.

- Presidential Security Force Chief Camille Oko dies.

- Five French nationals, a German and a Dane are held hostage by the National Movement for the Liberation of Congo.

February

- The national army claims a victory over Ninja forces in Loumou.

- Former President Pascal Lissouba denies that he is gathering resources to stage a coup, when found purchasing arms.

March

- Army Chief of Staff Major General Jacques Yvon Ndolou accuses his own forces of looting the capital, Brazzaville, and selling supplies and arms to rebel forces.

- The Republic of Congo agrees to protect its' forests with the World Wildlife Fund.

- Jean-Claude Ganga, from the Republic of Congo, is expelled for corruption from the International Olympic Committee.

- A cease-fire is signed in Zambia, yet fighting continues.

June

- Minister for Information Francois Ibovi claims that a scheduled mediation through Central African Republic President Ange-Felix Patasse will not take place.

July

- The United Nations claims that eight times as much aid is given to Kosovo refugees as for African refugees, while thousands of Congolese refugees flood neighboring Gabon.

- Bisso Na Bisso from Congo-Brazzaville wins best group at the Kora All Africa Music Awards at Sun City, South Africa.

August

- Eight former members of the ousted government present a five-year transition proposal under the present administration to introduce multi-party democracy to the Congo.

September

- Students from Congo-Brazzaville demand scholarship money at the embassy in the Central African Republic.

October

- Floods leave thousands homeless.

December

- Four European men (two French, one Italian, and one Croat) are convicted of plotting to kill President Denis Sassou-Nguesso. The four, who have already spent eight months in jail, are given jail sentences ranging from two to seven years.

1999 ANALYSIS OF EVENTS

BUSINESS AND THE ECONOMY

From 1979–92, President Denis Sassou-Nguesso ruled the Republic of Congo-Brazzaville as a one-party, Marxist state. The 1992 elections brought Pascal Lissouba into power for five years, but Sassou-Nguesso returned to challenge his rule in 1997, prompting Lissouba to send the militia in order to keep the incumbent out of the race. This began a bitter civil war between the followers of Pascal Lissouba and Denis Sassou-Nguesso. The effect on the Congolese economy has, to say the least, been devastating.

The Republic of Congo is the most indebted country per citizen and thousands have fled to the neighboring nations of Gabon, Cameroon and Angola in the wake of fighting. Once a French colony, the Congo still retains close economic ties with France. Its currency is the CFA franc, fixed at 100 to the French franc with the other central and west African countries. Oil production remains the main source of income for the country, but terms of trade fell by more than 20 percent in 1998 as oil prices collapsed. The Central African Economic and Monetary Community (CEMAC), including Gabon, Cameroon and Congo-Brazzaville, is working to improve the situation, but in essence the area is neo-colonial and dependent upon French investment and direction. The civil war makes transportation of goods almost impossible, with bombed railways and stations held by armed forces.

The Congo is one of the only three countries in the world to not have direct Internet access, making advanced communication for businesses next to impossible. To top it all off, the nation's army itself loots the town and countryside and floods in October added to the economic duress that citizens of the Republic of Congo find themselves under.

GOVERNMENT AND POLITICS

The six-month war in 1997 which sent President Lissouba into exile in Britain and sparked off the current civil war resulted in more than 10,000 deaths and thousands of refugees. President Denis Sassou-Nguesso's coup was conducted with the aid of the Angolan government, and recent fighting has occurred with the help of hired militiamen from Uganda and other African countries, although allegations of Cuban troops aiding the Congolese government have been denied. In the beginning of the year, President Sassou-Nguesso reshuffled his cabinet in order to prepare for military conflict with rebel forces—the Coroyes, led by former Prime Minister Bernard Kolelas and the Ninjas, led by supporters of Lissouba. The ex-President, residing in Britain, has reportedly been purchasing supplies to stage his coup, but there is no definite evidence of this.

For the most part, President Sassou-Nguesso has been winning the fight, but his resources are falling dangerously low and he has the added responsibility, unlike Lissouba, for retaining social order in the country. Unfortunately, even his own troops steal from the Congo's citizens, and rebels are reported to have used human shields and to have systematically executed civilians. In August, eight members of the former government presented a five-year transition plan to President Sassou-Nguesso which would bring a cease-fire and, ultimately, a multi-party democracy to the Congo. This plan is not promising considering the March cease-fire signed in Zambia which immediately failed, and the Minister of Information Francois Ibovi's statement that they would not "negotiate with Dracula."

CULTURE AND SOCIETY

As a former colonial state, the Republic of Congo retains some of the French culture and language, but the allegiance to Europe is not strong. Over the past couple of years, European embassies, officials and tourists have been kidnapped, tortured and killed. In a state of war, this is likely to happen to anyone who crosses an army's path, but the targeting of Europeans has occurred for reasons that some would say are validated by the history of colonial exploitation. During the civil war in the Congo, the Kosovo crisis also took place in the Balkans: more than eight times the United Nations aid given to Congolese refugees was given to Albanians, when greater need existed in the countries surrounding the Republic of Congo. Although this figure needs to be adjusted for monetary purchasing power in each country, the amounts still add up to be grossly unequal at $32 compared to $265. Despite the civil war and economic problems, the Republic of Congo has received attention for its' popular musical group Bisso Na Bisso, which won best group at the Kora All Africa Music Awards in Sun City, South Africa.

The country has also signed up with other Central African nations to protect its' forests through the World Wildlife Fund. Forest management is crucial to saving the disappearing natural resources in the Republic of Congo, which comprise more than half of Africa's wild plants and animals, located in the Congo Basin. If the Republic of Congo could but end the civil strife in its political life, then the natural riches of this nation could pull it out of an economic and social quagmire.

DIRECTORY

CENTRAL GOVERNMENT
Head of State

President
Denis Sassou-Nguesso, Office of the President, Palais Presidentiel, Brazzaville, Congo
PHONE: +242 31197

Ministers

Minister of Defense
Justin Itihi Lekoundzou Ossetoumba, Ministry of Defense

Minister of the Presidency in Charge of the Presidential Cabinet and State Control
Gerard Bitsindou, Ministry of the Presidential Cabinet and State Control

Minister of Agriculture and Livestock
Celestin Nkoua Gongara, Ministry of Agriculture
and Livestock

**Minister of Commerce and Small and
Medium-Sized Enterprises**
Pierre Damien Boussoukou Boumba, Ministry of
Commerce and Small and Medium-Sized
Enterprises

**Minister of Communication and Relations
with Parliament**
Francois Ibovi, Ministry of Communication and
Relations with Parliament

Minister of Culture and Tourism
Aimee Mambou Gnali, Ministry of Culture and
Tourism

Minister of Education and Scientific Research
Pierre Nzila, Ministry of Education and
Scientific Research

Minister of Energy and Water Resources
Jean-Marie Tassoua, Ministry of Energy and
Water Resources

Minister of Economy, Finance and Budget
Mathias Dzon, Ministry of Economy, Finance
and Budget

Minister of Foreign Affairs and Cooperation
Rodolphe Adada, Ministry of Foreign Affairs
and Cooperation

Minister of Forestry and Fisheries
Henri Djombo, Ministry of Forestry and
Fisheries

Minister of Health and National Solidarity
Leon Alfred Opimbat, Ministry of Health and
National Solidarity

Minister of Industry, Mines and Environment
Michel Mampouya, Ministry of Industry, Mines
and Environment

**Minister of Industrial Development and
Private Sector Promotion**
Alphonse Obama, Ministry of Industrial
Development and Private Sector Promotion

Minister of Interior
Pierre Oba, Ministry of Interior

Minister of Justice and Keeper of the Seals
Jean Martin Mbemba, Ministry of Justice and
Keeper of the Seals

Minister of Labor and Social Security
Lambert Ndouane, Ministry of Labor and Social
Security

Minister of Petroleum Affairs
Jean-Baptiste Taty Loutard, Ministry of
Petroleum Affairs

Minister of Posts and Telecommunications
Jean Dello, Ministry of Posts and
Telecommunications

**Minister of Public Service, Administrative
Reform and Women's Affairs**
Jeanne Dambenze, Ministry of Public Service,
Administrative Reform and Women's Affairs

Minister of Public Works
Florent Tsiba, Ministry of Public Works

**Minister of Reconstruction and Urban
Development**
Martin Mberi, Ministry of Reconstruction and
Urban Development

Minister of Regional Development
Pierre Moussa, Ministry of Regional
Development

**Minister of Technical Education, Professional
Training, Youth, Civic Education, and Sports**
Andre Okombi Salissan, Ministry of Technical
Education, Professional Training, Youth, Civic
Education, and Sports

**Minister of Transport, Civil Aviation, and
Merchant Marine**
Isidore Mvouba, Ministry of Transport, Civil
Aviation, and Merchant Marine

Director, Central Bank
Ange Edouard Poungui, Central Bank

POLITICAL ORGANIZATIONS
Congolese Labor Party (PCT)

TITLE: President
NAME: Denis Sassou-Nguesso

Association for Democracy and Development (RDD)

TITLE: President
NAME: Joachim Yhombi-Opango

Association for Democracy and Social Progress (RDPS)

TITLE: President
NAME: Jean-Pierre Thystere Tchicaya

Congolese Movement for Democracy and Integral Development (MCDDI)

NAME: Michel Mampouya

Pan-African Union for Social Development (UPADS)

NAME: Martin Mberi

Union of Democratic Forces (UFD)

NAME: Sebastian Ebao

Union for Democratic Renewal (URD)

Union for Development and Social Progress (UDPS)

NAME: Jean-Michael Bokamba-Yangouma

DIPLOMATIC REPRESENTATION

Embassies in Congo (ROC)

Belgium
BP 2251, Brazzaville, Congo
PHONE: +242 831120

China
BP 213, Brazzaville, Congo
PHONE: +242 832963

Czech Republic
BP 292, Brazzaville, Congo
PHONE: +242 820837

Egypt
BP 917, Brazzaville, Congo
PHONE: +242 834428

France
rue Alfassa BP 2089, Brazzaville, Congo
PHONE: +242 831423

Germany
BP 2022, Brazzaville, Congo
PHONE: +242 832990

Italy
2-3 Blvd Lyautey BP 2484, Brazzaville, Congo
PHONE: +242 834047

Nigeria
BP 790, Brazzaville, Congo
PHONE: +242 831316

Russia
BP 2132, Brazzaville, Congo
PHONE: +242 834439
FAX: +242 836917

United States
Avenue Amilcar Cabral BP 1015, Brazzaville, Congo
PHONE: +242 832070
FAX: +242 836338

JUDICIAL SYSTEM
Supreme Court

FURTHER READING
Articles

"Africa's Franc Zone—A Tale of Two Regions." BBC World Service, 7 September 1999.

"Africa's Refugees Lose Out on Aid." BBC World Service, 21 July 1999.

"Congo Republic Army Kills Four Rebel Militiamen." Reuters, 22 October 1999.

"Congo-Brazzaville: Duel to the Death." *The Economist* (April 10, 1999): 45.

"Congo-Brazzaville Opposition Militia Loses Stronghold." BBC World Service, 22 September 1999.

"Congo Brazzaville Rejects Mediation." BBC World Service, 16 June 1999.

"Congo-Brazzaville Students in Protest." BBC World Service, 5 September 1999.

"Congo Republic Floods Leave Thousands Homeless." Reuters, 22 October 1999.

"Fassie and Kuti Take the Prize." BBC World Service, 27 July 1999.

"Gabon Asks for Help." BBC World Service, 1 October 1999.

"Peace Initiative Launched for Congo-Brazzaville." BBC World Service, 24 August 1999.

"UN Calls for Aid to Congo." BBC World Service, 28 September 1999.

Books

Republic of Congo: An Old Generation of Leaders in New Carnage. New York: Amnesty International, USA, 1999.

Internet

Republic of Congo. Available Online @ http://www.congoweb.org/english.html. (November 1, 1999).

CONGO, REPUBLIC OF THE: STATISTICAL DATA

For sources and notes see "Sources of Statistics" in the front of each volume.

GEOGRAPHY

Geography (1)

Area:

Total: 342,000 sq km.

Land: 341,500 sq km.

Water: 500 sq km.

Area—comparative: slightly smaller than Montana.

Land boundaries:

Total: 5,504 km.

Border countries: Angola 201 km, Cameroon 523 km, Central African Republic 467 km, Democratic Republic of the Congo 2,410 km, Gabon 1,903 km.

Coastline: 169 km.

Climate: tropical; rainy season (March to June); dry season (June to October); constantly high temperatures and humidity; particularly enervating climate astride the Equator.

Terrain: coastal plain, southern basin, central plateau, northern basin.

Natural resources: petroleum, timber, potash, lead, zinc, uranium, copper, phosphates, natural gas.

Land use:

Arable land: 0%

Permanent crops: 0%

Permanent pastures: 29%

Forests and woodland: 62%

Other: 9% (1993 est.).

HUMAN FACTORS

Demographics (2A)

	1990	1995	1998	2000	2010	2020	2030	2040	2050
Population	2,206.4	2,484.3	2,658.1	2,775.7	3,367.6	3,944.6	4,577.8	5,324.1	6,081.0
Net migration rate (per 1,000 population)	NA	NA	NA	NA	NA	NA	NA	NA	NA
Births	NA	NA	NA	NA	NA	NA	NA	NA	NA
Deaths	NA	NA	NA	NA	NA	NA	NA	NA	NA
Life expectancy - males	45.7	44.9	45.3	45.5	47.3	50.7	59.6	68.5	71.9
Life expectancy - females	48.2	48.8	48.9	48.9	50.8	54.5	64.9	75.2	79.0
Birth rate (per 1,000)	41.7	39.8	38.5	37.5	32.1	27.6	23.9	20.2	17.5
Death rate (per 1,000)	17.1	16.8	16.5	16.2	14.8	12.9	8.6	5.7	5.6
Women of reproductive age (15-49 yrs.)	514.7	586.9	642.9	675.4	844.8	1,035.1	1,247.4	1,459.4	1,626.1
of which are currently married	NA	NA	NA	NA	NA	NA	NA	NA	NA
Fertility rate	5.6	5.2	5.0	4.8	4.0	3.2	2.7	2.4	2.2

Except as noted, values for vital statistics are in thousands; life expectancy is in years.

Ethnic Division (6)

Kongo 48%

Sangha 20%

M'Bochi 12%

Teke 17%

Europeans . . . .

Note - Europeans estimated at 8,500, mostly French, before the 1997 civil war; may be half of that in 1998, following the widespread destruction of foreign businesses in 1997.

Religions (7)

Christian 50%

Animist 48%

Muslim 2%

Languages (8)

French (official), Lingala and Monokutuba (lingua franca trade languages), many local languages and dialects (of which Kikongo has the most users).

EDUCATION

Educational Attainment (10)

Age group (1984) . . . . .25+

Total population 646,626

Highest level attained (%)

No schooling 58.8

First level

Not completed 13.0

Completed 8.5

Entered second level

S-1 . . . . .11.0

S-2 . . . . .5.9

Postsecondary 3.0

Literacy Rates (11A)

In thousands and percent[1]	1990	1995	2000	2010
Illiterate population (15+ yrs.)	393	354	306	214
Literacy rate - total adult pop. (%)	67.8	74.9	81.0	90.1
Literacy rate - males (%)	77.8	83.1	87.7	94.0
Literacy rate - females (%)	58.6	67.2	74.8	86.5

GOVERNMENT & LAW

Government Budget (13B)

Revenues . . . .$870 million

Expenditures . . . .$970 million

Capital expenditures . . . . .NA

Data for 1997 est. NA stands for not available.

Military Affairs (14A)

Military age . . . . .20 years of age

Availability of manpower

Males age 15-49 (1998 est.) 623,924

Fit for military service

Males (1998 est.) 317,997

Reaching military age annually

Males (1998 est.) 27,354

Total expenditures (1993) . . . .$110 million

Expenditures as % of GDP (1993) 3.8%

LABOR FORCE

Unemployment Rate (17)

Rate not available.

PRODUCTION SECTOR

Electric Energy (18)

Capacity . . . . .118,000 kW (1995)

Production . . . . .438 million kWh (1995)

Consumption per capita . . . . .220 kWh (1995)

Transportation (19)

Highways:

total: 12,800 km

paved: 1,242 km

unpaved: 11,558 km (1996 est.)

Waterways: the Congo and Ubangi (Oubangui) Rivers provide 1,120 km of commercially navigable water transport; other rivers are used for local traffic only

Pipelines: crude oil 25 km

Merchant marine:

total: 1 cargo ship (1,000 GRT or over) totaling 2,918 GRT/4,100 DWT (1997 est.)

Airports: 37 (1997 est.)

Airports—with paved runways:

total: 4

over 3,047 m: 1

1,524 to 2,437 m: 3 (1997 est.)

Airports—with unpaved runways:

total: 33

1,524 to 2,437 m: 8

914 to 1,523 m: 15

under 914 m: 10 (1997 est.)

Top Agricultural Products (20)

Cassava (tapioca) accounts for 90% of food output, sugar, rice, corn, peanuts, vegetables, coffee, cocoa; forest products.

MANUFACTURING SECTOR

GDP & Manufacturing Summary (21)

Detailed value added figures are listed by both International Standard Industry Code (ISIC) and product title.

	1980	1985	1990	1994
GDP ($-1990 mil.)[1]	1,722	2,887	2,851	2,674
Per capita ($-1990)[1]	1,032	501	1,277	1,063
Manufacturing share (%) (current prices)[1]	7.7	5.7	8.2	8.6
Manufacturing				
Value added ($-1990 mil.)[1]	139	278	227	200
Industrial production index	100	172	127	113
Value added ($ mil.)	61	54	90	75
Gross output ($ mil.)	163	154	260	233
Employment (000)	6	9	8	8
Profitability (% of gross output)				
Intermediate input (%)	62	65	65	68
Wages and salaries inc. supplements (%)	13	17	15	15
Gross operating surplus	24	18	20	18
Productivity ($)				
Gross output per worker	13,445	17,546	34,506	30,370
Value added per worker	5,062	6,209	11,957	9,774

	1980	1985	1990	1994
Average wage (inc. supplements)	3,411	3,032	5,248	4,435
Value added ($ mil.)				
311/2 Food products	11	10	22	20
313 Beverages	11	11	23	19
314 Tobacco products	3	3	7	5
321 Textiles	3	2	2	1
322 Wearing apparel	2	1	1	1
323 Leather and fur products	—	—	—	—
324 Footwear	3	2	2	1
331 Wood and wood products	5	5	5	3
332 Furniture and fixtures	3	3	3	2
341 Paper and paper products	1	—	1	1
342 Printing and publishing	1	—	1	1
351 Industrial chemicals	2	2	3	3
352 Other chemical products	3	2	4	3
353 Petroleum refineries	—	—	—	—
354 Miscellaneous petroleum and coal products	—	—	—	—
355 Rubber products	1	1	2	1
356 Plastic products	—	—	—	—
361 Pottery, china and earthenware	—	—	—	—
362 Glass and glass products	—	—	—	—
369 Other non-metal mineral products	1	2	1	1
371 Iron and steel	—	—	—	—
372 Non-ferrous metals	—	—	—	—
381 Metal products	4	4	5	5
382 Non-electrical machinery	1	1	1	1
383 Electrical machinery	2	2	2	2
384 Transport equipment	2	2	3	3
385 Professional and scientific equipment	—	—	—	—
390 Other manufacturing industries	—	—	—	—

FINANCE, ECONOMICS, & TRADE

Economic Indicators (22)

National product: GDP—purchasing power parity—
$5.25 billion (1996 est.)

National product real growth rate: 4% (1996 est.)

National product per capita: $2,000 (1996 est.)

Inflation rate—consumer price index: 3% (1996 est.)

Exchange Rates (24)

Exchange rates:

CFA francs (CFAF) per US$1

January 1998	608.36
1997	583.67
1996	511.55
1995	499.15
1994	555.20
1993	283.16

Beginning 12 January 1994, the CFA franc was devalued to
CFAF 100 per French franc from CFAF 50 at which it had
been fixed since 1948

Top Import Origins (25)

$670 million (f.o.b. 1995) Data are for 1995 est.

Origins	%
France	31.2
Netherlands	24.6
Italy	11.4
United States	6.9

Top Export Destinations (26)

$1.2 billion (f.o.b., 1995) Data are for 1995 est.

Destinations	%
Belgium-Luxembourg	24.3
Taiwan	20.2
United States	14.9
Italy	14.8

Economic Aid (27)

Recipient: ODA, $NA. NA stands for not available.

Import Export Commodities (28)

Import Commodities	Export Commodities
Intermediate manufactures	Crude oil 90%
	Lumber
Capital equipment	Plywood
Construction materials	Sugar
Foodstuffs	Cocoa
Petroleum products	Coffee
	Diamonds

COOK ISLANDS

INTRODUCTORY SURVEY

RECENT HISTORY

Tahitian and Samoan Polynesians likely first settled the Cook Islands. An upper class emerged, the *ariki*, who ruled over the broad scatter of fifteen islands clustered in two groupings midway between the Hawaiian Islands and New Zealand. A European presence in the area first came when Spanish explorer Alvaro de Mendaña de Neira sighted Pukapuka Island of the northern group in 1595. Many of the islands were later explored by British explorer Captain James Cook in the 1770s. A Russian cartographer named the islands after Cook in 1824. Christianization arrived in 1821 with John Williams of the London Missionary Society. So effective was the Society that by the late 1990s over 60% of the population were still members of the Christian Church founded by the Society. While the southern group of islands were governed by missionaries in combination with the *ariki*, the northern group suffered Peruvian slave raids in the 1860s. In 1888 Britain established a protectorate over Rarotonga Island. By 1892 the protectorate status extended to other southern group islands with each island being self-governed.

In 1901 New Zealand was assigned administrative control and annexed the entire island group. Through World War II the Cook Islands were administered by an appointed minister and resident commissioner. U.S. airbases were established on two islands during the war. In 1946 New Zealand created a Cook Islands Legislative Council which became the Legislative Assembly in 1957. Seeking

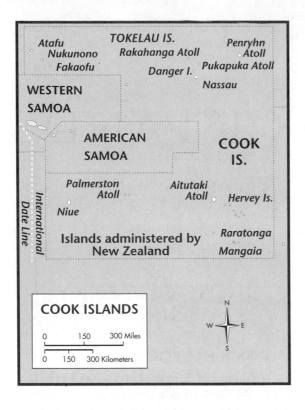

Atafu
Nukunono
Fakaofu
TOKELAU IS.
Rakahanga Atoll
Danger I.
Penryhn Atoll
Pukapuka Atoll
Nassau

WESTERN SAMOA

AMERICAN SAMOA

COOK IS.

International Date Line

Palmerston Atoll
Niue

Aitutaki Atoll
Hervey Is.

Islands administered by New Zealand

Raratonga
Mangaia

COOK ISLANDS

0   150   300 Miles

0   150   300 Kilometers

even greater autonomy, residents voted in 1965 for self-government in free association with New Zealand. The Islands retained the right to unilaterally establish complete independence. The 1965 constitution was amended in 1981 and 1991 steadily increasing parliament and cabinet size. To further reduce dependence on New Zealand, the Cook Islands increased economic arrangements with France in 1991 and the People's Republic of China in 1997. By the 1990s over 80% of Cook Islanders were still of Polynesian descent.

GOVERNMENT

A self-governing parliamentary democracy, the chief of state is the British monarch. Queen Elizabeth II has served that capacity since 1952. The United Kingdom and New Zealand each appoint representatives to the island's government with the High Commissioner representing New Zealand. The island's head of government is a prime minister, usually leader of the party winning most parliament seats, assisted by a deputy prime minister. The prime minister selects seven others to form the nine-member cabinet which also includes the deputy prime minister. The cabinet exercises executive powers and is responsible to the twenty-five-seat unicameral parliament, which is the legislative branch of Cook Island government. Parlia-

ment members are elected by universal adult suffrage for five-year terms.

Fifteen traditional hereditary island chiefs compose the House of Arikis which advises parliament on traditional issues but holds no legislative power. A council locally governs each island along with an elected mayor and an administer officer appointed by the Islands' prime minister.

Judiciary

The Cook Islands' judiciary system is primarily based on New Zealand law and English common law. The principal judicial body is the High Court with jurisdiction in all civil and criminal matters and in land title cases on all islands except three. Land title disputes on Mitiaro, Pukapuka, and Mangaia are settled according to custom. High Court decisions may be appealed to the Court of Appeal. Civil and criminal cases may be further appealed to the United Kingdom's Privy Council.

Political Parties

Political parties active in the mid-1990s were the Cook Islands Party (CIP) founded in 1965, the Democratic Party (DP) founded in 1971, the Alliance Party which split from the DP in 1992, the Labour Party founded in 1988, and the Democratic Tumu Party founded in 1985. The CIP was dominate in the 1997 parliament elections.

DEFENSE

New Zealand has responsibility for the Cook Islands' defense and foreign affairs when requested by the Islands. However, the Islands have steadily assumed greater control over its foreign policy.

ECONOMIC AFFAIRS

With the northern group of islands being low coral atolls and the south islands being volcanic and hilly, less than 10% of the land is cultivatable. Besides limited natural resources, other factors inhibiting economic growth include isolation from foreign markets, poor infrastructure, and vulnerability to cyclones. Agricultural products of copra and citrus fruit are the primary exports with papayas alone constituting 25% of total exports in 1996. Other agricultural crops and products include pineapple, mangoes, bananas, black pearls and pearl shells, fish, and coffee. A major economic setback occurred in late 1997 when a devastating cyclone struck the northern island group essentially destroying all crops and infrastructure.

Imports greatly exceed exports. In 1994 imports were estimated at NZ $85 million while exports were only NZ $4.2 million. Many Cook Islanders must emigrate to New Zealand to find jobs.

In 1997 the Cook Islands' parliament passed the Outer Islands Local Government Act to facilitate outer islands' development by altering the funding system and increasing local control. As a result, three new local government bodies were elected in 1998.

Tourism is the island's most important industry. Almost 23% of the GDP in 1995 was contributed by the tourism industry. Close to 50,000 foreign visitors arrived in 1996. Two new resorts in the outer islands were scheduled for construction in the mid-1990s.

The Cook Islands is a member of Pacific Community, the South Pacific Forum, and the UN Economic and Social Commission for Asia and the Pacific. The Development Investment Board was founded in 1996 and the Cook Islands Investment Corporation in 1998 to promote foreign investment in private development on the islands.

Public Finance

With limited products, the Cook Islands' debt was NZ $160 million in 1994. Revenue primarily came from customs duties and tariffs, income tax, and stamp sales. Foreign aid, primarily from New Zealand, amounted to over NZ $11 million in 1996/97 as a series of financial crises developed. New Zealand authorities charged some Cook Islands' financial institutions with tax evasion. By 1996 the government was near bankruptcy. In agreement with New Zealand, Cook Islands' government services, including the number of civil servants, were significantly reduced to cut costs in addition to selling public assets. Controversy over the government spending cuts continued through the following years. A government commission was established in 1998 to assess possible political reforms that would be the subject of 1999 elections.

Income

The gross domestic product (GDP) in 1997/98 was estimated at NZ $148 million, with per capita GDP at U.S. $5,600.

Industry

Besides fruit processing, other light industry includes coffee brewing, clothing manufacture, and handicrafts. Efforts at further expanding tourism, fishing, and mining industries have met limited success. Industrial production amounted to less than 10% of the GDP in 1995. Aquaculture involved development of giant clam and pearl oyster farming in the 1980s. Tuna fisheries became significantly depleted by 1990. Patrol of the Cook Island 200 nautical mile exclusive economic zone around the islands began guarding against unauthorized foreign fishing incursions. The sale of fishing licenses to foreign countries was an important source of income.

The government signed a 1997 agreement with a consortium of Norwegian mining companies to develop deep-sea cobalt, nickel, copper, and manganese sources. Mineral extraction was expected to begin in 2002 and produce up to U.S. $600 million dollars in revenue.

Banking and Finance

The Monetary Board, founded in 1981, exercises control of currency, trade, and industry. The Cook Islands Development Bank, founded in 1978, provides loans and advisory services to small businesses and industries.

In 1982 offshore banking operations began and grew quickly. The Trustee Companies Association was established as a controlling body for offshore financial activity. Commercial banks on the Cook Islands include the state owned Cook Islands Savings Bank, the Australia and New Zealand Banking Corporation, and the Westpac Banking Corporation. Offshore banking practices came under scrutiny in 1999 spurred by significantly increased accounts by Russian nationals raising suspicions of organized criminal activity.

SOCIAL WELFARE

With the mid-1990s financial crises and significant public debt, social services were significantly reduced in 1996.

Healthcare

A user pay scheme for health care was introduced in 1996 with residents under sixteen and over sixty years of age exempted. Dental services were privatized though free dental care persisted for school children. In 1992 eighteen government hospitals totaling 154 beds were available with the main 80-bed hospital located on Rarotonga and dispensaries or cottage hospitals available on other inhabited islands. In 1999 life expectancy at birth for the total population was 71.1 years, 69.2 years for males, and 73.1 years for females. Dengue fever, carried by mosquitos in the region, poses a health threat in the islands.

Housing

Following the catastrophic 1997 cyclone, the government constructed two cyclone shelters, each capable of holding 200-300 people, on Manihiki Island at the cost of U.S. $5 million.

EDUCATION

Education is free and compulsory for ten years between ages five and sixteen. In 1994 twenty public and church-sponsored primary schools, eight high schools, and seven other secondary schools were available. Higher education includes a teacher-training college and a nursing school. Overseas scholarships are available from the government to institutions in New Zealand, Fiji, Australia and other countries. The University of the South Pacific, based in Fiji, operates an extension center in the Cook Islands.

1999 KEY EVENTS TIMELINE

March

- "Plant, Adopt, Protect a Tree" program launched.

April

- The International triathlon is held in Rarotonga.
- The Olympic torch passes through Cook Islands.

June

- General elections are held.
- Prime Minister Geoffrey Henry builds an alliance with the New Alliance Party to retain power.
- Chief Justice Sir Peter Quilliam strikes down an electoral amendment that would have restricted the campaign period for general elections.

July

- Election outcomes challenged in 4 of 25 constituencies.
- Three elected members of Cooks Island Party form a coalition with the Democratic Alliance Party.
- The Cook Islands' first prime minister warns against a return to government led by Sir Geoffrey Henry.

August

- The Cook Islands apply to be included in LOME IV agreement successor.

September

- Dr. Joe Williams, Prime Minister of the Cook Islands, is sued for medical malpractice.
- An ocean-going Cook Islands canoe sails for New Zealand for the ceremonial opening of the Americas Cup yacht race.

October

- The Cook Islands send delegates to the Climate Convention in Bonn, Germany.

November

- Pa Ariki elected to a seventh consecutive term as president of House of Ariki.
- Parliament reconvenes.

ANALYSIS OF EVENTS: 1999

BUSINESS AND THE ECONOMY

In 1999 the Cook Island government applied to be part of the successor agreement to the LOME IV Convention, which is due to expire early next year. This convention is a multifaceted cooperative agreement between the fifteen members of the European Union and seventy nations in the African, Caribbean, and Pacific (ACP) grouping. LOME IV involves trade relations, commodity stabilization, financial aid, and technical development. It seems likely that this application will be approved.

In addition, the government announced plans to boost the Cook Islands' black pearl production by converting Suwarrow, an uninhabited sanctuary for native birds and marine life, into a black pearl farm. Environmental groups, including Save Our Suwarrow and the World Wildlife Fund, have expressed concern over this planned development.

GOVERNMENT AND POLITICS

General elections were held in June 1999. Months later, however, the results were still inconclusive due to shifting alliances among the three political parties. The original vote counts gave the ruling Cook Islands Party (CIP) eleven of twenty-five seats, while the Democratic Alliance Party

(DAP) and New Alliance Party (NAP) took ten seats and four seats, respectively. After the election, the NAP formed an alliance with the CIP, giving the CIP fifteen seats, but a subsequent by-election for one of the CIP seats shifted the seat to the DAP on a preliminary count, and two disaffected CIP members shifted to the DAP. These changes left the CIP with only twelve uncontested seats, no longer a clear majority. The NAP then pulled out of the NAP-CIP coalition, giving the combined DAP-NAP opposition sixteen of twenty-five seats.

The opposition pledges to bring numerous changes to the nation's government. They propose a Freedom of Information Act that would make the actions of the government more transparent to its citizens. They also propose an investigation into the building of the Vaimaanga Hotel, and give the public expenditure review committee increased powers. It is not clear that they will be able to act on these plans for the queen's representative, Sir Apenera Short, has refused DAP leader Dr. Terepai Moatate's request to swear in a new government. Dr. Moatate and CIP leader Sir Geoffrey Henry each claim to have enough support to form a government. In the meantime, Dr. Joe Williams, incumbent Prime Minister for what is now the minority party, refuses to resign. He has publicly stated that the only clear solution to the Cook Islands' political woes is a coalition among all three parties.

Pa Ariki, elected in November to her seventh consecutive term as President of the House of Ariki, a consultative and advisory body for the Cook Islands, has expressed a similar sentiment. In her speech before the House of Ariki, she stated that the Westminster system of government currently in place in the Cook Islands does not encourage consensus building, and that political parties have led politicians to put the needs of their parties before the needs of their country. She expressed her belief that while the failure of any party to win an absolute majority may lead to a less stable government, it may also force the parties to work together more effectively for the country's good.

CULTURE AND SOCIETY

This year the Cook Islands sent a delegation to an international climate convention held in Bonn, Germany. At this convention they presented studies showing that Pacific nations such as the Cook Islands produce far lower levels of greenhouse gas emissions than the global per capita average. While they do not produce high levels of emissions, the Pacific island nations are very likely to suffer the environmental consequences of these emissions, most dramatically in the form of land loss related to rising sea-level. Along with representatives of nine other Pacific island states, the Cook Island delegates urged that there be strong compliance with commitments made under the convention, and that the international community take an organized approach to helping small island nations deal with sea-level rise and other climatic disruptions.

DIRECTORY

CENTRAL GOVERNMENT
Head of State

Queen
Elizabeth II, Monarch

Queen's Representative
Apenera Short

New Zealand High Commissioner
Jon Jonessen

Ministers

Prime Minister
Terepai Maoate, Office of the Prime Minister
PHONE: +682 25494

Deputy Prime Minister
Norman George, Office of the Deputy Prime Minister
PHONE: +682 25494

Minister of Finance
Papamama Pokino, Ministry of Finance, PO Box 99, Rarotonga, Cook Islands
PHONE: +682 22878
FAX: +682 21511

Minister of Foreign Affairs
Robert Woonton, Ministry of Foreign Affairs, PO Box 105, Rarotonga, Cook Islands
PHONE: +682 29347
FAX: +682 21247

Minister of Health
Norman George, Ministry of Health, PO Box 109, Rarotonga, Cook Islands
PHONE: +682 22664
FAX: +682 23109

Minister of Justice

Tangata Vavia, Ministry of Justice, PO Box 111, Rarotonga, Cook Islands

PHONE: +682 29410

FAX: +682 29610

Minister of Works, Energy and Physical Planning

Ngamau Munokoa, Ministry of Works, Energy and Physical Planning, PO Box 102, Rarotonga, Cook Islands

PHONE: +682 20034

FAX: +682 21134

POLITICAL ORGANIZATIONS

Cook Islands Party

NAME: Geoffrey Henry

Democratic Party

NAME: Thomas Davis

Democratic Alliance Party

NAME: Norman George

New Alliance

DIPLOMATIC REPRESENTATION

Embassies in Cook Islands

New Zealand

P.O. Box 21, Rarotonga, Cook Islands

PHONE: +682 22201

FAX: +682 21241

JUDICIAL SYSTEM
High Court

FURTHER READING
Articles

"Cooks' Government Proposes Major Pearl Farm in Wildlife Sanctuary." *Pacific Islands Monthly* (February 1999): 38.

"Freedom Muzzle Broken." *Pacific Islands Monthly* (June 1999): 49.

"Hiding the Piggy Bank." Wall Street Journal (June 7, 1999): 7.

"Improved Investor Confidence in Cooks." *Pacific Islands Monthly* (May 1999): 25.

"To Rate or Not to Rate—That is the Question." *Pacific Islands Monthly* (March 1999): 55.

"Vast Empty Hotel Might Save Cooks Islands' Economy." *Pacific Islands Monthly* (January 1999): 18.

Books

Idiens, Dale. *Cook Islands Art.* Shire Publications, 1999.

Kernahan, Mel. *White Savages in the South Seas.* New York: Verso, 1995.

Stanley, David. *Tahiti Handbook: Including Easter Island and the Cooks.* Chico, Calif.: Moon Publications, 1999.

Internet

Central Intelligence Agency. *World Factbook, 1998.* Available Online @ http://www.odci.gov/cia/publications/factbook/cw.html/ (November 11, 1999).

Cook Island Information. Available Online @ http://www.webcentral.co.ck/information.htm/ (November 11, 1999).

Cook Island News. Available Online @ http://www.cinews.co.ck/ (November 11, 1999).

COOK ISLANDS: STATISTICAL DATA

For sources and notes see "Sources of Statistics" in the front of each volume.

GEOGRAPHY

Geography (1)

Area:

Total: 240 sq km.

Land: 240 sq km.

Water: 0 sq km.

Area—comparative: 1.3 times the size of Washington, DC.

Land boundaries: 0 km.

Coastline: 120 km.

Climate: tropical; moderated by trade winds.

Terrain: low coral atolls in north; volcanic, hilly islands in south.

Natural resources: NEGL.

Land use:

Arable land: 9%

Permanent crops: 13%

Permanent pastures: NA%

Forests and woodland: NA%

Other: 78% (1993 est.).

HUMAN FACTORS

Demographics (2B)

Population (July 1998 est.) 19,989

Age structure:

   0-14 years . . . . .NA

   15-64 years . . . . .NA

   65 years and over . . . . .NA

Population growth rate (1998 est.) 1.06%

Birth rate, 1998 est. (births/1,000 population) 22.52

Death rate, 1998 est. (deaths/1,000 population) 5.2

Net migration rate, 1998 est.
  (migrant(s)/1,000 population) . . . .-6.71

Infant mortality rate, 1998 est.
  (deaths/1,000 live births) 24.7

Life expectancy at birth (years):

   Total population 71.14

   Male 69.2

   Female (1998 est.) 73.1

Total fertility rate, 1998 est.
  (children born/woman) .3.19

Infants and Malnutrition (5)

Under-5 mortality rate (1997) 30

% of infants with low birthweight (1990-97) 1

Births attended by skilled health staff % of total[a] . . .NA

% fully immunized (1995-97)

   TB 84

   DPT 91

   Polio 91

   Measles 86

Prevalence of child malnutrition under age 5
  (1992-97)[b] . . . . .NA

Ethnic Division (6)

Polynesian (full blood) .81.3%

Polynesian and European 7.7%

Polynesian and non-European 7.7%

European 2.4%

Other 0.9%

Religions (7)

Christian (majority of populace are members of the Cook Islands Christian Church).

Languages (8)

English (official), Maori.

GOVERNMENT & LAW

Political Parties (12)

Parliament	No. of seats
Cook Islands Party	.20
Democratic Party	.3
Democratic Alliance Party	.2

Government Budget (13B)

Revenues	NA
Expenditures	NA
Capital expenditures	NA

NA stands for not available.

Military Affairs (14A)

Defense is the responsibility of New Zealand, in consultation with the Cook Islands and at its request.

LABOR FORCE

Labor Force (16)

Total	.6,601
Agriculture	.29%
Government	.27%
Services	.25%
Industry	.15%
Other	.4%

Data for 1993. Percent distribution for 1981.

Unemployment Rate (17)

Rate not available.

PRODUCTION SECTOR

Electric Energy (18)

Capacity	.6,000 kW (1995)
Production	.15 million kWh (1995)
Consumption per capita	.775 kWh (1995)

Transportation (19)

Highways:

total: 187 km

paved: 35 km

unpaved: 152 km (1980 est.)

Merchant marine:

total: 1 cargo ship (1,000 GRT or over) totaling 1,464 GRT/2,181 DWT (1997 est.)

Airports: 7 (1997 est.)

Airports—with paved runways:

total: 1

1,524 to 2,437 m: 1 (1997 est.)

Airports—with unpaved runways:

total: 6

1,524 to 2,437 m: 3

914 to 1,523 m: 3 (1997 est.)

Top Agricultural Products (20)

Copra, citrus, pineapples, tomatoes, beans, pawpaws, bananas, yams, taro, coffee.

FINANCE, ECONOMICS, & TRADE

Economic Indicators (22)

National product: GDP—purchasing power parity—$79 million (1994 est.)

National product real growth rate: NA%

National product per capita: $4,000 (1994 est.)

Inflation rate—consumer price index: 2.6% (1994 est.)

Exchange Rates (24)

Exchange rates:

New Zealand dollars (NZ$) per US$1

January 1998	1.7283
1997	1.5083
1996	1.4543
1995	1.5235
1994	1.6844
1993	1.8495

Top Import Origins (25)

$85 million (c.i.f., 1994) Data are for 1993.

Origins	%
NZ	.49
Italy	NA
Australia	NA

NA stands for not available.

Top Export Destinations (26)

$4.2 million (f.o.b., 1994 est.) Data are for 1993.

Destinations	%
NZ	.80
Japan	NA
Hong Kong	NA

NA stands for not available.

Economic Aid (27)

Recipient: roughly $16 million annually, 1985-95, with New Zealand furnishing 88% of the total.

Import Export Commodities (28)

Import Commodities	Export Commodities
Foodstuffs	Copra
Textiles	Fresh and canned citrus
Fuels	fruit
Timber	Coffee; fish; pearls and
Capital goods	pearl shells; clothing

COSTA RICA

Republic of Costa Rica
República de Costa Rica

CAPITAL: San José.

FLAG: The national flag consists of five horizontal stripes of blue, white, red, white, and blue, the center stripe being wider than the others. The national seal is on the red stripe near the hoist.

ANTHEM: *Himno Nacional,* beginning "Noble patria, tu hermosa bandera" ("Noble native land, your beautiful flag").

MONETARY UNIT: The colón (c) is a paper currency of 100 céntimos. There are coins of 1, 5, 10, 25, and 50 céntimos and of 1, 2, 5, 10, and 20 colones, and notes of 5, 10, 20, 50, 100, 500, and 1,000 colones. c1 = $0.0463 (or $1 = c216.07).

WEIGHTS AND MEASURES: The metric system is the legal standard, but local measures also are used.

HOLIDAYS: New Year's Day and Solemnity of Mary, 1 January; Day of St. Joseph (Costa Rica's patron saint), 19 March; Anniversary of the Battle of Rivas, 11 April; Labor Day, 1 May; Day of St. Peter and St. Paul, 29 June; Anniversary of the Annexation of Guanacaste, 25 July; Feast of Our Lady of the Angels, 2 August; Assumption (Mother's Day), 15 August; Independence Day, 15 September; Columbus Day, 12 October; Immaculate Conception, 8 December; Abolition of Armed Forces Day, 1 December; Christmas, 25 December. Movable religious holidays include Holy Thursday, Good Friday, Holy Saturday, and Corpus Christi.

TIME: 6 AM = noon GMT.

LOCATION AND SIZE: The third-smallest country in Central America, Costa Rica has an area of 51,100 square kilometers (19,730 square miles), including some small islands. The area occupied by Costa Rica is slightly smaller than the state of Virginia.

CLIMATE: There are three climatic zones: torrid, temperate, and cold. The average annual rainfall is more than 250 centimeters (100 inches).

INTRODUCTORY SURVEY

RECENT HISTORY

Costa Rica enjoyed political stability from the turn of the century until just after World War II. Between 1948 and 1949, there was a brief period of upheaval, when a dictatorship was imposed on the country by its outgoing president. José Figueres Ferrer, leader of a successful civilian uprising, restored democratic government under the legally elected president, Otilio Ulate Blanco. In 1949, a new constitution restored free elections and banned a standing army.

Figueres was elected president by an overwhelming majority in 1952 (with women voting for the first time), and under his leadership, Costa Rica was one of the most democratic and prosperous countries in Latin America. Costa Rica joined the Central American Common Market (CACM) in 1963. It has benefited from Central American economic cooperation, especially in the area of industrialization.

During the 1980s, Costa Ricans were confronted with a severe economic crisis and increasing political violence, including some terrorist activity in San José. The Monge government introduced a government program to aid economic recovery and avoided being drawn into the war in neighboring Nicaragua between the rebel "contras" and the Sandinista government. Costa Rica resisted pressure from the United States to support the contras and refused to accept U.S. aid toward the building of a military establishment.

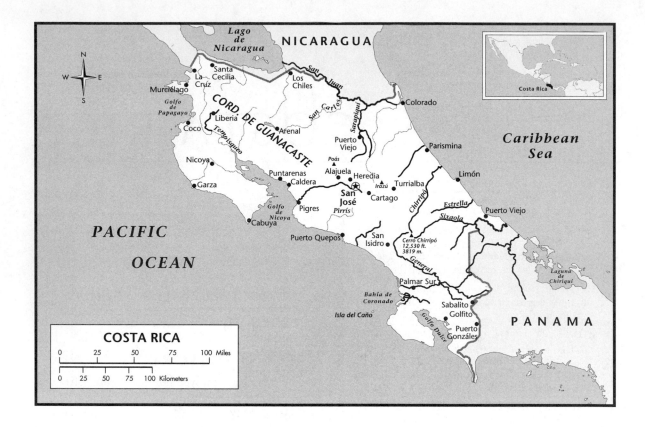

In August 1987, a peace plan for Central America outlined by Costa Rican president Oscar Arias Sánchez was signed in Guatemala by Nicaragua, Guatemala, Costa Rica, El Salvador, and Honduras. Among the provisions were free elections and an eventual reduction in the armed forces in all countries; a guarantee of basic democratic freedoms in Nicaragua; a cease-fire by both Sandinistas and contras; and an end to outside aid to the contras. Arias won the Nobel Prize for peace later that year.

With the pressures of regional warfare and refugees eased, the Costa Rican economy improved. In 1994, José María Figueres Olsen, son of former president Figueres, was elected president of Costa Rica. Economic hardship plagued his presidency. In 1998, Miguel Angel Rodríguez of the Christian Social Unity party was elected president.

GOVERNMENT

Costa Rica is a republic organized under the constitution of 1949. A president, two vice-presidents, and a single-chamber congress (the Legislative Assembly) of sixty-one members (in 1997) are all directly elected for four-year terms. The cabinet and the president form the Council of Government. Voting is universal and compulsory for all persons of 18 years or more.

Judiciary

The judiciary consists of justices of the peace, lower courts, labor courts, a court of cassation, two civil courts of appeal, two penal courts of appeal, and the Supreme Court, the highest court in the land. The Supreme Court comprises seventeen justices chosen for eight-year terms by the Legislative Assembly. The Supreme Court, by a two-thirds majority, can declare legislative and executive acts unconstitutional.

Political Parties

The largest political grouping is the PLN, a reformist party that has been the nation's leading party since its formation in 1948. The other major party is the more conservative Social Christian Unity Party (Partido Unidad Social Cristiana—PUSC), which, since World War II, has held the presidency only during 1978–82, 1990–94, and since 1998. There are also several minor parties. Support for the two main parties was weak in the 1998 elections.

DEFENSE

The 1949 constitution prohibits armed forces. A 3,000-member (in 1995) Civil Guard and a 2,000-member Rural Assistance Guard perform security and police functions. An antiterrorist battalion serves as the presidential guard. Small coast guard and air units patrol the coast for revenue purposes. Security expenditures were $26 million in 1996 with no significant arms imports.

ECONOMIC AFFAIRS

As of 1994, Costa Ricans enjoyed the highest per person income in Central America, although it decreased during the first half of the 1990s. Gross domestic product (GDP) declined by 0.5% in 1996.

Agriculture continues to be the backbone of the economy. By the end of 1993, it accounted for 26% of total employment, 18% of the economy, and roughly half of exports. The main crops are coffee, bananas and sugar.

Public Finance

The central government budget is passed upon by the Legislative Assembly. Municipal budgets are of minor importance, and local government funds are mainly grants from the national government. The financial range of the public sector extends to a large number of publicly owned entities.

The CIA estimates that, in 1995, government revenues totaled approximately $1.1 billion and expenditures $1.34 billion, including capital expenditures of $110 million. External debt totaled $4 billion.

The government of Costa Rica announced establishment of a high-level commission to resolve the problem of internal debt, which in 1996 rose to the equivalent of $2.3 billion in local currency and required about one-third of the government's budget for servicing.

Income

In 1998, Costa Rica's gross national product (GNP) was $9.78 billion, or $2,780 per person. For the period 1985–95, the average inflation rate was 18.5%, resulting in a real growth rate in GNP of 2.9% per person.

Industry

Costa Rica is one of the most industrialized countries in Central America, although industries are mostly small scale and mainly involve assembling or finishing imported semifinished components. In 1996, industry contributed 22% to gross domestic product. Larger-scale manufacturing includes chemical fertilizers, textiles, coffee and cocoa processing, chemicals, and plastics. Commerce and tourism (40% of gross domestic product) was divided among hotels, restaurants, tourist services, banks and insurance.

Banking and Finance

The Central Bank (Banco Central de Costa Rica), an autonomous governmental body established in 1950, issues currency, holds the nation's gold reserves, formulates general banking policy, and regulates commercial banks. The Central Bank held reserves of $190.3 billion at the end of 1992. Monetary variables reflect the cautious monetary policy followed by the Central Bank. However, a slight relaxation of previous stringency appears to have taken place in the last few months of 1996 in an effort to counter the persistent recessionary trend in the economy.

Economic Development

Following an economic crisis in the early 1980s, Costa Rica made significant progress toward macroeconomic stability, structural adjustment, and growth through increasingly diversified exports. Gross domestic product (GDP) growth has averaged 5% since 1987, nontraditional exports and tourism have increased rapidly and now account for almost 60% of foreign currency earnings, official unemployment declined to 4%, and inflation declined to 10% in 1993. A debt-buyback program under the U.S. "Brady Plan" was completed in May 1990, enabling Costa Rica to repurchase 60% of its commercial bank debt and to stabilize its foreign debt servicing.

SOCIAL WELFARE

The national Social Security Fund administers social insurance and pension programs. Most of the population is covered by these social services, which have been extended throughout the country and include workers' compensation and family assistance benefits. The social security program is compulsory for all employees under 65 years of age. The program, however, suffered as a result of the fiscal crisis of the 1980s and was overtaxed by an increase in the number of refugees.

A 1990 law reinforces existing provisions barring sex discrimination and improves women's property rights. Women and men are usually paid equally for equal work. In 1995, a vice president, two cabinet ministers, seven vice ministers and nine members of the Legislative Assembly were women.

Healthcare

About 95% of the nation's hospital beds are in urban areas. From 1992 to 1996, Costa Rica had one physician per 1,011 people. Health services for the rural population are generally inadequate, and the refugee problem has severely taxed urban services. In 1995, it was estimated that 97% of the population had access to health care services and 100% had access to safe drinking water.

Health standards have steadily improved in Costa Rica. During the 1980s, the greatest health problem was protein-calorie malnutrition, particularly among infants and children. Diseases of the circulatory system are the leading cause of death. Life expectancy at birth is an average of 77 years.

Housing

Sources for housing mortgages include private funds, the Central Bank, the Social Security Fund, and the national banking system. The National Institute of Housing and Urban Affairs, established in 1954, administers a national low-cost housing program.

EDUCATION

Costa Rica has one of the most literate populations in Latin America; adult literacy is about 95%. Nearly one-fifth of the government's expenditure is on education. Primary education lasts for six years followed by three years of secondary education. This again is followed by a two-year highly specialized course. Primary and secondary education is free, and primary school attendance is compulsory. In 1994, enrollment in primary schools was 495,879, with 15,086 teachers; in secondary schools, enrollment was 169,777 with 8,845 teachers.

The country has five universities, including an open university. The University of Costa Rica (founded in 1843) is supported by the government and enrolls about 28,000 students. The Open University, in San José, operates 28 regional centers for all students who apply.

1999 KEY EVENTS TIMELINE

January
- The social and economic effects of Hurricane Mitch are still felt in Costa Rica and Central America; thousands of Nicaraguan refugees are still in Costa Rica.

February
- Rafael Angel Calderón, the former president of Costa Rica, announces his intention to run for Secretary General of the Organization of American States, a post presently occupied by César Gaviria, Colombia's former president. Eventually, Calderón desists from his attempt and Costa Rica backs the re-election of Gaviria.

March
- Although a majority of Costa Ricans oppose the privatization of state enterprises, President Miguel Angel Rodríguez promises to go on with his plan to privatize state enterprises.

April
- As one of the most valuable ecological sanctuaries in the world, the Costa Rican rain forest is being affected by urbanization and the use of arable land for agricultural production.

June
- Costa Rica and other Central American nations ask the international community for support to rebuild the areas devastated by Hurricane Mitch in late 1998; Costa Rica leads the plea in a Summit with European and Latin American leaders held in Rio de Janeiro in late June.

August
- A 6.7 magnitude earthquake hits Costa Rica; minor damages and injuries are reported.
- A Dutch female tourist is found dead in the countryside. The cause of her death is not established immediately, but the incident occurs after the Costa Rican police arrested several foreigners who entered the country as tourists but were apparently involved in a prostitution ring.

September
- The International Coffee Organization announced that a new coffee negotiating group would meet in November to discuss coffee pro-

duction in light of recent changes in international supply and demand.

December

• Strict regulations for the registration of firearms go into effect as the government tries to stem dramatic increases in violence involving guns.

ANALYSIS OF EVENTS: 1999

BUSINESS AND THE ECONOMY

As most other Latin American countries, Costa Rica suffered the effects of the Asian economic crisis in 1999. Production and exports fell, the balance of payments suffered and inflationary pressures occupied most of the government's efforts. As foreign capitals fled the region, Costa Rica had to respond by reducing government spending, fostering internal savings and coping with growing unemployment. A fluctuating price of coffee did not help long term planning on the part of the government. President Rodríguez moved forward with his plan to privatize some of the state owned enterprises in order to attract foreign investment, foster economic development, and reduce the level of poverty in the country. Although Costa Rica has historically had low levels of poverty by Latin American standards, recent urban migration and population growth have aggravated the problem in some areas. In recent years, Costa Rica actively sought foreign investment by offering access to its vast natural resources. Timber production became one of the country's leading exports. Some headway was made in seafood production and offshore projects to search for oil were also enthusiastically announced by the government. In general, however, given the reduced size of the country, massive exploitation of natural resources has not reached the levels known to Brazil's Amazon jungle.

GOVERNMENT AND POLITICS

President Miguel Angel Rodríguez was elected in 1998. As a member of the Social Christian Unity Party, Rodríguez moved to fulfill some of his campaign promises. He has vowed to restore sustainable economic growth before his term expires in 2002. However, he has also begun moving to make some constitutional changes that would allow for the immediate re-election of members of congress and other elected officials. Although there has not been talk of immediate presidential re-election, some of the former presidents have quietly begun lobbying to lift a ban on non-immediate presidential re-election.

Costa Rica is not only the longest running democracy in Latin America, it is also the nation with the most former presidents who are still alive. Some of them are also young and have expressed interest in returning to politics. Former president Figueres, Calderón Sol and Nobel Prize laureate Oscar Arias could still be viable political candidates in countries where presidential re-election is not forbidden.

With the consolidation of the peace process in Central America, Costa Rica's main foreign concerns lie with its southern neighbor, Panama, which will receive control of the Canal on December 31, 1999, from the United States. Although there are no immediate threats to the normal operations of the canal, potential social conflicts might erupt in Panama as a result of the growing poverty and inequality in that country. As an ally of the United States and because it is the most consolidated democracy in the region, Costa Rica would be asked to play an active role in securing stability in the region. President Rodríguez drew some criticism when he publicly criticized the government in Cuba run by dictator Fidel Castro. Rodríguez joined the conservative president of Nicaragua in calling for a transition to democracy in the Caribbean island.

CULTURE AND SOCIETY

One of Costa Rica's two engines of development has been coffee production. In recent years, coffee production has seen ups and downs and Costa Rica's economy has not been immune to price fluctuations. The Rodríguez government has not taken decisive steps to reduce Costa Rica's dependence on coffee. In part, this has resulted from the historic role coffee has played in Costa Rica's economy and society. The second engine of growth in the country is tourism. Costa Rica has become an international paradise for eco-tourism. Because of the wealth of natural resources, including vast rain forests and thousands of animal species, and because of the stable political environment, Costa Rica has become the destination of choice for many American and European tourists in recent years. A good infrastructure and modern communication systems have also helped

Costa Rica position itself as a viable alternative to more traditional tourist oriented centers in Mexico and the Caribbean. The effect tourism has had on Costa Rican society has begun to surface in recent years. A large percentage of urban Costa Ricans work in the service sector and the middle class grows more and more integrated with the global community in their daily life concerns. In that sense, the traditional coffee producing country is changing into a service-based economy open to the world.

DIRECTORY

CENTRAL GOVERNMENT

Head of State

President
Miguel Ángel Rodríguez Echeverría, Office of the President

Vice President
Astrid Fischel Volio, Office of the Vice President

Ministers

Minister of Agriculture and Livestock
Esteban Brenes Castro, Ministry of Agriculture
PHONE: (506) 2905463
FAX: (506) 2312062

Minister of Economy and Foreign Trade
Samuel Guzowski Rose, Ministry of Economy and Foreign Trade

Minister of Finance
Leonel Baruch Goldberg, Ministry of Finance

Minister of Foreign Relations and Religion
Roberto Rojas Lopez, Ministry of Foreign Relations and Religion

Minister of Health
Rogelio Pardo Evans, Ministry of Health

Minister of Housing
Jose Antonio Lobo, Ministry of Housing

Minister of Justice
Monica Nagel Berger, Ministry of Justice

Minister of Labor and Social Security
Victor Morales Mora, Ministry of Labor and Social Security

Minister of the Presidency
Roberto Tovar Faja, Ministry of the Presidency

Minister of Public Education
Claudio Gutierrez Carranza, Ministry of Public Education

Minister of Public Security, Government, and Police
Juan Rafael Lizano Saenz, Ministry of Public Security, Government, and Police

Minister of Public Works and Transportation
Rodolfo Mendez Maia, Ministry of Public Works and Transportation

Minister of Women's Affairs
Yolanda Ingianna, Ministry of Women's Affairs

POLITICAL ORGANIZATIONS

Acción Democratica Alajuelense-ADA (Alajuelense Democratic Action)

Agrícola Cartagines-AC (Cartagena Agrarian)

Fuerza Democrática-FD (Democratic Force)
NAME: Vladimir De La Cruz de Lemos

Movimiento Libertario-ML (Libertarian Movement)
NAME: Federico Malavasi Calvo

Marxist Popular Vanguard Party
NAME: Humberto Vargas Carbonell

Agrario Nacional-AN (National Agrarian Party)

Integración Nacional-IN (National Integration Party)
NAME: Walter Munoz Cespedes

Partido Liberación Nacional-PLN (National Liberation Party)
NAME: Jose Miguel Corrales Bolanos

MNR (New Republic Movement)
NAME: Sergio Erick Ardon Ramirez

PPC (People's Party of Costa Rica)
NAME: Lenin Chacon Vargas

PRD (Radical Democratic Party)
NAME: Juan Jose Echeverria Brealey

**Partido de Unidad Socialcristiana-PUSC
(Social Christian Unity Party)**

NAME: Miguel Angel Rodriguez Echeverria

DIPLOMATIC REPRESENTATION
Embassies in Costa Rica

Italy
Barrio Los Yoses, San José, Costa Rica
PHONE: (506) 2342326; 2246574
FAX: (506) 2258200

JUDICIAL SYSTEM
Corte Suprema de Justicia

FURTHER READING
Articles

"Costa Rica. Your Pollution, Our Forests. PALMITAL." *The Economist* (June 28, 1998).

"Jorge Cabrera, 29: An Architect of Biodiversity Law who Joins Nature to a Vision of Responsible Eco-business." *Time International* 153 (May 24, 1999): 87(1).

"Patriotism, Central American Style." *The Economist* (August 22, 1998).

"A Silver Lining." *The Economist* (August 14, 1999): 30.

Torras, Mariano. "Inequality, Resource Depletion, and Welfare Accounting: Applications to Indonesia and Costa Rica." *World Development* 27 (July 1999): 1191(1).

Internet

Central America Weekly. Available Online @ http://www.centralamericaweekly.com/ (November 17, 1999).

Tico Times Online. Available Online @ http://ticotimes.co.cr/ (November 17, 1999).

COSTA RICA: STATISTICAL DATA

For sources and notes see "Sources of Statistics" in the front of each volume.

GEOGRAPHY

Geography (1)

Area:

Total: 51,100 sq km.

Land: 50,660 sq km.

Water: 440 sq km.

Note: includes Isla del Coco.

Area—comparative: slightly smaller than West Virginia.

Land boundaries:

Total: 639 km.

Border countries: Nicaragua 309 km, Panama 330 km.

Coastline: 1,290 km.

Climate: tropical, dry season (December to April); rainy season (May to November).

Terrain: coastal plains separated by rugged mountains.

Natural resources: hydropower potential.

Land use:

Arable land: 6%

Permanent crops: 5%

Permanent pastures: 46%

Forests and woodland: 31%

Other: 12% (1993 est.).

HUMAN FACTORS

Demographics (2A)

	1990	1995	1998	2000	2010	2020	2030	2040	2050
Population	3,022.5	3,391.4	3,604.6	3,743.7	4,416.1	5,043.8	5,584.8	6,011.6	6,320.8
Net migration rate (per 1,000 population)	NA	NA	NA	NA	NA	NA	NA	NA	NA
Births	NA	NA	NA	NA	NA	NA	NA	NA	NA
Deaths	11.4	NA	NA	NA	NA	NA	NA	NA	NA
Life expectancy - males	73.3	73.2	73.5	73.7	74.6	75.3	76.0	76.6	77.2
Life expectancy - females	78.2	78.1	78.5	78.7	79.9	80.8	81.7	82.4	83.1
Birth rate (per 1,000)	27.5	24.3	22.9	22.0	19.4	17.0	15.2	14.0	13.2
Death rate (per 1,000)	4.1	4.2	4.2	4.2	4.6	5.3	6.5	7.9	9.1
Women of reproductive age (15-49 yrs.)	772.9	874.5	937.9	981.4	1,161.5	1,276.7	1,378.4	1,413.8	1,425.9
of which are currently married	NA	NA	NA	NA	NA	NA	NA	NA	NA
Fertility rate	3.2	2.9	2.8	2.7	2.4	2.2	2.1	2.1	2.0

Except as noted, values for vital statistics are in thousands; life expectancy is in years.

Health Personnel (3)

Total health expenditure as a percentage of GDP, 1990-1997[a]

Public sector 6.0

Private sector 2.2

Total[b] 8.5

Health expenditure per capita in U.S. dollars, 1990-1997[a]

Purchasing power parity 544

Total 215

Availability of health care facilities per 100,000 people

Hospital beds 1990-1997[a] 250

Doctors 1993[c] 126

Nurses 1993[c] 95

Health Indicators (4)

Life expectancy at birth

1980 73

1997 77

Daily per capita supply of calories (1996) 2,822

Total fertility rate births per woman (1997) 2.8

Maternal mortality ratio per 100,000 live births (1990-97) . . . . .55[c]

Safe water % of population with access (1995) 100

Sanitation % of population with access (1995) 97

Consumption of iodized salt % of households (1992-98)[a] 89

Smoking prevalence

Male % of adults (1985-95)[a] 35

Female % of adults (1985-95)[a] 20

Tuberculosis incidence per 100,000 people (1997) 18

Adult HIV prevalence % of population ages 15-49 (1997) 0.55

Infants and Malnutrition (5)

Under-5 mortality rate (1997) 14

% of infants with low birthweight (1990-97) 7

Births attended by skilled health staff % of total[a] . . .97

% fully immunized (1995-97)

TB 91

DPT 91

Polio 93

Measles 99

Prevalence of child malnutrition under age 5 (1992-97)[b] 5

Ethnic Division (6)

White (including Mestizo) 96%

Black 2%

Amerindian 1%

Chinese 1%

Religions (7)

Roman Catholic 95%

Languages (8)

Spanish (official), English spoken around Puerto Limon.

EDUCATION

Public Education Expenditures (9)

Public expenditure on education (% of GNP)

1980 . . . . .7.8

1996 . . . . .5.3

Expenditure per student

Primary % of GNP per capita

1980 . . . . .13.1

1996 . . . . .13.4

Secondary % of GNP per capita

1980 . . . . .25.8

1996 . . . . .23.0

Tertiary % of GNP per capita

1980 . . . . .76.1

1996 . . . .

Expenditure on teaching materials

Primary % of total for level (1996) 0.4

Secondary % of total for level (1996) . . . .

Primary pupil-teacher ratio per teacher (1996) 30

Duration of primary education years (1995) 6

Literacy Rates (11A)

In thousands and percent[1]	1990	1995	2000	2010
Illiterate population (15+ yrs.)	117	115	111	93
Literacy rate - total adult pop. (%)	93.9	94.8	95.6	97.1
Literacy rate - males (%)	93.9	94.7	95.5	96.9
Literacy rate - females (%)	94.0	95.0	95.8	97.4

GOVERNMENT & LAW

Political Parties (12)

Legislative Assembly	No. of seats
Social Christian Unity Party (PUSC)	27
National Liberation Party (PLN)	23
Minority parties	7

Government Budget (13A)

Year: 1996

Total Expenditures: 572.97 Billions of Colones

Expenditures as a percentage of the total by function:

General public services and public order 11.49

Defense . . . .-

Education 16.80

Health 22.11

Social Security and Welfare 20.47

Housing and community amenities 29

Recreational, cultural, and religious affairs 88

Fuel and energy 48

Agriculture, forestry, fishing, and hunting 1.62

Mining, manufacturing, and construction . . . .-

Transportation and communication 5.46

Other economic affairs and services 59

Crime (15)

Crime rate (for 1994)

Crimes reported 45,662

Total persons convicted 5,913

Crimes per 100,000 population 1,487

Persons responsible for offenses

Total number of suspects 10,314

Total number of female suspects 842

Total number of juvenile suspects . . . . .NA

Military Affairs (14B)

	1990	1991	1992	1993	1994	1995
Military expenditures						
Current dollars (mil.)	75	67	99	104	98	50
1995 constant dollars (mil.)	86	74	106	109	101	50
Armed forces (000)	8	8	8	8	8	8
Gross national product (GNP)						
Current dollars (mil.)	6,149	6,500	7,222	7,935	8,488	8,930
1995 constant dollars (mil.)	7,066	7,183	7,768	8,319	8,700	8,930
Central government expenditures (CGE)						
1995 constant dollars (mil.)	1,294	1,349	1,417	1,518	1,904	1,882
People (mil.)	3.0	3.1	3.2	3.2	3.3	3.4
Military expenditure as % of GNP	1.2	1.0	1.4	1.3	1.2	.6
Military expenditure as % of CGE	6.6	5.5	7.5	7.2	5.3	2.7
Military expenditure per capita (1995 $)	28	24	33	33	30	15
Armed forces per 1,000 people (soldiers)	2.6	2.6	2.5	2.5	2.4	2.4
GNP per capita (1995 $)	2,338	2,319	2,449	2,563	2,621	2,633
Arms imports[6]						
Current dollars (mil.)	0	0	0	0	0	0
1995 constant dollars (mil.)	0	0	0	0	0	0
Arms exports[6]						
Current dollars (mil.)	0	0	0	0	0	0
1995 constant dollars (mil.)	0	0	0	0	0	0
Total imports[7]						
Current dollars (mil.)	1,990	1,877	2,440	2,885	3,025	3,274
1995 constant dollars (mil.)	2,287	2,074	2,625	3,025	3,101	3,274
Total exports[7]						
Current dollars (mi)	1,448	1,598	1,829	2,049	2,215	2,611
1995 constant dollars (mil.)	1,664	1,766	1,967	2,148	2,271	2,611
Arms as percent of total imports[8]	0	0	0	0	0	0
Arms as percent of total exports[8]	0	0	0	0	0	0

LABOR FORCE

Labor Force (16)

Total 868,300

Industry and commerce 35.1%

Government and services 33%

Agriculture 27%

Other 4.9%

Data for 1985 est.

Unemployment Rate (17)

5.7% (1997 est.); much underemployment.

PRODUCTION SECTOR

Electric Energy (18)

Capacity . . . . .1.094 million kW (1995)

Production . . . . .4.53 billion kWh (1995)

Consumption per capita . . . . .1,323 kWh (1995)

Transportation (19)

Highways:

total: 35,597 km

paved: 6,051 km

unpaved: 29,546 km (1996 est.)

Waterways: about 730 km, seasonally navigable

Pipelines: petroleum products 176 km

Merchant marine: none

Airports: 158 (1997 est.)

Airports—with paved runways:

total: 27

2,438 to 3,047 m: 2

1,524 to 2,437 m: 1

914 to 1,523 m: 18

under 914 m: 6 (1997 est.)

Airports—with unpaved runways:

total: 131

914 to 1,523 m: 31

under 914 m: 100 (1997 est.)

Top Agricultural Products (20)

Coffee, bananas, sugar, corn, rice, beans, potatoes; beef; timber (depletion of forest resources has resulted in declining timber output).

MANUFACTURING SECTOR

GDP & Manufacturing Summary (21)

Detailed value added figures are listed by both International Standard Industry Code (ISIC) and product title.

	1980	1985	1990	1994
GDP ($-1990 mil.)[1]	4,496	4,560	5,710	6,902
Per capita ($-1990)[1]	1,969	1,726	1,881	2,062
Manufacturing share (%) (current prices)[1]	18.4	21.9	19.2	*18.4*
Manufacturing				
Value added ($-1990 mil.)[1]	882	891	1,095	1,359
Industrial production index	100	103	123	153
Value added ($ mil.)	788	761	968	1,300
Gross output ($ mil.)	2,743	2,466	3,197	4,407
Employment (000)	77	104	134	*157*
Profitability (% of gross output)				
Intermediate input (%)	71	69	70	71
Wages and salaries inc. supplements (%)	12	9	12	*13*
Gross operating surplus	17	22	19	*17*
Productivity ($)				
Gross output per worker	*35,669*	*23,786*	*23,834*	*28,082*
Value added per worker	*13,796*	*7,341*	*7,217*	*8,291*
Average wage (inc. supplements)	*4,118*	*2,201*	*2,781*	*3,528*
Value added ($ mil.)				
311/2 Food products	241	247	292	379
313 Beverages	96	94	128	185
314 Tobacco products	24	28	31	26
321 Textiles	33	23	32	29
322 Wearing apparel	31	34	32	48
323 Leather and fur products	7	5	5	5
324 Footwear	10	9	8	10
331 Wood and wood products	30	25	22	25
332 Furniture and fixtures	26	14	21	17
341 Paper and paper products	20	22	45	42

	1980	1985	1990	1994
342 Printing and publishing	18	21	34	49
351 Industrial chemicals	19	26	33	45
352 Other chemical products	40	42	50	112
353 Petroleum refineries	40	45	35	33
354 Miscellaneous petroleum and coal products	—	—	—	—
355 Rubber products	14	15	17	19
356 Plastic products	19	26	36	51
361 Pottery, china and earthenware	1	2	3	4
362 Glass and glass products	3	7	11	11
369 Other non-metal mineral products	25	19	36	43
371 Iron and steel	4	—	10	15
372 Non-ferrous metals	1	—	1	1
381 Metal products	18	12	20	30
382 Non-electrical machinery	8	10	13	22
383 Electrical machinery	25	21	33	71
384 Transport equipment	31	10	16	22
385 Professional and scientific equipment	—	—	—	—
390 Other manufacturing industries	2	3	4	5

FINANCE, ECONOMICS, & TRADE

Economic Indicators (22)

National product: GDP—purchasing power parity—$19.6 billion (1997 est.)

National product real growth rate: 3% (1997 est.)

National product per capita: $5,500 (1997 est.)

Inflation rate—consumer price index: 11.2% (1997 est.)

Exchange Rates (24)

Exchange rates:

Costa Rican colones (C) per US$1

December 1997	243.55
1997	232.60
1996	207.69
1995	179.73
1994	157.07
1993	142.17

Top Import Origins (25)

$3.4 billion (c.i.f., 1996)

Origins	%
United States	NA
Japan	NA
Mexico	NA
Guatemala	NA
Venezuela	NA
Germany	NA

NA stands for not available.

Balance of Payments (23)

	1991	1992	1993	1994	1995
Exports of goods (f.o.b.)	1,498	1,739	1,867	2,122	2,480
Imports of goods (f.o.b.)	−1,698	−2,211	−2,628	−2,728	−2,954
Trade balance	−200	−472	−761	−606	−473
Services - debits	−820	−1,026	−1,153	−1,143	−1,287
Services - credits	803	954	1,150	1,350	1,464
Private transfers (net)	91	85	58	47	48
Government transfers (net)	50	88	85	119	106
Overall balance	−75	−370	−620	−234	−143

Top Export Destinations (26)

$2.9 billion (f.o.b., 1996).

Destinations	%
United States	NA
Germany	NA
Italy	NA
Guatemala	NA
El Salvador	NA
Netherlands	NA
United Kingdom	NA
France	NA

NA stands for not available.

Economic Aid (27)

Recipient: ODA, $NA. NA stands for not available.

Import Export Commodities (28)

Import Commodities	Export Commodities
Raw materials	Coffee
Consumer goods	Bananas
Capital equipment	Textiles
Petroleum	Sugar

CÔTE D'IVOIRE

Republic of Côte d'Ivoire
République de Côte d'Ivoire

INTRODUCTORY SURVEY

RECENT HISTORY

On 7 August 1960, the Republic of Côte d'Ivoire proclaimed its complete independence from France and a new constitution providing for a presidential system was adopted. In elections held on 27 November, Félix Houphouët-Boigny was unanimously elected the country's first president.

Outbreaks of unrest plagued the Houphouët-Boigny government during the late 1960s and early 1970s. However, throughout this period, the government worked to win over new adherents. By the end of the 1970s, Houphouët-Boigny was firmly in control, and Côte d'Ivoire became one of black Africa's most prosperous nations. Houphouët-Boigny continued to control the government and won an unopposed sixth term as president in October 1985. He reportedly received 100% of the vote in a turnout of over 99% of the eligible voters. These results were disputed, for in the following month, fewer than 30% turned out for the National Assembly elections.

In 1990, Côte d'Ivoire entered a new political era as months of prodemocracy demonstrations and labor unrest led to the legalization of opposition parties, previously banned. The first multiparty presidential and legislative elections were held, and Houphouët-Boigny was reelected as president with 81% of the vote. Again, outside observers saw the elections as less than free and fair.

Early in 1992, the president rejected the findings of his own investigative commission, which

had found army chief of staff General Robert Guei responsible for the shootings of students at Yopougon University in May 1991. Upon doing so, Houphouët-Boigny left for a four-month ''private visit'' to France. Rioting followed a mass demonstration in February 1992, and the government used this as an excuse to jail opposition leaders. Houphouët-Boigny continued to manage affairs from Paris. He returned in June to release the opposition leaders as part of an amnesty that also shielded the soldiers.

After Houphouët-Boigny's death in 1993, power was transferred smoothly to Henri Konan Bédíe. Opposition parties have claimed, however, that the government has engaged in anti-democratic tactics and they boycotted presidential elections held in 1995. The opposition did participate in legislative elections, however. Still, the ruling party maintained its vast majority.

GOVERNMENT

The unicameral National Assembly consists of 175 members, elected by direct voting for a five-year term in the same year as the president. The country had a one-party system until May 1990, when opposition parties were allowed. The post of prime minister was created after the November 1990 elections.

Judiciary

The Supreme Court has four chambers—constitutional, judicial, administrative, and financial. Appeals courts sit at Abidjan and Bouaké. There are twenty-eight courts of first instance (magistrates' courts). The High Court of Justice, comprising members elected from and by the National Assembly, has the power to impeach any government official, including the president.

Political Parties

From 1959 to 1990, the only political party was the Democratic Party of Côte d'Ivoire, headed by Félix Houphouët-Boigny. In May 1990, opposition parties were legalized and contested the 1990 elections.

DEFENSE

Côte d'Ivoire's armed forces in 1995 included 6,800 in the army, 900 in the navy, and 700 in the air force. There is also a paramilitary force of about 7,800.

ECONOMIC AFFAIRS

Côte d'Ivoire's wealth rests essentially on the production for export of coffee, cocoa, cotton, and tropical woods. The nation is the world's sixth-largest producer of coffee and the world's largest producer of cocoa. Industrial activity, consisting chiefly of processing industries, is well developed.

In January 1994, France suddenly devalued the CFA franc, cutting its value in half overnight. This had a devastating impact on all of francophone Africa. Within days, there was considerable consumer unrest as people scrambled to purchase necessary goods before they became any more expensive. Despite this initial trauma, the devaluation led to growth rates averaging 7% per year during 1995–97.

Public Finance

The CIA estimates that, in 1993, government revenues totaled approximately $1.9 billion and expenditures $3.4 billion, including capital expenditures of $408 million. External debt totaled $18 billion in 1997. In 1997, interest and principal repayments accounted for 51% of government revenues, down from 84% in 1993.

Income

In 1998, Côte d'Ivoire's gross national product (GNP) was $10.1 billion at current prices, or about $700 per person. For the period 1985–95, the average inflation rate was 2.1%, resulting in a decline in GNP of 4.3% per person.

Industry

Côte d'Ivoire's industrial activity is substantial by African standards. The development of processing industries, especially in the Abidjan region, has been significant. Numerous thriving industries have been built up in the forest zone of the southern coastal region. In 1995, industrial gross domestic product (GDP) grew 10.2%.

Banking and Finance

In 1959, the Central Bank of the West African States (Banque Centrale des États de l'Afrique de l'Ouest—BCEAO) succeeded the Currency Board (Institut d'Émission) of French West Africa and Togo as the bank of issue for the former French West African territories. In 1962, it was reorganized as the joint note-issue bank of Dahomey (now Benin), Côte d'Ivoire, Mauritania (which withdrew in 1973), Niger, Senegal, Togo, and Upper Volta (now Burkina Faso). The board of directors of the BCEAO consists of representatives of each participating African country, as well as of France.

Public credit institutions provide credit to farmers and agricultural cooperatives, mortgages and personal loans, real estate financing, and loans to small industries.

The Abidjan stock exchange is the local securities market. It was created in 1976 to encourage domestic investment and to provide Ivoirian industries with access to the international financial market.

Economic Development

Since independence, Côte d'Ivoire has engaged in an economic program aimed at ending its reliance on outside assistance and at achieving self-sustained growth. Under current conditions, however, the Côte d'Ivoire economy will remain highly vulnerable to commodity price variations and dependent upon outside assistance into the foreseeable future, a future mortgaged by its earlier levels of borrowing. The 1994 devaluation of the CFA franc provided a new framework for improving sales of Côte d'Ivoire's products. Increased efforts to liberalize the economy by privatizing state-owned companies have also helped to improve economic performance.

SOCIAL WELFARE

A social welfare service was established in 1950 to coordinate public and private social assistance activities; it occupies itself mainly with casework in the large towns. A system of family allowances for wage earners was instituted in 1956, and workers' compensation has also been introduced. In 1964, the National Assembly abolished polygamy and set the legal marriage age at 18 for boys and 16 for girls. There is a cabinet-level Ministry of Women's Affairs.

Healthcare

Malaria, yellow fever, sleeping sickness, yaws, leprosy, trachoma, and meningitis are widespread. As of 1990, malnutrition affected 12% of children under 5 years old. Studies show that 1995, 60% of the population had access to health care services. That year, about 80% of the population had access to safe drinking water. In 1990, there were 1,020 doctors.

Housing

Housing remains an issue of major concern, particularly in Abidjan, which has been the focus of continued migration from rural areas. Extensive slum clearance has been carried out in the former capital, but shantytowns (poor areas) still persist on the outskirts.

EDUCATION

Education is free at all levels. Primary education lasts for six years and secondary for seven years (four years followed by three years). Adult illiteracy rates in 1995 were estimated at 60%. The National University of Côte d'Ivoire is located in Abidjan.

1999 KEY EVENTS TIMELINE

January

- Three leftist fringe parties, the Parti Ivoirien du Travail (PIT), the Union des Sociaux-Démocrates (USD), and the Renaissance party, form a coalition to strengthen their bid for leadership in 2000.

- Bowing to International Monetary Fund conditions, the government dissolves the state marketing board for coffee, cocoa, and agricultural products.

- The RDR party, allied with Alassane Ouattara, prepares to launch a daily newspaper.

- The FPI party of Laurent Gbagbo and the ruling party reach an agreement on political reforms, including the creation of a national commission on elections, equal access of all political parties to state media, public financing of political parties, and public assistance for presidential candidates.

- The Minister of Foreign Affairs, Amara Essy, travels to Sierra Leone to broker an agreement between the Kabbah government and the RUF.

- The state price stabilization company for agricultural produce (CAISTAB) is officially dissolved, though it reappears in a privatized, sleeker form.

February

- Four hundred government employees are retrenched, but the World Bank wants to trim the number to 30.

- The results of the census, commenced in November 1998, are still unknown as the counting presumably continues.

- The Commerce Ministry organizes the first annual meeting for the promotion of exports (Apex-CI), a World Bank-funded initiative to diversify Côte d'Ivoire's reliance on cocoa and coffee.

March

- There is an overall fall in commodity prices and agricultural production.

- The government party, PDCI and the opposition RDR, fail to agree on key political reforms, including the establishment of an independent election commission.

- The wives of Bédié and Ouattara host charity functions in a dual to increase their husbands' recognition and popularity.

April

- The cost for making local telephone calls rises by 4.7 percent($1) for five instead of six minutes. International calling becomes cheaper, however, by a general reduction of 7.7 percent.

- The government announces its interest in doubling the output of small and medium enterprises in the country, which presently make up 80 percent of all businesses, but account for only 18 percent of the GDP.

May

- Following three years of negotiations, the huge state coffee and cocoa commodities marketing board is privatized allowing the state to retain 35 percent control.

- The government and the IMF engage in talks to restructure the nation's debt and to establish disciplined financial policies.

- The Federation of Ivorian Students calls off its month-long boycott of classes.

June

- College students and high school pupils resume their boycott of classes in a five-day protest against the government's "insensitivity" to their problems. The government closes residence halls.

- Trading at the regional stock exchange suffers from the student unrest.

- The Ivorian Oil Refinery (SIR) signs a contract with Foxboro of France to increase oil production to 4.5 million tons by the end of 2000.

- The government announces the creation of a national literacy fund, especially to improve girls' enrollment rates.

- UNDP announces that more than 500,000 people have moved above the poverty line, indicating improvement in the economy.

July

- Côte d'Ivoire and Ghana announce a harmonization of cocoa production and commercialization policy to counter falling prices on the international market.

August

- Canada commits $1.2 million to assist Ivorians in computerizing voter lists in preparation for next year's elections. The United States approves $200,000 in foreign elections assistance toward this effort.

September

- President Bédié travels to France and to Italy for talks with European partners.

October

- Leading opposition figure, Laurent Gbagbo, calls on the government to end speculation about Ouattara's ancestry and to allow all candidates to run for president in the 2000 elections.

- President Bédié returns from a month-long trip to Europe.

November

- The government's tactics to ensure victory in next year's election jeopardize the usually conflict-free Côte d'Ivoire as eleven of 20 leading members of the main opposition party, including four members of parliament and Henriette Diabate, the opposition party's secretary-general, are jailed for two years upon being found guilty of public-order offenses.

December

- Rioting begins just before Christmas as the army, led by General Robert Guei, takes control of the country. President Henri Konan Bédié is deposed and flees the country, arriving in neighboring Togo December 26. A nine-member junta is officially ruling the country.

ANALYSIS OF EVENTS: 1999

BUSINESS AND THE ECONOMY

Côte d'Ivoire, formerly the Ivory Coast, is named for the ivory once taken in abundance from elephants roaming its coastal forests and northern savannas. That was 400 years ago when the uncontrolled extraction of ivory all but killed off the elephants. Today, the economy is still extractive, but depends mainly on cocoa and coffee. In 1999, Côte d'Ivoire was the world's number one producer of cocoa and third largest coffee producer. It also was one of the top producers of bananas, rubber, and palm oil. However, the double digit growth in the GDP that became known as the "Ivory Coast Economic Miracle" is now a distant shadow as Ivorians struggle to pay the annual servicing of an estimated $650 million on an external debt of $19 billion.

The collapse of commodity prices in the 1980s helped cause the economic downturn, but the government must be held responsible for corrupt practices and mismanagement of public revenues. It has repeatedly violated International Monetary Fund (IMF) rules by its extra-budgetary spending. The ruling party dismissed the IMF's criticisms as politicking by Alassane Ouattara, a senior IMF deputy who was poised to run against President Bédié in

2000. In the first quarter of 1999, the government admitted to a budget shortfall of $125 million, which it explained as loss of import duties and tax and customs fraud.

A major effort to redress the economic predicament came to fruition in 1999. After many delays in implementing the IMF's Enhanced Structural Adjustment Facility (ESAP), the government agreed to privatize the cocoa and coffee sectors within the state marketing company, the Caisse de stabilisation des prix des produits agricoles (CAISTAB). However, the process has not been transparent, fueling speculation that CFA 130 billion ($26 million) has been illegally diverted.

Under the privatization agreement, producers obtain a 33 percent share, the government retains 25 percent, exporters 20 percent, cocoa and coffee processors 8 percent, banks 8 percent, and buyers 6 percent. Total staffing is supposed to stay under 100 persons, and coffee prices will be set daily. The new arrangement is not without risks. Growers have formed a new producers association (FIPCC), but are nervous about prices that have dropped to between 50-82 cents a kilogram (2.2 pounds) down from nearly a dollar a kg.

The outlook for growth in 1999–2000 is somewhat gloomy given the fall in prices for Côte d'Ivoire's commodity exports, cocoa, coffee, and oil. An anticipated 20% drop in production in coffee to around 160,000 tons also will reduce government revenues. These losses might be countered by rising fruit production. By the end of 1999, banana exports are expected to reach 224,000 tons, 37,000 tons over 1998, and pineapples are expected to produce 160,000 tons, compared with 50,000 in 1998. Privatization is bound to attract more foreign direct investment, as might the prospect of a future common market among the member states of UEMOA. Real GDP growth is predicted at 6 percent for 1999, and 5 percent for 2000.

On the bright side, Abidjan brought a new power plant online in January 1999, fueled by offshore gas. The country also is negotiating a connection to the West African Gas Pipeline, which would link Côte d'Ivoire and four West African countries: Nigeria, Benin, Togo, and Ghana. Abidjan is West Africa's key transit harbor, having increased traffic to landlocked Mali, Niger, and Burkina Faso by more than a million tons (31 percent) in 1998. Additionally, the regional stock exchange that opened in September 1998 represents a future magnet for investment in Côte d'Ivoire.

GOVERNMENT AND POLITICS

Since gaining its independence from France in 1960, Côte d'Ivoire has established a reputation for pragmatic "democratic authoritarianism" in Africa. Houphouët-Boigny ruled Côte d'Ivoire with absolute authority, and kept opponents off balance by dispensing political patronage. While more ideological neighbors expelled expatriates, Houphouët-Boigny welcomed French cooperation, and permitted French troops to be garrisoned on Ivorian soil. The party he founded, the PDCI, still maintains 153 of 179 seats in the national assembly.

In 1995, the PDCI stirred up ethnic, anti-foreigner, and anti-Muslim sentiments to unsettle Alassane Ouattara. His RDR boycotted the elections, damaging Côte d'Ivoire's image abroad as a model for constitutional stability in a troubled region. In 1999, the U.S. State Department released a Human Rights report criticizing police brutality, "life-threatening" prison conditions, and arbitrary arrest in Côte d'Ivoire. One newspaper editor, accused of libel, has been in prison for five months, exceeding the 120 day limit for detention without trial.

Several issues within government control threatened national unity. By October 1999, the government had not yet released the results of the 1998 census, leading to speculation that the census was so methodologically flawed that it could not be trusted, or that the government was tampering with the results to rig voter rolls. Until 1993, any person of legal age with a resident's card could vote. Because of anti-immigrant rhetoric, many of the country's immigrants feared discrimination and deportation.

The government's failure to handle Alassane Ouattara's candidacy in a transparent and even-handed manner posed the most significant threat to peace. Ouattara, a former prime minister and IMF operations director, is a Northerner, and was a credible threat to Bédié. The government's insistence that he is not an Ivorian citizen, and therefore ineligible to run for president, was perceived by many to be anti-Muslim and anti-Northerners. The issue was further complicated by the country's malleable citizenship laws, which are open to varying interpretation. In October, Laurent Gbagbo of the opposition FPI party declared that he would rather see Ouattara allowed to run than to have the country thrown into civil war.

Given its reputation as an oasis of stability in a turbulent continent, Côte d'Ivoire surprised the world in December when the army, led by General Robert Guei, took control of the country. President Henri Konan Bédié was deposed and fled to neighboring Togo. Guei said that the constitution had been suspended, but not abolished, and he insisted that civilian rule would be restored, but did not specify when. This coup, the country's first, proved that peace in Côte d'Ivoire cannot be taken for granted.

CULTURE AND SOCIETY

Côte d'Ivoire has long been a social and cultural melting pot. Some sixty ethnic groups and four major language families comprise the country with the Akan groups constituting about 40% of the immigrant population. The Baoulé make up 25-30 percent. Other groups with significant representation are the Bété, Malinké, and Sénoufou. As many as 40 percent of the population may be immigrants from neighboring countries or as far away as the Democratic Republic of the Congo (former Zaire). When released, the 1998 census is expected to reveal a total population approaching 19 million.

Cultural cleavages are mainly regional and tied to religion. Ten years ago, 39 percent of the population declared itself Muslim, while 27 percent claimed the Christian faith. The predominantly Catholic south has had more exposure to Europe, while the Northerners historically have been linked with ethnic and linguistic groups of Mali and Burkina Faso, and their Muslim traditions. French influence in culture, language, and business is considerable. From 1960–80, the French expatriate community doubled in size reaching nearly 60,000.

Abidjan has become a magnet for African musicians. In the 1970s, Ernesto Djédjé was crowned as the king of "Ziglibithy," a Congolese rumba-style of dance music using drums, guitars, and organ. More recently, Côte d'Ivoire's recording studios have attracted world famous musicians like Sam Mangwana and Tshala Muana of Congo-Zaire. Ivorian Alpha Blondy became a superstar of international reggae, producing "Cocody Rock," "Jerusalem," and "Apartheid is Nazism." "Zouglou," "Zoblazo," and "Polihet" define new Ivorian pop themes that blend traditional and modern rhythms, transforming folkloric dances into hot rhythms with modern instrumentation.

Côte d'Ivoire, particularly Abidjan, is struggling with high crime and unemployment. In 1998 car thefts were up 31 percent and sexual offenses have risen more than three times their level in 1996. It is now considered unsafe to drive around Abidjan with unlocked doors due to armed carjackers. Poverty in the face of opulence is a factor. Ten years ago, over half of the population had no electric appliances, and 67 percent of the population used kerosene storm lanterns for lighting.

A high number of people with HIV/AIDS poses the greatest menace to Ivorian society. Overall, about one million people are seropositive and about 90,000 of them are AIDS patients. However, significantly higher prevalence rates are recorded in Treichville and other densely populated areas in and near Abidjan. At least 50 percent of the HIV seropositives are too poor to afford antiretroviral treatment in spite of subsidized care backed by UNAIDS, and a National Solidarity Fund created by the government. Despite this sobering reality, a major prevention and awareness campaign is underway to combat the epidemic.

DIRECTORY

CENTRAL GOVERNMENT
Head of State

Acting President
General Robert Guei, Office of the President, Abidjan, Boulevard Clozel, Côte d'Ivoire
FAX: +225 211425; 331425

Ministers

Minister of State for Religious Affairs and Dialogue with the Opposition
Leon Konan Koffi, Ministry of Religious Affairs

Minister of State in Charge of Foreign Affairs
Amara Essy, Ministry of Foreign Affairs
PHONE: +225 227160
FAX: +225 332308

Minister of State in Charge of Interior and Decentralization
Emile Constant Bombet
PHONE: +225 216823
FAX: +225 324735

Minister of State in Charge of National Solidarity
Laurent Dona Fologo, Ministry of National Solidarity
PHONE: +225 220488

FAX: +225 329077

Minister of State in Charge of Relations with Institutions

Timothee Ahoua N'Guetta, Ministry of Relations with Institutions
PHONE: +225 220020
FAX: +225 220341

Minister of Agriculture and Animal Resources

Lambert Kouassi Konan, Ministry of Agriculture and Animal Resources
PHONE: +225 212881
FAX: +225 214818

Minister of Commodities

Guy Emmanuel Alain Gauze, Ministry of Commodities
PHONE: +225 216341
FAX: +225 219172

Minister of Communications

Danielle Boni-Claverie, Ministry of Communications
PHONE: +225 211116
FAX: +225 222297

Minister of Culture

Bernard Zadi Zaourou, Ministry of Culture
PHONE: +225 214034
FAX: +225 213359

Minister of Defense

Vincent Bandama N'Gatta, Ministry of Defense
PHONE: +225 212574
FAX: +225 213425

Minister of Economic Infrastructure

Jean Michel Moulod, Ministry of Economic Infrastructure
PHONE: +225 347314
FAX: +225 347322

Minister of Economy and Finance

Niamien N'Goran, Ministry of Economy and Finance
PHONE: +225 216681
FAX: +225 211090

Minister of Employment, Civil Service, and Social Welfare

Pierre Achi Atsain, Ministry of Employment, Civil Service, and Social Welfare
PHONE: +225 210400
FAX: +225 228415

Minister of Energy

Safiatou Ba-N'daw, Ministry of Energy
PHONE: +225 344857
FAX: +225 344855

Minister of Environment and Forestry

Jean-Cleaude Kouassi, Ministry of Environment and Forestry
PHONE: +225 214078

Minister of Family and Promotion of Women

Leopoldine Coffie, Ministry of Family and Promotion of Women
PHONE: +225 217703
FAX: +225 214460

Minister of Foreign Trade Promotion

Guy Emmanuel Alain Gauze, Ministry of Foreign Trade Promotion
PHONE: +225 216341
FAX: +225 219172

Minister of Higher Education and Scientific Research

Francis Wodie, Ministry of Higher Education and Scientific Research
PHONE: +225 213316
FAX: +225 212225

Minister of Housing and Urban Planning

Albert Kacou Tiapani, Ministry of Housing and Urban Planning
PHONE: +225 219406
FAX: +225 214561

Minister of Industrial Development and Small- and Medium-Scale Enterprises

Theophile Ahoua N'Doli, Ministry of Industrial Development and Small- and Medium-Scale Enterprises
PHONE: +225 218473
FAX: +225 216474

Minister of Information

Danielle Boni-Claverie, Ministry of Information
PHONE: +225 211116
FAX: +225 222297

Minister of Interior and National Integration

Emile Constant Bombet, Ministry of Interior and National Integration
PHONE: +225 216823
FAX: +225 324735

Minister of Internal Trade Promotion

Adou Kouadio, Ministry of Internal Trade Promotion
PHONE: +225 222004
FAX: +225 212334

Minister of Justice and Public Freedom, Keeper of the Seals

Jean Kouakou Brou, Ministry of Justice and Public Freedom

PHONE: +225 211727
FAX: +225 331259

Minister of Mines and Petroleum Resources
Lamine Mohamed Fadika, Ministry of Mines
and Petroleum Resources
PHONE: +225 221596
FAX: +225 215320

**Minister of National Education and Basic
Training**
Pierre Kipre, Ministry of National Education and
Basic Training
PHONE: +225 224417
FAX: +225 226908

**Minister of Planning and Development
Programs**
Tidrane Thiam, Ministry of Planning and
Development Programs
PHONE: +225 446926
FAX: +225 445666

Minister of Presidential Affairs
Faustin Kouame, Ministry of Presidential Affairs

**Minister of Presidential Affairs and
Government Spokesman**
Paul Akoto Yau, Ministry of Presidential Affairs

Minister of Public Health
Maurice Kacou Guikahue, Ministry of Public
Health
PHONE: +225 210871
FAX: +225 222220

Minister of Security
Marcel Dibona Kone, Ministry of Security
PHONE: +225 218536
FAX: +225 213981

**Minister of Technical Education and
Professional Training**
Dossongui Kone, Ministry of Technical
Education and Professional Training

Minister of Tourism and Handicrafts
Norbert Anney Kablan, Ministry of Tourism and
Handicrafts
PHONE: +225 210534
FAX: +225 229322

Minister of Transport
Adama Coulibaly, Ministry of Transport
PHONE: +225 216055
FAX: +225 213095

Minister of Youth and Sports
Siguide Soumahoro, Ministry of Youth and
Sports

PHONE: +225 215251
FAX: +225 224821

POLITICAL ORGANIZATIONS

**Front Populaire Ivorienne (Ivorian
People's Front)**

**Parti Démocratique de la Côte d'Ivoire
(Democratic Party of Ivory Coast)**

**Rassemblement des Républicains (Rally of
the Republicans)**

DIPLOMATIC REPRESENTATION

Embassies in Côte d'Ivorie

Cameroon
P.O. Box 326, Abidjan, Côte d'Ivoire
PHONE: +225 322086; 323331; 322701

Israel
9e etage, avenue Chardy Immeubel Nour-El-
Hayat, BP 1877, Abidjan 01, Côte d'Ivoire
PHONE: +225 213178; 227191
FAX: +225 218704

Italy
16, rue de la Canebiere, BP 1905, Abidjan 01,
Côte d'Ivoire
PHONE: +225 446361; 446170
FAX: +225 443587

United Kingdom
3rd Floor, Immeuble 'Les Harmonies', BP 2581,
Abidjan 01, Côte d'Ivoire
PHONE: +225 226850; 226851; 226852; 228209
FAX: +225 223221

United States
5 rue Jesse Owens, BP 1712, Abidjan 01, Côte
d'Ivoire
PHONE: +225 210979; 214672
FAX: +225 223259
TITLE: Chief of Mission, Ambassador
NAME: George Mu

JUDICIAL SYSTEM

Court of Arbitration of Côte d'Ivoire

Secretariat of CACI, BP 2847, Abidjan 06, Côte
d'Ivoire
PHONE: +225 331414
FAX: +225 331413
E-MAIL: info@caci.or.ci

Cour de Supreme

FURTHER READING

Books

Ajayi, J.F. Ade, and Michael Crowder, eds. *History of West Africa, 2.* New York: Colombia University Press, 1974.

Central Intelligence Agency. *World Factbook, 1998.* Washington, DC: GPO, 1999.

Clark, John F. and David E. Gardinier, eds. *Political Reform in Francophone Africa.* Boulder: Westview Press, 1997.

Handloff, Robert E. *Côte d'Ivoire: A Country Study.* Area Handbook Series. Third Edition. Washington, DC: Federal Research Division, Library of Congress, 1991.

Jackson, Robert H. and Carl G. Rosberg. *Personal Rule in Black Africa: Prince, Autocrat, Prophet, Tyrant.* Berkeley: University of California Press, 1982.

Morgenthau, Ruth Schachter. *Political Parties in French-Speaking West Africa.* Oxford: Clarendon Press, 1964.

Naipaul, V.S. *Finding the Center.* New York: Vintage Books, 1984.

———. *The Crocodiles of Yamoussoukro.* N.p., n.d.

Pedler, Frederick. *Main Currents of West African History 1940–1978.* London: Macmillan Press Ltd., 1979.

Internet

Africaonline. Available Online @ http://www.africaonline.com (October 28, 1999).

Africa News Online. Available Online @ http://www.africanews.org/west/stories/1999_feat1.html (October 28, 1999).

Integrated Regional Information Network (IRIN). Available Online @ http://www.reliefweb.int/IRIN (October 28, 1999).

Panafrican News Agency. Available Online @ http://www.africanews.org/PANA/news/1999/feat19.html (October 28, 1999).

CÔTE D'IVOIRE: STATISTICAL DATA

For sources and notes see "Sources of Statistics" in the front of each volume.

GEOGRAPHY

Geography (1)

Area:

Total: 322,460 sq km.

Land: 318,000 sq km.

Water: 4,460 sq km.

Area—comparative: slightly larger than New Mexico.

Land boundaries:

Total: 3,110 km.

Border countries: Burkina Faso 584 km, Ghana 668 km, Guinea 610 km, Liberia 716 km, Mali 532 km.

Coastline: 515 km.

Climate: tropical along coast, semiarid in far north; three seasons—warm and dry (November to March), hot and dry (March to May), hot and wet (June to October).

Terrain: mostly flat to undulating plains; mountains in northwest.

Natural resources: petroleum, diamonds, manganese, iron ore, cobalt, bauxite, copper.

Land use:

Arable land: 8%

Permanent crops: 4%

Permanent pastures: 41%

Forests and woodland: 22%

Other: 25% (1993 est.).

HUMAN FACTORS

Demographics (2A)

	1990	1995	1998	2000	2010	2020	2030	2040	2050
Population	11,904.2	14,204.0	15,446.2	16,190.1	20,565.3	25,267.5	30,709.8	37,391.0	44,509.1
Net migration rate (per 1,000 population)	NA	NA	NA	NA	NA	NA	NA	NA	NA
Births	NA	NA	NA	NA	NA	NA	NA	NA	NA
Deaths	NA	NA	NA	NA	NA	NA	NA	NA	NA
Life expectancy - males	46.2	45.5	44.7	44.2	45.4	49.0	58.5	68.0	71.5
Life expectancy - females	48.4	48.2	47.8	47.5	47.9	51.9	63.3	74.7	78.6
Birth rate (per 1,000)	46.4	43.5	42.2	41.4	37.4	32.7	28.2	23.9	20.2
Death rate (per 1,000)	16.5	16.0	16.1	16.2	15.4	13.3	8.4	4.9	4.5
Women of reproductive age (15-49 yrs.)	2,592.5	3,109.9	3,424.6	3,619.5	4,808.3	6,235.3	8,089.9	10,172.2	12,102.4
of which are currently married	NA	NA	NA	NA	NA	NA	NA	NA	NA
Fertility rate	6.7	6.2	6.0	5.8	4.9	4.0	3.3	2.7	2.4

Except as noted, values for vital statistics are in thousands; life expectancy is in years.

Health Indicators (4)

Life expectancy at birth

1980 49

1997 47

Daily per capita supply of calories (1996) 2,421

Total fertility rate births per woman (1997) 5.1

Maternal mortality ratio per 100,000 live births
(1990-97) . . . . .810[d]

Safe water % of population with access (1995) 72

Sanitation % of population with access (1995) 51

Consumption of iodized salt % of households
(1992-98)[a] . . . .

Smoking prevalence

Male % of adults (1985-95)[a] . . . .

Female % of adults (1985-95)[a] . . . .

Tuberculosis incidence per 100,000 people
(1997) 290

Adult HIV prevalence % of population ages
15-49 (1997) 10.06

Infants and Malnutrition (5)

Under-5 mortality rate (1997) 150

% of infants with low birthweight (1990-97) 12

Births attended by skilled health staff % of total[a] . . .45

% fully immunized (1995-97)

TB 73

DPT 70

Polio 70

Measles 68

Prevalence of child malnutrition under age 5
(1992-97)[b] 24

Ethnic Division (6)

Baoule 23%

Bete 18%

Senoufou 15%

Malinke 11%

Agni, foreign Africans (mostly Burkinabe and Malians, about 3 million), non-Africans 130,000 to 330,000 (French 30,000 and Lebanese 100,000 to 300,000).

Religions (7)

Muslim 60%

Christian 12%

Indigenous 25%

Some of the indigenous are also numbered among the Christians and Muslims.

Languages (8)

French (official), 60 native dialects with Dioula the most widely spoken

EDUCATION

Public Education Expenditures (9)

Public expenditure on education (% of GNP)

1980 . . . . .7.2

1996 . . . . .5.0

Expenditure per student

Primary % of GNP per capita

1980 . . . . .22.7

1996 . . . . .16.9

Secondary % of GNP per capita

1980 . . . .

1996 . . . .

Tertiary % of GNP per capita

1980 . . . . .378.3

1996 . . . . .210.1[1]

Expenditure on teaching materials

Primary % of total for level (1996) . . . .

Secondary % of total for level (1996) . . . .

Primary pupil-teacher ratio per teacher (1996) . . . . .41[1]

Duration of primary education years (1995) 6

Educational Attainment (10)

Age group (1988)[1] . . . . .25+

Total population 739,179

Highest level attained (%)

No schooling . . . . .NA

First level

Not completed . . . . .NA

Completed 48.2

Entered second level

S-1 . . . . .43.1

S-2 . . . . .NA

Postsecondary 8.7

Literacy Rates (11A)

In thousands and percent[1]	1990	1995	2000	2010
Illiterate population (15+ yrs.)	4,077	4,339	4,532	4,798
Literacy rate - total adult pop. (%)	34.2	40.1	46.7	60.1
Literacy rate - males (%)	44.2	49.9	55.8	67.4
Literacy rate - females (%)	23.6	30.0	37.3	52.7

GOVERNMENT & LAW

Political Parties (12)

National Assembly	No. of seats
Democratic Party of the Côte d'Ivoire (PDCI) 150	
Rally of the Republicans (RDR) 13	
Ivorian Popular Front (FPI) 12	

Government Budget (13B)

Revenues . . . .$2.4 billion
Expenditures . . . .$2.7 billion

Capital expenditures . . . .$600 million

Data for 1996 est.

Crime (15)

Crime rate (for 1997)

Crimes reported 113,600

Total persons convicted 68,500

Crimes per 100,000 population 950

Persons responsible for offenses

Total number of suspects 14,800

Total number of female suspects 950

Total number of juvenile suspects 350

Military Affairs (14B)

	1990	1991	1992	1993	1994
Military expenditures					
Current dollars (mil.)	85	86	94	88[e]	61[e]
1994 constant dollars (mil.)	95	93	98	90[e]	61[e]
Armed forces (000)	15	15	15	15	15
Gross national product (GNP)					
Current dollars (mil.)	5,211	5,347	5,492	5,515	5,445
1994 constant dollars (mil.)	5,799	5,732	5,727	5,628	5,445
Central government expenditures (CGE)					
1994 constant dollars (mil.)	NA	NA	NA	NA	NA
People (mil.)	12.4	12.9	13.3	13.8	14.3
Military expenditure as % of GNP	1.6	1.6	1.7	1.6	1.1
Military expenditure as % of CGE	NA	NA	NA	NA	NA
Military expenditure per capita (1994 $)	8	7	7	7	4
Armed forces per 1,000 people (soldiers)	1.2	1.2	1.1	1.1	1.0
GNP per capita (1994 $)	468	446	430	408	381
Arms imports[6]					
Current dollars (mil.)	0	0	0	0	0
1994 constant dollars (mil.)	0	0	0	0	0
Arms exports[6]					
Current dollars (mil.)	0	0	0	0	0
1994 constant dollars (mil.)	0	0	0	0	0
Total imports[7]					
Current dollars (mil.)	2,098	2,103	5,347	2,212[e]	NA
1994 constant dollars (mil.)	2,335	2,254	5,576	2,258[e]	NA
Total exports[7]					
Current dollars (mil.)	2,817[e]	2,777[e]	6,220	3,272[e]	NA
1994 constant dollars (mil.)	3,135[e]	2,977[e]	6,486	3,339[e]	NA
Arms as percent of total imports[8]	0	0	0	0	0
Arms as percent of total exports[8]	0	0	0	0	0

LABOR FORCE

Unemployment Rate (17)

Rate not available.

PRODUCTION SECTOR

Electric Energy (18)

Capacity . . . . .1.173 million kW (1995)

Production . . . . .1.875 billion kWh (1995)

Consumption per capita . . . . .127 kWh (1995)

Transportation (19)

Highways:

total: 50,400 km

paved: 4,889 km

unpaved: 45,511 km (1996 est.)

Waterways: 980 km navigable rivers, canals, and numerous coastal lagoons

Merchant marine:

total: 1 oil tanker (1,000 GRT or over) totaling 1,200 GRT/1,500 DWT (1997 est.)

Airports: 36 (1997 est.)

Airports—with paved runways:

total: 7

over 3,047 m: 1

2,438 to 3,047 m: 2

1,524 to 2,437 m: 4 (1997 est.)

Airports—with unpaved runways:

total: 29

1,524 to 2,437 m: 8

914 to 1,523 m: 12

under 914 m: 9 (1997 est.)

Top Agricultural Products (20)

Coffee, cocoa beans, bananas, palm kernels, corn, rice, manioc (tapioca), sweet potatoes, sugar; cotton, rubber; timber.

MANUFACTURING SECTOR

GDP & Manufacturing Summary (21)

Detailed value added figures are listed by both International Standard Industry Code (ISIC) and product title.

	1980	1985	1990	1994
GDP ($-1990 mil.)[1]	9,965	10,439	9,899	10,136
Per capita ($-1990)[1]	1,216	1,051	827	736

Manufacturing share (%) (current prices)[1]	11.7	13.5	11.3	*14.4*
Manufacturing				
Value added ($-1990 mil.)[1]	1,246	1,487	1,120	*1,141*
Industrial production index	100	100	96	111
Value added ($ mil.)	1,273	*914*	2,029	*1,022*
Gross output ($ mil.)	4,006	*2,608*	5,137	*3,337*
Employment (000)	67	56	53	53
Profitability (% of gross output)				
Intermediate input (%)	68	*65*	60	69
Wages and salaries inc. supplements (%)	10	*10*	8	8
Gross operating surplus	22	25	32	22
Productivity ($)				
Gross output per worker	59,630	*46,337*	*93,963*	*58,698*
Value added per worker	18,950	*16,241*	*37,429*	*18,078*
Average wage (inc. supplements)	6,026	*4,739*	*7,540*	*5,241*
Value added ($ mil.)				
311/2 Food products	303	*230*	599	289
313 Beverages	75	*38*	66	*42*
314 Tobacco products	66	*17*	22	*4*
321 Textiles	169	*113*	224	*104*
322 Wearing apparel	8	*6*	14	7
323 Leather and fur products	*5*	*7*	*10*	*7*
324 Footwear	*5*	*2*	*1*	*1*
331 Wood and wood products	67	*32*	109	*74*
332 Furniture and fixtures	21	*2*	*1*	—
341 Paper and paper products	*14*	*7*	*8*	*3*
342 Printing and publishing	*22*	*9*	*20*	*12*
351 Industrial chemicals	*22*	*19*	*54*	*26*
352 Other chemical products	*53*	*32*	*78*	*39*
353 Petroleum refineries	*167*	*194*	*427*	*193*
354 Miscellaneous petroleum and coal products	*14*	*17*	*32*	*19*
355 Rubber products	4	*4*	22	*14*

	1980	1985	1990	1994
356 Plastic products	1	—	—	—
361 Pottery, china and earthenware	2	—	—	—
362 Glass and glass products	—	—	—	1
369 Other non-metal mineral products	27	13	32	20
371 Iron and steel	5	2	5	2
372 Non-ferrous metals	3	1	2	1
381 Metal products	70	36	80	54
382 Non-electrical machinery	3	1	—	—
383 Electrical machinery	20	5	18	3
384 Transport equipment	106	95	151	74
385 Professional and scientific equipment	—	—	—	—
390 Other manufacturing industries	20	29	51	32

FINANCE, ECONOMICS, & TRADE

Economic Indicators (22)

National product: GDP—purchasing power parity—$25.8 billion (1997 est.)

National product real growth rate: 6.5% (1997 est.)

National product per capita: $1,700 (1997 est.)

Inflation rate—consumer price index: 3.4% (1997 est.)

Exchange Rates (24)

Exchange rates:

CFA francs (CFAF) per US$1

January 1998	.608.36
1997	.583.67
1996	.511.55
1995	.499.15
1994	.555.20
1993	.283.16

Beginning 12 January 1994, the CFA franc was devalued to CFAF 100 per French franc from CFAF 50 at which it had been fixed since 1948

Top Import Origins (25)

$3.2 billion (f.o.b., 1996)

Origins	%
France	.32
Nigeria	.20
United States	.6
Ghana	.NA
Germany	.NA
Italy	.NA

NA stands for not available.

Balance of Payments (23)

	1992	1993	1994	1995	1996
Exports of goods (f.o.b.)	2,947	2,519	2,811	3,820	4,375
Imports of goods (f.o.b.)	−1,952	−1,770	−1,507	−2,474	−2,515
Trade balance	995	748	1,304	1,345	1,860
Services - debits	−2,577	−2,219	−1,940	−2,258	−2,452
Services - credits	668	774	646	763	771
Private transfers (net)	324	187	720	186	159
Government transfers (net)	−423	−381	−363	−482	−540
Overall balance	−1,013	−892	368	−447	−204

Top Export Destinations (26)

$4.2 billion (f.o.b., 1996).

Destinations	%
France	18
Germany	8
Italy	8
Netherlands	8
Burkina Faso	NA
Mali	NA
United States	NA
United Kingdom	NA

NA stands for not available.

Economic Aid (27)

Recipient: ODA, $552 million (1993).

Import Export Commodities (28)

Import Commodities	Export Commodities
Food	Cocoa 36%
Consumer goods; capital goods	Coffee 22%; tropical woods 4%
Fuel	Petroleum
Transport equipment	Cotton
	Bananas
	Pineapples
	Palm oil
	Cotton
	Fish

CROATIA

Republic of Croatia
Republika Hrvatska

INTRODUCTORY SURVEY

RECENT HISTORY

Macedonia, Croatia, Slovenia, and Yugoslavia (the former Federal Socialist Republic of Yugoslavia) share a common history between 1945 and 1991, the year of Yugoslavia's break-up. The World War II Partisan Resistance Movement, controlled by the Communist Party of Yugoslavia and led by Marshal Josip Tito, won a civil war waged against nationalist groups. They had both recognition and aid from the Western powers and the Soviet Union.

Being more open to Western influences, the Yugoslav communist regime allowed the development of more liberal wings of communist parties, especially in Croatia and Slovenia. Also, nationalism reappeared, with tensions especially strong between Serbs and Croats in the Croatian republic, leading to the repression by Tito of the Croatian and Slovenian "Springs" (freedom movements like the one in Czechoslovakia in 1968) in 1970–71.

The 1974 constitution shifted much of the decision-making power from the federal level to the republics, further decentralizing the political process. Following Tito's death in 1980, there was an economic crisis. Severe inflation and the inability to pay the nation's foreign debts led to tensions between the different republics and demands for a reorganization of the Yugoslav federation into a confederation of sovereign states.

Pressure toward individual autonomy for the regions, as well as a market economy, grew stronger, leading to the formation of non-communist political parties. By 1990, they were able to win majorities in multiparty elections in Slovenia and then in Croatia, ending the era of Communist Party monopoly of power.

Slovenia and Croatia declared their independence on 25 June 1991. Within a few weeks, ethnic violence broke out between Croats and the Serbs in the northern region of Croatia, backed by Serbian president Slobodan Miloević. The fighting caused tremendous destruction. Entire cities (such as

Vukovar) were destroyed, and large-scale damage was inflicted on Dubrovnik.

Croatia, poorly armed and caught by surprise, fought over a seven-month period and suffered some 10,000 deaths, 30,000 wounded, and over 14,000 missing. Croatia lost about one-third of its territory to the Serbs.

The European community made efforts to stop the killing and destruction in Croatia, as did the UN special envoy, Cyrus Vance. Vance was able to conclude a peace accord on 3 January 1992 that called for a major UN peace-keeping force in Croatia. The Serbian side agreed to hand over their heavy weapons to the United Nations units and to allow thousands of refugees to return home.

In August 1995, more than 100,000 Croatian troops entered and retook the occupied northern region from rebel Serbs. The Croats also linked up with Bosnian forces to protect the UN-designated Muslim ''safe area'' of Bihać in western Bosnia that had been under Serb attack.

In 1996, an uneasy peace was imposed on the warring factions of the former Yugoslavia. Croatia maintained its control of the Krajina and signed an accord giving it partial control, along with Serbs and Bosnians, of disputed territory in Bosnia and Herzegovina.

On 15 January 1998, eastern Slavonia was transferred to Croatia, after two years under UN administration. It was the last Serbian enclave in Croatia and a frequent combat site during the war.

GOVERNMENT

Croatia is a united republic with a mix of parliamentary and presidential forms of government. The parliament of Croatia, as formed on 30 May 1990, adopted a constitution for Croatia on 22 December 1990. The executive authority is held by a president, elected for five years, and a government cabinet headed by a prime minister.

The two-chamber parliament comprises the House of Representatives (127 seats) and the House of Counties (68 seats) with the chairman of the House of Representatives serving as the Parliament chairman.

The president appoints the prime minister and the cabinet, is the Supreme Commander of the armed forces, declares war, and concludes peace on the basis of the parliament's decisions.

Judiciary

The judicial system comprises municipal and district courts, a Supreme Court, and a Constitutional Court. A High Judicial Council (made up of the president and fourteen other members) appoints judges and public prosecutors.

Political Parties

Some fifty political parties are registered in Croatia. The last presidential elections were held in May 1997, when Dr. Franjo Tudjman, leader of the HDZ, was reelected president.

DEFENSE

Upon declaring its independence in 1991, Croatia formed an active armed force of 105,000 plus 100,000 reservists. The separate air defense service has 4,000 members; the air force, 250 and increasing; and the navy, 5,000 sailors. There are also 40,000 armed police. Croatia's total defense spending in 1995 was $1.9 billion.

ECONOMIC AFFAIRS

Before the dissolution of the Yugoslav SFR (Federal Socialist Republic of Yugoslavia), Croatia was its second-most prosperous and industrialized area (after Slovenia). Many of Croatia's current economic problems not caused by the war are largely inherited from communist mismanagement and a large foreign debt.

As a result of the war and loss in output capacity, gross domestic product fell by more than 40%.

Retail inflation, which was nearly 1,150% in 1993, fell to just 4% in 1995.

Public Finance

The fiscal year follows the calendar year. The IMF and World Bank have granted Croatia $192 million and $100 million, respectively, to repair economic imbalances from war and to curb hyperinflation. The EBRD has approved financial support totaling $230 million for infrastructure, telecommunications, and energy projects which otherwise would be unobtainable by the Croatian government.

Income

In 1998, Croatia's gross domestic product (GDP) was estimated to be $20.6 billion in current U.S. dollars, or about $4,520 per person.

The CIA estimates that, in 1995, government revenues totaled approximately $3.86 billion and expenditures $3.72 billion, including capital expenditures of $320 million. External debt totaled $3.15 billion, approximately 54% of which was financed abroad.

Industry

Light industry, especially for the production of consumer goods, is relatively advanced in Croatia. Croatia's main manufacturing industries include chemicals and plastics, machine tools, fabricated metal products, electronics, pig iron and rolled steel products, and aluminum processing.

Banking and Finance

The National Bank of Croatia was founded in 1992. It has the responsibility of issuing currency and regulating the commercial banking sector. The Croatian dinar was issued 23 December 1991, and was replaced in 1994 by the kuna.

As of February 1996 Croatia had fifty-seven banks. In 1995, Raiffeisenbank Austria d.d. Zagreb began operating in Croatia as the first bank with 100% foreign capital.

The Croatian Bank for Reconstruction and Development (HBOR) was established in 1992 as a 100% government-owned institution, with the tasks of financing reconstruction and development and promoting exports through credits and credit guarantees.

The Zagreb Stock Exchange started operations in 1991.

Economic Development

In October 1993, the government adopted an ambitious three-phase program intended to stabilize the economy through fiscal stabilization, currency reform, and accelerated privatization. The plan, however, relies upon cooperation with international financial organizations.

Economic development has been closely tied with privatization. By 1995, the process of ownership transformation had been fully completed by 2,554 companies. There were 221 companies that had the two Croatian Pension Funds and Croatian Privatization Funds (CPF) as majority owners, and 1,225 companies having the same funds as minority owners. The CPF is legally obliged to offer the shares of its portfolio for sale at auction, and as a rule sells its shares through the Zagreb Stock Exchange.

SOCIAL WELFARE

The effects of the 1991 war, the great refugee burden, and the absence of significant international aid have strained the country's social fabric and economy. In 1993, the average standard of living stood at less than 50% of its level before 1991. Over 400,000 Croats were displaced by the war and its aftermath.

Zagreb and several other major cities have started family crisis associations, such as the Women of Vukovar, for women who have missing relatives, and Tresnjevka, a group working to open a support center for wartime rape victims from Bosnia.

Healthcare

Availability of Croatia's health care statistics has been limited by the civil war that has raged since 1991. Between 1991 and 1992, there were 25,000 war-related deaths. There were 50,000 new births in 1994. Life expectancy is 72, and infant mortality was 16 per 1,000 live births in 1995.

Housing

As of mid-1994, nearly 800,000 displaced persons and refugees from Bosnia and occupied Croat territories were in Croatia, of whom approximately 640,000 have found housing with families in Croatia. The remainder are housed in refugee centers and hotels. By 1997, thousands of refugees, mainly from eastern Slavonia, still remained housed in coastal hotels.

EDUCATION

Education at the elementary level is free and compulsory for children between the ages of 6 to 15 years. Secondary education lasts from two to five years. In 1995, approximately 82% of children were enrolled in primary school.

There are four universities and three polytechnic institutes. During the 1994–95 academic year, 83,600 students were enrolled in Croatia's institutions of higher learning.

1999 KEY EVENTS TIMELINE

January

- A new banking law allows the National Bank of Croatia to interfere with, merge, and close down financially weak banks.

February

- Suspected war criminal Nada Sakic is released for lack of evidence in a case against Croatia's Ustashe regime, which ran a concentration camp in Jasenovac during World War II.

March

- Israel agrees to upgrade Croatia's 25 MIG-21 fighters.

April

- Holiday reservations for Easter, made primarily by Germans and Austrians, are canceled because of the nearby Kosovo conflict.

May

- The United States supports Croatia's bid to enter the Partnership for Peace Program and offers $2 billion to help settle refugees, but allows the country to import American defense equipment.

June

- Croatia gives up sovereignty over part of the Dalmatian coastline to Czech holidaymakers, in return for relief in the $4 million debt to the Czech Republic.

- Enron Corporation of the U.S. and the Croatian electric company announce plans to build a power plant in Jertovec.

July

- The Canadian government announces a military investigation in the alleged altering of medical records for Canadian peacekeepers stationed in Croatia during 1993, many of whom are chronically sick.

November

• On November 24, the ruling party pushes through parliament a measure to declare the critically ill President Franco Tudjman temporarily disabled. This action paves the way for the speaker of parliament, Vlatko Pavletic, to sign into law important bills awaiting presidential ratification, and enables the ruling party to avoid calling an early presidential election.

December

• President Franco Tudjman, hospitalized since November 1, dies at age 77.

ANALYSIS OF EVENTS: 1999

BUSINESS AND THE ECONOMY

Considering the series of Balkan conflicts which have disturbed commerce and tourism for a decade, Croatia had a difficult time in 1999. Had the nation been left undisturbed, it would be recovering from the former communist dependency on state planning and climbing slowly out of debt, like other post-communist nations. The wars in Bosnia and Kosovo can be partly blamed on the instability caused by the end of General Tito's reign in the area, who at least held a tight grip on the many ethnic groups that inhabit the Balkan countries. A slow but constant march towards privatization in Croatia since 1989 has not done much for the overall economy, which languishes at a growth rate of 3 percent or less. This coastal nation, comprised of the Dalmatian coastline and hundreds of islands, depends upon tourism for the majority of its income. Unfortunately, no one wants to vacation in or near a war zone, making the country unappealing to business investments as well. President Franjo Tudjman was working on a macroeconomic stabilization plan that should help the region become more attractive to companies, but it will take some time.

In the banking sector, a Bank Rehabilitation Agency will consolidate and privatize some of the 61 different banks to strengthen and streamline the financial situation. The exchange rate, pegged to the Deutschmark since 1994, is steady and inflation remains normal, although Croatian debt is a large problem. In June, the government even signed a deal with the Czech Republic giving up some of its coastline to tourists in order to help repay a $4 million debt. The war-prone neighbors of Croatia have supplied the country with at least one major source of income—gun running—that cannot be adequately measured, but probably is the most profitable business in Croatia. As the economy shifts to more peaceful times, major investments in utility companies such as Enron's deal with Hrvatska Elektropriveda to provide electricity to the country, will support reconstruction.

GOVERNMENT AND POLITICS

Franjo Tudjman's presidency was accused of excessively nationalist tactics in regards to the war in Kosovo and country planning. His ruling HDZ (Croatian Democratic Union) party was supported by only 20 percent of the population. Multi-party democracy is a new concept in this nation, which makes political activism somewhat unheard of, except to preserve the status quo and ruling party. In another holdover from the communist era, many of the utilities and industry in Croatia are still government owned and run, although there are plans for mass privatization. The government wants prompt entrance into the European Union and the improved image of a "European" country instead of being seen as part of the Balkan tragedy. However, there are economic and ideological reasons that stand in the way. The country cannot meet the requirements for entrance to the European Union without major restructuring and financial aid, and nationalist sentiments still run high. Covert arms shipments during the two wars, and banking and oil agreements with Iran tie Croatia firmly into the Muslim world, which bothers some potential allies in Europe. The United States has offered $2 billion in aid for refugees from the Kosovo conflict, and the International Monetary Fund (IMF) lends money to Croatia annually, but this aid is seen mostly as a method of assuaging war-like tendencies. Croatia is a place of great political instability and international controversy that will continue to spawn difficult political situations.

CULTURE AND SOCIETY

The Croatian culture has been forged in the blood and tears of Yugoslavian conflicts that have taken place for centuries. In the face of such contention, growth in the arts and other expressions of societal unity have been stunted. The country takes many of its cues from German and Austrian cultural identities because much of the economy depends upon these benevolent tourists and investors, but the traditional Roman Catholic religion and way of life dominates at home. The majority of Croatia's citizens are Roman Catholic, while a sizable percentage of Orthodox Christian Serbians and Muslims also inhabit the country, although they often suffer from discrimination. In 1998, Croatia was granted custodianship of Eastern Slavonia, from which almost half of the predominantly Serbian population had fled. Many of the more talented scientists and artists have emigrated from Croatia seeking a better life, but they keep close ties with family that remains in the country.

DIRECTORY

CENTRAL GOVERNMENT

Head of State

Acting President
Vlatko Pavletic, Office of the President, Pantovcak 241, 10000 Zagreb, Croatia
PHONE: +385 (1) 4565191

Ministers

Prime Minister
Zlatko Mateša, Office of the Prime Minister, Trg Sv Marka 2, 10000 Zagreb, Croatia
PHONE: +385 (1) 4569201
FAX: +385 (1) 6303019

Deputy Prime Minister and Minister of Finance
Borislav Škegro, Ministry of Finance, Katanciceva 5, 10000 Zagreb, Croatia
PHONE: +385 (1) 4591333

Deputy Prime Minister and Minister of Foreign Affairs
Mate Granic, Ministry of Foreign Affairs, Trg Nikole Šubica Zrinskog 7-8, 10000 Zagreb, Croatia
PHONE: +385 (1) 4569964
FAX: +385 (1) 4569988

Deputy Prime Minister and Minister for Development, Immigration and Reconstruction
Jure Radic, Ministry for Development, Immigration and Reconstruction, Nazorova 61, 10000 Zagreb, Croatia

PHONE: +385 (1) 3784500
FAX: +385 (1) 3784598

Deputy Prime Minister and Minister for European Integration
Ljerka Mintas-Hodak, Ministry for European Integration, Trg Sv. Marka 2, 10000 Zagreb, Croatia
PHONE: +385 (1) 4569203
FAX: +385 (1) 4569326

Minister of Defense
Pavao Miljavac, Ministry of Defense, Trg Kralja Petra Kresimira IV 1, 10000 Zagreb, Croatia

Minister of Interior
Ivan Penic, Ministry of the Interior, Savska 35, 10000 Zagreb, Croatia
PHONE: +385 (1) 6122111
FAX: +385 (1) 6122771

Minister of Agriculture and Forestry
Ivan Djurkic, Ministry of Agriculture and Forestry, Ulica grada Vukovara 78, 10000 Zagreb, Croatia
PHONE: +385 (1) 6106200
FAX: +385 (1) 6109200

Minister of Culture
Ministry of Culture, Trg burze 6, 10000 Zagreb, Croatia
PHONE: +385 (1) 4610477
FAX: +385 (1) 4610489

Minister of Economy
Nenad Porges, Ministry of Economy, Ulica grada Vukovara 78, 10000 Zagreb, Croatia
PHONE: +385 (1) 6106111
FAX: +385 (1) 6109111

Minister of Education and Sports
Nansi Ivaniševic, Ministry of Education and Sports, Trg burze 6, 10000 Zagreb, Croatia
PHONE: +385 (1) 4610485
FAX: +385 (1) 4569087

Minister of Health
Ministry of Health, Ulica baruna Trenka 6, 10000 Zagreb, Croatia
PHONE: +385 (1) 4591333

Minister for Homeland War Veterans
Juraj Njavro, Ministry for Homeland War Veterans, Park Stara Trešnjevka 4, 10000 Zagreb, Croatia
PHONE: +385 (1) 3657800
FAX: +385 (1) 3657852

Minister of Justice
Zvonimir Šeparovic, Ministry of Justice, Ulica
Republike Austrije 14, 10000 Zagreb, Croatia
PHONE: +385 (1) 3710600
FAX: +385 (1) 3710602

Minister of Labor and Social Welfare
Joso Škara, Ministry of Labor and Social
Welfare, Prisavlje 14, 10000 Zagreb, Croatia
PHONE: +385 (1) 6169200
FAX: +385 (1) 6113593

Minister of Maritime Affairs, Transportation, and Communications
Ivan Pavlovic, Ministry of Maritime Affairs,
Transportation, and Communications, Prisavlje
14, 10000 Zagreb, Croatia
PHONE: +385 (1) 6169111
FAX: +385 (1) 6196473

Minister of Science and Technology
Ministry of Science and Technology,
Strossmaycrov trg 4, 10000 Zagreb, Croatia
PHONE: +385 (1) 4594444
FAX: +385 (1) 4594469
E-MAIL: office@science.hr www.mzt.hr

Minister of Tourism
Ivan Herak, Ministry of Tourism, Ul. Grada
Vukovara 78, 10000 Zagreb, Croatia
PHONE: +385 (1) 6106300
FAX: +385 (1) 6109300

Minister of Zoning, Construction and Housing
Marko Širac, Ministry of Zoning, Construction
and Housing, Ulica Republike Austrije 20,
10000 Zagreb, Croatia
PHONE: +385 (1) 3782143
FAX: +385 (1) 3772555

Minister in the Government
Milan Kovac, Ministry in the Government
PHONE: +385 (1) 4569103
FAX: +385 (1) 4569133

POLITICAL ORGANIZATIONS

Hrvatska cista stranka prava-HCSP (Croatian Pure Party of Rights)

Frankopanska 2/II, 10000 Zagreb, Croatia
PHONE: +385 (1) 4848473
FAX: +385 (1) 4848473
TITLE: President
NAME: Ivan Gabelica

Hrvatska demokratska zajednica-HDZ (Croatian Democratic Union)

Trg hrvatskih velikana 4, 10000 Zagreb, Croatia
PHONE: +385 (1) 4553000
FAX: +385 (1) 4552600
TITLE: President
NAME: Franjo Tudjman

Hrvatska kršcanska demokratska unija-HKDU (Croatian Christian Democratic Union)

Tkalciceva 4, 10000 Zagreb, Croatia
PHONE: +385 (1) 4816282
FAX: +385 (1) 4816282
TITLE: President
NAME: Marko Veselica

Hrvatska narodna stranka-HNS (Croatian People's Party)

Branimirova 3, 10000 Zagreb, Croatia
PHONE: +385 (1) 4839425
FAX: +385 (1) 4839424
TITLE: President
NAME: Radimir Cacic

Hrvatska seljaeka stranka-HSS (Croatian Peasant Party)

Zvonimirova 17/III, 10000 Zagreb, Croatia
PHONE: +385 (1) 4553627
FAX: +385 (1) 4553631
E-MAIL: hss-sredisnjica@hss.hr
TITLE: President
NAME: Zlatko Tomcic

Hrvatska socijalno liberalna stranka-HSLS (Croatian Social Liberal Party)

Zrinjevac 17, 10000 Zagreb, Croatia
PHONE: +385 (1) 4810402
FAX: +385 (1) 4810404

Hrvatska stranka prava-HSP (Croatian Party of Rights)

Primorska 1/II, 10000 Zagreb, Croatia
PHONE: +385 (1) 3778016
FAX: +385 (1) 3778736
TITLE: President
NAME: Anto Đapic

Istarski demokratski forum-IDF (Istrian Democratic Forum)

Sergijevaca 12, CT-52100 Pula, Croatia
TITLE: President

NAME: Luciano Delbianco

Istarski demokratski sabor (Istrian Democratic Assembly)

Splitska 3, CT-52100 Pula, Croatia
TITLE: President
NAME: Ivan Jakovcic

Krščanski demokrati Mecimurja-KDM (Christian Democrats of Mecimurje)

Strossmayerova 9, CT-42300 Cakovec, Croatia
TITLE: President
NAME: Vladimir Mesaric

Liberalna stranka-LS (Liberal Party)

Ilica 16/I, 10000 Zagreb, Croatia
E-MAIL: liberali@varazdin.com
TITLE: President
NAME: Vlado Gotovac

Primorsko-goranski savez-PGS (Alliance of Croatian Coast and Mountains Department)

Ciottina 19, CT-51000 Rijeka, Croatia
TITLE: President
NAME: Luciano Sušanj

Samostalna demokratska srpska stranka-SDSS (Independent Democratic Serbian Party)

N. Pašica 1/III, CT-32010 Borovo naselje, Croatia
TITLE: President
NAME: Vojislav Stanimirovic

Socijaldemokratska partija Hrvatske-SDP (Social Democratic Party of Croatia)

Trg Drage Iblera 9, 10000 Zagreb, Croatia
PHONE: +385 (1) 4552055
FAX: +385 (1) 4552842
E-MAIL: sdp@sdp.tel.hr
TITLE: President
NAME: Ivica Racan

Srpska narodna stranka-SNS (Serbian People's Party)

Mazuranicev trg 3, 10000 Zagreb, Croatia
PHONE: +385 (1) 4855631
FAX: +385 (1) 4855631
TITLE: President
NAME: Milan Dukic

Stranka Hrvatske ravnice-SHR (Party of the Croatian Plains)

Šupanijska 7, CT-31000 Osijek, Croatia
TITLE: President
NAME: Slavko Vukšic

DIPLOMATIC REPRESENTATION

Embassies in Croatia

Albania
Jurišiceva 2a, 10000 Zagreb, Croatia
PHONE: +385 (1) 4810679
FAX: +385 (1) 4810681
TITLE: Ambassador
NAME: Miriam Bisha

Austria
Jabukovac 39, 10000 Zagreb, Croatia
TITLE: Ambassador
NAME: Rudolf Bogner

Belgium
Pantovcak 125 B I, 10000 Zagreb, Croatia
PHONE: +385 (1) 4578901
FAX: +385 (1) 4578902
TITLE: Ambassador
NAME: Frans Hintjens

Bosnia and Herzegovina
Torbarova 9, 10000 Zagreb, Croatia
PHONE: +385 (1) 4683761
FAX: +385 (1) 4683764
TITLE: Ambassador
NAME: Hasan Muratovic

Bulgaria
Novi Goljak 25, 10000 Zagreb, Croatia
PHONE: +385 (1) 4823336
FAX: +385 (1) 4823338
TITLE: Ambassador
NAME: Velizar Encev

Canada
Prilaz Gjure Dezelica 4, 10000 Zagreb, Croatia
PHONE: +385 (1) 4848055
FAX: +385 (1) 4848063
TITLE: Ambassador
NAME: Donald W. Smith

Chile
Rackoga 8, 10000 Zagreb, Croatia
PHONE: +385 (1) 4550468
FAX: +385 (1) 4552054
TITLE: Ambassador
NAME: Patricio Rodriguez Renteria

China
Mlinovi 132, 10000 Zagreb, Croatia
PHONE: +385 (1) 4637011
FAX: +385 (1) 4637012
TITLE: Ambassador
NAME: Li Guobang

Czech Republic
Savska cesta 41, 10000 Zagreb, Croatia
PHONE: +385 (1) 6177246
FAX: +385 (1) 6176630
TITLE: Ambassador
NAME: Jiry Kudela

Côte d'Ivoire
Pantovcak 131, 10000 Zagreb, Croatia
PHONE: +385 (1) 4579081
FAX: +385 (1) 4578898
TITLE: Honorary Consul
NAME: Boris Mocan

Egypt
Tuškanac 58a, 10000 Zagreb, Croatia
PHONE: +385 (1) 4818426
FAX: +385 (1) 4818427
TITLE: Ambassador
NAME: Moustafa Mohamed El Feki

Finland
Berislaviceva 2/II, 10 000 Zagreb, Croatia
PHONE: +385 (1) 4811662
FAX: +385 (1) 4819946
TITLE: Ambassador
NAME: Osmo Liponen

France
Schlosserove stube 5, 10000 Zagreb, Croatia
PHONE: +385 (1) 4818110
FAX: +385 (1) 4816899
TITLE: Ambassador
NAME: Jean-Jacques Gaillarde

Germany
Ulica Grada Vukovara 64, 10000 Zagreb, Croatia
PHONE: +385 (1) 6158100; 6108101
FAX: +385 (1) 6158103
TITLE: Ambassador
NAME: Volker Haak

Greece
Babukiceva 3a, 10000 Zagreb, Croatia
PHONE: +385 (1) 2335834
FAX: +385 (1) 2302893
TITLE: Ambassador
NAME: Stavros-Georges-Kristian Vasilopoulos

Hungary
Krlezin gvozd 11a, 10000 Zagreb, Croatia
TITLE: Ambassador
NAME: Gyorgy Csoti

India
Boškoviceva ulica 7A, 10000 Zagreb, Croatia
FAX: +385 (1) 4817907
TITLE: Ambassador
NAME: Udai Singh

Iran
Pantovcak 125 b, 10000 Zagreb, Croatia
PHONE: +385 (1) 4578983; 4578984
FAX: +385 (1) 4578987
TITLE: Ambassador
NAME: Keyvan Imani

Italy
Meduliceva 22, 10000 Zagreb, Croatia
PHONE: +385 (1) 4846386; 4846387
FAX: +385 (1) 4846384
TITLE: Ambassador
NAME: Fabio Pigliapoco

Japan
Ksaver 211, 10000 Zagreb, Croatia
PHONE: +385 (1) 4677755
FAX: +385 (1) 4677766
TITLE: Ambassador
NAME: Oba Keisuke

Macedonia
Petrinjska 29/I, 10000 Zagreb, Croatia
TITLE: Ambassador
NAME: Servet Avziu

Malaysia
Slavujevac 4A, 10000 Zagreb, Croatia

Malta
Beciceve stube 2, 10000 Zagreb, Croatia
PHONE: +385 (1) 4677999
TITLE: Ambassador
NAME: Nikola Barun Adamovich

The Netherlands
PHONE: +385 (1) 4819533
TITLE: Ambassador
NAME: Ida Leonore Van Veldhuizer-Rothenbuecher

Norway
Petrinjska 9/1, 10000 Zagreb, Croatia
TITLE: Ambassador
NAME: Knut Morkved

Poland
Krlezin Gvozd 3, 10000 Zagreb, Croatia
PHONE: +385 (1) 4819 233

TITLE: Ambassador
NAME: Jerzy Mieczyslav Chmielewski

Romania

Srebrnjak 150A, 10000 Zagreb, Croatia
PHONE: +385 (1) 2430137
FAX: +385 (1) 2430138
TITLE: Ambassador
NAME: Contantin Ghirda

Russian Federation

Bosanska 44, 10000 Zagreb, Croatia
PHONE: +385 (1) 3755038; 3755039
FAX: +385 (1) 3755040
TITLE: Ambassador
NAME: Eduard Leonidovic-Kuzmin

Serbia

Mesiceva 19, 10000 Zagreb, Croatia
PHONE: +385 (1) 4680552; 4680553; 4680671
FAX: +385 (1) 4680770
TITLE: Ambassador
NAME: Veljko Knezevic

Slovakia

Prilaz Gjure Deelica 10, 10000 Zagreb, Croatia
PHONE: +385 (1) 4848941; 4848944
FAX: +385 (1) 4848942

Slovenia

Savska c. 41, 10000 Zagreb, Croatia
PHONE: +385 (1) 6311000; 6311011
FAX: +385 (1) 6177236
TITLE: Ambassador
NAME: Boštjan Kovacic

Spain

Meduliceva 5, 10000 Zagreb, Croatia
PHONE: +385 (1) 4848603; 4848606
FAX: +385 (1) 4848605
NAME: Antonio Pedauye y Gonzales

Sudan

Andrijeviceva 21, 10000 Zagreb, Croatia
PHONE: +385 (1) 3777808
FAX: +385 (1) 3777809

Sweden

Frankopanska 22, 10000 Zagreb, Croatia
PHONE: +385 (1) 4849322; 4849333
FAX: +385 (1) 4849244; 4849329
TITLE: Ambassador
NAME: Ingemar Borjesson

Switzerland

Bogoviceva 3, 10000 Zagreb, Croatia
PHONE: +385 (1) 4810891; 4810895
FAX: +385 (1) 4810890
TITLE: Ambassador

NAME: Petar Troendle

Turkey

Masarykova 3/II, 10000 Zagreb, Croatia
PHONE: +385 (1) 4855200
FAX: +385 (1) 4855606
TITLE: Ambassador
NAME: Salahattin Alpar

Ukraine

Vocarska 52, 10000 Zagreb, Croatia
PHONE: +385 (1) 4616296; 4556128
FAX: +385 (1) 4553824
TITLE: Ambassador
NAME: Anatoliy Shostak

United Kingdom

Vlaška 121/III, 10000 Zagreb, Croatia
PHONE: +385 (1) 4555310
FAX: +385 (1) 4551685
TITLE: Ambassador
NAME: Colin Andrew Munroe

United States

Andrije Hebranga 2-4, 10000 Zagreb, Croatia
PHONE: +385 (1) 4555500; 4555281
FAX: +385 (1) 4553126; 4550892
TITLE: Ambassador
NAME: William Dale Montgomery

Vatican City

Ksaverska cesta 10a, 10000 Zagreb, Croatia
PHONE: +385 (1) 4673996
FAX: +385 (1) 4673997
TITLE: Papal Nuncio
NAME: Giulio Einaudi

JUDICIAL SYSTEM

Supreme Court

Trg Nikole Subica Zrinskog 3, 10000 Zagreb, Croatia
PHONE: +385 (1) 4810022
FAX: +385 (1) 4810035

Constitutional Court

Trg sv. Marka 4, 10000 Zagreb, Croatia
PHONE: +385 (1) 4569222

FURTHER READING

Government Publications

Country Finance: Croatia. New York, NY:
Economic Intelligence Unit, 1999.

Articles

"Another Buffeting for Dubrovnic." *The Economist* (May 22, 1999): 54.

"Enron Plans Plant in Croatia." *The Oil Daily* (May 24, 1999).

Giarelli, Andrew. "The Coast of Bohemia." *The World Press Review* (June 1999): 21.

"Israel, Croatia Mend Fences." *Business Week* (March 1, 1999): 53.

Jones, Colin. "On a Tight Rein." *The Banker* (April 1999): 47.

"West of the War." *The American Spectator* (July 1999): 60.

Books

Croatia. Oakland, CA: Lonely Planet Publications, 1999.

Croatia: Second Class Citizens: The Serbs of Croatia. New York, NY: Human Rights Watch, 1999.

The Former Yugoslavia Through Documents: From its Dissolution to the Peace Settlement. Boston, MA: Nijhoff Publications, 1999.

Internet

Croatia. Available Online @ http://croatia.net (October 26, 1999).

Croatian Bureau of Statistics. Available Online @ http://www.dzs.hr/Eng/default2.htm (October 26, 1999).

Croatian Government Bulletin. Available Online @ http://www.vlada.hr/english/contents.html (October 26, 1999).

CROATIA: STATISTICAL DATA

For sources and notes see "Sources of Statistics" in the front of each volume.

GEOGRAPHY

Geography (1)

Area:

Total: 56,538 sq km.

Land: 56,410 sq km.

Water: 128 sq km.

Area—comparative: slightly smaller than West Virginia.

Land boundaries:

Total: 2,197 km.

Border countries: Bosnia and Herzegovina 932 km, Hungary 329 km, Serbia and Montenegro 266 km (241 km with Serbia; 25 km with Montenego), Slovenia 670 km.

Coastline: 5,790 km (mainland 1,778 km, islands 4,012 km).

Climate: Mediterranean and continental; continental climate predominant with hot summers and cold winters; mild winters, dry summers along coast.

Terrain: geographically diverse; flat plains along Hungarian border, low mountains and highlands near Adriatic coast, coastline, and islands.

Natural resources: oil, some coal, bauxite, low-grade iron ore, calcium, natural asphalt, silica, mica, clays, salt.

Land use:

Arable land: 21%

Permanent crops: 2%

Permanent pastures: 20%

Forests and woodland: 38%

Other: 19% (1993 est.).

HUMAN FACTORS

Demographics (2A)

	1990	1995	1998	2000	2010	2020	2030	2040	2050
Population	NA	4,700.5	4,671.6	4,681.0	4,634.5	4,469.5	4,208.8	3,875.0	3,486.3
Net migration rate (per 1,000 population)	NA	NA	NA	NA	NA	NA	NA	NA	NA
Births	NA	NA	NA	NA	NA	NA	NA	NA	NA
Deaths	NA	NA	NA	NA	NA	NA	NA	NA	NA
Life expectancy - males	NA	69.6	70.4	71.0	73.3	75.2	76.8	78.0	79.0
Life expectancy - females	NA	76.5	77.3	77.8	79.9	81.6	83.0	84.2	85.0
Birth rate (per 1,000)	NA	10.9	10.5	10.2	8.9	7.5	6.8	6.1	5.6
Death rate (per 1,000)	NA	11.3	11.1	11.2	12.0	12.8	13.8	15.7	17.1
Women of reproductive age (15-49 yrs.)	NA	1,166.4	1,162.1	1,156.8	1,062.3	972.0	850.5	716.0	610.7
of which are currently married	NA	NA	NA	NA	NA	NA	NA	NA	NA
Fertility rate	NA	1.6	1.5	1.5	1.4	1.3	1.3	1.3	1.3

Except as noted, values for vital statistics are in thousands; life expectancy is in years.

Health Personnel (3)

Total health expenditure as a percentage of GDP, 1990-1997[a]

Public sector 8.4

Private sector 1.6

Total[b] 9.9

Health expenditure per capita in U.S. dollars, 1990-1997[a]

Purchasing power parity 414

Total 302

Availability of health care facilities per 100,000 people

Hospital beds 1990-1997[a] 590

Doctors 1993[c] 201

Nurses 1993[c] 470

Health Indicators (4)

Life expectancy at birth

1980 70

1997 72

Daily per capita supply of calories (1996) 2,458

Total fertility rate births per woman (1997) 1.6

Maternal mortality ratio per 100,000 live births (1990-97) . . . . .12[b]

Safe water % of population with access (1995) 63

Sanitation % of population with access (1995) 61

Consumption of iodized salt % of households (1992-98)[a] 70

Smoking prevalence

Male % of adults (1985-95)[a] . . . .

Female % of adults (1985-95)[a] . . . .

Tuberculosis incidence per 100,000 people (1997) 64

Adult HIV prevalence % of population ages 15-49 (1997) 0.01

Infants and Malnutrition (5)

Under-5 mortality rate (1997) 9

% of infants with low birthweight (1990-97) . . . . . .NA

Births attended by skilled health staff % of total[a] . . .NA

% fully immunized (1995-97)

TB 98

DPT 92

Polio 92

Measles 91

Prevalence of child malnutrition under age 5 (1992-97)[b] 1

Ethnic Division (6)

Croat 78%

Serb 12%

Muslim 0.9%

Hungarian 0.5%

Slovenian 0.5%

Others 8.1% (1991)

Religions (7)

Catholic 76.5%

Orthodox 11.1%

Slavic Muslim 1.2%

Protestant 0.4%

Others and unknown 10.8%

Languages (8)

Serbo-Croatian 96%, other 4% (including Italian, Hungarian, Czechoslovak, and German).

EDUCATION

Public Education Expenditures (9)

Public expenditure on education (% of GNP)

1980 . . . .

1996 . . . . .5.3[1]

Expenditure per student

Primary % of GNP per capita

1980 . . . .

1996 . . . .

Secondary % of GNP per capita

1980 . . . .

1996 . . . .

Tertiary % of GNP per capita

1980 . . . .

1996 . . . .

Expenditure on teaching materials

Primary % of total for level (1996) . . . .

Secondary % of total for level (1996) . . . .

Primary pupil-teacher ratio per teacher (1996) 19

Duration of primary education years (1995) 4

Educational Attainment (10)

Age group (1991)[23] . . . . .25+

Total population 2,969,584

Highest level attained (%)

No schooling 10.2

First level

Not completed 43.6

Completed . . . . .NA

Entered second level

S-1 . . . . .39.5

S-2 . . . . .NA

Postsecondary 6.4

Literacy Rates (11B)

Adult literacy rate

1980

  Male ....-

  Female ....-

1995

  Male 98%

  Female 97%

GOVERNMENT & LAW

Political Parties (12)

House of Representatives	No. of seats
Croatian Democratic Union (HDZ) 75	
Croatian Social Liberal Party (HSLS) 12	
Croatian Peasants' Party (HSS) 10	
Social Democratic Party of Croatia (SDP) 10	
Istrian Democratic Assembly (IDS) 4	
Croatian Party of Rights 1861 (HSP 1861) 4	
Croatian People's Party (HNS) 2	
Serbian National Party (SNS) 2	
Croatian Democratic Independents (HND) 1	
Action of the Social Democrats of Croatia (ASII) 1	
Croatian Christian Democratic Union (HKDU) 1	
Slanvonsko-Baranja Croatian Party (SBHS) 1	
Independents 4	

Government Budget (13A)

Year: 1997

Total Expenditures: 58,795.41 Millions of Kunas

Expenditures as a percentage of the total by function:

  General public services and public order 10.42

  Defense 11.83

  Education 6.55

  Health 14.11

  Social Security and Welfare 36.23

  Housing and community amenities 5.89

  Recreational, cultural, and religious affairs 95

  Fuel and energy ....-

  Agriculture, forestry, fishing, and hunting 1.13

  Mining, manufacturing, and construction 1.27

  Transportation and communication 6.24

  Other economic affairs and services 94

Military Affairs (14B)

	1992	1993	1994	1995
Military expenditures				
Current dollars (mil.)	1,441	1,537	1,827	2,114
1995 constant dollars (mil.)	1,550	1,611	1,873	2,114
Armed forces (000)	103[e]	NA	80	60
Gross national product (GNP)				
Current dollars (mil.)	18,610	18,570	19,310	20,100
1995 constant dollars (mil.)	20,010	19,470	19,800	20,100
Central government expenditures (CGE)				
1995 constant dollars (mil.)	8,019	10,640	6,719	6,608
People (mil.)	4.8	4.9	4.9	5.0
Military expenditure as % of GNP	7.7	8.3	9.5	10.5
Military expenditure as % of CGE	19.3	15.1	27.9	32.0
Military expenditure per capita (1995 $)	320	330	380	425
Armed forces per 1,000 people (soldiers)	21.3	NA	16.2	12.1
GNP per capita (1995 $)	4,135	3,986	4,019	4,045
Arms imports[6]				
Current dollars (mil.)	0	150	40	110
1995 constant dollars (mil.)	0	157	41	110
Arms exports[6]				
Current dollars (mil.)	0	0	0	0
1995 constant dollars (mil.)	0	0	0	0
Total imports[7]				
Current dollars (mil.)	4,500	4,666	5,231	7,582
1995 constant dollars (mil.)	4,840	4,892	5,362	7,582
Total exports[7]				
Current dollars (mil.)	4,597	3,913	4,259	4,633
1995 constant dollars (mil.)	4,945	4,102	4,366	4,633
Arms as percent of total imports[8]	0.0	3.2	.8	1.5
Arms as percent of total exports[8]	0.0	0	0	0

Crime (15)

Crime rate (for 1997)

Crimes reported 55,100

Total persons convicted 42,100

Crimes per 100,000 population 1,150

Persons responsible for offenses

Total number of suspects 29,500

Total number of female suspects 2,750

Total number of juvenile suspects 2,500

LABOR FORCE

Labor Force (16)

Total (million) 1.444

Industry and mining .31.1%

Agriculture 4.3%

Government 19.1%

Other 45.5%

Data for 1995 Percent distribution for 1993. Government
includes education and health.

Unemployment Rate (17)

15.9% (yearend 1997 est.)

PRODUCTION SECTOR

Electric Energy (18)

Capacity . . . . .3.593 million kW (1995)

Production . . . . .7.15 billion kWh (1995)

Consumption per capita . . . . .2,315 kWh (1995)

Transportation (19)

Highways:

total: 27,247 km

paved: 22,206 km (including 318 km of expressways)

unpaved: 5,041 km (1996 est.)

Waterways: 785 km perennially navigable; Sava
blocked by downed bridges

Pipelines: crude oil 670 km; petroleum products 20
km; natural gas 310 km (1992); note—under repair
following territorial dispute

Merchant marine:

total: 72 ships (1,000 GRT or over) totaling 793,114
GRT/1,187,908 DWT ships by type: bulk 13, cargo 31,
chemical tanker 2, combination bulk 5, container 5,
liquefied gas 1, multi-function large load carrier 3, oil
tanker 2, passenger 2, roll-on/roll-off cargo 3, short-sea
passenger 5 note: Croatia owns an additional 80 ships

(1,000 GRT or over) totaling 2,057,523 DWT operating
under the registries of Malta, Liberia, Cyprus, Panama,
and Saint Vincent and the Grenadines (1997 est.)

Airports: 71 (1997 est.)

Airports—with paved runways:

total: 20

over 3,047 m: 2

2,438 to 3,047 m: 6

1,524 to 2,437 m: 2

914 to 1,523 m: 3

under 914 m: 7 (1997 est.)

Airports—with unpaved runways:

total: 51

1,524 to 2,437 m: 1

914 to 1,523 m: 8

under 914 m: 42 (1997 est.)

Top Agricultural Products (20)

Wheat, corn, sugar beets, sunflower seed, alfalfa,
clover, olives, citrus, grapes, vegetables; livestock
breeding, dairy farming.

MANUFACTURING SECTOR

GDP & Manufacturing Summary (21)

Detailed value added figures are listed by both International
Standard Industry Code (ISIC) and product title.

	1980	1985	1990	1994
GDP ($-1990 mil.)[1]	16,339	16,475	12,672	7,783
Per capita ($-1990)[1]	3,733	3,685	2,805	1,728
Manufacturing share (%) (current prices)[1]	21.4	24.6	22.9	26.5
Manufacturing				
Value added ($-1990 mil.)[1]	NA	NA	NA	NA
Industrial production index	NA	NA	NA	NA
Value added ($ mil.)	4,792	3,498	3,389	5,227
Gross output ($ mil.)	19,701	12,136	8,527	12,129
Employment (000)	620	562	533	322
Profitability (% of gross output)				
Intermediate input (%)	75	71	60	57
Wages and salaries inc. supplements (%)	17	14	26	14
Gross operating surplus	9	15	14	29

	1980	1985	1990	1994
Productivity ($)				
Gross output per worker	31,697	21,579	16,011	37,554
Value added per worker	8,033	6,228	6,364	16,194
Average wage (inc. supplements)	5,246	2,957	4,101	5,334
Value added ($ mil.)				
311/2 Food products	659	397	572	895
313 Beverages	88	75	110	194
314 Tobacco products	54	41	61	190
321 Textiles	306	251	207	285
322 Wearing apparel	284	172	168	260
323 Leather and fur products	83	50	29	33
324 Footwear	144	123	90	84
331 Wood and wood products	121	112	92	188
332 Furniture and fixtures	160	97	85	140
341 Paper and paper products	144	88	100	115
342 Printing and publishing	234	142	195	167
351 Industrial chemicals	179	120	75	176
352 Other chemical products	195	117	188	361
353 Petroleum refineries	138	76	61	171
354 Miscellaneous petroleum and coal products	36	22	−1	18
355 Rubber products	72	44	31	19
356 Plastic products	108	66	67	86
361 Pottery, china and earthenware	21	18	22	23
362 Glass and glass products	55	33	52	60
369 Other non-metal mineral products	145	111	121	203
371 Iron and steel	108	113	114	142
372 Non-ferrous metals	51	39	53	49
381 Metal products	355	273	203	244
382 Non-electrical machinery	490	412	256	302
383 Electrical machinery	335	258	247	362
384 Transport equipment	372	225	168	425
385 Professional and scientific equipment	17	10	10	19
390 Other manufacturing industries	18	11	14	16

FINANCE, ECONOMICS, & TRADE

Economic Indicators (22)

National product: GDP—purchasing power parity—$22.7 billion (1997 est.)

National product real growth rate: 4.4% (1997 est.)

National product per capita: $4,500 (1997 est.)

Inflation rate—consumer price index: 3.7% (1997 est.)

Balance of Payments (23)

	1993	1994	1995	1996
Exports of goods (f.o.b.)	3,904	4,260	4,633	4,512
Imports of goods (f.o.b.)	−4,200	−4,706	−6,759	−7,009
Trade balance	−296	−446	−2,126	−2,497
Services - debits	−1,894	−2,303	−2,974	−3,456
Services - credits	1,918	2,394	2,743	3,723
Private transfers (net)	250	235	280	155
Government transfers (net)	126	224	366	624
Overall balance	104	103	−1,712	−1,452

Exchange Rates (24)

Exchange rates:

Croatian kuna per US$1

January 1998	.6.369
1997	.6.101
1996	.5.434
1995	.5.230
1994	.5.996
1993	.3.577

Top Import Origins (25)

$9.1 billion (c.i.f., 1997) Data are for 1994.

Origins	%
Germany	.21
Italy	.19
Slovenia	.10

Top Export Destinations (26)

$4.3 billion (f.o.b., 1997) Data are for 1994.

Destinations	%
Germany	.22
Italy	.21
Slovenia	.18

Economic Aid (27)

Recipient: ODA, $NA. Note: IMF has given Croatia $192 million; World Bank has given Croatia $100 million. NA stands for not available.

Import Export Commodities (28)

Import Commodities	Export Commodities
Machinery and transport equipment 23.1%	Machinery and transport equipment 13.6%
Fuels and lubricants 8.8%	Miscellaneous manufactures 27.6%
Food and live animals 9.0%	Chemicals 14.2%
Chemicals 14.2%	Food and live animals 12.2%
Miscellaneous manufactured articles 16.0%	Raw materials 6.1%
Raw materials 3.5%	Fuels and lubricants 9.4%
Beverages and tobacco 1.4%	Beverages and tobacco 2.7%

CUBA

Republic of Cuba
República de Cuba

CAPITAL: Havana (La Habana).

FLAG: The flag consists of five alternating blue and white horizontal stripes penetrated from the hoist side by a red triangle containing a white five-pointed star.

ANTHEM: *Himno de Bayamo (Hymn of Bayamo),* beginning "Al combate corred bayameses" ("March to the battle, people of Bayamo").

MONETARY UNIT: The Cuban peso (c $) of 100 centavos is a paper currency with one exchange rate. There are coins of 1, 2, 3, 5, 20, 40, and 100 centavos and notes of 1, 3, 5, 10, 20, 50, and 100 pesos. c $1 = us $1 (or us $1 = c $1).

WEIGHTS AND MEASURES: The metric system is the legal standard, but older Spanish units and the imperial system are still employed. The standard unit of land measure is the caballería (13.4 hectares/133.1 acres).

HOLIDAYS: Day of the Revolution, Liberation Day, 1 January; Labor Day, 1 May; Anniversary of the Revolution, 25–27 July; Proclamation of Yara, 10 October. Celebration of religious holidays falling during the workweek was prohibited by a 1972 law.

TIME: 7 AM = noon GMT.

LOCATION AND SIZE: The Republic of Cuba consists of one large island and several small ones situated on the northern rim of the Caribbean Sea, about 160 kilometers (100 miles) south of Florida. With an area of 110,860 square kilometers (42,803 square miles), Cuba is the largest country in the Caribbean. The area occupied by Cuba is slightly smaller than the state of Pennsylvania. Cuba's total coastline is 3,764 kilometers (2,339 miles).

CLIMATE: Except in the mountains, the climate of Cuba is semitropical or temperate. The average minimum temperature is 21°C (70°F), the average maximum 27°C (81°F). The mean temperature at Havana is about 25°C (77°F).

The mountain areas have an average precipitation of more than 180 centimeters (70 inches); most of the lowland area has from 90 to 140 centimeters (35–55 inches) annually; and the area around Guantánamo Bay has less than 65 centimeters (26 inches).

INTRODUCTORY SURVEY

RECENT HISTORY

Fulgencio Batista y Zaldívar assumed power and ruled Cuba from 1934 until 1940, often through a series of puppet presidents. In 1934, Batista got President Franklin D. Roosevelt to revoke the Platt Amendment, although the United States retained its naval base at Guantánamo Bay (which is currently scheduled to revert to Cuban authority in 2000).

Under a new constitution, adopted in 1940, Batista became president. In 1944, he was succeeded by Grau San Martín, whose eight years of rule were ineffective and corrupt. In 1952, with elections scheduled, Batista seized power in a military coup and, for the next seven years, used increasingly harsh measures to keep himself in office. Under the Batista regime, social services suffered, poverty and illiteracy were widespread, and the bureaucracy was glaringly corrupt.

Exiled after a failed 1953 raid on an army barracks, the young revolutionary Fidel Castro gathered supporters in Mexico for a second revolt and in 1956 landed in Cuba. Overcome by Batista's troops, Castro escaped into the Sierra Maestra mountains with only a dozen supporters. His forces never grew to more than a few thousand, but clever use of guerrilla tactics made them a match for Batista's poorly trained army. In addition, there was almost no popular support for Batista, and in 1958, the United States ended its military aid to the falling government.

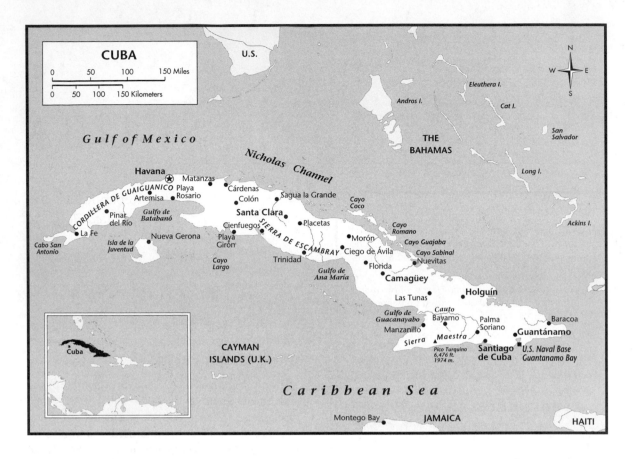

On 1 January 1959, the Batista regime collapsed. Castro seized control of the government and began to rule by decree. Castro instituted a revolutionary government that began large-scale land reforms and other measures aimed at solving Cuba's desperate economic problems.

After June 1960, Cuban-U.S. relations worsened as communist influence on the Cuban government grew. Castro's government took control of about $2 billion in U.S.-owned property in Cuba; the United States severed diplomatic relations with the Castro government and stopped importing Cuban sugar.

In April 1961, a group of 1,500 Cuban exiles—financed, trained and equipped by the CIA—invaded Cuba at the Bay of Pigs. The invasion turned out to be a politically embarrassing blunder for the newly installed administration of President John F. Kennedy. The brigade was defeated within seventy-two hours, and the survivors were captured. They were later released in exchange for a ransom of $50 million in food and medical supplies.

In 1961, Castro declared himself a Marxist-Leninist and part of the Socialist world. All major means of production, distribution, communication, and services were taken over by the government. Cuba's trade and other relations shifted to the Soviet bloc.

In October 1962, U.S. planes photographed missile bases operated by the Soviet Union in Cuba. In what came to be known as the Cuban Missile Crisis, the United States blockaded Cuba until the Soviet Union agreed to withdraw the missiles in exchange for a U.S. government pledge to launch no more offensive operations against the island.

However, the United States did continue its attempt to isolate Cuba politically and economically from Latin America and the rest of the non-communist world. Castro responded by trying to weaken certain Central and South American governments. Guerrilla movements became active throughout the region, often with Cuban support.

During the administration of U.S. President Jimmy Carter, there were moves to normalize relations with Cuba. However, the advent of the administration of President Ronald Reagan brought increased tensions between the two countries. Citing Cuban involvement in Angola, Ethiopia,

Nicaragua, and Grenada, the United States took a more hostile stance toward Cuba.

Domestically, Castro's administration has had mixed success. Cuba has a strong social welfare system, including free health care and subsidized housing. However, economic mismanagement has led to economic decline. Cubans live frugally under a highly controlled system of rationing.

Cuba was dealt a serious blow in the late 1980s with the collapse of the Soviet Union. This meant a cutoff in economic and military aid, on which Cuba had come to rely. However, Castro remains committed to the original goals of his revolution. He continues to blame Cuba's economic woes on the continuing U.S. trade embargo.

In the 1990s, Cuba's economy began to show signs of strength. But in 1992, the United States tightened its embargo, leading to another wave of emigration. This in turn led to increased isolationist policies by the United States. In 1997, Cuba's tourist economy was threatened by a wave of bombings at luxury hotels. The Cuban government blamed the United States. In January 1998, Pope John Paul II visited Cuba. It was the first time that Castro had invited a prominent international figure who opposed his socialist dictatorship to visit Cuba.

GOVERNMENT

A new constitution, adopted in 1975 and ratified in 1976, establishes the National Assembly of People's Power as the supreme state organ. The National Assembly elects the Council of State, which includes the president, who is both head of state and head of government.

In December 1986, the third National Assembly, with 510 delegates, reelected Castro as president of the Council of State. He remains the key figure in domestic and foreign policy making. As of 1996, there were 589 seats in the National Assembly. Suffrage is universal for citizens age 16 and over, excluding those who have applied for permanent emigration.

Judiciary

The 1976 constitution established the People's Supreme Court, which proposes laws, issues regulations, and makes decisions to be implemented by the people's courts. There are also seven regional courts of appeal, as well as district courts with civil and criminal jurisdiction.

Political Parties

The constitution recognizes the Cuban Communist Party (Partido Comunista Cubano—PCC) as the "highest leading force of the society and of the state," which, in practice, outlaws other political parties. At the third party congress in 1986, Fidel Castro was reelected as first secretary.

DEFENSE

The Castro government has maintained a military draft since 1963. It now requires two years of military service from men between the ages of 16 and 50. Total armed strength in 1995 was estimated at 100,000. The army has 85,000 personnel, the navy has 5,000 personnel, and the air force 10,000. Paramilitary forces included 15,000 state security troops; 4,000 border guards; 50,000 civil defense forces; 65,000 youth labor army, and the 1 million-member territorial militia.

Cuba's 1996 budget for defense and internal security was $335 million, or about 1.6% of gross national product.

ECONOMIC AFFAIRS

The collapse of the Soviet Union in 1991 resulted in a cutoff of important assistance and the breakdown of traditional markets for Cuban exports. The Cuban economy slowed significantly in the period 1990–91.

In response, the Castro government has restricted public spending, restructured the economy, and begun trading with market economies. The government has put special emphasis on the promotion of foreign investment and the development of sugar and tourism. And, in 1992, tourism surpassed sugar as Cuba's principal source of foreign exchange.

Beginning in the late 1990s, Cuba was experimenting with limited market-economics, such as pay incentives and bonuses, in an attempt to improve productivity. In 1996, Cuba's economy grew by 7.8%. The growth was led by tourism, with gross revenues from tourism rising 18% to $1.3 billion.

Public Finance

Under the Economic Management System, developed during the 1970s and approved by the PCC Congress in 1975, state committees for statistics and finances have been established, and formal state budgets, abandoned in 1967, have been reintroduced. State revenues come from the nationalized enterprises, income tax, social security contributions, and foreign aid. Cuba's debt to Western nations in 1991 was estimated at $6.5 billion, while debt to the former USSR was estimated at $24 billion.

Income

In 1995, Cuba's gross domestic product (GDP) was estimated to be $14.7 billion in current U.S. dollars, or about $1,300 per person. That year, the real growth rate of GDP was 2.5%.

Industry

All Cuban industrial production was nationalized after the revolution. The last privately owned companies were nationalized in 1968. Castro has allowed limited market economics into the economy in recent years.

Sugar is the second largest contributor to gross national product (GNP) after tourism. In 1996, construction expanded by 31%, agriculture by 17%, mining by 12%, and manufacturing by 8%.

Banking and Finance

All banks in Cuba were nationalized in 1960. The National Bank of Cuba, established in 1948, was restructured in 1967. Commercial banks include Banco Financiero International (1984). Savings banks include Banco Popular dul Ahorro. There are no securities exchanges.

Although no figures have been given as of 1997, repeated references to financial shortages and the policy emphasis on financial control suggest that the situation is difficult. Hard-currency reserves, already depleted by import growth in excess of export growth, were strained further by purchases needed to repair the damage caused by Hurricane Lili in October 1996.

Economic Development

Until 1959, the Cuban government followed a policy of free enterprise; government ownership was largely limited to local utilities. When the Castro government came to power in 1959, it proceeded to create a centrally planned economy. By means of nationalization and expropriation, all producer industries, mines, refineries, communications, and export-import concerns were brought under government control by 1968.

More recently, Cuba has been applying timid market reforms while actively seeking foreign investment. Economic growth in the late 1990s was projected to come from an expansion of manufacturing, tourism, mining, and services. Other positive factors include the improved tourist industry and a sharp recovery of the cigar industry. The creation of a new Central Bank completed financial sector reforms begun in 1995. These reflected the increased role of the private sector in financial transactions.

SOCIAL WELFARE

A single system of social security covering almost all workers and protecting them against the risks of old age, disability, and death was enacted in 1963. Family-planning services are integrated within the general health care system. Pensions are set at a rate of 50% of average earnings. The national health system covers all citizens. The Family Code of 1975 outlaws gender discrimination. Women receive equal access to education and are found in all professions.

There were reports of serious human rights abuses in 1995. Prison conditions are harsh, medical care is inadequate, and abuse and torture are common. The government does not allow international organizations to monitor prison conditions.

Healthcare

Health conditions improved greatly after the 1959 revolution. All health services are provided free of charge. From 1992 to 1995, 100% of the country had access to health care services. Life expectancy was an average of 76 years for women and men in 1995. Infant mortality in 1995 was 9 per 1,000 live births. In 1999, there was one doctor for every 200 people.

Housing

Cuban housing has not kept pace with the population increase. All large cities have slum problems, despite the construction of 200,000 housing units between 1959 and 1975, 83,000 units between 1976 and 1980, and 335,000 units between 1981 and 1985.

EDUCATION

In 1995, UNESCO reported the illiteracy rate of persons aged 15 years and over as 4% (males, 3.8%; females, 4.7%). Education is free and compulsory for five years (6–11 years of age). Secondary education lasts for another five years. The Castro government added agricultural and technical programs to the secondary-school curriculum; the work-study principle is now central to Cuban secondary education. Cuba has five universities. In

1993, 176,228 students were enrolled in higher education; 57% were female.

1999 KEY EVENTS TIMELINE

January

- January 1 marks the 40th anniversary of the communist revolution.

- President Fidel Castro announces a crackdown on crime and calls for greater U.S. cooperation against drug trafficking.

February

- Cuba's National Assembly approves harsh penalties for political opposition and violent crime, including the death penalty for drug trafficking and prison terms of up to 30 years for "collaborating" with the United States.

- The Cuban phone company cuts most service to the U.S.

March

- Salvadorans Raul Ernesto Cruz Leon and Otto Rene Rodriguiez Llerena are convicted of terrorism and sentenced to death for their roles in the 1997 hotel bombings in Cuba.

- Vladimiro Roca, one of Cuba's best-known dissidents and the son of the late Cuban Communist Party leader Blas Roca, is sentenced to five years in prison for his 1997 criticism of a Communist Party document.

- Havana announces plans to replace the U.S. dollar with the euro.

- A baseball game between the Baltimore Orioles of the United States and the Cuban national team takes place in Havana's Latinoamericano stadium.

April

- Many farmers now exceed their quota and can earn up to double the average wage, thanks to sustainable farming methods implemented since the end of Soviet-supported agricultural practices. Nearly all Cuban farms are now run by co-ops rather than the state.

May

- New U.S. regulations go into effect that allow the sale of food, medical equipment, and agricultural supplies to nongovernmental entities in Cuba.

- The Baltimore Orioles and Cuban national team play baseball again, this time at Baltimore's Camden Yards.

June

- The first Protestant open-air services in Cuba in 40 years are held in the Plaza of the Revolution in Havana.

July

- Cuban officials claim that the economy grew by 6 percent in the first half of 1999.

- Cuban fans of Ernest Hemingway, who lived in Cuba for 31 years, celebrate the 100th anniversary of the writer's birth.

August

- Cuba makes a bid to host the 2008 Summer Olympics.

- The United States announces the easing of travel restrictions to Cuba.

- Castro accuses the U.S. of encouraging illegal immigration by granting automatic asylum to all Cubans who succeed in reaching U.S. soil.

- United States Senators Tom Daschle and Byron Dorgan meet with Fidel Castro in Havana for more than seven hours and call for an end to restrictions on shipments of food and medicine to Cuba.

- Cuban high-jump champion Javier Sotomayor fails a drug test at the Pan American Games in Winnipeg, Manitoba. Two Cuban weightlifters also fail drug tests at the games.

September

- Leaders from the African nations of Zimbabwe, Guinea-Bissau, and Namibia visit Cuba.

- Cambodian Prime Minister Hun Sen meets in Havana with Castro.

- Cuban doctors are barred from permanently leaving the country.

- Cuban dissident journalist Raul Rivero wins a prestigious American journalism award, the Maria Moors Cabot Prize.

- Fidel Castro designs and donates a shark cage for Australian swimmer Susie Maroney's 90.3 nautical mile (145 km) swim from Jamaica to Cuba.

November

- The Ibero-American summit—a gathering of Spain, Portugal, and the countries of Latin America—is held in Cuba; dissidents demonstrate in the streets and get as much attention from visiting officials as does Castro.

- A six-year-old Cuban boy, the sole survivor of a boatload of Cubans who drowned while illegally attempting to enter the United States, triggers a controversy over whether he should be allowed to stay in Florida with relatives or be returned to his father living in Cuba. Fidel Castro demands the boy be returned to Cuba, while Cuban Americans demonstrate in Miami, demanding that he be allowed to stay in the United States.

December

- A Cuban jet crashes into a mountain in Venezuela. All twenty-two on board are killed.

ANALYSIS OF EVENTS: 1999

BUSINESS AND THE ECONOMY

Although Cuban officials claim that the nation's economy grew by 6 percent in the first half of 1999, most indications are that Cuba is still struggling to recover from the collapse of the Soviet Union, which accounted for 85 percent of its overseas market. The island nation's underground economy appears to be thriving, however. Because government rations and salaries are often inadequate for survival, many Cubans supplement their official incomes by moonlighting "on the left" at occupations that pay primarily in United States dollars. Cuban farmers, who have abandoned Soviet-style agricultural practices in favor of sustainable farming methods, appear to be the rare exception to this practice. Most Cuban farms are now run by cooperatives rather than the state, and farmers exceeding their quotas can earn up to double the average wage.

In March, Havana announced that it planned to start using the euro in its transactions with European Union nations. More than 40 percent of Cuba's international trade is with European nations, and half its tourists are from Europe. The Cuban government hopes the move will strengthen its ties with European markets, although a Central Committee spokesperson said that it is unlikely that the dollar will ever be phased out entirely.

In January, U.S. President Bill Clinton announced that U.S. citizens could send up to $1200 a year to any individual or non-governmental group in Cuba. Such cash infusions from overseas relatives total about $800 million annually and constitute Cuba's largest single source of hard currency. Dozens of Western Union offices have opened in Havana, to which dollars can be wired directly from the U.S. In addition, the U.S. government lifted some restrictions on shipments of food and medicine to Cuba. Other U.S. plans include improving cooperation with Cuba in tracking drug smugglers and increasing the number of commercial passenger flights to the island, making it easier for American citizens to visit relatives in Cuba.

GOVERNMENT AND POLITICS

Cuba's National Assembly approved new, harsher penalties for political opposition and violent crime, including the death penalty for drug trafficking and prison terms of up to 30 years for "collaborating" with the United States. Vladimiro Roca, one of Cuba's best-known dissidents and the son of the late Cuban Communist Party leader Blas Roca, was sentenced to five years in prison for his 1997 criticism of a Communist Party document. Three co-defendants received lesser terms. Salvadorans Raul Ernesto Cruz Leon and Otto Rene Rodriguiez Llerena were convicted of terrorism and sentenced to death for their roles in 1997 hotel bombings in Cuba.

On July 13, dozens of Cuban exiles formed a flotilla in international waters off Havana to mark the five-year anniversary of the deaths of a group of Cubans trying to flee the country. The 41 Cubans drowned when the tugboat they had hijacked was capsized by Cuban border patrols in 1994.

The number of Cubans willing to risk their lives to leave the country rose in 1999. In keeping with a 1994 accord between Cuba and the U.S., refugees picked up at sea are returned to Cuba, but those who reach U.S. shores are given automatic asylum. In the year between October 1997 and October 1998, a total of 615 Cubans reached Florida beaches; in the nine months following, nearly 2,000 completed the journey. Speedboats have replaced the rowboats and rafts previously used by fleeing Cubans. According to the U.S. Border Patrol, up to 80 percent of asylum-seekers are paying smugglers as much as $10,000 per person to be transported to U.S. shores. In August, Fidel Castro accused the United States of encouraging illegal immigration by granting automatic asylum to Cubans who reach U.S. soil and announced a $10,000 fine to operators of boats used for smuggling Cubans to the U.S.

Cuba's national telephone company cut most service to the U.S. in 1999 because American phone companies had been withholding payment since December 1998 pending a federal-court case against the communist nation. The case involved relatives of four Cuban-Americans whose unarmed aircraft were shot down by Cuba in February 1996.

Foreign visitors to Cuba in 1999 included the Trans-Africa Forum, a group of approximately 25 prominent African Americans, attempting to strengthen ties with Cuban blacks and push for an end to the U.S. trade ban. Other visitors included leaders from the African nations of Zimbabwe, Guinea-Bissau, and Namibia. After an August meeting with Fidel Castro in Havana, U.S. Senate minority leader Tom Daschle, the highest-ranking American official to visit Cuba in years, called for an end to the United States embargo on food and medicine to Cuba. The U.S. announced plans to increase the number of charter flights to Cuba, to improve Radio Marti transmissions, and to restore mail service.

CULTURE AND SOCIETY

In June, tens of thousands of Cuban evangelicals attended a three-hour "Love Peace Unity" revival in Havana's Plaza of the Revolution, the first open-air Protestant services held in Cuba in 40 years. The Rev. Joan Brown Campbell, general secretary of the United States National Council of Churches, apologized for U.S. policies toward Cuba. The historic services were also broadcast on Cuban television and radio. Government officials pointed to the event as an indication of growing religious tolerance in Cuba. Fidel Castro attended the services, as did Vice President Carlos Lage, Havana Communist Party chief Esteban Lazo, Foreign Minister Felipe Perez Roque and other Cabinet members.

In July, Cuban fans of Ernest Hemingway celebrated the 100th anniversary of the writer's birth. Hemingway spent nearly half his life in Cuba. Among those attending the festivities was 102-year-old Gregorio Fuentes, the captain of Hemingway's boat, El Pilar.

At the Pan American Games in Winnipeg, Manitoba, two Cuban weightlifting gold medalists, William Vargas and Rolando Delgado, tested positive for steroids. Javier Sotomayor, a Cuban highjumper, tested positive for cocaine. Two exhibition baseball games—one in Cuba and one in the U.S.—were played between the Cuban national team and the Baltimore Orioles.

Even without Soviet aid, Cuba maintains public health standards unheard of in other poor nations, and health care services are free to Cuba's 11 million citizens. Cuba's infant mortality is 7.1 per thousand, and its average life expectancy is 75 years. Despite the fact that the country has a glut of doctors—more than one per 200 citizens—in 1999, the government barred doctors from permanently leaving the country.

DIRECTORY

CENTRAL GOVERNMENT

Head of State

President of the Council of State and President of the Council of Ministers, Fidel Castro Ruz, Palacio de la Revolucion, Havana, Cuba

First Vice President

Raul Castro Ruz, Office of the First Vice President, Palacio de la Revolucion, Havana, Cuba

Vice President

Juan Almeida Bosque, Office of the Vice President, Palacio de la Revolucion, Havana, Cuba

Vice President

Abelardo Colome Ibarra, Office of the Vice President, Palacio de la Revolucion, Havana, Cuba

Vice President

Carlos Lage Davila, Office of the Vice President, Palacio de la Revolucion, Havana, Cuba

Vice President of the Council of State

Esteban Lazo Hernandez, Office of the Vice President, Palacio de la Revolucion, Havana, Cuba

Vice President
Jose Ramon Machado Ventura, Office of the Vice President, Palacio de la Revolucion, Havana, Cuba

Ministers

Ministers of Foreign Affairs
Felipe Perez Roque; Roberto Robaina Gonzalez, Ministry of Foreign Affairs, Calzada #360, e/ G Y H, Vedado, Havana, Cuba
PHONE: +53 (7) 312206; 311628
FAX: +53 (7) 333085

Minister of Agriculture
Alfredo Jordan Morales, Ministry of Agriculture, Avda Independencia, entre Conill y Sta. Ana, Havana, Cuba
PHONE: +53 (99) 701434

Minister of Basic Industries
Marcos Portal Leon, Ministry of Basic Industries, Avda Salvador Allende, No. 666, Havana, Cuba
PHONE: +53 (99) 707722

Minister of Communications
Silvano Colas Sanchez, Ministry of Communications, Plaza de le Revolucion, Havana, Cuba
PHONE: +53 (99) 705581

Minister of Construction
Juan Mario Junco del Pino, Ministry of Construction, Avda Carlos M. de Cespedes y Calle 35, Havana, Cuba
PHONE: +53 (99) 709411

Minister of Culture
Abel Prieto Jimenez, Ministry of Culture, Calle 2, No. 258, entre 11 y 13, Vedado, Havana, Cuba
PHONE: +53 (99) 39945

Minister of Domestic Trade
Barbara Castillo Cuesta, Ministry of Domestic Trade

Minister of Economy and Planning
Jose Luis Rodriguez Garcia, Ministry of Economy and Planning, 20 de Mayo y Ayestaran, Plaza de la Revolucion, Havana, Cuba
PHONE: +53 (99) 796115

Minister of Education
Luis I. Gomez Gutierrez, Ministry of Education, Obispo No. 160, Havana, Cuba
PHONE: +53 (99) 614888

Minister of Finance and Prices
Manuel Millares Rodriguez, Ministry of Finance and Prices, Obispo 211, Havana, Cuba
PHONE: +53 (99) 604111

Minister of the Fishing Industry
Orlando Felipe Rodriguez Romay, Ministry of the Fishing Industry, Barlovento, Santa Fe, Havana, Cuba
PHONE: +53 (99) 227474

Minister of the Food Industry
Alejandro Roca Iglesias, Ministry of the Food Industry, Calle 41, No. 4455, Playa, Havana, Cuba
PHONE: +53 (99) 26801

Minister of Foreign Investment and Economic Cooperation
Ibrahim Ferradaz, Ministry of Foreign Investment and Economic Cooperation, Calle 1, No. 201 Vedado, Havana, Cuba
PHONE: +53 (99) 36661

Minister of Foreign Trade
Ricardo Cabrisas Ruiz, Ministry of Foreign Trade, Infanta No. 16, Vedado, Havana, Cuba
PHONE: +53 (99) 709341
FAX: +53 (99) 76234

Minister of Higher Education
Fernando Vecino Alegret, Ministry of Higher Education, Calle 23, No. 565, esq. A F, Vedado, Havana, Cuba
PHONE: +53 (99) 36655
FAX: +53 (99) 333096

Minister of Interior
Corps. General Abelardo Colome Ibarra, Ministry of Interior, Plaza de la Revolucion, Havana, Cuba

Minister of Justice
Roberto Diaz Sotolongo, Ministry of Justice, Calle O, No. 216e 23 y Humboldt, Vedado, Havana, Cuba
PHONE: +53 (99) 326319

Minister of Labor and Social Security
Salvador Valdes Mesa, Ministry of Labor and Social Security

Minister of Light Industry
Jesus Perez Othon, Ministry of Light Industry, Empedrado No. 302, Havana, Cuba
PHONE: +53 (99) 624041

Minister of Metallurgy and Electronics Industry

Ignacio Gonzalez Planas, Ministry of Metallurgy and Electronics Industry, Avda Rancho Boyeros y Calle 100, Havana, Cuba

Minister of Public Health

Carlos Dotres Martinez, Ministry of Public Health, Calle 23, No. 301, Vedado, Havana, Cuba
PHONE: +53 (99) 322561

Minister of the Revolutionary Armed Forces

General Raul Castro Ruz, Ministry of the Revolutionary Armed Forces, Plaza de la Revolucion, Havana, Cuba

Minister of Science, Technology, and Environment

Rosa Elena Simeon Negrin, Ministry of Science, Technology, and Environment

Minister of the Sugar Industry

Ulises Rosales del Toro, Ministry of the Sugar Industry, Calle 23, No. 171, Vedado, Havana, Cuba
PHONE: +53 (99) 305061

Minister of Tourism

Osmany Cienfuegos Gorriaran, Ministry of Tourism

Minister of Transportation

Alvaro Perez Morales, Ministry of Transportation, Avda Independencia y Tulipan, Havana, Cuba
PHONE: +53 (99) 812076

Minister Without Portfolio

Wilfredo Lopez Rodriguez, Ministry Without Portfolio

Minister-President, Central Bank of Cuba

Francisco Soberon Valdes

POLITICAL ORGANIZATIONS

Partido Communista da Cuba-PCC (Cuban Communist Party)

TITLE: First Secretary
NAME: Fidel Castro Ruz

Coordinadora Social Demócrata de Cuba (Cuban Social Democratic Coordinator Party)

P.O. Box 248171, University Station, Coral Gables, FL 33124-8171, USA
PHONE: (305) 8222746
FAX: (305) 2219494

E-MAIL: webmaster@activo.com

Partido Solidaridad Democrática (Democratic Solidarity Party)

PHONE: (305) 4082659
E-MAIL: gladyperez@aol.com
NAME: Fernando Sánchez López—Presidente

DIPLOMATIC REPRESENTATION

Embassies in Cuba

Argentina
Calle 36, No. 511 E/ 5ta. y 7ma. Ave., Miramar, Havana, Cuba
PHONE: +53 (3) 332972; 332565; 332549
FAX: +53 (7) 332140

Austria
Calle 4, No. 101 esq. a 1 Ra., Miramar, Havana, Cuba
PHONE: +53 (7) 332825; 332394
FAX: +53 (7) 331235

Belgium
5ta. Ave. No. 7408 esq. a 76, Miramar, Havana, Cuba
PHONE: +53 (7) 332410; 332561
FAX: +53 (7) 331318

Bolivia
Calle 26, No. 113 E/ 1ra. y 3ra., Miramar, Havana, Cuba
PHONE: +53 332426; 332127
FAX: +53 (7) 332739

Brazil
Calle 16, No. 503, entre 5 y 7, Miramar, Havana, Cuba
PHONE: +53 (7) 332026
FAX: +53 (7) 332139

Canada
Calle 30, No. 518, esq. a 7ma. Avenida, Miramar, Havana, Cuba
PHONE: +53 (7) 332516; 332527; 332517
FAX: +53 (7) 331249

Chile
Avda 33, No. 1423, entre 16 y 18, Miramar, Havana, Cuba

China
Calle 13, No. 551, Vedado, Havana, Cuba
PHONE: +53 (7) 325205

Czech Republic
Avda Kohly 259, entre 41 y 43, Nuevo Vedado, Havana, Cuba

PHONE: +53 (7) 333201
FAX: +53 (7) 333596

Denmark
Paseo De Marti 20, Apto 4-C, Havana, Cuba
PHONE: +53 (7) 338128
FAX: +53 (7) 338127

Ecuador
Avenida 5ta., No. 4407 E/ 44 y 46, Miramar,
Havana, Cuba
PHONE: +53 (3) 332034; 332820
FAX: +53 (7) 332868

Egypt
5ta. Avenida, No. 1801, esq. a 18, Miramar,
Havana, Cuba
PHONE: +53 (1) 332441; 332542

France
Calle 14, No. 312 E/ 3ra. y 5ta., Miramar,
Havana, Cuba
PHONE: +53 (3) 332308; 332132; 332080
FAX: +53 (7) 331439

Germany
Calle 28, No. 313 E/ 3ra. y 5ta., Miramar,
Havana, Cuba
PHONE: +53 (7) 332539
FAX: +53 (7) 331586

Greece
5ta Ave., No. 7802, esq. a 78, Miramar, Havana,
Cuba
PHONE: +53 332995; 332854
FAX: +53 (7) 331784

Hungary
Calle 6, No. 458 E/ 19 y 21, Vedado, Havana,
Cuba
PHONE: +53 333365; 333474
FAX: +53 (7) 333286

India
Calle 21, No. 202, esq. a K, Vedado, Havana,
Cuba
PHONE: +53 333777; 333106; 333169
FAX: +53 (7) 333287

Iran
5ta. Ave., No. 8201, E/ 82 y 84, Havana,
Miramar, Cuba
PHONE: +53 332461; 332326
FAX: +53 (7) 332157

Italy
54 Paseo, No. 606, E/ 25 y 27, Vedado, Havana,
Cuba
PHONE: +53 333378; 333334; 333390
FAX: +53 (7) 333416

Japan
Calle 62, esq. a 15, Vedado, Havana, Cuba
PHONE: +53 333454; 333355; 333507
FAX: +53 (7) 333172

Laos
5ta. Ave., No. 2808, esq. a 30, Miramar,
Havana, Cuba
PHONE: +53 331057; 331056

Mexico
Calle 12, No. 518, E/ 5ta. y 7ma., Havana, Cuba
PHONE: +53 332498; 332583; 332909
FAX: +53 (7) 332717; 332294

Nicaragua
Calle 20, No. 709, E/ 7ma. y 9na., Miramar,
Havana, Cuba
PHONE: +53 331025
FAX: +53 (7) 336323

Peru
Calle 36, No. 109, E/ Ira. y 3ra., Miramar,
Havana, Cuba
PHONE: +53 332477; 332632
FAX: +53 (7) 332636

Poland
Avda 5, No. 4405, esq. a 46, Miramar, Havana,
Cuba
PHONE: +53 (7) 291015

Portugal
Avda 5, No. 6604, Miramar, Havana, Cuba
PHONE: +53 (7) 332871
FAX: +53 (7) 332593

Russia
5ta. Avenida, No. 6402, E/ 62 y 66, Miramar,
Havana, Cuba
PHONE: +53 331749; 331085; 332688
FAX: +53 (7) 331038

Spain
Calle Carcel No. 51, esq. a, Zulueta, Havana,
Cuba
PHONE: +53 338025; 338026; 338093
FAX: +53 (7) 338006

Sweden
Ave. 31, No. 1411, E/ 14 y 18, Miramar,
Havana, Cuba
PHONE: +53 (3) 332563; 332831; 332971
FAX: +53 (7) 331194

Switzerland
5ta. Ave., No. 2005, E/ 20 y 22, Miramar,
Havana, Cuba
PHONE: +53 (3) 332611; 332989; 332729
FAX: +53 (7) 331148

United Kingdom
Calle 34, No. 708, E/ 7ma. y 17, Miramar,
Havana, Cuba
PHONE: +53 331771; 331772; 331299
FAX: +53 (7) 338104

United States
Interests Section of the United States, Calzada,
E/ L y M, Vedado, Havana, Cuba
PHONE: +53 333551; 333543

Vatican City
Calle 12, No. 514, Miramar, Havana, Cuba
PHONE: +53 (7) 332700
FAX: +53 (7) 332257

Venezuela
R-Alle 36a, No. 704, E/ 7ma. y 42, Miramar,
Havana, Cuba
PHONE: +53 (3) 332662; 332497; 332612
FAX: +53 (7) 332773

JUDICIAL SYSTEM
The People's Supreme Court
Provincial Courts
Municipal Courts
Military Courts

FURTHER READING
Articles
Adams, Marilyn. "Cuba: Today and
Tomorrow." *Florida Trend* (June 1999): 46-
48.

Books
"Cuba." *The Columbia Encyclopedia*, 5th ed.
New York: Columbia University Press, 1993.

Fernandez Revuelta, A. *Castro's Daughter: an
Exile's Memoir of Cuba.* Trans. Dolores M.
Koch. New York: St. Martin's Press, 1998.

Hatchwell, E., and Simon Calder. *Cuba: a Guide
to the People, Politics and Culture.* New
York: Interlink Books, 1999.

Quirk, R. E. *Fidel Castro.* New York: Norton,
1993.

Rice, E. *The Cuban Revolution.* San Diego:
Lucent Books, 1995.

Rudolph, J. D. (ed.). *Cuba: A Country Study/
Foreign Area Studies.* 3rd ed. Washington,
D.C.: U.S. Government Printing Office, 1993.

Sale, R. *Essential Cuba.* Lincolnwood, IL:
Passport Books, 1998.

Sheehan, S. *Cuba.* New York: Marshall
Cavendish, 1995.

Suchlicki. *Cuba: from Columbus to Castro and
Beyond.* 4th ed. Washington, D.C.: Brassey's,
1997.

Tanter, R. *Rogue regimes: terrorism and
proliferation.* New York: St. Martin's Press,
1998.

Williams, S. *Cuba: the land, the history, the
people, the culture.* Philadelphia: Running
Press, 1994.

Internet
Florida International University. "Cuban
Research Center." Available Online @ http://
lacc.fiu.edu/cri/ (October 21, 1999).

University of Texas at Austin. "Cuba Reference
Desk." Available Online @ http://
lanic.utexas.edu/la/ca/cuba/, 1999 (October 21,
1999).

CUBA: STATISTICAL DATA

For sources and notes see "Sources of Statistics" in the front of each volume.

GEOGRAPHY

Geography (1)
Area:

Total: 110,860 sq km.

Land: 110,860 sq km.

Water: 0 sq km.

Area—comparative: slightly smaller than Pennsylvania.

Land boundaries:

Total: 29 km.

Border countries: US Naval Base at Guantanamo Bay 29 km.

Note: Guantanamo Naval Base is leased by the US and thus remains part of Cuba.

Coastline: 3,735 km.

Climate: tropical; moderated by trade winds; dry season (November to April); rainy season (May to October).

Terrain: mostly flat to rolling plains with rugged hills and mountains in the southeast.

Natural resources: cobalt, nickel, iron ore, copper, manganese, salt, timber, silica, petroleum.

Land use:

Arable land: 24%

Permanent crops: 7%

Permanent pastures: 27%

Forests and woodland: 24%

Other: 18% (1993 est.).

HUMAN FACTORS

Demographics (2A)

	1990	1995	1998	2000	2010	2020	2030	2040	2050
Population	10,544.8	10,900.0	11,050.7	11,139.4	11,497.6	11,721.4	11,641.3	11,259.1	10,594.0
Net migration rate (per 1,000 population)	NA	NA	NA	NA	NA	NA	NA	NA	NA
Births	NA	NA	NA	NA	NA	NA	NA	NA	NA
Deaths	72.1	NA	NA	NA	NA	NA	NA	NA	NA
Life expectancy - males	72.8	73.0	73.3	73.5	74.6	75.6	76.4	77.1	77.7
Life expectancy - females	77.6	77.8	78.1	78.5	79.9	81.2	82.3	83.1	83.8
Birth rate (per 1,000)	17.7	13.5	13.1	12.7	11.0	10.1	9.1	8.8	8.6
Death rate (per 1,000)	6.8	7.2	7.3	7.4	8.1	9.3	11.1	13.4	15.8
Women of reproductive age (15-49 yrs.)	2,977.6	3,022.3	3,010.9	3,021.7	3,070.5	2,660.9	2,404.8	2,197.1	1,990.7
of which are currently married	NA	NA	NA	NA	NA	NA	NA	NA	NA
Fertility rate	1.8	1.5	1.6	1.6	1.6	1.6	1.7	1.7	1.7

Except as noted, values for vital statistics are in thousands; life expectancy is in years.

Health Personnel (3)

Total health expenditure as a percentage of GDP, 1990-1997[a]

Public sector 7.9

Private sector ....NA

Total[b] ....NA

Health expenditure per capita in U.S. dollars, 1990-1997[a]

Purchasing power parity ....NA

Total ....NA

Availability of health care facilities per 100,000 people

Hospital beds 1990-1997[a] 540

Doctors 1993[c] 518

Nurses 1993[c] 752

Health Indicators (4)

Life expectancy at birth

1980 74

1997 76

Daily per capita supply of calories (1996) 2,357

Total fertility rate births per woman (1997) 1.5

Maternal mortality ratio per 100,000 live births (1990-97) ....36[b]

Safe water % of population with access (1995) 91

Sanitation % of population with access (1995) 92

Consumption of iodized salt % of households (1992-98)[a] 45

Smoking prevalence

Male % of adults (1985-95)[a] 49

Female % of adults (1985-95)[a] 25

Tuberculosis incidence per 100,000 people (1997) 18

Adult HIV prevalence % of population ages 15-49 (1997) 0.02

Infants and Malnutrition (5)

Under-5 mortality rate (1997) 8

% of infants with low birthweight (1990-97) 7

Births attended by skilled health staff % of total[a] ...99

% fully immunized (1995-97)

TB 99

DPT 100

Polio 97

Measles 100

Prevalence of child malnutrition under age 5 (1992-97)[b] ....NA

Ethnic Division (6)

Mulatto 51%

White 37%

Black 11%

Chinese 1%

Religions (7)

Nominally Roman Catholic 85% prior to CASTRO assuming power; Protestants Jehovah's Witnesses, Jews, and Santeria are also represented.

Languages (8)

Spanish

EDUCATION

Public Education Expenditures (9)

Public expenditure on education (% of GNP)

1980 ....7.2

1996 ....

Expenditure per student

Primary % of GNP per capita

1980 ....10.4

1996 ....

Secondary % of GNP per capita

1980 ....

1996 ....

Tertiary % of GNP per capita

1980 ....28.5

1996 ....

Expenditure on teaching materials

Primary % of total for level (1996) ....5.7[1]

Secondary % of total for level (1996) 1.0

Primary pupil-teacher ratio per teacher (1996) 12

Duration of primary education years (1995) 6

Educational Attainment (10)

Age group (1981) 25-49

Total population 3,013,315

Highest level attained (%)

No schooling[12] 3.7

First level

Not completed 22.6

Completed 27.6

Entered second level

S-1 ....40.2

S-2 ....NA

Postsecondary 5.9

Literacy Rates (11A)

In thousands and percent[1]	1990	1995	2000	2010
Illiterate population (15+ yrs.)	468	364	279	166
Literacy rate - total adult pop. (%)	94.3	95.7	96.8	98.3
Literacy rate - males (%)	95.1	96.2	97.0	98.4
Literacy rate - females (%)	93.5	95.3	96.6	98.2

GOVERNMENT & LAW

Political Parties (12)

The National Assembly of People's Power, with 601 seats, is the legislative branch. All seats are held by the Cuban Communist Party (PCC).

Government Budget (13B)

Revenues . . . . .NA

Expenditures . . . . .NA

  Capital expenditures . . . . .NA

NA stands for not available.

Military Affairs (14B)

	1990	1991	1992	1993	1994	1995
Military expenditures						
Current dollars (mil.)[3]	1,400	1,160e	NA	600e	600e	350e
1995 constant dollars (mil.)[3]	1,609	1,282e	NA	629e	615e	350*
Armed forces (000)	297	297	175	175	140	70
Gross national product (GNP)						
Current dollars (mil.)	33,690	26,950	23,850	21,460	22,000	22,550
1995 constant dollars (mil.)	38,720	29,780	25,650	22,500	22,550	22,550
Central government expenditures (CGE)						
1995 constant dollars (mil.)	NA	NA	NA	NA	NA	NA
People (mil.)	10.5	10.6	10.7	10.8	10.8	10.9
Military expenditure as % of GNP	4.2	4.3	NA	2.8	2.7	1.6
Military expenditure as % of CGE	NA	NA	NA	NA	NA	NA
Military expenditure per capita (1995 $)	153	120	NA	58	57	32
Armed forces per 1,000 people (soldiers)	28.1	27.9	16.3	16.2	12.9	6.4
GNP per capita (1995 $)	3,672	2,798	2,392	2,086	2,079	2,068
Arms imports[6]						
Current dollars (mil.)	1,400	525	100	100	0	0
1995 constant dollars (mil.)	1,609	580	108	105	0	0
Arms exports[6]						
Current dollars (mil.)	0	0	0	0	0	0
1995 constant dollars (mil.)	0	0	0	0	0	0
Total imports[7]						
Current dollars (mil.)	7,416	4,233	2,315	1,977	1,898	2,467
1995 constant dollars (mil.)	8,523	4,678	2,490	2,073	1,946	2,467
Total exports[7]						
Current dollars (mil.)	5,415	2,980	1,779	1,137	1,314	1,576
1995 constant dollars (mil.)	6,223	3,293	1,914	1,192	1,347	1,576
Arms as percent of total imports[8]	18.9	12.4	4.3	5.0	0	0
Arms as percent of total exports[8]	0	0	0	0	0	0

LABOR FORCE

Labor Force (16)

Total (million) . . . . .4.5 economically active population

Services and government .30%

Industry 22%

Agriculture 20%

Commerce 11%

Construction 10%

Transportation and communications 7%

State sector 76%

Non-state sector 24%

Data for 1996 est. Percent distribution for 1996 est. Total includes economically active population. Transport and communications data for June 1990.

Unemployment Rate (17)

8% (1996 est.)

PRODUCTION SECTOR

Electric Energy (18)

Capacity . . . . .3.988 million kW (1995)

Production . . . . .10.105 billion kWh (1995)

Consumption per capita . . . . .924 kWh (1995)

Transportation (19)

Highways:

total: 27,700 km

paved: 15,484 km

unpaved: 12,216 km (1996 est.)

Waterways: 240 km

Merchant marine:

total: 17 ships (1,000 GRT or over) totaling 91,981 GRT/126,416 DWT ships by type: cargo 9, liquefied gas tanker 1, oil tanker 1, refrigerated cargo 6

Airports: 171 (1997 est.)

Airports—with paved runways:

total: 77

over 3,047 m: 7

2,438 to 3,047 m: 9

1,524 to 2,437 m: 14

914 to 1,523 m: 11

under 914 m: 36 (1997 est.)

Airports—with unpaved runways:

total: 94

914 to 1,523 m: 33

under 914 m: 61 (1997 est.)

Top Agricultural Products (20)

Sugarcane, tobacco, citrus, coffee, rice, potatoes and other tubers, beans; livestock.

MANUFACTURING SECTOR

GDP & Manufacturing Summary (21)

Detailed value added figures are listed by both International Standard Industry Code (ISIC) and product title.

	1980	1985	1990	1994
GDP ($-1990 mil.)[1]	12,800	18,663	17,453	11,239
Per capita ($-1990)[1]	1,318	1,847	1,647	1,025
Manufacturing share (%) (current prices)[1]	35.8	34.1	*33.1*	NA
Manufacturing				
Value added ($-1990 mil.)[1]	3,609	6,863	5,782	*3,471*
Industrial production index	100	132	125	*81*
Value added ($ mil.)	4,909	5,148	*5,942*	*5,560*
Gross output ($ mil.)	9,779	12,098	*17,699*	*16,548*
Employment (000)	501	654	*701*	*652*
Profitability (% of gross output)				
Intermediate input (%)	50	57	*66*	*66*
Wages and salaries inc. supplements (%)	*13*	*14*	*13*	*14*
Gross operating surplus	*37*	*29*	*21*	*20*
Productivity ($)				
Gross output per worker	19,527	18,488	*25,255*	*25,354*
Value added per worker	9,802	7,867	*8,515*	*8,682*
Average wage (inc. supplements)	*2,620*	*2,528*	*3,194*	*3,576*
Value added ($ mil.)				
311/2 Food products	658	962	*1,014*	*870*
313 Beverages	247	275	*352*	*300*
314 Tobacco products	1,815	2,015	*2,580*	*2,210*
321 Textiles	51	41	*119*	*196*
322 Wearing apparel	147	98	*97*	*101*
323 Leather and fur products	53	32	*33*	*26*
324 Footwear	79	49	*52*	*50*

	1980	1985	1990	1994
331 Wood and wood products	58	53	52	57
332 Furniture and fixtures	48	44	43	47
341 Paper and paper products	47	45	14	10
342 Printing and publishing	97	59	80	67
351 Industrial chemicals	80	54	71	108
352 Other chemical products	327	222	288	440
353 Petroleum refineries	NA	NA	NA	NA
354 Miscellaneous petroleum and coal products	NA	NA	NA	NA
355 Rubber products	99	67	87	133
356 Plastic products	86	59	76	116
361 Pottery, china and earthenware	8	6	8	9
362 Glass and glass products	17	13	19	21
369 Other non-metal mineral products	189	105	115	109
371 Iron and steel	27	44	37	32
372 Non-ferrous metals	41	48	61	49
381 Metal products	108	92	84	90
382 Non-electrical machinery	114	164	127	95
383 Electrical machinery	60	58	58	51
384 Transport equipment	232	331	254	192
385 Professional and scientific equipment	17	24	19	14
390 Other manufacturing industries	202	189	203	165

FINANCE, ECONOMICS, & TRADE

Economic Indicators (22)

National product: GDP—purchasing power parity—$16.9 billion (1997 est.)

National product real growth rate: 2.5% (1997 est.)

National product per capita: $1,540 (1997 est.)

Inflation rate—consumer price index: NA%

Exchange Rates (24)

Exchange rates: Cuban pesos (Cu$) per US$1—1.0000 (non-convertible, official rate, linked to the US dollar)

Top Import Origins (25)

$3.2 billion (c.i.f., 1997 est.) Data are for 1997 est.

Origins	%
Spain	14
Russia	12
Mexico	9

Top Export Destinations (26)

$1.9 billion (f.o.b., 1997 est.).

Destinations	%
France	16
Belgium-Luxembourg	40.1
Italy	NA
Japan	NA
United States	NA
Spain	NA
Iran	NA
Democratic Republic of the Congo	NA
Republic of the Congo	NA

NA stands for not available.

Economic Aid (27)

Recipient: ODA, $46 million (1997 est.).

Import Export Commodities (28)

Import Commodities	Export Commodities
Petroleum	Sugar
Food	Nickel
Machinery	Tobacco
Chemicals	Shellfish
	Medical products
	Citrus
	Coffee

CYPRUS

Republic of Cyprus

Kypriaki Dimokratia

CAPITAL: Nicosia.

FLAG: The national flag consists of the map of Cyprus in gold set above two green olive branches on a white field.

ANTHEM: *Ethnikos Hymnos (National Hymn).*

MONETARY UNIT: The Cyprus pound (c£) is a paper currency of 100 cents. There are coins of 1, 2, 5, 10, 20, and 50 cents and 1 pound, and notes of 50 cents, and 1, 5, 10, and 20 pounds. c£1 = $2.1692 (or $1 = c£0.4461). The Turkish lira (TL) of 100 kuruş is the currency in the Turkish Cypriot zone.

WEIGHTS AND MEASURES: The metric system is the legal standard. Imperial and local measures are also used.

HOLIDAYS: New Year's Day, 1 January; Epiphany, 6 January; Late President Makarios' Day, 19 January; Greek Independence Day, 25 March; Cyprus National Day, 1 April; Labor Day, 1 May; Cyprus Independence Day, 1 October; Greek Resistance Day, 28 October; Christmas, 25 December; Boxing Day, 26 December. Holidays observed by the Turkish Cypriot community include Founding of the Turkish Federated State of Cyprus, 13 February; Turkish National Sovereignty and Children's Day, 23 April; Turkish Youth and Sports Day, 19 May; Turkish Victory Day, 30 August; Turkish Independence Day, 29 October. Movable Christian religious holidays include Green Monday, Good Friday, Holy Saturday, and Easter Monday. Movable Muslim religious holidays are observed in the Turkish Cypriot zone.

TIME: 2 PM = noon GMT.

LOCATION AND SIZE: Cyprus is the third largest Mediterranean island, after Sicily and Sardinia. Its area is 9,250 square kilometers (3,571 square miles), about three-fourths the size of the state of Connecticut. Cyprus has a total coastline of 648 kilometers (403 miles).

CLIMATE: Cyprus's climate is mostly dry and sunny. The mean annual temperature is about 20°C (68°F).

INTRODUCTORY SURVEY

RECENT HISTORY

For centuries, under Ottoman and British rule, Greek Cypriots had regarded Greece as their mother country and had sought union (enosis) with it as Greek nationals. In 1931, this desire led to violence, which the British colonial administration put a stop to with severe repressive measures. At the close of World War II (1939–45) demands that the United Kingdom yield the island to Greece were renewed. The National Organization of Cypriot Fighters was led by Colonel George Grivas (a retired Greek army officer). They began a campaign of terrorism in 1955 in which upward of 2,000 casualties were recorded.

The prime ministers of Greece and Turkey met in Zürich, Switzerland, early in 1959 in an attempt to reach a settlement. Unexpectedly, the Greek Cypriots set aside their demands for union with Greece and accepted instead proposals for an independent republic. The new republic would have representation from both the Greek and Turkish Cypriot communities. By 1 July 1960, an agreement was reached on all outstanding differences, and independence was officially declared on 16 August.

From the beginning, the two Cypriot communities differed on how the Zürich agreement would be carried out, and how much autonomy the Turkish minority would enjoy. Throughout the 1960s, there were outbreaks of violence on the island. The United Nations (UN) maintained peace with a peacekeeping force of about 3,500 troops. In addi-

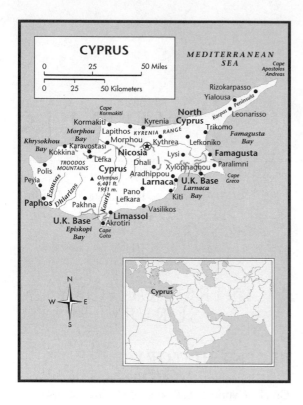

tion to the UN forces, both Greek Cypriot National Guard and Turkish Cypriot militia maintained sizable troops of their own.

Although talks continued between the two communities, no agreement was reached on the two basic points of dispute. Politically, the Turks wanted full freedom, whereas the Greeks demanded a continued single majority rule. Territorially, the Turks wanted Cyprus divided into Greek- and Turkish-controlled zones, a position that clashed with the Greek Cypriot concept of a unified state.

When peace talks in Geneva broke down, a full-scale Turkish offensive began, and by mid-August, Turkish forces controlled about 38% of the island. On 13 February 1975, the Turkish-held area broke away and proclaimed itself the Turkish Cypriot Federated State.

On 15 November 1983, the Turkish sector proclaimed itself an independent state. It was named the Turkish Republic of Northern Cyprus (TRNC). However, only Turkey recognizes the TRNC. The UN, which condemned the TRNC's declaration of independence, tried repeatedly to end the partition between north and south, but all proposals were rejected by both sides.

Talks between both sides have taken place at intervals since 1988. In 1991, the United Nations Security Council called on both sides to complete an overall framework agreement. To date, no one has been able to find a solution to the problem. In 1997, both sides met in Geneva, but little progress was made. Also that year, the European Union (EU) made good on its progress to invite the Greek half of the island to join the trading block. Turkish-Cypriot leaders denounced the invitation.

GOVERNMENT

The 1960 constitution of the Republic of Cyprus respects the two existing ethnic communities, Greek and Turkish, by providing for representation from each in the government. The president must be Greek and the vice-president Turkish. Legislative authority is vested in the fifty-member House of Representatives, elected by the two chief communities in the proportion of thirty-five Greek and fifteen Turkish.

On 13 February 1975, after the Turkish invasion of Cyprus, the Turkish Cypriot Federated State (TCFS) was proclaimed in the northern part of the island, and Rauf Denktash became its president. A draft constitution was ratified by the Turkish Cypriot community in a referendum on 8 June. On 15 November 1983, the TCFS proclaimed itself the Turkish Republic of Northern Cyprus (TRNC), separate and independent from the Republic of Cyprus. In June 1985, TRNC voters approved a new constitution that embodied most of the old constitution's articles.

Judiciary

In the Greek Cypriot area, the Supreme Court is the final court of appeal and has final authority in constitutional and administrative cases. The seven Orthodox Church courts have sole jurisdiction in matrimonial cases involving Greek Orthodox Church members. Appeals go from these courts to the appeals tribunal of the Church.

In the Turkish-held area, a Supreme Court acts as a final appeals court, with powers similar to those of the Supreme Court in the Greek Cypriot area. In addition to district courts, there are two Turkish communal courts, as well as a communal appeals court.

Political Parties

The four principal political parties of the Greek community in 1996 were the center-right Democratic Party (Demokratiko Komma—

DIKO); the Progressive Party of the Working People (Anorthotikon Komma Ergazomenou Laou—AKEL); the right-wing Democratic Rally (Demokratikos Synagermos—DISY); and the Socialist Party (Eniea Demokratiki Enosi Kyprou—EDEK). The Democratic Rally won the largest number of seats in the 1996 elections.

The Turkish Republic of Northern Cyprus held elections for a fifty-seat Legislative Assembly in 1993, with the vote split fairly evenly among the right-wing National Unity Party, the Democratic Party, and the Republican Turkish Party.

DEFENSE

Under the Zürich agreement, Cyprus was to have an army of 2,000 men, of whom 60% were to be Greek and 40% Turkish. The Cypriot national guard, which is wholly Greek, comprised 10,000 men and 400 women in 1995, backed by 88,000 reservists. About 1,000 troops and advisors from Greece were stationed in the south in 1986.

The Turkish community has its own police force and army of 4,000 regulars and 26,000 reserves. A sizable military force from the country of Turkey (about 30,000 in 1996) has supported these native forces since the 1974 intervention.

ECONOMIC AFFAIRS

The 1974 coup and the Turkish armed intervention badly disrupted the economy. Physical destruction and the displacement of about a third of the population reduced the output of the economy's manufacturing, agricultural, and service areas. In general, the Greek Cypriot zone recovered much more quickly and successfully than the Turkish-held region, which was burdened with the weaknesses of Turkey's economy as well as its own. In the south, on the other hand, tourism has exceeded prewar levels, and foreign assistance has been readily available.

Public Finance

The fiscal year follows the calendar year. Import duties and income tax are the principal sources of government revenue. The principal ordinary expenditures are education, defense, and police and fire services.

Turkish Cypriots use the Turkish lira for currency, and the Turkish government reportedly provides a large part of the TRNC annual budget, most recently a $100 million loan in November 1992 for economic development projects.

The CIA estimates that, in 1995, government revenues totaled approximately $2.3 billion and expenditures of $3.4 billion, including capital expenditures of $500 million. External debt totaled $1.4 billion, approximately 25% of which was financed abroad.

Income

In 1995, Cyprus's gross national product (GNP) was $7.8 billion at current prices, or about $14,920 per person. For the years 1985 to 1995, inflation was 43%, resulting in a real growth rate in GNP of 4.6% per person.

Industry

Industries are numerous and small in scale, most of them employing fewer than 10 workers. Manufacturing, encouraged by income tax breaks and protected by import tariffs, primarily involves the processing of local products for both export and the home market, or the production of consumer items including foods, beverages, apparel, plastic products, and tobacco products.

Banking and Finance

In 1963, the Ottoman Bank (since renamed the Central Bank of Cyprus) was designated as the government's banking and currency clearing agent. Credit growth was expected to have risen by around 13% during 1996, exceeding the Central Bank of Cyprus (CBC)'s original target of 10% for the year.

The Cyprus Stock Exchange, which opened in March 1996, ended 1996 with gains of just 0.2%.

Economic Development

Since 1975, multi-year emergency economic action plans inaugurated by the Republic of Cyprus have provided for increased employment, incentives to reactivate the economy, more capital investment, and measures to maintain economic stability. The 1994–98 Strategic Development Plan emphasized a free-market, private-sector economic approach with a target GDP growth of 4% annually.

Since its military intervention in 1974, Turkey has provided substantial financial aid to the Turkish Cypriot area. In 1996, this assistance was estimated to be approximately one-third of the area's GDP, or approximately $175 million.

SOCIAL WELFARE

Social insurance is required of all employees and self-employed persons in the Greek Cypriot zone. It provides unemployment and sickness benefits; old-age, widows', and orphans' pensions; maternity benefits; missing persons' allowances; injury and disablement benefits; and death and marriage grants. A law requiring equal pay for both sexes in private employment was in effect by late 1992.

Healthcare

In 1994, there were 1,255 doctors in Cyprus. There are both public and private medical facilities, including nearly 50 rural health centers. The island has a low incidence of infectious diseases, but hydatid disease (echinococcosis) is widespread. Average life expectancy is 78 years. In 1996, 95% of the population had access to health care services, and 100% had access to safe water.

Housing

Village homes in Cyprus are generally constructed of stone, mud bricks, and other locally available materials; in the more prosperous rural centers, there are houses of burnt brick or concrete. The total number of housing units grew from about 75,000 in 1976 to about 138,000 in 1994.

EDUCATION

Adult literacy in Cyprus in 1996 was 94%. Education is compulsory for nine years with children attending six years of primary school and six years of secondary. In 1994, there were 383 primary schools with 3,528 teachers and 63,884 students attending them. At the secondary level, there were 4,641 teachers and 57,804 students attending.

1999 KEY EVENTS TIMELINE

January

- The Greek Cypriot Socialist party withdraws from the ruling coalition to protest President Glafcos Clerides's decision not to deploy Russian-built S-300 surface-to-air missiles on Cyprus.

February

- Cyprus sentences two Israeli undercover agents to three-year jail terms for encroaching on its territory.

April

- Diplomatic efforts by the speaker of the Cypriot parliament to win release of three American sol-

diers captured by Yugoslavia are rebuffed by Slobodan Milosevic.

June

- Turkish Cypriot leader Rauf Denktash rejects proposed United Nations-sponsored peace talks in which Greek Cypriot president Clerides would participate.

August

- Cyprus frees two imprisoned Israeli agents as a goodwill gesture toward new Israeli prime minister, Ehud Barak.

- Prices on the Cyprus Stock Exchange rise more than 25 percent in a single day.

September

- Turkish prime minister Bulent Ecevit meets with U.S. President Clinton in Washington, D.C., to discuss a resolution to Cyprus partition and other issues.

- The stock exchange closes for three weeks to catch up on backlog of unprocessed transfers.

December

- Leaders of Cyprus visit United Nations headquarters in New York, where Kofi Annan, the secretary-general, attempts to lead talks between Rauf Denktash, Turkish Cypriot leader, and Glafcos Clerides, the Greek Cypriot leader, in an effort to reunite Greeks and Turks in their long dispute over the islands.

ANALYSIS OF EVENTS: 1999

BUSINESS AND THE ECONOMY

In spite of the troubling political impasse on Cyprus, the nation's economy continued to prosper in 1999, led by the tourist industry that had flourished on the island in the previous two decades. More than 2,000,000 people had visited Cyprus in 1998, drawn to the recreational activities afforded by its scenic landscape, as well as a multitude of historic and cultural attractions. Income from tourism was expected to reach $1.6 billion in 1999. The tourist industry had fueled Cyprus's transition from a poor and backward country to one with a modern, Westernized service economy. Economic growth had averaged over 6 percent in real terms for 15 years, per capita income was nearing $15,000, inflation was under 3 percent, and employment was booming for the island's well-educated work force.

The most dramatic economic phenomenon of 1999, however, was a major boom on the three-year-old Cyprus Stock Exchange, where share prices rose by 300 percent in the first eight months of the year. Business was so frenetic that the exchange had been forced to shut down twice by September to catch up on its backlog of unprocessed stock transfers. On a single day in August—normally a slow month—stock prices surged. Contributing factors in creating the stock boom included Cyprus's overall economic health, the cancellation of a planned missile deployment early in the year, and investment money from the new market economies of former Communist countries.

Amid the general speculation euphoria, there was some concern that individual investors who were sinking large sums into the market could be badly hurt if the boom was followed by a serious market correction.

GOVERNMENT AND POLITICS

Although the political and ethnic divisions in place since 1974 continued through the last year of the century, tensions between the nation's Greek and Turkish sectors, and between Cyprus and Turkey, were at least temporarily lessened by a decision made by Greek Cypriot president Glafcos Clerides. At the end of 1998, he announced the cancellation of the planned deployment of a Russian surface-to-air missile system. Turkey had threatened to take military action if the missiles were deployed. Although it defused tension with Turkey and helped smooth the way for eventual admission to the European Union, Clerides's decision created internal division within the Greek Cypriot community, where it was highly unpopular. The Socialist party withdrew from the governing coalition, and two Socialist ministers resigned their positions in protest.

Although an immediate crisis had been avoided by the cancellation of the planned missile deployment, there was little progress toward a longtime resolution to the political impasse on the divided island.

In June, Turkish Cypriot leader Rauf Denktash rejected a United Nations-proposed framework for peace talks with Clerides. The two leaders had last met two years earlier. The situation on Cyprus was a major topic of discussion in September when Turkish prime minister Bulent Ecevit traveled to Washington, D.C., to meet with President Clinton and congressional leaders.

In February two Israeli undercover agents who had been found near a restricted military zone on Cyprus with illegal listening devices received three-year jail sentences. However, both were freed in August in a goodwill gesture by the Greek Cypriot government toward new Israeli prime minister Ehud Barak.

CULTURE AND SOCIETY

A quarter of a century after Turkish forces occupied part of the island, Cyprus remained a divided society. Its ethnic Greeks and Turks, who had previously lived side by side, were rigidly separated by a buffer zone that even divided the capital city of Nicosia in two. All movement and communication between the two sides was completely cut off.

As the 1990s drew to a close, another, and less obvious, social division became apparent on Cyprus—the generation gap between older Cypriots who remembered the era before the partition of the country and those who had come of age in the 1980s and 1990s. The older generation was known for such traditional values as respect for authority, a strict work ethic, and loyalty to employers. Younger, better-educated Cypriots demonstrated many of the qualities that characterized their generation in other Westernized countries, including a preference for autonomy and flexibility in their jobs and lifestyles and fewer expectations of job security.

In spite of two decades of material progress and prosperity, Cypriots were still haunted by the political division of their country and, in particular, by the large number of their compatriots—about 1,500 Greeks and 500 Turks—who had been missing since the fighting that took place in 1974. The possibility of closure for relatives of those who died was raised by forensic experts who proposed that DNA technology, together with a computer database of missing persons, could aid in identifying the remains of many Cypriots who lost their lives in the conflict.

DIRECTORY

CENTRAL GOVERNMENT
Head of State

President
Glafcos Clerides, Office of the President, Presidential Palace, Dem. Severis Ave, 1400 Nicosia, Cyprus
PHONE: +357 661333
FAX: +357 665016
E-MAIL: grafio.proedrou@cytanet.com.cy

Ministers

Minister of Foreign Affairs
Ioannis Kasoulides, Ministry of Foreign Affairs, Dem. Severis Ave., 1447 Nicosia, Cyprus
PHONE: +357 300713
FAX: +357 661881
E-MAIL: minforeign1@cytanet.com.cy

Minister of Finance
Takis Klerides, Ministry of Finance, Ex-Secretariat Compound, 1439 Nicosia, Cyprus
PHONE: +357 679888
FAX: +357 676080

Minister of Interior
Christodoulos Christodoulou, Ministry of the Interior, Dem. Severis Ave., Ex-Secretariat Offices, 1453 Nicosia, Cyprus
PHONE: +357 302105
FAX: +357 671465

Minister of Labor and Social Insurance
Andreas Moushouttas, Ministry of Labor and Social Insurance, Byron Ave., 1463 Nicosia, Cyprus
PHONE: +357 673580
FAX: +357 670993

Minister of Defense
Socrates Hasikos, Ministry of Defense, 4 Emm. Roides Ave., 1432 Nicosia, Cyprus
PHONE: +357 807501
FAX: +357 366225
E-MAIL: roc-amin@cytanet.com.cy

Minister of Justice and Public Order
Nicos Koshis, Ministry of Justice and Public Order, 12 Ilioupoleos St., 1461 Nicosia, Cyprus
PHONE: +357 303917
FAX: +357 461427

Minister of Education and Culture
Ouranios Ioannides, Ministry of Education and Culture, Corner Thoucydides and Kimon, 1434 Nicosia, Cyprus
PHONE: +357 427033
FAX: +357 305974
E-MAIL: roc1@cytanet.com.cy

Minister of Commerce, Industry and Tourism
Nicos Rolandis, Ministry of Commerce, Industry and Tourism, 6 A. Araouzos St., 1424 Nicosia, Cyprus
PHONE: +357 867196
FAX: +357 375120

Minister of Health
Frixos Savvides, Ministry of Health, Byron Ave., 1448 Nicosia, Cyprus
PHONE: +357 303452
FAX: +357 305803
E-MAIL: sg@spidernet.com.cy

Minister of Communications and Works
Averof Neophytou, Ministry of Communications and Works, Dem. Severis Ave., 1424 Nicosia, Cyprus
PHONE: +357 670842
FAX: +357 675024
E-MAIL: mcw@cytanet.com.cy

Minister of Agriculture, Natural Resources and Environment
Costas Themistocleous, Ministry of Agriculture, Natural Resources and Environment, Loukis Akritas Ave., 1411 Nicosia, Cyprus
PHONE: +357 774214
FAX: +357 781156

POLITICAL ORGANIZATIONS
Dimokratikos Synagermos-DISY (Democratic Rally)

E-MAIL: disy@disy.org.cy

Anorthotikon Komma Ergazemenou Laou-AKEL (Progressive Party of the Working People)

E-MAIL: k.e.akel@cytanet.com.cy
TITLE: General Secretary
NAME: Demetris Christofias

Socialistiko Komma Kyprou-EDEK (Socialist Party of Cyprus)

Kinima ton Eleftheron Dimokratikon-KED (Movement of Free Democrats)

Oikologoi Perivallontistes (Cyprus Green Party)

38 Kyriacos Matsis Str., Flat 16, Ayios
Dhometios, 1722 Nicosia, Cyprus
PHONE: +357 (2) 778820
FAX: +357 (2) 777417
E-MAIL: cyprusgreens@hotmail.com

Dimokratikon Komma-DIKO (Democratic Party)

Neoi Orizontes-NEO (New Horizons)

E-MAIL: neo@logos.cy.net

DIPLOMATIC REPRESENTATION

Embassies in Cyprus

Canada
Suite 403, 15 Margarita House, P.O. Box 2125,
Themistocles Dervis St., Nicosia, Cyprus
PHONE: +357 (2) 451630
FAX: +357 (2) 459096

United Kingdom
P.O. Box 1978, Alexander Pallis Street, Nicosia,
Cyprus
PHONE: +357 (2) 473131
FAX: +357 (2) 473131

United States
P.O. Box 4536, Metochiou and Ploutarchou
Streets, Engomi, Nicosia, Cyprus
PHONE: +357 (2) 677143
FAX: +357 (2) 465944
E-MAIL: amcenter@spidernet.com.cy

TITLE: Ambassador
NAME: Donald Bandler

JUDICIAL SYSTEM
Supreme Court of the Republic

PHONE: +357 (2) 302746
FAX: +357 (2) 304500
E-MAIL: frgn@cyntanet.com.cy

FURTHER READING
Articles

"DNA Detectives on Divided Cyprus." *The Christian Science Monitor* (May 28, 1999): 6.

"Keep on Trying." *The Economist* (July 24, 1999): 48.

"Market Mania in Cyprus." *Time International* (Sept. 13, 1999): 50.

"Too Late, Perhaps." *The Economist* (Jan. 9, 1999): 46.

Books

The Almanac of Cyprus, 1998. Nicosia: Press and Information Office, 1998.

Dodd, C. H. *The Cyprus Imbroglio.* Huntingdon, England: Eothen Press, 1998.

Joseph, Joseph S. *Cyprus: Ethnic Conflict and International Politics: From Independence to the Threshold of the European Union.* Basingstoke: Macmillan, 1999.

Sonyel, Salahi Ramadan. *Cyprus: The Destruction of a Republic: British Documents, 1960 65.* Huntingdon, England: Eothen Press, 1997.

CYPRUS:
STATISTICAL DATA

For sources and notes see "Sources of Statistics" in the front of each volume.

GEOGRAPHY

Geography (1)

Area:

Total: 9,250 sq km (note—3,355 sq km are in the Turkish Cypriot area).

Land: 9,240 sq km.

Water: 10 sq km.

Area—comparative: about 0.6 times the size of Connecticut.

Land boundaries: 0 km.

Coastline: 648 km.

Climate: temperate, Mediterranean with hot, dry summers and cool, wet winters.

Terrain: central plain with mountains to north and south; scattered but significant plains along southern coast.

Natural resources: copper, pyrites, asbestos, gypsum, timber, salt, marble, clay earth pigment.

Land use:

Arable land: 12%

Permanent crops: 5%

Permanent pastures: 0%

Forests and woodland: 13%

Other: 70% (1993 est.).

HUMAN FACTORS

Demographics (2A)

	1990	1995	1998	2000	2010	2020	2030	2040	2050
Population	681.3	733.2	749.0	759.0	808.9	855.4	878.8	884.4	877.9
Net migration rate (per 1,000 population)	NA	NA	NA	NA	NA	NA	NA	NA	NA
Births	NA	NA	NA	NA	NA	NA	NA	NA	NA
Deaths	NA	NA	NA	NA	NA	NA	NA	NA	NA
Life expectancy - males	72.4	73.9	74.6	75.2	77.3	78.7	79.5	80.1	80.4
Life expectancy - females	76.7	78.3	79.1	79.7	82.0	83.7	84.8	85.5	86.0
Birth rate (per 1,000)	18.7	15.2	13.9	13.4	13.4	12.1	10.7	10.7	10.1
Death rate (per 1,000)	8.4	7.7	7.5	7.3	7.4	8.2	9.7	11.1	11.8
Women of reproductive age (15-49 yrs.)	171.5	181.6	185.2	188.0	196.7	192.9	195.2	184.4	175.0
of which are currently married	NA	NA	NA	NA	NA	NA	NA	NA	NA
Fertility rate	2.4	2.1	2.0	2.0	1.8	1.8	1.8	1.8	1.8

Except as noted, values for vital statistics are in thousands; life expectancy is in years.

Infants and Malnutrition (5)

Under-5 mortality rate (1997) 9

% of infants with low birthweight (1990-97) . . . . . .NA

Births attended by skilled health staff % of total[a] . . .NA

% fully immunized (1995-97)

TB . . . . .NA

DPT 98

Polio 98

Measles 90

Prevalence of child malnutrition under age 5
(1992-97)[b] . . . . .NA

Ethnic Division (6)

Greek 78%

Turkish 18%

Other . . . .

Of Greeks, 99.5% live in the Greek Cypriot area; 0.5% of the Greeks live in the Turkish Cypriot area. Of Turks, 1.3% live in the Greek Cypriot area; 98.7% of the Turks live in the Turkish Cypriot area.

Religions (7)

Greek Orthodox 78%

Muslim 18%

Maronite, Armenian Apostolic, and other 4%

Languages (8)

Greek, Turkish, English.

EDUCATION

Educational Attainment (10)

Age group (1992) . . . . .25+

Total population 363,573

Highest level attained (%)

No schooling 5.1

First level

Not completed 13.0

Completed 30.6

Entered second level

S-1 . . . . .34.2

S-2 . . . . .NA

Postsecondary 17.0

Literacy Rates (11B)

Adult literacy rate

1980

Male . . . .-

Female . . . .-

1995

Male 98x

Female 91x

GOVERNMENT & LAW

Political Parties (12)

Legislatures	% of seats
House of Representatives (Greek area)	
Democratic Rally (DISY)	34.5
Restorative Party of the Working People (AKEL) (Communist)	33.0
Democratic Party (DIKO)	16.4
United Democratic Union of Cyprus (EDEK) . . .	8.1
United Democrats Movement (EDI/KED)	3.7
Others	4.1
Assembly of the Republic (Turkish area)	
Unity Party (UBP)	29.9
Democratic Party (DP)	29.2
Republican Turkish Party (CTP)	24.2
Communal Liberation Party (TKP)	13.3
Others	3.4

Government Budget (13A)

Year: 1995

Total Expenditures: 1,306.14 Millions of Pounds

Expenditures as a percentage of the total by function:

General public services and public order 12.52

Defense 3.54

Education 11.54

Health 6.21

Social Security and Welfare 23.96

Housing and community amenities 4.59

Recreational, cultural, and religious affairs 1.37

Fuel and energy . . . .-

Agriculture, forestry, fishing, and hunting 6.59

Mining, manufacturing, and construction 01

Transportation and communication 5.70

Other economic affairs and services 2.66

Crime (15)

Crime rate (for 1997)

Crimes reported 3,950

Total persons convicted 5,300

Crimes per 100,000 population 600

Persons responsible for offenses

    Total number of suspects 1,100

    Total number of female suspects 91

    Total number of juvenile suspects 94

LABOR FORCE

Labor Force (16)

Total Greek Cypriot area 299,700

    Services 62%

Industry 25%

    Agriculture 13%

Total Turkish Cypriot area 76,500

    Services 66%

    Industry 11%

    Agriculture 23%

Data for 1996. Percent distribution for 1995.

Unemployment Rate (17)

Greek Cypriot area: 3.3% (1997 est.); Turkish Cypriot area: 6.4% (1996).

GOVERNMENT & LAW

Military Affairs (14B)

	1990	1991	1992	1993	1994	1995
Military expenditures						
Current dollars (mil.)	223	443	NA	262	369	495
1995 constant dollars (mil.)	257	489	NA	275	378	495
Armed forces (000)	10	10	10	NA	NA	10
Gross national product (GNP)						
Current dollars (mil.)	6,032	6,307	7,083	7,383	7,908	8,510[e]
1995 constant dollars (mil.)	6,932	6,969	7,618	7,740	8,106	8,510[e]
Central government expenditures (CGE)						
1995 constant dollars (mil.)	2,268	2,335	2,491	2,521	2,720	2,897
People (mil.)	.7	.7	.7	.7	.7	.7
Military expenditure as % of GNP	3.7	7.0	NA	3.6	4.7	5.8
Military expenditure as % of CGE	11.3	20.9	NA	10.9	13.9	17.1
Military expenditure per capita (1995 $)	377	705	NA	382	520	672
Armed forces per 1,000 people (soldiers)	14.7	14.4	14.1	NA	NA	13.6
GNP per capita (1995 $)	10,170	10,040	107,700	10,770	11,104	11,560
Arms imports[6]						
Current dollars (mil.)	50	40	150	30	60	50
1995 constant dollars (mil.)	57	44	161	31	62	50
Arms exports[6]						
Current dollars (mil.)	0	0	0	0	0	0
1995 constant dollars (mil.)	0	0	0	0	0	0
Total imports[7]						
Current dollars (mil.)	2,568	2,621	3,313	2,590	3,018	3,694
1995 constant dollars (mil.)	2,951	2,896	3,564	2,715	3,094	3,694
Total exports[7]						
Current dollars (mil.)	957	964	987	867	967	1,229
1995 constant dollars (mil.)	1,100	1,065	1,062	909	991	1,229
Arms as percent of total imports[8]	1.9	1.5	4.5	1.2	2.0	1.4
Arms as percent of total exports[8]	0	0	0	0	0	0

PRODUCTION SECTOR

Electric Energy (18)

Capacity .666,000 kW (1995)

Production . . . . .2.6 billion kWh (1995)

Consumption per capita . . . . .3,530 kWh (1995)

Transportation (19)

Highways:

total: Greek Cypriot area: 10,415 km; Turkish Cypriot area: 2,350 km

paved: Greek Cypriot area: 5,947 km; Turkish Cypriot area: 1,370 km

unpaved: Greek Cypriot area: 4,468 km (1996 est.); Turkish Cypriot area: 980 km

Merchant marine:

total: 1,533 ships (1,000 GRT or over) totaling 23,330,565 GRT/37,272,825 DWT

Airports: 15 (1997 est.)

Airports—with paved runways:

total: 12

2,438 to 3,047 m: 8

914 to 1,523 m: 3

under 914 m: 1 (1997 est.)

Airports—with unpaved runways:

total: 3

914 to 1,523 m: 1

under 914 m: 2 (1997 est.)

Top Agricultural Products (20)

Potatoes, citrus, vegetables, barley, grapes, olives, vegetables.

MANUFACTURING SECTOR

GDP & Manufacturing Summary (21)

Detailed value added figures are listed by both International Standard Industry Code (ISIC) and product title.

	1980	1985	1990	1994
GDP ($-1990 mil.)[1]	3,051	4,010	5,574	6,600
Per capita ($-1990)[1]	4,850	6,030	7,939	8,992
Manufacturing share (%) (current prices)[1]	18.2	16.4	14.8	*12.5*
Manufacturing				
Value added ($-1990 mil.)[1]	513	641	796	774
Industrial production index	100	117	143	139
Value added ($ mil.)	406	378	792	899
Gross output ($ mil.)	1,134	1,122	2,196	2,302
Employment (000)	34	39	43	40
Profitability (% of gross output)				
Intermediate input (%)	64	66	64	61
Wages and salaries inc. supplements (%)	*15*	18	19	*22*
Gross operating surplus	*21*	16	17	*17*
Productivity ($)				
Gross output per worker	29,417	25,804	46,057	53,226
Value added per worker	10,525	8,697	16,606	20,782
Average wage (inc. supplements)	*5,062*	5,143	9,738	*12,616*
Value added ($ mil.)				
311/2 Food products	42	49	101	136
313 Beverages	37	29	73	84
314 Tobacco products	36	26	41	63
321 Textiles	16	14	32	31
322 Wearing apparel	53	54	118	90
323 Leather and fur products	5	6	11	7
324 Footwear	21	19	30	25
331 Wood and wood products	19	23	39	48
332 Furniture and fixtures	17	22	36	42
341 Paper and paper products	11	8	17	21
342 Printing and publishing	15	18	37	44
351 Industrial chemicals	3	2	3	5
352 Other chemical products	12	12	28	46
353 Petroleum refineries	6	5	7	10
354 Miscellaneous petroleum and coal products	—	—	—	—
355 Rubber products	3	2	3	4
356 Plastic products	11	11	25	29
361 Pottery, china and earthenware	—	1	2	2

	1980	1985	1990	1994
362 Glass and glass products	—	—	1	2
369 Other non-metal mineral products	44	24	69	85
371 Iron and steel	—	—	—	—
372 Non-ferrous metals	—	—	—	—
381 Metal products	23	26	55	58
382 Non-electrical machinery	11	12	24	26
383 Electrical machinery	5	6	12	12
384 Transport equipment	8	4	9	10
385 Professional and scientific equipment	—	—	—	1
390 Other manufacturing industries	7	7	19	18

FINANCE, ECONOMICS, & TRADE

Economic Indicators (22)

National product: GDP—purchasing power parity—$11.19 billion (Greek Cypriot area— purchasing power parity—$9.75 billion; Turkish Cypriot area: purchasing power parity — $1.44 billion) (1997 est.)

National product real growth rate: 2.4% (Greek Cypriot area: 2.5%; Turkish Cypriot area: 1.7%) (1997 est.)

National product per capita: $13,500 (Greek Cypriot area: $15,000; Turkish Cypriot area: $8,000)(1997 est.)

Inflation rate—consumer price index: Greek Cypriot: 3.5% (1997 est.); Turkish Cypriot: 87.5% (1997 est.)

Exchange Rates (24)

Exchange rates:

Cypriot pounds per US1$

January 1998	.0.5326
1997	.0.5135
1996	.0.4663
1995	.0.4522
1994	.0.4915
1993	.0.4970

Turkish liras (TL) per US$1

November 1997	.187,477
1996	.81,405
1995	.45,845.1
1994	.29,608.7
1993	.10,984.6

Top Import Origins (25)

Greek Cypriot area: $3.6 billion (f.o.b., 1996) Data are for 1993.

Origins	%
NZ	.49
Italy	.NA
Australia	.NA

NA stands for not available.

Top Export Destinations (26)

Turkish Cypriot area: $70.5 million (f.o.b., 1996).

Destinations	%
Turkey	.48.2
United Kingdom	.21.3
other EU	.13.7

Balance of Payments (23)

	1991	1992	1993	1994	1995
Exports of goods (f.o.b.)	952	986	868	967	1,229
Imports of goods (f.o.b.)	−2,553	−3,301	−2,374	−2,703	−3,314
Trade balance	−1,602	−2,315	−1,507	−1,735	−2,085
Services - debits	−960	−1,119	−963	−1,073	−1,347
Services - credits	2,032	2,678	2,467	2,768	3,102
Private transfers (net)	23	15	15	15	20
Government transfers (net)	86	103	98	100	97
Overall balance	−420	−638	110	74	−213

Economic Aid (27)

Greek Cypriot area: recipient—$187 million (1990-94) in grants; Turkish Cypriot area: recipient—$700 million (1990-97) from Turkey in grants and loans that are usually forgiven.

Import Export Commodities (28)

Import Commodities	Export Commodities
Consumer goods	Citrus
Petroleum and lubricants	Potatoes
Food and feed grains	Textiles
Machinery	

CZECH REPUBLIC

Czech Republic
Ceskaá Republika

INTRODUCTORY SURVEY

RECENT HISTORY

At the end of World War II (1939–45), negotiations between Eduard Benes (the president), Klement Gottwald (the communist leader), and Josef Stalin of the Soviet Union established the basis for a postwar Czechoslovakian government.

The new National Front government ran Czechoslovakia as a democracy until 1948, when a military coup with Soviet backing forced President Benes to accept a government headed by Gottwald. A wave of purges and arrests rolled over the country from 1949 to 1954. Gottwald died a few days after Stalin died, in March 1953. His successors, presidents Zapotocky and Novotny, both clung to harsh methods of control, holding Czechoslovakia in a tight grip until well into the 1960s.

The liberalization in the Soviet Union led by president Nikita Khrushchev encouraged liberals within the Czechoslovak party to try to imitate Moscow. In January 1968, the presidency was separated from the Communist Party chairmanship, and Alexander Dubček was named head of the Czechoslovak Communist Party, the first Slovak ever to hold the post.

Novotny resigned in March 1968, and, under Dubček, Czechoslovakia embarked on a radical liberalization, termed "socialism with a human face." The leaders of the other communist nations viewed the developments of the "Prague Spring" with alarm and issued warnings to Dubček.

Finally, on the night of 20–21 August 1968, military units from almost all the Warsaw Pact nations invaded Czechoslovakia to ''save it from counter-revolution.'' Dubček and other officials were arrested, and the country was placed under the control of the Soviet Union. A purge of liberals followed, and Dubček was expelled from the party.

Between 1970 and 1975 nearly one-third of the party was dismissed, as the new Communist Party leader Gustav Husak consolidated his power, re-uniting the titles of party head and republic president.

Once again it was liberalization in the Soviet Union, under the policies of *perestroika* (restructuring) and *glasnost* (openness), which set off political change in Czechoslovakia. Husak ignored calls for Party reform from Mikhail Gorbachev, the Soviet Union's leader. In 1987, Husak announced his retirement and his replacement by Milos Jakes.

On 17 November 1989, a group of about 3,000 youths gathered in Prague's Wenceslas Square, de-manding free elections. On Jakes's orders, they were attacked and beaten by security forces; this ignited a swell of public indignation, expressed in ten days of nonstop meetings and demonstrations. This so-called ''velvet revolution'' ended on 24 November, when Jakes and all his government resigned.

Vaclav Havel, a playwright and founder of the Charter 77 dissident group, was named president on 29 December 1989. The old struggle between the Czechs and Slovaks resulted in the country being renamed the Czech and Slovak Federal Republic. Following the June 1990 elections, economic transformation of the country began.

Meanwhile, pressure for separation by Slovakia continued to build. Legislative attempts to strengthen the central government failed, and the republics increasingly began to behave as though they were already separate. Their prime ministers eventually agreed to separate, in the so-called velvet divorce, which took effect 1 January 1993.

Havel was reconfirmed as president of the Czech Republic by a vote of the 200-member Czech parliament on 26 January 1993. In January 1998, Josef Todovsky became prime minister after Vaclav Klaus was forced to resign because of a campaign finance scandal.

On March 12, 1999, together with Hungary and Poland, the Czech Republic joined the North Atlantic Treaty Organization (NATO).

GOVERNMENT

The constitution of the Czech Republic was adopted in December 1992. It calls for a two-chamber legislative body, consisting of an 81-member senate and a 200-member lower body, or parliament. The former Czech assembly was transformed into the parliament upon the dissolution of Czechoslovakia. In 1996 the eighty-one-member senate was established.

The head of the executive branch is the president, who will eventually be elected by popular election. The present president, Vaclav Havel, was elected by the parliament at the time of the republic's formation. The government is headed by the prime minister, who comes from the majority party, or a coalition.

Judiciary

Under the 1992 constitution, the judiciary has been completely reorganized to provide for a system of courts which includes a Supreme Court, a Supreme Administrative Court, high, regional, and district courts, and a Constitutional Court. The fifteen-member Constitutional Court created in 1993 rules on the constitutionality of legislation. Criminal defendants are entitled to fair and open public trials. They have the right to counsel and are presumed innocent.

Political Parties

As of the late 1990s, the strongest political grouping in the republic was the Civic Democratic Party (CDP). The CDP had an unbreakable majority in parliament because of its coalition with three other parties, the Civic Democratic Alliance, Christian Democratic Union, and Christian Democratic Party. There were two more left-leaning parties, the Czech Social Democrats, and the Czech People's Party, and a number of small nationalist parties.

DEFENSE

The Czech Republic had 37,400 army personnel in 1995, including 21,400 conscripts. Paramilitary forces that year consisted of 4,000 border guards and 1,600 internal security personnel.

ECONOMIC AFFAIRS

In 1993, the Czech Republic emerged from forty years of centralized economic planning in the communist era with a more prosperous and less debt-ridden economy than most other post-communist countries. It has significant industrial production and is strong in both heavy and precision engineering.

After recovering from a recession following the separation from Slovakia, the republic enjoyed gross domestic product (GDP) growth of 5.9% in 1995.

Public Finance

The CIA estimates that, in 1995, government revenues totaled approximately $16.5 billion and expenditures. External debt totaled $14.9 billion, approximately 31% of which was financed abroad.

Income

In 1998, the Czech Republic's gross domestic product (GNP) was $51.8 billion at current prices, or about $5,040 per person. For the period 1985–95, the average inflation rate was 12.2%, resulting in a decline in real growth rate of the GNP of 1.8% per person.

Industry

Light industry, including consumer goods—such as pilsner beer, ham, and sugar—were important in the pre-World War II export trade. Machinery was predominant under the communist regime. Major industries in the Czech Republic include textiles, glass, china, wood and paper, iron, steel, coal, machine tools, and chemicals.

Banking and Finance

The Czech National Bank (CNB) is the country's central bank, charged with issuing currency and regulating the state's commercial banking sector. Since mid-1996 domestic credit and M2 growth have fallen sharply. Growth in M2 stood at 7.8% at the end of December 1996, well below the central bank's 13-17% growth target for 1996 and in the middle of its 8-12% target range for 1997.

In 1990, eight banks became members of the Preparatory Committee on Stock Exchange Foundation. In 1992, this institution transformed itself into a stock exchange. The Prague Stock Exchange has been trading debt securities (mostly government and bank issues) since April 1993.

Economic Development

Economic recovery has been implemented by development of the private sector, increased exports to industrialized nations, control of inflation, and achievement of a positive trade balance. At the end of 1996, approximately 80% of the Czech Republic's large companies had been privatized, most via voucher privatization, through which nearly six million Czechs bought vouchers exchangeable for shares in companies that were to be privatized.

SOCIAL WELFARE

Social welfare programs in the Czech Republic include old-age pensions, disability, survivor benefits, sickness and maternity leave, work injury, unemployment, and family allowances.

More women than men are employed in farming, trade, health and social welfare, and education. However, they hold a larger share of lower-paying positions.

Healthcare

Factories and offices have health services, ranging from first-aid stations to hospitals. All school children receive medical attention, including inoculations, X-rays, and annual examinations. An insurance scheme is already in place to encourage private medical practice.

Special attention has been devoted to preventive medicine, with campaigns waged against tuberculosis, venereal diseases, cancer, poliomyelitis, diphtheria, and mental disturbances. Average life expectancy in 1996 was 74 years for men and women.

Housing

The lack of affordable housing, which keeps people from relocating for better job opportunities, is a major factor slowing economic growth in the Czech Republic. Housing starts totaled 10,000 in 1991, down nearly 80% from 1990.

EDUCATION

Education in the Czech Republic is free through the university level, for all who can obtain admission. There is 99% literacy. At the start of the 1994 school year, 1.9 million students were enrolled in 6,319 primary schools; 1.1 million students attended secondary schools; and 5,172 attended teacher-training schools

Over 36 universities, colleges, and advanced schools in the Czech Republic had a total of 165,106 students in 1994.

1999 KEY EVENTS TIMELINE

January

- A Czech recession causes banks to cut interest rates.

- Volkswagen AG plans to build a new engine and transmission plant in the Czech Republic.

February

- The Czech cabinet votes to re-nationalize ailing firms.

March

- The Czech Republic is formally admitted into the North Atlantic Treaty Organization (NATO).

- An international panel of energy experts claims that Temelin nuclear power plant is unnecessary.

April

- Medusa Oil and Gas begins Czech oil production.

May

- The Central European Visegrad group reunites to discuss economics in Slovakia's capital.

June

- The Czech Republic's fourth biggest bank, Ceskoslovenska obchodni banka (CSOB) is sold to Belgium's KBC Banking and Insurance Group.

August

- Ronald Lauder, primary owner of CME broadcasting, sues the Czech Republic for allowing Nova TV general manager to change broadcasts.

September

- The Czech unit of Austrian steelmaker Voest Alpine Stahl AG agrees to supply steel for a new car made by Skoda Auto AS.

November

- The Czech lower house of parliament passes a reform allowing creditors to seize and sell debtors' assets without requiring their permission first.

- The tenth anniversary of Czechoslovakia's "velvet revolution" prompts celebration of freedom but also underscores disappointments of the past decade.

December

- Pope John Paul II apologizes for the execution in 1415 of Jan Hus, a religious reformer who was burned at the stake. The apology is issued to mark the visit to the Vatican by president Vaclav Havel, who is delivering a Christmas tree to St. Peter's Basilica.

ANALYSIS OF EVENTS: 1999

BUSINESS AND THE ECONOMY

The Czech Republic has found itself in the grips of a recession during the past year, driving away much of the investment that took place following communist occupation. It is speculated that former Prime Minister Vaclav Klaus and President Vaclav Havel's administration is to blame for the 1997 financial collapse and subsequent ineffectively imposed austerity measures in 1998. Russia's financial collapse in August 1998 also negatively affected the Czech economy, because a large number of banks were financed primarily by Russians. The new, left-leaning government—led by Prime Minister Milos Zemen—implemented a series of interest rate cuts combined with an increased government budget deficit and further privatization of government-owned firms. This last process has proven harder to do than originally envisioned, causing the new administration to backtrack from liberalization on some accounts. Out of the variety of banks in the Czech Republic, only a handful are large enough, and solvent enough for sale to investors, and those expressing interest are foreigners that could potentially subvert national goals. Czech analysts were calling for a stronger, nationally owned and supported central bank before privatization could begin for other firms, but the country's four largest banks were sold in September to foreign investors. This may seem like an alarming turn for the Czech banking system, but the majority of shares for these banks are held by the State despite privatization schemes.

The most successful enterprises continue to be foreign run, while State intervention has wreaked havoc on domestic organizations. For example, the auto industry in the Czech Republic, led by Germany's Volkswagen AG, has found great success manufacturing and exporting cars from the country, but the locally owned Temelin nuclear power plant has been entangled in a web of politics that may even shut it down. The plant has disturbed environmentalists, including the powerful Green Party and some groups claim that the extra power is unnecessary to Czech growth. This is only one of many utilities controversies that still face the post-communist Czech government.

GOVERNMENT AND POLITICS

After 1989 and the "Velvet Revolution," the Czech Republic was challenged with the transformation to a liberal economy and government. Originally, under the leadership of President Vaclav Havel, the ideals of a liberal democracy were extremely popular while revolting against the established communist regime. Now, however, the revolutionaries have become the establishment and the administration is caught having to deal with a post-communist fallout using democratic methods that sometimes fall short of the ideal. Deputy Prime Minister for Economic Policy, Pavel Mertlik, has found out that State planning is actually necessary for the transition to a free-market economy. This has caused some dissension because the minority government run by Social Democrat Milos Zeman has pursued policies to strengthen the economy that reflect leftist leanings for the first time since communist rule. But this government intervention has done little to put off proponents for the participation in Western society through NATO and the European Union.

In March, the Czech Republic joined the NATO alliance with Poland and Hungary, during the first addition of former communist states. A significant move away from Russia, analysts feared that this would bring instability to the balance of power in the region, much like the effect of American-led, NATO bombing runs in Kosovo that drew the ire of Russia's President Boris Yeltsin. This has not occurred as of yet, but the walls between Russia and the rest of Europe are growing in the Czech Republic, as the country strives for European Union membership and closer ties with Eastern and Central Europe. In May the Central European Free Trade Area (CEFTA) group met to discuss regional policies and cooperation, alienating Russia and, some say, snubbing Western Europe. Nevertheless, participation in regional politics will ultimately spell the success or demise of the Czech Republic's national goals.

CULTURE AND SOCIETY

The frozen world of communism after 1989 caused an exodus of Czech intellectuals and immense influx of Western ideals, culture, music and art. One could say that the composition of the society completely changed, leaving an older generation of intellectual, democratic revolutionaries, and another generation of youthful counterculturists. Especially in Prague, students speak English and German instead of Czech and watch American television programs. The relatively new, free-market economy has brought foreign influences to the Czech Republic, replacing traditional entertainment like theater and opera. The most popular television station, TV Nova, has been criticized for it's cheap, meaningless programming, but this is what the majority of citizens want to see and shows just how far the Czech Republic has come towards a market-dominated society. One major cultural problem stemming from the capitalist transformation is the activity of powerful black marketeers from the Ukraine. This Mafia deals mostly with human transport, providing extremely cheap labor and prostitutes through the Czech border, and helping illegal immigrants into the European Union. This does not improve economic or health conditions in the Czech Republic, and damages relations with the European Union, when most Czech citizens support regional integration. The country has a long way to go in managing the freedoms of democracy, while simultaneously protecting the Czech culture and tradition.

DIRECTORY

CENTRAL GOVERNMENT

Head of State

President
Vaclav Havel, The Office of the President of the Czech Republic, Prague Castle, 119 08 Prague 1, Czech Republic
PHONE: +420 (2) 24371111
FAX: +420 (2) 24373300
E-MAIL: president@hrad.cz

Prime Minister
Milos Zeman

Ministers

Deputy Prime Minister
Egon Lansky, Office of the Deputy Prime Minister

Deputy Prime Minister
Pavel Mertlik, Office of the Deputy Prime Minister

Deputy Prime Minister
Pavel Rychetsky, Office of the Deputy Prime Minister

Deputy Prime Minister
Vladimir Spidla, Office of the Deputy Prime Minister

Minister of Agriculture
Jan Fencl, Ministry of Agriculture, Tesnov 17, 117 05 Prague 1, Czech Republic
PHONE: +420 (2) 21811111
FAX: +420 (2) 24810478

Minister of Culture
Pavel Dostal, Ministry of Culture, Valdstejnske nam. 4, 118 11 Prague 1, Czech Republic
PHONE: +420 (2) 5131111
FAX: +420 (2) 24510897

Minister of Defense
Vladimir Vetchy, Ministry of Defense, Tychonova 1, 160 00 Prague 6, Czech Republic
PHONE: +420 (2) 20201111

Minister of Economic Competition
Ministry of Economic Competition, Jostova 8, 601 56 Brno, Czech Republic
PHONE: +420 (5) 42161111
FAX: +420 (5) 42210023

Minister of Economy
Ministry of Economy, Staromestske nam. 6, 110 15 Prague 1, Czech Republic
PHONE: +420 (2) 24861111
FAX: +420 (2) 24861333

Minister of Education
Eduard Zeman, Ministry of Education, Youth and Sport, Karmelitska 5,7,8, 118 12 Prague 1, Czech Republic

Minister of Environment
Milos Kuzvart, Ministry of Environment, Vrsovicka 65, 110 00 Prague 10, Czech Republic
PHONE: +420 (2) 67121111
FAX: +420 (2) 67310308

Minister of Finance
Pavel Mertlik, Ministry of Finance, Letenska 15,
118 10 Prague 1, Czech Republic
PHONE: +420 (2) 24541111
FAX: +420 (2) 24542788

Minister of Foreign Affairs
Jan Kavan, Ministry of Foreign Affairs,
Loretanske nam. 5, 118 00 Prague 1, Czech
Republic
PHONE: +420 (2) 24181111
FAX: +420 (2) 24310017

Minister of Health
Ivan David, Ministry of Health, Palackeho nam.
4, 128 01 Prague 2, Czech Republic
PHONE: +420 (2) 24971111
FAX: +420 (2) 249721111

Minister of Industry and Trade
Miroslav Gregr, Ministry of Industry and Trade,
Na Frantisku 32, 110 15 Prague 1, Czech
Republic
PHONE: +420 (2) 24851111
FAX: +420 (2) 24811089

Minister of Interior
Vaclav Grulich, Ministry of Interior, Nad Stolou
3, 170 00 Prague 7, Czech Republic
PHONE: +420 (2) 61421115

Minister of Justice
Otakar Motejl, Ministry of Justice, Vyschradska
16, 128 10 Prague 2, Czech Republic
PHONE: +420 (2) 21997111

Minister of Labor and Social Affairs
Vladimir Spidla, Ministry of Labor and Social
Affairs, Na poricnim pravu 1, 128 00 Prague 2,
Czech Republic
PHONE: +420 (2) 24902111
FAX: +420 (2) 24902664

Minister of Local Development
Jaromir Cisar, Ministry of Local Development

Minister of Transport and Communication
Antonin Peltram, Ministry of Transport, Nabr. L.
Svobody 12, 110 15 Prague 1, Czech Republic
PHONE: +420 (2) 23031111
FAX: +420 (2) 24810596

Minister Without Portfolio
Jaroslav Basta, Office of the Minister Without
Portfolio

POLITICAL ORGANIZATIONS
Czech Social Democratic Party
TITLE: Chairman

NAME: Miloš Zeman

Civic Democratic Party
TITLE: Chairman
NAME: Václav Klaus

Freedom Union
TITLE: Chairman
NAME: Jan Ruml

Communist Party
TITLE: Chairman
NAME: Miroslav Grebenícek

Pensioners for a Secure Life
TITLE: Chairman
NAME: Eduard Kremlicka

Civic Democratic Alliance
TITLE: Chairman
NAME: Daniel Kroupa

Democratic Union
TITLE: Chairman
NAME: Ratibor Majzlik

Green Party
TITLE: Chairman
NAME: Emil Zeman

Civic Coalition-Political Club
TITLE: Chairman
NAME: Jozef Wagner

DIPLOMATIC REPRESENTATION
Embassies in the Czech Republic
Argentina
Washingtonova 25, Prague 1, Czech Republic
PHONE: +420 24212448

Australia
Cinska 4, Prague 6, Czech Republic
PHONE: +420 24310070

Austria
Victora Huga 10, Prague 5, Czech Republic
PHONE: +420 24511677

Belgium
Valdstejnska 6, Prague 1, Czech Republic
PHONE: +420 24510532
FAX: +420 24510966

Brazil
Suciska 12, 160 41 Prague 6, Czech Republic

Bulgaria
Krakovska 6, Prague 1, Czech Republic
PHONE: +420 24228647

Canada
Mickiewiczova 6, Prague 6, Czech Republic
PHONE: +420 24311108
FAX: +420 24310294

China
Pelleova 11, Prague 6, Czech Republic
PHONE: +420 24311323

Denmark
U pate baterie 7, Prague 6, Czech Republic

Egypt
Pelleova 14, Prague 6, Czech Republic
PHONE: +420 24311506
FAX: +420 24311157

Finland
Drevna 2, Prague 2, Czech Republic
PHONE: +420 24913594
FAX: +420 24915556

France
Velkoprevorske nam. 2, Prague 1, Czech Republic
PHONE: +420 24510402
FAX: +420 24511313

Germany
Vlasska 19, Prague 1, Czech Republic
PHONE: +420 24510323
FAX: +420 24510156

Greece
Na Orechovce 19, Prague 6, Czech Republic
FAX: +420 24311235

Hungary
Badeniho 1, Prague 6, Czech Republic

India
Valdstejnska 6, Prague 1, Czech Republic
PHONE: +420 24510665

Israel
Badeniho 2, Prague 6, Czech Republic

Italy
Nerudova 20, Prague 1, Czech Republic
PHONE: +420 24510089
FAX: +420 24510363

Japan
Maltezske nam. 6, Prague 1, Czech Republic
PHONE: +420 24510753

Mexico
Nad Kazankou 8, Prague 7, Czech Republic

Netherlands
Maltezske nam 1, Prague 1, Czech Republic
PHONE: +420 24510189
FAX: +420 24510188

Norway
Na Orechovce 69, Prague 6, Czech Republic

Poland
Valdstejnska 8, Prague 1, Czech Republic
PHONE: +420 24510891
FAX: +420 24510811

Portugal
Bubenska 3, Prague 7, Czech Republic
PHONE: +420 66711065
FAX: +420 66710208

Romania
Nerudova 5, Prague 1, Czech Republic
PHONE: +420 24510414

Russia
Pod kastany 1, Prague 6, Czech Republic

South Africa
Ruska 65, Prague 10, Czech Republic
PHONE: +420 67311114
FAX: +420 67311395

Spain
Pevnostni 9, Prague 6, Czech Republic
PHONE: +420 24311441

Sweden
Uvoz 13, Prague 1, Czech Republic
PHONE: +420 24510436
FAX: +420 24510301

Switzerland
PHONE: +420 24311228
FAX: +420 24311312

United Kingdom
Thunovska 14, Prague 1, Czech Republic
PHONE: +420 24510439
FAX: +420 24511314

United States
Trziste 15, Prague 1, Czech Republic
PHONE: +420 24510847
FAX: +420 24511001
TITLE: Ambassador
NAME: John Shattuck

JUDICIAL SYSTEM
The Supreme Court

Czech Constitutional Court

Jostova 8, 660 83 Brno 2, Czech Republic
PHONE: +420 (5) 42161111
FAX: +420 (5) 42218326
E-MAIL: kessler@concourt.cz

FURTHER READING

Government Publications

Czech Republic: Capital Market Review
Washington, DC: World Bank, 1999.

Articles

"Come Back, Visegrad," *The Economist* (May 22, 1999): 56.

"Czech Renationalisation: For Turning," *The Economist* (February 6, 1999): 65-66.

"Czech Youth: Wicked, Really," *The Economist* (February 20, 1999): 47-48.

"The Disappearing Czech Intellectual," *The Economist* (August 21, 1999): 41.

Jones, Colin. "A Tale of Two Economies," *The Banker* (February 1999): 42.

Madigan, James Cooper. "Unease, Even After the Easing," *Business Week* (January. 1999): 31.

Meils, Cathy. "CME's Lauder Seeks Arbitration," *Variety* (August 30, 1999): 159.

"Plenty of Muck, Not Much Money," *The Economist* (May 8, 1999): 52.

"Poland, Hungary and Czechs Join NATO," *International Journal on World Peace* (March 1999): 81.

"A Right-Winger Veers Left?" *The Economist* (23 Jan. 1999): 48.

Solana, Javier. "Growing the Alliance," *The Economist* (March 13, 1999): 23.

Stojaspal, Jan. "Nothing to Toast About: Czechs Struggle to Mend the Tattered Remnants of their 'Velvet Revolution,'" *Time International* (March 15, 1999): 18.

Tomass, Mark. "A Decade of Conflicts in Czech Economic Transformation," *Journal of Economic Issues* (June 1999): 315.

"Under New Management," *The Banker* (September 1999): 56.

"Unprecedented Success in Czech Telecommunications Market," *Harvard Business Review* (January-February 1999): 163.

Wesolowsky, Tony. "Tough Choices on Temelin," *Bulletin of the Atomic Scientists* (May 1999): 16.

Books

Bebler, Anton A., ed. *The Challenge of NATO Enlargement* Westport, CN: Praeger, 1999.

Goetz-Strankelviz and Phyllis Carey, eds. *Critical Essays on Václav Havel* New York, NY: G.K. Hall, Twayne, 1999.

Pluckrose, Henry. *Czech Republic* New York, NY: Franklin Watts, 1999.

CZECH REPUBLIC: STATISTICAL DATA

For sources and notes see "Sources of Statistics" in the front of each volume.

GEOGRAPHY

Geography (1)

Area:

Total: 78,703 sq km.

Land: 78,645 sq km.

Water: 58 sq km.

Area—comparative: slightly smaller than South Carolina.

Land boundaries:

Total: 1,881 km.

Border countries: Austria 362 km, Germany 646 km, Poland 658 km, Slovakia 215 km.

Coastline: 0 km (landlocked).

Climate: temperate; cool summers; cold, cloudy, humid winters.

Terrain: Bohemia in the west consists of rolling plains, hills, and plateaus surrounded by low mountains; Moravia in the east consists of very hilly country.

Natural resources: hard coal, soft coal, kaolin, clay, graphite.

Land use:

Arable land: 41%

Permanent crops: 2%

Permanent pastures: 11%

Forests and woodland: 34%

Other: 12% (1993 est.).

HUMAN FACTORS

Demographics (2A)

	1990	1995	1998	2000	2010	2020	2030	2040	2050
Population	NA	10,326.6	10,286.5	10,283.8	10,457.8	10,309.1	9,912.3	9,345.8	8,626.0
Net migration rate (per 1,000 population)	NA	NA	NA	NA	NA	NA	NA	NA	NA
Births	NA	NA	NA	NA	NA	NA	NA	NA	NA
Deaths	NA	NA	NA	NA	NA	NA	NA	NA	NA
Life expectancy - males	NA	69.7	70.8	71.3	73.5	75.4	76.9	78.1	79.0
Life expectancy - females	NA	76.7	77.6	78.1	80.1	81.8	83.1	84.2	85.1
Birth rate (per 1,000)	NA	9.3	9.0	10.7	10.6	8.2	8.3	7.3	6.6
Death rate (per 1,000)	NA	11.5	10.9	10.8	10.8	11.4	13.0	14.3	15.5
Women of reproductive age (15-49 yrs.)	NA	2,662.9	2,620.6	2,589.3	2,447.4	2,309.3	2,004.8	1,766.6	1,643.1
of which are currently married	NA	NA	NA	NA	NA	NA	NA	NA	NA
Fertility rate	NA	1.3	1.2	1.4	1.6	1.5	1.5	1.4	1.4

Except as noted, values for vital statistics are in thousands; life expectancy is in years.

Health Personnel (3)

Total health expenditure as a percentage of GDP, 1990-1997[a]

Public sector 6.4

Private sector 0.6

Total[b] 7.0

Health expenditure per capita in U.S. dollars, 1990-1997[a]

Purchasing power parity 806

Total 360

Availability of health care facilities per 100,000 people

Hospital beds 1990-1997[a] 670

Doctors 1993[c] 293

Nurses 1993[c] 944

Health Indicators (4)

Life expectancy at birth

1980 70

1997 74

Daily per capita supply of calories (1996) 3,177

Total fertility rate births per woman (1997) 1.2

Maternal mortality ratio per 100,000 live births (1990-97) . . . . .2[b]

Safe water % of population with access (1995) . . . .

Sanitation % of population with access (1995) . . . .

Consumption of iodized salt % of households (1992-98)[a] . . . .

Smoking prevalence

Male % of adults (1985-95)[a] 43

Female % of adults (1985-95)[a] 31

Tuberculosis incidence per 100,000 people (1997) 20

Adult HIV prevalence % of population ages 15-49 (1997) 0.04

Infants and Malnutrition (5)

Under-5 mortality rate (1997) 7

% of infants with low birthweight (1990-97) 6

Births attended by skilled health staff % of total[a] . .100

% fully immunized (1995-97)

TB 97

DPT 98

Polio 97

Measles 97

Prevalence of child malnutrition under age 5 (1992-97)[b] 1

Ethnic Division (6)

Czech 94.4%

Slovak 3%

Polish 0.6%

German 0.5%

Gypsy 0.3%

Hungarian 0.2%

Other 1%

Religions (7)

Atheist 39.8%

Roman Catholic 39.2%

Protestant 4.6%

Orthodox 3%

Other 13.4%

Languages (8)

Czech, Slovak.

EDUCATION

Public Education Expenditures (9)

Public expenditure on education (% of GNP)

1980 . . . .

1996 . . . . .5.4

Expenditure per student

Primary % of GNP per capita

1980 . . . .

1996 . . . . .16.3[1]

Secondary % of GNP per capita

1980 . . . .

1996 . . . . .23.7[1]

Tertiary % of GNP per capita

1980 . . . .

1996 . . . . .40.3[1]

Expenditure on teaching materials

Primary % of total for level (1996) . . . .

Secondary % of total for level (1996) . . . . .36.1[1]

Primary pupil-teacher ratio per teacher (1996) . . . . .19[1]

Duration of primary education years (1995) 4

Educational Attainment (10)

Age group (1991) . . . . .25+

Total population 6,580,525

Highest level attained (%)

No schooling 0.3

First level

Not completed 31.4

Completed . . . . .NA

Entered second level

S-1 . . . . .58.6

S-2 . . . . .NA

Postsecondary 8.5

GOVERNMENT & LAW

Political Parties (12)

Chamber of Deputies	No. of seats
Governing coalition	
Civic Democratic Party (ODS) 68	
Christian Democratic Union-Czech People's Party (KDU-CSL) 18	
Civic Democratic Alliance (ODA) 13	
Opposition	
Czech Social Democrats (CSSD) 61	
Communist Party (KSCM) 22	
Assembly for the Republic (SPR-RSC) 18	

Government Budget (13A)

Year: 1997

Total Expenditures: 592,070 Millions of Koruny

Expenditures as a percentage of the total by function:

General public services and public order 8.63

Defense 4.66

Education 11.34

Health 17.83

Social Security and Welfare 36.63

Housing and community amenities 3.99

Recreational, cultural, and religious affairs 1.10

Fuel and energy 56

Agriculture, forestry, fishing, and hunting 2.46

Mining, manufacturing, and construction 24

Transportation and communication 5.45

Other economic affairs and services 3.64

Military Affairs (14B)

	1993	1994	1995
Military expenditures			
Current dollars (mil.)	2,386	2,495	2,368
1995 constant dollars (mil.)	2,501	2,558	2,368
Armed forces (000)	107	90	68

Gross national product (GNP)			
Current dollars (mil.)	89,640	93,970	101,000
1995 constant dollars (mil.)	93,980	96,330	101,000
Central government expenditures (CGE)			
1995 constant dollars (mil.)	36,040	35,310	36,130
People (mil.)	10.3	10.3	10.3
Military expenditure as % of GNP	2.7	2.7	2.3
Military expenditure as % of CGE	6.9	7.2	6.6
Military expenditure per capita (1995 $)	242	248	229
Armed forces per 1,000 people (soldiers)	10.3	8.7	6.6
GNP per capita (1995 $)	9,101	9,328	9,779
Arms imports[6]			
Current dollars (mil.)	5	90	0
1995 constant dollars (mil.)	5	92	0
Arms exports[6]			
Current dollars (mil.)	210	300	120
1995 constant dollars (mil.)	220	308	120
Total imports[7]			
Current dollars (mil.)	13,340	15,640	26,530
1995 constant dollars (mil.)	13,990	16,030	26,530
Total exports[7]			
Current dollars (mil.)	13,200	14,250	21,650
1995 constant dollars (mil.)	13,840	14,610	21,650
Arms as percent of total imports[8]	0.0	.6	0
Arms as percent of total exports[8]	1.6	2.1	.6

Crime (15)

Crime rate (for 1997)

Crimes reported 403,700

Total persons convicted 174,800

Crimes per 100,000 population 3,900

Persons responsible for offenses

Total number of suspects 118,400

Total number of female suspects 11,400

Total number of juvenile suspects 12,800

LABOR FORCE

Labor Force (16)

Total (million) 5.124

Industry 33.1%

Agriculture 6.9%

Construction 9.1%

Transport and communications 7.2%

Services 43.7%

Data for 1997. Percent distribution for 1994.

Unemployment Rate (17)

5% (1997 est.)

PRODUCTION SECTOR

Electric Energy (18)

Capacity . . . . .13.85 million kW (1994)

Production . . . . .53.285 billion kWh (1995)

Consumption per capita . . . . .5,069 kWh (1995)

Transportation (19)

Highways:

total: 55,489 km

paved: 55,489 km (including 423 km of expressways)

unpaved: 0 km (1996 est.)

Waterways: NA km; the Elbe (Labe) is the principal river

Pipelines: natural gas 5,400 km

Merchant marine:

total: 5 ships (1,000 GRT or over) totaling 110,233 GRT/192,998 DWT ships by type: bulk 3 under Maltese flag, cargo 2 under the Cypriot flag (1997 est.)

Airports: 66 (1997 est.)

Airports—with paved runways:

total: 33

over 3,047 m: 2

2,438 to 3,047 m: 7

1,524 to 2,437 m: 10

914 to 1,523 m: 1

under 914 m: 13 (1997 est.)

Airports—with unpaved runways:

total: 33

914 to 1,523 m: 17

under 914 m: 16 (1997 est.)

Top Agricultural Products (20)

Grains, potatoes, sugar beets, hops, fruit; pigs, cattle, poultry; forest products.

MANUFACTURING SECTOR

GDP & Manufacturing Summary (21)

Detailed value added figures are listed by both International Standard Industry Code (ISIC) and product title.

	1980	1985	1990	1994
GDP ($-1990 mil.)[1]	NA	29,214	31,604	25,597
Per capita ($-1990)[1]	NA	2,835	3,067	2,486
Manufacturing share (%) (current prices)[1]	NA	NA	NA	NA
Manufacturing				
Value added ($-1990 mil.)[1]	NA	NA	NA	NA
Industrial production index	NA	NA	NA	NA
Value added ($ mil.)	NA	NA	NA	NA
Gross output ($ mil.)	30,577	28,725	*36,458*	*46,951*
Employment (000)	NA	*1,758*	1,577	*1,186*
Profitability (% of gross output)				
Intermediate input (%)	NA	NA	NA	NA
Wages and salaries inc. supplements (%)	NA	NA	NA	NA
Gross operating surplus	NA	NA	NA	NA
Productivity ($)				
Gross output per worker	NA	*16,336*	*23,119*	*39,599*
Value added per worker	NA	NA	NA	NA
Average wage (inc. supplements)	NA	*2,151*	2,223	*2,685*
Value added ($ mil.)				
311/2 Food products	NA	NA	NA	NA
313 Beverages	NA	NA	NA	NA
314 Tobacco products	NA	NA	NA	NA
321 Textiles	NA	NA	NA	NA
322 Wearing apparel	NA	NA	NA	NA
323 Leather and fur products	NA	NA	NA	NA
324 Footwear	NA	NA	NA	NA
331 Wood and wood products	NA	NA	NA	NA

	1980	1985	1990	1994
332 Furniture and fixtures	NA	NA	NA	NA
341 Paper and paper products	NA	NA	NA	NA
342 Printing and publishing	NA	NA	NA	NA
351 Industrial chemicals	NA	NA	NA	NA
352 Other chemical products	NA	NA	NA	NA
353 Petroleum refineries	NA	NA	NA	NA
354 Miscellaneous petroleum and coal products	NA	NA	NA	NA
355 Rubber products	NA	NA	NA	NA
356 Plastic products	NA	NA	NA	NA
361 Pottery, china and earthenware	NA	NA	NA	NA
362 Glass and glass products	NA	NA	NA	NA
369 Other non-metal mineral products	NA	NA	NA	NA
371 Iron and steel	NA	NA	NA	NA
372 Non-ferrous metals	NA	NA	NA	NA
381 Metal products	NA	NA	NA	NA
382 Non-electrical machinery	NA	NA	NA	NA
383 Electrical machinery	NA	NA	NA	NA
384 Transport equipment	NA	NA	NA	NA
385 Professional and scientific equipment	NA	NA	NA	NA
390 Other manufacturing industries	NA	NA	NA	NA

FINANCE, ECONOMICS, & TRADE

Economic Indicators (22)

National product: GDP—purchasing power parity—$111.9 billion (1997 est.)

National product real growth rate: 0.7% (1997 est.)

National product per capita: $10,800 (1997 est.)

Inflation rate—consumer price index: 10% (1997)

Exchange Rates (24)

Exchange rates:

Koruny (Kcs) per US$1

January 1998	35.357
1997	31.698
1996	27.145
1995	26.541
1994	28.785
1993	29.153

Values before 1993 reflect Czechoslovak exchange rates

Top Import Origins (25)

$27.7 billion (f.o.b., 1996) Data are for 1996.

Origins	%
European Union	61.1
CEFTA	16.3
Slovakia	11.8
EFTA	2.2

Balance of Payments (23)

	1993	1994	1995	1996
Exports of goods (f.o.b.)	14,201	16,003	21,477	21,693
Imports of goods (f.o.b.)	−14,672	−17,369	−25,162	−27,571
Trade balance	−471	−1,366	−3,685	−5,877
Services - debits	−4,373	−5,497	−6,183	−8,156
Services - credits	5,269	5,958	7,922	9,351
Private transfers (net)	—	—	103	130
Government transfers (net)	—	—	469	254
Overall balance	512	−778	−1,373	−4,298

Top Export Destinations (26)

$21.7 billion (f.o.b., 1996) Data are for 1996.

Destinations	%
European Union	.60.9
CEFTA	.21.4
Slovakia	.13.9
EFTA	.1.7

Economic Aid (27)

$NA. NA stands for not available.

Import Export Commodities (28)

Import Commodities	Export Commodities
Machinery and equipment 38.2%	Machinery and equipment 32.7%
Manufactured goods 19.3%	Manufactured goods 28.8%
Raw materials and fuels 12.4%	Raw materials and fuel 9.2%
Food 5.6%	Food 4.1%

DENMARK

Kingdom of Denmark
Kongeriget Danmark

INTRODUCTORY SURVEY

RECENT HISTORY

After World War II (1939–45), Denmark became a charter member of the United Nations (UN) and of the North Atlantic Treaty Organization (NATO). In 1952, it joined with the other Scandinavian nations to form the Nordic Council. Having joined the European Free Trade Association (EFTA) in 1960, Denmark left that association for the European Community (EC) in 1973. Meanwhile, during the 1950s and 1960s, agricultural and manufacturing production rose impressively, a high level of employment was maintained, and foreign trade grew.

However, the expense of maintaining Denmark's highly developed social security system, persistent inflation, rising unemployment, and increases in the price of imported oil posed political as well as economic problems for Denmark in the 1970s and 1980s, as one weak coalition government followed another.

Economic performance continued to be a major issue in the 1990s. Voters narrowly rejected the Maastricht Treaty on European Union in 1992, but later approved it in 1994 after modifications were made in Denmark's favor.

GOVERNMENT

Denmark is a constitutional monarchy. Legislative power is vested jointly in the monarch and in a single-chamber parliament *(Folketing)*. Execu-

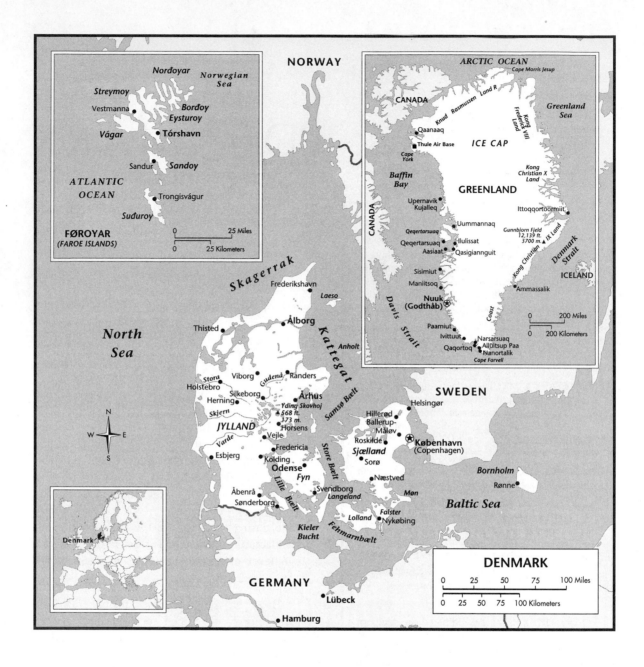

tive power belongs to the sovereign—through his or her ministers—and judicial power is exercised by the courts.

The sovereign must belong to the Lutheran Church. The crown is hereditary in the royal house (family) of Lyksborg, which ascended the throne in 1863.

The single-chamber Folketing is elected every four years by direct, secret ballot by Danish subjects 18 years of age and older. There are 179 members, two of whom are elected in the Faroe Islands and two in Greenland.

Judiciary

As a rule, cases have their first hearing before the Copenhagen city court, the Aarhus city court, or one of eighty-four local courts. Certain major cases, however, come under the High Courts (Landsrettes) in Copenhagen and Viborg; otherwise, these courts function as courts of appeal. The Supreme Court (Hojesteret), made up of fifteen judges, serves solely as a court of appeal for cases coming from the High Courts.

Political Parties

The major parties support the United Nations and NATO, and favor inter-Scandinavian cooperation. Aims of the leading Social Democratic Party are to break up monopolies, redistribute personal incomes by taxation and other measures, divide large farm properties into smaller units, and raise working-class living standards through full employment.

The Conservative Party advocates an economic policy based on the rights of private property and private enterprise. It calls for a national pension system that would encourage personal initiative and savings.

DEFENSE

All young men must register for military service at the age of 18 and are subject to nine to twelve months of service. Women may volunteer for service, including service on combat vessels. The army consists of 19,000 personnel, the navy 6,000, and the air force 7,900. There are also 70,450 members of the reserves and 64,300 in the volunteer home guard. Military expenditures for 1995 amounted to $3.1 billion.

ECONOMIC AFFAIRS

Denmark is traditionally an agricultural country. Since the end of World War II (1939–45), however, manufacturing has gained rapidly in importance and now contributes more than agriculture to national income. Denmark has always been a prominent shipping nation.

Since the Danes joined the European Community (EC) in January 1973, their trade position has improved. The gross domestic product (GDP) increased by 2.7% in 1995 and 2.5% in 1996.

Public Finance

The finance bill is presented to the Folketing yearly; the fiscal year follows the calendar year. As a general rule, the budget is prepared on the ''net'' principle, the difference between receipts and expenditures—surplus or deficit—of public undertakings being posted to the revenue accounts. By far the largest amounts of public expenditure are for social security, health, education and research, unemployment insurance, pensions, allowances, and rent subsidies.

The CIA estimates that, in 1994, government revenues totaled approximately $56.5 billion and expenditures $64.4 billion. External debt totaled $40.9 billion.

Income

In 1998, Denmark's gross national product (GNP) was $176 billion at current prices, or about $33,260 per person. For the period 1985–95, the average inflation rate was 2.8%, resulting in a real growth rate in per person GNP of 1.5%.

Industry

Manufacturing has greatly expanded since the end of World War II and now accounts for a far greater share of national income than does agriculture. The chemical, metalworking, and pharmaceutical industries have made notable progress. Handicrafts remain important, and Danish stone, clay, glass, wood, and silver products are world famous.

Machinery is by far the most important industrial export. Other important exports are canned foods, chemicals and pharmaceuticals, furniture, metal and paper products, ships, and textiles.

Banking and Finance

In 1936 the Danish National Bank, the bank of issue since 1818, was converted from an independent to an official government corporation. The bank performs all the usual functions of a central bank, and it holds almost all the nation's foreign exchange reserves.

Originally a commodity exchange equipped with booths and storage rooms, the Bourse is now almost exclusively a stock exchange. In 1970, the Stock Exchange was placed under the jurisdiction of the Ministry of Commerce with a governing committee of eleven members.

Economic Development

For many years, Danish governments followed a full-employment policy and relied chiefly on promotion of private enterprise to achieve this end. Beginning in the late 1970s, however, the government increased its intervention in the economy, in response to rising unemployment, inflation, and budget deficits. Inflation has been curbed and budget deficits reduced. This bolstered the currency from devaluation, but at the cost of restraining growth, and unemployment continued to rise.

In 1978, Denmark reached the UN target for official developmental assistance in the mid-1970s: 0.7% of GNP. It reached 0.96% of GNP in 1991, second only to Norway. Denmark's official assistance to developing countries amounted to $1.34 million in 1993.

SOCIAL WELFARE

Denmark was one of the first countries in the world to establish efficient social services. As of 1988, the nation was ninth in the world in expenditures on social security and housing, allotting 40.4% of its budget to these areas.

Family allowances are paid to families with incomes below a certain threshold, as are rent subsidies. The 1976 Social Assistance Act provides for an advisory service for persons undergoing social hardship; cash grants in situations not covered by pension law; a home-help service; and assistance in caring for young people experiencing difficulties.

All Danish citizens over 67 years of age may draw old-age pensions. Disability pensions are paid to persons with a certain degree of disablement. The state is primarily responsible for the care, education, and support of physically and mentally handicapped persons. There are allowances for unmarried mothers, for the children of widows, and in some cases for the children of widowers.

Laws guarantee equal pay for equal work, and women have and use legal recourse if they encounter discrimination.

Healthcare

Approximately $3,000 is invested in the social and medical well-being of every Dane annually, although health care expenditures have declined over the last decade. Anyone can go to a physician for free, and the public health system entitles each Dane to his or her own doctor. Costs are borne by public authorities, but high taxes help pay these costs.

In 1993, there was one physician for every 360 people. Public health authorities have waged large-scale campaigns against tuberculosis, venereal diseases, diphtheria, and poliomyelitis. In 1996, there were 1,866 AIDS cases. Life expectancy averages 75 years (72 for males and 78 for females).

Housing

Extensive government support helped to reduce the wartime and immediate postwar housing shortage. The total number of dwellings in 1996 was 2.4 million, of which 979,586 were detached one-family houses. In 1997, an estimated 15,790 new dwellings were completed, down from 27,237 in 1990.

EDUCATION

Practically the entire Danish adult population is literate. Primary, secondary, and, in general, university and other higher education are free, and public expenditure on education is therefore high.

Among the over one million students receiving education in 1994, 605,798 were in basic schools; 75,793 were in upper secondary schools; and 155,661 were in higher educational institutions such as colleges and universities.

1999 KEY EVENTS TIMELINE

January

- The new fiscal year begins with major changes in old age and early retirement pension programs.

- Denmark remains outside the new European Monetary Union but keeps the Danish *krone* fixed in value to the Euro.

February

- The Danish Supreme Court declares an Act of Parliament unconstitutional. The act sought to remove state subsidies from a controversial folk college.

March

- A new local government is formed in the autonomous territory of Greenland under Social Democratic Premier Jonathan Motzfeldt in coalition with leftist nationalists.

- Prostitution is decriminalized, although organized vice is still an offense.

April

- Collective bargaining agreements are reached for most public sector employees (about 30 percent of the labor force), largely in line with a 1998 private sector agreement. Additional paid vacation (5-6 weeks) is also gained.

- Danish military units participate in NATO military action against Serbia.

May

- Denmark negotiates an offshore economic zone between the autonomous Faroe Islands and the United Kingdom. This will allow oil prospecting in Faroese waters to commence.

- Government legislation ends a national strike by 5,000 nurses enforcing the public sector labor agreements reached in April.

June

- The 150th anniversary of a democratic constitution is celebrated nationally.

- National elections yield 16 Danish members of the European Parliament.

August

- Finance Minister Mogens Lykketoft proposes a 2000 governmental budget emphasizing surplus and falling national debt.

- The birth of a Danish prince, the first grandchild of Queen Margrethe II to Prince Joachim and Princess Alexandra, is announced. The child is baptized in November as Prince Nikolaj William Alexander Frederik.

September

- The renovated and expanded Royal (national) Library re opens in Copenhagen.

October

- Prime Minister Poul Nyrup Rasmussen opens Parliament and promises continuity in economic policies, improvements in education, health care, and public safety.

November

- A severe riot in Copenhagen by young Danish and immigrant activists takes place. Police unpreparedness is roundly criticized.

- Danish Queen Margrethe II and Prince Henrik visit New York City as part of the "Danish Waves" cultural program.

- President Akayev of Kyrgyzstan travels to Denmark for a three-day visit, during which he meets with Prime Minister Poul Nyrup Rasmussen and Danish industrial leaders.

- Police clash with anti-Nazi demonstrators outside a concert supported by neo-Nazis commemorating the anniversary of the death of the Spanish military dictator Franciso Franco (1892-1975).

- A program of visas is reinstated for Slovak citizens to control the flow of Slovaks seeking asylum in Denmark.

December

- Prime Minister Rasmussen reveals that he was shocked to learn recently that his father was a Nazi during World War II.

ANALYSIS OF EVENTS: 1999

BUSINESS AND THE ECONOMY

The Danish economy continued its expansion at a slower pace during 1999 following the government's tightening of the economic reins in June 1998. GDP was expected to grow by 1.7 percent for the year with unemployment averaging 5.7 percent. The national debt continued to decline as did public sector borrowing costs. Public sector labor relations were stormy in the spring as the government offered roughly the same deal that the private sector received the previous year. Most dissatisfied were the nurses (nearly all of whom are employed in the public health services). Their labor actions were ended by legislation in May. Overall Denmark's international economic standing continued to improve; one international credit agency gave Denmark its top rating.

The private sector did well; the Danish shipping company Maersk bought its American competitor Sealand and consolidated its position as the world's largest shipping concern. Danisco purchased a Finnish company to expand its international food products while preparing to sell off its distilling company which produces Denmark's famous "snaps." Legoland opened its first American amusement park in southern California in March.

The government's 1999 budget included some significant and controversial reforms in the Danish pension system. As part of a broad agreement with the principal center-right opposition parties, the Social Democratic-Liberal coalition lowered the general old-age pension age from 67 to 65 while tightening subsidies for early retirement. The reforms will require extra pension contributions by those intending to take early retirement in the future, and will reward those who delay their retirement until 65. Overall the budget sought to expand resources for the health care sector and education while running a revenue surplus to reduce the national debt. Despite the vigor of its economy, Denmark chose not to join the new European Monetary

Union which went into effect in January. The Danish *krone* will remain firmly linked to the new "Euro," and overall Danish economic policies will not diverge significantly from its EU partners.

The government continues to promote competition by deregulating utilities. Following the liberalization of telecommunications, 1999 saw similar measures for the electrical power industry. Globalization is forcing mergers on Danish firms, including this year's merger between two large insurance companies (Unidanmark and Tryg-Baltica) and the dairy industry (MD Foods and Klover).

Issues of food quality and safety remained prominent in Denmark, with strong support for the European Union's reluctance to allow foreign meats (mainly from the U.S.A.) treated with hormones or genetically modified foods. On the home front, Danish poultry continued to be plagued by bacteria and questions about consumer safety.

GOVERNMENT AND POLITICS

Prime Minister Poul Nyrup Rasmussen's center-left coalition remains solid despite its single vote parliamentary majority. His ability to maneuver first to the left (the fiscal tightening in 1998) and then to the right (the 1999 budget agreement) was not without costs. Particularly, the cuts in early pension schemes hurt Rasmussen's popularity as he had promised not to touch this popular but expensive public program in the 1998 parliamentary elections. By year's end the anger was subsiding because the popularity of Rasmussen's Social Democrats remained at historic lows. This may have been what was behind the party's modest performance in the June elections to the European Parliament. That election produced no fundamental changes; the leftist anti-European Union forces held on to their four seats (of Denmark's 16) while the equally anti-EU rightist Danish People's party gained its first seat. Among the mainstream parties, the Conservatives continued their decline while the pro-EU Liberals and Social Democrats each picked up a seat. Only 51.7 percent of eligible Danish voters went to the polls.

European Union issues centered on the monetary union and a timetable for a Danish decision on whether or not to join (which would require yet another national referendum). Such an election is unlikely before 2001. Danes generally supported the European Parliament's dismissal of the Santer European Commission. Danish Commissioner Ritt

Bjerregaard was replaced by fellow Social Democrat Poul Nielsson.

The government hammered out a five year defense policy agreement (a year longer than usual) with the center and right parties. There will be significant cuts each year including base closings, but there will also be accelerated defense equipment modernization. This is important given Denmark's participation in NATO and UN peacekeeping efforts. Danish air and naval units supported the NATO enforcement measures against Serbia, while Denmark joined its allies in receiving numerous refugees from the war zone.

CULTURE AND SOCIETY

Denmark celebrated the 150th anniversary of its first democratic constitution in June. Consensus around its democratic political principles remains nearly universal despite the daily partisan squabbles. The current constitution dates from 1953 and there are growing calls for revision. Likewise, the future relationship of the autonomous Faroe Islands in the North Atlantic remains unsettled.

Refugees and immigrants continued to stir passions in Danish politics as right wing parties focussed on the immigration issue. Strong antiforeigner comments emanate regularly from the Danish People's party and its rightwing competitor, the Progress party. The latter party split further following the return of its controversial founder Mogen Glistrup, whose anti-foreigner rhetoric is exceptionally strident. Although less than a sixth of the Danish electorate supports these extreme parties, problems with the integration of some non-European immigrants dominated the domestic debate. Violence by immigrant gangs in Odense and by similar groups—joined by Danish young anarchists—in Copenhagen stirred passions and concerns.

Danish films continue to attract international attention while at home new films have been well received. A major international cultural exposition called "Danish Wave," opened in Australia early in 1999 and a similar event attracted considerable attention in New York City in October. At home, new cultural facilities included the renovated and expanded State Art Museum and Royal Library in Copenhagen.

DIRECTORY

CENTRAL GOVERNMENT

Head of State

Queen
Margrethe

Prime Minister
Poul Nyrup Rasmussen, Office of the Prime
Minister, Christiansborg, Prins Jorgens Gaard 11,
DK-1218 Copenhagen, Denmark
PHONE: +45 33923300
FAX: +45 33111665
E-MAIL: stm@stm.dk

Ministers

Minister of Education
Margrethe Vestager, Ministry of Education,
Frederiksholms Kanal 21, DK-1220 Copenhagen
K, Denmark
PHONE: +45 33925000
FAX: +45 33925547
E-MAIL: uvm@uvm.dk

Minister of Environment and Energy
Ministry of Environment and Energy, Højbro
Plads 4, DK-1200 Copenhagen K, Denmark
PHONE: +45 33927600
FAX: +45 33322227
E-MAIL: mem@mem.dk

Minister for Foreign Affairs
Niels Helveg Petersen, Ministry for Foreign
Affairs, Asiatisk Plads 2, DK-1448 Copenhagen
K, Denmark
PHONE: +45 33920000
FAX: +45 32540533
E-MAIL: um@um.dk

**Minister for Research and Information
Technology**
Birte Weiss, Ministry for Research and
Information Technology, Bredgade 43, DK-1260
Copenhagen K, Denmark
PHONE: +45 33929700
FAX: +45 33323501
E-MAIL: fsk@fsk.dk

Minister of the Interior
Ministry of the Interior, Christiansborg
Slotsplads 1, DK-1218 Copenhagen K, Denmark
PHONE: +45 33923380
FAX: +45 33111239
E-MAIL: inm@inm.dk

Minister of Justice
Frank Jensen, Ministry of Justice,
Slotsholmsgade 10, DK-1218 Copenhagen K,
Denmark
PHONE: +45 33923340
FAX: +45 33933510
E-MAIL: jm@jm.dk

Minister of Food, Agriculture and Fisheries
Ministry of Food, Agriculture and Fisheries,
Holbergsgade 2, DK-1057 Copenhagen K,
Denmark
PHONE: +45 33923301
E-MAIL: fvm@fvm.dk

Minister of Culture
Ministry of Culture, Nybrogade 10, DK-1203
Copenhagen K, Denmark
PHONE: +45 33923040
FAX: +45 33146428
E-MAIL: kultips@inet.uni-c.dk

Minister of Health
Ministry of Health, Holbergsgade 6, DK-1057
Copenhagen K, Denmark
PHONE: +45 33923360
FAX: +45 33931563
E-MAIL: sum@sum.dk

Minister of Labor
Ove Hygum, Ministry of Labor, Holmens Kanal
20, DK-1060 Copenhagen K, Denmark
PHONE: +45 33925900

Minster of Social Affairs
Ministry of Social Affairs, Holmens Kanal 22,
DK-1060 Copenhagen K, Denmark
PHONE: +45 33929300

Minister of Transport
Ministry of Transport, Frederiksholms Kanal 27,
DK-1220 Copenhagen K, Denmark
PHONE: +45 33923355
FAX: +45 33123893
E-MAIL: trm@trm.dk

Minister of Defense
H. E. Hans Haekkerup, Ministry of Defense,
Holmens Kanal 42, DK-1060 Copenhagen K,
Denmark
PHONE: +45 33923320
FAX: +45 33320655
E-MAIL: fmn@fmn.dk

Minister of Business and Industry
Pia Gjellerup, Ministry of Business and Industry,
Slotsholmsgade 10-12, DK-1216 Copenhagen K,
Denmark

PHONE: +45 33923350
FAX: +45 33123778
E-MAIL: em@em.dk

Minister of Economy

Marianne Jelved, Ministry of Economy, Ved
Stranden 8, DK-1061 Copenhagen K, Denmark
PHONE: +45 33923322
FAX: +45 33936020
E-MAIL: oem@oem.dk

Minister of Treasury

Ole Stavad, Ministry of Treasury,
Slotsholmsgade 12, DK-1216 Copenhagen K,
Denmark
PHONE: +45 33923392
E-MAIL: km@skm.dk

POLITICAL ORGANIZATIONS

Social Democrats

2 Thorvaldsensvej, DK-1780 Copenhagen V,
Denmark
PHONE: +45 31391522
FAX: +45 31394030
E-MAIL: socialdemokratiet@net.dialog.dk
NAME: Poul Nyrup Rasmussen

Liberals

30 Søllerødvej, DK-2840 Holte, Denmark
PHONE: +45 45802233
FAX: +45 45803830
E-MAIL: venstre@venstre.dk
NAME: Uffe Ellemann-Jensen

Conservatives

Press Service, Christiansborg, DK-1240
Copenhagen K, Denmark
PHONE: +45 33374388; 33120266
FAX: +45 33931431
E-MAIL: konservative@konservative.dk
NAME: Hans Engell

Socialist People's Party

Christiansborg, DK-1240 Copenhagen K,
Denmark
PHONE: +45 33374491
FAX: +45 33147010
E-MAIL: sf@sf.dk
NAME: Holger K. Nielsen

Danish People's Party

Christiansborg, DK-1240 Copenhagen K,
Denmark

PHONE: +45 33375199
FAX: +45 33375191
E-MAIL: dfcceb@ft.dk

Centre Democrats

7 Ny Vestergade, DK-1471 Copenhagen K,
Denmark
PHONE: +45 33127115
FAX: +45 33120115
E-MAIL: cd@pol.dk
NAME: Mimi Stilling Jakobsen

Social Liberals

Christiansborg, DK-1240 Copenhagen K,
Denmark
PHONE: +45 33374747
FAX: +45 33137251
E-MAIL: radikale@radikale.dk

Red-Green Alliance

24 Studiestraede, DK-1455 Copenhagen K,
Denmark
PHONE: +45 33933324; 33375050
FAX: +45 33320372
E-MAIL: elhebj@ft.dk

Progress Party

Christiansborg, DK-1240 Copenhagen K,
Denmark
PHONE: +45 33374699
FAX: +45 33151399
E-MAIL: fp@ft.dk
TITLE: Group Chairman
NAME: Kim Behnke

Christian People's Party

Christiansborg, DK-1240 Copenhagen K,
Denmark
PHONE: +45 33374999
FAX: +45 33374998
E-MAIL: krf@ft.dk
NAME: Jann Sjursen

DIPLOMATIC REPRESENTATION

Embassies in Denmark

Algeria
Amaliegade 36, DK-1256 Copenhagen K,
Denmark
PHONE: +45 33119440; 33119640
FAX: +45 33115850
E-MAIL: ambalda@post10.Telephonee.dk

TITLE: Ambassador
NAME: Mohamed Benhocine

Argentina
Borgergade 16, 1st fl., DK-1300 Copenhagen K, Denmark
PHONE: +45 33158082; 33159526
FAX: +45 33155574
E-MAIL: embardin@post1.Telephonee.dk
TITLE: Ambassador
NAME: Vicente Ernesto Berasategui

Australia
Strandboulevarden 122, 5th fl., DK-2100 Copenhagen Ø, Denmark
PHONE: +45 39292077
FAX: +45 39296077

Austria
Sølundsvej 1, DK-2100 Copenhagen Ø, Denmark
PHONE: +45 39294141
FAX: +45 39292086
E-MAIL: austria@post7.Telephonec.dk
TITLE: Ambassador
NAME: Robert Marschik

Belgium
Øster Allé 7, DK-2100 Copenhagen Ø, Denmark
PHONE: +45 35250200
FAX: +45 35250211
E-MAIL: mi612063@inet.uni2.dk or Copenhagen@diplobel.org
TITLE: Ambassador
NAME: Baudouin de la Kethulle de Ryhove

Bolivia
Amaliegade 16 C, 2nd fl., DK-1256 Copenhagen K, Denmark
PHONE: +45 33124900
FAX: +45 33124903
TITLE: Charge d'Affaires
NAME: Jorge Heredia

Botswana
c/o Microtronic A/S, Byleddet 12-14, DK-4000 Roskilde, Denmark
PHONE: +45 46365691
FAX: +45 46365113
TITLE: Consul
NAME: Kjell A. Nilsson

Brazil
Ryvangs Alle'e9 24, DK-2100 Copenhagen Ø, Denmark
PHONE: +45 39206478
FAX: +45 39273607
E-MAIL: ambassade@brazil.dk

TITLE: Ambassador
NAME: Carlos Luiz Coutinho Perez

Bulgaria
Gamlehave Allé 7, DK-2920 Charlottenlund, Denmark
PHONE: +56 39642484; 39635634; 39633872
FAX: +56 39634923
TITLE: Ambassador
NAME: Kroum Dimitrov Slavov

Burkina Faso
Svanemøllevej 20, DK-2100 Copenhagen Ø, Denmark
PHONE: +56 39184022
FAX: +56 39271886
TITLE: Ambassador
NAME: Anna Konaté

Canada
Kr. Bernikowsgade 1, DK-1105 Copenhagen K, Denmark
PHONE: +45 33483200
FAX: +45 33483221
TITLE: Ambassador
NAME: Brian Ellison Baker

Chile
Kassvej 15, 3rd Fl., DK-2100 Copenhagen Ø, Denmark
PHONE: +45 35385834; 35437755
FAX: +45 35384201
TITLE: Ambassador
NAME: Raefal Schmidt

China
Øregårds Allé 25, DK-2900 Hellerup, Denmark
PHONE: +45 39460889
FAX: +45 39625484
TITLE: Ambassador
NAME: Yang Hexiong

Colombia
Kassvej 15, Gr. Fl., DK-2100 Copenhagen Ø, Denmark
PHONE: +56 35263026; 35263103
FAX: +56 35262297
TITLE: Chargé d'Affaires
NAME: Carlos Arturo Morales

Costa Rica
Kvesthusgade 3, DK-1251 Copenhagen K, Denmark
PHONE: +45 33110885
FAX: +45 33937530
TITLE: Consul-General
NAME: Mads Marstrand-Jørgensen

Croatia
Dronningens Tærgade 5, 1st Fl., DK-1302
Copenhagen K, Denmark
PHONE: +45 33919095; 33915121
FAX: +45 33917131
TITLE: Ambassador
NAME: Mario Mikolic

Cuba
Carolinevej 12, Gr. Fl., left, DK-2900 Hellerup,
Denmark
PHONE: +45 39401510
FAX: +45 39401510
TITLE: Chargé d'Affaires
NAME: Carlos Alfredo Amores

Cyprus
Aurikelvej 22, DK-2000 Frederiksberg, Denmark
PHONE: +45 36462980
FAX: +45 31317141
TITLE: Vice-Consul
NAME: Ove Linde

Czech Republic
Ryvangs Allé 14-16, DK-2100 Copenhagen Ø,
Denmark
PHONE: +45 39291888; 39291598
FAX: +45 39291888; 39291598
TITLE: Ambassador
NAME: Alois Buchta

Ecuador
c/o J.C. Hempels Skibsfarve-Fabrik A/S,
Lundtoftevej 150, DK-2800 Lyngby, Denmark
PHONE: +45 45933800
FAX: +45 45885518
TITLE: Consul
NAME: Leif Juul Jørgensen

Egypt
Kristianiagade 19, DK-2100 Copenhagen Ø,
Denmark
PHONE: +45 35437070
FAX: +45 35433649
TITLE: Ambassador
NAME: Mohammad Shaaban

El Salvador
Gatnervej 18, DK-2630 Taastrup, Denmark
PHONE: +45 43998530
FAX: +45 43998530
TITLE: Consul
NAME: Torben Alstrup Jensen

Estonia
Aurehøjvej 19, DK-2900 Hellerup, Denmark
PHONE: +45 39463070
FAX: +45 39463076

TITLE: Ambassador
NAME: Jüri Kahn

Finland
Sankt Anné Plads 24, DK-1250 Copenhagen K,
Denmark
PHONE: +45 33134214
FAX: +45 33324710
TITLE: Ambassador
NAME: Ralf Friberg

France
Kongens Nytorv 4, DK-1050 Copenhagen K,
Denmark
PHONE: +45 33155122
FAX: +45 33939752
TITLE: Ambassador
NAME: Jean Pierre Masset

Germany
Stockholmsgade 57, Box 2712, DK-2100
Copenhagen Ø, Denmark
PHONE: +45 35261622
FAX: +45 35267105

Ghana
Egebjerg Allé 13, DK-2900 Hellerup, Denmark
PHONE: +45 39628222
FAX: +45 39621652
TITLE: Ambassador
NAME: Martha Dodoo Tamakloe

Greece
Borgergade 16, DK-1300 Copenhagen K,
Denmark
PHONE: +45 33114533; 33115139
FAX: +45 33931646
TITLE: Ambassador
NAME: Anastase Scopelitis

Guatemala
Immortellevej 4, DK-2950 Vedbék, Denmark
PHONE: +45 45891584
FAX: +45 45893322
TITLE: Consul
NAME: Knud-Ole Larsen

Guinea
Illumgaard, Hveensvej 6, DK-2950 Vedbæk,
Denmark
PHONE: +45 45892000
FAX: +45 45893100
TITLE: Consul
NAME: Axel Juhl-Jørgensen

Honduras
Telegrafvej 5, DK-2750 Ballerup, Denmark
PHONE: +45 44973626

FAX: +45 44683304
TITLE: Consul-General
NAME: Carl G. Sander

Hungary

Strandvejen 170, DK-2920 Charlottenlund,
Denmark
PHONE: +45 39631688; 39631929
FAX: +45 39630052
TITLE: Ambassador
NAME: Andrés Hajdu

Iceland

Dantes Plads 3, DK-1556 Copenhagen V,
Denmark
PHONE: +45 33159604; 33159675
FAX: +45 33930506
TITLE: Ambassador
NAME: Helgi Ágústsson

India

Vangehusvej 15, DK-2100 Copenhagen Ø,
Denmark
PHONE: +45 39182888; 39299201
FAX: +45 39270218
TITLE: Ambassador
NAME: Mr. Shashank

Indonesia

Ørehøj Allé 1, DK-2900 Hellerup, Denmark
PHONE: +45 39624422
FAX: +45 39624483
TITLE: Ambassador
NAME: Andjar Soejito Mangkoewijoto

Iran

Engskiftevej 6, DK-2100 Copenhagen Ø,
Denmark
PHONE: +45 39160071; 39160072
FAX: +45 39160075; 39160076
TITLE: Ambassador
NAME: Nasser Jafar Jasbi

Ireland

Østbanegade 21, DK-2100 Copenhagen Ø,
Denmark
PHONE: +45 35423233
FAX: +45 35431858
TITLE: Ambassador
NAME: James Anthony Sharkey

Israel

Lundevangsvej 4, DK-2900 Hellerup, Denmark
PHONE: +45 39626288
FAX: +45 39621938
TITLE: Ambassador
NAME: Abraham Setton

Italy

Gammel Vartov Vej 7, DK-2900 Hellerup,
Denmark
PHONE: +45 39626877
FAX: +45 39622599
TITLE: Ambassador
NAME: Giacomo Ivancich-Biaggini

Jamaica

Tagesmindevej 8, DK-2820 Gentofte, Denmark
PHONE: +45 39654313
FAX: +45 39650263
TITLE: Consul
NAME: Hans Jørgen Petersen

Japan

Pilestrae 61, DK-1112 Copenhagen K, Denmark
PHONE: +45 33113344; 33455090
FAX: +45 33113377
TITLE: Ambassador
NAME: Masaki Orita

Jordan

H. C. Andersens Boulevard 9, 2nd Fl., DK-1553
Copenhagen V, Denmark
PHONE: +45 33338677
FAX: +45 33338986
TITLE: Consul
NAME: Jørgen Stockfleth Carlé

South Korea

Svanemøllevej 104, DK-2900 Hellerup, Denmark
PHONE: +45 39460400
FAX: +45 39460422
TITLE: Ambassador
NAME: Kwon Young-min

Kuwait

Strandvejen 203, DK-2900 Hellerup, Denmark
PHONE: +45 39611420
FAX: +45 39610677
TITLE: Consul
NAME: Børge Emil Hansen

Latvia

Rosbæksvej 17, DK-2100 Copenhagen Ø,
Denmark
PHONE: +45 39276000
FAX: +45 39276173
TITLE: Ambassador
NAME: Aivars Baumanis

Lebanon

Mantziusvej 18, DK-2900 Hellerup, Denmark
TITLE: Consul
NAME: Karoli L. Nemeth

Liberia

Pakhus 12, Amerikakaj Dampfergevej 10, DK-2100 Copenhagen Ø, Denmark
PHONE: +45 35262995
FAX: +45 35266995
TITLE: Consul-General
NAME: Jørgen Galst

Libya

Rosenvaengets Hovedvej 4, DK-2100 Copenhagen Ø, Denmark
PHONE: +56 35263611; 35263664
FAX: +56 35265606
TITLE: Chargè d'Affaires
NAME: Fauzi Milad Abu-Argub

Luxembourg

Fridtjof Nansens Plads 5, 1st Fl., DK-2100 Copenhagen Ø, Denmark
PHONE: +45 35268200
FAX: +45 35268208
TITLE: Ambassador
NAME: Francois Bremer

United Kingdom

Kastelsvej 36-40, DK-2100 Copenhagen Ø, Denmark
PHONE: +45 35445200
FAX: +45 35445293
TITLE: Ambassador
NAME: Philip Astley

United States

Dag Hammarskjølds Alle 24, DK-2100 Copenhagen Ø, Denmark
PHONE: +45 35553144
FAX: +45 35430223
TITLE: Ambassador
NAME: Richard N. Swett

Vatican City

Apostolic Nunciature, Immorlevej 11, 2950 Vedbék, Denmark
PHONE: 45893536, 45893637
FAX: 45661771
TITLE: Ambassador

NAME: Piero Biggio

JUDICIAL SYSTEM

The Supreme Court

High Courts

City Courts

FURTHER READING

Government Publications

International Monetary Fund. *IMF Concludes Article IV Consultation with Denmark*. Public Information Notice no. 99/83 (August 1999).

Organisation for Economic Co-operation and Development. *Economic Outlook*. No. 65 (June 1999).

Books

Einhorn, Eric S. and John Logue. ''Scandinavia: Still the Middle Way?'' *Europe Today*. Edited by Ronald Tiersky. Lanham, MD: Rowman and Littlefield, 1999. 197-240.

Ingebritsen, Christine. *The Nordic States and European Union: From Economic Interdependence to Political Integration*. Ithaca, NY: Cornell University Press, 1998.

Internet

Danmarks Statistik. Available Online @ http://www.dst.dk (November 11, 1999).

Politiken Available Online @ http://www.politiken.dk (November 11, 1999).

News from Denmark. Available Online @ http://www.denmarkemb.org/press (November 11, 1999).

Statens Information. Available Online @ http://www.danmark.dk (November 11, 1999).

DENMARK: STATISTICAL DATA

For sources and notes see "Sources of Statistics" in the front of each volume.

GEOGRAPHY

Geography (1)

Area:

Total: 43,094 sq km.

Land: 42,394 sq km.

Water: 700 sq km.

Note: includes the island of Bornholm in the Baltic Sea and the rest of metropolitan Denmark, but excludes the Faroe Islands and Greenland.

Area—comparative: slightly less than twice the size of Massachusetts.

Land boundaries:

Total: 68 km.

Border countries: Germany 68 km.

Coastline: 7,314 km.

Climate: temperate; humid and overcast; mild, windy winters and cool summers.

Terrain: low and flat to gently rolling plains.

Natural resources: petroleum, natural gas, fish, salt, limestone, stone, gravel and sand.

Land use:

Arable land: 60%

Permanent crops: 0%

Permanent pastures: 5%

Forests and woodland: 10%

Other: 25% (1993 est.).

HUMAN FACTORS

Demographics (2A)

	1990	1995	1998	2000	2010	2020	2030	2040	2050
Population	5,141.0	5,234.3	5,333.6	5,374.6	5,452.7	5,401.4	5,223.1	4,887.0	4,476.1
Net migration rate (per 1,000 population)	NA	NA	NA	NA	NA	NA	NA	NA	NA
Births	NA	NA	NA	NA	NA	NA	NA	NA	NA
Deaths	36.5	NA	NA	NA	NA	NA	NA	NA	NA
Life expectancy - males	71.8	73.0	73.6	74.0	75.7	77.1	78.2	79.0	79.7
Life expectancy - females	77.7	78.5	79.1	79.5	81.4	82.9	84.1	85.0	85.7
Birth rate (per 1,000)	12.4	13.3	12.2	11.0	8.6	8.8	7.9	6.6	6.6
Death rate (per 1,000)	11.9	11.5	11.1	10.9	10.6	11.3	13.0	14.5	16.1
Women of reproductive age (15-49 yrs.)	1,309.7	1,299.0	1,276.8	1,265.0	1,253.8	1,174.9	1,043.8	961.3	809.2
of which are currently married	NA	NA	NA	NA	NA	NA	NA	NA	NA
Fertility rate	1.7	1.8	1.7	1.5	1.5	1.4	1.4	1.3	1.3

Except as noted, values for vital statistics are in thousands; life expectancy is in years.

Health Personnel (3)

Total health expenditure as a percentage of GDP,
1990-1997[a]

Public sector 5.1

Private sector 2.7

Total[b] 7.8

Health expenditure per capita in U.S. dollars,
1990-1997[a]

Purchasing power parity 1,811

Total 2,388

Availability of health care facilities per 100,000 people

Hospital beds 1990-1997[a] 490

Doctors 1993[c] 283

Nurses 1993[c] . . . . .NA

Health Indicators (4)

Life expectancy at birth

1980 74

1997 75

Daily per capita supply of calories (1996) 3,808

Total fertility rate births per woman (1997) 1.8

Maternal mortality ratio per 100,000 live births
(1990-97) . . . . .9[c]

Safe water % of population with access (1995) . . . .

Sanitation % of population with access (1995) 100

Consumption of iodized salt % of households
(1992-98)[a] . . . .

Smoking prevalence

Male % of adults (1985-95)[a] 37

Female % of adults (1985-95)[a] 37

Tuberculosis incidence per 100,000 people
(1997) 11

Adult HIV prevalence % of population ages
15-49 (1997) 0.12

Infants and Malnutrition (5)

Under-5 mortality rate (1997) 6

% of infants with low birthweight (1990-97) 6

Births attended by skilled health staff % of total[a] . . .NA

% fully immunized (1995-97)

TB . . . . .NA

DPT 89%

Polio 100%

Measles 84%

Prevalence of child malnutrition under age 5
(1992-97)[b] . . . . .NA

Ethnic Division (6)

Scandinavian, Eskimo, Faroese, German.

Religions (7)

Evangelical Lutheran 91%

Other Protestant and Roman Catholic 2%

Other 7% (1988)

Languages (8)

Danish, Faroese, Greenlandic (an Eskimo dialect),
German (small minority).

EDUCATION

Public Education Expenditures (9)

Public expenditure on education (% of GNP)

1980 . . . . .6.8

1996 . . . . .8.2[1]

Expenditure per student

Primary % of GNP per capita

1980 . . . . .38.4

1996 . . . . .25.9[1]

Secondary % of GNP per capita

1980 . . . . .11.6

1996 . . . . .36.6[1]

Tertiary % of GNP per capita

1980 . . . . .51.5

1996 . . . . .55.3[1]

Expenditure on teaching materials

Primary % of total for level (1996) 4.3

Secondary % of total for level (1996) . . . .

Primary pupil-teacher ratio per teacher (1996) . . . . .10[1]

Duration of primary education years (1995) 6

Educational Attainment (10)

Age group (1991)[16] . . . . .25+

Total population 2,742,734

Highest level attained (%)

No schooling . . . .-

First level

Not completed 38.7

Completed . . . . .NA

Entered second level

S-1 . . . . .3.4

S-2 . . . . .38.2

Postsecondary 19.6

GOVERNMENT & LAW

Political Parties (12)

Parliament	No. of seats
Social Democrats	.65
Socialist People's Party	.13
Radical Liberal Party	.7
Unity Party	.5
Progress Party	.42
Conservative People's Party	.16
Danish People's Party	.13
Center Democrats	.8
Other parties	.10

Government Budget (13A)

Year: 1995

Total Expenditures: 419,725 Millions of Kroner

Expenditures as a percentage of the total by function:

General public services and public order	.9.28[p]
Defense	.4.03[p]
Education	.9.37[p]
Health	.82[p]
Social Security and Welfare	.43.22[p]
Housing and community amenities	.1.61[p]
Recreational, cultural, and religious affairs	.1.58[p]
Fuel and energy	.60[p]
Agriculture, forestry, fishing, and hunting	.90[p]
Mining, manufacturing, and construction	.39[p]
Transportation and communication	.2.46[p]
Other economic affairs and services	.3.51[p]

Military Affairs (14B)

	1990	1991	1992	1993	1994	1995
Military expenditures						
Current dollars (mil.)	3,025	3,210	3,246	3,340	3,336	3,118
1995 constant dollars (mil.)	3,477	3,547	3,491	3,502	3,420	3,118
Armed forces (000)	31	30	28	27	28	27
Gross national product (GNP)						
Current dollars (mil.)	141,100	149,100	155,300	162,200	173,200	170,100[e]
1995 constant dollars (mil.)	162,100	164,700	167,000	170,100	177,600	170,100[e]
Central government expenditures (CGE)						
1995 constant dollars (mil.)	68,680	70,910	73,330	78,050	81,680	75,580
People (mil.)	5.1	5.2	5.2	5.2	5.2	5.2
Military expenditure as % of GNP	2.1	2.2	2.1	2.1	1.9	1.8
Military expenditure as % of CGE	5.1	5.0	4.8	4.5	4.2	4.1
Military expenditure per capita (1995 $)	676	688	675	675	657	596
Armed forces per 1,000 people (soldiers)	6.0	5.8	5.4	5.2	5.4	5.2
GNP per capita (1995 $)	31,540	31,960	32,290	34,100	34,100	32,540
Arms imports[6]						
Current dollars (mil.)	110	60	70	100	40	80
1995 constant dollars (mil.)	126	66	75	105	41	80
Arms exports[6]						
Current dollars (mil.)	80	20	10	10	10	20
1995 constant dollars (mil.)	92	22	11	10	10	20
Total imports[7]						
Current dollars (mil.)	32,230	32,400	35,170	30,540	34,880	43,220
1995 constant dollars (mil.)	37,040	35,800	37,830	32,020	35,750	43,220
Total exports[7]						
Current dollars (mil.)	35,130	36,000	41,050	37,170	41,420	49,040
1995 constant dollars (mil.)	40,380	39,780	44,160	38,970	42,460	49,040
Arms as percent of total imports[8]	.3	.2	.2	.3	.1	.2
Arms as percent of total exports[8]	.2	.1	0	0	0	0

Crime (15)

Crime rate (for 1997)

Crimes reported 531,100

Total persons convicted 106,200

Crimes per 100,000 population 10,100

Persons responsible for offenses

Total number of suspects . . . . .NA

Total number of female suspects . . . . .NA

Total number of juvenile suspects . . . . .NA

LABOR FORCE

Labor Force (16)

Total 2,895,950

Private services 40%

Government services 30%

Manufacturing and mining 19%

Construction 6%

Agriculture, forestry, and fishing 5%

Data for 1995.

Unemployment Rate (17)

7.9% (1997 est.)

PRODUCTION SECTOR

Electric Energy (18)

Capacity . . . . .10.604 million kW (1995)

Production . . . . .34.244 billion kWh (1995)

Consumption per capita . . . . .6,432 kWh (1995)

Transportation (19)

Highways:

total: 71,600 km

paved: 71,600 km (including 880 km of expressways)

unpaved: 0 km (1996 est.)

Waterways: 417 km

Pipelines: crude oil 110 km; petroleum products 578 km; natural gas 700 km

Merchant marine:

total: 327 ships (1,000 GRT or over) totaling 4,972,331 GRT/6,894,091 DWT ships by type: bulk 14, cargo 118, chemical tanker 16, container 76, liquefied gas tanker 24, livestock carrier 6, oil tanker 25, railcar carrier 1, refrigerated cargo 14, roll-on/roll-off cargo 22, short-sea passenger 9, specialized tanker 2 note: Denmark has created its own internal register, called the Danish International Ship register (DIS); DIS ships do

not have to meet Danish manning regulations, and they amount to a flag of convenience within the Danish register (1997 est.)

Airports: 118 (1997 est.)

Airports—with paved runways:

total: 28

over 3,047 m: 2

2,438 to 3,047 m: 7

1,524 to 2,437 m: 3

914 to 1,523 m: 13

under 914 m: 3 (1997 est.)

Airports—with unpaved runways:

total: 90

1,524 to 2,437 m: 1

914 to 1,523 m: 7

under 914 m: 82 (1997 est.)

Top Agricultural Products (20)

Grain, potatoes, rape, sugar beets; meat, dairy products; fish.

MANUFACTURING SECTOR

GDP & Manufacturing Summary (21)

Detailed value added figures are listed by both International Standard Industry Code (ISIC) and product title.

	1980	1985	1990	1994
GDP ($-1990 mil.)[1]	104,994	119,647	129,116	139,659
Per capita ($-1990)[1]	20,495	23,396	25,120	26,998
Manufacturing share (%) (current prices)[1]	19.7	19.6	18.3	*19.0*
Manufacturing				
Value added ($-1990 mil.)[1]	18,562	21,047	20,992	22,453
Industrial production index	100	122	133	148
Value added ($ mil.)	11,944	10,451	22,988	*26,633*
Gross output ($ mil.)	29,347	25,713	52,700	*61,511*
Employment (000)	381	405	511	*494*

	1980	1985	1990	1994
Profitability (% of gross output)				
Intermediate input (%)	59	59	56	57
Wages and salaries inc. supplements (%)	26	24	28	26
Gross operating surplus	15	17	15	17
Productivity ($)				
Gross output per worker	76,623	63,316	99,957	123,541
Value added per worker	31,187	25,734	43,602	54,677
Average wage (inc. supplements)	19,697	15,021	29,241	33,017
Value added ($ mil.)				
311/2 Food products	2,232	1,925	4,072	4,964
313 Beverages	484	381	757	945
314 Tobacco products	108	95	203	260
321 Textiles	366	324	610	631
322 Wearing apparel	204	176	259	253
323 Leather and fur products	27	18	25	16
324 Footwear	55	38	65	100
331 Wood and wood products	252	193	486	537
332 Furniture and fixtures	271	305	642	721
341 Paper and paper products	300	262	628	726
342 Printing and publishing	845	675	1,592	1,746

	1980	1985	1990	1994
351 Industrial chemicals	534	482	1,107	1,404
352 Other chemical products	604	599	1,537	1,900
353 Petroleum refineries	53	51	118	193
354 Miscellaneous petroleum and coal products	64	59	207	205
355 Rubber products	75	56	122	113
356 Plastic products	238	264	635	767
361 Pottery, china and earthenware	83	40	71	67
362 Glass and glass products	94	58	114	120
369 Other non-metal mineral products	568	432	941	968
371 Iron and steel	167	118	281	292
372 Non-ferrous metals	67	42	73	69
381 Metal products	825	798	1,837	2,178
382 Non-electrical machinery	1,616	1,387	3,050	3,443
383 Electrical machinery	703	622	1,319	1,311
384 Transport equipment	644	572	1,128	1,316
385 Professional and scientific equipment	275	294	622	701
390 Other manufacturing industries	192	185	489	685

FINANCE, ECONOMICS, & TRADE

Balance of Payments (23)

	1992	1993	1994	1995	1996
Exports of goods (f.o.b.)	40,504	36,948	41,741	48,901	50,735
Imports of goods (f.o.b.)	−33,446	−29,229	−34,300	−42,080	−43,203
Trade balance	7,058	7,719	7,441	6,820	7,532
Services - debits	−32,018	−37,947	−39,452	−47,056	−57,230
Services - credits	30,039	35,655	36,404	43,233	54,128
Private transfers (net)	−749	−462	−1,111	−1,299	−1,453
Government transfers (net)	−131	−133	−93	−92	−113
Overall balance	4,199	4,832	3,189	1,606	2,864

FINANCE, ECONOMICS, & TRADE

Economic Indicators (22)

National product: GDP—purchasing power parity—$122.5 billion (1997 est.)

National product real growth rate: 3% (1997 est.)

National product per capita: $23,200 (1997 est.)

Inflation rate—consumer price index: 2.2% (1997 est.)

Exchange Rates (24)

Exchange rates:

Danish kroner (DKr) per US$1

January 1998	.6.916
1997	.6.604
1996	.5.799
1995	.5.602
1994	.6.361
1993	.6.484

Top Import Origins (25)

$43.2 billion (c.i.f., 1996) Data are for 1995.

Origins	%
Germany	.21.7
Sweden	.11.7
Netherlands	.7.0
United Kingdom	.6.6
France	.5.2
Norway	.4.9

United States	.4.7
Japan	.3.5
FSU	.1.7

Top Export Destinations (26)

$48.8 billion (f.o.b., 1996) Data are for 1995.

Destinations	%
Germany	.22.5
Sweden	.9.7
United Kingdom	.7.9
Norway	.5.9
France	.5.4
Netherlands	.4.4
United States	.4.0

Economic Aid (27)

Donor: ODA, $1.34 billion (1993).

Import Export Commodities (28)

Import Commodities	Export Commodities
Machinery and equipment	Machinery and instruments 25%
Petroleum 25%	Meat and meat products
Chemicals	Fuels
Grain and foodstuffs	Dairy products
Textiles	Ships
Paper	Fish
	Chemicals 4.4%

DJIBOUTI

Republic of Djibouti
République de Djibouti
Jumhouriyya Djibouti

INTRODUCTORY SURVEY

RECENT HISTORY

After World War II, French Somaliland gradually gained a measure of local autonomy. In 1957, it obtained a territorial assembly and a local executive council. These bodies were able to advise the French-appointed governor-general. In 1967, French Somaliland joined the French Community as an overseas territory. The territory elected one deputy and one senator to the French National Assembly.

During this period, there were ongoing disagreements between the two ethnic groups in the country, the Afars and the Issas. Although the Afars were in the minority, they dominated the government. The Issas complained that the laws unfairly favored the Afars. Consequently, the Issas continued to press the French for full independence. Their movement was opposed by the Afars, who feared Issa domination.

Finally, in 1975, the French began to accommodate demands for independence. In a referendum in May 1977, the Issa majority voted decisively for independence, which was officially established on 27 June 1977. Hassan Gouled Aptidon, the territory's premier, was elected the nation's first president and reelected without opposition by universal suffrage in June 1981 and April 1987.

Dissatisfaction with Gouled grew in the late 1980s. This led to uprisings by Afar guerrillas which began in late 1991. Their group was called

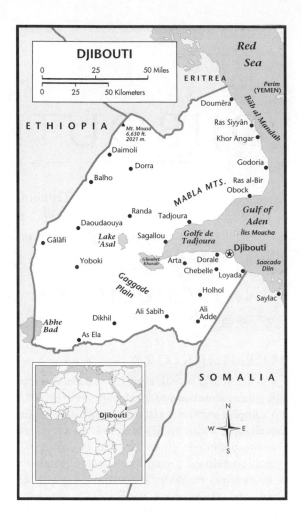

DJIBOUTI

0   25   50 Miles

0   25   50 Kilometers

Red Sea

ERITREA

Perim (YEMEN)

ETHIOPIA

Mt. Mousa 6,630 ft. 2021 m.

Doumêra

Ras Siyyân

Khor Angar

Daimoli

Dorra

Balho

MABLA MTS.

Godoria

Ras al-Bir

Obock

Randa

Tadjoura

Daoudaouya

Gâlâfi

Lake 'Asal

Sagallou

Gulf of Aden

Îles Moucha

Golfe de Tadjoura

Ghoubet Kharab

Yoboki

Arta

Dorale

Djibouti

Chebelle

Loyada

Saacada Diin

Gaggade Plain

Holhol

Saylac

Abhe Bad

Dikhil

Ali Sabîh

Ali Adde

As Ela

SOMALIA

Djibouti

N W E S

the Front for the Restoration of Unity and Democracy (FRUD). FRUD gained control of some areas of the north and west. In early 1992, French troops came to the aid of the Djibouti government and the Afars declared a cease-fire. However, fighting continued until mid-1992 when the rebel bases were occupied and their leaders imprisoned.

The military occupation of the north has been expensive for the government. By the end of 1993, about 35% of the government's budget went toward maintaining security in the north. In March 1995, a cease-fire was negotiated between the rebels and the government. Most of the FRUD guerrillas were then disarmed.

GOVERNMENT

Djibouti is a parliamentary republic. The president must be an Issa, according to the constitution. The president is elected by universal adult suffrage. The prime minister, who heads the cabinet, must be an Afar.

The legislature consists of the unicameral Chamber of Deputies, whose sixty-five members are elected for five-year terms. Before 1992, candidates came from a single list submitted by the ruling party, the People's Rally for Progress (RPP). In that year, voters approved a new constitution permitting multiparty democracy.

Judiciary

The judicial system consists of courts of first instance, a High Court of Appeal, and a Supreme Court. Each of the five administrative districts also has a customary court. The judiciary is not completely independent of the executive branch.

Political Parties

Despite the 1992 constitutional changes that legalized opposition party political activity, Djibouti is a de facto one-party system. However, there are also illegal Issa and Afar parties.

The RPP (People's Rally for Progress) holds all seats in the legislature and the presidency. However, two opposition groups, the Democratic Renewal Party (PRD) and the Democratic National Party (PND), function openly. The Front for the Restoration of Unity and Democracy (FRUD) formed in 1991 and was engaged in armed rebellion until a peace accord was reached in 1995.

DEFENSE

About 4,000 French troops are based near the city of Djibouti to deal with threats to French interests in the region. Djibouti's own armed force of 9,600 members is divided into an 8,000-man army, a 200-man navy, and a 200-man air force.

ECONOMIC AFFAIRS

Djibouti has a free-enterprise economy. The country's main economic advantage is its strategic position at the southern entrance to the Red Sea.

Public Finance

The CIA estimates that, in 1993, government revenues totaled approximately $164 million and expenditures of $201 million, including capital expenditures of $16 million. External debt totaled $227 million. Increased military expenditures, declining tax receipts, and political unrest in bordering countries have exacerbated the deterioration of public finance in recent years.

Income

No reliable estimates of Djibouti's gross national product (GNP) are available. In 1995, GNP was estimated between $766 and $3,035 per person.

Industry

Shipbuilding and urban construction are the only major industrial undertakings. Local manufacturing is limited to a mineral-water bottling facility and small plants that produce food, dairy products, beverages, furniture, building materials, and bottled gas.

Banking and Finance

The Djibouti franc was created in 1949 by the government of France. The Djibouti Treasury was replaced in 1983 as the bank of issue and central bank by the new National Bank of Djibouti. There were five commercial banks in 1993 and a National Development Bank, 51% government owned. There is no securities exchange.

Economic Development

In 1990, the Djibouti government significantly expanded its public investment program. Projects in communications, agriculture, and fisheries, as well as in social and environmental areas, were planned. Execution of these plans was put on hold as a result of subsequent domestic disturbances. The Persian Gulf War also disrupted investment programs sponsored by Iraq, Kuwait, and Saudi Arabia.

French budgetary support of the Djibouti economy is crucial to its stability, providing some 45% of foreign aid. The long-standing French financial commitment has weakened since 1989, and the IMF in 1992 expressed serious concern over key budget and trade deficits.

SOCIAL WELFARE

A social service fund covers medical and pension benefits. Although women can vote, they do not play a leadership role.

Healthcare

Malnutrition is severe, and the incidence of tuberculosis high; malaria is widespread. Life expectancy is 50 years.

Housing

Djiboutian nomads generally live in transportable huts (toukouls), which are covered with woven mats or boiled bark pulled into fine strands and plaited. Good-quality urban housing is in short supply.

EDUCATION

In 1994, there were eighty-one primary schools. Secondary schools had a total of 11,384 students. Education is compulsory for six years at the primary level followed by seven years of secondary education. Adult illiteracy is about 54%.

1999 KEY EVENTS TIMELINE

February

- President Hassan Gouled Aptidon, age 83 and president since the country won its independence from France in 1977, announces his intention to retire from office in April. His announcement came during a speech to his party, the Popular Rally for Progress.

- The Popular Rally for Progress party names President Aptidon's chief of staff, Ismael Omar Guellah, as its candidate for president.

March

- The first of a series of landmine explosions takes place in northern Djibouti. A radical branch of the Afar group, FRUD (Front for the Restoration of Unity and Democracy) has claimed responsibility for landmine atackes in the past.

April

- Voting takes place April 4 to elect a new president. Twenty international monitors are in the country to observe the voting. The two candidates are Ismael Omar Guelleh, candidate of the current party in power, Popular Rally for Progress; and Moussa Ahmed Idriss, candidate of opposition coalition.

- One week after the election, the losing candidate, Moussa Ahmed Idriss, complains that government security forces are harrassing him and his supporters, ten of whom were arrested after the election and remain in police custody.

May

- Ismail Omar Guelleh is sworn into office at a May 8 ceremony attended by a number of leaders from neighboring African nations.

- A landmine explodes in northern Djibouti, killing three, two of whom were young girls.

May

- The newly elected president, Ismail Omar Guellah, takes office, becoming the second president since the country's independence from France.

- President Guellah, in a radio broadcast, orders the release of about forty political prisoners, some of whom had been engaged in a hunger strike. Among those released are activist and lawyer, Mohammed Aref, and a number of suspected members of the radical organization FRUD who had been extradited from Ethiopia.

- President Guelleh leaves from Nairobi, Kenya, for a trip to Europe that will include stops in France and Italy.

- Police order the closing of bars and nightclubs in an ongoing battle against illegal activities such as male and female prostitiution, public intoxication, brawling, and pedophilia in the city of Djibouti. The authorities close about forty night clubs and dance halls catering mainly to personnel from a French military base, where 3,200 personnel are stationed.

August

- A landmine explodes on the only railroad track connecting Djibouti and Ethiopia, derailing a train and causing injury to two railroad personnel on board.

September

- Moussa Ahmed Idriss, leader of Unified Djiboutian Opposition and the losing candidate in April's presidential election, is arrested at his home. He is charged with violations of press laws and with ''threatening the morale of the armed forces'' because of articles in his monthly newspaper, *Le Temps*. He and nineteen of his supporters are jailed.

October

- A crew from the French television station, France Deux, is expelled from Djibouti and their documentary film footage is seized. The documentary explores how funds from the French government intended for economic development are being used. The French government and France Deux protests the expulsion, claiming the filming had been cleared in advance by the Djibouti government.

- The World Food Programme organization is sending food to drought-stricken Djibouti.

- Dallo Airline of Djibouti halts the illegal export to United Arab Emirates of six cheetahs and other exotic animals.

November

- President Guellah visits Ethiopia, where he holds talks with President Negasso Gidada concerning trade and commerce. The two leaders discuss ways to achieve economic integration of their respective countries. President Guellah agrees to make Djibouti's port available to Ethiopia for trade imports and exports.

- President Guelleh hosts a meeting of the Intergovernmental Authority on Development (IGAD), where he leads discussions on plans for peace in Somalia, among other issues of regional interest.

- Leaders in the breakaway republic of Somaliland, part of Somalia, charge the Djibouti government with interfering in their internal affairs.

ANALYSIS OF EVENTS: 1999

BUSINESS AND THE ECONOMY

Djibouti remains economically dependent on its main port, which borders the Red Sea. Revenue from the use of its port, along with imports and exports run its meager economy. Djibouti has formed an alliance with Ethiopia, and continues to allow Ethiopia to use its port. Leaders from the two nations agree to cooperate on security and trade.

Djibouti is largely dependent on support from other countries to manage its economy. Following talks between President Guelleh and French president Jacques Chirac in Paris, France pledged increased aid. The French government also promised to use its influence with the European Union and International Monetary Fund to secrure more economic assistance for Djibouti.

GOVERNMENT AND POLITICS

In 1999, Djibouti had less internal strife and enjoyed relative peace with its African neighbors. Following the April elections, long-time president Hassan Goulad Aptidon retired. His aide, Ismail Omar Guellah, defeated opposition candidate Moussa Ahmed Idriss. The prime minister, Barkat

Goural Hamadou (b.1930) remained in office following the election. Freedom of the press remains one of the main issues of concern in Djibouti. Even though the government is an elected democracy, the one-party government retains tight control over the distribution of information. Foreign journalists, as well as opposition journalists within the country, have complained about the lack of access to government information and about suppression by the government of any reports it deems negative.

CULTURE AND SOCIETY

The population of Djibouti is divided between the Issas and Afar tribes. Both are Islamic nomadic people, engaged primarily in herding. The Issas come from Somalia and the Afars come from Ethiopia. FRUD, the radical wing of the Afar tribe, has claimed responsibility for landmine explosions, although they repeatedly deny injuring any civilians.

The nations of Africa, including Djibouti, have been experiencing a severe drought; as a result, international economic and medical aid has been sent to Djibouti.

DIRECTORY

CENTRAL GOVERNMENT
Head of State

President
Ismail Omar Guelleh, Office of the President
PHONE: +253 350201
FAX: +253 355049

Prime Minister
Barkat Gourad Hamadou, Office of the Prime Minister

Ministers

Minister of Agriculture, Livestock and Fishing
Ali Mohamed Daoud, Ministry of Agriculture, Livestock and Fishing

Minister of Commerce, Industry and Crafts
Elmi Obsieh Wais, Ministry of Commerce, Industry and Crafts

Minister of Defense
Ougoureh Kifleh Ahmed, Ministry of Defense

Minister of Economy, Finance and Privatization
Yacin Elmi Bouh, Ministry of Economy, Finance and Privatization

Minister of Education
Abdi Ibrahim Absieh, Ministry of Education

Minister of Employment and National Solidarity
Mohamed Barkat Abdillahi, Ministry of Employment and National Solidarity

Minister of Energy and Natural Resources
Mohamed Ali Mohamed, Ministry of Energy and Natural Resources

Minister of Equipment and Transportation
Osman Idriss Djama, Ministry of Equipment and Transportation

Minister of Foreign Affairs, International Cooperation and Parliamentary Relations
Ali Abdi Farah, Ministry of Foreign Affairs, International Cooperation and Parliamentary Relations

Minister of Health
Dini Farah Mohamed, Ministry of Health

Minister of Interior
Abdallah Aboillahi Miguil, Ministry of Interior

Minister of Justice, Muslim and Penal Affairs and Human Rights
Ibrahim Idriss Djibril, Ministry of Justice, Muslim and Penal Affairs and Human Rights

Minister of Presidential Affairs and Investment Promotion
Osman Ahmed Moussa, Ministry of Presidential Affairs and Investment Promotion

Minister of Urban Planning, Housing, Environment and National and Regional Development
Souleiman Omar Oudine, Ministry of Urban Planning, Housing, Environment and National and Regional Development

Minister of Youth, Sports, Leisure and Tourism
Dini Abdallah Bililis, Ministry of Youth, Sports, Leisure and Tourism

POLITICAL ORGANIZATIONS
Parti National Démocratique (Democratic National Party)

NAME: Aden Robleh Awaleh

Parti du Renouveau Démocratique (Democratic Renewal Party)

NAME: Mohamed Jama Elabe

Front pour la Restauration de l'Unit et de la Démocratie (Front for the Restoration of Unity and Democracy)

Rassemblement populaire pour le Progres (People's Rally for Progress)

NAME: Hassan Gouled Aptidon

DIPLOMATIC REPRESENTATION
Embassies in Djibouti

United Kingdom
BP 81, Gellatly Hankey et Cie, Djibouti, Djibouti
PHONE: +253 353844
FAX: +253 353294

United States
Plateau du Serpent, boulevard Marechal Joffre, BP 185, Djibouti, Djibouti
PHONE: +253 353995
FAX: +253 353940
TITLE: Ambassador
NAME: Lange Schermerhorn

JUDICIAL SYSTEM
Supreme Court
High Court of Appeals

FURTHER READING
Articles
"Djibouti: Picking a President." *New York Times,* 10 April 1999, p. A4.

"Djibouti President in Ethiopia." BBC Online, 1 November 1999.

"Djibouti—Ethiopia Railway Blast." BBC Online, 21 August 1999.

"Djibouti Expels French TV Team." BBC Online, 24 October 1999.

"Djibouti Releases Afar Prisoners." BBC Online, 10 May 1999.

"News Brief: Djibouti." *New York Times,* 5 February 1999, p. A8.

"Opposition Leader Arrested in Djibouti." BBC Online, 23 September 1999.

"Opposition Members Jailed in Djibouti." BBC Online, 7 October 1999.

Internet

Africa Online. Available Online @ www.africaonline.com (November 3, 1999).

BBC Online. Available Online @ www.bbc.co.uk/ (November 3, 1999).

Worldwide EP Inc. Africa News Online. Available Online @ www.africanews.org (November 3, 1999.)

Zarate's Political Collections (ZPC) Available Online @ personales.jet.es/ziaorarr (November 3, 1999).

DJIBOUTI: STATISTICAL DATA

For sources and notes see "Sources of Statistics" in the front of each volume.

GEOGRAPHY

Geography (1)

Area:

Total: 22,000 sq km.

Land: 21,980 sq km.

Water: 20 sq km.

Area—comparative: slightly smaller than Massachusetts.

Land boundaries:

Total: 508 km.

Border countries: Eritrea 113 km, Ethiopia 337 km, Somalia 58 km.

Coastline: 314 km.

Climate: desert; torrid, dry.

Terrain: coastal plain and plateau separated by central mountains.

Natural resources: geothermal areas.

Land use:

Arable land: NA%

Permanent crops: NA%

Permanent pastures: 9%

Forests and woodland: 0%

Other: 91% (1993 est.).

HUMAN FACTORS

Demographics (2A)

	1990	1995	1998	2000	2010	2020	2030	2040	2050
Population	370.1	421.3	440.7	454.3	587.8	750.9	934.7	1,130.8	1,329.4
Net migration rate (per 1,000 population)	NA	NA	NA	NA	NA	NA	NA	NA	NA
Births	NA	NA	NA	NA	NA	NA	NA	NA	NA
Deaths	NA	NA	NA	NA	NA	NA	NA	NA	NA
Life expectancy - males	45.8	47.8	49.1	49.9	54.1	58.3	62.2	65.8	68.9
Life expectancy - females	49.1	51.6	53.2	54.2	59.4	64.4	69.0	73.0	76.3
Birth rate (per 1,000)	43.6	42.8	41.8	41.0	37.2	32.6	27.9	23.8	20.5
Death rate (per 1,000)	16.8	15.5	14.7	14.1	11.6	9.3	7.5	6.2	5.8
Women of reproductive age (15-49 yrs.)	81.0	92.2	95.3	97.6	131.8	183.0	240.3	302.7	359.1
of which are currently married	NA	NA	NA	NA	NA	NA	NA	NA	NA
Fertility rate	6.4	6.2	5.9	5.8	5.0	4.1	3.3	2.8	2.4

Except as noted, values for vital statistics are in thousands; life expectancy is in years.

Infants and Malnutrition (5)

Under-5 mortality rate (1997) 156

% of infants with low birthweight (1990-97) 11

Births attended by skilled health staff % of total[a] . . .NA

% fully immunized (1995-97)

TB 58

DPT 49

Polio 49

Measles 47

Prevalence of child malnutrition under age 5
(1992-97)[b] . . . . .NA

Ethnic Division (6)

Somali 60%

Afar 35%

French, Arab, Ethiopian, Italian 5%

Religions (7)

Muslim 94%

Christian 6%

Languages (8)

French (official), Arabic (official), Somali, Afar.

EDUCATION

Literacy Rates (11A)

In thousands and percent[1]	1990	1995	2000	2010
Illiterate population (15+ yrs.)	173	181	187	192
Literacy rate - total adult pop. (%)	41.1	46.2	51.4	61.0
Literacy rate - males (%)	55.4	60.3	64.9	72.9
Literacy rate - females (%)	27.4	32.7	38.3	49.5

GOVERNMENT & LAW

Political Parties (12)

Chamber of Deputies	No. of seats
People's Progress Assembly (RPP) 65	

Government Budget (13B)

Revenues . . . .$156 million

Expenditures . . . .$175 million

Capital expenditures . . . . .NA

Data for 1997 est. NA stands for not available.

LABOR FORCE

Labor Force (16)

Total 282,000

Agriculture 75%

Industry 11%

Services 14%

Data for 1991 est.

Unemployment Rate (17)

40%-50% (1996 est.)

PRODUCTION SECTOR

Electric Energy (18)

Capacity . . . . .85,000 kW (1995)

Production . . . . .180 million kWh (1995)

Consumption per capita . . . . .427 kWh (1995)

Transportation (19)

Highways:

total: 2,890 km

paved: 364 km

unpaved: 2,526 km (1996 est.)

Merchant marine:

total: 1 cargo ship (1,000 GRT or over) totaling 1,369
GRT/3,030 DWT (1997 est.)

Airports: 11 (1997 est.)

Airports—with paved runways:

total: 2

over 3,047 m: 1

2,438 to 3,047 m: 1 (1997 est.)

Airports—with unpaved runways:

total: 9

1,524 to 2,437 m: 2

914 to 1,523 m: 5

under 914 m: 2 (1997 est.)

Top Agricultural Products (20)

Fruits, vegetables; goats, sheep, camels.

GOVERNMENT & LAW

Military Affairs (14B)

	1990	1991	1992	1993	1994	1995
Military expenditures						
Current dollars (mil.)	36[e]	44[e]	43[e]	30	26	22
1995 constant dollars (mil.)	41[e]	49[e]	46[e]	31	27	22
Armed forces (000)	4	3	8	8	8	8
Gross national product (GNP)						
Current dollars (mil.)	501[e]	490	514	500	496[e]	493[e]
1995 constant dollars (mil.)	576[e]	542	553	524	509[e]	493[e]
Central government expenditures (CGE)						
1995 constant dollars (mil.)	204[e]	256[e]	NA	226[e]	NA	NA
People (mil.)	.4	.4	.4	.4	.4	.4
Military expenditure as % of GNP	7.1	9.1	8.3	6.0	5.3	4.5
Military expenditure as % of CGE	20.1	19.2	NA	13.9	NA	NA
Military expenditure per capita (1995 $)	111	129	118	78	65	52
Armed forces per 1,000 people (soldiers)	11.3	8.9	20.5	19.9	19.4	19.0
GNP per capita (1995 $)	1,556	1,423	1,415	1,306	1,233	1,170
Arms imports[6]						
Current dollars (mil.)	5	5	10	0	0	0
1995 constant dollars (mil.)	6	6	11	0	0	0
Arms exports[6]						
Current dollars (mil.)	0	0	0	0	0	0
1995 constant dollars (mil.)	0	0	0	0	0	0
Total imports[7]						
Current dollars (mil.)	215	214	219	NA	384[e]	NA
1995 constant dollars (mil.)	247	236	236	NA	394[e]	NA
Total exports[7]						
Current dollars (mil.)	25	17	16	NA	NA	NA
1995 constant dollars (mil.)	29	19	17	NA	NA	NA
Arms as percent of total imports[8]	2.3	2.3	4.6	NA	0	NA
Arms as percent of total exports[8]	0	0	0	NA	NA	NA

MANUFACTURING SECTOR

GDP & Manufacturing Summary (21)

	1980	1985	1990	1992	1993	1994
Gross Domestic Product						
Millions of 1990 dollars	353	367	418	424	426	428
Growth rate in percent	4.72	0.57	8.91	−1.00	0.30	0.50
Per capita (in 1990 dollars)	1,256.8	937.6	807.6	777.1	764.1	755.7
Manufacturing Value Added						
Millions of 1990 dollars	15	15	17	17	18	18
Growth rate in percent	4.08	0.49	11.79	1.17	1.76	1.88
Manufacturing share in percent of current prices	4.2	4.7	4.8	4.4	4.5	NA

FINANCE, ECONOMICS, & TRADE

Economic Indicators (22)

National product: GDP—purchasing power parity—$520 million (1997 est.)

National product real growth rate: 0.5% (1997 est.)

National product per capita: $1,200 (1997 est.)

Inflation rate—consumer price index: 3% (1997 est.)

Balance of Payments (23)

	1992	1993	1994	1995
Exports of goods (f.o.b.)	53	71	56	34
Imports of goods (f.o.b.)	−271	−255	−237	−205
Trade balance	−218	−184	−181	−172
Services - debits	−119	−118	−97	−96
Services - credits	175	187	176	177
Private transfers (net)	87	91	66	80
Government transfers (net)	−12	−10	−11	−13
Overall balance	−88	−34	−46	−23

Exchange Rates (24)

Exchange rates: Djiboutian francs (DF) per US$1—177.721 (fixed rate since 1973)

Top Import Origins (25)

$200.5 million (f.o.b., 1996 est.) Data are for 1996.

Origins	%
France	NA
Ethiopia	NA
Italy	NA
Saudi Arabia	NA
Thailand	NA

NA stands for not available.

Top Export Destinations (26)

$39.6 million (f.o.b., 1996 est.) Data are for 1996.

Destinations	%
Ethiopia	.45
Somalia	NA
Yemen	NA
Saudi Arabia	NA

NA stands for not available.

Economic Aid (27)

Recipient: ODA, $NA. NA stands for not available.

Import Export Commodities (28)

Import Commodities	Export Commodities
Foods	Hides and skins
Beverages	Coffee (in transit)
Transport equipment	
Chemicals	
Petroleum products	

DOMINICA

Commonwealth of Dominica
Dominica

INTRODUCTORY SURVEY

RECENT HISTORY

Dominica was governed as part of the Leeward Islands from 1871 until 1939. In 1940, it was transferred to the Windward Islands administration. From 1958 to 1962, the island was a member of the Federation of the West Indies. Dominica became an associated state of the Commonwealth of Nations in 1967 and in 1978 became an independent republic.

In its first years of independence, Dominica had several problems. Some were brought about by destructive hurricanes, especially Hurricane David in 1979. Others were attributable to the corrupt and tyrannical administration of Premier Patrick John. John was ousted in June 1979, and after a year of interim rule, Mary Eugenia Charles became prime minister in July 1980. She was the first female prime minister in the Caribbean. Charles's party lost its majority in 1995 and Edison James became the new prime minister.

GOVERNMENT

Under its 1978 constitution, Dominica has a single-chamber parliament, the House of Assembly, with twenty-one elected and nine appointed members. Parliament elects a president as head of state, who in turn appoints the prime minister and cabinet.

Judiciary

The lowest-level courts are the four magistrates' courts; at the second level is the Court of

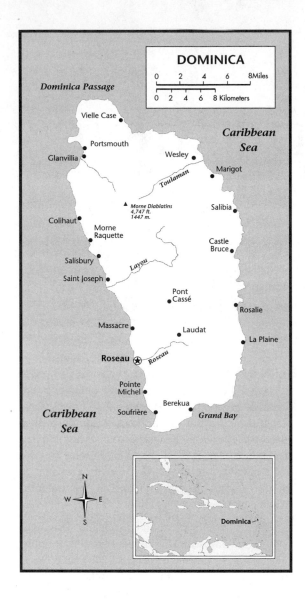

DOMINICA

Summary Jurisdiction. The highest court is the Eastern Caribbean Supreme Court, based in St. Lucia.

Political Parties

Dominica's major political parties are the Dominican Freedom Party (DFP), the Dominica Labour Party (DLP), and the United Workers Party (UWP). The DFP held the majority from 1980 until 1995. That year, the UWP won eleven of the twenty-one seats and made Edison James prime minister.

DEFENSE

There is a police force of 300. Defense from foreign attack would come from the United States or United Kingdom.

ECONOMIC AFFAIRS

Practically the entire economy is based on agriculture, fishing, and forestry. Bananas are the main crop, and coconuts, from which copra is extracted for export, are also important.

Public Finance

Operating revenues come mostly from customs duties, excise taxes, and other taxes and fees for government services. The leading areas of expenditure are education, health, public services, housing, and defense. The U.S. Central Intelligence Agency estimates that, in 1995, government revenues totaled approximately $80 million and expenditures $95.8 million. External debt totaled $92.8 million.

Income

In 1998, Dominica's gross national product (GNP) was $222 million at current prices, or $3,010 per person. For the period 1985–95, the average inflation rate was 4.4%, resulting in a real growth rate in GNP of 4.0% per person.

Industry

Dominica has only light industry, most of it connected with the processing of agricultural products. Soap and toiletries are exported. Home industries produce ceramics, straw products, and some leather work.

Banking and Finance

The principal national banks are the National Commercial and Development Bank of Dominica and the Dominica Agricultural Industrial and Development (AID) Bank. Private commercial banks include Barclays (UK), the Royal Bank of Canada, and the Banque Française Commerciale. Dominica is a member of the Eastern Caribbean Central Bank, which issues a common currency. Dominica has no stock market.

Economic Development

Dominica seeks to foster private enterprise, but the Charles government has been willing to intervene in the economy where it perceives a need.

The economy is dependent on agriculture and thus is highly vulnerable to climatic conditions. Agriculture accounts for about 30% of GDP and employs 40% of the labor force. Principal products include bananas, citrus, mangoes, root crops, and coconuts. Development of the tourist industry remains difficult because of the rugged coastline and the lack of an international airport.

SOCIAL WELFARE

In 1976, the government established the Social Security Scheme, which covers all workers from 16 to 60 years of age. Benefits include retirement and disability pensions, maternity benefits, and survivors' pensions. Apart from the constitution, there is no specific legislation in force to protect women from sex discrimination.

Healthcare

Medical facilities include one general hospital and twelve health centers. Serious tropical diseases have been eliminated, but due to the high humidity and rainy conditions, tuberculosis and other respiratory diseases continue to be a problem. Average life expectancy is 74 years.

Housing

Hurricane David destroyed the homes of over four-fifths of the population. Under an emergency housing program, construction supplies were brought into the island, and shelters were built for most of the population.

EDUCATION

Much of Dominica's school system had to be rebuilt after the 1979 hurricane. In 1994, there were 64 primary schools, with 641 teachers and 12,607 students enrolled. Higher educational facilities include a teacher training institute, a technical college, and a nursing school. There were 34 teaching staff and 484 students in higher level institutions in 1992.

1999 KEY EVENTS TIMELINE

February

- The Prime Minister of Dominica, Edison James, announces a gun amnesty. In his address to the nation, he says residents have until February 12 to deliver illegally held guns and ammunition to the government without penalty.

April

- The World Trade Organization upholds the United States government's right to impose trade penalties on Europe over its banana import rules. At issue are Caribbean bananas from countries like Dominica that enjoy special tariffs in Europe.

- Heavy rains damage homes and roads in Dominica. Landslides cut off a few communities, and some residents have to abandon their flooded homes.

May

- A U.S. judge freezes the accounts of a Dominica-based company accused of fraud for using email messages to entice web users to call an international phone number. The line connects callers to an adult sex site that charged $2 per minute.

June

- The owner of a for-profit medical school in Dominica tries to open a similar institution in Wyoming, but faces resistance. The national accrediting agency for medical schools refuses to consider the project.

July

- Dominica considers closer economic ties with Cuba. The government considers a Cuban proposal to eliminate tariffs on some products and strengthen bilateral trade.

August

- The Dominica government offers $5.92 million for a 600-acre private estate it wants to use for an international airport.

October

- A plan by English-speaking countries in the Caribbean to create a regional supreme court to replace London's Privy Council may not be completed until 2000.

- Dominica celebrates its 21st anniversary of independence on October 2 with a cultural exposition; independence and millenium celebrations will continue through April 2000.

- The government announces that at least three cruise lines are considering adding Dominica to their ports of call by late 1999 or the 2000-2001 travel season.

ANALYSIS OF EVENTS: 1999

BUSINESS AND THE ECONOMY

Finance Minister Julius Timothy said the nation could not expect to move forward with single digit growth rates; double-digit growth, at least for a short time, was needed to boost the economy. The government hopes that the construction of an international airport will boost the economy. Timothy made his remarks as he delivered the 1999–2000 budget, the final budget in the five-year administration of the United Workers Party.

At least three cruise lines were considering adding Dominica to their ports of call during the 1999 tourist season or by the 2000-01 season, government officials announced. Much like their Caribbean neighbors, Dominica hopes cruise ship visitors will be impressed by the island, and return for extended stays.

GOVERNMENT AND POLITICS

In July, some of the nation's most prominent business leaders criticized government heads for using their political position to further their business interests. The Chamber of Commerce called for greater accountability and transparency in business deals executed by government officials.

Prime Minister Edison James rejected the criticism, saying it was lawful and legitimate for his ministers to set up businesses under Dominica's laws. The Dominica Association of Industry and Commerce also showed concern, releasing a statement that said government officials should set higher standards for themselves, and remember that public trust should be held in the highest regard.

Partly as an attempt to persuade his fellow Dominicans, prime minister James began to promote social partnerships between governments and business and social organizations. The purpose, James said, was part of an effort to create a modern economy with sustained growth and more employment. For James, the partnership could foster more consultation and cooperation instead of confrontation.

In other political matters, Dominica and other Caribbean nations spent most of 1999 lobbying in Europe and the United States to protect their banana industries, which make up a considerable portion of their economies. Prime Minister James visited Spain, Portugal, Finland, and Brussels on a banana lobbying mission. James and other Caribbean leaders believe that a quota allocation is the best option to continue the preferential access that Caribbean fruit producers have to the European market.

Several European nations have rules that favor bananas imported from their former colonies in the Caribbean, while restricting bananas imported from places like Honduras, Ecuador and Colombia. The United States, under lobbying pressure by U.S. fruit companies that grow bananas in Central and South America, challenged the preferential treatment at the World Trade Organization (WTO). In February, the WTO upheld the U.S. government's right to impose trade penalties on Europe over its banana import rules. Following the decision, the United States announced it would impose 100 percent tariffs on many European products, including clothes, food, and jewelry. While Europe and the United States argued about fair trade practices, small Caribbean nations like Dominica, St. Lucia, St. Vincent and the Grenadines joined lobbying efforts in an attempt to be heard. No solution to the issue was expected anytime soon.

CULTURE AND SOCIETY

Dominica's farmers are getting older, and the younger generations, it seems, have no interest in taking over. Government officials estimate the average age for a Dominican farmer is 50, which could create labor problems and shortages in food production in the not too distant future. Farming remains the main economic activity in Dominica, with bananas a leading export crop. Dominica's Ministry of Agriculture has decided to start a Young Farmer Recruitment and Development Program that will at first target 120 people. They will be taught about crop production, animal husbandry, farm management and marketing, among other skills. Government officials hope the young farmers will someday establish their own farms.

The Caribs, Dominica's indigenous people, have made important strides in recent years, and established a strong community in the island, The Chronicle of Dominica reported in 1999. About 3,500 people live in Carib Territory, in an area of about 3,700 acres on the island's east coast. It is reportedly the largest Carib community in the Caribbean. The Chronicle reports that the community had begun to allow visitors, telling them about their long struggle for survival, their resistance against slavery, and the near destruction of their people. The Caribs also share their art and culture, and show visitors how they made the canoes that were used to establish themselves throughout the Caribbean long before Christopher Columbus arrived in the Americas.

The Caribs are working with the government to build a model village similar to the ones that existed in pre-Columbian times. The village, which is expected to be finished in three years, will feature craft shops, restaurants and an archival center on Carib studies.

The Chronicle reported that despite some progress, many Carib youths felt discrimination, and were treated as second-class citizens. "Students make certain disparaging remarks about the cannibalistic nature of our forefathers. People say in upsetting ways that Caribs are foolish. At college, for example, they say we are fools," one Carib youth told the Chronicle. Community leaders said people still have too many misconceptions about the Carib people.

"We in the Carib Territory should unite," a more positive Carib youth told the Chronicle. "We were the first people and we must unite to gain recognition through representation. We need to be educated on culture. We should stand for who we are and should be proud as indigenous people."

DIRECTORY

CENTRAL GOVERNMENT

Head of State

President
Vernon Shaw, Office of the President, Government Headquarters, Roseau, Dominica
PHONE: +809 (767) 4482401
FAX: +809 (767) 4485200

Prime Minister
Edison James, Office of the Prime Minister, Government Headquarters, Roseau, Dominica
PHONE: +809 (767) 4482401
FAX: +809 (767) 4488960

Ministers

Deputy Prime Minister
Julius Timothy, Office of the Prime Minister, Government Headquarters, Roseau, Dominica
PHONE: +809 (767) 4482401
FAX: +809 (767) 4488960

Minister of Agriculture and Environment
Peter Carbon, Ministry of Agriculture and Environment, Government Headquarters, Roseau, Dominica
PHONE: +809 (767) 4482401

Minister of Communications, Housing, and Public Works
Earl Williams, Ministry of Communications, Housing, and Public Works, Government Headquarters, Roseau, Dominica
PHONE: +809 (767) 4482401

Minister of Community Development and Women's Affairs
Gertrude Roberts, Ministry of Community Development and Women's Affairs, Government Headquarters, Roseau, Dominica
PHONE: +809 (767) 4482401

Minister of Education and Sports
Ron Green, Ministry of Education and Sports, Government Headquarters, Roseau, Dominica
PHONE: +809 (767) 4482401

Minister of Finance, Industry, and Planning
Julius Timothy, Ministry of Finance, Industry, and Planning, Government Headquarters, Roseau, Dominica
PHONE: +809 (767) 4482401

Minister of Foreign Affairs, Trade, and Marketing
Charles Norris, Ministry of Foreign Affairs, Trade, and Marketing, Government Headquarters, Roseau, Dominica
PHONE: +809 (767) 4482401

Minister of Health and Social Services
Doreen Paul, Ministry of Health and Social Services, Government Headquarters, Roseau, Dominica
PHONE: +809 (767) 4482401
E-MAIL: health@cwdom.dm

Minister of Legal Affairs and Labor
Edison James, Ministry of Legal Affairs and Labor, Government Headquarters, Roseau, Dominica
PHONE: +809 (767) 4482401

Minister of Tourism, Ports, and Employment
Norris Prevost, Ministry of Tourism, Ports, and Employment, Government Headquarters, Roseau, Dominica
PHONE: +809 (767) 4482401

POLITICAL ORGANIZATIONS

Dominica Freedom Party
NAME: Charles Saverin

Dominica United Workers' Party
E-MAIL: uwp@cwdom.dm

NAME: Edison James

Labor Party of Dominica

NAME: Rosie Douglas

DIPLOMATIC REPRESENTATION

Embassies in Dominica

United Kingdom
Lower Collymore Rock, PO Box 676,
Bridgetown, Barbados
PHONE: +(809) 4366694
FAX: +(809) 4267916

JUDICIAL SYSTEM

Supreme Court

Government Headquarters, Roseau, Dominica
PHONE: +809 (767) 4482401
FAX: +809 (767) 4485200

FURTHER READING
Articles

"A Fruitless Confrontation about more than Bananas." *The Seattle Times*, 16 March 1999.

"Government Completes Record Land Acquisition." *Caribbean Week*, 3 August 1999.

"Lavish Party for 21st Birthday." *The Chronicle of Dominica*, 24 September 1999.

"Prime Minister James Calls for Social Partnership." *Caribbean Week*, 29 April 1999.

"Regional Supreme Court Plans Delayed for Discussion." *The Miami Herald*, 18 October 1999.

"Ruling Allows Sanctions: World Trade Organization Favors U.S. in Banana Dispute." *The Miami Herald,* 7 April 1999.

"SOS Saves Two in Rough Seas." *The Miami Herald*, 28 October 1999.

DOMINICA: STATISTICAL DATA

For sources and notes see "Sources of Statistics" in the front of each volume.

GEOGRAPHY

Geography (1)

Area:

Total: 750 sq km.

Land: 750 sq km.

Water: 0 sq km.

Area—comparative: slightly more than four times the size of Washington, DC.

Land boundaries: 0 km.

Coastline: 148 km.

Climate: tropical; moderated by northeast trade winds; heavy rainfall.

Terrain: rugged mountains of volcanic origin.

Natural resources: timber.

Land use:

Arable land: 9%

Permanent crops: 13%

Permanent pastures: 3%

Forests and woodland: 67%

Other: 8% (1993 est.).

HUMAN FACTORS

Infants and Malnutrition (5)

Under-5 mortality rate (1997) 20

% of infants with low birthweight (1990-97) 10

Births attended by skilled health staff % of total[a] . . .NA

% fully immunized (1995-97)

TB 100

DPT 100

Polio 100

Measles 100

Prevalence of child malnutrition under age 5
(1992-97)[b] . . . . .NA

HUMAN FACTORS

Demographics (2A)

	1990	1995	1998	2000	2010	2020	2030	2040	2050
Population	72.1	68.2	65.8	63.9	61.0	65.1	68.5	70.1	69.4
Net migration rate (per 1,000 population)	NA	NA	NA	NA	NA	NA	NA	NA	NA
Births	NA	NA	NA	NA	NA	NA	NA	NA	NA
Deaths	NA	NA	NA	NA	NA	NA	NA	NA	NA
Life expectancy - males	73.2	74.3	74.9	75.3	76.9	78.1	79.0	79.6	80.0
Life expectancy - females	79.0	80.2	80.8	81.2	82.9	84.1	84.9	85.6	86.0
Birth rate (per 1,000)	19.6	18.3	17.4	16.5	13.6	12.6	11.3	10.4	10.1
Death rate (per 1,000)	6.0	6.1	6.3	6.4	6.6	6.6	7.4	9.6	12.6
Women of reproductive age (15-49 yrs.)	18.2	17.7	17.4	17.1	16.7	15.9	15.4	14.7	13.9
of which are currently married	NA	NA	NA	NA	NA	NA	NA	NA	NA
Fertility rate	2.1	2.0	1.9	1.9	1.8	1.8	1.8	1.8	1.8

Except as noted, values for vital statistics are in thousands; life expectancy is in years.

Ethnic Division (6)

Black, Carib Amerindian.

Religions (7)

Roman Catholic 77%
Protestant 15%
  Methodist 5%
  Pentecostal 3%
  Seventh-Day Adventist 3%
  Baptist 2%
  Other 2%
None 2%
Unknown 1%
Other 5%

Languages (8)

English (official), French patois.

EDUCATION

Educational Attainment (10)

Age group (1981) . . . . .25+
Total population 27,508
Highest level attained (%)
  No schooling 6.6
  First level
    Not completed 80.5
    Completed . . . . .NA
  Entered second level
    S-1 . . . . .11.1
    S-2 . . . . .NA
  Postsecondary 1.7

GOVERNMENT & LAW

Political Parties (12)

House of Assembly	No. of seats
United Workers Party (UWP) 12	
Dominica Labor Party (DLP) 5	
Dominica Freedom Party (DFP) 4	

Government Budget (13B)

Revenues . . . .$77 million
Expenditures . . . .$78 million
  Capital expenditures . . . .$22 million
Data for FY95/96.

Military Affairs (14A)

Total expenditures . . . .$NA
Expenditures as % of GDP . . . . .NA%
NA stands for not available.

Crime (15)

Crime rate (for 1997)
  Crimes reported 5,750
  Total persons convicted . . . . .NA
  Crimes per 100,000 population 7,550
Persons responsible for offenses
  Total number of suspects . . . . .NA
  Total number of female suspects . . . . .NA
  Total number of juvenile suspects . . . . .NA

LABOR FORCE

Labor Force (16)

Total 25,000
Agriculture 40%
Industry and commerce .32%
Services 28%
Data for 1984.

Unemployment Rate (17)

15% (1992 est.)

PRODUCTION SECTOR

Electric Energy (18)

Capacity . . . . .8,000 kW (1995)
Production . . . . .37 million kWh (1995)
Consumption per capita . . . . .448 kWh (1995)

Transportation (19)

Highways:
total: 780 km
paved: 393 km
unpaved: 387 km (1996 est.)
Merchant marine: none
Airports: 2 (1997 est.)
Airports—with paved runways:
total: 2
914 to 1,523 m: 1
under 914 m: 1 (1997 est.)

Top Agricultural Products (20)

Bananas, citrus, mangoes, root crops, coconuts; forestry and fisheries potential not exploited.

FINANCE, ECONOMICS, & TRADE

Economic Indicators (22)

National product: GDP—purchasing power parity—$208 million (1996 est.)

National product real growth rate: 3.7% (1996 est.)

National product per capita: $2,500 (1996 est.)

Inflation rate—consumer price index: 1.7% (1996)

Exchange Rates (24)

Exchange rates: East Caribbean dollars (EC$) per US$1—2.7000 (fixed rate since 1976)

Top Import Origins (25)

$98.1 million (f.o.b., 1996)

Origins	%
United States	.41
Caricom	.25
United Kingdom	.13
Netherlands	NA
Canada	NA

NA stands for not available.

Top Export Destinations (26)

$51.8 million (f.o.b., 1996) Data are for 1996 est.

Destinations	%
Caricom countries	.47
United Kingdom	.36
United States	.7

Economic Aid (27)

Recipient: ODA, $NA. NA stands for not available.

Import Export Commodities (28)

Import Commodities	Export Commodities
Manufactured goods	Bananas 50%
Machinery and equipment	Soap
	Bay oil
Food	Vegetables
Chemicals	Grapefruit
	Oranges

Balance of Payments (23)

	1990	1991	1992	1993	1994
Exports of goods (f.o.b.)	56	56	55	47	44
Imports of goods (f.o.b.)	−104	−96	−93	−94	−96
Trade balance	−48	−41	−38	−47	−52
Services - debits	−39	40	−42	−40	−47
Services - credits	37	40	47	50	55
Private transfers (net)	−1	−0	−0	−1	1
Government transfers (net)	7	8	8	10	7
Overall balance	−44	−34	−26	−28	−36

MANUFACTURING SECTOR

GDP & Manufacturing Summary (21)

	1980	1985	1990	1992	1993	1994
Gross Domestic Product						
Millions of 1990 dollars	5,946	6,419	7,080	7,603	7,830	8,170
Growth rate in percent	6.05	−2.59	−5.41	8.03	2.99	4.34
Per capita (in 1990 dollars)	1,043.7	1,006.8	995.8	1,027.4	1,038.1	1,063.2
Manufacturing Value Added						
Millions of 1990 dollars	910	884	955	1,070	1,077	*1,120*
Growth rate in percent	5.03	−7.11	−7.80	12.70	0.63	*4.04*
Manufacturing share in percent of current prices	15.3	13.6	13.5	14.2	*14.2*	NA

DOMINICAN REPUBLIC

Republica Dominicana

INTRODUCTORY SURVEY

RECENT HISTORY

In 1930, Rafael Leonidas Trujillo Molina was elected president. For the next thirty-one years, he ruled the Dominican Republic either directly or indirectly. At one point, Trujillo arranged for his brother to become president and then, in 1960, installed Joaquín Balaguer as president. However, no matter who was the president, Trujillo was in control. Under Trujillo and his associates, the country achieved some economic progress. However, they brutally suppressed fundamental human rights. Only one party was allowed, the press was totally controlled, and constant purges weeded out all but his most loyal supporters.

Trujillo was assassinated on 30 May 1961. A period of instability followed as various military and political factions competed for power. With anarchy—and rumored communist intervention—threatening, the United States sent 23,000 troops into the Dominican Republic. Balaguer went into exile. Within weeks, the Organization of American States (OAS) had set up an Inter-America Peace Force in the country, and order was restored to the country. After the 1966 elections, all U.S. and OAS troops left the island.

In the 1978 elections, the major opposition parties remained active and vocal. Silvestre Antonio Guzmán Fernández of the PRD (Dominican Revolutionary Party) won with a 158,000-vote plurality, and his party gained a majority in the Chamber of Deputies.

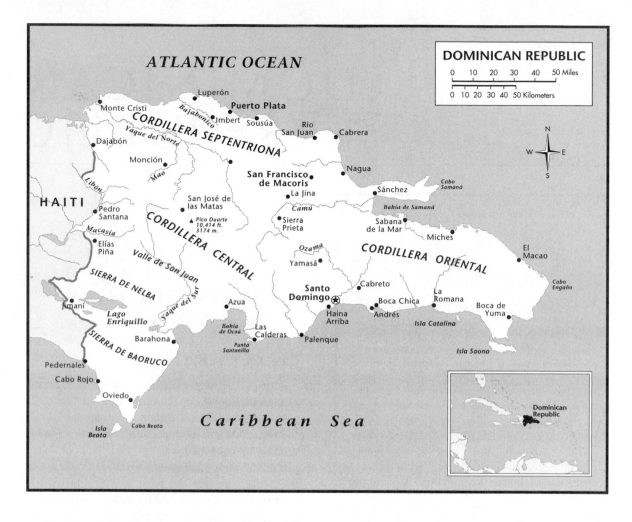

During Guzmán's term, political prisoners were freed, press censorship was practically abolished, and political parties engaged in open activity. At the same time, however, there were mounting economic difficulties. In May 1982, a left-wing PRD senator, Salvador Jorge Blanco, was elected president.

President Blanco's administration struggled with the country's growing foreign debt and other economic difficulties. In May 1986, former president Joaquín Balaguer was returned to office with 41.6% of the vote. Balaguer embarked on an ambitious program of public works that created employment for nearly 100,000 people. But by 1988, inflation was on the rise, and the peso had become unstable.

In 1990, Balaguer won a narrow, hotly contested victory amid claims of fraud by the opposition. His unpopular economic reforms brought national strikes in August and November of 1990, and demands for resignation. Balaguer won another term in 1994, but the electoral board voided the election results. A new election in 1996 brought Leonel Fernandez to power.

GOVERNMENT

The constitution of 1966 established a republic consisting of twenty-six provinces and a single National District. The government is controlled by the chief executive, a president directly elected for a four-year term. The National Congress consists of a 30-member Senate and a 120-member Chamber of Deputies.

Judiciary

The judicial system is headed by a Supreme Court with nine judges, and serves as the highest court of appeals. There are twenty-six provincial courts.

Political Parties

The Dominican Republic has four major parties: the Social Christian Reform Party (Partido Reformista Social Christiano—PRSC), the Dominican Revolutionary Party (Partido Revolucionario Dominicano—PRD), the Dominican Liberation Party (Partido de la Liberación Dominicana—PLD), and the Independent Revolutionary Party (PRI).

DEFENSE

The army has 15,000 personnel; the air force, 5,500 personnel; and the navy, 4,000 personnel. The national police number 15,000. In 1995, the armed forces budget was $112 million.

ECONOMIC AFFAIRS

Manufacturing and agriculture are the mainstays of the economy.

Light manufacturing contributes an important share of national production, exports, and employment. In 1994 and 1995, the country's economy rapidly grew, due to the expansion of tourism, mining, and the export processing zones.

Public Finance

Between 1968 and 1975, dependence on foreign loans and grants to finance the budget was substantially decreased, and by 1975 tax revenues amounted to about 12% of the GNP. In the late 1970s, this trend was reversed, with rising expenditures and increased assistance from abroad.

The U.S. CIA estimates that, in 1994, government revenues totaled approximately $1.8 billion and expenditures $2.2 billion. External debt totaled $4.6 billion.

Income

In 1998, the Dominican Republic's gross national product (GNP) was $14.6 billion at current prices, or about $1,770 per person. For the period 1985–95, the average inflation rate was 26.3%, resulting in a real growth rate in GNP of 2.1% per person.

Industry

Manufacturing is limited largely to the processing of agricultural and mineral commodities. Including the processing of sugar, food processing represents more than half of total industrial production.

Banking and Finance

The Central Bank of the Dominican Republic (Banco Central de la República Dominicana—BCRD) is the sole bank of issue. The state-owned Banco de Reservas, established in 1941, is the largest commercial bank in the country and acts as the fiscal agent and depository for the government. The Agricultural and the Industrial Credit Bank promotes the development of agriculture as well as industry by granting medium-term and long-term credit. The National Housing Bank (Banco Nacional de Vivienda) is a primary investor in low-cost housing.

Securities are traded on the Santo Domingo Securities Exchange.

Economic Development

Caribbean Basin Initiative (CBI) and Generalized Systems of Preferences—government programs that allow the import of raw materials, equipment, and goods for re-export duty-free—benefit the economy. Duty-free access to the EC market was granted by joining the Lome Convention in 1989, which also provides inexpensive financing for economic development projects.

Standard & Poor's assigned a B+ rating in February 1997 to the Dominican Republic's $519 million discount and past-due interest Brady Bonds.

SOCIAL WELFARE

Social assistance is administered by the Department of Public Health and Welfare, which administers medical, disability, maternity, old age, and survivors' benefits, as well as workers' compensation. An Institute for the Development of Women was created in 1975.

Haitian immigrants face discrimination. Human rights violations include police brutality, arbitrary detention, and mistreatment of suspects in custody.

Healthcare

During 1985–95, 80% of the population had access to health care services. There is 1 doctor for every 949 people. Average life expectancy is 71 years.

Housing

Rapid population growth and migration to urban areas have combined to create a serious housing shortage. The 1979 and 1998 hurricanes prompted a construction boom to replace units that had been destroyed by the storms.

EDUCATION

The 1995 estimated adult illiteracy rate was 18%. Nine years of education is compulsory. In 1994, there were 4,001 primary schools with

42,135 teachers and 1.5 million students. In addition to the state-run Autonomous University of Santo Domingo, there are four private universities.

1999 KEY EVENTS TIMELINE

January

- Former President Joaquin Balaguer, 92, is flown to the United States for medical treatment. Despite frail health, he is still mentioned as a possible candidate for the 2000 presidential election.

- Political parties struggle for control: the controversy stems from a dispute over the Municipal League, which distributes national government funds to local governments.

- After a senator and a local journalist are injured in a fracas with police, 20,000 armed soldiers are called in to control the situation in the capital city.

- Disputes between the nation's three political parties spill into the streets of Santo Domingo; vandals damage city buses.

March

- Popular unrest erupts as citizens become frustrated with the government's failure to curb rising prices. Three are killed and 20 injured in rioting.

April

- Heads of states from more than 20 Caribbean nations gather for a summit in Santo Domingo; one of Cuban leader Fidel Castro's bodyguards defects during the stay.

- Santo Domingo hosts talks of the Caribbean Community trade bloc.

- The nation continues to recover from damage wrought by Hurricane Georges; some families are still living in improvised shelters.

- AES Corporation of Virginia (U.S.) announces that its subsidiary purchased a 50 percent interest in the electricity distributor Empresa Distribudora Eléctrica Este from the Dominican Republic.

May

- The government announces plans to restructure its debt.

- A general strike paralyzes the nation.

July

- U.S. Marshals capture a fugitive, one of its fifteen most wanted, who had escaped to the Dominican Republic.

August

- Tricom announces expanded telecommunications services to the country's northern region.

- At the Pan American Games in Winnipeg, Manitoba (Canada), women's high jump gold medalist Juana Rosario Arrendel of the Dominican Republic team tests positive for steroids and is stripped of her medal.

- Chicago Cubs baseball star Sammy Sosa announces plan to develop a network of clinics in his homeland.

September

- Coastal Corporation of Houston, Texas (U.S.), and Gener S.A. (South America) buy 50 percent of the Itabo Generation Company, one of two power companies to be partially privatized by the Dominican Republic government, which retains the other 50-percent interest.

- Part of the government-owned sugar industry is sold to private interests.

- The British magazine *The Economist* reports that the Dominican Republic's GDP is expected to grow by more than 6 percent this year.

- Public opinion polls give President Leonel Fernández a 45 percent approval rating.

- The government announces it is considering raising the price of fuel.

October

- President Leonel Fernandez returns home after a 12-day trip to the United States and Taiwan.

- The government increases the price of gas between 15 and 25 percent; police are put on alert as the nation prepares for unrest in the wake of the announcement.

- On October 12, a general strike is called by labor and activist groups to protest the gas hike; police round up an estimated 1,000 political leaders to prevent staging of protests.

- On October 13, commerce returns to normal.

- Presidential candidates for the 2000 election outline their foreign trade platforms aimed at reducing the country's trade deficit.

- The National Office of Statistics reports the nation's population will reach 8.5 million by 2000, with the the national district (greater Santo Domingo) accounting for nearly 2.6 million people.

- The *Listín Diario* newspaper reports the diversification in 1999 of the country's free (trade) zones.

- President Fernández announces plans to support a congressional bill that would add a fixed tax to the price of petroleum.

- During a Latin American Travel Press Conference, developer Juan Dolio announces a $900-million development of a stretch of a southeastern beach.

- Chicago Cubs baseball star and national hero Sammy Sosa returns home with his family.

- An international, 12-day drug raid, conducted in 15 Caribbean countries results in nearly 1,300 arrests; the operation is coordinated, in part, from the Dominican Republic capital.

November

- Leaders of 71 nations in Africa, the Caribbean, and the Pacific region, known as the ACP group, meet in the Dominican Republic to discuss trade. The ACP group is currently negotiating favorable trade status for its members with the European Union.

December

- The central bank reports that the economy closed the year with an 8.3 percent growth in gross domestic product, one of the strongest in the world.

ANALYSIS OF EVENTS: 1999

BUSINESS AND THE ECONOMY

Under the leadership of President Fernández, the Dominican government continued its plan to privatize government-held interests, selling off 50 percent of its interest in its electrical power companies, and also selling off part of its sugar industry.

The nation's free (trade) zone became less textiles-intensive during the year. More than half of the new industries in the free zone are non-apparel manufacturers. Their products include office sup-

plies, boats, leather goods, and windows. The diversification could ease the nation's foreign trade deficit.

The Dominican Republic hosted many high-profile meetings during the year. Heads of state from more than 20 Caribbean nations gathered in Santo Domingo for a trade summit. In preparation for the establishment of Free Trade Area of the Americas (slated to begin 2005), attendees approved a plan to impose a regional tariff, but each country was left to move toward a common tariff based on its own priorities.

Santo Domingo also hosted talks of the Caribbean Community trade bloc. The body's leaders resolved that unity is imperative among the smaller nations to protect their economies, they must work together to promote the region's tourism industry, and Western nations must stop transporting nuclear and toxic waste through the Caribbean. Tourism got a boost as the Latin American Travel Press Conference was held in the Dominican Republic.

Though there was popular unrest due to inflation, the British magazine *The Economist* reported that the nation's economy was performing well; its GDP was expected to grow by more than 6 percent in 1999.

GOVERNMENT AND POLITICS

With a presidential election looming in 2000 and the current president prohibited by law from running, political tensions ran high in the Dominican Republic—even precipitating unrest in the capital. Two of the nation's three political parties allied against the third to dispute the leadership of the Municipal League, which distributes national funds to local governments; each side elected its own leader to head the administrative body. In Santo Domingo, protesters accused President Leonel Fernández of being a "fledgling dictator"-ostensibly for trying to secure his party's leadership of the league. After a senator and a reporter were injured in a fracas with police at the capitol, 20,000 armed soldiers were called in to bring the situation under control.

President Fernández continued government efforts to reform the nation's economy, but growth failed to reach many citizens. Mounting frustration with the Fernández administration's failure to deliver on the campaign promises prompted a general strike in May, the first of two this year; demonstrators demanded more government services and lower prices for gasoline, electricity, and food.

Public opinion of the president continued to run low through the year; his approval rating was only 45 percent in September. The following month saw an increase in gas prices. Police were put on alert as the nation prepared for unrest in the wake of the announcement. Fernández explained the increase was necessary to help pay the nation's $4-billion foreign debt (which was restructured earlier in the year). He later announced plans to support a congressional bill that would add a fixed tax to the price of petroleum, allowing fuel prices to fluctuate according to world market prices-without political and social implications.

After a year of political and social instability, largely caused by an economy that cannot seem to grow fast enough to meet the needs of the Dominican Republic's population, many looked forward to the May 2000 elections. The most important issues for that election appeared to be foreign debt, the trade deficit, and bringing inflation under control.

CULTURE AND SOCIETY

For many it was a year of hardships as the nation continued to recover from damage wrought by Hurricane Georges (fall 1998), which left 180,000 people homeless and claimed 260 lives. Frustration with government relief efforts and with rising consumer prices resulted in sporadic outbreaks of civil unrest. Following a hike in gas prices, a general strike was called by labor and activist groups on October 12; it was the second general strike of the year. Privately run public transportation came to a standstill, and schools, shops, and most small businesses closed. Army troops and police patrolled the streets. The strike, which cost an estimated 663 million pesos ($42 million), ended after one day. Those who supported it said it sent a strong message of intolerance to the nation's government.

Chicago Cubs star Sammy Sosa announced that his foundation will provide free immunizations to 50,000 youths in the Dominican Republic in 2000. The program, which is in collaboration with the U.S. Agency of International Development and the Centers for Disease Control (CDC), is part of a three-year plan aimed at developing a network of clinics in the athlete's homeland. The American baseball season over, Sosa returned home with his family for several months.

DIRECTORY

CENTRAL GOVERNMENT

Head of State

President

Leonel Antonio Fernández Reyna, Office of the President, Palacio Nacional, Calle Moisés García, esq. Dr. Delgado, Santo Domingo, Dominican Republic
PHONE: +(809) 6864771
FAX: +(809) 6867040
E-MAIL: correspondencias@presidencia.gov.do

Vice President

Jaime David Fernandez Mirabal, Office of the President, Palacio Nacional, Calle Moisés García, esq. Dr. Delgado, Santo Domingo, Dominican Republic
PHONE: +(809) 6864771
FAX: +(809) 6867040

Cabinet

Secretary of State for Agriculture

Amilcar Romero, Secretariat of State for Agriculture, Autopista Duarte, Santo Domingo, Dominican Republic
PHONE: +(809) 5473800
FAX: +(809) 5676609

Secretary of State for the Armed Forces

Manuel de Jesus Florentino, Secretariat of State for the Armed Forces, Plaza de la Independencia, Ave. 27 de Febrero, Santo Domingo, Dominican Republic
PHONE: +(809) 5305193
FAX: +(809) 5310461; 5305180

Secretary of State for Education, Fine Arts, and Public Worship

Ligia Amada Melo de Cardona, Secretariat of State for Education, Fine Arts, and Public Worship, Ave. Máximo Gómez, Santo Domingo, Dominican Republic
PHONE: +(809) 6855010
FAX: +(809) 6890788

Secretary of State for Finance

Daniel Toribio, Secretariat of State for Finance, Ave. Mexico, Santo Domingo, Dominican Republic
PHONE: +(809) 6879246
FAX: +(809) 6886561

Secretary of State for Foreign Relations
Eduardo Latorre, Secretariat of State for Foreign Relations, Ave. Independencia, Santo Domingo, Dominican Republic
PHONE: +(809) 5356280; 5334121
FAX: +(809) 5355752

Secretary of State for Industry and Commerce
Luis Manuel Bonetti, Secretariat of State for Industry and Commerce, Ave. México, esq. Leopoldo Navarro, Edificio Oficinas Gubernamentales, Piso 7, Santo Domingo, Dominican Republic
PHONE: +(809) 6855171
FAX: +(809) 6861973

Secretary of State for Interior and Police
Norge Botello, Secretariat of State for Interior and Police, Ave. Mexico, esq. Leopoldo Navarro, Edificio Oficinas Gubernamentales, Piso 3, Santo Domingo, Dominican Republic
PHONE: +(809) 6889565; 6865923

Secretary of State for Judicial Reform
Ramon Andres Blanco Fernandez, Secretariat of State for Judicial Reform

Secretary of State for Labor
Rafael Alburquerque de Castro, Secretariat of State for Labor, Centro de los Héroes, Santo Domingo, Dominican Republic
PHONE: +(809) 5324144, 5354404
FAX: +(809) 5354590
E-MAIL: tabajo@ codetel.net.do

Secretary of State for Public Health and Social Welfare
Altagracia Guzman, Secretariat of State for Public Health and Social Welfare, Avenida Tiradentes esq. Avenida San Cristobal, Apartado Postal 1344, Santo Domingo, Dominican Republic
PHONE: +(809) 5413121
FAX: +(809) 5444337
E-MAIL: sespas@codetel.net.do

Secretary of State for Public Works and Communications
Diandino Pena, Secretariat of State for Public Works and Communications, Ave. Tiradentes, Ensanche la Fe, Santo Domingo, Dominican Republic
PHONE: +(809) 5678251
FAX: +(809) 5623382

Secretary of State for Sports, Physical Education, and Recreation
Juan Marichal, Secretariat of State for Sports, Physical Education, and Recreation, Ave. Pedro Henríquez Ureña, Santo Domingo, Dominican Republic
PHONE: +(809) 5404010
FAX: +(809) 5636878

Secretary of State for Tourism
Félix Jiménez, Secretariat of State for Tourism, Ave. México, esq. 30 de Marzo, Oficinas Gubernamentales, Bloque D, Santo Domingo, Dominican Republic
PHONE: +(809) 2214660
FAX: +(809) 6823806

Secretary of State for the Presidency
Alejandrina German, Secretariat of State for the Presidency, Palacio Nacional, Calle Moisés Garcia, esq. Dr. Delgado, Santo Domingo, Dominican Republic
PHONE: +(809) 6864771
FAX: +(809) 6867040

Secretary of State Without Portfolio
Lidio Cadet, Secretariat of State Without Portfolio

Secretary of State Without Portfolio
Rafael Augusto Collado, Secretariat of State Without Portfolio

Secretary of State Without Portfolio
Julian Serrule, Secretariat of State Without Portfolio

Administrative Secretary of the Presidency
Simon Lizardo, Secretariat of the Presidency, Palacio Nacional, Calle Moisés Garcia, esq. Dr. Delgado, Santo Domingo, Dominican Republic
PHONE: +(809) 6864771
FAX: +(809) 6867040

Technical Secretary of the Presidency
Temistocles Montas, Technical Secretariat of the Presidency, Palacio Nacional, Calle Moisés García, esq. Dr. Delgado, Santo Domingo, Dominican Republic
PHONE: +(809) 6825430
FAX: +(809) 6867040

POLITICAL ORGANIZATIONS
Social Christian Reformist Party
NAME: Ricardo Joaquin Balaguer

Dominican Liberation Party

NAME: Lidio Cadet

Partido Revolucionario Dominicano (Dominican Revolutionary Party)

NAME: Emanuel Esquea

Independent Revolutionary Party

Unidad Democrática (Democratic Unity)

DIPLOMATIC REPRESENTATION

Embassies in Dominican Republic

Canada
Fimaca Building, 1st Floor, 30 Maximo Gomez, PO Box 2054, Santo Domingo, Dominican Republic
PHONE: +(809) 6890002
FAX: +(809) 6822691

France
Avenida Georges Washington 353, 2ndo piso, Santo Domingo, Dominican Republic
PHONE: +(809) 6892161
FAX: +(809) 2218408
E-MAIL: ambafrance@ambafrance-do.org
TITLE: Ambassador
NAME: François-Xavier Deniau

United States
Unit 5500, APO AA 34041-5500, Santo Domingo, Dominican Republic
PHONE: +(809) 2212171
FAX: +(809) 6867437
TITLE: Charge d'Affaires
NAME: Linda E. Watt

JUDICIAL SYSTEM

Supreme Court

Calle Porfirio Herrera Billini, esq. Juan B. Pérez, Apartado Postal 1485, Santo Domingo, Dominican Republic
PHONE: +(809) 5333191
FAX: +(809) 5322906
E-MAIL: suprema.corte@codetel.net.do

FURTHER READING

Government Publications

Central Intelligence Agency. *CIA World Factbook, 1998.*Washington, DC: GPO, 1999.

U.S. Department of State. *Background Notes: Dominican Republic, 1997.* Washington, DC: GPO, 1998.

U.S. Department of State. *Country Reports on Human Rights Practices for 1997.* Washington, DC: GPO, 1998.

Sources of Statistical Information

International Monetary Fund. *Government Finance Statistics Yearbook.* Washington, DC.

UNESCO. *Statistical Yearbook.* Lanham, MD: Bernam Press.

ARTICLES

"AES of Virginia is in Dominican Republic Venture." *New York Times*, April 17, 1999.

"Armed Soldiers, Police Block Dominican Congress in Election." CNN.com, January 26, 1999.

"Balaguer Flown to United States for Medical Treatment." CNN.com, January 18, 1999.

"Calling the Blind Man's Bluff." *The Economist*, September 25, 1999.

"Caribbean Nations Seek Regional Tariff System." CNN.com, April 17, 1999.

"Coastal and GENER Purchase Interest in Dominican Power Company." PR Newswire, September 8, 1999.

"Cuban Defection Reported." *New York Times*, April 22, 1999.

"Dominican Political Parties Struggle for Control." CNN.com, January 28, 1999.

"Dominican Republic Gold Medalist Tests Positive." Reuters, August 1999.

"Dominican Republic Population for 2000." *Dominican Republic One: Daily News*, October 15, 1999.

"Dominican Republic Resumes Normal Commerce after General Strike." CNN.com, October 13, 1999.

"Ex-Strongman's Next Move Intrigues Dominicans." *New York Times*, April 25, 1999.

"Fixed Petroleum Tax." *Dominican Republic One: Daily News*, October 15, 1999.

"Free Zones Diversify." *Dominican Republic One: Daily News*, October 15, 1999.

"Fugitive is Apprehended in Dominican Republic." *New York Times*, July 27, 1999.

"General Strike Called in Dominican Republic."
CNN.com, October 12, 1999.

"One Dead in Dominican General Strike."
CNN.com, October 12, 1999.

"Police on Alert as Dominican Republic Braces
for Gasoline Price Rise." CNN.com, October
4, 1999.

"Politicians Make Promises to Exporters."
Dominican Republic One: Daily News,
October 15, 1999.

"Sammy Sosa Comes Home." *Dominican
Republic One: Daily News*, October 15, 1999.

"Sammy Sosa Opening Clinic for Kids in His
Native Country." Business Wire, August 4,
1999.

"Senator, Journalist Shot in Confrontation over
Disputed Election." CNN.com, January 26,
1999.

"Tricom Installs the Most Advanced
International Gateway Switch in the
Caribbean." PR Newswire, August 18, 1999.

BOOKS

Brown, Isabel Zakrzewski. *Cultures and
Customs of the Dominican Republic.*
Westport, CT: Greenwood Publications, 1999.

Creed, Alexander. *Dominican Republic.*
Broomall, PA: Chelsea House, 1999.

Howard, David. *Dominican Republic: A Guide
to the People, Politics and Culture. In Focus*
series. Northampton, MA: Interlink Publishing
Group, 1999.

Kelly, Robert C. et. al., editors. *Dominican
Republic Country Review 1999/2000.*
Houston, TX: Commercial Data International,
1999.

Velton, Ross. *Haiti and the Dominican Republic:
The Island of Hispaniola.* Bucks, England:
Bradt Publications, 1999.

Wucker, Michele. *Why the Cocks Fight:
Dominicans, Haitians, and the Struggle for
Hispaniola.* New York: Hill and Wang, 1999.

DOMINICAN REPUBLIC: STATISTICAL DATA

For sources and notes see "Sources of Statistics" in the front of each volume.

GEOGRAPHY

Geography (1)

Area:

Total: 48,730 sq km.

Land: 48,380 sq km.

Water: 350 sq km.

Area—comparative: slightly more than twice the size of New Hampshire.

Land boundaries:

Total: 275 km.

Border countries: Haiti 275 km.

Coastline: 1,288 km.

Climate: tropical maritime; little seasonal temperature variation; seasonal variation in rainfall.

Terrain: rugged highlands and mountains with fertile valleys interspersed.

Natural resources: nickel, bauxite, gold, silver.

Land use:

Arable land: 21%

Permanent crops: 9%

Permanent pastures: 43%

Forests and woodland: 12%

Other: 15% (1993 est.).

HUMAN FACTORS

Demographics (2A)

	1990	1995	1998	2000	2010	2020	2030	2040	2050
Population	6,997.1	7,611.7	7,998.8	8,261.5	9,642.0	11,084.6	12,439.3	13,620.7	14,586.3
Net migration rate (per 1,000 population)	NA	NA	NA	NA	NA	NA	NA	NA	NA
Births	NA	NA	NA	NA	NA	NA	NA	NA	NA
Deaths	NA	NA	NA	NA	NA	NA	NA	NA	NA
Life expectancy - males	64.8	66.6	67.5	68.2	71.0	73.3	75.2	76.6	77.7
Life expectancy - females	69.1	71.0	72.0	72.8	75.9	78.4	80.5	82.1	83.3
Birth rate (per 1,000)	29.3	27.8	26.4	25.5	22.4	20.1	17.8	16.3	15.0
Death rate (per 1,000)	6.4	6.0	5.7	5.6	5.3	5.4	5.9	6.9	7.8
Women of reproductive age (15-49 yrs.)	1,766.0	1,939.0	2,046.1	2,119.0	2,493.0	2,784.7	3,054.6	3,258.7	3,372.8
of which are currently married	NA	NA	NA	NA	NA	NA	NA	NA	NA
Fertility rate	3.3	3.2	3.1	3.0	2.7	2.5	2.4	2.3	2.2

Except as noted, values for vital statistics are in thousands; life expectancy is in years.

Health Personnel (3)

Total health expenditure as a percentage of GDP, 1990-1997[a]

Public sector 1.8

Private sector 3.9

Total[b] 5.7

Health expenditure per capita in U.S. dollars, 1990-1997[a]

Purchasing power parity 227

Total 77

Availability of health care facilities per 100,000 people

Hospital beds 1990-1997[a] 200

Doctors 1993[c] 77

Nurses 1993[c] 20

Health Indicators (4)

Life expectancy at birth

1980 64

1997 71

Daily per capita supply of calories (1996) 2,316

Total fertility rate births per woman (1997) 3.0

Maternal mortality ratio per 100,000 live births (1990-97) . . . . .110[c]

Safe water % of population with access (1995) 73

Sanitation % of population with access (1995) 80

Consumption of iodized salt % of households (1992-98)[a] 13

Smoking prevalence

Male % of adults (1985-95)[a] 66

Female % of adults (1985-95)[a] 14

Tuberculosis incidence per 100,000 people (1997) 114

Adult HIV prevalence % of population ages 15-49 (1997) 1.89

Infants and Malnutrition (5)

Under-5 mortality rate (1997) 53

% of infants with low birthweight (1990-97) 16

Births attended by skilled health staff % of total[a] . . .96

% fully immunized (1995-97)

TB 88

DPT 80

Polio 79

Measles 80

Prevalence of child malnutrition under age 5 (1992-97)[b] 6

Ethnic Division (6)

White 16%

Black 11%

Mixed 73%

Religions (7)

Roman Catholic 95%

Languages (8)

Spanish.

EDUCATION

Public Education Expenditures (9)

Public expenditure on education (% of GNP)

1980 . . . . .2.2

1996 . . . . .2.0

Expenditure per student

Primary % of GNP per capita

1980 . . . . .3.1

1996 . . . . .3.3[1]

Secondary % of GNP per capita

1980 . . . .

1996 . . . . .4.4[1]

Tertiary % of GNP per capita

1980 . . . .

1996 . . . . .9.8

Expenditure on teaching materials

Primary % of total for level (1996) . . . .

Secondary % of total for level (1996) . . . .

Primary pupil-teacher ratio per teacher (1996) . . . . .35[1]

Duration of primary education years (1995) 8

Literacy Rates (11A)

In thousands and percent[1]	1990	1995	2000	2010
Illiterate population (15+ yrs.)	905	908	911	892
Literacy rate - total adult pop. (%)	79.8	82.1	84.0	87.2
Literacy rate - males (%)	79.9	82.0	83.6	86.5
Literacy rate - females (%)	79.6	82.2	84.4	88.0

GOVERNMENT & LAW

Political Parties (12)

Chamber of Deputies	No. of seats
Social Christian Reformist Party (PRSC)	.50
Dominican Revolutionary Party (PRD)	.57
Dominican Liberation Party (PLD)	.13

Government Budget (13A)

Year: 1996

Total Expenditures: 28,653.1 Millions of Pesos

Expenditures as a percentage of the total by function:

General public services and public order	.8.92
Defense	.4.01
Education	.12.60
Health	.11.16
Social Security and Welfare	.4.58
Housing and community amenities	.13.20
Recreational, cultural, and religious affairs	.1.14
Fuel and energy	.4.69
Agriculture, forestry, fishing, and hunting	.8.92
Mining, manufacturing, and construction	.7.70
Transportation and communication	.13.51
Other economic affairs and services	.1.77

Military Affairs (14B)

	1990	1991	1992	1993	1994	1995
Military expenditures						
Current dollars (mil.)	76	59	82	117	122	154
1995 constant dollars (mil.)	88	65	88	123	125	154
Armed forces (000)	21	21	22	22	22	22
Gross national product (GNP)						
Current dollars (mil.)	7,904	8,325	9,224	9,921	10,640	11,430
1995 constant dollars (mil.)	9,084	9,200	9,922	10,400	10,900	11,430
Central government expenditures (CGE)						
1995 constant dollars (mil.)	1,034	879	1,403	1,901	1,832	1,704
People (mil.)	7.2	7.4	7.5	7.7	7.8	7.9
Military expenditure as % of GNP	1.0	.7	.9	1.2	1.1	1.4
Military expenditure as % of CGE	8.5	7.4	6.3	6.5	6.8	9.1
Military expenditure per capita (1995 $)	12	9	12	16	16	19
Armed forces per 1,000 people (soldiers)	2.9	2.9	2.9	2.9	2.8	2.8
GNP per capita (1995 $)	1,259	1,249	1,321	1,358	1,397	1,438
Arms imports[6]						
Current dollars (mil.)	5	5	5	5	20	10
1995 constant dollars (mil.)	6	6	5	5	21	10
Arms exports[6]						
Current dollars (mil.)	0	0	0	0	0	0
1995 constant dollars (mil.)	0	0	0	0	0	0
Total imports[7]						
Current dollars (mil.)	2,062	1,988	2,501	2,436	2,626	2,976
1995 constant dollars (mil.)	2,370	2,197	2,690	2,554	2,692	2,976
Total exports[7]						
Current dollars (mil.)	735	658	562	511	633	765
1995 constant dollars (mil.)	845	727	605	536	649	765
Arms as percent of total imports[8]	.2	.3	.2	.2	.8	.3
Arms as percent of total exports[8]	0	0	0	0	0	0

Crime (15)

Crime rate (for 1997)

Crimes reported 70,700

Total persons convicted . . . . .NA

Crimes per 100,000 population 850

Persons responsible for offenses

Total number of suspects . . . . .NA

Total number of female suspects . . . . .NA

Total number of juvenile suspects . . . . .NA

LABOR FORCE

Labor Force (16)

Agriculture 50%

Services and government 32%

Industry 18%

Data for 1991 est.

Unemployment Rate (17)

30% (1996 est.)

PRODUCTION SECTOR

Electric Energy (18)

Capacity . . . . .1.447 million kW (1995)

Production . . . . .6.5 billion kWh (1995)

Consumption per capita . . . . .865 kWh (1995)

Transportation (19)

Highways:

total: 12,600 km

paved: 6,224 km

unpaved: 6,376 km (1996 est.)

Pipelines: crude oil 96 km; petroleum products 8 km

Merchant marine:

total: 1 cargo ship (1,000 GRT or over) totaling 1,587 GRT/1,165 DWT (1997 est.)

Airports: 36 (1997 est.)

Airports—with paved runways:

total: 14

over 3,047 m: 2

2,438 to 3,047 m: 2

1,524 to 2,437 m: 5

914 to 1,523 m: 3

under 914 m: 2 (1997 est.)

Airports—with unpaved runways:

total: 22

1,524 to 2,437 m: 1

914 to 1,523 m: 6

under 914 m: 15 (1997 est.)

Top Agricultural Products (20)

Sugarcane, coffee, cotton, cocoa, tobacco, rice, beans, potatoes, corn, bananas; cattle, pigs, dairy products, meat, eggs.

FINANCE, ECONOMICS, & TRADE

Economic Indicators (22)

National product: GDP—purchasing power parity— $38.3 billion (1997 est.)

National product real growth rate: 7% (1997 est.)

National product per capita: $4,700 (1997 est.)

Inflation rate—consumer price index: 10.9% (1997 est.)

Balance of Payments (23)

	1992	1993	1994	1996	1996
Exports of goods (f.o.b.)	562	3,114	3,361	3,653	3,963
Imports of goods (f.o.b.)	−2,174	−4,654	−4,903	−5,145	−5,727
Trade balance	−1,612	−1,540	−1,542	−1,492	−1,764
Services - debits	−931	−1,380	−1,495	−1,628	−1,677
Services - credits	1,403	1,616	1,846	2,027	2,251
Private transfers (net)	85	35	71	64	69
Government transfers (net)	347	848	893	928	1,011
Overall balance	−708	−421	−227	−101	−110

Exchange Rates (24)

Exchange rates:

Dominican pesos (RD$) per US$1

December 1997 . . . . .14.332

1997 . . . . .14.265

1996 . . . . .13.775

1995 . . . . .13.597

1994 . . . . .13.160

1993 . . . . .12.676

Top Import Origins (25)

$3.7 billion (f.o.b., 1996)

Origins	%
United States	.41
Caricom	.25
United Kingdom	.13
Netherlands	NA
Canada	NA

NA stands for not available.

Top Export Destinations (26)

$815 million (f.o.b., 1996) Data are for 1995.

Destinations	%
United States	.45
European Union	.34
Canada	NA
Japan	NA
Puerto Rico	NA

NA stands for not available.

Economic Aid (27)

Recipient: ODA, $21 million (1993).

Import Export Commodities (28)

Import Commodities	Export Commodities
Foodstuffs	Ferronickel
Petroleum	Sugar
Cotton and fabrics	Gold
Chemicals and pharmaccuticals	Coffee
	Cocoa

·ECUADOR

Republic of Ecuador
República del Ecuador

INTRODUCTORY SURVEY

RECENT HISTORY

From 1944 to 1961, a succession of elected governments held office. In 1961, with Ecuadorian currency in a slump and consumers heavily taxed, the air force revolted and sent president Velasco Ibarra into exile.

After a period, which included rule by a four-man military junta, Velasco once again won the presidency in 1968. However, in 1970 following a fiscal crisis, he suspended the 1967 constitution and assumed dictatorial power. Velasco was overthrown in a bloodless coup in 1972, but military rule continued.

Democracy returned to Ecuador in 1979 with the election of Jaime Roldós Aguilera, and elected governments have run the country since that time.

In 1992, voters elected a conservative government, headed by President Sixto Durán-Ballén of the Republican Unity Party (PUR), and Vice President Alberto Dahik of the Conservative Party (CP).

In January 1995 a long-standing border dispute with Peru erupted when Ecuadoran troops attacked a Peruvian post. Ecuador and Peru fought until March, with 80 casualties and 200 wounded. In 1998, the two countries agreed to begin talks to resolve the dispute.

In July 1996, Abdalá Bucaram was elected president. An eccentric populist, he alienated most of the political establishment and was removed from office by Ecuador's congress in February 1997. Congress elected Fabián Alarcón as interim

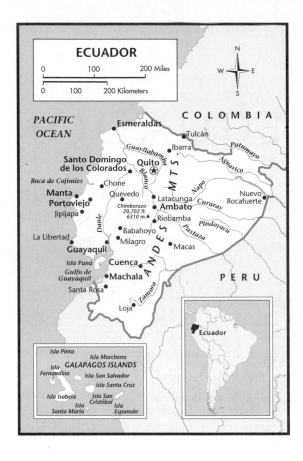

ECUADOR

0 100 200 Miles

0 100 200 Kilometers

PACIFIC OCEAN

COLOMBIA

Esmeraldas
Tulcán
Guayllabamba
Ibarra
Putumayo
Santo Domingo de los Colorados
Quito
Aguarico
Boca de Cojimíes
Chone
Napo
Quevedo
Nuevo Rocafuerte
Manta
Latacunga
Curaray
Portoviejo
Chimborazo 20,702 ft. 6310 m.
Ambato
Jipijapa
Riobamba
Pindoyacu
Babahoyo
Pastaza
La Libertad
Milagro
Macas
Guayaquil
Isla Puná
Cuenca
Gulfo de Guayaquil
Machala
PERU
Santa Rosa
Loja
Zamora

Ecuador

Isla Pinta
Isla Marchena
GALAPAGOS ISLANDS
Isla Fernandina
Isla San Salvador
Isla Santa Cruz
Isla Isabela
Isla San Cristóbal
Isla Santa Maria
Isla Espanola

president. In July 1998, Jamal Mahuad, mayor of Quito, narrowly defeated businessman Alvaro Noboa in presidential elections. Naboa challenged the result, but international observers judged the elections to be fair. Mahuad took office in August 1998.

GOVERNMENT

Ecuador's Chamber of Representatives consists of seventy-seven provincial and national members. The president and vice-president are elected for four-year terms, and the president cannot be reelected. The president controls the armed forces and can declare a state of siege.

Judiciary

There are five levels of courts. The parochial judge handles only minor civil cases. Cantonal courts try minor civil and criminal actions. Provincial courts handle most criminal cases and serious civil and commercial suits. Superior courts handle appeals from the lower courts. The highest court is the Supreme Court, which has thirty-one justices and three alternates chosen by the Chamber of Representatives for six-year periods.

Political Parties

There are currently eighteen parties active in Ecuadorian politics. Modern parties on the right include the Social Christian Party (PSC), the Republican Unity Party (PUR), and the Conservative Party (CE). On the left are the Democratic Left (ID), the Popular Democracy Party (DP) of former President Hurtado, and the traditional Radical Liberal Party (PLR). In the 1996 elections, the PSC won twenty-seven of eighty-two seats; the DP won ten seats; the populist Roldosist Party won twenty-one seats; and an Amerindian political movement called Pachakutik (Quichua for "cataclysmic change") won eight seats, increasing the representation of indigenous peoples in Ecuadoran politics.

DEFENSE

The armed forces of 57,100 are designed for internal security more than external defense. A one-year draft supports an army of 50,000. The navy numbers 4,100 (including 1,500 marines), and the air force 3,000.

ECONOMIC AFFAIRS

Ecuador's economy grew by less than 2% in 1996, mainly as a result of the border dispute with Peru, electricity shortages, and high interest rates. The inflation rate was 60% at the end of 1992, but fell to 25% by 1995.

Public Finance

Economic reforms instituted in 1992 caused domestic fuel prices and utility rates to rise, eliminated subsidies, and brought the government budget into balance. These changes helped eliminate the budget deficit by 1994. The government was able to maintain tight budgetary control in 1995 when faced with increased military expenditures because of the boarder conflict with Peru. The U.S. Central Intelligence Agency estimates that, in 1995, government revenues totaled approximately $3.3 billion and expenditures $3.3 billion. External debt totaled $12.6 billion.

Income

In 1998, Ecuador's gross national product (GNP) was $18.6 billion at current prices, or about $1,530 per person. For the period 1985–95, the average inflation rate was 45.5%, resulting in a real growth rate in GNP of 0.8% per person.

Industry

In 1990–95, manufacturing output increased by an average of 3.2% per year. Ecuador's industrial sector manufactures tobacco products, textiles, wood and paper, chemicals, and metallic minerals.

Banking and Finance

The Central Bank of Ecuador, founded as a private bank in 1927, was declared an organ of the state in 1948 by the Monetary Board. It is owned by the national government and by private banks, which are required to invest at least 5% of their capital and reserves in it. The Central Bank issues and stabilizes currency, holds and manages foreign-exchange reserves, issues import and export permits, and regulates international transactions.

Trading in securities is relatively minor. Ecuador has two stock exchanges, one in Quito and the other in Guayaquil, both established in 1969.

Economic Development

In 1992–93, a major macroeconomic adjustment program was introduced, featuring a sizable currency devaluation (35%) and substantial increases in domestic fuel and electricity prices. Free trade agreements with Colombia, Venezuela, and Bolivia were signed, and new investment regulations were adopted to open up the economy to foreign investment and eliminate previous bureaucratic impediments. In April 1993, Ecuador qualified for Andean Trade Preference Act benefits, and has officially submitted an application to join the GATT.

SOCIAL WELFARE

The benefits of Ecuador's social security program, for those who fulfill the requirements, consist of health and maternity insurance with free medical service, accident insurance, old-age pensions, survivors' pensions, funeral expenses, and unemployment insurance.

Despite equal legal status, women have fewer educational and employment opportunities than men.

Healthcare

It is estimated that 88% of the population has access to health care services. There is one doctor for every 957 people in Ecuador. In 1994, the country spent over $440 million on health care.

Malnutrition and infant mortality are the country's two basic health problems. Life expectancy was estimated at 70 years.

Housing

Almost all rural homes and many city dwellings on the coast are made with split bamboo siding and a palm thatch or corrugated iron roof.

EDUCATION

Illiteracy for persons 15 years of age and over fell from 12% in 1990 to 10% in 1995. At the primary level, there were 63,347 teachers and 2 million students in 1992. The secondary level had 814,359 students in 1992. At the universities and all higher level institutions, there were 206,541 students enrolled and 12,856 teaching staff in 1990. The Central University of Ecuador dates from 1594.

1999 KEY EVENTS TIMELINE

January

- The largest bank merger in the nation's history will take place as soon as final regulatory approval is completed. Banco del Pacífico and Banco Popular will merge to become Ecuador's new financial leader.

- Low oil prices continue to hurt the economy. Ecuador is experiencing its worst economic crisis of the decade.

February

- The teacher union goes on strike to demand better salaries. The government argues that rather than increasing public spending, the nation needs a swift reduction in spending to balance the budget.

March

- President Mahuad sends an emergency bill to Congress to reduce public spending. He also moves to begin the process of privatization of telecommunications and electricity companies. The austerity package includes a proposed hike in value added tax from 10 to 15%.

- President Mahuad declares a State of Emergency in the country as a result of political upheaval caused by the economic crisis.

April

- Private transportation buses and taxi drivers continue their strike protesting a 100% increase in fuel prices. Ecuador is a net exporter of oil and historically, oil prices have been subsidized in the country.

May

- President Mahuad lifts the state of emergency as the economic crisis worsens. Opposition leader Jaime Nabot demands that steps be taken to alleviate the suffering of the poor.

- The presidents of Perú (Alberto Fujimori) and Ecuador (Jamil Mahuad) formally end a 40-year old border conflict between the two countries.

June

- Ten of the 40 banks existing in Ecuador have collapsed in the last 10 months, worsening the economic and financial crisis.

- President Mahuad's hopes rest with signing an agreement with the International Monetary Fund (IMF) to obtain a $1.4 billion loan to rescue Ecuador's economy. The agreement is expected to be signed in August.

July

- The government reaches an agreement with protesting indigenous groups who were demanding government support to face the economic crisis.

August

- A private place crashes in the port city of Guayaquil killing five.

- Members of Congress continue to block much needed government reforms. Without the reforms, the government is unlikely to balance the budget, reduce government spending and overcome the economic crisis.

- President Mahuad marks his first year anniversary in power with Ecuador suffering its worst economic crisis in decades.

- Ecuador's currency has lost 119% of its value in one year.

- Ecuador announces it is closer than ever to signing an agreement with the IMF to restructure its $13 billion public debt.

- Mahuad announces Ecuador will default on a $96 million interest payment-due on August 31- on previously signed restructured commercial bank loans.

September

- The IMF announces that it has reached a deal with Ecuador on a rescue package for that country. Ecuador will get access to much needed credit but it must comply with several economic reforms and privatization plans.

- Twelve foreigners are kidnapped in Ecuador's northern Amazonian border with Colombia; a Canadian government official flies to Ecuador to negotiate the release of the hostages.

- Ecuador promises to pay part of the $96 million interest payment on its debt defaulted on August 31.

- One of the twelve hostages kidnapped earlier this month is found safe and unhurt.

- Economic minister Guillermo Lasso resigns. He lasted for 42 days and was the first economic minister appointed by president Mahuad after that office was created to coordinate the government's financial strategy.

- Ecuador delivers on its promise to pay half of the interest payment due in late August. Ecuador had defaulted on August 31.

November

- Ecuador, the world's biggest producer of bananas, reaches an agreement with Caribbean exporters on a quota arrangement, which they hope will satisfy U.S. concerns about the European Union's import regime.

- The provincial council of Guyas, which includes the country's largest city and main port, Guayaquil, votes to hold a referendum on autonomy. Their goal is to keep half of its tax revenues.

- In a desperate attempt to stabilize the downward spiral of the sucre, Ecuador's currency, the central bank pushes its overnight lending rate from 62% to 160%, ignoring fiscal targets agreed to with the International Monetary Fund.

- The United States closes its embassy in Quito and its consulate in Guayaquil, citing threats to security.

ANALYSIS OF EVENTS: 1999

BUSINESS AND THE ECONOMY

Ecuador continued to suffer its worst economic crisis in decades. President Mahuad was elected in 1998 on a platform of anti-corruption, responsibility and accountability. However, soon after taking office, he had to cope with a banking crisis. The entire banking system was at risk of collapsing. In addition, the opposition in congress was directly linked with the strong financial sector in the port city of Guayaquil and opposed Mahuad's move to restructure the banking sector. The negative effects caused by the El Niño weather system also affected Ecuador's agricultural production. Many rural areas were devastated by the floods and heavy rains. Poverty in the rural areas increased and agricultural production fell drastically. Together with the banking and agricultural crisis, the fall in the price of oil in international markets reduced Ecuador's net gains from exports significantly. Ecuador is a net oil exporter and most government revenues come from oil export profits. When international oil prices fall, the government of Ecuador needs to resort to foreign lending to meet its fiscal demands. Borrowing abroad had become a tradition in past years, but Ecuador's public foreign debt mounted to more than $13 billion in early 1999. As a result of the Asian economic crisis, access to foreign lending declined sharply for all developing countries in 1998 and 1999. President Mahuad faced two challenges in early 1999 in this area: Ecuador did not have access to credit, and interest payments on previously contracted government's public debt had to be made.

A rescue package from the International Monetary Fund was negotiated throughout the year. However, the inability of President Mahuad to muster a congressional majority to pass much needed legislation to reform the banking sector and adopt fiscal reforms to reduce government spending and balance the budget delayed the signing of the agreement. In late September, Ecuador finally signed an agreement with the IMF and a much needed line of credit was open to Mahuad's government. The agreement, however, came after Ecuador had defaulted on a $96 million interest payment on Brady bonds. Ecuador's rating among foreign creditors was hurt. Having defaulted on its financial obligations will continue to hurt Ecuador's economy in the future.

GOVERNMENT AND POLITICS

President Mahuad was inaugurated in 1998 and he set out to restore economic growth and solve a border dispute with Peru. The border dispute had led the two nations into armed confrontation at least twice since 1980. Mahuad's first move as president was to meet with Peru's president Alberto Fujimori. A general agreement was signed in 1998 and by mid 1999 the two presidents announced that all border disputes had been solved. Mahuad, however, could not enjoy the gratification of reveling in this accomplishment. During his first year in office, Ecuador sank deeper into an economic recession triggered by a crisis in the financial system.

As the former mayor of the capital city of Quito, Mahuad had to deal with a political opposition led by powerful Guayaquil bankers. Quito and Guayaquil are Ecuador's largest and most powerful cities and have traditionally opposed each other by forming regional political parties and by attempting to curtail each other's political influence in congress. Opposition leader Jaime Nebot, a politician from Guayaquil, rejected president Mahuad's effort to reform the banking sector and Mahuad unsuccessfully attempted to muster a congressional majority to pass his economic reform package.

For many years, Ecuador has been characterized by bad economic management on the part of the government. Corruption has been rampant in recent years and populist politicians have successfully blocked economic reforms in Congress. Government spending has increased and clientilism and pork-barrel politics abound. The fiscal sector has run a deficit year after year as presidents have been unable or unwilling to reduce government spending. President Mahuad's effort to balance the budget, launch a privatization program to attract foreign investment, and reduce the size of the government found strong opposition in Congress.

A deadlock between a president who has been willing to adopt painful reforms and a Congress that has vowed to defend subsidies has worsened the crisis. Corruption and opportunism on the part of Congress and the inability on the part of President Mahuad to muster enough congressional votes to carry on his reforms have led Ecuador to a new political crisis. Although a democratic breakdown is not expected, few analysts expect that Mahuad and Congress will find ways to cooperate during the next three years Mahuad has left in office.

CULTURE AND SOCIETY

Quito's Guagua Pichincha volcano eruption in September and October has made many Ecuadorians believe that their country is suffering unduly weather-related crises. The negative effects of the El Niño weather system were felt in the entire country. Floods and significant losses in agricultural production were experienced in the last two years.

Together with the economic and political crises, Ecuador's climate has added an additional element of concern to most Ecuadorians. Today, Ecuador is a poorer country than a decade ago. This has led many Ecuadorians to leave the country. A growing number of Ecuadorians have migrated to the United States and many have ventured into neighboring Peru, Colombia and other Latin American regions.

DIRECTORY

CENTRAL GOVERNMENT

Head of State

President
Jamil Mahuad, Office of the President, Garcia Moreno 1043, Quito, Ecuador
PHONE: +593 (2) 210300
FAX: +593 (2) 580735

Ministers

Minister of Foreign Affairs
Benjamin Ortiz, Ministry of Foreign Affairs, Carrion y 10 de Agosto, Quito, Ecuador
PHONE: +593 (2) 561215; 503159
FAX: +593 (2) 507077

Minister of Government
Vladimiro Alvarez Grau, Ministry of Government, Quito, Ecuador
PHONE: +593 (2) 517481
FAX: +593 (2) 580067

Minister of Defense
Jose Gallardo, Ministry of Defense, Exposicion 208, Quito, Ecuador
PHONE: +593 (2) 572580
FAX: +593 (2) 580431

Minister, Secretary of Production
Xavier Espinosa, Ministry of Production, Benalcazar entre Chile y Espejo, Quito, Ecuador

Minister, Secretary of Human Development
Carlos Larreategui, Minister of Human Development, Benalcazar entre Chile y Espejo, Quito, Ecuador

Minister of Finance
Alfredo Arizaga, Ministry of Finance, Ave. 10 de Agosto 1661 y Jorge Washington, Quito, Ecuador
PHONE: +593 (2) 503328
FAX: +593 (2) 500702

Minister of Energy and Mining
Rene Ortiz, Ministry of Energy and Mining, Santa Prisca 223, Quito, Ecuador
PHONE: +593 (2) 570141
FAX: +593 (2) 580724

Minister of External Trade
José Luis Icaza, Ministry of External Trade, Avs. Eloy Alfaro y Amazonas, Quito, Ecuador
PHONE: +593 (2) 529076
FAX: +593 (2) 507549

Minister of Agriculture
Salomon Larrea, Agricultural Information and Census, Ave. Amazonas y Eloy Alfaro, Quito, Ecuador
PHONE: +593 (2) 548708
FAX: +593 (2) 564531

Ministry of Tourism
Reina Victoria 514 y Roca, Quito, Ecuador
PHONE: +593 (2) 522387
FAX: +593 (2) 228301

Minister of Environment
Yoland Kakabadse, Ministry of Environment
PHONE: +593 (2) 540920
FAX: +593 (2) 255172

Minister of Public Works
Jose Macchiavello, Ministry of Public Works, Ave. 6 de Diciembre 1184, Quito, Ecuador
PHONE: +593 (2) 222749
FAX: +593 (2) 223077

Minister of Housing and Development
Teodoro Pena, Ministry or Housing and Urban Development
PHONE: +593 (2) 502785
FAX: +593 (2) 566785

Minister of Education
Rosangela Adoum, Ministry of Education, Mejia 321, Quito, Ecuador
PHONE: +593 (2) 216224
FAX: +593 (2) 580174

Minister of Public Health
Edgar Rodas, Ministry of Public Health, Juan Larrea 445, Quito, Ecuador
PHONE: +593 (2) 521733
FAX: +593 (2) 569786

Minister of Labor
Angel Polibio Chavez, Ministry of Labor, Luis Felipe Borja y C. Ponce, Quito, Ecuador
PHONE: +593 (2) 526666
FAX: +593 (2) 503122

Minister of Social Welfare
Guillermo Celi, Ministry of Social Welfare,
Robles 850 y Amazonas, Quito, Ecuador
PHONE: +593 (2) 540750
FAX: +593 (2) 563497

Minister of Industry, Commerce, Integration,
and Fisheries
Jose Luis Icaza, Minister of Industry,
Commerce, Integration, and Fisheries

POLITICAL ORGANIZATIONS

Partido Izquierda Democrática (Democratic Left Party)

TITLE: Leader
NAME: Rodrigo Borja Cevallos

Partido Roldosista Ecuatoriana (Ecuadorian Roldosist Party)

TITLE: Director
NAME: Abdalá Bucaram Ortiz

Partido Liberal Radical Ecuatoriana-FRA-PLRE Coalition (Ecuadorian Radical Liberal Party)

TITLE: Leader
NAME: Medardo Mora

Frente Radical Alfarista-FRA (Radical Alfarista Front)

TITLE: Director
NAME: Fabian Alarcon

Movimiento Unidad Plurinacional Pachakutik-MUPP (Pluri-National Pachakutik Movement)

Democracia Popular-Unión Demócrata Cristiana-DP-UDC (Popular Democracy-Christian Democratic Union)

TITLE: Leader
NAME: Jamil Mahuad Witt

Movimiento Popular Democrático-MPD (Popular Democratic Movement)

TITLE: Leader
NAME: Juan Jose Castello

Partido Conservador Ecuatoriana-PCE (Ecuadorian Conservative Party)

TITLE: President
NAME: Sixto Duran-Ballen

Partido Social Cristiano-PSC (Social Christian Party)

TITLE: President
NAME: Jaime Nebot Saadi

DIPLOMATIC REPRESENTATION

Embassies in Ecuador

France
Plaza 107 y Av. Patria, Casilla 21005, Quito,
Ecuador
PHONE: +593 (2) 560789; 562347
FAX: +593 (2) 566424
E-MAIL: francic@uio.satnet

United States
corner of 12 de Octubre and Patria, Quito,
Ecuador
PHONE: +593 (2) 562890
FAX: +593 (2) 502052
E-MAIL: cons@mail.amembquito.org.ec
TITLE: Ambassador
NAME: Gwen C. Clare

JUDICIAL SYSTEM

Constitutional Assembly

Supreme Court

Palacio de Justicia, Av. 6 de Diciembre y
Piedrahita, Quito, Ecuador
PHONE: +593 (2) 543803

Parochial Court

Cantonal Court

Provincial Court

FURTHER READING

Articles

"Bail In, Bail Out." *The Economist* (October 2, 1999).

"Ecuador. Chaos, Continued." *The Economist* (March 20, 1999).

"Ecuador. The Furies Wait." *The Economist* (March 6, 1999).

"Ecuador's Default Latin Bondage." *The Economist* (October 9, 1999).

"Fuming in Ecuador." *The Economist* (October 9, 1999): 40.

"The Message in Letting Ecuador Default." *Business Week* (October 25, 1999): 22.

Internet

Embassy of Ecuador, Washington D.C..
Available Online @ http: //www.ecuador.org.
(November 17, 1999).

Yahoo Full Coverage. Available Online @ http:
//fullcoverage.yahoo.com/Full_Coverage/
World/Ecuador/ (November 17, 1999).

ECUADOR: STATISTICAL DATA

For sources and notes see "Sources of Statistics" in the front of each volume.

GEOGRAPHY

Geography (1)

Area:

Total: 283,560 sq km.

Land: 276,840 sq km.

Water: 6,720 sq km.

Note: includes Galapagos Islands.

Area—comparative: slightly smaller than Nevada.

Land boundaries:

Total: 2,010 km.

Border countries: Colombia 590 km, Peru 1,420 km.

Coastline: 2,237 km.

Climate: tropical along coast becoming cooler inland.

Terrain: coastal plain (costa), inter-Andean central highlands (sierra), and flat to rolling eastern jungle (oriente).

Natural resources: petroleum, fish, timber.

Land use:

Arable land: 6%

Permanent crops: 5%

Permanent pastures: 18%

Forests and woodland: 56%

Other: 15% (1993 est.).

HUMAN FACTORS

Demographics (2A)

	1990	1995	1998	2000	2010	2020	2030	2040	2050
Population	10,307.7	11,628.7	12,336.6	12,782.2	14,861.3	16,876.4	18,658.1	20,071.4	21,059.2
Net migration rate (per 1,000 population)	NA	NA	NA	NA	NA	NA	NA	NA	NA
Births	NA	NA	NA	NA	NA	NA	NA	NA	NA
Deaths	50.2	NA	NA	NA	NA	NA	NA	NA	NA
Life expectancy - males	66.2	68.1	69.2	69.9	72.9	75.1	76.8	78.1	78.9
Life expectancy - females	71.5	73.5	74.5	75.3	78.3	80.7	82.4	83.8	84.7
Birth rate (per 1,000)	31.6	25.8	23.2	21.4	18.4	16.3	14.5	13.0	12.5
Death rate (per 1,000)	6.5	5.6	5.2	5.0	4.7	4.9	5.8	7.1	8.7
Women of reproductive age (15-49 yrs.)	2,533.8	2,975.3	3,242.8	3,420.5	4,252.2	4,627.8	4,737.4	4,662.9	4,547.8
of which are currently married	2,011.3	NA	NA	NA	NA	NA	NA	NA	NA
Fertility rate	4.0	3.1	2.8	2.5	2.1	2.0	2.0	2.0	2.0

Except as noted, values for vital statistics are in thousands; life expectancy is in years.

Health Personnel (3)

Total health expenditure as a percentage of GDP, 1990-1997[a]

Public sector 2.0

Private sector 3.2

Total[b] 5.3

Health expenditure per capita in U.S. dollars, 1990-1997[a]

Purchasing power parity 259

Total 78

Availability of health care facilities per 100,000 people

Hospital beds 1990-1997[a] 160

Doctors 1993[c] 111

Nurses 1993[c] 34

Health Indicators (4)

Life expectancy at birth

1980 63

1997 70

Daily per capita supply of calories (1996) 2,592

Total fertility rate births per woman (1997) 3.0

Maternal mortality ratio per 100,000 live births (1990-97) . . . . .150[c]

Safe water % of population with access (1995) 55

Sanitation % of population with access (1995) 53

Consumption of iodized salt % of households (1992-98)[a] 97

Smoking prevalence

Male % of adults (1985-95)[a] . . . .

Female % of adults (1985-95)[a] . . . .

Tuberculosis incidence per 100,000 people (1997) 165

Adult HIV prevalence % of population ages 15-49 (1997) 0.28

Infants and Malnutrition (5)

Under-5 mortality rate (1997) 39

% of infants with low birthweight (1990-97) 13

Births attended by skilled health staff % of total[a] . . .64

% fully immunized (1995-97)

TB 100

DPT 76

Polio 77

Measles 75

Prevalence of child malnutrition under age 5 (1992-97)[b] 17

Ethnic Division (6)

Mestizo 55%

Amerindian 25%

Spanish 10%

Black 10%

Mestizos are mixed Amerindian and Spanish.

Religions (7)

Roman Catholic 95%

Languages (8)

Spanish (official), Amerindian languages (especially Quechua).

EDUCATION

Public Education Expenditures (9)

Public expenditure on education (% of GNP)

1980 . . . . .5.6

1996 . . . . .3.5

Expenditure per student

Primary % of GNP per capita

1980 . . . . .5.6

1996 . . . . .7.6

Secondary % of GNP per capita

1980 . . . .

1996 . . . .

Tertiary % of GNP per capita

1980 . . . . .24.2

1996 . . . .

Expenditure on teaching materials

Primary % of total for level (1996) . . . .

Secondary % of total for level (1996) . . . .

Primary pupil-teacher ratio per teacher (1996) 25

Duration of primary education years (1995) 6

Educational Attainment (10)

Age group (1990) . . . . .25+

Total population 3,953,452

Highest level attained (%)

No schooling 1.7

First level

Not completed 43.7

Completed . . . . .NA

Entered second level

S-1 . . . . .22.6

S-2 . . . . .NA

Postsecondary 12.7

Literacy Rates (11A)

In thousands and percent[1]	1990	1995	2000	2010
Illiterate population (15+ yrs.)	691	719	678	553
Literacy rate - total adult pop. (%)	87.3	90.1	91.9	94.8
Literacy rate - males (%)	90.4	92.0	93.5	95.8
Literacy rate - females (%)	86.5	88.2	90.3	93.7

GOVERNMENT & LAW

Political Parties (12)

National Congress	No. of seats
Social Christian Party (PSC)	.27
Roldosista Party (PRE)	.19
Popular Democracy (DP)	.12
Pachakutik-New Country (P-NP)	.8
Democratic Left (ID)	.4
Radical Alfarista Front (FRA)	.3
Popular Democratic Movement (MPD)	.2
Conservative Party (PCE)	.2
Concentration of Popular Forces (CFP)	.1
Independents and other	.4

Military Affairs (14B)

	1990	1991	1992	1993	1994	1995
Military expenditures						
Current dollars (mil.)[1]	392	475	515	467	574	611
1995 constant dollars (mil.)[1]	450	525	554	490	589	611
Armed forces (000)	53	53	57	57	57	58
Gross national product (GNP)						
Current dollars (mil.)	12,250	13,650	14,700	15,560	16,000	16,600
1995 constant dollars (mil.)	14,080	15,080	15,810	16,310	16,400	16,600
Central government expenditures (CGE)						
1995 constant dollars (mil.)	2,211	2,132	2,180	2,330	2,695	3,340
People (mil.)	10.1	10.3	10.6	10.8	11.0	11.2
Military expenditure as % of GNP	3.2	3.5	3.5	3.0	3.6	3.7
Military expenditure as % of CGE	20.4	24.6	25.4	21.0	21.8	18.3
Military expenditure per capita (1995 $)	45	51	52	45	53	54
Armed forces per 1,000 people (soldiers)	5.2	5.1	5.4	5.3	5.2	5.2
GNP per capita (1995 $)	1,391	1,458	1,497	1,511	1,489	1,476
Arms imports[6]						
Current dollars (mil.)	20	20	30	50	50	50
1995 constant dollars (mil.)	23	22	32	52	51	50
Arms exports[6]						
Current dollars (mil.)	0	0	0	0	0	0
1995 constant dollars (mil.)	0	0	0	0	0	0
Total imports[7]						
Current dollars (mil.)	1,862	2,399	2,501	2,562	3,690	4,193
1995 constant dollars (mil.)	2,140	2,651	2,690	2,686	3,783	4,193
Total exports[7]						
Current dollars (mil.)	2,714	2,852	3,007	2,904	3,820	4,307
1995 constant dollars (mil.)	3,119	3,152	3,234	3,044	3,916	4,307
Arms as percent of total imports[8]	1.1	.8	1.2	2.0	1.4	6.2
Arms as percent of total exports[8]	0	0	0	0	0	0

Government Budget (13B)

Revenues . . . .$3.6 billion

Expenditures . . . .$3.6 billion

  Capital expenditures .NA

Data for 1997. Data for 1996 est. NA stands for not available.

Crime (15)

Crime rate (for 1997)

  Crimes reported 68,000

  Total persons convicted . . . . .NA

  Crimes per 100,000 population 575

Persons responsible for offenses

  Total number of suspects 31,500

  Total number of female suspects . . . . .NA

  Total number of juvenile suspects . . . . .NA

LABOR FORCE

Labor Force (16)

Total (million) 4.2

Agriculture 29%

Manufacturing 18%

Commerce 15%

Services and other 38%

Data for 1990.

Unemployment Rate (17)

6.9% with widespread underemployment (August 1997 est.)

PRODUCTION SECTOR

Electric Energy (18)

Capacity . . . . .2.754 million kW (1996)

Production . . . . .9.27 billion kWh (1996)

Consumption per capita . . . . .600 kWh (1996)

Transportation (19)

Highways:

total: 43,249 km

paved: 5,752 km

unpaved: 37,497 km (1996 est.)

Waterways: 1,500 km

Pipelines: crude oil 800 km; petroleum products 1,358 km

Merchant marine:

total: 18 ships (1,000 GRT or over) totaling 84,423 GRT/137,272 DWT ships by type: liquefied gas tanker 1, oil tanker 14, passenger 3 (1997 est.)

Airports: 183 (1997 est.)

Airports—with paved runways:

total: 52

over 3,047 m: 2

2,438 to 3,047 m: 6

1,524 to 2,437 m: 10

914 to 1,523 m: 16

under 914 m: 18 (1997 est.)

Airports—with unpaved runways:

total: 131

1,524 to 2,437 m: 3

914 to 1,523 m: 38

under 914 m: 90 (1997 est.)

Top Agricultural Products (20)

Bananas, coffee, cocoa, rice, potatoes, manioc, plantains, sugarcane; cattle, sheep, pigs, beef, pork, dairy products; balsa wood; fish, shrimp.

MANUFACTURING SECTOR

GDP & Manufacturing Summary (21)

Detailed value added figures are listed by both International Standard Industry Code (ISIC) and product title.

	1980	1985	1989	1990
GDP ($-1980 mil.)	8,755	9,730	10,686	12,257
Per capita ($-1980)	1,100	1,069	1,041	1,092
Manufacturing share (%) (current prices)	17.8	19.3	20.1	*30.7*
Manufacturing				
Value added ($-1981 mil.)	2,017	2,160	2,068	*2,329*
Industrial production index	100	110	128	*162*
Value added ($ mil.)	1,289	1,322	1,196	3,095
Gross output ($ mil.)	3,571	4,379	3,934	7,834
Employment (000)	112	97	112	124
Profitability (% of gross output)				
Intermediate input (%)	64	70	70	60
Wages and salaries inc. supplements (%)	*16*	13	9	*4*
Gross operating surplus	*21*	18	21	*36*

	1980	1985	1989	1990
Productivity ($)				
Gross output per worker	31,623	45,072	35,083	63,021
Value added per worker	11,414	13,606	10,667	24,896
Average wage (inc. supplements)	*4,976*	*5,677*	*3,137*	*2,461*
Value added ($ mil.)				
311/2 Food products	294	328	228	366
313 Beverages	96	65	33	86
314 Tobacco products	46	17	1	7
321 Textiles	134	146	95	103
322 Wearing apparel	20	15	10	13
323 Leather and fur products	7	6	4	5
324 Footwear	6	7	6	7
331 Wood and wood products	35	18	16	25
332 Furniture and fixtures	28	23	9	11
341 Paper and paper products	42	41	34	27
342 Printing and publishing	40	35	27	54
351 Industrial chemicals	25	32	17	40
352 Other chemical products	90	76	75	923
353 Petroleum refineries	29	38	374	989
354 Miscellaneous petroleum and coal products	4	14	4	10
355 Rubber products	25	29	17	27
356 Plastic products	34	57	42	57
361 Pottery, china and earthenware	7	15	7	7
362 Glass and glass products	9	15	8	11
369 Other non-metal mineral products	100	101	60	99
371 Iron and steel	25	56	19	33
372 Non-ferrous metals	5	10	2	8
381 Metal products	93	78	44	73
382 Non-electrical machinery	4	7	3	4
383 Electrical machinery	59	58	32	57
384 Transport equipment	23	23	22	42
385 Professional and scientific equipment	2	9	3	5
390 Other manufacturing industries	7	5	3	5

FINANCE, ECONOMICS, & TRADE

Economic Indicators (22)

National product: GDP—purchasing power parity—$53.4 billion (1997 est.)

National product real growth rate: 3.4% (1997 est.)

National product per capita: $4,400 (1997 est.)

Inflation rate—consumer price index: 31% (1997 est.)

Balance of Payments (23)

	1992	1993	1994	1995	1996
Exports of goods (f.o.b.)	3,101	3,066	3,843	4,411	4,890
Imports of goods (f.o.b.)	−2,083	−2,474	−3,280	−4,057	−3,488
Trade balance	1,018	592	563	354	1,402
Services - debits	−1,912	−2,080	−2,184	−2,256	−2,330
Services - credits	652	680	797	936	931
Private transfers (net)	120	130	145	231	290
Government transfers (net)	—	—	—	—	—
Overall balance	−122	−678	−679	−735	293

Exchange Rates (24)

Exchange rates:

Sucres (S) per US$1

January 1998	.4,498.0
1997	.3,988.3
1996	.3,189.5
1995	.2,564.5
1994	.2,196.7
1993	.1,919.1

Top Import Origins (25)

$2.9 billion (c.i.f., 1997)

Origins	%
United States	.41
Caricom	.25
United Kingdom	.13
Netherlands	.NA
Canada	.NA

NA stands for not available.

Top Export Destinations (26)

$3.4 billion (f.o.b., 1997).

Destinations	%
United States	.39
Latin America	.25
European Union countries	.22
Asia	.12

Economic Aid (27)

Recipient: ODA, $153 million (1993). Note: received $12.7 million from the US and $160 million from other countries in 1995.

Import Export Commodities (28)

Import Commodities	Export Commodities
Transport equipment	Petroleum 30%
Consumer goods	Bananas 26%
Vehicles	Shrimp 16%
Machinery	Cut flowers 2%
Chemicals	Fish 1.9%

EGYPT

Arab Republic of Egypt
Jumhuriat Misr al-ʿArabiyah

INTRODUCTORY SURVEY

RECENT HISTORY

After the World War I, in 1922, England recognized Egypt as an officially sovereign country under King Fuad. Egyptian nationalism gathered momentum in World War II (1939–45), during which Egypt was used as an Allied base of operations. Many political and social problems motivated a successful coup in 1952, and in 1954 Lieutenant Colonel Gamal Abdel Nasser, leader of the revolution, came to power.

To increase the production in his country, Nasser entered into preliminary agreements with the United States, Britain, and the United Nations to finance a new dam at Aswân. At the same time, he negotiated economic aid and arms shipments from the Soviet Union and its allies in Eastern Europe. This angered the United States. In response, the United States withheld its financial backing for the dam. In retaliation President Nasser took control of the Suez Canal and announced that he would use the profits from its operations to build the dam. The dam was completed with aid and technical assistance from the Soviet Union.

In 1956 there was a three-nation plot to bring down Nasser and reassert control over the Canal. Israeli armed forces swept into Egypt's Sinai Peninsula. Britain and France then issued an ultimatum to both sides to cease fire. When Egypt rejected the ultimatum, Britain and France landed troops in the Port Said area and bombed Egyptian cities from the air. The intervention of the United States and the Soviet Union, acting through the

United Nations, led to the withdrawal of the British, French, and Israeli forces by March 1957.

On 1 February 1958, Egypt and Syria proclaimed their union in the United Arab Republic (UAR) with Nasser as president. However, differing economic and political conditions prevented a complete fusion of the two regions. On 28 September 1961, the Syrian army revolted, and two days later it proclaimed Syrian independence. Egypt continued to try for Arab unity, signing agreements with Iraq, Yemen, Syria, and Libya during the 1960s and early 1970s. None of these agreements produced a lasting political union.

On 5 June 1967, Egypt closed the Gulf of Aqaba to Israeli shipping. In what later became known as the "Six-Day War," Israel quickly crippled the Egyptian air force and occupied the Gaza Strip and the Sinai and blocked the Suez Canal. During the years after 1967, a "War of Attrition" was fought along the Canal with each side shelling the other and Israeli planes bombing Egyptian cities.

When Nasser died on 28 September 1970, his vice-president, Anwar al-Sadat, became president. President Sadat firmly established his hold on the government and began to implement pragmatic economic and social policies, including improved relations with the United States.

Frustrated in his ambition to recover the Sinai, President Sadat broke the 1967 cease-fire agreement on 6 October 1973, initiating the "Yom Kippur War." He attacked Israeli forces in the Sinai Peninsula while Syria attacked Israeli forces occupying the Syrian Golan Heights. After initial successes, the Egyptian strike forces were defeated by Israeli troops, who then crossed the Canal south of Ismâ'ilîyah. A cease-fire that came into effect on 24 October left Egyptian troops in the Sinai and Israeli troops on the west bank of the Canal. United States Secretary of State Henry Kissinger negotiated an agreement that left Egypt in full control of the Canal and established a UN-supervised buffer zone in the Sinai between the Egyptian and Israeli forces. In November 1975, the Sinai oil fields at Abu Rudeis and Sudr were returned to Egypt.

President Sadat went to Jerusalem in November 1977 and received Israeli Prime Minister Menachem Begin at Ismâ'ilîyah the following month. In September 1978, Sadat entered into negotiations with Begin, mediated by U.S. President Jimmy Carter, at Camp David, Maryland. Following further negotiations, Sadat signed the Egyptian-Israeli Peace Treaty in Washington, D.C., on 26 March 1979. For their roles as peacemakers, Sadat and Begin were jointly awarded the 1978 Nobel Peace Prize. But other Arab leaders denounced the accords and sought to isolate Egypt within the Arab world.

In early September 1981, Sadat ordered the arrest of 1,536 Muslims, Christian Copts, leftists, and other persons accused of violent acts. One month later, on 6 October, Sadat was assassinated in Cairo by four Muslim fundamentalists. The vice-president, Muhammad Hosni (Husni) Mubarak, who had been Sadat's closest adviser, succeeded him as president. Mubarak pledged to continue Sadat's policies, particularly the terms of the peace treaty with Israel. Relations with Israel cooled during 1982, however, especially after Israeli troops moved into Lebanon.

Following the Amman Arab summit conference in November 1987, Egypt renewed diplomatic relations with a number of Arab states and in May 1989 rejoined the Arab League. Mubarak continued Sadat's policies of moderation and peacemaking abroad and gradual political liberalization and movement toward the free market at home. In 1990, Egypt played a key role in the coalition to expel Iraq from Kuwait and in 1993 and 1994 was active in promoting the Israeli-Palestinian peace accord.

Mubarak was reelected president in 1987 and 1993. The most serious opposition to the Mubarak government is from outside the political system. Religious parties are banned and, as a consequence, Islamic militants have resorted to violence against the regime. Security forces have cracked down hard, but the militant movement has gathered strength, fueled by discontent with poor economic conditions, corruption, secularism, and Egypt's ties with the United States and Israel.

GOVERNMENT

The president of the republic is the head of state and supreme commander of the armed forces. The president's power to declare war and make treaties with foreign countries is subject to the approval of the People's Assembly. The assembly is a unicameral legislative body consisting of 444 elected and 10 appointed members serving five-year terms. A 210-member advisory body, the Shura Council, was formed in 1980. The People's Assembly nominates the president, who must then be confirmed by plebiscite (popular vote) for a six-year term.

Judiciary

Simple police offenses, misdemeanors, and civil cases involving small amounts of money are subject to the jurisdiction of a single judge. The trial courts of the central tribunals, consisting of three judges each, hear more serious cases and also consider appeals. Traffic in narcotics and press offenses, considered serious crimes, are tried by the courts of appeals. The highest tribunal is the Court of Cassation.

Political Parties

The Arab Socialist Union (ASU; founded by President Nasser as the Egyptian National Union in 1957) was the sole legal political party until 1976, when President Sadat allowed three minor parties to participate in parliamentary elections. In 1978, Sadat replaced the ASU with his own organization, the National Democratic Party (NDP), of which he became chairman. In January 1982, President Mubarak was elected without opposition as chairman of the NDP. The New Wafd (Delegation) Party is the middle-class successor of the dominant party of the pre-Nasser period, now allied with the Muslim Brotherhood. In the 1995 parliamentary elections, the NDP won 316 of 444 seats. Most of the 100 independents elected were closely allied with the NDP.

DEFENSE

Military service is compulsory for all males over 18. In 1995, the armed forces consisted of 440,000 men. The army had 310,000 men, and the army reserves totaled about 150,000 men. The air force had 30,000 men, plus 80,000 personnel in the air defense command. The navy had 20,000 men.

ECONOMIC AFFAIRS

Historically, the Egyptian economy was mostly agricultural, with cotton as the mainstay. Land prices are extremely high because of the shortage of arable land. Not enough food is produced to meet the needs of a rapidly growing population. Although Egypt has expanded its private sector in recent years, industry remains centrally controlled and for the most part government owned. Since the 1950s, the government has developed the petroleum, services, and construction sectors, largely at the expense of agriculture. The collapse of world oil prices in the early 1990s led Egypt to restructure its debt. Tourism has plunged in recent years because of attacks by Islamic extremists on tourist groups. The economy is not growing fast enough to reduce unemployment, which stood at 20% in 1995.

Public Finance

The government's current budget covers revenues and expenses of government agencies rendering services free of charge. The capital budget includes investments by state and local governments and by servicing authorities, plus capital investment transfers. In 1990, a reform program was implemented, which has decreased the overall fiscal deficit to only 0.8% of GDP in 1997.

The CIA estimates that, in 1994, government revenues totaled approximately $18 billion and expenditures $19.4 billion, including capital expenditures of $3.8 billion. External debt totaled $33.6 billion.

Income

In 1998, Egypt's gross national product (GNP) was $79.2 billion at current prices, or $1,290 per person. For the period 1985–95, the average inflation rate was 15.7%.

Industry

Egyptian industry produces cement, glass, iron and steel products, fertilizers, paper, petroleum refining, electric power, textiles, and sugar. Newer industries include tires, refrigerators, air conditioners, sewing machines, bicycles, electric meters, batteries, wire, and cable. Egypt and South Africa are the largest producers of petroleum refinery products in Africa. Industrial output accounted for 34% of the gross domestic product (GDP) in 1995.

Banking and Finance

The National Bank of Egypt, founded in 1898, had as a private institution the exclusive right to issue currency and act as the government's banker. In January 1961, although permitted to retain its commercial banking business, it was divested of its central banking function, which was given to the newly established Central Bank of Egypt.

In addition to the Central Bank, there were, until 1962, 25 other Arab and foreign banks and branches. In 1957, when foreign banks refused to finance Egypt's cotton crop after the Suez Canal was nationalized, the government took over British and French banks and insurance companies; those of other countries were taken over by January 1962. By the end of 1962, all banks, domestic and foreign, had been nationalized. The number of registered banks dwindled to only four by 1971. As of 1996, there were 69 banks operating in Egypt. Four state-owned commercial banks dominate the sector due to their size in terms of assets, deposit base, and branches, accounting for 55% of the banking system's total assets.

Egypt's stock exchange had a record year in 1996. The value of trading soared to E£11 billion ($3.24 billion) from E£3.85 billion in 1985, according to the regulatory body, the Capital Markets Authority, and the volume of shares traded rose by 188% to 207.8 million from 72.2 million in the previous year. The government issued bonds worth E£4 billion in 1996.

Economic Development

Development expenditures for 1986–87 totaled E£5,320 million. The current plan aims at the privatization of several sectors by encouraging the private sector to invest more capital. Total investment is planned to reach E£154 billion, of which E£89.5 billion is provided by the private sector.

SOCIAL WELFARE

Social programs focus on services including health care and family planning. Other social insurance programs include workers' compensation, old-age pensions, and death and disability benefits. Unemployed workers receive 60% of their last monthly wage. Women have won employment opportunities in a number of fields, but Egyptian feminists fear these gains will be lost if Islamic fundamentalists gain control.

Healthcare

Serious diseases in Egypt include schistosomiasis, malaria, hookworm, trachoma, tuberculosis, dysentery, beriberi, and typhus. Of children under five years of age in 1995, 9% were considered malnourished. Life expectancy is 66 years.

Housing

Prior to 1952, most Egyptians lived in mud huts. Postrevolutionary governments, however, have actively concerned themselves with housing. In order to encourage rural housing activities on nonfertile soil, "extension areas" have been allocated for villages, and efforts have been made to provide low-rent housing in towns. Despite these efforts, Egypt's housing shortage remains serious, with about one million units needed in urban areas.

EDUCATION

In 1994 there were 7.3 million students in 16,088 primary schools and 6.1 million students in secondary schools.

Education is free and compulsory for all children between the ages of 6 and 12. Entry to preparatory schools is by competitive examination, which children take at the age of 10. Preparatory schools offer four-year courses leading to a certificate. This certificate then allows a student to go on for three-year courses in secondary schools.

A decree of 23 July 1962 provided free tuition at all Egyptian universities. The traditional center for religious education in the Muslim world is Al-Azhar in Cairo. It is the oldest continuously operating school in the world. All universities and higher-level institutions had a total of 620,145 students in 1993. Universities and equivalent institutions had a faculty of 38,828 personnel. The American University in Cairo offers a wide range of undergraduate and graduate courses.

1999 KEY EVENTS TIMELINE

January

- Egypt celebrates the 100th anniversary of the birth of its most revered singing star, Umm Kalthoum, who died in 1975.

April

- Egyptian ministers vote to repeal a controversial law which exempts a rapist from punishment if he marries his victim.

May

- President Hosni Mubarak travels to Libya to discuss Arab unity, his first visit to the country since the suspension of United Nations sanctions against Libya in April.

June

- The European Union (EU) endorses an accord that creates an Egypt-EU free trade zone, following four years of heated negotiations. Egypt hopes that it will make it the center of Arab trade with the EU, its main trading partner.

July

- President Mubarak returns from Washington after talks regarding the Palestinian peace process.

August

- In his first visit to Egypt since the suspension of United Nations sanctions against Libya, Libyan leader Muammar Gaddafi meets with President Hosni Mubarak in the northern Egyptian town of Mersa Matruh to discuss trade reconciliation.

- As part of an effort to increase exports Prime Minister Kamal Ganzouri issues a decree granting all exporters a holiday on all taxes.

September

- In Sharm el-Sheikh, Egypt hosts the signing of the latest stage in the peace accord between the Palestinian Authority and Israel, which gives a timeframe for the implementation of the Wye River Agreement. Joining President Mubarak in the ceremony are Palestinian President Yasser Arafat, Israeli Prime Minister Ehud Barak, King Abdullah of Jordan and U.S. Secretary of State Madeleine Albright.

- The day following the peace accord, as President Hosni Mubarak's motorcade drives through Port

Said, El-Sayed Seliman, a street vendor, lunges at the president with a knife, nicking him in the arm. The assailant is shot dead by security forces, and President Mubarak continues with his scheduled events for that day.

- A host of disciplinary measures against security forces follow the attempted assassination, including the sacking of three generals.

- Egypt's 24 million voters go to the polls and re-elect President Hosni Mubarak to his fourth six-year term in office.

October

- Atef Obeid, 67-year-old architect of the Egyptian privatization program begun in 1991, is named as prime minister by President Hosni Mubarak.

- Obeid names his new government, which retains nineteen ministers of the previous cabinet. Thirteen new people receive ministerial portfolios, and new ministries are created for technological development, information technology, and youth issues.

- The World Bank issues a report highly critical of Egypt's widespread sales taxes, bureaucratic red tape, and corrupt businesspeople operating in the banking sector.

November

- In response to prosecutors moving the trials of twenty people suspected of membership in the banned Muslim Brotherhood from civilian to military justice courts, the New York-based Human Rights Watch issues an open letter to President Mubarak criticizing the trials of civilians in Egypt in military courts.

- An investigation of an Egypt Air flight that crashed without explanation off the northeast coast of the United States brings tension between Egypt and the United States. This is due in part to preliminary suggestions by U.S. investigators that an Egyptian relief pilot may have deliberately crashed the plane, killing all on board, in a suicide.

- Yale University scientist Dr. John Darnell discovers what is believed to be the world's oldest alphabet, believed to be nearly 4,000 years old, at Wadi el-Hol west of Luxor.

- Officials from Egypt, Ethiopia, and Sudan agree to cooperate on the use of water resources from the Nile River.

- President Zinc el Abidine Ben ali of Tunisia meets with president Hosni Mubarak to discuss a joint effort to combat terrorism and organized crime, and Egypt's interest in becoming a member of the Arab Maghreb Union made up of the nations of northern Africa.

December

- The government rejects a request from the Sharia Party, a militant Muslim group seeking recognition as a political party.

- At a ceremony televised from Cairo, president Hosni Mubarak awards the country's highest honor—the Nile Necklace—to chemist Ahmed Zewall, winner of the 1999 Nobel Prize for Chemistry.

- President Mubarak calls for the formation of a common market for Arab nations.

- Egypt and Sudan announce jointly that they have restored diplomatic relations.

- Egypt legalizes the drug used for treatment of male impotence, Viagra.

ANALYSIS OF EVENTS: 1999

BUSINESS AND THE ECONOMY

In the first part of the year, Egypt was touted as a prize pupil of the International Monetary Fund (IMF) for its stabilization and restructuring program. Most of the macroeconomic indicators are good, with a 5 percent growth rate in 1998 expected to be closer to 6 percent in 1999; inflation below 4 percent; a budget deficit of 1 percent of GDP; $18 billion in foreign reserves, and more open access to economic information. By 2000 up to 80 percent of the economy is expected to be in private hands, with the details of continuing privatization moves being announced in September. Egypt pushes the "build-operate-transfer" formula, used in the construction of the Suez Canal, to encourage foreign companies to invest in transportation and other new projects. Egypt's economy is diversified and has a strong domestic market. In addition, it benefits from expatriate remittances, Suez Canal dues, oil exports (though with very modest reserves), and $3 billion a year in foreign aid, two-thirds of which comes from the United States.

However, privatization of insurance and banking is behind schedule. In October, the World Bank issued a critical report of Egypt's economic environment and especially criticized the government's program in the areas of industry and exports, terming Egypt's shipping and export services "incompetent." Exports have fallen to less than one-third of the exports in each of the previous three years, and only represent 17 percent of Egypt's Gross National Product (GNP). The report also criticized a cumbersome bureaucracy in customs, which increases costs and also identified a lax banking system that allows businesspeople to obtain loans without collateral, and then to smuggle out the cash without fear of government reprisal.

Though the government's programs have assisted in producing a rosier picture in macroeconomic statistics, it is also clear that there has been a steep rise in poverty. The government attempts to censor figures that conflict with its more optimistic picture. The poor have been hurt in particular by the removal of food subsidies, though the new prime minister has assured the public that the subsidy on bread would be maintained. The restructuring measures introduced by the government have led to an increase in malnutrition with studies showing 30 percent of young people stunted, an increase of 35 percent in the early 1990s. The problem is worse in southern/Upper Egypt, highlighting a continuing regional disparity having access to government services and employment opportunities. Government statistics place the unemployment rate at 10-13 percent; most economists place it a good deal higher. Health care and education increasingly have hidden fees, belying the claims that they are free to all citizens.

Egypt's millennia-old problem is its aridity and very small proportion of land open for settlement. This government has responded with vast irrigation schemes in the deep south and the northeast, in order to move people beyond the Nile delta and narrow Nile valley. At present, 95 percent of Egypt's people live in 5 percent of the country. The Al-Salam canal is projected to feed Nile water into the Sinai peninsula for agro-industry and labor-intensive farming, and the Toshka canal in the far south will carry water from Lake Nasser behind the Aswan dam, to the west. East Oweinat in the far south is also projected to be irrigated from underground aquifers. It remains to be seen if these projects will live up to the government pronouncements.

GOVERNMENT AND POLITICS

Egyptians voted in September to continue under the same president, Hosni Mubarak, 71, of the National Democratic Party, as they have had for the past eighteen years, electing him to his fourth six-year term in office in a referendum vote where he was the sole candidate. Theoretically, Egypt is a democracy with an elected parliament, 14 officially-recognized political parties, and an opposition press. However, political Islam is still not allowed a public voice, with the government only having to point to the Islamic Salvation Front in Algeria, and the associated violence to allow it to overrule civil liberties. Increasingly, military courts are used to try all parties accused of "terrorism" or association with "terrorist" groups. This process has brought increasing outcries from both Egyptian and international human rights organizations. The government has established a six-man committee, which rules on the application for the establishment of new political parties. No Islamic political parties have ever passed this vetting procedure.

Still plodding, inefficient bureaucracy dominates the scene despite economic reforms. One-third of the work force is employed by government. This total is only being reduced by attrition and early-retirement offers, which remove 2 percent of bureaucrats each year.

Terrorism from southern Egypt brought one positive result—more government attention and investment. There have been no attacks on tourists since the 1997 attack in Luxor, which killed 58. The response to this attack was an intense security hike and a drop in prices in attempt to lure tourists back to Egypt.

Despite the Sept. 26 yes or no referendum on a sole candidate, Hosni Mubarak, for a fourth term as president, Mubarak would have probably won even if he were running against other candidates. The National Democratic Party has dominated the Parliament for two decades. There is strong concern because a vice president has never been nominated and because Mubarak gives no indication of a likely successor.

Egypt now goes along with the idea of lifting sanctions imposed on Iraq due to the suffering they cause the Iraqi people.

CULTURE AND SOCIETY

There is an emergency session of Arab information ministers of the Arab League in Cairo. A boycott of Walt Disney company is announced in September if Disney allows Jerusalem to be depicted as Israel's capital.

Female circumcision is still strongly supported by Egyptians, and little progress has been made in stopping it.

In September, changes are made in the laws banning proxy marriages between foreigners and Egyptian women and in the laws decreeing that the age difference can be no more than 25 years. Under the new rules, the embassy of a foreign husband-to-be must provide official documents guaranteeing his financial, social and medical conditions before the marriage contract is signed. In addition, $7,500 must be deposited in an Egyptian bank for the sole use of the bride.

Although known for religious tolerance, Copts, Egypt's minority Christian community, feels increasingly uneasy. Complaints of discrimination and violence against Copts continue to increase.

The law gives the Social Affairs Ministry a wide array of powers, including the right to disband the management of private groups, overturn their decisions and control their sources of income.

DIRECTORY

CENTRAL GOVERNMENT
Head of State

President
Mohammed Hosni Mubarak, Office of the President

Prime Minister
Kamal Ahmed el-Ganzouri, Office of the Prime Minister

Deputy Prime Minister
Youssef Amin Wally, Office of the Deputy Prime Minister

Ministers

Minister of Agriculture and Land Reclamation
Youssef Amin Wally, Ministry of Agriculture and Land Reclamation

Minister of Awqaf (Religious Affairs)
Mahmoud Hamdi Zakzuk, Ministry of Awqaf (Religious Affairs)

Minister of Culture
Faruq Husni, Ministry of Culture

Minister of Defense and Military Production
Mohamed Hussein Tantawi, Ministry of Defense and Military Production

Minister of Economy
Yousef Boutros-Ghali, Ministry of Economy
E-MAIL: minecon@idsc1.gov.eg

Minister of Education
Kamel Bahaa al-Din, Ministry of Education

Minister of Electricity and Energy
Mohamed Maher Abaza, Ministry of Electricity and Energy

Minister of Finance
Mohieddin el-Gharib, Ministry of Finance

Minister of Foreign Affairs
Amre Mahmoud Moussa, Ministry of Foreign Affairs

Minister of Health and Population
Ismail Sallam, Ministry of Health and Population

Minister of Higher Education and Scientific Research
Munfid Shinab, Ministry of Higher Education and Scientific Research

Minister of Housing, Utilities, Reconstruction, and New Communities
Mohammed Ibrahim Soliman, Minister of Housing, Utilities, Reconstruction, and New Communities

Minister of Industry
Suleiman Reda, Ministry of Industry

Minister of Information
Mohamed Safwat el-Sherif, Ministry of Information

Minister of Insurance and Social Affairs
Mirvat Muhanna el-Tilawi, Ministry of Insurance and Social Affairs

Minister of Interior
Habib el-Adli, Ministry of Interior

Minister of International Co-Operation
Kamal Ahmed el-Ganzouri, Ministry of International Co-Operation

Minister of Justice
Faruq Sayf al-Nasr, Ministry of Justice

Minister of Local Administration
Mahmud Sayid Ahmad Sharif, Ministry of Local Adminstration

Minister of Manpower
Ahmed el-Amawi, Ministry of Manpower

Minister of Petroleum
Hamdi Ali Abdel Wahhab Banbi, Ministry of
Petroleum

Minister of Planning
Kamal Ahmed el-Ganzouri, Ministry of Planning

Minister of Public Enterprises
Atef Ebeid, Ministry of Public Enterprises

**Minister of Public Works and Water
Resources**
Mahmoud Abd al-Halim Abu Zayd, Ministry of
Public Works and Water Resources

Minister of Rural Development
Mahmoud Sharif, Minister of Rural Development

**Minister of State for Administrative
Development**
Mohammed Zaki Abu Amer, Ministry of State
for Administrative Development

Minister of State for Cabinet Affairs
Talaat Hammad, Ministry of State for Cabinet
Affairs

Minister of State for Environmental Affairs
Nadia Riad Makram Ebeid, Ministry of State for
Environmental Affairs

Minister of State for Military Production
Mohammed el-Ghamrawi, Ministry of State for
Military Production

**Minister of State for People's Assembly and
Consultative Council Affairs**
Kamal el-Shazli, Ministry of State for People's
Assembly and Consultative Council Affairs

**Minister of State for Planning and
International Co-Operation**
Zafir Salim El-Bishri, Ministry of State for
Planning and International Co-Operation

Minister of State for Scientific Research
Venice Kamil Gouda, Ministry of State for
Scientific Research

Minister of Supply and Trade
Ahmed Goweili, Ministry of Supply and Trade

Minister of Tourism
Mamdouh el-Beltagui, Ministry of Tourism, Misr
Travel Tower, Abbasia St., Cairo, Egypt
FAX: +20 2859551

**Minister of Transport, Communication,
Maritime Transport, and Civil Aviation**
Soliman Metwalli Soliman, Ministry of
Transport, Communication, Maritime Transport,
and Civil Aviation

POLITICAL ORGANIZATIONS

**Hizb al Dimuqratiyah al Wataniyah-
HDW (National Democratic Party)**
NAME: Mohammed Hosni Mubarak

**Hizb al Tajamaa al Wataniyah al
Tagadamm al Wahdwa-HTWTW
(National Progressive Unionist Grouping)**
NAME: Khalid Muhi al-Din

**Hizb al-Wafd-al-Jadid-HJW (New
Delegation Party)**
NAME: Fu'ad Siraj al-Din

The Socialist Liberals
TITLE: Chairman
NAME: Mostafa Kamel Murad

Egypt Arab Socialist
TITLE: Chairman
NAME: Gamal Eldin Rabie Youssef

The Egyptian Greens
TITLE: Chairman
NAME: Abdul Moneim El Aasar

Social Justice
TITLE: Chairman
NAME: Mohammad Abdul Aal

The Democratic Unionist
TITLE: Chairman
NAME: Ibrahim Abdul Moneim Tork

Misr El-Fatah (Young Egypt)
TITLE: Chairman
NAME: Gamal Rabie

El-Takaful (Solidarity)
TITLE: Chairman
NAME: Dr. Usama Mohammad Shaltout

Al-Ummah (The Nation)
TITLE: Chairman
NAME: Ahmad Al Sabahi Awad Allah

The Nasserist
TITLE: Chairman
NAME: Diaa Eldin Daoud

DIPLOMATIC REPRESENTATION

Embassies in Egypt

Austria
Chancellory and Consular Section, el-Riyadh Tower, 5th floor, 5, Wissa Wassef St., Corner el-Nile St., Giza, Egypt
PHONE: +20 5702975
FAX: +20 5702979
E-MAIL: aec@gega.net

Denmark
12, Hassan Sabri Street, 11211 Zamalek, Cairo, Egypt
PHONE: +20 (2) 3402502
FAX: +20 (2) 3411780
E-MAIL: rdemb@commnet.com.eg

France
Poste d'Expansion Economique du Caire, 10, rue Aziz Osman, Zamalek, Cairo, Egypt
PHONE: +20 (2) 3415694
FAX: +20 (2) 3418238
E-MAIL: peecaire@soficom.com.eg

United States
5 Latin America St., Garden City, Cairo, Egypt
PHONE: +20 (2) 3557371

JUDICIAL SYSTEM

Court of Cassation

Supreme Constitutional Court

Shura Council

FURTHER READING

Articles
"Egypt." *The Economist* (March 20, 1999).

"Egypt Attracted 348,000 Tourists in June." Reuters, 16 September 1999.

"Egypt Moves to Protect Women Marrying Foreigners." Reuters, 10 September 1999.

"Egypt Sacks Three Generals After Mubarak Attack." Reuters, 13 September 1999.

"Egypt Signs Contract to Purchase 24 Lockheed Martin F-16s." PR Newswire, 25 August 1999.

"Egypt to Privatize 94 Companies Next Year." Reuters, 14 September 1999.

"Egyptian, Libyan Leaders Meet in Northern Egypt." Reuters, 4 August 1999.

"Egypt's FM Moussa Leaves for OAU Summit in Libya." Reuters, 6 September 1999.

"Egypt's Mubarak Hurt, Attacker Killed." Reuters, 9 September 1999.

"Egypt's Mubarak Meets Saudi Foreign Minister." Reuters, 13 September 1999.

"Egypt's State Broadcasters Plan Disney Boycott." Reuters, 21 September 1999.

"Egypt's Waiting Game." *The Economist* (September 25, 1999).

"EU Deal to Make Egypt Link to Arab World." Reuters, 16 September 1999.

"Faith, Fear and Feuding: Complaints of Growing Religious and Political Bias in Egypt Cause Anxiety among Coptic Christians." *Time International* (18 January 1999) p. 28.

"FOCUS-Egypt Sets Tax Break on Exports." Reuters, 30 August 1999.

"The Nile Flows On." *Africa Confidential* 40 (June 11, 1999).

"Sudan to Ask Egypt for Pipeline Bomb Suspect." Reuters, 28 September 1999.

Internet
Africa News. Available Online @ http://www.africanews.org/north/egypt/ (November 29, 1999).

Amnesty International. Available Online @ http://www.amnesty.org/ailib/countries/indx512.htm (November 29, 1999).

BBC World Service. Available Online @ http://news2.thls.bbc.co.uk/scripts/query.asp (November 29, 1999).

EGYPT: STATISTICAL DATA

For sources and notes see "Sources of Statistics" in the front of each volume.

GEOGRAPHY

Geography (1)

Area:

Total: 1,001,450 sq km.

Land: 995,450 sq km.

Water: 6,000 sq km.

Area—comparative: slightly more than three times the size of New Mexico.

Land boundaries:

Total: 2,689 km.

Border countries: Gaza Strip 11 km, Israel 255 km, Libya 1,150 km, Sudan 1,273 km.

Coastline: 2,450 km.

Climate: desert; hot, dry summers with moderate winters.

Terrain: vast desert plateau interrupted by Nile valley and delta.

Natural resources: petroleum, natural gas, iron ore, phosphates, manganese, limestone, gypsum, talc, asbestos, lead, zinc.

Land use:

Arable land: 2%

Permanent crops: 0%

Permanent pastures: 0%

Forests and woodland: 0%

Other: 98% (1993 est.).

HUMAN FACTORS

Demographics (2A)

	1990	1995	1998	2000	2010	2020	2030	2040	2050
Population	56,105.9	62,373.8	66,050.0	68,494.6	80,725.4	92,234.2	102,218.1	110,604.7	117,121.0
Net migration rate (per 1,000 population)	NA	NA	NA	NA	NA	NA	NA	NA	NA
Births	NA	NA	NA	NA	NA	NA	NA	NA	NA
Deaths	NA	NA	NA	NA	NA	NA	NA	NA	NA
Life expectancy - males	57.7	59.2	60.1	60.7	63.5	66.1	68.4	70.4	72.2
Life expectancy - females	61.4	63.1	64.1	64.8	68.1	71.0	73.7	76.0	78.0
Birth rate (per 1,000)	32.0	28.9	27.3	26.3	22.4	19.1	16.7	15.2	13.9
Death rate (per 1,000)	9.9	8.9	8.4	8.1	7.3	7.2	7.6	8.2	9.1
Women of reproductive age (15-49 yrs.)	13,552.2	15,554.0	16,765.7	17,552.5	21,457.3	24,680.7	26,894.3	27,756.6	28,015.8
of which are currently married	NA	NA	NA	NA	NA	NA	NA	NA	NA
Fertility rate	4.2	3.7	3.4	3.2	2.6	2.3	2.1	2.1	2.0

Except as noted, values for vital statistics are in thousands; life expectancy is in years.

Health Personnel (3)

Total health expenditure as a percentage of GDP, 1990-1997[a]

Public sector 1.7

Private sector 2.1

Total[b] 3.7

Health expenditure per capita in U.S. dollars, 1990-1997[a]

Purchasing power parity 103

Total 38

Availability of health care facilities per 100,000 people

Hospital beds 1990-1997[a] 2.10

Doctors 1993[c] 202

Nurses 1993[c] 222

Health Indicators (4)

Life expectancy at birth

1980 56

1997 66

Daily per capita supply of calories (1996) 3,289

Total fertility rate births per woman (1997) 3.2

Maternal mortality ratio per 100,000 live births (1990-97) . . . . .170[c]

Safe water % of population with access (1995) 84

Sanitation % of population with access (1995) 70

Consumption of iodized salt % of households (1992-98)[a] 0

Smoking prevalence

Male % of adults (1985-95)[a] 40

Female % of adults (1985-95)[a] 1

Tuberculosis incidence per 100,000 people (1997) 36

Adult HIV prevalence % of population ages 15-49 (1997) 0.03

Infants and Malnutrition (5)

Under-5 mortality rate (1997) 73

% of infants with low birthweight (1990-97) 10

Births attended by skilled health staff % of total[a] . . .46

% fully immunized (1995-97)

TB 98

DPT 94

Polio 94

Measles 92

Prevalence of child malnutrition under age 5 (1992-97)[b] 15

Ethnic Division (6)

Eastern Hamitic stock (Egyptians, Bedouins, and Berbers) 99%, Greek, Nubian, Armenian, other European (primarily Italian and French) 1%.

Religions (7)

Muslim (mostly Sunni) 94%

Coptic Christian and other 6%

Data are official estimates.

Languages (8)

Arabic (official), English and French widely understood by educated classes.

EDUCATION

Public Education Expenditures (9)

Public expenditure on education (% of GNP)

1980 . . . . .5.7[1]

1996 . . . . .4.8[1]

Expenditure per student

Primary % of GNP per capita

1980 . . . .

1996 . . . .

Secondary % of GNP per capita

1980 . . . .

1996 . . . . .25.9

Tertiary % of GNP per capita

1980 . . . . .57.9

1996 . . . .

Expenditure on teaching materials

Primary % of total for level (1996) . . . .

Secondary % of total for level (1996) . . . . .0.7[1]

Primary pupil-teacher ratio per teacher (1996) 23

Duration of primary education years (1995) 5

Educational Attainment (10)

Age group (1986) . . . . .25+

Total population .19,441,903

Highest level attained (%)

No schooling[2] 64.1

First level

Not completed 16.5

Completed . . . . .NA

Entered second level

S-1 . . . . .14.8

S-2 . . . . .NA

Postsecondary 4.6

Literacy Rates (11A)

In thousands and percent[1]	1990	1995	2000	2010
Illiterate population (15+ yrs.)	17,816	18,954	20,047	21,557
Literacy rate - total adult pop. (%)	47.5	51.4	55.3	62.2
Literacy rate - males (%)	60.5	63.6	66.8	71.9
Literacy rate - females (%)	34.2	38.8	43.4	52.2

GOVERNMENT & LAW

Political Parties (12)

People's Assembly—	% of seats
National Democratic Party (NDP) 72	
Independents 25	
Opposition 3	

Military Affairs (14B)

	1990	1991	1992	1993	1994	1995
Military expenditures						
Current dollars (mil.)	1,468	1,599	1,710[e]	1,816[e]	1,835	2,653[e]
1995 constant dollars (mil.)	1,687	1,767	1,840[e]	1,904[e]	1,881	2,653[e]
Armed forces (000)	434	434	424	424	430	430
Gross national product (GNP)						
Current dollars (mil.)	36,610	39,460	40,970	42,310	44,360	46,490
1995 constant dollars (mil.)	42,080	43,600	44,070	44,360	45,470	46,490
Central government expenditures (CGE)						
1995 constant dollars (mil.)	16,690	17,630	21,720	20,410	21,030[e]	19,390[e]
People (mil.)	56.1	57.5	58.7	59.9	61.1	62.4
Military expenditure as % of GNP	4.0	4.1	4.2	4.3	4.1	5.7
Military expenditure as % of CGE	10.1	10.0	8.5	9.3	8.9	13.7
Military expenditure per capita (1995 $)	30	31	31	32	31	43
Armed forces per 1,000 people (soldiers)	7.7	7.5	7.2	7.1	7.0	6.9
GNP per capita (1995 $)	750	758	750	470	744	746
Arms imports[6]						
Current dollars (mil.)	800	825	1,100	1,400	1,200	1,900
1995 constant dollars (mil.)	919	912	1,183	1,468	1,230	1,900
Arms exports[6]						
Current dollars (mil.)	80	0	20	10	10	0
1995 constant dollars (mil.)	92	0	22	10	10	0
Total imports[7]						
Current dollars (mil.)	9,216	7,862	8,245	8,184	10,180	11,740
1995 constant dollars (mil.)	10,590	8,688	8,869	8,580	10,440	11,740
Total exports[7]						
Current dollars (mil.)	2,585	3,659	3,051	2,244	3,463	3,435
1995 constant dollars (mil.)	2,971	4,043	3,282	2,353	3,550	3,435
Arms as percent of total imports[8]	8.7	10.5	13.3	17.1	11.8	16.2

Government Budget (13A)

Year: 1995

Total Expenditures: 68,689 Millions of Pounds

Expenditures as a percentage of the total by function:

General public services and public order 6.97

Defense 9.13

Education 13.84

Health 2.50

Social Security and Welfare 13.25

Housing and community amenities 4.38

Recreational, cultural, and religious affairs 7.61

Fuel and energy 28

Agriculture, forestry, fishing, and hunting 4.39

Mining, manufacturing, and construction 12

Transportation and communication 4.27

Other economic affairs and services 36

Crime (15)

Crime rate (for 1994)

Crimes reported 20,957

Total persons convicted 198,249

Crimes per 100,000 population 36

Persons responsible for offenses

Total number of suspects . . . . .NA

Total number of female suspects . . . . .NA

Total number of juvenile suspects . . . . .NA

LABOR FORCE

Labor Force (16)

Total (million) 17.4

Agriculture 40%

Services, including government 38%

Industry 22%

Data for 1996 est. Percent distribution 1990 est.

Unemployment Rate (17)

9.4% (1997 est.)

PRODUCTION SECTOR

Electric Energy (18)

Capacity . . . . .13.04 million kW (1995)

Production . . . . .48.5 billion kWh (1995)

Consumption per capita . . . . .778 kWh (1995)

Transportation (19)

Highways:

total: 64,000 km

paved: 49,984 km

unpaved: 14,016 km (1996 est.)

Waterways: 3,500 km (including the Nile, Lake Nasser, Alexandria-Cairo Waterway, and numerous smaller canals in the delta); Suez Canal, 193.5 km long (including approaches), used by oceangoing vessels drawing up to 16.1 m of water

Pipelines: crude oil 1,171 km; petroleum products 596 km; natural gas 460 km

Merchant marine:

total: 161 ships (1,000 GRT or over) totaling 1,225,989 GRT/1,899,818 DWT ships by type: bulk 24, cargo 60, liquefied gas tanker 1, oil tanker 15, passenger 42, refrigerated cargo 1, roll-on/roll-off cargo 15, short-sea passenger 3 (1997 est.)

Airports: 89 (1997 est.)

Airports—with paved runways:

total: 70

over 3,047 m: 11

2,438 to 3,047 m: 39

1,524 to 2,437 m: 15

914 to 1,523 m: 2

under 914 m: 3 (1997 est.)

Airports—with unpaved runways:

total: 19

2,438 to 3,047 m: 2

1,524 to 2,437 m: 2

914 to 1,523 m: 6

under 914 m: 9 (1997 est.)

Top Agricultural Products (20)

Cotton, rice, corn, wheat, beans, fruits, vegetables; cattle, water buffalo, sheep, goats; annual fish catch about 140,000 metric tons.

MANUFACTURING SECTOR

GDP & Manufacturing Summary (21)

Detailed value added figures are listed by both International Standard Industry Code (ISIC) and product title.

	1980	1985	1990	1994
GDP ($-1990 mil.)[1]	15,986	26,438	32,907	38,104
Per capita ($-1990)[1]	365	531	584	618
Manufacturing share (%) (current prices)[1]	12.9	15.4	18.0	*13.0*

	1980	1985	1990	1994
Manufacturing				
Value added ($-1990 mil.)[1]	2,041	3,612	5,502	*5,920*
Industrial production index	100	183	155	*169*
Value added ($ mil.)	1,769	2,938	4,498	*6,405*
Gross output ($ mil.)	6,986	10,260	15,664	*19,566*
Employment (000)	868	907	1,077	*1,155*
Profitability (% of gross output)				
Intermediate input (%)	75	71	71	*67*
Wages and salaries inc. supplements (%)	*17*	*18*	*12*	*10*
Gross operating surplus	*8*	*10*	*17*	*22*
Productivity ($)				
Gross output per worker	7,984	11,232	14,550	*16,945*
Value added per worker	2,023	3,216	4,178	*5,549*
Average wage (inc. supplements)	*1,360*	*2,058*	*1,756*	*1,751*
Value added ($ mil.)				
311/2 Food products	308	421	712	*860*
313 Beverages	14	71	35	*65*
314 Tobacco products	21	131	100	*190*
321 Textiles	506	509	635	*1,264*
322 Wearing apparel	6	15	40	*28*
323 Leather and fur products	3	7	5	*17*
324 Footwear	22	9	17	*29*
331 Wood and wood products	9	24	13	*14*
332 Furniture and fixtures	7	19	10	*10*
341 Paper and paper products	42	76	63	*124*
342 Printing and publishing	39	101	57	*96*
351 Industrial chemicals	69	145	254	*272*
352 Other chemical products	87	205	365	*314*
353 Petroleum refineries	40	59	867	*1,329*
354 Miscellaneous petroleum and coal products	61	78	27	*83*
355 Rubber products	12	28	6	*23*
356 Plastic products	33	21	54	*54*
361 Pottery, china and earthenware	6	12	47	*50*
362 Glass and glass products	17	22	31	*57*
369 Other non-metal mineral products	78	167	248	*365*
371 Iron and steel	88	98	235	*303*
372 Non-ferrous metals	64	279	132	*176*
381 Metal products	42	95	108	*235*
382 Non-electrical machinery	54	83	107	*131*
383 Electrical machinery	69	181	120	*136*
384 Transport equipment	65	106	178	*132*
385 Professional and scientific equipment	4	13	28	*44*
390 Other manufacturing industries	1	6	6	*5*

FINANCE, ECONOMICS, & TRADE

Balance of Payments (23)

	1992	1993	1994	1995	1996
Exports of goods (f.o.b.)	3,670	3,545	4,044	4,670	4,779
Imports of goods (f.o.b.)	−8,901	−9,923	−9,997	−12,267	−13,169
Trade balance	−5,231	−6,378	−5,953	−7,597	−8,390
Services - debits	−7,664	−7,334	−7,759	−6,856	−6,640
Services - credits	8,631	9,005	9,400	10,168	11,172
Private transfers (net)	1,430	1,581	917	1,003	749
Government transfers (net)	6,104	5,664	3,426	3,028	2,917
Overall balance	3,270	2,538	31	−254	−192

FINANCE, ECONOMICS, & TRADE

Economic Indicators (22)

National product: GDP—purchasing power parity—$267.1 billion (1997 est.)

National product real growth rate: 5.2% (1997 est.)

National product per capita: $4,400 (1997 est.)

Inflation rate—consumer price index: 4.9% (1997)

Exchange Rates (24)

Exchange rates:

Egyptian pounds (£E) per US$1

November 1994	.3.4
November 1993	.3.369
November 1992	.3.345

Market rate

January 1998	.3.3880
1997	.3.3880
1996	.3.3880
1995	.3.3900
1994	.3.3910
1993	.3.3718

Top Import Origins (25)

$15.5 billion (c.i.f., FY96/97 est.)

Origins	%
United States	NA
European Union	NA
Japan	NA

NA stands for not available.

Top Export Destinations (26)

$5.1 billion (f.o.b., FY96/97 est.).

Destinations	%
European Union	NA
United States	NA
Japan	NA

NA stands for not available.

Economic Aid (27)

Recipient: ODA, $1.713 billion (1993).

Import Export Commodities (28)

Import Commodities	Export Commodities
Machinery and equipment	Crude oil and petroleum products
Foods	Cotton yarn
Fertilizers	Raw cotton
Wood products	Textiles
Durable consumer goods	Metal products
Capital goods	Chemicals

EL SALVADOR

Republic of El Salvador
República de El Salvador

INTRODUCTORY SURVEY

RECENT HISTORY

In 1931 General Maximiliano Hernández Martínez seized power, a fifty-year period of military rule began. Hernández ruled for thirteen years, brutally suppressing a peasant uprising in 1932, in which 30,000 people were killed. None of the military governments that followed Hernández was able to reduce the economic gap between the landowners and the landless classes.

Landless Salvadorans found land available in neighboring Honduras and migrated there. When the flow of Salvadorans increased during the 1960s, the Honduran government took steps to limit it. Tensions rose between the two nations, and on 14 July 1969, they went to war for four days. A total of 3,000–4,000 people were killed on both sides.

In 1972, José Napoleón Duarte of the Christian Democratic Party (PDC) ran for president against the military candidate. Duarte was denied election by fraud and sent into exile. Armed resistance arose from leftist guerrilla groups, and the right unleashed "death squads" to counter it. By the late 1970s, the situation had escalated into a civil war. In 1979, a coup brought to power a five-member military-civilian junta. Attacked by both the left and the right, the junta was unable either to suppress left-wing guerrillas or to control its own security forces.

In December 1980, Duarte was appointed president by the junta. Following his taking office, a state of siege was proclaimed in an attempt to

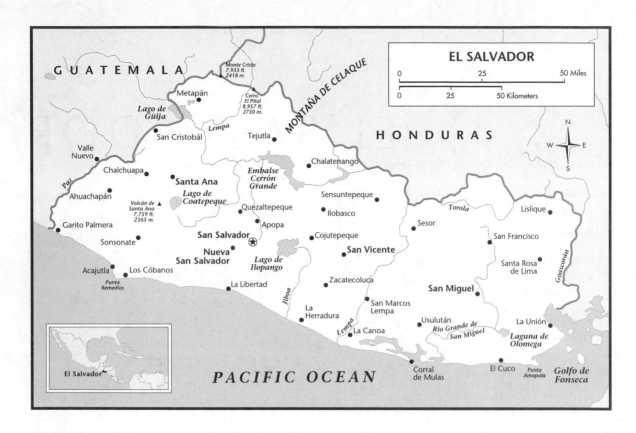

control widespread violence and human rights violations. It is estimated that at least 62,000 people died between October 1979 and April 1987, most of them civilians murdered by death squads and government security forces.

In 1984, Duarte defeated Roberto D'Aubuisson Arrieta of the National Republican Alliance in a runoff election in May, becoming the first constitutionally elected president in over fifty years. Duarte's regime was a difficult balancing act between right and left, but his overriding problem was the ongoing civil war.

Eventually, El Salvador's economic troubles and charges of government corruption led to the election in 1989 of Alfredo Félix Christiani Burkard of the National Republican Alliance (ARENA). On 31 December 1991, the government and the guerrillas, known as the Farabundo Martí National Liberation Front (*Frente Farabundo Martí de Liberacíon Nacional—FMLN*), signed an agreement, Chapultepec Accord, which ended the civil war.

New elections were held in 1994, and voters returned ARENA to power, with Armando Calerón Sol winning the presidential run-off election. In the elections of March 1997, the FMLN significantly increased its role as a major political force by nearly doubling its number of seats in parliament.

GOVERNMENT

The constitution, adopted on 20 November 1983, defines El Salvador as a republic. It vests executive power in the president, who is to be elected by direct popular vote for a term of five years. Legislative power is exercised by a single-chamber National Assembly comprising eighty-four deputies.

Judiciary

The court system includes justices of the peace, lower-level courts, intermediate level appeals courts, and the Supreme Court, made up of thirteen justices selected by the National Assembly.

Political Parties

The leading party of the right in El Salvador is the National Republican Alliance (Alianza Republicana Nacionalista—ARENA). The National Conciliation Party (Partido de Conciliación Nacional-PCN), the party of the former military government, is allied with ARENA. Together, the two parties control a majority of seats in the legislature.

The moderate Christian Democratic Party (Partido Demócrata Cristiano—PDC) was founded by former president José Napoleón Duarte. The PDC now makes up the largest opposition party, holding twenty-six of eighty-four seats in the National Assembly.

Leftist groups include the Democratic Convergence (CD), a coalition of three leftist parties, and the Farabundo Martí National Liberation Front (Frente Farabundo Martí de Liberación Nacional—FMLN). As part of the peace agreement ending the civil war, FMLN is now a legal party after having ceased its military operations.

DEFENSE

All Salvadoran males between 18 and 30 years of age are eligible for military service. In 1995, 28,380 personnel were in service, 25,700 of whom were in the army, 1,100 in the navy and marine corps, and 1,600 in the air force. National police and village militia forces numbered an additional 12,000. In 1995, $126 million was budgeted for national defense. U.S. military assistance during the civil war (1979–92) reached over $1 billion.

ECONOMIC AFFAIRS

Agriculture is the foundation of El Salvador's economy, providing about two-thirds of the nation's exports and employing one-third of its labor force. In the 1970s, El Salvador was the most industrialized nation in Central America, although a dozen years of civil war have eroded this position.

Recent administrations have carried out a comprehensive economic reform plan oriented toward a free-market economy. The gross domestic product (GDP) annually grew by an average of 6.5% between 1990 and 1995.

Public Finance

Most current public revenues come from taxes, fees, and fines. Municipal taxes and fees are subject to approval by the Ministry of the Interior. Until the early 1980s, government fiscal operations had generally shown surpluses; these enabled the government to sustain a growing volume of capital expenditures, resulting in a higher government share in total investments.

The CIA estimates that, in 1992, government revenues totaled approximately $846 million and expenditures $890 million. External debt totaled $2.6 billion, approximately 63% of which was financed abroad.

Income

In 1998, El Salvador's gross national product (GNP) was $11.2 billion, or $1,850 per person. For the period 1985–95, the average inflation rate was 14.7%, resulting in real growth in GNP of 2.9% per person.

Industry

Although industry plays a secondary role in the country's economy, it is the most developed in Central America. In 1993, industrial production grew by 7.6%, fueled mainly by clothing production.

Banking and Finance

The banking system, nationalized in March 1980, consisted in 1993 of the Central Reserve Bank of El Salvador, 10 commercial and mortgage banks, four development banks, and six savings and loan associations. The central bank of El Salvador, established in 1934, was nationalized in 1961. It is the sole bank of issue and the fiscal agent for the government. As of December 31, 1995, the money supply, as measured by M2, was C 31,494 million.

A stock exchange was established in San Salvador on April 27, 1992, with five government issues of long-term bonds. In the first twelve months of activity, stock market transactions were nearly $100 million; the rate of growth in 1993–95 was rapid, and by the end of 1995 transactions reached an estimated $2.4 billion.

Economic Development

Aided by the government's economic reforms and the IMF and World bank supported macroeconomic programs, the country's economy will continue to prosper. The rising influx of private remittances, official transfer, and the return of local capital will boost domestic demand as well as construction activity, especially in transportation infrastructure and other public projects. The industrial sector should also benefit from this upturn.

El Salvador's external debt decreased sharply in 1993, chiefly as a result of an agreement under which the U.S. forgave about $461 million of official debt. Total external debt went down from $2.25 billion in 1994 to $2.20 billion in 1995 and did not rise significantly in 1996.

SOCIAL WELFARE

The Salvadoran Social Security Institute provides national insurance for health, accidents, unemployment, invalidism, old age, and death. The

Ministry of Public Health and Social Welfare supervises institutions and hospitals for the infirm and aged, as well as child welfare and maternal care services. Women are paid lower wages than men and lack equal access to credit and property ownership. Child abandonment and the use of child labor are growing social problems.

Healthcare

Much of the progress since the 1930s was undermined by the civil war, which overtaxed health care facilities, while shrinking their funding. The National Medical School was shut down in 1980. Between 1985 and 1994, only 54% of the population had access to health care services. In 1993, there were 70 physicians per 100,000 people.

The principal causes of death remain gastroenteritis (inflammation of lining of stomach or intestines), influenza, malaria, measles, pneumonia, and bronchitis, caused or complicated by malnutrition, bad sanitation, and poor housing. The average life expectancy is 69 years for women and men.

Housing

Inadequate housing, most critically felt in cities and towns, is widespread throughout El Salvador. In the early 1990s, an estimated 47% of all households did not have easy access to drinking water, and 59% lacked plumbing. Housing problems have been aggravated by the civil war, which has created hundreds of thousands of refugees.

EDUCATION

By 1995, illiteracy had been reduced to about 29% (males, 26.5%; females, 30.2%). Primary education is free and compulsory. Primary education lasts for nine years followed by three years of secondary education. Twelve private and three public universities offer higher education.

1999 KEY EVENTS TIMELINE

February

- Salvadoran farmers seek economic relief. They demand pardons for agrarian and banking debts.
- Coffee producers face a year of losses after Hurricane Mitch.

March

- The right-wing Nationalist Republican Alliance holds on to power. In the presidential race, Francisco Flores defeats Facundo Guardado of the leftist Farabundo Martí National Liberation Front. Flores receives 52 percent of the vote, and Guardado receives 29 percent.
- United States President Bill Clinton visits El Salvador and promises economic aid.
- A Salvadoran admits to conducting bombings in Cuba and is sentenced to death there.

May

- Families of slain churchwomen sue two Salvadoran generals.
- U.S. officials say Salvadoran immigrants may stay in the United States.

June

- Francisco Flores, leader of the Nationalist Republican Alliance, is sworn in as president.

September

- Hundreds of Salvadoran teachers go on strike, demanding better pay.

October

- Thousands of health workers walk off the job, demanding increased pay and a halt to the government's plan to privatize health care.

December

- The Inter-American Commission for Human Rights issues a report that implicates the El Salvador government in the killing of ten Jesuit priests in 1989, but the government refuses to reopen the investigation.
- President Francisco Flores delivers the keynote address at the Miami Conference on the Caribbean and Latin America on December 7.

ANALYSIS OF EVENTS: 1999

BUSINESS AND THE ECONOMY

Salvadorans spent most of 1999 recovering from devastating Hurricane Mitch, which hit the small nation in October 1998, killing 239 people, and left thousands homeless. El Salvador was not hit as hard as neighboring countries, but the hurricane devastated coffee production. By some estimates, it will take many years for coffee producers to recover in El Salvador, where losses topped more than fifty percent. Despite the damages that slowed down the economy, some economic analysts said the country remained the most aggressive reformer in the region.

In March, during a visit to El Salvador, U.S. President Bill Clinton promised nearly $1 billion in aid for the region. The Americans signed a bilateral investment treaty with El Salvador meant to promote U.S. exports and protect U.S. investments. U.S. officials applauded the country's continued efforts at market reforms.

The precarious legal situation of thousands of undocumented Salvadoran immigrants living in the United States was a special concern for the small nation. Salvadoran workers in the U.S. sent $1.34 billion to families in El Salvador in 1998. Remittances reached $319 million in the first quarter of 1999, 8 percent higher than the same period a year ago.

Leaders from El Salvador and other Central American countries wanted Clinton to stop or slow the deportation of undocumented workers. Clinton said the United States would continue to discourage illegal immigration. But in May, the White House announced it would implement guidelines to give legal residency to more than 500,000 Guatemalans and Salvadorans already living in the United States. The measure placed Guatemalans and Salvadorans on par with Nicaraguans, who had fled a leftist government and had an easier time getting permanent residency. Salvadorans and Guatemalans were not as favored because they fled governments supported by the United States.

El Salvador continued to lead Central America in market reforms, a good sign for foreign investors. While foreign investment was not expected to reach 1998 levels—when more than $1 billion poured into the country with the privatization of electrical power plants and telecommunications— El Salvador remained a viable place for business, with about $250 million in direct investments in 1999. One of those investors was Microsoft, which in June reaffirmed its commitment to software development in the country by investing more than $1 million.

Despite the positive signs, the economy showed signs of recession. The Central Reserve Bank forecast economic growth of 3 percent for 1999, but there was cumulative deflation of 1.5 percent through May 1999. GDP growth may end up at 1.5 percent for the year.

GOVERNMENT AND POLITICS

In 1997, Former leftist guerrillas won major victories at the polls, including San Salvador's mayoralty. By early 1999, a confident Farabundo Martí National Liberation Front had its hopes on the presidency.

Early in the campaign, the leftists appeared to have a chance behind the candidacy of Facundo Guardado, whose party espoused political views not typical of the left. The party supported a free trade agreement with the United States, and the sale of some state enterprises. And they were not opposed to the privatization of the country's social security system.

The right-wing Nationalist Republican Party (ARENA by its Spanish acronym) was trying to capture its third straight presidential election, this time behind Francisco Flores, a 39-year-old U.S.-educated academic. The young candidate built support by moving away from the harsh rhetoric of the right. Roberto D'Aubuisson, a wealthy anti-Communist who created the notorious death-squads, founded ARENA, and remains a popular figure among the country's conservatives. Running on the pledge to curb unemployment and lawlessness, Flores won the election with 52 percent of the vote, with Guardado receiving 29 percent.

CULTURE AND SOCIETY

Emboldened by democratic reforms, Salvadorans showed their displeasure with the government with short strikes and public protests. In February, farmers showed up in the capital to ask the government to forgive farm and banking debts. During a one-day bus strike in June, Salvadorans were forced to find other ways to get to work. Bus drivers wanted the government to forgive $28 million in traffic fines. Trash piled in San Salvador streets after sanitation workers went on strike in July. Two months later, hundreds of teachers took to the streets demanding higher pay.

On the human rights front, lawsuits against former high-ranking military officers reminded the nation of its bloody civil war, when more than 70,000 people died between 1980 and 1992. More frequently, victims were filing their cases in United States courts. In May, families filed suit in U.S. District Court against former military officers implicated in the murders of four American churchwomen in 1980. The suit named National Guard director Carlos Eugenio Vides Casanova, and former defense minister Jose Guillermo Garcia, both living in Florida since 1989. The suit was field under provisions of the Federal Torture Victims Prevention Act. It allows U.S. citizens to sue foreigners living in the United States for damages from human rights abuses committed in other countries

Drinking water continued to be a problem for Salvadorans, with health problems affecting a large number of children. In March, Clinton announced $16.5 million in aid to improve drinking-water quality. Dysentery and diarrhea are the leading causes of death for children under five years of age.

DIRECTORY

CENTRAL GOVERNMENT
Head of State
President
Francisco Guillermo Flores, Office of the President, Casa Presidencial, San Salvador, El Salvador
PHONE: +503 2715544
FAX: +503 2710950

Vice President
Carlos Quintanilla Schmidt, Office of the Vice President, Casa Presidencial, San Salvador, El Salvador
PHONE: +503 2715544
FAX: +503 2710950

Ministers
Minister of Agriculture and Livestock
Ingeniero Salvador Urrutia, Ministry of Agriculture and Livestock, Final Primera Ave. Norte y Ave. Manuel Gallardo, Santa Tecla, El Salvador
PHONE: +503 2889983
FAX: +503 2885040

Minister of Defense
Juan Antonio Martínez Varela, Ministry of National Defense, Alameda Dr. Manuel Enrique Araujo, San Salvador, El Salvador
PHONE: +503 2981033
FAX: +503 2982005

Minister of Economy
Miguel Lacayo, Ministry of Economy, Alameda Juan Pablo II y Calle Guadalupe,, Centro de Gobierno, San Salvador, El Salvador
PHONE: +503 2810531; 2213571
FAX: +503 2212797

Minister of Education
Evelyn Jacir de Lovo, Ministry of Education, Alameda Juan Pablo II y Calle Guadalupe, Centro de Gobierno, San Salvador, El Salvador
PHONE: +503 2810254
FAX: +503 2810257

Minister of Environment and Natural Resources
Miguel Eduardo Araujo, Ministry of Environment and Natural Resources, Torre El Salvador, 55 Ave. Sur y Alameda Roosevelt, San Salvador, El Salvador
PHONE: +503 2608900
FAX: +503 2603117

Minister of Finance
Jose Luis Trigueros, Ministry of Finance, Edificio Ministerio de Hacienda, Sexta Planta, Blvd. de Los Héroes, San Salvador, El Salvador
PHONE: +503 2255500
FAX: +503 2257491

Minister of Foreign Affairs
Maria Eugenia Brizuela de Avila, Ministry of Foreign Affairs, Alameda Dr. Manuel Enrique Araujo, San Salvador, El Salvador
PHONE: +503 2433802; 2433805
FAX: +503 2433710

Minister of Health
José López Beltrán, Ministry of Health

Minister of Housing
Ministry of Housing, Diagonal Centroamérica y Av. Alvarado, Condominio Tres Torres, San Salvador, El Salvador
PHONE: +503 2251022
FAX: +503 2267170

Minister of Interior
Mario Acosta Oertel, Ministry of Interior, Centro de Gobierno, San Salvador, El Salvador
PHONE: +503 2216574
FAX: +503 2815959

Minister of Justice
Nelson Segovia, Ministry of Justice
PHONE: +503 2211808
FAX: +503 2213956

Minister of Labor and Social Welfare
Jorge I. Nieto Menéndez, Ministry of Labor and Social Welfare, Paseo Escalon 4122, Col. Escalon, San Salvador, El Salvador
PHONE: +503 2635439
FAX: +503 2635272

Minister of the Presidency
Enrique Borgo Bustamante, Ministry of the
Presidency, Casa Presidencial, San Salvador, El
Salvador
PHONE: +503 2715544
FAX: +503 2710950

**Minister of Public Health and Social
Assistance**
Eduardo Interiano, Ministry of Public Health and
Social Assistance, Calle Arce 827, San Salvador,
El Salvador
PHONE: +503 2710008
FAX: +503 2210985

Minister of Public Security
Francisco Bertrand Galindo, Ministry of Public
Security, 6a. Calle Oriente 42, San Salvador, El
Salvador
PHONE: +503 2213688
FAX: +503 2213956

Minister of Public Works
Jose Quiros, Ministry of Public Works, Edificio
Dirección General de Caminos, Final Ave.
Peralta, San Salvador, El Salvador
PHONE: +503 2936585
FAX: +503 2936583

POLITICAL ORGANIZATIONS

Alianza Republicana Nacionalista (ARENA)

Prolongación Calle Arce 2429, San Salvador, El
Salvador
PHONE: +503 2604400
FAX: +503 2604400
TITLE: President
NAME: Félix Alfredo Cristiani

Frente Farabundo Marti para la Liberacion Nacional (FMLN)

27 Calle Pte. 1316 y 25 Ave. Nte., Col. Layco,
San Salvador, El Salvador
PHONE: +503 2265220
FAX: +503 2252961
TITLE: General Coordinator
NAME: Francisco Jovel

Partido De Conciliacion Nacional (PCN)

15 Ave. Norte y 3a Calle Poniente No.244, San
Salvador, El Salvador
PHONE: +503 2213752
FAX: +503 2213752
TITLE: Secretary General

NAME: Ciro Cruz Zepeda Peña

Partido Democrata Cristiano (PDC)

3a Calle Poniente No. 924, San Salvador, El
Salvador
PHONE: +503 2221815
FAX: +503 2216320
TITLE: Secretary General
NAME: René Aguiluz

Partido Union Social Cristiana (USC)

No. 1701, Col. Flor Blanca, San Salvador, El
Salvador
PHONE: | 503 2216090
TITLE: President
NAME: Carlos Abraham Rodríguez

Convergencia Democratica (CD)

Final Blvd. Tutunichapa, Calle Guadalupe No.
1313, Urb. La Esperanza, San Salvador, El
Salvador
PHONE: +503 2220592
FAX: +503 2229269
TITLE: Secretary General
NAME: Ruben Zamora

Partido Liberal Democratico (PLD)

Ave. Las Palmas No. 129, Col. San Benito, San
Salvador, El Salvador
PHONE: +503 2980625
FAX: +503 2980625
TITLE: Secretary General
NAME: Dr. Kirio Waldo Salgado

Partido Democrata (PD)

Boulevard María Cristina No. 128, Urb. La
Esperanza, San Salvador, El Salvador
PHONE: +503 2265706
FAX: +503 2265719
TITLE: President
NAME: Ana Guadalupe Martínez

Partido Popular Laborista (PPL)

23 Calle Poniente No. 1518, Col. Layco, San
Salvador, El Salvador
PHONE: +503 2356260
FAX: +503 2357260
TITLE: Secretary General
NAME: Jose Ernesto Vilanova

DIPLOMATIC REPRESENTATION
Embassies in El Salvador

Argentina
79 Ave. Norte y 11 Calle Pte. No. 704, Col. Escalón, San Salvador, El Salvador
PHONE: +503 2633564
FAX: +503 2633867
TITLE: Ambassador
NAME: Jorge T. Pereira

Brazil
Blvd. del Hipódromo No. 305, Col. San Benito, San Salvador, El Salvador
PHONE: +503 2982751
FAX: +503 2793934
TITLE: Ambassador
NAME: Luiz Henrique Pereira Da Fonsecaa

Chile
Pje. Bellavista No. 121, Col. Escalón, San Salvador, El Salvador
PHONE: +503 2634285; 2634346
FAX: +503 2634308
TITLE: Ambassador
NAME: Horacio Wood Armas

China
Paseo Gral. Escalón No. 5333, Condominio Penthouse, 7o. Piso, Col. Escalón, San Salvador, El Salvador
PHONE: +503 2983464
FAX: +503 2691331
TITLE: Ambassador
NAME: Bing F. Yen

Colombia
Calle el Mirador No. 5021, Col. Escalón, San Salvador, El Salvador
PHONE: +503 2631947
FAX: +503 2631942
TITLE: Ambassador
NAME: Hernando Piedraheta Currea

Costa Rica
Ave. Albert Einstein No. 11-A, Col. Lomas de San Francisco, San Salvador, El Salvador
PHONE: +503 2733111
FAX: +503 2731455
TITLE: Ambassador
NAME: José Alberto Brenes

Dominican Republic
Ave. República Federal de Alemania No. 163, Col. Escalón, San Salvador, El Salvador
PHONE: +503 2631816
FAX: +503 2983439
TITLE: Ambassador
NAME: Jorge Alberto Santiago Pérez

Ecuador
77 Ave. Nte. No. 208, Col. Escalón, San Salvador, El Salvador
PHONE: +503 2635323
FAX: +503 2635258
TITLE: Ambassador
NAME: Ing. Eustorgio Mendoza Cubillo

Egypt
9a. Calle Pte. y 93 Ave. Nte. 12-97, Col. Escalón, San Salvador, San Salvador
PHONE: +503 2632426
FAX: +503 2632411
TITLE: Encargado de los Intereses
NAME: Mohamed Hassan Ghanem

France
1a. Calle Pte. No. 3718, Col. Escalón, San Salvador, El Salvador
PHONE: +503 2794016; 2981455
FAX: +503 2981536
TITLE: Ambassador
NAME: Michele Dantec

Guatemala
15 Ave. Norte No. 135, San Salvador, El Salvador
PHONE: +503 2712225; 2222903
FAX: +503 2213019
TITLE: Ambassador
NAME: Oscar Augusto Zelaya Coronado

Honduras
3a. Calle Pte. No. 3597, Col. Escalón, San Salvador, El Salvador
PHONE: +503 2234975
FAX: +503 2232221
TITLE: Ambassador
NAME: Ramón Valladares Soto

Israel
85 Ave. Nte. No. 619, Col. Escalón, San Salvador, El Salvador
PHONE: +503 2985331; 2793086
FAX: +503 2790040
TITLE: Ambassador
NAME: Yosef Livne

Italy
Calle La Reforma No. 158, Col. San Benito, San Salvador, El Salvador
PHONE: +503 2234806; 2235184
FAX: +503 2983050
TITLE: Ambassador
NAME: Eugenio Di Mattei

Japan
Calle Loma Linda No. 258, Col. San Benito,
San Salvador, El Salvador
PHONE: +503 2244740
FAX: +503 2986685
TITLE: Ambassador
NAME: Katsu Iwamoto

Malta
7a. Calle Pte. No. 4016, Col. Escalón, San
Salvador, El Salvador
PHONE: +503 2239600; 2793056
FAX: +503 2239155
TITLE: Ambassador
NAME: Louis Chiurato

Mexico
Calle Circunvalación Pje. 12, Col. San Benito,
San Salvador, El Salvador
PHONE: +503 2433458
FAX: +503 2430437
TITLE: Ambassador
NAME: José Ignacio Piña Rojas

Nicaragua
71 Ave. Nte. y 1a. Calle Pte. No. 164, Col.
Escalón, San Salvador, El Salvador
PHONE: +503 2237729; 2240970
FAX: +503 2237201
TITLE: Ambassador
NAME: Luis Cardenal Arguello

Panama
Alameda Roosevelt, 2o. Piso, Edif. COPA, San
Salvador, El Salvador
PHONE: +503 2980884
FAX: +503 2980884
TITLE: Ambassador
NAME: Eduardo Ritter Aislán

Paraguay
Ave. Las Palmas No. 226, Col. San Benito, San
Salvador, El Salvador
PHONE: +503 2237541
FAX: +503 2237541
TITLE: Encargado de Negocios
NAME: Emilio Balbuena

Peru
7 Calle Pte #4111, Col. Escalón, San Salvador,
El Salvador
PHONE: +503 2633312
FAX: +503 2633310
TITLE: Ambassador
NAME: Antonio Gruter Vasquez

Spain
Calle La Reforma No. 167, Col. San Benito, San
Salvador, El Salvador
PHONE: +503 2981188; 2236168
FAX: +503 2980402
TITLE: Ambassador
NAME: Arturo Avello Diez Del Corral

United States
Urb. Sta. Elena, Antiguo Cuscatlán, La Libertad,
El Salvador
PHONE: +503 2784444
FAX: +503 2786011
TITLE: Ambassador
NAME: Anne Patterson

Venezuela
7a. calle Pte., entre 75 y 77 Ave. Nte., Col.
Escalón, San Salvador, El Salvador
PHONE: +503 2633977
FAX: +503 2633979
TITLE: Ambassador
NAME: Doña Elsa Boccheciampe de Crovati

JUDICIAL SYSTEM
Supreme Court
Edificio Adebien II, Blvd. Merliot No. 5,
Jardínes de la Hacienda, Ciudad Merliot, El
Salvador
PHONE: +503 2893660
FAX: +503 2893657

FURTHER READING
Articles
"Central America Coffee Producers Face Years
of Losses after Hurricane Mitch." *Journal of
Commerce and Commercial* (February 25,
1999): 6A.

"Childhood Malnutrition and Postwar
Reconstruction in Rural El Salvador: A
Community-Based Survey." *The Journal of
the American Medical Association* (January
13, 1999): 184.

"Clinton Celebrates Peace, Progress in El
Salvador." The Associated Press, 10 March
1999.

"El Salvador and Guatemala Immigrants can
Stay in U.S." *The Seattle Times*, 20 May
1999.

"In Salvador, a Cycle Salvager Thrives." *Los
Angeles Times,* 6 July 1999.

''A New Kind of University Grows in the Salvadoran Countryside.'' *The Chronicle of Higher Education* (May 7, 1999): A53.

''Politics of War Still Defines Relationship of Salvadoran Government and Uuniversities.'' *The Chronicle of Higher Education* (May 7, 1999): A54.

''Relatives of Slain Churchwomen Sue Two Implicated Salvadorans.'' *America* (May 29, 1999): 5.

''Rightist Party Retains Power in El Salvador.'' *The Miami Herald,* 9 March 1999.

''Salvadoran Ex-officials Sued in Slayings.'' *The Miami Herald,* 14 May 1999.

''Talking Trash? Sanitation Workers on Strike.'' *The Miami Herald,* 8 July 1999.

''Torture Victim Uses U.S. Courts in Quest for Justice.'' *The Miami Herald,* 27 June 1999.

''Transport Strike in El Salvador.'' *The Miami Herald,* 4 June 1999.

EL SALVADOR: STATISTICAL DATA

For sources and notes see "Sources of Statistics" in the front of each volume.

GEOGRAPHY

Geography (1)

Area:

Total: 21,040 sq km.

Land: 20,720 sq km.

Water: 320 sq km.

Area—comparative: slightly smaller than Massachusetts.

Land boundaries:

Total: 545 km.

Border countries: Guatemala 203 km, Honduras 342 km.

Coastline: 307 km.

Climate: tropical; rainy season (May to October); dry season (November to April).

Terrain: mostly mountains with narrow coastal belt and central plateau.

Natural resources: hydropower, geothermal power, petroleum.

Land use:

Arable land: 27%

Permanent crops: 8%

Permanent pastures: 29%

Forests and woodland: 5%

Other: 31% (1993 est.).

HUMAN FACTORS

Demographics (2A)

	1990	1995	1998	2000	2010	2020	2030	2040	2050
Population	NA	5,481.2	5,752.1	5,925.4	6,850.5	7,851.7	8,913.3	9,921.6	10,813.6
Net migration rate (per 1,000 population)	NA	NA	NA	NA	NA	NA	NA	NA	NA
Births	NA	NA	NA	NA	NA	NA	NA	NA	NA
Deaths	NA	NA	NA	NA	NA	NA	NA	NA	NA
Life expectancy - males	NA	65.1	66.3	67.1	70.8	73.7	75.8	77.4	78.5
Life expectancy - females	NA	72.1	73.2	73.9	77.1	79.6	81.5	83.0	84.1
Birth rate (per 1,000)	NA	28.1	26.7	25.6	21.7	19.1	17.2	15.8	14.8
Death rate (per 1,000)	NA	6.7	6.3	6.1	5.4	5.2	5.4	6.1	7.2
Women of reproductive age (15-49 yrs.)	NA	1,401.6	1,501.5	1,564.0	1,876.2	2,130.3	2,298.8	2,419.6	2,492.2
of which are currently married	NA	NA	NA	NA	NA	NA	NA	NA	NA
Fertility rate	NA	3.3	3.0	2.9	2.5	2.3	2.3	2.2	2.2

Except as noted, values for vital statistics are in thousands; life expectancy is in years.

Health Personnel (3)

Total health expenditure as a percentage of GDP, 1990-1997[a]

Public sector 2.4

Private sector 3.4

Total[b] 5.9

Health expenditure per capita in U.S. dollars, 1990-1997[a]

Purchasing power parity .153

Total 86

Availability of health care facilities per 100,000 people

Hospital beds 1990-1997[a] 140

Doctors 1993[c] 91

Nurses 1993[c] 38

Health Indicators (4)

Life expectancy at birth

1980 57

1997 69

Daily per capita supply of calories (1996) 2,515

Total fertility rate births per woman (1997) 3.2

Maternal mortality ratio per 100,000 live births (1990-97) . . . . .300[c]

Safe water % of population with access (1995) 53

Sanitation % of population with access (1995) 77

Consumption of iodized salt % of households (1992-98)[a] 91

Smoking prevalence

Male % of adults (1985-95)[a] 38

Female % of adults (1985-95)[a] 12

Tuberculosis incidence per 100,000 people (1997) 74

Adult HIV prevalence % of population ages 15-49 (1997) 0.58

Infants and Malnutrition (5)

Under-5 mortality rate (1997) 36

% of infants with low birthweight (1990-97) 11

Births attended by skilled health staff % of total[a] . . .87

% fully immunized (1995-97)

TB 93

DPT 97

Polio 96

Measles 97

Prevalence of child malnutrition under age 5 (1992-97)[b] 11

Ethnic Division (6)

Mestizo 94%

Amerindian 5%

White 1%

Religions (7)

Roman Catholic 75%. There is extensive activity by Protestant groups throughout the country; by the end of 1992 there were an estimated 1 million Protestant evangelicals in El Salvador.

Languages (8)

Spanish, Nahua (among some Amerindians).

EDUCATION

Public Education Expenditures (9)

Public expenditure on education (% of GNP)

1980 . . . . .3.9

1996 . . . . .2.2[1]

Expenditure per student

Primary % of GNP per capita

1980 . . . . .12.5

1996 . . . . .7.0[1]

Secondary % of GNP per capita

1980 . . . .

1996 . . . . .5.5[1]

Tertiary % of GNP per capita

1980 . . . . .141.5

1996 . . . .

Expenditure on teaching materials

Primary % of total for level (1996) . . . .

Secondary % of total for level (1996) . . . .

Primary pupil-teacher ratio per teacher (1996) 33

Duration of primary education years (1995) 9

Educational Attainment (10)

Age group (1980) . . . . .25+

Total population 2,064,258

Highest level attained (%)

No schooling[2] 37.2

First level

Not completed 46.0

Completed . . . . .NA

Entered second level

S-1 . . . . .9.8

S-2 . . . . .NA

Postsecondary 6.4

Literacy Rates (11A)

In thousands and percent[1]	1990	1995	2000	2010
Illiterate population (15+ yrs.)	914	975	1,015	1,091
Literacy rate - total adult pop. (%)	68.7	71.5	74.1	78.5
Literacy rate - males (%)	71.2	73.5	75.8	79.4
Literacy rate - females (%)	66.5	69.8	72.7	77.7

GOVERNMENT & LAW

Political Parties (12)

Legislative Assembly	% of seats
National Republican Alliance (ARENA)	.35.4
Farabundo Marti National Liberation Front (FMLN)	.34.3
National Conciliation Party (PCN)	.8.1
Christian Democratic Party (PDC)	.7.9
Democratic Convergence (CD)	.3.8
Social Christian Union (USC)	.5.5
Liberal Democratic Party (PLD)	.3.2
Democratic Party (PD)	.1.0
Other	.0.8

Government Budget (13A)

Year: 1997
Total Expenditures: 12,027.3 Millions of Colones
Expenditures as a percentage of the total by function:

General public services and public order	.29.96
Defense	.7.09
Education	.19.64
Health	.10.27
Social Security and Welfare	.5.44
Housing and community amenities	.1.83
Recreational, cultural, and religious affairs	.1.69
Fuel and energy	..03
Agriculture, forestry, fishing, and hunting	.2.19
Mining, manufacturing, and construction	..06
Transportation and communication	.12.37
Other economic affairs and services	.2.43

Military Affairs (14B)

	1990	1991	1992	1993	1994	1995
Military expenditures						
Current dollars (mil.)	223[e]	213[e]	143	117	113	101
1995 constant dollars (mil.)	256[e]	235[e]	154	123	116	101
Armed forces (000)	55	60	49	49	30	22
Gross national product (GNP)						
Current dollars (mil.)	6,016	6,484	7,239	7,979	8,690	9,564
1995 constant dollars (mil.)	6,914	7,165	7,787	8,365	8,908	9,564
Central government expenditures (CGE)						
1995 constant dollars (mil.)	751	902	1,192	1,182	1,260	1,358
People (mil.)	5.2	5.3	5.4	5.5	5.6	5.7
Military expenditure as % of GNP	3.7	3.3	2.0	1.5	1.3	1.4
Military expenditure as % of CGE	34.1	26.1	12.9	10.4	9.2	7.4
Military expenditure per capita (1995 $)	49	44	28	22	21	18
Armed forces per 1,000 people (soldiers)	10.5	11.3	9.1	8.9	5.3	3.8
GNP per capita (1995 $)	1,325	1,348	1,438	1,516	1,585	1,671
Arms imports[6]						
Current dollars (mil.)	90	60	70	40	30	20
1995 constant dollars (mil.)	103	66	75	42	31	20
Arms exports[6]						
Current dollars (mil.)	0	0	0	0	0	0
1995 constant dollars (mil.)	0	0	0	0	0	0
Total imports[7]						
Current dollars (mil.)	1,263	1,406	1,699	1,912	2,249	2,853
1995 constant dollars (mil.)	1,452	1,554	1,828	2,004	2,305	2,853
Total exports[7]						
Current dollars (mil.)	582	588	598	732	844	998
1995 constant dollars (mil.)	669	650	643	767	865	998
Arms as percent of total imports[8]	7.1	4.3	4.1	2.1	1.3	.7
Arms as percent of total exports[8]	0	0	0	0	0	0

LABOR FORCE

Labor Force (16)

Total (million) 2.26

Agriculture 40%

Commerce 16%

Manufacturing 15%

Government 13%

Financial services 9%

Transportation 6%

Other 1%

Data for 1997 est.

Unemployment Rate (17)

7.7% (1997 est.)

PRODUCTION SECTOR

Electric Energy (18)

Capacity ....900,000 kW (1996)

Production ....3.5 billion kWh (1997)

Consumption per capita ....603 kWh (1997 est.)

Transportation (19)

Highways:

total: 9,977 km

paved: 1,985 km (including 266 km of expressways)

unpaved: 7,992 km (1996 est.)

Waterways: Rio Lempa partially navigable

Merchant marine: none

Airports: 88 (1997 est.)

Airports—with paved runways:

total: 4

over 3,047 m: 1

1,524 to 2,437 m: 1

914 to 1,523 m: 2 (1997 est.)

Airports—with unpaved runways:

total: 84

914 to 1,523 m: 18

under 914 m: 66 (1997 est.)

Top Agricultural Products (20)

Coffee, sugarcane, corn, rice, beans, oilseed, cotton, sorghum; beef, dairy products; shrimp.

MANUFACTURING SECTOR

GDP & Manufacturing Summary (21)

Detailed value added figures are listed by both International Standard Industry Code (ISIC) and product title.

	1980	1985	1990	1994
GDP ($-1990 mil.)[1]	5,119	4,660	5,113	6,479
Per capita ($-1990)[1]	1,131	983	989	1,149
Manufacturing share (%) (current prices)[1]	15.0	16.4	18.6	22.6
Manufacturing				
Value added ($-1990 mil.)[1]	943	828	952	1,216
Industrial production index	100	88	101	129
Value added ($ mil.)	448	393	569	521
Gross output ($ mil.)	1,130	860	1,272	1,111
Employment (000)	39	25	26	48
Profitability (% of gross output)				
Intermediate input (%)	60	54	55	53
Wages and salaries inc. supplements (%)	15	12	10	13
Gross operating surplus	24	34	34	34
Productivity ($)				
Gross output per worker	28,857	34,129	46,893	22,960
Value added per worker	11,426	15,593	21,162	10,823
Average wage (inc. supplements)	4,376	3,991	5,012	3,060
Value added ($ mil.)				
311/2 Food products	78	55	90	83
313 Beverages	63	59	65	21
314 Tobacco products	26	29	39	26
321 Textiles	62	40	74	45
322 Wearing apparel	16	10	18	28
323 Leather and fur products	5	5	5	5
324 Footwear	13	1	2	5
331 Wood and wood products	1	—	1	—
332 Furniture and fixtures	3	4	5	6
341 Paper and paper products	40	24	16	22
342 Printing and publishing	8	8	16	27

	1980	1985	1990	1994
351 Industrial chemicals	4	7	19	15
352 Other chemical products	46	57	100	91
353 Petroleum refineries	14	20	43	60
354 Miscellaneous petroleum and coal products	2	—	2	3
355 Rubber products	4	3	4	5
356 Plastic products	13	15	16	20
361 Pottery, china and earthenware	—	—	—	—
362 Glass and glass products	—	—	—	—
369 Other non-metal mineral products	11	13	13	16
371 Iron and steel	9	7	3	3
372 Non ferrous metals	1	1	1	—
381 Metal products	10	12	8	11
382 Non-electrical machinery	6	7	1	2
383 Electrical machinery	9	12	21	19
384 Transport equipment	1	—	1	1
385 Professional and scientific equipment	—	1	1	3
390 Other manufacturing industries	4	2	4	4

FINANCE, ECONOMICS, & TRADE

Economic Indicators (22)

National product: GDP—purchasing power parity—$17.8 billion (1997 est.)

National product real growth rate: 4% (1997 est.)

National product per capita: $3,000 (1997 est.)

Inflation rate—consumer price index: 2% (1997)

Exchange Rates (24)

Exchange rates:

Salvadoran colones (C) per US$1 (end of period)

January 1998-1995	8.755
1994	8.750
1993	8.670

As of 1 June 1990, the rate is based on the average of the buying and selling rates, set on a weekly basis, for official receipts and payments, imports of petroleum, and coffee exports; prior to that date, a system of floating was in effect.

Top Import Origins (25)

$3.5 billion (c.i.f., 1997 est.)

Origins	%
United States	NA
Guatemala	NA
Mexico	NA
Panama	NA
Venezuela	NA
Japan	NA

NA stands for not available.

Balance of Payments (23)

	1991	1992	1993	1994	1995
Exports of goods (f.o.b.)	587	598	731	1,252	1,660
Imports of goods (f.o.b.)	−1,291	1,560	−1,766	−2,407	−3,184
Trade balance	−705	−962	−1,035	−1,155	−1,523
Services - debits	−474	−494	−524	−574	−630
Services - credits	341	409	437	423	442
Private transfers (net)	178	229	222	285	159
Government transfers (net)	492	710	823	1,004	1,230
Overall balance	−167	−109	−77	−18	−322

Top Export Destinations (26)

$1.96 billion (f.o.b., 1997 est.).

Destinations	%
United States	.NA
Guatemala	.NA
Germany	.NA
Costa Rica	.NA
Honduras	.NA

NA stands for not available.

Economic Aid (27)

Recipient: ODA, $763 million (1996). Note: US has committed $280 million in economic assistance to El Salvador for 1995-97 (excludes military aid).

Import Export Commodities (28)

Import Commodities	Export Commodities
Raw materials	Coffee
Consumer goods	Sugar
Capital goods	Shrimp
Fuels	Textiles

EQUATORIAL GUINEA

Republic of Equatorial Guinea
República de Guinea Ecuatorial

CAPITAL: Malabo (formerly Santa Isabel).

FLAG: The flag is a tricolor of green, white, and red horizontal stripes; a blue triangle joins them at the hoist. The arms in the center of the white stripe hold a cotton tree (the national symbol), six stars—one for each physical division of the country—and the motto ''Unidad, Justicia, Paz.''

ANTHEM: *Himno Nacional*, beginning ''Caminemos pisando la senda de nuestra inmensa felicidad'' (''Let us walk on the path of our immense happiness'').

MONETARY UNIT: Communauté Financière Africaine franc (CFA Fr), introduced in 1985, is a paper currency tied to the French franc at the rate of CFA Fr 100 = Fr 1. CFA Fr 1 = $0.00196 (or $1 = CFA Fr510.65). There are coins of 1, 2, 5, 10, 25, 50, 100, and 500 CFA francs and notes of 50, 100, 500, 1,000, 5,000, and 10,000 francs.

WEIGHTS AND MEASURES: The metric system is the legal standard.

HOLIDAYS: New Year's Day, 1 January; Independence Day, 5 March; Labor Day, 1 May; OAU Day, 25 May; President's Birthday, 5 June; Armed Forces Day, 3 August; Human Rights Day, 10 December; Christmas, 25 December. Movable Christian holidays include Good Friday and Easter Monday.

TIME: 1 PM = noon GMT.

LOCATION AND SIZE: Located on the west coast of Africa, Equatorial Guinea consists of a mainland enclave, Río Muni, and five inhabited islands: Bioko, Annobón, Corisco, and the two small Elobeys (known together as Islas Elobey—Elobey Chico and Elobey Grande). Comparatively, the area occupied by Equatorial Guinea is slightly larger than the state of Maryland. The total boundary length of Equatorial Guinea is 835 kilometers (519 miles). The capital city of Equatorial Guinea, Malabo, is located on the island of Bioko.

CLIMATE: Equatorial Guinea has a tropical climate with distinct wet and dry seasons. From June to August, Río Muni is dry and Bioko wet; from December to February, the reverse is true. The temperature at Malabo, Bioko, ranges from 16°C to 33°C (61–91°F).

INTRODUCTORY SURVEY

RECENT HISTORY

Equatorial Guinea became a province of Spain in 1958. On 12 October 1968, the colony became the independent Republic of Equatorial Guinea. On 23 August 1972, Francisco Macías Nguema was proclaimed president for life. Seven years later, he was overthrown in a military coup. Under the rule of Macías Nguema's nephew, Lieutenant-Colonel Teodoro Obiang Nguema Mbasogo, corruption continued to flourish, with political opponents and others imprisoned or put to death. He was elected head of state without opposition on 25 June 1989. Since 17 November 1991, Equatorial Guinea has officially had a constitutional democracy with multiparty elections. In reality, Obiang's Democratic Party of Equatorial Guinea (PDGE) controls the country.

GOVERNMENT

On 17 November 1991, a new constitution was adopted, and opposition parties sought official recognition in 1992. In the 21 November 1993 election, the PDGE (the ruling party) won sixty-eight of eighty seats, but the major opposition parties boycotted the election.

Judiciary

The court system includes a Supreme Court, military courts, and customary (traditional) courts. Under the 1991 constitution, the judiciary is not independent of the executive branch.

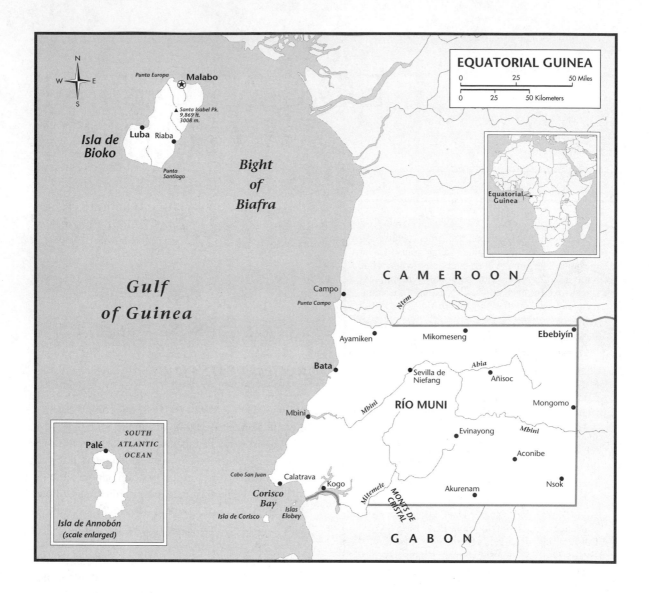

Political Parties

In 1979, the Democratic Party for Equatorial Guinea (PDGE) became the only legal party. In 1992, the government began to recognize other political parties, and there were thirteen legal opposition parties by mid-1993. In the 1993 elections, eight of the opposition parties boycotted the election, and the PDGE won sixty-eight of eighty seats. As of 1995, party membership was restricted to those who had lived continuously in Equatorial Guinea for five years.

DEFENSE

As of 1993, military personnel numbered 1,320—army, 1,100; navy, 120; and air force, 100.

ECONOMIC AFFAIRS

The agricultural sector supports 50% of the population. The country exports cocoa, coffee, and timber, and imports large quantities of foodstuffs. Production of oil began in 1991, and the exploration for additional reserves continues.

In 1994, France suddenly devalued the CFA franc by 50%. Prices for almost all imported goods soared. The devaluation encouraged people to buy goods that were made locally instead of imports. The devaluation stalled economic growth in 1994, but double digit growth rates returned in 1995 and 1996.

Public Finance

Equatorial Guinea made its first standby loan agreement with the IMF in 1985 and negotiated a structural adjustment agreement in 1988. Government problems with budget overruns and a continuing, structural imbalance of trade have frustrated IMF technicians, who stopped payments in 1990. Nonetheless, the government reduced the 1990 budget and enacted key portions of the structural adjustment program—import price liberalization, economic diversification, utility rate increases, clarification of property rights, and private sector stimulus. With these steps taken and with petroleum revenues increasing, the IMF restarted the blocked structural adjustment program in December 1991. By 1996, however, repeated human rights violations and the failure to enact economic reform led to the suspension of most foreign economic assistance.

The CIA estimates that, in 1993, government revenues totaled approximately $32.5 million and expenditures $35.9 million, including capital expenditures of $3 million. External debt totaled $268 million.

Income

In 1998, Equatorial Guinea's gross national product (GNP) was $647 million at current prices, or $1,500 per person. During 1985–95, the annual average inflation rate was 4.1%.

Industry

Equatorial Guinea's manufacturing sector is small. Two sawmills lead industrial production, followed by cement, bleach, and tuna canning plants.

Banking and Finance

The Bank of Issue of Equatorial Guinea was established on 12 October 1969 as the central bank. In January 1985, the country joined the franc zone, and the Bank of the Central African States (*Banque des États de l'Afrique Centrale*—BEAC) became its central bank. There are no securities exchanges.

Economic Development

In the 1990s, in conjunction with Spain, Equatorial Guinea is focusing on education, health, administrative reform, and economic infrastructures.

SOCIAL WELFARE

There is little provision for social welfare. The great majority of the population goes without safe drinking water, electricity, basic education, or minimal health care. Women have the same legal rights as men, but in practice face discrimination.

Healthcare

Residents of Equatorial Guinea have a life expectancy of 50 years. Major health problems are preventable diseases (mainly malaria), parasitic disease, upper respiratory infections, gastroenteritis, and complications of pregnancy.

Housing

No recent information is available.

EDUCATION

Education is free and compulsory from 6 to 14 years of age, and there are four years of secondary education. In 1993, 75,751 pupils attended primary schools and 16,616 attended secondary schools.

1999 KEY EVENTS TIMELINE

January

- President Obiang attends the swearing-in ceremony for Gabon's re-elected president, Omar Bongo.

March

- The ruling Democratic Party wins 75 out of 80 seats in the parliamentary election.

- The opposition charges massive electoral fraud in protest of their losses in the election.

April

- Equatorial Guinea participates in African trade talks with United States business leaders.

May

- The government protests a Spanish investigation into Equatorial Guinea's recent elections.

- The Bank of Central African States raises interest rates on the CFA franc.

September

- The first bidding round for offshore oil blocks is greeted with apathy.

ANALYSIS OF EVENTS: 1999

BUSINESS AND THE ECONOMY

In 1999 Equatorial Guinea continued the economic recovery which began four years earlier, when it became the first Spanish-speaking country to join the CFA franc zone, and also saw the inauguration of production at the offshore Zafiro oil field. By 1999, oil had replaced timber as the country's major export, and it accounted for approximately 70 percent of its GNP. Economic growth had risen dramatically in the intervening years as the investment climate improved. The Planning Ministry's three-year plan covering 1999–2001 emphasized continued rapid improvement of the country's infrastructure, including roads and other transportation projects, energy development, and telecommunications.

In April Equatorial Guinea was among the African nations that sent trade representatives to the United States to confer with top American oil industry and financial services executives at a three-day conference in Texas.

The Bank of Central African States raised interest rates on the CFA franc in May in response to falling commodity prices affecting the six member states of the CFA franc zone (which Equatorial Guinea had joined in 1995). Rates declined from 7.6 percent to 7 percent.

Equatorial Guinea held its first bidding round for exploration rights to offshore oil blocks in the spring of 1999. Observers attributed the general lack of interest shown by major oil companies to low world oil prices and also to charges of government favoritism toward Elf and Mobil, whom competitors claimed were assured from the outset of winning certain blocks.

GOVERNMENT AND POLITICS

In March 1999, Equatorial Guinea held its second multiparty election since the dictatorship of Francisco Macias Nguema ended in 1979. Nearly 700 candidates from 13 parties contested 80 seats in the nation's legislature. The resulting vote—in which 75 of the seats were won by candidates of the ruling Partido Democratico de Guinea Ecuatorial (PDGE)—was greeted with mixed reactions. Some observers declared the polling free and fair and termed it an important step toward true multiparty democracy for a country still recovering from one of Africa's most brutal dictatorships. However, critics were dissatisfied with the wide margin maintained by the dominant party, and opposition politicians contested the results, charging massive electoral fraud and calling for an annulment of the vote. The five opposition politicians elected to the legislature (all belonged to either the Popular Union or the Convergence for Social Democracy) refused to take their seats at the first meeting of the new parliament. On March 27 it was reported that dozens of Popular Union members had been arrested near the Cameroon border by security forces.

Spain, Equatorial Guinea's former colonial ruler, officially voiced doubts about the legitimacy of the election and announced that it wanted to send a delegation to investigate the situation. The government of Equatorial Guinea heatedly rejected the Spanish initiative, which it labeled as an unacceptable intervention into its domestic affairs, and repeated its assertions that there had been no irregularities in the voting.

In January, President Obiang was one of seven African heads of state present at the inauguration of re-elected president Omar Bongo in Gabon.

CULTURE AND SOCIETY

In 1999, Equatorial Guinea's capital city of Malabo displayed a renewed vibrancy thanks to the economic revival spearheaded by offshore oil production. Foreign oil workers from a variety of countries added to the growing level of activity in the city, which was also undergoing major infrastructure improvements. However, some observers questioned whether the majority of the nation's population would realize any substantial benefit from its new-found oil wealth, and whether the economic gulf between the rich and the poor would narrow. Critics of the government charged that oil industry profits were being funneled to President Obiang, his political associates, and members of his clan, which had now ruled Equatorial Guinea for three decades. Continuing human rights abuses toward the government's opponents were also alleged.

In March, Equatorial Guinea was one of five central African nations to sign the Yaounde declaration, a measure designed to protect and conserve large areas of tropical rainforest in the Congo Basin. In signing the agreement, the leaders of these nations agreed to adopt a variety of measures mandated by the World Wildlife Federation (WWF), including the establishment of new protected areas and forest reserves and the adoption of animal welfare measures.

Also in March, the only passenger plane operated by Equatorial Guinea's national airline, EGA, crashed during takeoff from the city of Bata. All thirty-two passengers were unharmed, but two crew members were injured in the crash, which occurred after the plane struck some trees.

DIRECTORY

CENTRAL GOVERNMENT

Head of State

President
Teodoro Obiang Nguema Mbasogo, Office of the President

Prime Minister and Head of Government
Serafin Seriche Dougan, Office of the Prime Minister

First Deputy Prime Minister
Miguel Oyono Ndong, Office of the Prime Minister

Deputy Prime Minister
Demetrio Elo Ndong, Office of the Prime Minister

Ministers

Minister Secretary General of the Government
Francisco Pascual Eyegue Obama Asue, Ministry of Secretary General of the Government

Minister Political Adviser to the Government
Demetrio Elo Ndong Ngefumu, Ministry of Political Adviser to the Government

Minister of Economy and Commerce
Marcelino Nguema Onguene, Ministry of Economy and Commerce

Minister of Planning and International Corporation
Anatolio Ndong Mba, Ministry of Planning and International Corporation

Minister of Interior and Local Corporations
Demetrio Elo Ndong, Ministry of Interior and Local Corporations

Minister of State for Missions
Alejandro Evuna Owono Asangono, Ministry of State for Missions

Minister of Relations with Assemblies and Legal Matters
Antonio Fernando Nve Ngu, Ministry of Relations with Assemblies and Legal Matters

Minister of Special Duties
Alejandro Evuna Owono Asangono, Ministry of Special Duties

Minister of Transport and Communication
Marcelino Oyono Ntutumu, Ministry of Transport and Communication

Minister of Agriculture, Fisheries, and Animal Husbandry
Constantine Eko Nsue, Ministry of Agriculture, Fisheries, and Animal Husbandry

Minister of Civil Service and Administrative Reforms
Fernando Mabale Mba, Ministry of Civil Service and Administrative Reforms

Minister of Culture, Tourism, and Francophone Affairs
Augustin Nse Nfumu, Ministry of Culture, Tourism, and Francophone Affairs

Minister of Economic Affairs and Finance
Baltasar Engonga Edjo, Ministry of Economic Affairs and Finance

Minister of Education, Science, and Francophone Affairs
Santiago Ngua Nfumu, Ministry of Education, Science, and Francophone Affairs

Minister of Employment and Social Security
Constantino Congue, Ministry of Employment and Social Security

Minister of Foreign Affairs and International Corporation
Santiago Nsobeya Efuman, Ministry of Foreign Affairs and International Corporation

Minister of Forestry and Environment
Teodoro Nguema Obiang, Ministry of Forestry and Environment

Minister of Health and Social Welfare
Juan Antonio Ntutumu, Ministry of Health and Social Welfare

Minister of Industry, Commerce, and Small and Medium Enterprises
Vidal Djoni Becoba, Ministry of Industry, Commerce, and Small and Medium Enterprises

Minister of Information, Tourism, and Culture
Lucas Nguema Esono, Ministry of Information, Tourism, and Culture

Minister of Justice and Religion
Ruben Maye Nsue, Ministry of Justice and Religion

Minister of Labor and Social Promotion
Ernesto Maria Cayetano Toherida, Ministry of Labor and Social Promotion

Minister of Mines and Energy
Cristobal Menana Ela, Ministry of Mines and Energy

Minister of Planning
Antonio Fernando Nve Ngu, Ministry of Planning

Minister of Public Works, Housing, and Urban Affairs
Florentino Nkogo Ndong, Ministry of Public Works, Housing, and Urban Affairs

Minister of Social Affairs and Women's Development
Margarita Alene, Ministry of Social Affairs and Women's Development

Minister of Territorial Administration and Local Government
Julio Ndong Ela Mangue, Ministry of Territorial Administration and Local Government

Minister of Youth and Sports
Ignacio Milam Ntang, Ministry of Youth and Sports

POLITICAL ORGANIZATIONS
Convergence for Social Democracy
TITLE: President
NAME: Santiago Obama Ndong

Partido Democratico Guinea Ecuatorial (Democratic Party for Equatorial Guinea)
TITLE: Leader
NAME: Teodoro Obiang Nguema Mbasogo

Union Democratico y Social (Democratic and Social Union)
TITLE: General Secretary
NAME: Camelo Modu

Popular Union
TITLE: President

NAME: Juan Bitui

Convencion Social Democratica y Popular (Social Democratic and Popular Convergence)
TITLE: General Secretary
NAME: Secundino Oyono Agueng Ada

DIPLOMATIC REPRESENTATION
Embassies in Equatorial Guinea

Cameroon
37 Calle Rey Boncoro, Apdo 292, Malabo, Equatorial Guinea

France
Carreterra del Aeropuerto, Apdo 326, Malabo, Equatorial Guinea

Gabon
Apdo 648, Douala, Malabo, Equatorial Guinea

Spain
Parque de las Avenidas de Africa, Malabo, Equatorial Guinea

JUDICIAL SYSTEM
Supreme Court of Justice
FAX: +240 09 4361

FURTHER READING
Articles
Akanni, Fred. "Why Equatorial Guinea's Bid Round Suffered from Apathy." *Offshore* (September 1999): 22.

"Brave New World: Old Revenue Brings Changes." *Institutional Investor International Edition* (August 1999): 2S2.

"Economy: Turning the Corner." *Institutional Investor International Edition* (August 1999): 2S5.

Young, Eric. "Equatorial Guinea." Africana: *The Encyclopedia of the African and African American Experience*. Edited by Kwame Anthony Appiah and Henry Louis Gates, Jr. New York: Basic Books, 1999.

Books
Klitgaard, Robert E. *Tropical Gangsters*. New York: Basic Books, 1990.

Sundiata, I. K. *Equatorial Guinea: Colonialism, State Terror, and the Search for Stability.* Boulder: Westview Press, 1990.

Internet

Africaonline. Available Online @ http://www.africaonline.com (October 28, 1999).

Africa News Online. Available Online @ http://www.africanews.org/west/stories/1999_feat1.html (October 28, 1999).

Integrated Regional Information Network (IRIN). Available Online @ http://www.reliefweb.int/IRIN (October 28, 1999).

EQUATORIAL GUINEA: STATISTICAL DATA

For sources and notes see "Sources of Statistics" in the front of each volume.

GEOGRAPHY

Geography (1)

Area:

Total: 28,050 sq km.

Land: 28,050 sq km.

Water: 0 sq km.

Area—comparative: slightly smaller than Maryland.

Land boundaries:

Total: 539 km.

Border countries: Cameroon 189 km, Gabon 350 km.

Coastline: 296 km.

Climate: tropical; always hot, humid.

Terrain: coastal plains rise to interior hills; islands are volcanic.

Natural resources: timber, petroleum, small unexploited deposits of gold, manganese, uranium.

Land use:

Arable land: 5%

Permanent crops: 4%

Permanent pastures: 4%

Forests and woodland: 46%

Other: 41% (1993 est.).

HUMAN FACTORS

Demographics (2A)

	1990	1995	1998	2000	2010	2020	2030	2040	2050
Population	369.0	420.3	454.0	477.8	614.8	782.8	974.4	1,181.4	1,393.6
Net migration rate (per 1,000 population)	NA	NA	NA	NA	NA	NA	NA	NA	NA
Births	NA	NA	NA	NA	NA	NA	NA	NA	NA
Deaths	NA	NA	NA	NA	NA	NA	NA	NA	NA
Life expectancy - males	48.3	50.4	51.6	52.5	56.6	60.5	64.2	67.5	70.3
Life expectancy - females	52.2	54.8	56.3	57.4	62.4	67.1	71.3	74.8	77.7
Birth rate (per 1,000)	42.5	40.2	38.9	38.1	34.8	31.0	27.0	23.7	20.9
Death rate (per 1,000)	16.2	14.4	13.3	12.6	9.9	7.8	6.4	5.8	5.7
Women of reproductive age (15-49 yrs.)	87.7	98.5	106.6	112.8	151.5	196.9	252.6	310.8	365.7
of which are currently married	NA	NA	NA	NA	NA	NA	NA	NA	NA
Fertility rate	5.5	5.2	5.1	4.9	4.3	3.8	3.3	2.9	2.6

Except as noted, values for vital statistics are in thousands; life expectancy is in years.

Infants and Malnutrition (5)

Under-5 mortality rate (1997) 172

% of infants with low birthweight (1990-97) . . . . . .NA

Births attended by skilled health staff % of total[a] . . .NA

% fully immunized (1995-97)

TB 99

DPT 81

Polio 81

Measles 82

Prevalence of child malnutrition under age 5
(1992-97)[b] . . . . .NA

Ethnic Division (6)

Bioko (primarily Bubi, some Fernandinos), Rio Muni (primarily Fang), Europeans less than 1,000, mostly Spanish.

Religions (7)

Nominally Christian and predominantly Roman Catholic, pagan practices.

Languages (8)

Spanish (official), French (official), pidgin English, Fang, Bubi, Ibo.

EDUCATION

Literacy Rates (11A)

In thousands and percent[1]	1990	1995	2000	2010
Illiterate population (15+ yrs.)	54	49	43	32
Literacy rate - total adult pop. (%)	73.2	78.5	83.3	90.6
Literacy rate - males (%)	86.3	89.6	92.3	95.8
Literacy rate - females (%)	60.8	68.1	74.7	85.7

GOVERNMENT & LAW

Political Parties (12)

House of Representatives	No. of seats
Democratic Party for Equatorial Guinea (PDGE)	68
Convergence Party for Social Democracy (CPDS)	6
Democratic Social Union (UDS)	5
Liberal Democratic Convention (CLD)	1

Government Budget (13B)

Revenues . . . .$47 million

Expenditures . . . .$43 million

Capital expenditures . . . .$7 million

Data for 1996 est.

LABOR FORCE

Unemployment Rate (17)

Rate not available.

PRODUCTION SECTOR

Electric Energy (18)

Capacity . . . . .5,000 kW (1995)

Production . . . . .20 million kWh (1995)

Consumption per capita . . . . .48 kWh (1995)

Transportation (19)

Highways:

total: 2,820 km

paved: 0 km

unpaved: 2,820 km (1995 est.)

Merchant marine:

total: 19 ships (1,000 GRT or over) totaling 66,766 GRT/84,780 DWT ships by type: bulk 1, cargo 16, passenger 1, passenger-cargo 1 (1997 est.)

Airports: 3 (1997 est.)

Airports—with paved runways:

total: 2

2,438 to 3,047 m: 1

1,524 to 2,437 m: 1 (1997 est.)

Airports—with unpaved runways:

total: 1

under 914 m: 1 (1997 est.)

Top Agricultural Products (20)

Coffee, cocoa, rice, yams, cassava (tapioca), bananas, palm oil nuts, manioc; livestock; timber.

FINANCE, ECONOMICS, & TRADE

Economic Indicators (22)

National product: GDP—purchasing power parity—$660 million (1997 est.)

National product real growth rate: NA%

National product per capita: $1,500 (1997 est.)

Inflation rate—consumer price index: 6% (1996 est.)

GOVERNMENT & LAW

Military Affairs (14B)

	1990	1991	1992	1993	1994	1995
Military expenditures						
Current dollars (mil.)	NA	NA	NA	NA	3	2
1995 constant dollars (mil.)	NA	NA	NA	NA	3	2
Armed forces (000)	1	1	1	1	1	1
Gross national product (GNP)						
Current dollars (mil.)	95	98	114	126	131	150
1995 constant dollars (mil.)	109	108	122	132	135	150
Central government expenditures (CGE)						
1995 constant dollars (mil.)	25	26[e]	30[e]	NA	NA	NA
People (mil.)	.4	.4	.4	.4	.4	.4
Military expenditure as % of GNP	NA	NA	NA	NA	2.2	1.6
Military expenditure as % of CGE	NA	NA	NA	NA	NA	NA
Military expenditure per capita (1995 $)	NA	NA	NA	NA	7	6
Armed forces per 1,000 people (soldiers)	2.7	2.6	2.6	2.5	2.4	3.1
GNP per capita (1995 $)	297	286	314	330	329	357
Arms imports[6]						
Current dollars (mil.)	0	0	0	0	0	0
1995 constant dollars (mil.)	0	0	0	0	0	0
Arms exports[6]						
Current dollars (mil.)	0	0	0	0	0	0
1995 constant dollars (mil.)	0	0	0	0	0	0
Total imports[7]						
Current dollars (mil.)	61	117	93	60	37	50
1995 constant dollars (mil.)	70	129	100	63	38	50
Total exports[7]						
Current dollars (mil.)	62	37	50	57	62	86
1995 constant dollars (mil.)	71	41	54	60	64	86
Arms as percent of total imports[8]	0	0	0	0	0	0
Arms as percent of total exports[8]	0	0	0	0	0	0

MANUFACTURING SECTOR

GDP & Manufacturing Summary (21)

	1980	1985	1990	1992	1993	1994
Gross Domestic Product						
Millions of 1990 dollars	117	131	145	171	183	199
Growth rate in percent	−9.94	6.55	4.74	13.72	7.35	8.90
Per capita (in 1990 dollars)	541.1	419.4	412.2	462.5	483.4	512.8
Manufacturing Value Added						
Millions of 1990 dollars	2	3	2	2	2	2
Growth rate in percent	−9.19	94.14	1.85	−0.22	11.28	2.47
Manufacturing share in percent of current prices	1.6	1.9	1.5	10.2	9.9	NA

FINANCE, ECONOMICS, & TRADE

Balance of Payments (23)

	1992	1993	1994	1995	1996
Exports of goods (f.o.b.)	50	61	62	90	175
Imports of goods (f.o.b.)	−56	−51	−37	−121	−292
Trade balance	−6	10	25	−31	−117
Services - debits	−40	−48	−33	−101	−230
Services - credits	9	9	3	4	5
Private transfers (net)	34	38	6	7	4
Government transfers (net)	−7	−6	−2	−3	−7
Overall balance	−11	3	−0	−123	−344

Exchange Rates (24)

Exchange rates:

CFA francs (CFAF) per US$1

January 1998	608.36
1997	583.67
1996	511.55
1995	499.15
1994	555.20
1993	283.16

Beginning 12 January 1994, the CFA franc was devalued to CFAF 100 per French franc from CFAF 50 at which it had been fixed since 1948.

Top Import Origins (25)

$248 million (c.i.f., 1996 est.)

Origins	%
Cameroon	40
Spain	18
France	14
United States	8

Top Export Destinations (26)

$197 million (f.o.b., 1996 est.).

Destinations	%
United States	34
Japan	17
Spain	13
China	13
Nigeria	NA

NA stands for not available.

Economic Aid (27)

Recipient: ODA, $NA. NA stands for not available.

Import Export Commodities (28)

Import Commodities	Export Commodities
Petroleum	Petroleum
Food	Timber
Beverages	Cocoa
Clothing	
Machinery	

ERITREA

State of Eritrea
Hagere Ertra

INTRODUCTORY SURVEY

RECENT HISTORY

In April 1941, British Commonwealth forces captured Eritrea from its Italian colonizers. After a decade of British rule, Eritrea was federated with neighboring Ethiopia in 1952, following a vote in the United Nations (UN). In September 1961, the Eritrean Liberation Front (ELF) launched the armed struggle for Eritrean independence. However, Ethiopia formally annexed Eritrea in 1962. After Emperor Haile Selassie was overthrown in 1974, Ethiopia's Marxist military dictatorship stepped up its campaign against the Eritreans. Between 1978 and 1981, the Eritrean People's Liberation Front (EPLF) fought and defeated the Eritrean Liberation Front (ELF) in a civil war. From 1981 until the end of the war in 1991, the EPLF continued to fight for Eritrean self-determination.

In May 1991, the EPLF captured the last Ethiopian outposts in Eritrea and formed a National Assembly, which elected Isaias Afwerki president of the provisional government. In July, the EPLF and the transitional Ethiopian government that had toppled the Mengistu regime issued a charter calling for Eritrean self-determination and mutual accommodation between the two nations. On 23–25 April 1993, 98.5% of the 1.2 million registered voters participated in a referendum on independence from Ethiopia. The UN certified the results, and on 24 May 1993, Eritrea became Africa's fifty-second independent state. Four days later, it was admitted to the United Nations and the Organization of African Unity (OAU).

In June 1998, heavy fighting erupted along the border with Ethiopia, even though the two countries had been on good terms with each other since Eritrea's independence in 1993. The battle began as a minor territorial dispute in two areas that both countries had claimed. The fighting escalated with Ethiopia conducting an air strike on the Red Sea port of Assab. The two sides agreed to stop any

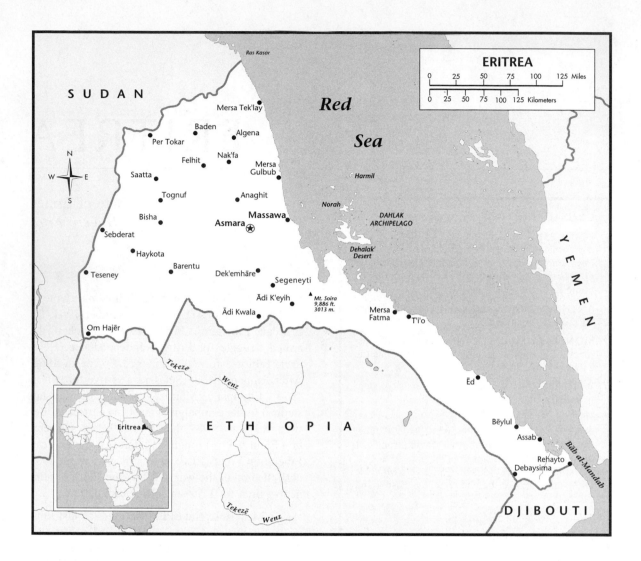

further air strikes, but fighting along the border continued.

GOVERNMENT

Upon official independence, a National Assembly was formed, consisting of the Central Committee of the EPLF and sixty other individuals, with ten seats reserved for women. The Constitutional Commission, appointed by the National Assembly in March 1994, developed a draft constitution in 1996. At the time of independence, the National Assembly set a deadline of May 1998 for election of a new government.

Judiciary

The court system consists of district courts, courts of appeals comprising five judges, and military courts that handle crimes committed by members of the military. Traditional courts play a major role in rural areas, where village elders determine property and family disputes under customary law or in the case of Muslims, the Koran.

Political Parties

The Eritrean Liberation Front (ELF) launched the modern phase of Eritrea's war of self-determination in September 1961. In 1970, the Eritrean People's Liberation Front (EPLF) joined the war against Ethiopia. From 1981 to 1991, only the EPLF was operating in Eritrea. At its February 1994 Congress, the EPLF was reformed as the People's Front for Democracy and Justice (PFDJ). The PFDJ elected an Executive Council of seventy-five members, and called on the government to increase the number of non-PFDJ members in the National Assembly to seventy-five.

DEFENSE

The process of demobilizing about 50–60% of the army began in July 1993. Following the second phase of demobilization in 1994, military forces stood at 48,000 soldiers, with expenditures estimated at $40 million in 1995.

ECONOMIC AFFAIRS

After years of armed struggle against the Ethiopian government, Eritrea is still largely dependent on food aid. Reversing the policies of Ethiopia's military regime, the post-independence government has denationalized housing and is committed to denationalization of business and services. The real growth rate of the gross domestic product (GDP) in 1995 was about 10%.

Public Finance

After independence, the state retained control over land, mineral resources, and infrastructure. Massive infusions of foreign aid and investment are needed to restore the infrastructure and services and to develop private sector growth. Membership into the IBRD and IMF were to have been approved in 1994.

Income

In 1998, Eritrea's gross national product (GNP) was $776 million, or $200 per person.

Industry

Ethiopia systematically dismantled the Eritrean industrial sector during the protracted civil war. The government of Eritrea is currently managing industries previously owned by the Ethiopian regime. Industry contributed about 18% to the gross domestic product (GDP) in 1995.

Banking and Finance

The Commercial Bank of Eritrea (CBE) functions as the country's central bank. Since Eritrea's independence from Ethiopia, the CBE has focused on establishing a national network and on offering international banking and credit. In the mid-1990s the bank suffered from excess liquidity, but several banking acts issued by the government sought to resolve that matter, as well as initiate the management of the national currency.

SOCIAL WELFARE

During its struggle for independence, Eritrea created an elaborate and effective system of social services. It launched a literacy program, a health care system (including hospitals), and a food distribution network. The government has allocated a significant budget for construction of housing, schools, and clinics to aid homeless returning refugees.

Healthcare

Average life expectancy is 55 years. Government estimates report that there is 1 doctor for every 28,000 people; other estimates report 1 doctor for every 48,000 people.

Housing

Thousands of refugees remain homeless after returning to Eritrea, and the government has placed a high priority on providing funding for housing construction.

EDUCATION

Primary school enrollment is reported to be 42% of school-age children.

1999 KEY EVENTS TIMELINE

February

- War resumes between Eritrea and Ethiopia in the contested territory of Badme, a conflict which began in May 1998.

- Eritrea's Ambassador is expelled from Ethiopia.

March

- A three-day battle with Ethiopia ends in the Badme region, with up to 40,000 killed or wounded.

- Eritrea agrees to Organization of African Unity (OAU) peace proposals and a cease-fire, but Ethiopia does not.

April

- Eritrea claims to have shot down an Ethiopian MiG-23.

June

- The United Nations Security Council demands an end to fighting, and to the sale of arms and munitions to Ethiopia and Eritrea.

July

- Eritrea and Ethiopia sign an updated peace plan formulated at the OAU head of state and government summit in Algiers, calling for Eritrea's withdrawal from Badme and a cease-fire.

August

- Eritrean President Isaias Afwerki visits Washington, D.C. in an unofficial visit to discuss the conflict.

October

- Up to 1,300 Eritrean nationals are deported voluntarily in buses crossing the Ethiopian war zone, violating international conventions.

December

- The Commercial Bank of Ethiopia liquidates assets of tens of thousands of Eritreans who left Ethiopia for Eritrea to escape the violent border conflicts between the two nations.

- The European Union appoints Italian Rino Serri to help Ethiopia and Eritrea resolve their 18-months violent conflict and to implement the peace plan prepared by the Organization of African Unity.

ANALYSIS OF EVENTS: 1999

BUSINESS AND THE ECONOMY

Since war broke out between Eritrea and Ethiopia in May 1998, the Eritrean economy has experienced a downturn for several reasons. It is estimated that the country has spent about one million a day on the war, including the purchase of T-55 tanks from Bulgaria, SU-27 fighter bombers from Russia, weapons from Djibouti and MiG-29 fighters from the Ukraine. In the capital of Asmara, there is a massive labor shortage because tens of thousands of men and women have been killed or wounded over the year, and many more are still fighting on the front. Little to no foreign investment has entered the country since the conflict began, and, since the enemy country used to be Eritrea's main export market for refined oil, there is little income. Ethiopia has also withdrawn its business from the Red Sea port of Assab, diverting its coffee trade through Djibouti, costing Eritrea millions.

On top of the economic problems at home, some 60,000 of Eritrea's nationals living in Ethiopia have been expelled, sometimes willingly, back to Eritrea, leaving behind what President Isaias Afwerki claims to be $800 million in property. The roots of the present war can be traced in part to economic considerations. In 1997, Eritrea introduced its own currency, the Nacfa, to replace the Ethiopian Birr. This raised fears in Ethiopia that its people were destined to provide a cheap labor force for Eritrean industry and seaside trade. There were also suspicions that Eritrean businesses were smuggling Ethiopian coffee through Assab, and that the country was selling oil back to Ethiopia at inflated prices. Tensions grew in the disputed territory of Badme in 1998, because maps drawn by Italian colonists in the nineteenth century did not match up with Ethiopian maps published in 1997 for that region. The original demarcation did not reflect the ethnic population distribution in the first place, making the border rather arbitrary.

GOVERNMENT AND POLITICS

Eritrea fought a 31-year war for independence from Italy, colonization, and a Soviet puppet government, which ended in 1993. Eritrea and Ethiopian troops fought side by side to defeat the Soviet-backed army of Mengistu Haile Mariam in 1991, which successfully ended the possibility of a foreign dictatorship on Eritrean and Ethiopian soil. Those who fought in this war, The Eritrean People's Liberation Front (EPLF,) went on to create the Eritrean government, while the Tigray People's Liberation Front (TPLF) ruled Ethiopia. President Isaias Afwerki of Eritrea and Prime Minister Meles Zenawi of Ethiopia not only fought together, but are related to each other. The current border skirmish is over a barren piece of land in Badme, which symbolizes the strenuous relations between the 3.5 million Eritreans and 60 million Ethiopians.

In May 1998, Eritrea captured Badme in a move that was meant to show Eritrean independence. By February 1999, however, Ethiopia had claimed victory on the same soil, and the fighting continues. Tens of thousands have died on both sides in what is called Africa's first high-tech war. The UN, and OAU have drafted an eleven-point peace plan which calls for each side to leave land occupied after May 6th, 1998, including Eritrea's claim on Badme. But Eritrea also claims that Ethiopia invaded Badme before May 6th. A cease-fire and UN deployment of peacekeepers would ensue, but while Eritrea has signed the agreement, the country has changed some of the rules, and Ethiopia refuses to bargain. In a sign that Ethiopia will not give up its claim on the Badme region, the country signed a security accord with Yemen in October which strengthens the country militarily, and geographically surrounds Eritrea. If Eritrea wishes to continue as an independent nation, it may be necessary to give up Badme, but this may also prove the country's weakness to potential invaders.

CULTURE AND SOCIETY

The state of post-colonial countries in Africa is one of almost continual flare-ups of violence that lead to war and civil war. The arbitrary creation of colonial maps is partly to blame for ethnic land disputes, and in the case of Eritrea, definitely plays a part in the conflict. There is also, in the northeastern portion of Africa, a delicate balance between Christian and Muslim influences which is exacerbated by outside influences. The Eritrean and Ethiopian government's relationships with Muslim terrorist leaders in the Middle East make the U.S. government hesitant to provide aid and negotiation for peace in the region. The Eritrean society is geared for war, the production of arms and supplies for troops, and is eager to accept foreign aid to protect it's borders, but the trade-off may lose the country more sovereignty and cultural independence than it bargains for.

DIRECTORY

CENTRAL GOVERNMENT

Head of State

President
Isaias Afwerki, Office of the President
PHONE: +291 119701
FAX: +291 125123

Ministers

Minister of State
Berhane Abrehe, Ministry of State
PHONE: +291 117675
FAX: +291 126422

Minister of Agriculture
Arefaine Berhe, Ministry of Agriculture
PHONE: +291 181499
FAX: +291 181415

Minister of Defense
Sebhat Efrem, Ministry of Defense
PHONE: +291 201857
FAX: +291 124920

Minister of Education
Osman Saleh, Ministry of Education
PHONE: +291 116644
FAX: +291 118351

Minister of Energy and Mines
Tesfai Gebreselaise, Ministry of Energy and Mines
PHONE: +291 116872

FAX: +291 127652

Minister of Finance
Wolday Fitur, Ministry of Finance
PHONE: +291 118131
FAX: +291 127947

Minister of Fisheries
Petros Solomon, Ministry of Fisheries
PHONE: +291 552010
FAX: +291 552971

Minister of Foreign Affairs
Haile Weldensae, Ministry of Foreign Affairs
PHONE: +291 127108
FAX: +291 125058

Minister of Health
Saleh Meky, Ministry of Health
PHONE: +291 117549
FAX: +291 122899

Minister of Information
Beraki Gebreselassie, Ministry of Information
PHONE: +291 117111
FAX: +291 124847

Minister of Justice
Fawzia Hashim, Ministry of Justice
PHONE: +291 117603
FAX: +291 126985

Minister of Labor and Human Welfare
Askalu Menkorious, Ministry of Labor and Human Welfare
PHONE: +291 151986
FAX: +291 151749

Minister of Land, Water and Environment
Woldemicahel Gebremariam, Ministry of Land, Water and Environment
PHONE: +291 118021
FAX: +291 123285

Minister of Local Governments
Mahmud Ahmed Sherifo, Ministry of Local Governments
PHONE: +291 114254
FAX: +291 126930

Minister of Public Works
Abraha Asfaha, Ministry of Public Works
PHONE: +291 202763
FAX: +291 120661

Minister of Tourism
Ahmed Haj Ali, Ministry of Tourism
PHONE: +291 120073
FAX: +291 126949

Minister of Trade and Industry

Ali Said, Ministry of Trade and Industry
PHONE: +291 118386
FAX: +291 120586

Minister of Transportation and Communication

Saleh Kekia, Ministry of Transportation and Communication
PHONE: +291 114036
FAX: +291 127048

POLITICAL ORGANIZATIONS

People's Front for Democracy and Justice

PHONE: +291 117398
FAX: +291 120542
NAME: Alamin Mohammed Said

DIPLOMATIC REPRESENTATION

Embassies in Eritrea

Israel

Wodejio Ali Str. 10, PO Box 5600, Asmara, Eritrea
PHONE: +291 (1) 120137
FAX: +291 (1) 120187

United Kingdom

Mitchell Cotts Building, Emperor Yohannes Avenue 54, Asmara, Eritrea
PHONE: +291 (4) 120145
FAX: +291 (4) 120104

United States

Franklin Roosevelt Street, PO Box 211, Asmara, Eritrea
PHONE: +291 (1) 120004
FAX: +291 (1) 127584

JUDICIAL SYSTEM

High Court

PHONE: +291 119799
FAX: + 291 201828

FURTHER READING

Articles

"Africa's Forgotten War." *The Economist* (May 8, 1999): 41–43.

"Carnage on the Plain." *The Economist* (April 17, 1999): 50.

"Endless Wars." *Time International* (September 6, 1999): 36.

"Ethiopia, Eritrea Interpret Peace Deal Differently." CNN, 15 July 1999.

"Forgotten War: Tens of Thousands Lose Lives in Ethiopia-Eritrea Conflict." CNN, 19 June 1999.

"Heavy Fighting Breaks Out Between Eritrea, Ethiopia." CNN, 6 February 1999.

"Lethal Punch-Up." *The Economist* (September 25, 1999): 55–56.

"Trench Warfare." *The Economist* (March 13, 1999): 58.

Useem, Andrea and David Gough. "On Africa's Horn, 'The Stupidest War.'" *World Press Review* (June 1999): 12.

"War it Is." *The Economist* (February 13, 1999): 44.

Books

Iyob, Arwat. *Blankets of Sand: Poems of War and Exile*. Lawrenceville, NJ: Red Sea Press, 1999.

Stewart, Julia. *Eccentric Graces: Eritrea and Ethiopia Through the Eyes of a Traveler*. Lawrenceville, NJ: Red Sea Press, 1999.

Vestal, Theodore M. *Ethiopia: A Post-Cold War African State*. Westport, CN: Praeger, 1999.

Internet

Africaonline. Available Online @ http://www.africaonline.com. (October 28, 1999).

Africa News Online. Available Online @ http://www.africanews.org/west/stories/1999_feat1.html. (October 28, 1999).

Eritrea-Ethiopia Conflict Information Site. Available Online @ http://denden.com/conflict/ (November 3, 1999).

Eritrea Network Information Center. Available Online @ http://www.eritrea.org. (November 3, 1999).

Integrated Regional Information Network (IRIN). Available Online @ http://www.reliefweb.int/IRIN. (October 28, 1999).

ERITREA: STATISTICAL DATA

For sources and notes see "Sources of Statistics" in the front of each volume.

GEOGRAPHY

Geography (1)

Area:

Total: 121,320 sq km.

Land: 121,320 sq km.

Water: 0 sq km.

Area—comparative: slightly larger than Pennsylvania.

Land boundaries:

Total: 1,630 km.

Border countries: Djibouti 113 km, Ethiopia 912 km, Sudan 605 km.

Coastline: 2,234 km total; mainland on Red Sea 1,151 km, islands in Red Sea 1,083 km.

Climate: hot, dry desert strip along Red Sea coast; cooler and wetter in the central highlands (up to 61 cm of rainfall annually); semiarid in western hills and lowlands; rainfall heaviest during June-September except on coastal desert.

Terrain: dominated by extension of Ethiopian north-south trending highlands, descending on the east to a coastal desert plain, on the northwest to hilly terrain and on the southwest to flat-to-rolling plains.

Natural resources: gold, potash, zinc, copper, salt, probably oil and natural gas (petroleum geologists are prospecting for it), fish.

Land use:

Arable land: 12%

Permanent crops: 1%

Permanent pastures: 48%

Forests and woodland: 20%

Other: 19% (1993 est.).

HUMAN FACTORS

Demographics (2A)

	1990	1995	1998	2000	2010	2020	2030	2040	2050
Population	2,945.1	3,463.6	3,842.4	4,142.5	5,737.3	7,470.8	9,468.6	11,618.2	13,735.8
Net migration rate (per 1,000 population)	NA	NA	NA	NA	NA	NA	NA	NA	NA
Births	NA	NA	NA	NA	NA	NA	NA	NA	NA
Deaths	NA	NA	NA	NA	NA	NA	NA	NA	NA
Life expectancy - males	49.9	51.9	53.2	54.0	58.1	62.0	65.5	68.6	71.3
Life expectancy - females	54.0	56.2	57.5	58.4	62.6	66.7	70.3	73.5	76.2
Birth rate (per 1,000)	40.1	41.8	42.5	42.7	37.7	32.5	28.6	24.1	20.6
Death rate (per 1,000)	14.9	13.3	12.6	12.1	9.5	7.5	6.3	5.6	5.6
Women of reproductive age (15-49 yrs.)	648.8	802.5	897.3	964.5	1,317.2	1,826.5	2,383.3	3,024.9	3,664.7
of which are currently married	NA	NA	NA	NA	NA	NA	NA	NA	NA
Fertility rate	6.2	6.1	6.0	5.9	5.2	4.4	3.5	2.9	2.5

Except as noted, values for vital statistics are in thousands; life expectancy is in years.

Health Personnel (3)

Total health expenditure as a percentage of GDP, 1990-1997[a]

Public sector 1.1

Private sector 0.9

Total[b] 2.0

Health expenditure per capita in U.S. dollars, 1990-1997[a]

Purchasing power parity . . . . .NA

Total . . . . .NA

Availability of health care facilities per 100,000 people

Hospital beds 1990-1997[a] . . . . .NA

Doctors 1993[c] 2

Nurses 1993[c] . . . . .NA

Health Indicators (4)

Life expectancy at birth

1980 44

1997 51

Daily per capita supply of calories (1996) 1,585

Total fertility rate births per woman (1997) 5.8

Maternal mortality ratio per 100,000 live births
(1990-97) . . . . .1,000[c]

Safe water % of population with access (1995) 7

Sanitation % of population with access (1995) . . . .

Consumption of iodized salt % of households
(1992-98)[a] 80

Smoking prevalence

Male % of adults (1985-95)[a] . . . .

Female % of adults (1985-95)[a] . . . .

Tuberculosis incidence per 100,000 people
(1997) 227

Adult HIV prevalence % of population ages
15-49 (1997) 3.17

Infants and Malnutrition (5)

Under-5 mortality rate (1997) 116

% of infants with low birthweight (1990-97) 13

Births attended by skilled health staff % of total[a] . . .21

% fully immunized (1995-97)

TB 67

DPT 60

Polio 60

Measles 53

Prevalence of child malnutrition under age 5
(1992-97)[b] 44

Ethnic Division (6)

Ethnic Tigrinya 50%

Tigre and Kunama 40%

Afar 4%

Saho (Red Sea coast dwellers) 3%

Religions (7)

Muslim, Coptic Christian, Roman Catholic, Protestant.

Languages (8)

Afar, Amharic, Arabic, Tigre and Kunama, Tigrinya, minor ethnic group languages.

EDUCATION

Public Education Expenditures (9)

Public expenditure on education (% of GNP)

1980 . . . .

1996 . . . . .1.8

Expenditure per student

Primary % of GNP per capita

1980 . . . .

1996 . . . . .9.2

Secondary % of GNP per capita

1980 . . . .

1996 . . . . .9.9

Tertiary % of GNP per capita

1980 . . . .

1996 . . . .

Expenditure on teaching materials

Primary % of total for level (1996) . . . .

Secondary % of total for level (1996) . . . .

Primary pupil-teacher ratio per teacher (1996) 44

Duration of primary education years (1995) 5

GOVERNMENT & LAW

Political Parties (12)

The legislative branch is a unicameral National Assembly (150 seats; term limits not established). People's Front for Democracy and Justice (PFDJ) is the only party recognized by the government.

Government Budget (13B)

Revenues . . . .$226 million

Expenditures . . . .$453 million

Capital expenditures . . . .$88 million

Data for 1996 est.

Military Affairs (14A)

Total expenditures (1995) . . . .$40 million

Expenditures as % of GDP . . . . .NA%

NA stands for not available.

LABOR FORCE

Unemployment Rate (17)

Rate not available.

PRODUCTION SECTOR

Electric Energy (18)

Capacity . . . . .73,000 kW (1995)

Production . . . . .NA kWh

Consumption per capita . . . . .NA kWh

NA stands for not available.

Transportation (19)

Highways:

total: 4,010 km

paved: 874 km

unpaved: 3,136 km (1996 est.)

Merchant marine:

total: 2 ships (1,000 GRT or over) totaling 5,516 GRT/5,747 DWT ships by type: oil tanker 1, roll-on/roll-off cargo 1 (1997 est.)

Airports: 20 (1997 est.)

Airports—with paved runways:

total: 2

over 3,047 m: 1

2,438 to 3,047 m: 1 (1997 est.)

Airports—with unpaved runways:

total: 18

over 3,047 m: 2

2,438 to 3,047 m: 2

1,524 to 2,437 m: 5

914 to 1,523 m: 6

under 914 m: 3 (1997 est.)

Top Agricultural Products (20)

Sorghum, lentils, vegetables, maize, cotton, tobacco, coffee, sisal (for making rope); livestock (including goats); fish.

FINANCE, ECONOMICS, & TRADE

Economic Indicators (22)

National product: GDP—purchasing power parity—$2.2 billion (1996 est.)

National product real growth rate: 6.8% (1996 est.)

National product per capita: $600 (1996 est.)

Inflation rate—consumer price index: 4% (1997 est.)

Exchange Rates (24)

Exchange rates: nakfa per US$1 = 7.2 (March 1998 est.)

Following independence from Ethiopia, Eritrea continued to use Ethiopian currency until late in 1997 when Eritrea issued its own currency, the nakfa, at approximately the same rate as the birr, i.e., 7.2 nakfa per US$1.

Top Import Origins (25)

$499 million (1996 est.)

Origins	%
Ethiopia	NA
Saudi Arabia	NA
Italy	NA
United Arab Emirates	NA

NA stands for not available.

Top Export Destinations (26)

$71 million (1996 est.) Data are for 1996.

Destinations	%
Ethiopia	67
Sudan	10
Saudi Arabia	4
United States	3
Italy	NA
Yemen	NA

NA stands for not available.

Economic Aid (27)

Recipient: ODA, $NA. NA stands for not available.

Import Export Commodities (28)

Import Commodities	Export Commodities
Processed goods	Livestock
Machinery	Sorghum
Petroleum products	Textiles
	Food
	Small manufactures

ESTONIA

Republic of Estonia
Eesti Vabariik

INTRODUCTORY SURVEY

RECENT HISTORY

Adolf Hitler's forces invaded the Soviet Union in June 1941 and took control of Estonia shortly thereafter. They retreated in 1944, and the Soviet Union once again occupied Estonia.

Taking advantage of the greater freedom allowed by Soviet president Mikhail Gorbachev, an Estonian nationalist movement, the Popular Front, was launched in 1987. Estonia declared its independence from the Soviet Union on 20 August 1991. A new constitution was adopted on 28 June 1992.

In August 1994, Russia removed the last of its tanks and troops, ending fifty years of military presence in Estonia.

The parliamentary elections of 1995 signaled a change from the vigorous pro-market reforms that dominated Estonia's new independence. The results of the election, however, were unlikely to significantly change the government's commitment to a balanced budget, stable economy, and good climate for foreign investment.

GOVERNMENT

The 1992 constitution declares Estonia a parliamentary democracy with a single-chamber parliament (the *Riigikogu*). The president, prime minister, and the cabinet make up the executive branch.

ESTONIA

0   50   100 Miles

0   50   100 Kilometers

Judiciary

The 1992 constitution established a three-level court system of rural and city courts, district courts, and state courts. A new criminal code was adopted in 1994. New codes in many areas of law were still being drafted as of 1997.

Political Parties

The Independent Communist Party of Estonia split from the Communist Party of the Soviet Union (CPSU) in January 1991. The Pro Patria Party, the Estonian Social Democratic Party, and the Christian-Democratic Union of Estonia are among the many parties that have emerged since then. In the parliamentary elections of March 1995, the Coalition Party and Rural Union (a coalition of four parties) won the majority, with 41 of 101 seats.

DEFENSE

Estonian men must serve for fifteen months in the military, in a border guard, a rapid reaction force, or territorial defense battalions. There were about 3,450 men on duty in 1995, of which 3,300 are army personnel and 140 are in the navy. The Estonian Border Guard has about 2,000 personnel.

ECONOMIC AFFAIRS

Estonia has one of the strongest economies among the former republics of the Soviet Union. After the 1992 monetary reform, the economy started to revive from the instability caused by the breakup of the Soviet Union. The gross domestic product (GDP) grew by 5% in 1994 and 6% in 1995. Services account for 53% of the GDP; industry, 37%; and agriculture, 10%.

Public Finance

The new government exercises fiscal responsibility characterized by a strictly balanced budget. No transfers or preferential credits are given to public enterprises, and governmental borrowing from the central bank is forbidden. In January 1996, Estonia instituted a centralized treasury system for managing the government's budget.

The U.S. Central Intelligence Agency estimates that, in 1996, government revenues totaled approximately $620 million and expenditures $582 million. External debt totaled $270 million.

Income

In 1998, the gross national product (GNP) was $4.89 billion at current prices, or $3,390 per person. During 1985–95, the average annual inflation rate was 76.2% and the GNP per person declined by 4.3%. The monthly inflation rate has been under 5% since 1992.

Industry

Industry is the principal sector of Estonia's economy. The textile mills in Narva and Tallinn are the country's largest plants. During 1990–95, industrial output fell by an average of 15% per year. Most of the decline happened immediately after independence, and by 1994 industrial production was on the rise.

Banking and Finance

All links with the Soviet budget and financial system were severed in 1991. In January 1990, the Bank of Estonia was created, which merged two years later with the Estonian branch of Gosbank (the Soviet State Bank) to form the country's new central bank. In December 1988, the authorities established the first Estonian commercial bank, the Tartu Commercial Bank, and by September 1991, there were 20 commercial banks responsible for 27% of total credit extended by banks.

There are two stock exchanges in Estonia: the Estonian Stock Exchange and the Tallinn Stock Exchange, inaugurated in May 1996.

Economic Development

After passing an ownership act in June 1990, the government began a privatization program at the beginning of 1991. Most of the nearly 500 state-owned companies have since passed into new hands. The Estonian privatization Agency (EPA) was established to oversee major privatization programs. In late 1995, EPA announced privatization plans for Estonian Railways, Estonian Energy, Estonian Oil Shale, Estonian Telekom, and Tallinn Ports. Estonian Gas, Estonian Tobacco, and Estonian Air were privatized in 1996.

Net resource flows from international financial institutions in 1995 included $18 million from the World Bank and $30 million from the International Monetary Fund (IMF). Distribution of aid by Development Assistance Committee countries totaled $33 million in 1994.

SOCIAL WELFARE

New social insurance systems were introduced between 1991 and 1994. Discrimination based on race, sex, nationality, or religion is illegal under the constitution. Men and women generally receive equal pay for equal work. Public attention has focused increasingly on the welfare of children. Several safe havens for children have been established. Ethnic Russians sometimes face discrimination in housing and employment. Many ethnic Russians in Estonia are non-citizens who are not allowed to run for office or vote in elections.

Healthcare

There are about 330 people per physician in the country. In 1995, the infant mortality rate was 14 per 1,000. Life expectancy averages 69 years.

Housing

On 1 January 1991, 51,000 households (or 12%) were on waiting lists for urban housing. Housing space per person totaled 20.3 square meters at the end of 1991, and 34.3 million square meters altogether, of which 10.1 million were privately owned.

EDUCATION

The country's adult literacy rate in 1995 was 99.8% for both men and women.

Estonian-language schools provide nine years of primary and three years of secondary education.

There are two well-known universities: the University of Tartu and the Talliva Technical University. In 1994, all higher level institutions had 25,483 pupils.

1999 KEY EVENTS TIMELINE

January

- The Estonian town of Narva cuts off water and sewage treatment services to the Russian town of Ivangorod.
- The Estonian government fires 300 Russian-speaking policeman for their inability to speak Estonian.
- An Estonian man is convicted for spying for the Soviet secret police under Stalin and ordering the deportation of Estonians.

February

- Sweden announces its decision not to recover the bodies of victims from the wreck of the ferry *Estonia*, many of whom were Estonian.

March

- General elections are held.

July

- Sweden's SwedBank gains a majority interest in Hansabank, Estonia's largest banking institution.

October

- The European Union (EU) announces that Estonia may be eligible to join in 2003.

ANALYSIS OF EVENTS: 1999

BUSINESS AND THE ECONOMY

Integration into the larger European economy remains the primary issue in business and finance for Estonia, independent only since 1991. The European Commission announced in October that Estonia was close to meeting the economic requirements for membership in the European Union. The EU opened talks with Estonia on possible membership in March 1998 and announced in October 1999 that Estonia was one of twelve nations being considered for membership, which may be granted Estonia as early as 2003. The EU announced in a Berlin summit in March 1999 the committal of U.S. $70 billion over a seven-year period for building up the economies and infrastructures of prospective member countries in Central and Eastern Europe, Estonia among them. Germany, however, refuses to fund further spending in this direction.

Considering its geographical situation, Estonia has naturally developed strong economic ties with the Scandinavian countries. Scandinavian banks have aggressively sought to expand into the Baltics, where growing economies and underdeveloped markets make for prime investment territory. SwedBank gained a majority interest in Hansabank, the largest bank in Estonia and a pre-eminent Baltic financial institution. The banking industry is relatively nascent in Estonia due to its Soviet past, and total bank deposits in Estonia comprise only some 30 percent of its gross domestic product. The nation now has 5 commercial banks as the result of closures and mergers, including foreign mergers.

Relations between Estonia and its Scandinavian neighbors are not without tension, however. Strong diplomatic, military, and economic ties between Finland and Estonia have been tested by wage disparities between the countries. Finnish dock workers have refused to unload ships of the Estonian Shipping Company (partly Norwegian-owned) because the Estonian ships have been transporting cargo between Denmark and Finland much more cheaply than could a Finnish ship due to the lower wages paid Estonian shipworkers. Finnish sailors earn $2400 a month, whereas Estonian sailors are paid $600 a month, a high salary in Estonia. Estonia has presented its case to the European Union (EU) in Brussels for adjudication, a move that will probably prove futile since the shipping trade falls outside the purview of European competition laws.

GOVERNMENT AND POLITICS

Estonia held its third general election in March. There was a close race between 2000 candidates for 101 seats in the Riigikogu, the Estonian parliament. The 55 percent voter turnout was lower than expected and down from the 70 percent turnout in the last general election in 1995. Former Prime Minister Edgar Savisaar's Center Party won largest number of votes and gained 28 seats, but a coalition of Reform, Fatherland, and Moderate parties won a narrow majority of 53 seats. The election represents a political shift to the center and right and has put into place a government dedicated to continued economic reform in spite of current setbacks.

Like Estonian society as a whole, Estonian politics are complicated by the question of how to integrate ethnic Russians (who comprise 20 percent of the electorate) into Estonian national life. One third of Estonia's 1.5 million inhabitants speak Russian, and some areas are predominantly Russian, such as the depressed industrial border town of Narva, which is 95 percent Russian. Not unexpectedly, relations between Estonians and ethnic Russians are often strained. The Estonian government has imposed strict citizenship examinations which require a knowledge of the Estonian language, and Russians find these an obstacle to obtaining full Estonian citizenship. In January, Estonia fired 300 Russian-speaking policeman who failed the examination. Still, most ethnic Russians voted for Estonian rather than Russian parties in March.

Estonia also struggles to assert its new-found identity against the influence of its huge neighbor to the east. The Estonian town of Narva cut off water and sewage treatment it had provided to the Russian town of Ivangorod across the border after the latter failed to pay more than $1 million for services received. A 78-year-old man, a former member of the Soviet secret police, was convicted and given an eight-year suspended sentence for having ordered the deportation of over twenty families during the Stalinist era. For their part, Russian authorities expelled an Estonian man after he confessed to gathering secret information about the Russian air force for the intelligence wing of a militant group in Estonia. Yet the government in Estonia remains stable. According to Transparency International, a non-governmental group that monitors governmental corruption, Estonia is among the former Communist bloc nations least affected by government corruption.

CULTURE AND SOCIETY

In June, ethnic Russians objected when the remains of an Estonian officer, a former Nazi commander, were transferred from Germany to Tallinn. The officer had fought in the Estonian army until the Soviets occupied Estonia in 1944, when he joined the German army. The Estonian prime minister said the officer had been one of Estonia's outstanding soldiers and deserved reburial in Estonia, while Estonian Russians denounced the action as tantamount to supporting fascism.

The Lake Peipus Project, named after the lake which dominates the Russian-Estonian border region, cooperates with a group in Narva called "A Home For Every Child" to place Russian children from the city with Estonian families in the rural town of Rapina, near Lake Peipus. The cooperative project has three aims: to improve relations between Estonians and ethnic Russians living in Estonia, to teach Russian children the Estonian language, and to provide urban children from disadvantaged backgrounds with an opportunity to live with close-knit families in a peaceful environment in the country.

In June, Estonian relatives of victims of the 1994 wreck of the ferry *Estonia* accepted the Swedish government's decision to leave the bodies of 757 passengers and crew in the wreck. This decision was supported by the governments of Finland and Estonia, though Swedish relatives of the victims are contesting it.

DIRECTORY

CENTRAL GOVERNMENT

Head of State

President
Lennart Meri, Office of the President, Weizenbergi 39, 15050 Tallinn, Estonia
PHONE: +372 6316202
FAX: +372 6316250
E-MAIL: sekretar@vpk.ee

Prime Minister
Mart Laar, Office of the Prime Minister, Lossi plats 1a, 15165 Tallinn, Estonia
PHONE: +372 6316701
FAX: +372 6316704
E-MAIL: valitsus@rk.ee

Ministers

Minister of Foreign Affairs
Toomas Hendrick Ilves, Ministry of Foreign Affairs, Rävala 9, 150 49 Tallinn, Estonia
PHONE: +372 6317000
FAX: +372 6317099
E-MAIL: vminfo@vm.ee

Minister of Agriculture
Ivari Padar, Ministry of Agriculture, Lai 39/41, 15056 Tallinn, Estonia
PHONE: +372 6256101
FAX: +372 6256200
E-MAIL: pm@agri.ee

Minister of Culture
Signe Kivi, Ministry of Culture, Suur-Karja 23, 15076 Tallinn, Estonia
PHONE: +372 6282222
FAX: +372 6282200
E-MAIL: info@kul.ee

Minister of Defense
Juri Luik, Ministry of Defense, Sakala 1, 10141 Tallinn, Estonia
PHONE: +372 6406000
FAX: +372 6406001
E-MAIL: info@kmin.ee

Minister of Economy Affairs
Mihkel Parnoja, Ministry of Economy Affairs, Harju tn. 11, 15072 Tallinn, Estonia
PHONE: +372 6256304
FAX: +372 6313660
E-MAIL: info@mineco.ee

Minister of Education
Tonis Lukas, Ministry of Education, Tõnismägi 9/11, 10119 Tallinn, Estonia
PHONE: +372 6281212
FAX: +372 6281213
E-MAIL: hm@hm.ee

Minister of Environment
Heiki Kranich, Ministry of Environment, Toompuiestee 24,, 10149 Tallinn, Estonia
PHONE: +372 6262800
FAX: +372 6262801
E-MAIL: min@ekm.envir.ee

Minister of Finance
Siim Kallas, Ministry of Finance, Suur-Ameerika 1, 15006 Tallinn, Estonia
PHONE: +372 6113445
FAX: +372 6317810
E-MAIL: info@fin.ee

Minister of Internal Affairs
Jüri Mõis, Ministry of Internal Affairs, Pikk 61, 15065 Tallinn, Estonia
PHONE: +372 6125010
FAX: +372 6125077
E-MAIL: sisemin@sisemin.gov.ee

Minister of Justice
Mart Rask, Ministry of Justice, Tõnismägi 5A, 15191 Tallinn, Estonia
PHONE: +372 6208100
FAX: +372 6208109
E-MAIL: sekretar@just.ee

Minister of Ethnic Affairs
Katrin Saks, Ministry of Ethnic Affairs, Lossi
plats 1a, 10130 Tallinn, Estonia
PHONE: +372 6316720
FAX: +372 6316904
E-MAIL: AasaK@wp.rk.ee

Minister of Regional Affairs
Toivo Asmer, Ministry of Regional Affairs, Pikk
57, 10133 Tallinn, Estonia
PHONE: +372 6125151; 6125152
FAX: +372 6125101
E-MAIL: piret@wp.rk.ee

Minister of Social Affairs
Eiki Nestor, Ministry of Social Affairs, Gonsiori
29, 15027 Tallinn, Estonia
PHONE: +372 6269700
FAX: +372 6317909
E-MAIL: webmaster@fs1.sm.ee

Minister of Transport and Communications
Toivo Jurgenson, Ministry of Transport and
Communications, Viru 9, 10140 Tallinn, Estonia
PHONE: +372 6397613
FAX: +372 6397606
E-MAIL: info@tsm.ee

POLITICAL ORGANIZATIONS

Eesti Keskerakond (Estonian Center Party)
Toom-Rüütli 3/5, 10130 Tallinn, Estonia
PHONE: +372 6273460; 6273463; 6273478
FAX: +372 6273461
E-MAIL: keskerakond@teleport.ee
NAME: Edgar Savisaar

Eesti Koonderakond (Estonian Coalition Party)
Raekoja plats 16, 10146 Tallinn, Estonia
PHONE: +372 6314161
FAX: +372 6314041
E-MAIL: koondera@online.ee
TITLE: Chair
NAME: Mart Siimann

Eesti Maarahva Erakond (Estonian Country People's Party)
Marja 4D, 10617 Tallinn, Estonia
PHONE: +372 6112909
FAX: +372 6112908
E-MAIL: eme@klab.envir.ee
TITLE: Chair
NAME: Arnold Rüütel

Eesti Reformierakond (Estonian Reform Party)
Tõnismäe 3a-15, 10119 Tallinn, Estonia
PHONE: +372 6408740; 6408742
FAX: +372 6408741
E-MAIL: info@reform.ee
TITLE: Chair
NAME: Siim Kallas

Eestimaa Ühendatud Rahvapartei (Estonian United People's Party)
Estonia pst. 3/5 (3rd floor), 10141 Tallinn,
Estonia
PHONE: +372 6455335
FAX: +372 6455336; 6455446
E-MAIL: eurp@uninet.ee; eurp@nobema.ee
TITLE: Chair
NAME: Viktor Andrejev

Erakond Mõõdukad
p/k 3437, 101506 Tallinn, Estonia
PHONE: +372 6419023; 6419024; 6419025
FAX: +372 6419488
E-MAIL: kirjad@moodukad.ee;
moodukad@datanet.ee
TITLE: Chair
NAME: Andres Tarand

Erakond Isamaaliit (Pro Patria Union)
Endla 4a,, 10142 Tallinn, Estonia
PHONE: +372 6263324; 6263325
FAX: +372 6263324
E-MAIL: isamaa@ngonet.ee
TITLE: Chair
NAME: Mart Laar

DIPLOMATIC REPRESENTATION
Embassies in Estonia

Armenia
Kopli 25, 10412 Tallinn, Estonia
PHONE: +372 6418672
TITLE: Honorary Consul
NAME: Garik Iknoyan

Austria
Vambola 6, 10114 Tallinn, Estonia
PHONE: +372 6278740; 6278745
FAX: +372 6314365
E-MAIL: austroemb@teleport.ee
TITLE: Ambassador
NAME: Michael Miess

Canada
Toomkooli 13, 15186 Tallinn, Estonia
PHONE: +372 6273310; 6273311
FAX: +372 6273312
E-MAIL: canembt@zzz.ee
NAME: Marina Asari

China
Narva mnt. 98, 15009 Tallinn, Estonia
PHONE: +372 6015830; 6015831
FAX: +372 6015833
TITLE: Ambassador
NAME: Zou Mingrong

Denmark
Wismari 5, 15047 Tallinn, Estonia
PHONE: +372 6306400
FAX: +372 6306421
E-MAIL: dan.emb@online.ee
TITLE: Ambassador
NAME: Svend Roed Nielsen

Finland
Kohtu 4, 15180 Tallinn, Estonia
PHONE: +372 6103200
FAX: +372 6103281
TITLE: Ambassador
NAME: Pekka Artur Oinonen

France
Toom-Kuninga 20, 15185 Tallinn, Estonia
PHONE: +372 6311492
FAX: +372 6311385
E-MAIL: france@datanet.ee
TITLE: Ambassador
NAME: Jean-Jacques Subrenat

Germany
Toom-Kuninga 11, 15048 Tallinn, Estonia
PHONE: +372 6275300
FAX: +372 6275304
E-MAIL: saksasaa@online.ee
TITLE: Ambassador
NAME: Gerhard Enver Schrömbgens

Hungary
Narva mnt. 122, 10127 Tallinn, Estonia
PHONE: +372 6140945
FAX: +372 6140945
TITLE: Ambassador
NAME: Béla Jávorszky

Italy
Müürivahe 3, 15075 Tallinn, Estonia
PHONE: +372 6256444; 6256446
FAX: +372 6311370
TITLE: Ambassador
NAME: Luchino Cortese

Latvia
Tõnismägi 10, 15190 Tallinn, Estonia
PHONE: +372 6461313
FAX: +372 6311366
TITLE: Ambassador
NAME: Gints Jegermanis

Lithuania
Uus tn. 15, 15070 Tallinn, Estonia
PHONE: +372 6314030; 6314053
FAX: +372 6412013
TITLE: Ambassador
NAME: Rimantas Juozapas Tonkunas

Norway
Harju str. 6, 10502 Tallinn, Estonia
PHONE: +372 6271000
FAX: +372 6271001
E-MAIL: noramb@uninet.ee
TITLE: Ambassador
NAME: Kai Olaf Lie

Poland
Pärnu mnt. 8, 10503 Tallinn, Estonia
PHONE: +372 6278206; 6278210
FAX: +372 6445221
E-MAIL: ambrptal@netexpress.ee
TITLE: Ambassador
NAME: Jakub Wolasiewicz

Russian Federation
Pikk 19, 10133 Tallinn, Estonia
PHONE: +372 6464175; 6464169
FAX: +372 6464178
TITLE: Ambassador
NAME: Aleksei Gluhhov

Sweden
Pikk 28, 15055 Tallinn, Estonia
PHONE: +372 6405600
FAX: +372 6405695
E-MAIL: swedemb@estpak.ee
TITLE: Ambassador
NAME: Elisabet Borsiin Bonnier

Ukraine
Lahe t. 6, 15170 Tallinn, Estonia
PHONE: +372 6015815
FAX: +372 6015816
E-MAIL: embukr@eol.ee
TITLE: Ambassador
NAME: Mykola Makarevych

United Kingdom
Wismari 6, 10136 Tallinn, Estonia
PHONE: +372 6674700
FAX: +372 6674755
E-MAIL: uk.talli@netexpress.ee

TITLE: Ambassador
NAME: Timothy James Craddock

United States

Kentmanni 20, 15099 Tallinn, Estonia
PHONE: +372 6312021
FAX: +372 6312025
TITLE: Ambassador
NAME: Melissa F. Wells

Vatican City

Chancery of the Apostolic Nunciature in Tallinn, Poska 47, 10150 Tallinn, Estonia
PHONE: +372 6013079
FAX: +372 6013190

JUDICIAL SYSTEM

National Court

Lossi 17, Tartu 50093, Estonia
PHONE: +372 7441411
FAX: +372 7441433

FURTHER READING

Articles

"Estonia's Latest Challenge." *The Economist* 350 (March 13, 1999): 60.

"Estonia's Taxing Dilemma." *The Economist* 350 (March 20, 1999): 76.

"Fault Lines in the Sand." *The Economist* 351 (April 24, 1999): 16.

Jones, Colin. "Losing their Independence." *The Banker* 149, 884 (October 1999): 65(3).

———— "Starting from Scratch." *The Banker* 149, 884 (October 1999): 55(2).

Ishiyama, John T. "Representational Mechanisms and Ethnopolitics: Evidence from Transitional Democracies in Eastern Europe." *East European Quarterly* 33, 2 (Summer 1999): 251(29).

"Russian, Nordics and Balts: Cosy Up." *The Economist* 351 (June 12, 1999): 45.

Books

Estonia: the Transition to a Market Economy. Washington, D.C.: World Bank, 1993.

Fjuk, Ignar. *Estonia: Free and Independent.* Tallinn: Estonian Encyclopaedia Publishers, 1994.

Internet

Estonia Online. Available Online @ www.ciesin.ee/Estonia (November, 3, 1999).

Estonian News Agency. Available Online @ eta.www.ee (November 3, 1999).

Estonia-Wide Web. Available Online @ 222.ee./ www/State/welcome.html (November 3, 1999).

ESTONIA: STATISTICAL DATA

For sources and notes see "Sources of Statistics" in the front of each volume.

GEOGRAPHY

Geography (1)

Area:

Total: 45,226 sq km.

Land: 43,211 sq km.

Water: 2,015 sq km.

Note: includes 1,520 islands in the Baltic Sea.

Area—comparative: slightly smaller than New Hampshire and Vermont combined.

Land boundaries:

Total: 633 km.

Border countries: Latvia 339 km, Russia 294 km.

Coastline: 3,794 km.

Climate: maritime, wet, moderate winters, cool summers.

Terrain: marshy, lowlands.

Natural resources: shalc oil (kukersite), peat, phosphorite, amber, cambrian blue clay.

Land use:

Arable land: 22%

Permanent crops: 0%

Permanent pastures: 11%

Forests and woodland: 31%

Other: 36% (1993 est.).

HUMAN FACTORS

Demographics (2A)

	1990	1995	1998	2000	2010	2020	2030	2040	2050
Population	1,573.1	1,474.4	1,421.3	1,398.1	1,329.2	1,271.4	1,203.7	1,134.2	1,046.9
Net migration rate (per 1,000 population)	NA	NA	NA	NA	NA	NA	NA	NA	NA
Births	NA	NA	NA	NA	NA	NA	NA	NA	NA
Deaths	NA	NA	NA	NA	NA	NA	NA	NA	NA
Life expectancy - males	64.7	61.7	62.5	62.7	65.7	69.6	72.8	75.3	77.2
Life expectancy - females	74.9	74.4	74.8	75.2	76.8	79.2	81.2	82.8	84.0
Birth rate (per 1,000)	14.2	9.1	9.0	9.1	11.6	8.4	8.0	7.4	6.4
Death rate (per 1,000)	12.4	14.1	14.1	14.2	14.3	13.4	13.4	14.3	15.4
Women of reproductive age (15-49 yrs.)	381.5	364.3	356.2	353.0	330.4	295.8	268.2	219.0	199.7
of which are currently married	NA	NA	NA	NA	NA	NA	NA	NA	NA
Fertility rate	2.0	1.3	1.3	1.3	1.6	1.5	1.4	1.4	1.3

Except as noted, values for vital statistics are in thousands; life expectancy is in years.

Health Personnel (3)

Total health expenditure as a percentage of GDP, 1990-1997[a]

Public sector 5.8

Private sector . . . . .NA

Total[b] . . . . .NA

Health expenditure per capita in U.S. dollars, 1990-1997[a]

Purchasing power parity . . . . .NA

Total . . . . .NA

Availability of health care facilities per 100,000 people

Hospital beds 1990-1997[a] 810

Doctors 1993[c] 312

Nurses 1993[c] 636

Health Indicators (4)

Life expectancy at birth

1980 69

1997 70

Daily per capita supply of calories (1996) 3,004

Total fertility rate births per woman (1997) 1.2

Maternal mortality ratio per 100,000 live births (1990-97) . . . . .52[b]

Safe water % of population with access (1995) . . . .

Sanitation % of population with access (1995) . . . .

Consumption of iodized salt % of households (1992-98)[a] . . . .

Smoking prevalence

Male % of adults (1985-95)[a] 52

Female % of adults (1985-95)[a] 24

Tuberculosis incidence per 100,000 people (1997) 52

Adult HIV prevalence % of population ages 15-49 (1997) 0.01

Infants and Malnutrition (5)

Under-5 mortality rate (1997) 14

% of infants with low birthweight (1990-97) . . . . . .NA

Births attended by skilled health staff % of total[a] . .100

% fully immunized (1995-97)

TB 99

DPT 85

Polio 86

Measles 88

Prevalence of child malnutrition under age 5 (1992-97)[b] . . . . .NA

Ethnic Division (6)

Estonian 64.2%

Russian 28.7%

Ukrainian 2.7%

Byelorussian 1.5%

Finn 1%

Other 1.9%

Data are for 1995.

Religions (7)

Evangelical Lutheran, Russian Orthodox, Estonian Orthodox, others include Baptist, Methodist, 7th Day Adventist, Roman Catholic, Pentecostal, Word of Life, 7th Day Baptist, Judaism.

Languages (8)

Estonian (official), Russian, Ukrainian, other.

EDUCATION

Public Education Expenditures (9)

Public expenditure on education (% of GNP)

1980 . . . .

1996 . . . . .7.3

Expenditure per student

Primary % of GNP per capita

1980 . . . .

1996 . . . .

Secondary % of GNP per capita

1980 . . . .

1996 . . . . .44.8[1]

Tertiary % of GNP per capita

1980 . . . .

1996 . . . . .38.4

Expenditure on teaching materials

Primary % of total for level (1996) . . . .

Secondary % of total for level (1996) 4.5

Primary pupil-teacher ratio per teacher (1996) . . . . .17[1]

Duration of primary education years (1995) 6

Educational Attainment (10)

Age group (1989) . . . . .25+

Total population 1,001,198

Highest level attained (%)

No schooling 2.2

First level

Not completed . . . . .NA

Completed 39.0

Entered second level

S-1 .... .45.1

S-2 .... .NA

Postsecondary 13.7

GOVERNMENT & LAW

Political Parties (12)

Parliament	% of seats
Coalition Party and Rural Union (KMU)	.32.22
Reform Party (RE)	.16.18
Center Party (K)	.14.17
Pro Patria and National Independence Party (ERSP)	.7.85
Moderates (M)	.5.98
Our Home is Estonia and Right-Wingers	.5.0

Government Budget (13A)

Year: 1997

Total Expenditures: 20,551.8 Millions of Krooni

Expenditures as a percentage of the total by function:

General public services and public order	.14.57
Defense	.4.60
Education	.10.16
Health	.15.73
Social Security and Welfare	.32.02
Housing and community amenities	..40
Recreational, cultural, and religious affairs	.4.38
Fuel and energy	..04
Agriculture, forestry, fishing, and hunting	.4.31
Mining, manufacturing, and construction	.18
Transportation and communication	.5.71
Other economic affairs and services	..95

Military Affairs (14B)

	1992	1993	1994	1995
Military expenditures				
Current dollars (mil.)	48	77	96	118
1995 constant dollars (mil.)	52	81	99	118
Armed forces (000)	3	5	4	6
Gross national product (GNP)				
Current dollars (mil.)	10,900	10,610	10,400	10,980
1995 constant dollars (mil.)	11,720	11,120	10,660	10,980
Central government expenditures (CGE)				
1995 constant dollars (mil.)	3,810	3,269	3,368	NA
People (mil.)	1.5	1.5	1.5	1.5
Military expenditure as % of GNP	0.4	.7	.9	1.1
Military expenditure as % of CGE	1.4	2.5	2.9	NA
Military expenditure per capita (1995 $)	34	53	66	80
Armed forces per 1,000 people (soldiers)	1.6	3.3	2.7	4.1
GNP per capita (1995 $)	7,587	7,329	7,118	7,431
Arms imports[6]				
Current dollars (mil.)	0	20	30	5
1995 constant dollars (mil.)	0	21	31	5
Arms exports[6]				
Current dollars (mil.)	0	0	5	0
1995 constant dollars (mil.)	0	0	5	0
Total imports[7]				
Current dollars (mil.)	432	896	1,660	2,539
1995 constant dollars (mil.)	465	939	1,702	2,539
Total exports[7]				
Current dollars (mil.)	463	805	1,299	1,836
1995 constant dollars (mil.)	498	844	1,332	1,836
Arms as percent of total imports[8]	0.0	2.2	1.8	.2
Arms as percent of total exports[8]	0.0	0	.4	0

Crime (15)

Crime rate (for 1997)

Crimes reported	.41,000
Total persons convicted	.13,000
Crimes per 100,000 population	.2,800

Persons responsible for offenses

Total number of suspects	.10,500
Total number of female suspects	.975
Total number of juvenile suspects	.1,900

LABOR FORCE

Labor Force (16)

Total	785,000
Industry and construction	42%
Agriculture and forestry	20%
Other	38%

Data for 1996 est. Percent distribution for 1990.

Unemployment Rate (17)

3.6% (1997 est.)

PRODUCTION SECTOR

Electric Energy (18)

Capacity	3.287 million kW (1995)
Production	8.083 billion kWh (1995)
Consumption per capita	4,355 kWh (1995)

Transportation (19)

Highways:

total: 15,304 km

paved: 8,142 km (including 65 km of expressways)

unpaved: 7,162 km (1996 est.)

Waterways: 500 km perennially navigable

Pipelines: natural gas 420 km (1992)

Merchant marine:

total: 53 ships (1,000 GRT or over) totaling 368,340 GRT/455,696 DWT ships by type: bulk 6, cargo 27, combination bulk 1, container 5, oil tanker 2, roll-on/roll-off cargo 7, short-sea passenger 5 (1997 est.)

Airports: 5 (1997 est.)

Airports—with paved runways:

total: 5

over 3,047 m: 1 2,438 to 3,047 m : 1

914 to 1,523 m: 3 (1997 est.)

Top Agricultural Products (20)

Potatoes, fruits, vegetables; livestock and dairy products; fish.

MANUFACTURING SECTOR

GDP & Manufacturing Summary (21)

	1980	1985	1990	1992	1993	1994
Gross Domestic Product						
Millions of 1990 dollars	4,041	4,099	4,602	3,481	3,210	3,402
Growth rate in percent	NA	−8.70	−6.47	−12.43	−7.79	6.00
Per capita (in 1990 dollars)	2,730.3	2,668.9	2,921.8	2,227.0	2,068.1	2,207.9
Manufacturing Value Added						
Millions of 1990 dollars	1,735	1,944	1,976	NA	NA	NA
Growth rate in percent	NA	0.38	−5.09	NA	NA	NA
Manufacturing share in percent of current prices	45.1	42.2	42.9	32.6	24.0	22.5

FINANCE, ECONOMICS, & TRADE

Balance of Payments (23)

	1992	1993	1994	1995	1996
Exports of goods (f.o.b.)	461	812	1,327	1,856	2,064
Imports of goods (f.o.b.)	−551	−957	−1,682	−2,530	−3,121
Trade balance	−90	−145	−355	−674	−1,058
Services - debits	−174	−300	−477	−558	−719
Services - credits	204	361	553	940	1,220
Private transfers (net)	97	106	109	101	92
Government transfers (net)	−0	−0	6	26	17
Overall balance	36	22	−165	−165	−447

Economic Indicators (22)

National product: GDP—purchasing power parity—$9.34 billion (1997 est.)

National product real growth rate: 10% (1997 est.)

National product per capita: $6,450 (1997 est.)

Inflation rate—consumer price index: 11.2% (1997 est.)

Exchange Rates (24)

Exchange rates:

Krooni (EEK) per US$1

January 1998	14.527
1997	13.882
1996	12.034
1995	11.465
1994	12.991
1993	13.223

Krooni are tied to the German deutsche mark at a fixed rate of 8 to 1

Top Import Origins (25)

$3.2 billion (c.i.f., 1996) Data are for 1995.

Origins	%
Finland	NA
Russia	NA
Sweden	NA
Germany	NA

NA stands for not available.

Top Export Destinations (26)

$2 billion (f.o.b., 1996) Data are for 1995.

Destinations	%
Finland	NA
Russia	NA
Sweden	NA
Germany	NA
Latvia	NA

NA stands for not available.

Economic Aid (27)

Recipient: ODA, $147 million (1993). Note: Western commitments $285 million (including international financial institutions).

Import Export Commodities (28)

Import Commodities	Export Commodities
Machinery and equipment 29%	Textiles 16%
Foodstuffs 14%	Food products 16%
Minerals 13%	Machinery and equipment 16%
Textiles 13%	Metals 9%
Metals 12%	

ETHIOPIA

Yeltyop'iya Federalawi

CAPITAL: Addis Ababa.

FLAG: The national flag is a tricolor of green, yellow, and red horizontal stripes with a blue disk and a yellow outlined star and rays in the center.

ANTHEM: Traditional "Ityopia, Ityopia" is in use at the present time. A new anthem will be designated in the near future.

MONETARY UNIT: The birr (B) is a paper currency of 100 cents. There are coins of 1, 5, 10, 25, and 50 cents, and notes of 1, 5, 10, 50, and 100 birr. B1 = $0.15773 (or $1 = B6.34).

WEIGHTS AND MEASURES: The metric system is used, but some local weights and measures are also employed.

HOLIDAYS: Holidays generally follow the Old Style Coptic Church calendar. National holidays include Christmas, 7 January; Epiphany, 19 January; Victory of Adwa (1896), 2 March; Victory Day, 6 April; May Day, 1 May; New Year's Day, 11 September; Feast of the Holy Cross, 27 September. Movable Muslim holidays include 'Id al-Fitr and 'Id al-'Adha'.

TIME: 3 PM = noon GMT.

LOCATION AND SIZE: Situated in eastern Africa, Ethiopia (formerly called Abyssinia) has an area of approximately 1,127,127 square kilometers (435,186 square miles), with a length of 1,639 kilometers (1,018 miles) east to west and a width of 1,577 kilometers (980 miles) north to south. Comparatively, the area occupied by Ethiopia is slightly less than twice the size of the state of Texas. Ethiopia's capital city, Addis Ababa, is located near the center of the country.

CLIMATE: The central plateau has a moderate climate with minimal seasonal temperature variation. The mean minimum during the coldest season is 6°C (43°F), while the mean maximum rarely exceeds 26°C (79°F). Temperature variations in the lowlands are much greater, and the heat in the desert and Red Sea coastal areas is extreme, with occasional highs of 60°C (140°F). Heavy rainfall occurs in most of the country during June, July, and August.

INTRODUCTORY SURVEY

RECENT HISTORY

Ras Tafari Mekonnen of Shewa was selected as heir and head of the government. On 2 November 1930, he was crowned Emperor Haile Selassie I. When Italy invaded and conquered Ethiopia in 1935–36, he was forced to flee the country. He returned in 1941 (at the start of World War II) with the aid of British forces. After the war, Eritrea, which had been under British administration since 1941, was federated to Ethiopia in 1952 and was incorporated into the empire ten years later. By this time, an Eritrean secessionist movement was already stirring.

After an unsuccessful coup attempt in 1960, Selassie's political power began to lessen as political opposition increased. Guerrilla activity in Eritrea increased noticeably, and student and labor unrest grew. In 1974, armed forces overthrew the government. The emperor was deposed and the monarchy was abolished. Haile Selassie died in 1975.

The new Provisional Military Administrative Council, also called the Dergue, came under the leadership of Mengistu Haile Mariam. The economy was extensively nationalized in 1975. Mengistu declared himself a Marxist-Leninist in 1976 and established close relations with Moscow.

The war with Eritrean secessionists continued. In addition, in mid-1977, Somalia invaded the Ogaden area in Ethiopia in order to support the claims of ethnic Somalis in Ogaden for self-deter-

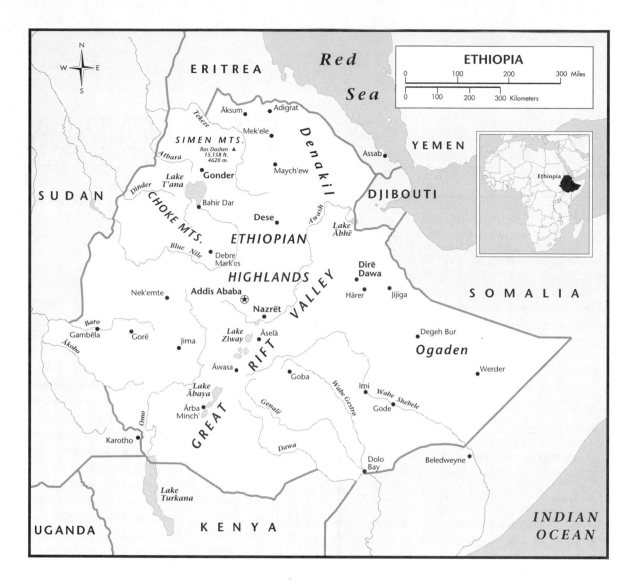

mination. The Somali assault was repulsed with the assistance of Soviet arms and Cuban soldiers. Ethiopia signed a twenty-year treaty with the Soviet Union, and close links with Libya and the People's Democratic Republic of Yemen were established.

Despite mobilizing one million troops and receiving massive military aid, the government was not able to defeat the Eritrean and Tigrayan insurgencies. The guerrillas finally prevailed, and on 21 May 1991, the Marxist dictator, Mengistu, was forced to resign as president. He fled into exile in Zimbabwe.

In July 1991, delegates from the guerrilla groups agreed to a plan establishing a transitional government and granting Eritrea the right to hold an internationally supervised referendum on independence. The vote, held on 23–25 April 1993, was for Eritrean independence. The UN certified the

results. On 24 May 1993, Eritrea became Africa's fifty-second independent state.

Ethiopia's new transitional government pledged to oversee the establishment of Ethiopia's first multiparty democracy. The one-party state was disbanded and freedom of the press was permitted. In June 1994, elections were held for the newly established Constituent Assembly. Elections were held in 1995 for the Federal Parliamentary Assembly. Opposition parties boycotted both elections, resulting in a large majority for the Ethiopian People's Revolutionary Democratic Front.

In June 1998, heavy fighting erupted along the border with Eritrea, even though the two countries had been on good terms with each other since Eritrea's independence in 1993. The battle began as a minor territorial dispute in two areas that both countries had claimed. The fighting escalated with

Ethiopia conducting an air strike on the Eritrean Red Sea port city of Assab. The two sides agreed to stop any further air strikes, but fighting along the border continued.

GOVERNMENT

After Mengistu's defeat in May 1991, a transitional government was established under the leadership of the Ethiopian People's Revolutionary Democratic Front (EPRDF). The first elections for a constituent assembly were held in June 1994. A new constitution was drafted, creating a directly elected president, a bicameral legislature, regional autonomy with the right to secede, and a nine-state national structure.

Judiciary

The government of Ethiopia is now putting into place a system of courts consisting of regional and central courts. Each region has a district (*woreda*), higher, and supreme courts. There are also local Shari'a (religious Muslim) courts which hear religion and family cases involving Muslims. The Federal High Court and Federal Supreme Court have jurisdiction over cases involving federal laws and issues of national import.

Political Parties

There were no established political parties in Ethiopia until the 1970s, when a number of illegal separatist groups became active militarily. The separatists successfully defeated Mengistu's forces, and after Mengistu fled in May 1991, they established a transitional government under their coalition banner, the Ethiopian People's Revolutionary Democratic Front (EPRDF). Elections for the newly created Federal Parliamentary Assembly were held in 1995. The EPRDF won 483 of 548 seats because most opposition parties refused to participate.

DEFENSE

As of the late 1990s, the military establishment was not yet formed. The two major rebel factions have perhaps 200,000 men armed with Russian weapons and vehicles captured from the Mengistu government in 1991. Soviet aviation and naval equipment also remains, but there is no Ethiopian air force or navy. All Russian and Cuban troops have departed.

ECONOMIC AFFAIRS

Ethiopia's economy has been undergoing major reforms since May 1991, when a market-oriented government came to power. Three major droughts, civil war, and cross-border conflicts have devastated the economy. Agriculture accounts for 57% of the gross domestic product (GDP).

Public Finance

The Ethiopian fiscal year begins 8 July, in the Ethiopian month of Hamle. Ethiopia's public finances are under great budgetary pressure, as years of war and poverty have taken a heavy toll on the countryside, population, and infrastructure.

The CIA estimates that, in 1994, government revenues totaled approximately $1.2 billion and expenditures $1.7 billion, including capital expenditures of $707 million. External debt totaled $3.7 billion, approximately 33% of which was financed abroad.

Income

In 1998, Ethiopia's gross national product (GNP) was $6.12 billion at current prices, or $100 per person. During 1985–95, the average annual decline in GNP per person was 0.5%.

Industry

While Ethiopia's industrial sector engages primarily in food processing, it also produces sugar, alcohol and soft drinks, cigarettes, cotton and textiles, footwear, soap, ethyl alcohol, and quicklime, and cement. Since 1991, privatization of Ethiopia's industry has been a major objective of the new government, reversing the policies of its predecessor.

Banking and Finance

All banking institutions were nationalized after the government's formal Declaration of Socialism on 20 December 1974. The country's three private commercial banks were placed under the management of the National Bank of Ethiopia (NBE) and, in 1981, under the state-owned Commercial Bank of Ethiopia (established in 1963), which had 151 branches in 1993. A proposal to deregulate the banking sector, giving greater autonomy to the NBE, was introduced by the Council of Ministers in September 1993. Legislation allowing for the establishment of private banks and insurance companies, but not the privatization of existing institutions, was passed in January 1994. There are no securities exchanges, and Ethiopians are legally barred from acquiring or dealing in foreign securities.

Economic Development

The policy of the Ethiopian government is to create the conditions necessary for sustained economic growth. Farmers have reacquired the economic freedom of price, of production, and of settlement. The government aspires to an agriculture-led industrialization and focuses its attention on food security, rural savings, and labor formation issues. The 1996 economic reform plan promotes free markets and liberalized trade laws as essential to economic growth.

SOCIAL WELFARE

Other than modest government allocations for pensions, labor and social welfare, and housing and community services, Ethiopia has no public welfare or social security programs. Women participated in the civil war and are better represented than in the past. There are still reports of human rights abuses committed by the military, Islamic militias, and opposition separatists.

Healthcare

The availability of modern health services reaches only a small portion of the population. In 1993, only 55% of the population had access to health care facilities.

Between 1974 and 1992, there were 575,000 war-related deaths. Hundreds of thousands of Ethiopians died during a famine in 1973, and as many as one million may have died between 1983 and 1985. Average life expectancy in 1995 was estimated at only 50 years. Widespread diseases include malaria, tuberculosis, syphilis, gonorrhea, leprosy, dysentery, and schistosomiasis.

Housing

Except in Addis Ababa, Dire Dawa, and a few other urban centers, most houses are built of mud or mortar and have thatched or tin roofs. In the rural areas, the traditional thatched hut (tukul) is still the most common dwelling.

EDUCATION

Compulsory and free public education exists at the primary level. In 1993, elementary schools had a total enrollment of 2.3 million pupils in 8,674 schools with 75,736 teachers. Junior and senior secondary schools had 720,825 pupils with 22,600 teachers. Universities and equivalent institutions had 26,218 pupils with 1,697 teachers.

1999 KEY EVENTS TIMELINE

February

- War resumes between Ethiopia and Eritrea in the contested territory of Badme, in a conflict which began in May 1998.

- Eritrea's Ambassador is expelled from Ethiopia.

- The United States criticizes Ethiopia for conducting bombing raids on Eritrea.

March

- A three-day battle with Eritrea ends in the Badme region, with up to 40,000 killed or wounded.

- Ethiopia claims a "total victory" in the Badme battle.

- Eritrea agrees to Organization of African Unity (OAU) peace proposals and cease-fire, but Ethiopia does not.

April

- Bombing runs by Ethiopian planes hit the transportation and water systems in Eritrea.

June

- The United Nations Security Council demands an end to fighting, and to the sale of arms and munitions to Ethiopia and Eritrea.

- Both Ethiopia and Eritrea claim to have killed, wounded or captured more than 18,000 troops.

July

- Ethiopia declares that it will continue the war because Eritrea is not taking peace plans seriously.

October

- Ethiopia deports 1,300 Eritreans in buses across the war zone.

- Ethiopia and Yemen agree to cooperate in security issues, signing an accord against Eritrea.

- Tens of thousands are homeless due to flooding from the Wabishebelle River in the eastern part of the country.

November

- Ethiopian businessman Sheik Mohammed al-Amoudi denies allegations that he finances the international terrorist Osama bin Laden.

December

- Former leader Mengistu Haile Mariam travels from Zimbabwe, where he has lived in exile since 1991, to South Africa for medical treatment. Ethiopia wants South Africa to extradite him back to Ethiopia, an action Zimbabwe has refused to take, so that he can be charged with crimes against humanity. Mengistu returns to Zimbabwe before South Africa can act on the request.

ANALYSIS OF EVENTS: 1999

BUSINESS AND THE ECONOMY

Ethiopia's main export and source of income is a product of the coffee trade, which pulled in about $450 million last year. The border clash with Eritrea has disturbed commerce to such an extent that Ethiopia's main port of trade on the coast of the Red Sea in Eritrea, Assab, has been re-routed through Djibouti. The Ethiopian government purchased six MiG-29's and SU fighter bombers from Russia, T-55 tanks from Bulgaria, and is estimated to spend $1 million a day on the war, while many of it's citizens starve. The per capita income for the average Ethiopian is $120 a year, but the country's economy is eight times as large as Eritrea's, and there are 60 million Ethiopians compared to only 3.5 million people in Eritrea.

The roots of this war stem from Ethiopia's economic concern that its people will be turned into a cheap labor pool for Eritrean industry which has sprung up around the coastline. The Ethiopian government has suspected the Eritrean oil refinery of setting high oil prices and Eritrean nationals of smuggling coffee out of Ethiopia for re-exportation. When Ethiopia introduced tariffs against Eritrea, the country started it's own currency called the Nacfa, to replace the Ethiopian Birr. Ethiopia claimed afterwards that all trade must be conducted in American dollars, angering Eritrean officials and setting the stage for war. But the conflict also has its roots in a 1997 Ethiopian map, commissioned by the Tigrayan provincial administration, which made claims on the Badme region. Earlier maps, drawn by Italian colonists, showed the region belonging to Eritrea, but Ethiopian Prime Minister Meles Zenawi does not accept either version, mak-ing the war now, more of an ideological battle for national pride.

GOVERNMENT AND POLITICS

In 1991, Ethiopian and Eritrean troops fought side by side to defeat the Soviet-backed Marxist dictatorship of Mengistu Haile Mariam, which successfully ended the possibility of a foreign dictatorship on Eritrean and Ethiopian soil. The Eritrean People's Liberation Front (EPLF), went on to create the Eritrean government with mutual consent in 1993, while the Tigray People's Liberation Front (TPLF) took over in Ethiopia. President Isaias Afwerki of Eritrea and Prime Minister Meles Zenawi of Ethiopia have not only fought together, but they are related to each other.

The current border skirmish is over a barren piece of land in Badme, which symbolizes the fight to remain independent. In May 1998, Eritrea captured Badme in a move that was meant to show Eritrean independence, but by February 1999, Ethiopia had claimed victory on the same soil, and the fighting continues. Tens of thousands have died on both sides in what is called Africa's first high-tech war. The United States has been quick to point out Ethiopia's blatant use of air force against Eritrea after signing a moratorium on air raids last year, but this has not stopped the use of Russian attack planes. The U.N. and OAU have drafted an 11-point peace plan which calls for each side to leave land occupied after May 6th, 1998, but each country adheres to the story that the land is theirs to keep. A cease-fire and U.N. deployment of peace-keepers would ensue under the peace plan, but while Eritrea has signed the agreement, the country has changed some of the rules, and Ethiopia refuses to bargain. In a sign that Ethiopia will not give up its claim on the Badme region, the country signed a security accord with Yemen in October which strengthens the country militarily, and geographically surrounds Eritrea. This may make Eritrea think twice about continuing hostilities into the next year.

CULTURE AND SOCIETY

The state of post-colonial countries in Africa is one of almost continual flare-ups of violence that lead to war and civil war. The arbitrary creation of colonial maps is partly to blame for ethnic land disputes, and in the case of Ethiopia, definitely plays a part in the conflict. There is also, in the northeastern portion of Africa, a delicate balance between Christian and Muslim influences which is exacerbated by outside influences. The Ethiopian government's relationships with Muslim terrorist leaders in the Middle East make the U.S. government hesitant to provide aid and negotiation for peace in the region. The Ethiopian society is geared for war, the production of arms and supplies for troops, and is eager to accept foreign aid to protect its borders, but this may be dangerous to the country weakened by battle. Ethiopian officials are still trying to recapture ancient Christian relics, including a fourth century obelisk, that were taken by the British in 1868, and by Mussolini's army in 1938.

DIRECTORY

CENTRAL GOVERNMENT

Head of State

President
Nagaso Gidada, Office of the President, P.O. Box 1031, Addis Ababa, Ethiopia
PHONE: +251 (1) 550224
FAX: +251 (1) 552041

Prime Minister
Meles Zenawi, Office of the Prime Minister, Addis Ababa, Ethiopia
PHONE: +251 (1) 550224
FAX: +251 (1) 514300

Ministers

Deputy Prime Minister and Minister of National Defense
Tefera Waluwa, Ministry of National Defense, P.O. Box 1373, Addis Ababa, Ethiopia
PHONE: +251 (1) 511717

Deputy Prime Minister and Minister of National Defense
Tefera Waluwa, Ministry of National Defense, P.O. Box 1373, Addis Ababa, Ethiopia
PHONE: +251 (1) 511717

Minister of Economic Affairs
Kassu Illala, Minister of Economic Affairs, P.O. Box 1037, Addis Ababa, Ethiopia
PHONE: +251 (1) 552800

Minister of Foreign Affairs
Seyoum Mesfin, Ministry of Foreign Affairs, P.O. Box 393, Addis Ababa, Ethiopia
PHONE: +251 (1) 517245

Minister of Justice
Worede-Wold Wolde, Ministry of Justice, P.O. Box 1370, Addis Ababa, Ethiopia
PHONE: +251 (1) 517390

Minister of Finance
Sufyan Ahmad, Ministry of Finance, P.O. Box 1905, Addis Ababa, Ethiopia
PHONE: +251 (1) 552400

Minister of Trade and Industry
Kasahun Ayele, Ministry of Trade and Industry, P.O. Box 704, Addis Ababa, Ethiopia
PHONE: +251 (1) 518025

Minister of Agriculture
Seifu Ketema, Ministry of Agriculture, P.O. Box 62347, Addis Ababa, Ethiopia
PHONE: +251 (1) 518040

Minister of Water Resources
Shiferaw Jarso, Ministry of Water Resources, P.O. Box 1034, Addis Ababa, Ethiopia
PHONE: +251 (1) 510455

Minister of Construction and Urban Development
Haile Aseged, Ministry of Construction and Urban Development, P.O. Box 5608, Addis Ababa, Ethiopia
PHONE: +251 (1) 514655

Minister of Transport and Communications
Abdulmejid Hussein, Ministry of Transport and Communications, P.O. Box 1238, Addis Ababa, Ethiopia
PHONE: +251 (1) 516166

Minister of Mines and Energy
Ezaddin Ali, Ministry of Mines and Energy, P.O. Box 486, Addis Ababa, Ethiopia
PHONE: +251 (1) 518256

Minister of Labor and Social Affairs
Hassan Abdella, Ministry of Labor and Social Affairs, P.O. Box 2056, Addis Ababa, Ethiopia
PHONE: +251 (1) 517080

Minister of Education
Genet Zewdie, Ministry of Education, P.O. Box 1367, Addis Ababa, Ethiopia
PHONE: +251 (1) 553133

Minister of Health
Adem Ibrahim, Ministry of Health, P.O. Box 1234, Addis Ababa, Ethiopia
PHONE: +251 (1) 517011

Minister of Information and Culture
Wolde Michael Chamo, Ministry of Information
and Culture, P.O. Box 1364, Addis Ababa,
Ethiopia
PHONE: +251 (1) 111124

POLITICAL ORGANIZATIONS

Oromo Liberation Front (OLF)

All Amhara People's Organization

**Southern Ethiopia People's Democratic
Coalition**

DIPLOMATIC REPRESENTATION

Embassies in Ethiopia

Austria
P.O. Box 1219, Addis Ababa, Ethiopia
PHONE: +251 (1) 712144
FAX: +251 (1) 712140

Canada
P.O. Box 1130, 6th floor, African Solidarity
Insurance Building, Addis Ababa, Ethiopia
PHONE: +251 (1) 713022
FAX: +251 (1) 710333

China
P.O. Box 5643, Addis Ababa, Ethiopia
PHONE: +251 (1) 711960
FAX: +251 (1) 711611

Egypt
P.O. Box 1611, Addis Ababa, Ethiopia
PHONE: +251 (1) 553077
FAX: +251 (1) 552722

France
P.O. Box 1464, Addis Ababa, Ethiopia
PHONE: +251 (1) 550066
FAX: +251 (1) 551180

Germany
P.O. Box 660, Addis Ababa, Ethiopia
PHONE: +251 (1) 550433
FAX: +251 (1) 551311

India
P.O. Box 528, Addis Ababa, Ethiopia
PHONE: +251 (1) 552394
FAX: +251 (1) 552521

Italy
P.O. Box 1105, Addis Ababa, Ethiopia
PHONE: +251 (1) 551565
FAX: +251 (1) 550218

Japan
P.O. Box 5650, Addis Ababa, Ethiopia
PHONE: +251 (1) 511088
FAX: +251 (1) 511350

Kenya
P.O. Box 3301, Addis Ababa, Ethiopia
PHONE: +251 (1) 610033
FAX: +251 (1) 611433

Russia
P.O. Box 3301, Addis Ababa, Ethiopia
PHONE: +251 (1) 610033
FAX: +251 (1) 611433

United Kingdom
P.O. Box 858, Fikre Mariam Abatechan Street,
Addis Ababa, Ethiopia
PHONE: +251 (1) 612354
FAX: +251 (1) 610588

United States
P.O. Box 1014, Entoto Street, Addis Ababa,
Ethiopia
PHONE: +251 (1) 550666
FAX: +251 (1) 551166

JUDICIAL SYSTEM

Federal Supreme Court

Federal High Court

Federal First Instance Court

Shari'a Court

FURTHER READING

Articles

"Africa's Forgotten War," *The Economist* (May
8, 1999): 41-43.

"Carnage on the Plain," *The Economist* (April
17, 1999): 50.

"Endless Wars," *Time International* (September
6, 1999): 36.

"Ethiopia, Eritrea Interpret Peace Deal
Differently," CNN (July 15, 1999).

"Forgotten War: Tens of Thousands Lose Lives
in Ethiopia-Eritrea Conflict," CNN (June 19,
1999).

"Heavy Fighting Breaks Out Between Eritrea,
Ethiopia," CNN (February 6, 1999).

"Lethal Punch-Up," *The Economist* (September
25, 1999): 55-56.

"Trench Warfare," *The Economist* (March 13,
1999): 58.

Useem, Andrea and David Gough. ''On Africa's Horn, 'The Stupidest War,'' *World Press Review* (June 1999): 12.

''War it Is,'' *The Economist* (February 13, 1999): 44.

Books

Iyob, Arwat. *Blankets of Sand: Poems of War and Exile*. Lawrenceville, NJ: Red Sea Press, 1999.

Stewart, Julia. *Eccentric Graces: Eritrea and Ethiopia Through the Eyes of a Traveler*. Lawrenceville, NJ: Red Sea Press, 1999.

Vestal, Theodore M. *Ethiopia: A Post-Cold War African State*. Westport, CN: Praeger, 1999.

Internet

Africaonline. Available Online @ http://www.africaonline.com (October 28, 1999).

Africa News Online. Available Online @ http://www.africanews.org/west/stories/1999_feat1.html (October 28, 1999).

Eritrea-Ethiopia Conflict Information Site. Available Online @ http://denden.com/conflict/ (November 3, 1999).

Eritrea Network Information Center. Available Online @http://www.eritrea.org (November 3, 1999).

Integrated Regional Information Network (IRIN). Available Online @ http://www.reliefweb.int/IRIN (October 28, 1999).

ETHIOPIA: STATISTICAL DATA

For sources and notes see "Sources of Statistics" in the front of each volume.

GEOGRAPHY

Geography (1)

Area:

Total: 1,127,127 sq km.

Land: 1,119,683 sq km.

Water: 7,444 sq km.

Area—comparative: slightly less than twice the size of Texas.

Land boundaries:

Total: 5,311 km.

Border countries: Djibouti 337 km, Eritrea 912 km, Kenya 830 km, Somalia 1,626 km, Sudan 1,606 km.

Coastline: 0 km (landlocked).

Climate: tropical monsoon with wide topographic-induced variation.

Terrain: high plateau with central mountain range divided by Great Rift Valley.

Natural resources: small reserves of gold, platinum, copper, potash, natural gas.

Land use:

Arable land: 12%

Permanent crops: 1%

Permanent pastures: 40%

Forests and woodland: 25%

Other: 22% (1993 est.).

HUMAN FACTORS

Demographics (2A)

	1990	1995	1998	2000	2010	2020	2030	2040	2050
Population	48,014.6	54,467.1	58,390.4	60,967.4	74,831.9	89,943.2	108,929.4	133,200.8	159,170.2
Net migration rate (per 1,000 population)	NA	NA	NA	NA	NA	NA	NA	NA	NA
Births	NA	NA	NA	NA	NA	NA	NA	NA	NA
Deaths	NA	NA	NA	NA	NA	NA	NA	NA	NA
Life expectancy - males	43.6	41.5	39.8	38.7	38.5	42.0	51.2	60.5	63.9
Life expectancy - females	44.8	42.7	42.0	41.5	38.7	42.6	53.8	65.0	68.9
Birth rate (per 1,000)	46.7	46.0	44.7	44.0	40.6	36.9	32.1	26.9	22.5
Death rate (per 1,000)	19.6	20.6	21.3	21.6	21.8	18.6	12.1	7.4	6.5
Women of reproductive age (15-49 yrs.)	10,709.3	12,014.5	12,891.6	13,440.7	16,978.8	21,561.1	27,868.9	35,855.8	43,623.5
of which are currently married	NA	NA	NA	NA	NA	NA	NA	NA	NA
Fertility rate	7.1	7.1	6.9	6.8	5.9	4.9	3.9	3.1	2.6

Except as noted, values for vital statistics are in thousands; life expectancy is in years.

Health Personnel (3)

Total health expenditure as a percentage of GDP, 1990-1997[a]

Public sector 1.6

Private sector 1.0

Total[b] 2.6

Health expenditure per capita in U.S. dollars, 1990-1997[a]

Purchasing power parity 13

Total 3

Availability of health care facilities per 100,000 people

Hospital beds 1990-1997[a] 20

Doctors 1993[c] 4

Nurses 1993[c] 8

Health Indicators (4)

Life expectancy at birth

1980 42

1997 43

Daily per capita supply of calories (1996) 1,845

Total fertility rate births per woman (1997) 6.5

Maternal mortality ratio per 100,000 live births (1990-97) ....1,400[c]

Safe water % of population with access (1995) 26

Sanitation % of population with access (1995) 8

Consumption of iodized salt % of households (1992-98)[a] 0

Smoking prevalence

Male % of adults (1985-95)[a] ....

Female % of adults (1985-95)[a] ....

Tuberculosis incidence per 100,000 people (1997) 251

Adult HIV prevalence % of population ages 15-49 (1997) 9.31

Infants and Malnutrition (5)

Under-5 mortality rate (1997) 175

% of infants with low birthweight (1990-97) 16

Births attended by skilled health staff % of total[a] 8

% fully immunized (1995-97)

TB 90

DPT 63

Polio 64

Measles 52

Prevalence of child malnutrition under age 5 (1992-97)[b] 48

Ethnic Division (6)

Oromo 40%

Amhara and Tigrean 32%

Sidamo 9%

Shankella 6%

Somali 6%

Afar 4%

Gurage 2%

Other 1%

Religions (7)

Muslim 45%-50%

Ethiopian Orthodox 35%-40%

Animist 12%

Other 3%-8%

Languages (8)

Amharic (official), Tigrinya, Orominga, Guaraginga, Somali, Arabic, English (major foreign language taught in schools).

EDUCATION

Public Education Expenditures (9)

Public expenditure on education (% of GNP)

1980 ....3.1[1]

1996 ....4.0

Expenditure per student

Primary % of GNP per capita

1980 ....17.7[1]

1996 ....34.0[1]

Secondary % of GNP per capita

1980 ....

1996 ....61.6[1]

Tertiary % of GNP per capita

1980 ....1,120.6[1]

1996 ....962.0

Expenditure on teaching materials

Primary % of total for level (1996) ....2.5[1]

Secondary % of total for level (1996) ....

Primary pupil-teacher ratio per teacher (1996) .....38[1]

Duration of primary education years (1995) 6

Educational Attainment (10)

Age group (1994) ....25+

Total population 18,716,940

Highest level attained (%)

  No schooling 80.1

  First level

    Not completed 6.3

    Completed 1.5

  Entered second level

    S-1 . . . . .2.1

    S-2 . . . . .3.4

  Postsecondary 1.0

Literacy Rates (11A)

In thousands and percent[1]	1990	1995	2000	2010
Illiterate population (15+ yrs.)	17,815	19,052	20,406	23,411
Literacy rate - total adult pop. (%)	30.8	35.5	40.4	50.6
Literacy rate - males (%)	40.8	45.5	50.3	59.7
Literacy rate - females (%)	20.8	25.3	30.3	41.5

GOVERNMENT & LAW

Military Affairs (14B)

	1990	1991	1992	1993	1994	1995
Military expenditures						
Current dollars (mil.)	472	370	153	139[e]	129	118
1995 constant dollars (mil.)	542	409	164	145[e]	132	118
Armed forces (000)	250	120	120	120	120	120[e]
Gross national product (GNP)						
Current dollars (mil.)	4,275	4,115	4,087	4,711	4,875	5,347
1995 constant dollars (mil.)	4,914	4,548	4,396	4,939	4,997	5,347
Central government expenditures (CGE)						
1995 constant dollars (mil.)	1,360	1,034	787	981	1,436	NA
People (mil.)	48.2	49.8	51.0	52.4	54.0	55.6
Military expenditure as % of GNP	11.0	9.0	3.7	2.9	2.6	2.2
Military expenditure as % of CGE	39.8	39.6	20.9	14.8	9.2	NA
Military expenditure per capita (1995 $)	11	8	3	3	2	2
Armed forces per 1,000 people (soldiers)	5.2	2.4	2.4	2.3	2.2	2.2
GNP per capita (1995 $)	102	91	86	94	93	96
Arms imports[6]						
Current dollars (mil.)	410	80	0	5	0	0
1995 constant dollars (mil.)	471	88	0	5	0	0
Arms exports[6]						
Current dollars (mil.)	10	0	0	0	0	0
1995 constant dollars (mil.)	11	0	0	0	0	0
Total imports[7]						
Current dollars (mil.)	1,081	472	799	787	1,003	NA
1995 constant dollars (mil.)	1,242	522	859	825	1,059	NA
Total exports[7]						
Current dollars (mil.)	298	189	169	199	372	423
1995 constant dollars (mil.)	342	209	182	209	381	423
Arms as percent of total imports[8]	37.9	16.9	0	6	0	NA
Arms as percent of total exports[8]	3.4	0	0	0	0	0

GOVERNMENT & LAW

Political Parties (12)

The legislative branch is a bicameral Parliament consists of the Council of the Federation (upper chamber (117 seats members are chosen by state assemblies to serve five-year terms) and the Council of People's Representatives, the lower chamber (548 seats members are directly elected by popular vote from single-member districts to serve five-year terms). The Ethiopian People's Revolutionary Democratic Front (EPRDF) holds most seats.

Government Budget (13A)

Year: 1995

Total Expenditures: 8,067.2 Millions of Birr

Expenditures as a percentage of the total by function:

General public services and public order 10.04

Defense 9.13

Education 14.04

Health 5.33

Social Security and Welfare 5.91

Housing and community amenities 5.67

Recreational, cultural, and religious affairs 1.08

Fuel and energy 2.66

Agriculture, forestry, fishing, and hunting 9.72

Mining, manufacturing, and construction 5.13

Transportation and communication 12.92

Other economic affairs and services 9.23

Crime (15)

Crime rate (for 1997)

Crimes reported 178,000

Total persons convicted 36,500

Crimes per 100,000 population 300

Persons responsible for offenses

Total number of suspects 281,300

Total number of female suspects 28,700

Total number of juvenile suspects 3,950

LABOR FORCE

Labor Force (16)

Total . . . . .NA

Agriculture and animal husbandry 80%

Government and services 12%

Industry and construction 8%

Data for 1985. NA stands for not available.

Unemployment Rate (17)

Rate not available.

PRODUCTION SECTOR

Electric Energy (18)

Capacity . . . . .464,000 kW (1995)

Production . . . . .1.143 billion kWh (1995)

Consumption per capita . . . . .20 kWh (1995)

Transportation (19)

Highways:

total: 28,500 km

paved: 4,275 km

unpaved: 24,225 km (1996 est.)

Merchant marine:

total: 13 ships (1,000 GRT or over) totaling 73,775 GRT/98,279 DWT ships by type: cargo 8, oil tanker 2, roll-on/roll-off cargo 3 (1997 est.)

Airports: 86 (1997 est.)

Airports—with paved runways:

total: 10

over 3,047 m: 3

2,438 to 3,047 m: 4

1,524 to 2,437 m: 2

914 to 1,523 m: 1 (1997 est.)

Airports—with unpaved runways:

total: 76

over 3,047 m: 3

2,438 to 3,047 m: 7

1,524 to 2,437 m: 10

914 to 1,523 m: 36

under 914 m: 20 (1997 est.)

Top Agricultural Products (20)

Cereals, pulses, coffee, oilseed, sugarcane, potatoes, other vegetables; hides, cattle, sheep, goats.

MANUFACTURING SECTOR

GDP & Manufacturing Summary (21)

Detailed value added figures are listed by both International Standard Industry Code (ISIC) and product title.

	1980	1985	1990	1994
GDP ($-1990 mil.)[1]	2,919	2,875	3,681	3,266
Per capita ($-1990)[1]	75	66	73	61
Manufacturing share (%) (current prices)[1]	10.8	11.2	11.2	8.8

	1980	1985	1990	1994
Manufacturing				
Value added ($-1990 mil.)[1]	260	311	375	358
Industrial production index	100	137	129	103
Value added ($ mil.)	273	311	532	529
Gross output ($ mil.)	604	741	1,155	1,105
Employment (000)	77	88	105	104
Profitability (% of gross output)				
Intermediate input (%)	55	58	54	52
Wages and salaries inc. supplements (%)	8	9	9	9
Gross operating surplus	37	33	37	39
Productivity ($)				
Gross output per worker	7,859	8,385	10,959	10,591
Value added per worker	3,551	3,519	5,049	5,069
Average wage (inc. supplements)	642	718	987	985
Value added ($ mil.)				
311/2 Food products	66	61	106	97
313 Beverages	50	76	129	130
314 Tobacco products	18	19	45	45
321 Textiles	63	37	52	57
322 Wearing apparel	2	6	8	8
323 Leather and fur products	9	7	21	18
324 Footwear	6	5	8	7
331 Wood and wood products	5	3	5	5
332 Furniture and fixtures	1	2	3	4
341 Paper and paper products	5	5	4	4
342 Printing and publishing	6	9	11	10
351 Industrial chemicals	1	1	1	1
352 Other chemical products	8	11	12	12
353 Petroleum refineries	12	29	78	88
354 Miscellaneous petroleum and coal products	—	—	—	—
355 Rubber products	4	7	6	6
356 Plastic products	2	6	7	7
361 Pottery, china and earthenware	—	—	—	—
362 Glass and glass products	1	2	1	1
369 Other non-metal mineral products	5	10	13	11
371 Iron and steel	5	4	4	3
372 Non-ferrous metals	—	—	—	—
381 Metal products	4	7	9	9
382 Non-electrical machinery	—	—	—	—
383 Electrical machinery	—	—	—	—
384 Transport equipment	—	4	8	7
385 Professional and scientific equipment	—	—	—	—
390 Other manufacturing industries	—	—	—	—

FINANCE, ECONOMICS, & TRADE

Balance of Payments (23)

	1992	1993	1994	1995	1996
Exports of goods (f.o.b.)	170	199	372	423	417
Imports of goods (f.o.b.)	−993	−706	−926	−1,137	−1,235
Trade balance	−823	−507	−554	−714	−817
Services - debits	−472	−377	−385	−445	−453
Services - credits	290	303	337	413	428
Private transfers (net)	544	280	421	379	369
Government transfers (net)	341	252	305	357	302
Overall balance	−120	−50	125	−10	−170

FINANCE, ECONOMICS, & TRADE

Economic Indicators (22)

National product: GDP—purchasing power parity—$29 billion (1997 est.)

National product real growth rate: 5% (1997 est.)

National product per capita: $530 (1997 est.)

Inflation rate—consumer price index: 0% (1996 est.)

Exchange Rates (24)

Exchange rates:

Birr (Br) per US$1 (end of period)

February 1998	.6.9530
September 1997	.6.8080
1996	.6.4260
1995	.6.3200
1994	.5.9500
fixed rate 1992-93	.5.0000

Since May 1993, the birr market rate has been determined in an interbank market supported by weekly wholesale auction; prior to that date, the official rate was pegged to US$1 = 5.000 birr.

Top Import Origins (25)

$1.23 billion (f.o.b., 1996 est.) Data are for 1994.

Origins	%
Saudi Arabia	.15
Italy	.11
United States	.12.3
Germany	.8

Top Export Destinations (26)

$418 million (f.o.b., 1996) Data are for 1994.

Destinations	%
Germany	.32
Japan	.14
Djibouti	.7
Saudi Arabia	.8
Italy	.8

Economic Aid (27)

Recipient: ODA, $367 million (FY95/96).

Import Export Commodities (28)

Import Commodities	Export Commodities
Food and live animals	Coffee
Petroleum and petroleum products	Leather products
	Gold
Chemicals	
Machinery	
Motor vehicles and aircraft	

FALKLAND ISLANDS

Colony of Falkland Islands
Islas Malvinas

CAPITAL: Stanley.

FLAG: The flag of the Falkland Islands is blue with the flag of the United Kingdom in the upper hoist-side quadrant and the Falkland Island coat of arms in a white disk centered on the outer half of the flag; the coat of arms contains a white ram (sheep raising is the major economic activity) above the sailing ship Desire (whose crew discovered the islands) with a scroll at the bottom bearing the motto "Desire the Right".

ANTHEM: God Save the Queen.

MONETARY UNIT: 1 Falkland pound (£F) = 100 pence.

WEIGHTS AND MEASURES: The imperial system is used.

HOLIDAYS: New Year's Day, 1 January; Good Friday, 28 March; HM Queen's Birthday, 21 April; Liberation Day, 14 June; Bank Holiday, 5 October; Anniversary of the Battle of the Falkland Islands, 8 December; Christmas, 25-29 December.

TIME: 8 AM = Noon GMT.

LOCATION AND SIZE: The Falkland Islands, a British crown colony in the South Atlantic, lie some 772 km (480 mi.) northeast of Cape Horn and 57° and 62°W, and have an area of 12,173 sq. km (4,700 sq. mi.).

CLIMATE: The climate is generally damp, cool and with strong westerly winds. Rain occurs on more than half the days in year with occasional snow all year, except in January and February. The summer season runs from December to March with temperatures averaging 16°C (60°F). Average temperature for the winter season, which runs from June to September, is about 0°C (32°F).

INTRODUCTORY SURVEY

RECENT HISTORY

For a small group of islands located in a remote area of the south Atlantic Ocean, the Falkland Islands were nevertheless a major part of the world's news in 1982 when Argentina invaded the islands they call Islas Malvinas in a dispute over ownership with the United Kingdom. Sovereignty arguments over the islands are traced back to unsubstantiated claims by both sides over which explorer first sighted the islands. The Argentines believe the first sighting was by a Spanish navigator while the English believe it to have been by an Englishman. However, the first settlement was by the French in 1764 who left in 1767. British and Argentine settlements traded places in the early 1800s; the islands were made a Crown Colony by Great Britain in 1892.

Since 1885, a self supporting community of 1,800 British citizens lived on the two main islands. After World War II, the dispute over sovereignty was taken to the United Nations, where debates were ongoing through a committee on decolonization. Argentina argued a position based upon centuries old papal bulls, the geographical location of the islands, and the need to end colonization throughout the world. The British argued a position based upon continuous possession and self-determination. The United Nations invited the two parties to negotiate. On April 2, 1982, with negotiations still ongoing, Argentina invaded the islands and claimed control. The act initiated the

SOUTH
ATLANTIC
OCEAN

EAST
FALKLAND

Port Howard

Stanley

Weddell

Goose Green

WEST
FALKLAND

Falkland
Sound

Scotia
Sea

N

W   E

S

Falkland
Islands

FALKLAND ISLANDS

0   25   50 Miles

0   25   50 Kilometers

Falkland Islands War. The United Kingdom immediately mobilized troops and took back the islands.

The war lasted about 10 weeks and cost the lives of more than 1,000 persons. Following the war, the military government of Argentina collapsed. The United Kingdom maintains about 4,300 troops on the islands to guarantee control. A constitution for the islands was enacted on October 3, 1985.

GOVERNMENT

As an overseas territory of the United Kingdom, the head of state for the islands is the British monarch, represented on the islands by an appointed governor. The government is based upon a constitution enacted on October 3, 1985, and amended in 1997. The executive branch of the government includes an Executive Council that serves as a cabinet for the governor. The Executive Council is comprised of three members elected by the Legislative Council, two ex officio members, and the governor. There are no direct elections to the executive branch positions.

The legislature is unicameral, and consists of the Legislative Council of ten seats, eight elected and two ex officio. Elected members serve for five year terms. There is universal suffrage for British citizens over the age of 18.

The Falkland Islands are not engaged in any international agreements as they are dependent on the United Kingdom for international relations and security. They do participate in the International

Confederation of Free Trade Unions (ICFTU). Additional British territories are administered from the Falklands: South Georgia, the South Sandwich Islands, and the Shag and Clerke rocks, all of whom lie hundreds of miles to the east.

Judiciary

The legal system is based upon English common law. The judicial branch is comprised of the Supreme Court, whose chief justice is a nonresident.

Political Parties

There are no formal political parties in the Falkland Islands.

DEFENSE

The United Kingdom has kept 4,300 troops stationed on the islands since the Falkland Islands War in 1982. The islands themselves have no armed forces, but there is a small police force.

ECONOMIC AFFAIRS

The Falkland Islands are located in a cool climate with a mean average annual temperature of just 42 degrees F. There are no indigenous land mammals and no trees. The grasslands of the islands has proven to be good for the raising of livestock. Consequently, sheep and sheep products are the major industry of the islands with over 700,000 sheep in the islands producing several thousand metric tons of wool annually. Wool, hides, and mutton are the islands' exports.

Agricultural products are otherwise limited to fodder for the sheep, and vegetables and dairy products for consumption by the islands' residents. There is a small industry involved in the sale of stamps and coins for collectors. Fuel, food and drink, building materials, and all machinery needs must be imported. Ample peat reserves on the islands are tapped for domestic fuel consumption.

In 1987, the government began selling fishing licenses for the islands' exclusive economic zone, fees that produce $40 million annually. The British Geological Survey established a 200-mile oil exploration zone around the islands in 1993. Although there had been no development of those fields by 1999, the surveys indicate as much as 500,000 barrels per day of oil could be realized from the reserves. To help defuse the still-antagonistic relations with Argentina, the United Kingdom entered into an agreement with them in 1995 to more clearly define the situation with the potential oil reserves.

Public Finance

The currency is the Falkland Island Pound, which is directly tied to the British Pound. Gross Domestic Product figures are not available, but the islands' government is self-sufficient other than defense. Domestic expenditures of $66.8 million in 1998 are nearly identical to the $66.1 million in revenues. Trade balance of payments are not favorable, with only $7.6 million in exports in 1995 to balance against $24.7 million in imports. However, the income from fishing licenses more than makes up the difference.

Income

Per capita income figures are not available for the islands. The is no unemployment and in fact, the islands suffer from a shortage of labor.

Industry

Sheep and sheep products are the Falkland Islands' major industry. Some agricultural efforts produce vegetables and dairy products for consumption on the islands. Licenses are sold for fishing rights in the exclusion zone surrounding the islands.

Economic Development

The islands have made some efforts to encourage tourism as a means of generating income Three small lodges have been built to draw visitors interested in the wildlife and trout fishing. Further development of offshore fishing licensing and the potential oil reserves are being pursued.

SOCIAL WELFARE

The Falkland Island government provides adequate social services for the islands' residents. There is no unemployment on the islands and labor is in short supply, but the shortage of housing impedes immigration. The government operates a radio station and two broadcast television stations.

Healthcare

Medical services are free and are provided by the government through a hospital at the capital of Stanley.

Housing

Housing is adequate but in short supply.

EDUCATION

Education is free and compulsory up to the age of 15. There is one secondary school at Stanley.

Outlying families may be served by distance education with traveling tutors and radio lessons.

1999 KEY EVENTS TIMELINE

January

- Argentina sends its foreign minister, Guido Di Tella, to New York this month to ask United Nations secretary-general Kofi Annan for help regarding the ongoing dispute over the Falkland Islands.

- President Carlos Menem of Argentina expresses in *Time International* the hope he feels at solving the long dispute with Great Britain over the Falkland Islands, based on his meetings with British Prime Minister Tony Blair in October 1998.

- Donald A. Lamont is named the next Governor of the Falkland Islands. He will take office in April 1999.

February

- Cambridge Mineral Resources starts its 1999 field exploration of the Falklands, targeting diamonds and sand.

March

- At the request of the Chilean government, the Chilean airline LAN ends its weekly service between Punta Arenas and Port Stanley, Falkland Islands. Chile's government is unhappy about Augusto Pinochet's detention in Britain.

- The Falklands begin to see some promise of recovery as the Asian economies stabilize and the Falklands begins to gain increased revenue as Asian fishing companies acquire licenses to fish in the Falkland Islands Cooperation Areas.

April

- The Executive Secretary of the Korean Deep Sea Fishing Association organizes a protest against the Falklands Fishery for not taking action to deter Taiwanese poachers.

May

- Due to ongoing tensions between Argentina, Britain, and the Falklands and because of the cessation of flights from Chile, a joint licensing round for oil exploration in a "Special Cooperation Area'' that straddles Argentine and Falkland waters has been unable to begin.

- The first formal negotiations between the Falklanders and Argentina since the 1982 war take place in Britain at the Falklands' request. Discussions concern illegal fishing, air links, and oil exploration in the waters between the Falklands and the mainland.

- A British-based company claims to have discovered gold in the Falklands.

July

- Argentina and Great Britain reach an agreement in London to allow Argentine citizens to visit the Falklands, to enhance existing levels of cooperation regarding fishing and conservation in the Falkland waters, and to build a memorial to commemorate those killed in the 1982 war.

September

- The Falklands celebrate the 100th anniversary of St. Mary's Catholic Church in Port Stanley. A special holy mass and buffet were held for the parishioners and 150 invited guests, with Reverend Maurice McGill, Superior General of Mill Hill Fathers in London, officiating.

October

- President Carlos Menem of Argentina claims sovereignty over the Falkland Islands as he dedicates a monument to honor those who died in the conflict with Great Britain over the islands in 1982.

- The first commercial flight between Argentina and Falklands in 17 years lands in Mount Pleasant containing 20 Argentine relatives of soldiers killed during the 1982 Falkland war.

ANALYSIS OF EVENTS: 1999

BUSINESS AND THE ECONOMY

Due to ongoing tensions between Argentina, Britain and the Falklands as well as because of the cessation of flights from Chile, a joint licensing round for oil exploration in a ''Special Cooperation Area'' that straddles Argentine and Falkland waters has been unable to begin. For some time, the only air link for the island was a bi-weekly flight to and from Britain by Royal Air Force (RAF). Re-

newed talks in Britain offered some hope that the presence of oil and gas sources in the SCA will begin, though many expect oil exploration won't begin until after 2000.

Cambridge Mineral Resources started its 1999 field exploration of the Falklands, targeting diamonds and sand. The company holds a license that allows them to search 12,000 square kilometers of the islands. The search is based on a theory that holds that the Falkland Islands' geological origins could be linked to a plate in the Earth's crust which originated from a location adjacent to the east side of South Africa—a region with significant collections of diamonds, gold, coal and base metals.

GOVERNMENT AND POLITICS

Falkland political news in 1999 largely concerned the ongoing disputes between Argentina and Britain over sovereignty; formal discussions were held for the first time since the 1982 war between the feuding nations.

Argentina sent its foreign minister, Guido Di Tella, to New York in January to ask U.N. secretary-general Kofi Annan for help in the ongoing dispute over the Falkland Islands. Argentina claims it inherited what it calls the *Islas Malvinas* from Spain, while Great Britain claims Spain never owned the islands and that they have been British owned since they took possession in 1833. Argentina invaded the island in 1982, igniting a war with Britain. Since then, no flights have been allowed from Argentine soil and cooperation with Britain has been largely over protecting the island's fishing industry. Most of the Falklands' 2,000 inhabitants are firmly opposed to Argentine rule and wish to maintain their self-governing status as a British colony. Argentina was recently given a seat on the United Nations Security Council, and called for the decolonization committee to begin talks concerning Britain and Argentina's sovereignty over the Falklands.

The first formal negotiations between the Falklanders and Argentina since the 1982 war took place in Britain at the Falklands' request to discuss illegal fishing, air links, and oil exploration in the waters between the Falklands and the mainland. Argentina continues to claim the Falkland Islands as its own, and has discussed buying or sharing sovereignty with Britain with little success. Islanders do not want to change their status as a self-governing British territory and though Britain and Argentina have not agreed to a solution, they have maintained normal relations in reference to oil exploration and fisheries. The Falklanders, however, still refuse Argentina's entry to the island, and have continued to reject Argentina's advances and attempts at winning them over.

President Carlos Menem of Argentina expressed his hope at solving the dispute with Britain over the Falklands in an article he authored appearing in *Time International*. Reporting on his meetings in London in October 1998, the first visit by an Argentine head of state to the United Kingdom since the 1982 war, Menem wrote that though the issue of sovereignty was not discussed, the meeting was symbolically and diplomatically important. He cites figures that indicated 73 percent of the British people believe it is time to solve the conflict over the Falklands, and that a majority believe that a better understanding between the two nations would be beneficial. Menem and British Prime Minister Tony Blair drafted a joint-action plan pledging to cover international trade, education, terrorism and joint ventures in the South Atlantic.

Donald A. Lamont was named the next governor of the Falkland Islands and took office in April. Lamont's previous post was as Chief of Staff and Deputy High Representative at the Office of High Representative in Bosnia-Herzegovina. Lamont had a long career in British foreign service and has also worked with the United Nations and served as Ambassador to Uruguay, among many posts.

CULTURE AND SOCIETY

The Falklands celebrated the 100th anniversary of the St. Mary's Catholic Church in Port Stanley. A special holy mass and buffet were held for the parishioners and 150 invited guests, with Reverend Maurice McGill, Superior General of Mill Hill Fathers in London, officiating.

DIRECTORY

CENTRAL GOVERNMENT
Head of State
Queen
Elizabeth, Monarch, Buckingham Palace, London, SW1 England

Governor
Donald Lamont, Office of the Governor

Chief Executive
A. M. Gurr, Office of the Chief Executive

Financial Secretary
D. F. Howatt, Office of Finance

POLITICAL ORGANIZATIONS
None

DIPLOMATIC REPRESENTATION
Embassies in The Falkland Islands

United Kingdom
Government House, Stanley, Falkland Islands
PHONE: +500 27433
FAX: +500 27434

JUDICIAL SYSTEM
Supreme Court

FURTHER READING
Articles

"Falklands Benefit As Confidence Returns as Asian Economies and Oil Prices Fluctuate Upwards." Falkland Islands News Network, 23 March 1999.

"Falklands Celebrate as St. Mary's Marks 100 Years of Service." Falkland Islands News Network, 27 September 1999.

"Flying and the Flag." *The Economist* 351 (May 29, 1999): 32.

"Fresh Air Over the South Atlantic." *Time International* 153, 3 (January 25, 1999): 20.

"Gold Discovered in Falkland Islands." *American Metal Market* 107 (May 25, 1999): 7.

"Governor Wanted." *World Press Review* 46, 7 (July 1999): 21.

"Is There Gold in Them There Hills?" Falkland Islands News Network, 10 February 1999.

"Koreans Protest as Poachers Vacuum Squid from Falklands Zone." Falkland Islands News Network, 19 April 1999.

"New Governor for the Falkland Islands." Falkland Islands News Network, 22 January 1999.

"Tensions, Lack of Success Stall Falkland Islands Exploration." *The Oil Daily*, 13 May 1999.

"Them? They Just Live There." *The Economist* (January 23, 1999): 32.

FALKLAND ISLANDS: STATISTICAL DATA

For sources and notes see "Sources of Statistics" in the front of each volume.

GEOGRAPHY

Geography (1)

Area:

Total: 12,173 sq km.

Land: 12,173 sq km.

Water: 0 sq km.

Note: includes the two main islands of East and West Falkland and about 200 small islands.

Area—comparative: slightly smaller than Connecticut.

Land boundaries: 0 km.

Coastline: 1,288 km.

Climate: cold marine; strong westerly winds, cloudy, humid; rain occurs on more than half of days in year; occasional snow all year, except in January and February, but does not accumulate.

Terrain: rocky, hilly, mountainous with some boggy, undulating plains.

Natural resources: fish, wildlife.

Land use:

Arable land: 0%

Permanent crops: 0%

Permanent pastures: 99%

Forests and woodland: 0%

Other: 1% (1993 est.).

HUMAN FACTORS

Demographics (2B)

Population (July 1998 est.) 2,805

Age structure:

  0-14 years . . . . .NA

  15-64 years . . . . .NA

  65 years and over . . . . .NA

Population growth rate (1998 est.) 4.13%

Birth rate (births/1,000 population) . . . . .NA

Death rate (deaths/1,000 population) . . . . .NA

Net migration rate (migrant(s)/1,000 population) . . .NA

Infant mortality rate (deaths/ 1,000 live births) . . . .NA

Life expectancy at birth:

  Total population . . . . .NA

  Male . . . . .NA

  Female . . . . .NA

Total fertility rate (children born/woman) . . . . .NA

Ethnic Division (6)

British.

Religions (7)

Primarily Anglican, Roman Catholic, United Free Church, Evangelist Church, Jehovah's Witnesses, Lutheran, Seventh-Day Adventist.

Languages (8)

English.

GOVERNMENT & LAW

Political Parties (12)

The legislative branch is a unicameral Legislative Council (10 seats, 8 elected, 2 ex officio members are elected by popular vote to serve five-year terms).

Government Budget (13B)

Revenues . . . .$53.4 million

Expenditures . . . .$53.1 million

  Capital expenditures . . . . .NA

Data for 1994-95 est. NA stands for not available.

Military Affairs (14A)

Total expenditures . . . .$NA

Expenditures as % of GDP . . . . .NA%

Defense is the responsibility of the UK. NA stands for not available.

LABOR FORCE

Labor Force (16)

Total 1,100 (est.); Agriculture 95% (mostly sheepherding).

Unemployment Rate (17)

Full employment; labor shortage.

PRODUCTION SECTOR

Electric Energy (18)

Capacity . . . . .9,000 kW (1995)

Production . . . . .10 million kWh (1995)

Consumption per capita . . . . .4,316 kWh (1995)

Transportation (19)

Highways:

total: 348 km

paved: 83 km

unpaved: 265 km

Merchant marine: none

Airports: 5 (1997 est.)

Airports—with paved runways:

total: 2

2,438 to 3,047 m: 1

under 914 m: 1 (1997 est.)

Airports—with unpaved runways:

total: 3

under 914 m: 3 (1997 est.)

Top Agricultural Products (20)

Fodder and vegetable crops; sheep farming, small dairy herds.

FINANCE, ECONOMICS, & TRADE

Economic Indicators (22)

No data available.

Exchange Rates (24)

Exchange rates:

Falkland pound (£F) per US$1

| January 1998 . . . . .0.6115 |
| 1997 . . . . .0.6106 |
| 1996 . . . . .0.6403 |
| 1995 . . . . .0.6335 |
| 1994 . . . . .0.6529 |
| 1993 . . . . .0.6658 |

The Falkland pound is at par with the British pound

Top Import Origins (25)

$24.7 million (1995) Data are for 1992.

Origins	%
United Kingdom	.NA
Netherlands Antilles	.NA
Japan	.NA

NA stands for not available.

Top Export Destinations (26)

$7.6 million (1995) Data are for 1992.

Destinations	%
United Kingdom	.NA
Netherlands	.NA
Japan	.NA

NA stands for not available.

Economic Aid (27)

Recipient: ODA, $NA. Note: UK, ODA and OOF bilateral commitments totaled $18 million (1993-94). NA stands for not available.

Import Export Commodities (28)

Import Commodities	Export Commodities
Fuel	Wool
Food and drink	Hides
Building materials	Meat
Clothing	

FAROE ISLANDS

Føroyar

INTRODUCTORY SURVEY

RECENT HISTORY

After first being settled by Irish monks around 700, the group of eighteen islands located about half way between Iceland and Norway in the North Atlantic Ocean were colonized by Vikings the following century. Later Christianized by the king of Norway around 1000, the islands became a Norwegian province. Denmark gained control over Norway and the islands in 1380. During the early nineteenth century Denmark's domination over the Faroe Islands grew. The Faroes formally became part of Denmark in 1849 with representation in the Danish legislature. With the native Faroese language discouraged, Danish became the official language in political and legal proceedings. In reaction, a Faroese nationalistic independence movement grew during the late nineteenth century eventually leading to formation of the Home Rule Party in 1906. Because the islands are strategically located along important sea lanes, Great Britain gained control of the Faroes in World War II when Germany occupied Denmark. Immediately following the war, control was restored to Denmark. The Faroes soon gained self-governance over domestic matters through the Home Rule Act of 1948. The islands remained part of the Danish state, dependent on Danish defense, foreign policy, the monetary system, and judicial matters. By 1998 the Faroes were seeking increased sovereignty from the Danish monarchy through negotiations with a possible public referendum vote scheduled in 2000.

GOVERNMENT

Part of the Kingdom of Denmark, the Faroe Islands operate under the 1953 Danish constitution. The chief of state is Denmark's Queen Margrethe II and head of government is an elected prime minister. An appointed High Commissioner represents Danish government in the Faroe's governmental proceedings. The thirty-two seats of the unicameral Faroese Parliament, or Logting, are filled by members elected by popular vote with suffrage enjoyed by all residents over eighteen years of age. Members serve four-year terms. Leader of the party winning the most seats is usually elected prime minister by the Faroese Parliament. The cabinet, known as Landsstyri, is elected by the Faroese Parliament.

Judiciary

A part of the Danish legal system, no judiciary operates on the islands.

Political Parties

Active political parties include the Social Democratic Party, the Workers' Party, Home Rule Party, Unionist Party, Republican Party, Center Party, Christian People's Party, and People's Party. The Republicans, People's Party, and Social Democrats received the most popular votes in 1998.

DEFENSE

With Faroe defense and foreign affairs a responsibility of Denmark, the islands have no organized military forces except for a small police force and a Coast Guard.

ECONOMIC AFFAIRS

With usually cool, foggy and windy summers and a rugged rocky terrain, only 6% of the land can be cultivated. Prior to the twentieth century a largely agrarian economy relied on sheep farming and wool exports. The main crop is potatoes, primarily grown for local consumption. By 1900 fishing and the export of dried cod became predominant. Following massive investments in its fishing fleets in the 1980s, the economy boomed. The Faroes enjoyed a remarkably high standard of living as fish and fish products constituted 96% of the Faroes' exports. But by the early 1990s, the aggressive fish harvests within the 200 nautical mile fisheries zone established around the Faroes in 1977 had significantly exhausted the supply of fish. The economy suffered with the gross domestic product (GDP) declining by some 20% in 1993. The Faroes became reliant on annual subsidies provided by Denmark. In 1995 exports exceeded imports, $362 million to $316 million.

As part of an economic recovery program, the Faroe Islands completed free trade agreements with Norway, Sweden, Iceland, Finland, and Austria in 1992 and 1993. As fish catches began to recover, agriculture and fishing constituted 14.5% of the gross domestic product (GDP) by 1996. New fish processing plants including fish farms were built to expand the economic base in the late 1990s.

Public Finance

The Faroes receive substantial annual subsidies from Denmark. Denmark provided approximately U.S. $150 million in 1995. In 1996, the aid accounted for about 24% of the total government revenue. Primary sources of revenue in 1998 were the income tax, customs, excise and production duties, and Danish transfer payments. Expenditures that year focused on social welfare, interest paid on debts, education and research, health, fishing and shipping, and communications in decreasing order.

Income

In 1996 the gross domestic product (GDP) was U.S. $700 million at an annual declining rate of 6%. Per capita GDP was U.S. $16,000. The prior economic income gross national product (GNP) increased in real terms from 1973 to 1988 at an average annual rate of 4.5%. But during financial hard times between 1989 and 1993 the GNP fell dramatically at an average rate of 9.4%.

Industry

In addition to the cod fishing industry, other industries include mining, shipbuilding, construction, and handicrafts. Industry constituted 18.7% of the GDP in 1996. Coal is mined on Sudhur Island. Offshore deep-water oil reserves were tested in the mid-1990s with favorable results. By 1996 the Faroese government began preparing to award drilling rights to bidders. However, ongoing continental shelf boundary disputes involving Denmark and Great Britain complicated plans to develop the region. To boost tourism, the Faroe Islands joined with Greenland and Iceland to form the West Nordic Tourist Board.

Banking and Finance

In an effort to stabilize the Faroes' economy following the financial crisis of the early 1990s and resolve the indebtedness to Denmark, Denmark restructured the island's banking system. The island banks include state-owned F roya Banki P/f which is the largest bank in addition to F roya Sparikassi, Landsbanki F roya, Nor oya Sparikassi, and the Su uroya Sparikassi.

SOCIAL WELFARE

The Faroe government spent 28% of its total budget in 1995 on social welfare programs. In 1998 key social security benefits included old-age pensions, disabled pensions, and cash benefits for sickness and unemployment.

Healthcare

Life expectancy was estimated at 78.6 years for the total population in 1999 with males averaging 75.7 years and females 81.6 years. Government medical services included three hospitals with almost 300 beds in the mid-1990s. In 1996, eighty-five physicians and thirty-nine dentists practiced on the islands.

Housing

Several of the key housing issues addressed by the Faroes' social services in 1998 included nursing homes for the infirm, housing for mentally handicapped, and an insulation program and heating fuel allowance for the lower income residents.

EDUCATION

The Faroe's educational system is similar to Denmark's except that Faroese is the language of instruction. Learning the Danish language, however, is compulsory. The Faroese Academy was founded in Torshavn in 1965 and in 1990 was upgraded to become the University of the Faroe Islands. Similar to Denmark, the literacy rate on the islands is high, as 99% of those over age fifteen can read and write.

1999 KEY EVENTS TIMELINE

March

- A labor dispute ended in the calling of both a lockout and general strike involving over 900 workers. Union demands include a 60 percent increase in wages. The government and unions eventually settle after three weeks with an agreement to raise wages 6.5 percent over two years, and to give workers an additional 3-1/2 days of paid leave annually.

May

- The twenty-year-old dispute over the 100,000 square kilometers between the United Kingdom and the Faroe Islands is resolved. The agreement, signed on May 18, sets the boundary halfway between the countries. The boundary was a crucial first step in the exploration for oil in the area.

- Reflecting the easing of laws restricting radio and television in the Faroe Islands, Atlantic Radio is the first of several commercial radio stations to begin broadcasts, following a light, easy listening format.

June

- ''Summartónar'' Festival of Classical and Contemporary Music is held from June 24-July 5.

July

- The two-day annual festival, Ólavsxka in Tórshavn, is held July 28-29. The festival opens with a parade, and includes rowing, football, and various others sports competitions.

- Saint Olav's Day, the national holiday and also the ceremonial official opening of parliament, is July 29. The day begins with a procession of government and religious officials, first to the cathedral and then to parliament. Horse races and an outdoor religious service follow in the afternoon, with folk and disco dancing in the evening.

August

- Newspapers in Denmark reveal that U.S. documents recently discovered prove that the United States and Denmark withheld information about an army base on Mount Sornfellio from the Faroese people. The documents show that U.S. and Danish officials wanted the Faroese people to believe the base was maintained by NATO, when it was really a U.S. base, forming a key link in a chain of military operations in Iceland, Scotland, Greenland, and the Faroes. The organization, Faroese People for Peace, had asserted that the base made the Faroes a bomb target.

- A bomb dropped by a German plane in World War II is found and detonated on Su*p*uroy. It is believed that there may be other unexploded bombs from World War II elsewhere in the Faroes.

- A strike of banks and insurance companies is settled hours before a midnight deadline, ending in a two-year contract that features wage increases of 6.5 percent over two years, and three-and-a-half new paid holidays.

- The Torshavnar Jazz, Folk, and Blues Festival, first held in 1984, is staged at the Nordic House August 11-14. Musicians, especially from Scandinavia, perform at the annual event.

October

- Sheep are herded from their mountainside pastures and slaughtered to provide meat over the winter. Formerly, all parts of the sheep including wool and sheepskin were used or sold. This is the first year that there were no buyers for the sheepskin, and it was all disposed of. The Farmers' Association is seeking a new market for the sheepskin.

November

- Results of a poll are released revealing that while the *Tjóðveldisflokkur* (Republicans) still have the support of the highest percentage of voters (more that 25 percent), support for the other parties has shifted. The poll also reveals that the majority of Faroese do not want to break away from Denmark next year, but ''sometime in the future.''

- Legislation is introduced regarding the procedures for awarding contracts for petroleum ex-

ploration. Bidding is expected to take place early in 2000.

ANALYSIS OF EVENTS: 1999

BUSINESS AND THE ECONOMY

The government has yet to reach a consensus on whether to provide public funding to the country's fleet of fishing boats. Fisheries Minister Jxrgen Niclassen and his supporters advocate the use of government funds to replace the fishing fleet, which averages thirty to forty years old, as a step toward making the fleet self-sufficient. However both of the other coalition parties consider that the fishing fleet should be completely self-supporting, without financial support from the government. The latter group believes that the fishing capacity, currently too great, will fall to a reasonable level in the absence of government funding.

The Farmers Association sought a new market for sheepskin and wool, and is investigating the possibility of marketing sheepskin to the United States. For the first time, the sheepskin from the annual slaughter of around 50,000 sheep could not find a market and was disposed of.

GOVERNMENT AND POLITICS

After a dispute with the U.K. was resolved over boundaries, the Faroe Islands government can now work to encourage the pursuit of exploration for oil. In addition, the government—comprised of a coalition of Republicans, Conservatives and the Self-Rule Party—has begun the exploration of establishing the Faroe Islands' independence from Denmark. Committees have been established to study the impact independence might have on the economy, how the country would fare without Danish financial support (currently around one billion Kroner), and to begin preliminary work on framing a constitution.

CULTURE AND SOCIETY

Faroe Islands is hoping to build on its scenic location to expand its tourism industry. Music festivals during the summer will continue to attract visitors. A popular activity is speed rowing. Beginning in May and on every other weekend through the summer months, rowing competitions, using

Faroese boats modeled after Viking boats, take place in every town and village. The boat is made in six-person, eight-person, ten-person, and occasionally even twelve-person models.

DIRECTORY

CENTRAL GOVERNMENT
Head of State

Queen
Margrethe II of Denmark, Monarch, Maalienborg, 1257 Copenhagen K, Denmark

Ministers

Prime Minister
Anfinn Kallsberg, Office of the Prime Minister

POLITICAL ORGANIZATIONS
Fólkaflokkurin (People's Party)
NAME: Arnfinn Kallsberg

Javnaðarflokkurin (Equality Party)
Kristiligi Fólkaflokkurin (Christian People's Party)
NAME: Niels Pauli Danielsen

Miðflokkurin (Centre Party)
NAME: Tordur Niclasen

Sambandsflokkurin (Union Party)
NAME: Edmund Joensen

Sjálvstýrisflokkurin (Self-Government Party)
NAME: Helena Dam A. Neystabo

Tjóðveldisflokkurin (Party for People's Government)
E-MAIL: jogvan@sam-teld.fo

Verkamannafylkingin (Workers' Movement)
NAME: Alis Jacobsen

JUDICIAL SYSTEM
Administered by Denmark

FURTHER READING
Articles

DeLuca, Marshall. "Faroes' Licensing Further Delayed Over Dispute." *Offshore* 59, 4 (April 1999): 12.

Swann, Richard. "Faroes Hopes to Award E and P Blocks by Summer 2000." *Platt's Oilgram News* 77, 92 (May 14, 1999): 1+.

"Will the Faeroes Flee the Nest?" *The Economist* 348 (September 5, 1998): 50.

Books

Taylor, Elizabeth, ed. *The Far Islands and Other Cold Places: Travel Essays of a Victorian Lady.* St. Paul, Minn.: Pogo Press, 1997.

Internet

Faroe Islands Review. Available Online @ review.fo (November 16, 1999).

Faroe Islands Travel Guide. Available Online @ 222.puffin.fo/travel (November 15, 1999).

FAROE ISLANDS: STATISTICAL DATA

For sources and notes see "Sources of Statistics" in the front of each volume.

GEOGRAPHY

Geography (1)

Area:

Total: 1,399 sq km.

Land: 1,399 sq km.

Water: 0 sq km (some lakes and streams).

Area—comparative: eight times the size of Washington, DC.

Land boundaries: 0 km.

Coastline: 1,117 km.

Climate: mild winters, cool summers; usually overcast; foggy, windy.

Terrain: rugged, rocky, some low peaks; cliffs along most of coast.

Natural resources: fish, whales.

Land use:

Arable land: 6%

Permanent crops: 0%

Permanent pastures: 0%

Forests and woodland: 0%

Other: 94% (1996).

HUMAN FACTORS

Ethnic Division (6)

Scandinavian.

Religions (7)

Evangelical Lutheran.

Languages (8)

Faroese (derived from Old Norse), Danish.

Demographics (2A)

	1990	1995	1998	2000	2010	2020	2030	2040	2050
Population	47.4	43.5	41.8	40.2	31.5	26.0	23.6	21.2	19.2
Net migration rate (per 1,000 population)	NA	NA	NA	NA	NA	NA	NA	NA	NA
Births	NA	NA	NA	NA	NA	NA	NA	NA	NA
Deaths	NA	NA	NA	NA	NA	NA	NA	NA	NA
Life expectancy - males	73.9	75.1	75.5	75.8	76.9	77.8	78.6	79.2	79.8
Life expectancy - females	81.0	81.1	81.4	81.7	82.9	83.8	84.6	85.2	85.8
Birth rate (per 1,000)	20.0	14.4	13.1	12.0	9.1	9.9	8.3	8.1	8.3
Death rate (per 1,000)	7.4	8.2	8.8	9.4	12.6	15.6	18.0	19.0	17.3
Women of reproductive age (15-49 yrs.)	11.3	9.6	9.0	8.4	5.9	4.0	4.1	4.2	3.7
of which are currently married	NA	NA	NA	NA	NA	NA	NA	NA	NA
Fertility rate	2.7	2.4	2.4	2.3	2.0	1.8	1.7	1.5	1.5

Except as noted, values for vital statistics are in thousands; life expectancy is in years.

GOVERNMENT & LAW

Political Parties (12)

Faroese Parliament	% of seats
Republicans	.23.8
People's Party	.21.3
Social Democrats	.21.9
Coalition Party (Union Party, Labor Front, Home Rule Party)	.15

Government Budget (13B)

Revenues	.$467 million
Expenditures	.$468 million
Capital expenditures	.$11 million

Data for 1996 est.

Military Affairs (14A)

Total expenditures	.$NA
Expenditures as % of GDP	.NA%

Defense is the responsibility of Denmark. NA stands for not available.

LABOR FORCE

Labor Force (16)

Total 20,345. Largely engaged in fishing, manufacturing, transportation, and commerce. Data for 1995 est.

Unemployment Rate (17)

11% (1996 est.)

PRODUCTION SECTOR

Electric Energy (18)

Capacity	.91,000 kW (1995)
Production	.200 million kWh (1995)
Consumption per capita	.4,092 kWh (1995)

Transportation (19)

Highways:

total: 458 km

paved: 450 km

unpaved: 8 km (1995 est.)

Merchant marine:

total: 6 ships (1,000 GRT or over) totaling 22,853 GRT/13,481 DWT ships by type: cargo 2, oil tanker 1, refrigerated cargo 1, roll-on/roll-off cargo 1, short-sea passenger 1 (1997 est.)

Airports: 1 (1997 est.)

Airports—with paved runways:

total: 1

914 to 1,523 m: 1 (1997 est.)

Top Agricultural Products (20)

Milk, potatoes, vegetables; sheep; salmon farming; fish.

FINANCE, ECONOMICS, & TRADE

Economic Indicators (22)

National product: GDP—purchasing power parity—$800 million (1996 est.)

National product real growth rate: 6% (1996 est.)

National product per capita: $16,300 (1996 est.)

Inflation rate—consumer price index: 2.8% (1996 est.)

Exchange Rates (24)

Exchange rates:

Danish kroner (DKr) per US$1

January 1998	.6.916
1997	.6.604
1996	.5.799
1995	.5.602
1994	.6.361
1993	.6.484

Top Import Origins (25)

$315.6 (c.i.f., 1995)

Origins	%
Denmark	.34.5
Norway	.15.9
United Kingdom 8.4% Germany	.7.8
Sweden	.5.8
United States	.1.5

Top Export Destinations (26)

$362 million (f.o.b., 1995).

Destinations	%
Japan	.NA
United States	.NA
Guam	.NA

NA stands for not available.

Economic Aid (27)

Receives an annual subsidy from Denmark of about $150 million (1995).

Import Export Commodities (28)

Import Commodities	Export Commodities
Machinery and transport equipment 17.0%	Fish and fish products 92%
Consumer goods 33%	Animal feedstuffs
Raw materials and semi manufactures 26.9%	Transport equipment (ships)
Fuels 11.4%	
Fish and salt 6.7%	

FIJI

Republic of Fiji

INTRODUCTORY SURVEY

RECENT HISTORY

Fiji was settled by Polynesian and Melanesian peoples at least 2,500 years ago. On 10 October 1970, Fiji became a sovereign and independent state within the Commonwealth of Nations, with Kamisese K. T. Mara, head of the Alliance Party, as prime minister. He and his majority party won elections in 1972, 1977, and 1982, but lost the April 1987 elections to an Indian-based coalition. Within a year, Lieutenant Colonel Sitivendi Rabuka led two military takeovers aimed at restoring political leadership to ethnic Fijians. He suspended the constitution, dissolved the parliament, and declared Fiji a republic. Full civilian rule returned in January 1990 when Rabuka gave up his position as minister of home affairs and became head of the armed forces.

The adoption in 1990 of a new constitution that favored rural Melanesian control of Fiji led to heavy Indian emigration causing serious economic difficulties. In 1996, the Constitutional Review Commission recommended the abolition of racial preferences in government.

GOVERNMENT

A new constitution went into effect in July 1990. It established Fiji as a sovereign, democratic republic with a two-chamber legislature. Fiji's president was to be appointed to a five-year term by the Great Council of Chiefs, which would also nominate twenty-four Melanesians to the thirty-four-member Senate. The seventy-member House

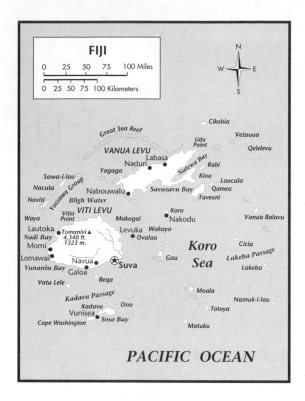

of Representatives was to be elected by the people every five years.

Judiciary

The 1990 constitution reorganized the judicial system. The courts include the Magistrate Courts, a High Court, and the Court of Appeals. A Supreme Court established by the 1990 constitution is not yet functioning.

Political Parties

Major political parties include the Fijian Political Party (SVT—primarily Fijian); the National Federation Party (NFP—primarily Indian); the Fijian Nationalist Party (FNP); the Fiji Labour Party (FLP); the All National Congress (ANC); and the General Voters Party (GVP). In the 1994 elections, SVT won a majority with thirty-one of seventy-one seats.

DEFENSE

Fiji's armed forces in 1995 consisted of 3,600 men, of whom 3,300 were in the army and 290 in the navy.

ECONOMIC AFFAIRS

Fiji's economy is mostly based on agriculture and tourism, and depends heavily on foreign trade. In 1995, agriculture accounted for 21% of gross domestic product (GDP); services, 61%; and industry, 18%.

Public Finance

The U.S. Central Intelligence Agency estimates that, in 1995, government revenues totaled approximately $495.6 million and expenditures $591.2 million. External debt totaled $670 million.

From 1985–95, Fiji suffered a crisis in both private and public investment. Total investment–both public and private–stood at 21.3% of GDP in 1985 and had dropped to 15.8% in 1994. Private investment fell from 13.6% to 5.4%, and public dropped from 3.5% to 2.4% in the period. Investment in public enterprises rose for the same period, however, from 3.2% of GDP in 1985 to 6.5% in 1994.

Income

In 1998, Fiji's gross national product (GNP) was about $1.75 billion, or about $2,110 per person. For the period 1985–92, the average inflation rate was 5.2%, resulting in a real growth rate of 2.6% per person in the GNP.

Industry

Fiji's industry is based primarily on the processing of agricultural products, mainly sugarcane and coconut, and on the mining and processing of minerals.

Banking and Finance

The Reserve Bank of Fiji is the central bank (formerly the Central Monetary Authority), created in 1983 to replace the Currency Board; the Fiji Development Bank is the main development finance agency. Commercial banking facilities consist of the National Bank of Fiji (NBF) and branches of several foreign banks.

Growth in money supply has fluctuated largely in response to trends in foreign trade, affecting the level of reserves. The government tends to follow a cautious monetary policy, which has concentrated on maintaining price stability and on managing high levels of liquidity in the commercial banking system resulting from low levels of private investment. There is no securities exchange in Fiji.

Economic Development

Under the ninth development plan (1986–90), the government emphasized diversification of industries and expansion of tourism, and set the goal for real GDP growth at 5% annually. Four key areas that will be crucial for future economic prospects are domestic and foreign development in the sugar sector; trade liberalization in major export markets; the resolution of industrial disputes; and the replacement of middle-level skills lost to emigration caused by political turmoil.

In 1995, Fiji received F$5.1 million in direct foreign grants. It additionally borrowed F$25.7 million from international lenders.

SOCIAL WELFARE

General welfare programs include poverty relief, maintenance of homes for the aged, free medical and legal aid to the needy, child care, and social casework to deal with delinquency. Most Fijian women fulfill traditional roles. The government has promoted the rights of ethnic Fijians over those of other ethnic groups.

Healthcare

The main health problem is influenza. The infant mortality rate was 27 per 1,000 live births in 1994. Estimated average life expectancy is 72 years.

Housing

In 1986, housing stock totaled 126,100 units, of which 30% were made of corrugated iron or tin, 30% were concrete, and 26% were wood.

EDUCATION

In 1992 there were 145,630 pupils in primary schools and 66,890 secondary school pupils. The University of the South Pacific had over 3,600 students in 1993. The illiteracy rate averages 8% (6.2% for males and 10.7% for females).

1999 KEY EVENTS TIMELINE

January

- At least seven people are dead, and several hundred are homeless after torrential rains drench Fiji. Some areas receive more than 15 inches of rain in 24 hours.

February

- Fiji allows a search for Amelia Earhart's bones.

May

- The arrival of television in Fiji in 1995 leads to eating disorders among young Fijian women, according to research data presented by a U.S. anthropologist and psychiatrist.

- Fijian Labor Party leader Mahendra Chaudhry becomes Fiji's first Prime Minister of Indian background.

July

- Seventeen people die when an Air Fiji passenger plane crashes into a mountainside. Investigators said the plane was flying too low.

August

- Fiji announces its plans to remove the valued added tax on basic foods. The removal of the tax was expected to reduce weekly food bills by 10 to 15 percent.

October

- A Fijian group announces that it wants to build a kava factory. The group's report says a processing facility will add more value to the mild narcotic root.

ANALYSIS OF EVENTS: 1999

BUSINESS AND THE ECONOMY

Former Prime Minister Sitiveni Rabuka's handling of the economy may have been his downfall in the May elections. Many Fijians blamed him for growing poverty and unemployment. By 1999, the country's economy was showing signs of improvement after two years of drought caused by the El Niño weather phenomena. The drought cut sugar exports in half, and gross domestic product (GDP) growth fell to −2.4 percent in 1998. The Fiji Reserve Bank was forecasting GDP growth of 7.4 percent for 1999, with tourism increasing by 10 percent over 1999.

Chaudhry's government has promised to reverse privatizations, lift the 10 percent value-added tax on some basic goods, and raise wages. ''Our first priority is to get the economy moving,'' he said after his inauguration.

GOVERNMENT AND POLITICS

In May, voters elected the country's first prime minister of Indian descent, a feat for Fiji, which has been caught in ethnic and political tensions for most of its history. Mahendra Chaudhry was challenged immediately for his post by a coalition partner who said the job should go to a native Fijian.

But President Ratu Sir Kamisese Mara persuaded the Fijian Association Party to maintain its support for the new government.

Following the elections, Chaudhry's Fijian Labor Party controlled 37 seats in the 71-seat parliament. Along with two Fijian parties in his coalition, he controlled 52 seats. About 51 percent of the population are indigenous Fijians, and 44 percent are Indian-Fijians. Other races make up about 5 percent of the population.

Chaudhry said he won by putting aside racial politics, and had faith in Fiji as a truly multi-racial society. Immediately after his election, he put into place a racial unity plan, and selected two indigenous Fijians, Adi Kuini Speed and Tupeni Baba, as deputy prime ministers. Eleven of 18 full ministries were assigned to native Fijians.

Fiji's defeated prime minister, Sitiveni Rabuka, who resigned just before the results of the election were announced, said Fiji remained a divided nation, and blamed Indian voters for engaging in racial politics. Rabuka led a 1987 coup that toppled Fiji's first Indian-dominated government. He said he would continue to defend indigenous Fijian rights in parliament.

Racial relations deteriorated after the 1987 coup, and Fiji was thrown out of the Commonwealth. By 1992, Rabuka had left the army and became prime minister in an election conducted under a constitution his regime drafted. That constitution guaranteed ethnic Fijians parliamentary supremacy and reserved the offices of president, prime minister and other key posts for them. In 1997, Rabuka softened his stance, and joined Indian rivals to push through constitutional amendments that restored the political and civil rights of Indians.

CULTURE AND SOCIETY

Anne Becker, an anthropologist at Harvard Medical School who had been studying Fijian eating habits since 1988, released a study in May showing how television had increased eating disorders such as anorexia and bulimia in the tiny Pacific island nation.

In her study, Becker said the concept of dieting was unknown in Fiji. But eating disorders increased fivefold among teenage girls since television arrived in 1995, 10 years after electricity arrived in the island. Becker said the changes happened rapidly. Within 38 months, the number of teenagers at risk for eating disorders more than doubled to 29 percent. The number of high-school girls who vomited for weight control went up five times to 15 percent. Becker also discovered that 74 percent of the teenagers in her study felt "too big or fat" at least some of the time. And 62 percent had dieted in the past month. Becker, who presented her research to the American Psychiatric Association, said a direct causal link between television and eating disorders could not be proved, but her results raised concerns.

The research gained attention throughout the world. "In just 38 months, and with only one channel, a television-free culture that defined a fat person as robust has become a television culture that sees robust as, well, repulsive," American commentator Ellen Goodman wrote. Fijian teenagers cited characters like Melrose's Amanda (Heather Locklear) as inspiration for changing their bodies.

Ranadi Johnston, who holds the Miss Fiji beauty queen title, told the BBC that slim women were traditionally seen as weak. "People are always telling me to put on weight."

In February, Fiji approved a search at Fiji Medical School for bones that may be the remains of missing American aviator Amelia Earhart, who was trying to become the first woman to fly around the world in 1937. She and her navigator, Fred Noonan, vanished during the flight. Most authorities believe she ran out of fuel and crashed into the Pacific while flying between Papua New Guinea and Hawaii.

In 1940, a Fiji naval officer reported finding the bones of two people in uninhabited Nikumaroro, a desolate Gilbert atoll north of Suva. A physician concluded they were the bones of men, and were ordered into storage. The crate containing them vanished. The Fiji Museum said records indicate that two wooden boxes arrived about 1940.

DIRECTORY

CENTRAL GOVERNMENT
Head of State

President
Ratu Kamisese, Office of the President, Berkley Crescent, P.O. Box 2513, Government Buildings, Suva, Fiji
PHONE: +679 314244
FAX: +679 301645

Prime Minister

Mahendra Chaudrhy, Office of the Prime
Minister, 4th Floor, New Government Buildings,
P.O. Box 2353, Suva, Fiji
PHONE: +679 211201
FAX: +679 306034
E-MAIL: pmsoffice@is.com.fj

Ministers

Minister of Finance

Mahendra Chaudrhy, Ministry of Finance, Ro
Lalabalavu House, Victoria Parade, P.O. Box
2212, Government Buildings, Suva, Fiji
PHONE: +679 307011
FAX: +679 300834

Minister of Information

Mahendra Chaudrhy, Ministry of Information,
Ground Floor, New Government Buildings, P.O.
Box 2225, Government Buildings, Suva, Fiji
PHONF: +679 211700
FAX: +679 303146
E-MAIL: info@fiji.gov.fj

Minister of Public Enterprises

Mahendra Chaudrhy, Ministry of Public
Enterprises, 3rd Floor, Civic Towers, P.O. Box
2278, Government Buildings, Suva, Fiji
PHONE: +679 315577
FAX: +679 315035

Deputy Prime Minster and Minister of Fijian Affairs

Adi Kuini Vuikaba Speed, Ministry of Fijan
Affairs, 61 Carnavon Street, P.O. Box 2100,
Government Bldgs, Suva, Fiji
PHONE: +679 304200
FAX: +679 302585

Deputy Prime Minister and Minister of Foreign Affairs

Tupeni Lebaivalu Baba, Ministry of Foreign
Affairs, 2nd Floor, New Government Buildings,
P.O. Box 2220, Government Buildings, Suva,
Fiji
PHONE: +679 211458
FAX: +679 301741
E-MAIL: foreignaffairs@govnet.gov.fi

Minister of Agriculture, Fisheries and Forests

Poseci Waqalevu Bune, Ministry of Agriculture,
Fisheries and Forests, Robinson Complex,
Grantham Road, Private Bag, Raiwaqa, Fiji
PHONE: +679 384233
FAX: +679 385048
E-MAIL: maffinfo@is.com.fj

Attorney General

Anand Kumar Singh, Office of the Attorney
General, 2nd Floor, Old Government Buildings,
Victoria Parade, P.O. Box 2213, Government
Buildings, Suva, Fiji
PHONE: +679 211580
FAX: +679 305421

Minister of Commerce, Business Development and Investment

Anup Kumar, Ministry of Commerce, Business
Development and Investment, Naibati House, 9
Goodenough Street, P.O. Box 2118, Government
Buildings, Suva, Fiji
PHONE: +679 305411
FAX: +679 302617

Minister of Communication and Civil Aviation

Meli Bogileka, Ministry of Communication and
Civil Aviation, Level 4, Civic Towers, P.O. Box
2264, Suva, Fiji
PHONE: +679 315577
FAX: +679 315035

Minister of Education

Pratap Chand, Ministry of Education, Marela
House, Thurston Street, Private Mail Bag, Suva,
Fiji
PHONE: +679 314477
FAX: +679 315245

Minister of Health

Isimeli Jale Cokanasiga, Ministry of Health, 3rd
Floor Dinem House, 88 Amy Street, P.O. Box
2223, Government Buildings, Suva, Fiji
PHONE: +679 306177
FAX: +679 306163
E-MAIL: lrokovada@health.gov.fj

Minister of Home Affairs

Joji Uluinakauvadra, Ministry of Home Affairs,
1st Floor, New Government Buildings, P.O. Box
2349, Suva, Fiji
PHONE: +679 211401
FAX: +679 300346

Minister of Labor and Industrial Relations

Ratu Tevita Momoedonu, Ministry of Labor and
Industrial Relations, 414 Victoria Parade, P.O.
Box 2216, Government Buildings, Suva, Fiji
PHONE: +679 211640
FAX: +679 304701
E-MAIL: minilabour@is.com.fj

Minister of Lands, ALTA and Mineral Resources

Ratu Mosese Volavola, Ministry of Lands,
ALTA and Mineral Resources, 1st Floor, Old

Government Buildings, P.O. Box 2222, Suva, Fiji
PHONE: +679 211556
FAX: +679 302730

Minister of Regional Development and Multi-Ethnic Affairs

Manoa Bale, Ministry of Regional Development and Multi-Ethnic Affairs, Regional House, 1 Knolly Street, P.O. Box 2219, Government Buildings, Suva, Fiji
PHONE: +679 313400
FAX: +679 313035

Minister of National Planning

Ganesh Chand, Ministry of National Planning, 8th Floor, Ro Lalabalavu House, Victoria Parade, P.O. Box 2351, Government Buildings, Suva, Fiji
PHONE: +679 313411
FAX: +679 304809

Minister of Local Government

Ganesh Chand, Ministry of Local Government, P.O. Box 2131, Government Buildings, Suva, Fiji
PHONE: +679 211310
FAX: +679 303515

Minister of Environment

Ganesh Chand, Ministry of Environment, P.O. Box 2131, Government Buildings, Suva, Fiji
PHONE: +679 311069
FAX: +679 312879
E-MAIL: msovaki@govnet.gov.fj

Minister of Tourism and Transport

Adi Koila Mara Nailatikau, Ministry of Tourism and Transport, 3rd Floor, Civil Towers, P.O. Box 1260, Suva, Fiji
PHONE: +679 312788
FAX: +679 302060
E-MAIL: infodesk@fijifvb.gov.fj

Minister of Women, Culture and Social Welfare

Lavinia K. Padarath, Ministry of Women, Culture and Social Welfare, 5th Floor, Civic Towers, P.O. Box 14068, Suva, Fiji
PHONE: +679 312199
FAX: +679 303829
E-MAIL: slomaloma@govnet.gov.fj

Minister of Works and Energy

Shiu Sharan Sharma, Ministry of Works and Energy, Nasilivata House, Kings Road, Private Bag, Samabula, Fiji
PHONE: +679 384111

FAX: +679 383198

Minister of Youth, Employment Opportunities and Sports

Ponipate Lesavua, Ministry of Youth, Employment Opportunities and Sports, Harm Bing Narm Building, 7 Brewster Street, P.O. Box 2448, Government Buildings, Suva, Fiji
PHONE: +679 315960
FAX: +679 305348

POLITICAL ORGANIZATIONS

Fijian Political Party (SVT)

TITLE: Major General
NAME: Sitivini Rabuka

National Federal Party (NFP)

NAME: Jai Ram Reddy

Fijian Nationalist Party (FNP)

NAME: Sakaesi Butadroka

Fiji Labor Party (FLP)

NAME: Mahendra Chaudhry

General Voters Party (GVP)

NAME: Leo Smith

Fiji Conservative Party (FCP)

Conservative Party of Fiji (CPF)

Fiji Indian Liberal Party

Fiji Indian Congress Party

Fiji Independent Labor (Muslim)

Four Corners Party

Fijian Association Party (FAP)

NAME: Adi Kuini Speed

General Electors' Association

NAME: David Pickering

National Unity Party

NAME: Apisai Tora

Veitokani ni Lewenivnua Vakarisito-VLV (Christian Fellowship Party)

DIPLOMATIC REPRESENTATION

Embassies in Fiji

Australia
37 Princes Road, P.O. Box 214, Suva, Fiji
PHONE: +679 382211
FAX: +679 382065
TITLE: Australian High Commissioner
NAME: Susan Boyd

China
147 Queen Elizabeth Drive, Private Mail Bag, Suva, Fiji
PHONE: | 679 310833; 300215
FAX: +679 300950
TITLE: Ambassador
NAME: Chen Jinghua

France
Dominion House, 1st Floor, Private Mail Bag, Suva, Fiji
PHONE: +679 312233; 300406; 312925
FAX: +679 301894
TITLE: Ambassador
NAME: Michael M Pierre Jolivet

Micronesia
37 Loftus Street, Suva, Fiji
PHONE: +679 304566
FAX: +679 300842
TITLE: Ambassador
NAME: Kodaro Martin Gallen

India
P.O. Box 471, Suva, Fiji
PHONE: +679 301125
ГAX: +679 301032
TITLE: High Commissioner
NAME: Ishwar Singh Chauhan

Japan
2nd Floor Dominion House, P.O. Box 13045, Suva, Fiji
PHONE: +679 302122
FAX: +679 301452
TITLE: Ambassador
NAME: Hisato Murayama

South Korea
Vanua House, 8th Floor, Private Mail Bag, Suva, Fiji
PHONE: +679 300977
FAX: +679 303410
TITLE: Ambassador
NAME: Lim Dae-taek

Malaysia
Pacific House, 5th Floor, P.O. Box 356, Suva, Fiji
PHONE: +679 312166
FAX: +679 303350
TITLE: High Commissioner
NAME: Mohammed Takwir Din

Marshall Islands
41 Borron Road, P.O. Box 2038, Government Buildings, Suva, Fiji
PHONE: +679 387899
FAX: +679 387115
TITLE: Ambassador
NAME: Mack Kaminaga

Nauru
Ratu Sukuna House, 7th Floor, P.O. Box 2420, Government Buildings, Suva, Fiji
PHONE: +679 313566
FAX: +679 302861
TITLF: High Commissioner
NAME: Millicent Aroi

New Zealand
Reserve Bank Building, P.O. Box 1378, Suva, Fiji
PHONE: +679 311422
FAX: +679 300842
TITLE: High Commissioner
NAME: John Richard Te Barrett

Papua New Guinea
Credit Corporation House, 3rd Floor, P.O. Box 2447, Government Buildings, Suva, Fiji
PHONE: +679 304244
FAX: +679 300178
TITLE: High Commissioner
NAME: Babani Maraga

Tuvalu
16 Gorrie Street, P.O. Box 14449, Suva, Fiji
PHONE: +679 301355
FAX: +679 301023
TITLE: High Commissioner
NAME: Sosene Sopoaga

United Kingdom
Victoria House, P.O. Box 1355, Government Buildings, Suva, Fiji
PHONE: +679 311033
FAX: +679 301406
TITLE: High Commissioner
NAME: Michael Dibben

United States
31 Loftus Street, P.O. Box 218, Suva, Fiji
PHONE: +679 314466

FAX: +679 300081
TITLE: Ambassador
NAME: Osman Siddique

JUDICIAL SYSTEM
Supreme Court
Court of Appeal
Magistrate Court
High Court

FURTHER READING
Articles
"Fiji Plans to Scrap Tax on Basic Foods." Reuters, 16 August 1999.

"Labor Leader Becomes Fiji's First Prime Minister of Indian Background." Associated Press, 19 May 1999.

"Millenium Hype Aside, Fiji Retains its Purity." *The Miami Herald*, 3 October 1999.

"Pacific Tourist Island may be a Sleeping Volcano." Associated Press, 23 June 1999.

"A Peaceful Change in Fiji." *The Economist* (May 22, 1999): 40.

"Plane Hits Jungle Mountain; 17 Die," Associated Press, 25 July 1999.

"Politics of Paradise: Fiji's First Free Elections since Coup." *Time International* (May 31, 1999): 42.

"The Skinny on Fiji's Loss of a Robust Cultural Identity." *The Seattle Times*, 28 May 1999.

"Study Finds Rise in Signs of Eating Disorders after TV Comes to Fiji." Associated Press, 20 May 1999.

"U.S. Team in Fiji Hopes it's on Trail of Amelia Earhart." Associated Press, 17 October 1999.

"World Rugby: Fiji Set to Test Coach's Foreign Policy." *The Guardian*, 16 October 1999.

FIJI:
STATISTICAL DATA

For sources and notes see "Sources of Statistics" in the front of each volume.

GEOGRAPHY

Geography (1)
Area:

Total: 18,270 sq km.

Land: 18,270 sq km.

Water: 0 sq km.

Area—comparative: slightly smaller than New Jersey.

Land boundaries: 0 km.

Coastline: 1,129 km.

Climate: tropical marine; only slight seasonal temperature variation.

Terrain: mostly mountains of volcanic origin.

Natural resources: timber, fish, gold, copper, offshore oil potential.

Land use:

Arable land: 10%

Permanent crops: 4%

Permanent pastures: 10%

Forests and woodland: 65%

Other: 11% (1993 est.).

HUMAN FACTORS

Infants and Malnutrition (5)

Under-5 mortality rate (1997) 24

% of infants with low birthweight (1990-97) 12

Births attended by skilled health staff % of total[a] . . .NA

% fully immunized (1995-97)

  TB 95

  DPT 86

  Polio 88

  Measles 75

Prevalence of child malnutrition under age 5

  (1992-97)[b] . . . . .NA

Demographics (2A)

	1990	1995	1998	2000	2010	2020	2030	2040	2050
Population	738.3	772.9	802.6	823.4	932.9	1,036.8	1,132.7	1,219.1	1,285.0
Net migration rate (per 1,000 population)	NA	NA	NA	NA	NA	NA	NA	NA	NA
Births	NA	NA	NA	NA	NA	NA	NA	NA	NA
Deaths	NA	NA	NA	NA	NA	NA	NA	NA	NA
Life expectancy - males	61.9	63.1	63.9	64.5	66.7	68.8	70.6	72.2	73.6
Life expectancy - females	66.3	67.8	68.8	69.4	72.1	74.5	76.6	78.4	79.9
Birth rate (per 1,000)	26.7	23.7	22.9	22.6	20.5	17.3	16.0	14.6	13.6
Death rate (per 1,000)	7.0	6.4	6.3	6.2	6.3	6.8	7.6	8.4	9.2
Women of reproductive age (15-49 yrs.)	188.2	201.1	213.3	221.4	250.7	271.4	292.7	296.3	302.6
of which are currently married	NA	NA	NA	NA	NA	NA	NA	NA	NA
Fertility rate	3.1	2.9	2.7	2.7	2.3	2.2	2.1	2.0	2.0

Except as noted, values for vital statistics are in thousands; life expectancy is in years.

Ethnic Division (6)

Fijian 49%

Indian 46%

European, other Pacific Islanders,
  overseas Chinese, and other 5%

Religions (7)

Christian 52%

  Methodist 37%

  Roman Catholic 9%

Hindu 38%

Muslim 8%

Other 2%

Fijians are mainly Christian, Indians are Hindu, and there is a
Muslim minority (1986).

Languages (8)

English (official), Fijian, Hindustani.

EDUCATION

Educational Attainment (10)

Age group (1986) . . . . .25+

Total population 287,175

Highest level attained (%)

  No schooling 10.9

  First level

    Not completed 35.9

    Completed 23.9

  Entered second level

    S-1 . . . . .24.9

    S-2 . . . . .NA

  Postsecondary 4.5

Literacy Rates (11A)

In thousands and percent[1]	1990	1995	2000	2010
Illiterate population (15+ yrs.)	49	43	37	26
Literacy rate - total adult pop. (%)	89.2	91.6	93.6	96.3
Literacy rate - males (%)	92.0	93.8	95.4	97.3
Literacy rate - females (%)	86.3	89.3	91.7	95.2

GOVERNMENT & LAW

Political Parties (12)

House of Representatives	No. of seats
Fijian Political Party (SVT)	31
National Federation Party (NFP)	20
Fiji Labor Party (FLP)	7
Fijian Association Party (FAP)	5
General Voters Party (GVP)	4
Independents	2
All National Congress (ANC)	1

Government Budget (13A)

Year: 1996

Total Expenditures: 881.44 Millions of Dollars

Expenditures as a percentage of the total by function:

  General public services and public order 31.00

  Defense 5.81

  Education 18.19

  Health 8.67

  Social Security and Welfare 4.13

  Housing and community amenities 2.88

  Recreational, cultural, and religious affairs 87

  Fuel and energy 23

  Agriculture, forestry, fishing, and hunting 3.59

  Mining, manufacturing, and construction 32

  Transportation and communication 7.98

  Other economic affairs and services 6.80

Crime (15)

Crime rate (for 1997)

  Crimes reported 22,100

  Total persons convicted 10,200

  Crimes per 100,000 population 2,850

Persons responsible for offenses

  Total number of suspects 11,000

  Total number of female suspects 1,200

  Total number of juvenile suspects 225

LABOR FORCE

Labor Force (16)

Total 235,000

Subsistence agriculture .67%

Wage earners 18%

Salary earners 15%

Data for 1987.

Unemployment Rate (17)

6% (1997 est.)

PRODUCTION SECTOR

Electric Energy (18)

Capacity .200,000 kW (1995)
Production . . . . .545 million kWh (1995)
Consumption per capita . . . . .705 kWh (1995)

Transportation (19)

Highways:
total: 3,440 km
paved: 1,692 km
unpaved: 1,748 km (1996 est.)
Waterways: 203 km; 122 km navigable by motorized craft and 200-metric-ton barges

Merchant marine:

total: 6 ships (1,000 GRT or over) totaling 17,800 GRT/18,034 DWT ships by type: chemical tanker 2, oil tanker 1, passenger 1, roll-on/roll-off cargo 2 (1997 est.)

Airports: 24 (1997 est.)

Airports—with paved runways:

total: 3

over 3,047 m: 1

1,524 to 2,437 m: 1

914 to 1,523 m: 1 (1997 est.)

Airports—with unpaved runways:

total: 21

914 to 1,523 m: 4

under 914 m: 17 (1997 est.)

GOVERNMENT & LAW

Military Affairs (14B)

	1990	1991	1992	1993	1994	1995
Military expenditures						
Current dollars (mil.)	33	34	31	27	34	32
1995 constant dollars (mil.)	38	37	34	28	35	32
Armed forces (000)	5	5	5	5	4	4
Gross national product (GNP)						
Current dollars (mil.)	1,446	1,523	1,610	1,680	1,773	1,863[e]
1995 constant dollars (mil.)	1,661	1,683	1,732	1,762	1,817	1,863[e]
Central government expenditures (CGE)						
1995 constant dollars (mil.)	488	434	444	546	624	538
People (mil.)	.7	.7	.7	.8	.8	.8
Military expenditure as % of GNP	2.3	2.2	1.9	1.6	1.9	1.7
Military expenditure as % of CGE	7.7	8.5	7.6	5.2	5.5	6.0
Military expenditure per capita (1995 $)	51	50	45	38	45	42
Armed forces per 1,000 people (soldiers)	6.8	6.7	6.7	6.6	5.2	5.2
GNP per capita (1995 $)	2,250	2,262	2,309	2,328	2,378	2,410
Arms imports[6]						
Current dollars (mil.)	0	0	0	0	0	20
1995 constant dollars (mil.)	0	0	0	0	0	20
Arms exports[6]						
Current dollars (mil.)	0	0	0	0	0	0
1995 constant dollars (mil.)	0	0	0	0	0	0
Total imports[7]						
Current dollars (mil.)	743	643	614	634	724	864
1995 constant dollars (mil.)	854	711	660	665	742	864
Total exports[7]						
Current dollars (mil.)	615	462	407	405	509	607
1995 constant dollars (mil.)	707	511	438	425	522	607
Arms as percent of total imports[8]	0	0	0	0	0	2.3
Arms as percent of total exports[8]	0	0	0	0	0	0

Top Agricultural Products (20)

Sugarcane, coconuts, cassava (tapioca), rice, sweet potatoes, bananas; cattle, pigs, horses, goats; fish catch 13,796 tons (1991).

MANUFACTURING SECTOR

GDP & Manufacturing Summary (21)

Detailed value added figures are listed by both International Standard Industry Code (ISIC) and product title.

	1980	1985	1990	1994
GDP ($-1990 mil.)[1]	1,097	1,153	1,381	1,492
Per capita ($-1990)[1]	1,730	1,650	1,902	1,936
Manufacturing share (%) (current prices)[1]	11.5	9.1	9.4	10.3
Manufacturing				
Value added ($-1990 mil.)[1]	99	97	122	146
Industrial production index	100	94	111	128
Value added ($ mil.)	121	90	142	210
Gross output ($ mil.)	489	395	642	834
Employment (000)	13	13	21	15
Profitability (% of gross output)				
Intermediate input (%)	75	78	80	75
Wages and salaries inc. supplements (%)	11	13	11	10
Gross operating surplus	14	8	9	15
Productivity ($)				
Gross output per worker	37,145	28,850	30,433	53,616
Value added per worker	9,230	7,197	9,240	14,184
Average wage (inc. supplements)	4,114	3,992	3,253	5,414
Value added ($ mil.)				
311/2 Food products	71	37	60	84
313 Beverages	6	7	11	15
314 Tobacco products	2	2	3	4
321 Textiles	—	—	—	—
322 Wearing apparel	2	4	16	28
323 Leather and fur products	—	—	—	—
324 Footwear	—	—	1	2
331 Wood and wood products	7	6	11	16
332 Furniture and fixtures	3	3	3	5
341 Paper and paper products	2	2	5	6
342 Printing and publishing	4	5	6	8
351 Industrial chemicals	—	—	—	—
352 Other chemical products	4	5	7	13
353 Petroleum refineries	—	—	—	—
354 Miscellaneous petroleum and coal products	—	—	—	—
355 Rubber products	1	1	1	1
356 Plastic products	2	2	3	5
361 Pottery, china and earthenware	—	—	—	—
362 Glass and glass products	—	—	—	—
369 Other non-metal mineral products	6	7	5	9
371 Iron and steel	—	—	—	—
372 Non-ferrous metals	—	—	—	—
381 Metal products	6	4	5	8
382 Non-electrical machinery	1	—	—	1
383 Electrical machinery	—	1	1	1
384 Transport equipment	4	3	1	2
385 Professional and scientific equipment	—	—	—	—
390 Other manufacturing industries	—	1	1	2

FINANCE, ECONOMICS, & TRADE

Economic Indicators (22)

National product: GDP—purchasing power parity—$5.1 billion (1996 est.)

National product real growth rate: 3% (1996)

National product per capita: $6,500 (1996 est.)

Inflation rate—consumer price index: 3% (1997 est.)

Balance of Payments (23)

	1992	1993	1994	1995	1996
Exports of goods (f.o.b.)	350	371	490	520	655
Imports of goods (f.o.b.)	−539	−653	−720	−761	−838
Trade balance	−189	−282	−230	−242	−182
Services - debits	−383	−401	−472	−493	−504
Services - credits	505	533	584	619	687
Private transfers (net)	26	27	72	106	—
Government transfers (net)	6	12	5	3	10
Overall balance	−35	−111	−41	−6	10

Exchange Rates (24)

Exchange rates:

Fijian dollars (F$) per US$1

January 1998	1.9064
1997	1.4437
1996	1.4033
1995	1.4063
1994	1.4641
1993	1.5418

Top Import Origins (25)

$947 million (c.i.f., 1996).

Origins	%
Australia	30
NZ	17
Japan	13
European Union	6
United States	6

Top Export Destinations (26)

$639 million (f.o.b., 1996).

Destinations	%
European Union	26
Australia	15
Other Pacific islands	11
Japan	6

Economic Aid (27)

Recipient: ODA, $14.35 million from Australia (FY96/97 est.); $3.5 million from New Zealand (FY95/96).

Import Export Commodities (28)

Import Commodities	Export Commodities
Machinery and transport equipment	Sugar 32%
Petroleum products	Clothing
Food	Gold
Consumer goods	Processed fish
Chemicals	Lumber

FINLAND

Republic of Finland
Suomen Tasavalta

CAPITAL: Helsinki.

FLAG: The civil flag contains an ultramarine cross with an extended right horizontal on a white background. The state flag flown on government buildings is the same but also includes, at the center of the cross, the coat of arms, consisting of a gold lion and nine white roses on a red background.

ANTHEM: *Maammelaulu* (in Swedish, *Vårt land; Our Land*).

MONETARY UNIT: The markkaa (M) of 100 penniä is a convertible currency with one official exchange rate. There are coins of 10 and 50 penniä and 1 and 5 markkaa, and notes of 10, 50, 100, 500 and 1,000 markkaa. M1 = $0.22099 (or $1 = M4.525).

WEIGHTS AND MEASURES: The metric system is the legal standard.

HOLIDAYS: New Year's Day, 1 January; May Day, 1 May; Independence Day, 6 December; Christmas, 25–26 December. Movable holidays include Good Friday, Easter Monday, Whitsun, and Midsummer Day (late June). Epiphany, Ascension, and All Saints' Day are adjusted to fall always on Saturdays.

TIME: 2 PM = noon GMT.

LOCATION AND SIZE: Finland has an area of 337,030 square kilometers (209,260 square miles), slightly smaller than the state of Montana. Its length, one-third of which lies above the Arctic Circle, is 1,160 kilometers (721 miles) from north to south; its width is 540 kilometers (336 miles) from east to west. Finland has a total boundary length of 3,754 kilometers (2,323 miles).

Finland's capital, Helsinki, is located on the country's southern coast.

CLIMATE: Because of the warming influence of the Gulf Stream, Finland's climate is quite mild for its high latitude. The average winter temperature ranges from −14°C to −3°C (7–27°F), while summer mean temperatures range from 13°C to 17°C (55–63°F). Average annual precipitation (including both rain and snow) ranges from 40 centimeters (16 inches) in northern Finland to 70 centimeters (28 inches) in southern Finland.

INTRODUCTORY SURVEY

RECENT HISTORY

Postwar Finland's economic recovery has been striking. Since World War II, Finland has followed a policy of neutrality and good relations with its neighbors. Traditional ties with other Nordic countries have been maintained and strengthened. The dominant figure of postwar politics was Urho Kekkonen, the Agrarian (later Center) Party leader who held the presidency from 1956 to 1981, when he resigned because of ill health.

The cornerstone of his policy was maintenance of a center-left coalition that included the Communists and good relations with the former Soviet Union. Social Democratic leader Mauno Koivisto, the prime minister, became acting president in October 1981 and was elected president in January 1982 and re-elected in 1988. In the presidential elections of February 1994, Martti Ahtisaari, of the Finnish Social Democratic Party, was elected president, defeating Elisabeth Rehn (Defense Minister) of the Swedish People's Party.

In March 1987, the conservative National Coalition Party made strong gains in parliamentary elections and formed Finland's first conservative-led government since World War II. The conservative trend continued in March 1991 with the Center Party leading a new four-party center-right coalition under Esko Aho.

The collapse of the Soviet Union in 1991 led Finland to reassess its relationship with Europe. In February 1993, Finland applied for membership in

FINLAND

0   100   200 Miles

0   100   200 Kilometers

the European Union. Finland officially joined the EU on 1 January 1995.

GOVERNMENT

Finland is a parliamentary republic. The constitution of 17 July 1919 vests supreme executive power in a president, who presides over and is assisted by a Council of State (cabinet). The president is elected directly (since 1991) for a six-year term. The president initiates legislation, issues decrees, directs foreign relations, and serves as commander-in-chief of the armed forces and appoints the highest civil servants.

The parliament (Eduskunta) is a single-chamber legislative body originally organized in 1906. Its 200 members are elected for four-year terms.

Finland was the first nation in Europe to grant suffrage to women in national elections (1906).

Judiciary

There are three levels of courts: local, appeals, and supreme. The final court of appeal, the Supreme Court (Korkeinoikeus), sits in Helsinki under a president and twenty-three justices.

Political Parties

Four major parties have dominated political life in Finland: the moderate Finnish Social Democratic Party (Suomen Sosialidemokraattinen Puolue—SSDP); the Center Party (Keskusrapuolue—KESK), which represents agricultural interests; the National Coalition Party (Kansallinen Kokoomus—KOK), which is considered ''conservative middle-class''; and the Finnish Christian League (Suomen Kristillinen Liitto—SKL), usually found on the political right with the KOK.

The Swedish People's Party (Svenska Folkpartiet—SFP) focuses on protecting the common interests of Finland's Swedish-speaking population. The Finnish People's Democratic League (Suomen Kansan Demokraattinen Liitto—SKDL) represents the extreme left. The Greens, an environmentalist alliance, won four seats in the Eduskunta in 1987, although they were not formally organized as a political party.

DEFENSE

In 1995, the army had 26,000 personnel; the navy, 4,500 personnel; and the air force, 3,000 personnel. Finland maintains 500,000 reservists.

Under the Paris Peace Treaty of 1947, Finland is prohibited from possessing or constructing atomic weapons, submarines, and bombers. There is compulsory military service for all males at age 17. Defense expenditures are around $2.1 billion a year.

ECONOMIC AFFAIRS

Despite being handicapped by relatively poor soil, a severe northern climate, and a lack of coal, oil, and most other mineral resources necessary for the development of heavy industry, the Finns have still been able to build a productive economy. This was made possible by unrivaled forests (Finland's ''green gold'') and waterpower resources (''white gold''), as well as by the Finnish disposition toward hard work and ingenuity.

Agriculture, long the traditional calling of the large majority of Finns, has been undergoing continuous improvement, with growing specialization in dairying and cattle breeding. The industries engaged in producing timber, wood products, paper, and pulp are highly developed, and these commodities make up an overwhelming proportion of the country's exports.

Dependent on foreign sources for a considerable portion of its raw materials, fuels, and machinery, and on exports as a source of revenue, the Finnish economy is very sensitive to changes at the international level. Finland's economy was hit hard by the collapse of the former Soviet Union, which had been its chief trading partner. Loss of export sales to the Soviet Union plus high labor costs and excessive borrowing created a deep recession in 1991. The regional economic recovery in Europe during 1994 helped Finland's economy turn around, growing by 4.4% that year. The gross domestic product (GDP) grew by 4.2% in 1995 and 3.3% in 1996.

Public Finance

Budget estimates are prepared by the Ministry of Finance and submitted to the legislature. They are referred to the finance committee and subsequently reported to the full body. Supplementary budgets are not unusual.

Finland's budget balance continued its sharp deterioration in 1992, as the deep recession resulted in decreased tax revenues and increased social expenditures. Extensive government support for the fragile banking system and increased interest expenditures were also responsible.

The CIA estimates that, in 1993, government revenues totaled approximately $21.7 billion and expenditures $31.7 billion. External debt totaled $30 billion, approximately 61% of which was financed abroad. By 1995, external public debt stood at an estimated $40.7 billion.

The Finnish government's budget for 1997 set the central government debt at 72% of GDP. State expenditures for 1997 were budgeted at M190.8 billion, a 5% reduction in real terms from 1996.

Income

In 1998, Finland's gross national product (GNP) was about $124 billion, or $24,110 per person. For the period 1985–95, the average inflation rate was 3.8%, resulting in a real growth rate in GNP of −0.2% per person.

Industry

Since the end of World War II (1939–45), industrial progress has been noteworthy. Contributing factors include the pressure of having to make World War II reparation payments; large quantities of available electric power; increased mining operations; development of transportation and communications; and steady foreign demand for Finnish exports.

In terms of value of production and size of labor force, the metals industry is the most important, accounting for 34% of industrial employment in 1993. Also highly significant are the food, pulp and paper, machinery, chemical, and electrical products and instruments industries.

Banking and Finance

The central bank is the Bank of Finland, established in 1811, with headquarters in Helsinki. Possessing extensive autonomy, though subject to parliamentary supervision, and endowed with extensive monetary and fiscal powers, the Bank is administered by a six-member board of management appointed by the president of the republic. It has an exclusive monopoly over the issuance of notes. Completing its preparations for Economic and Monetary Union (EMU), on 17 January 1997, the government submitted to the Eduskunta a proposal for a new Act of the Bank of Finland. The main purpose of the act is to institutionally prepare the Bank of Finland for Stage 3 of EMU by providing for its independence ahead of the move to a single currency, in line with the requirements set out in Maastricht.

An exchange at Helsinki (established in 1912) is authorized to deal in stocks. Stock prices have risen sharply since 1992, and in 1996 the Helsinki Stock Exchange (HEX) recorded a strong performance.

Economic Development

Problems arising from World War II—reparations, loss of resources in the ceded territories, compensation to the evacuated and displaced population, and reconstruction—have dictated the main lines of Finnish economic policy. Reparations were originally fixed at $300 million (1938 price level), payable in six years. They were subsequently scaled down to $226.5 million, payable in eight years. Extensive governmental control over supplies, prices, wages, rents, foreign trade, and foreign exchange was inevitable.

Finland remains principally a free enterprise economy, although government-owned enterprises play a part. The only true state monopoly is of the production, import, and sale of alcoholic beverages. Government interests, however, dominate the railroads, airlines, broadcasting, and telecommunications, and the government owns a majority of the shares in many joint stock companies, particularly in utilities, mining, and industry.

Finland does not engage in formal economic planning, but it is making a serious attempt at industrial expansion and diversification.

SOCIAL WELFARE

Social welfare legislation in Finland is patterned largely on Scandinavian models. Major benefits include employees' accident insurance, old-age and disability insurance, unemployment insurance, sickness insurance, compensation for war invalids, and family and child allowances.

Some private welfare organizations, like the Mannerheim Child Welfare League, have won widespread recognition. Each city operates a maternal and child-care clinic. There is a maternity allowance, which covered 170 weekdays as of 1 January 1991.

Women have a high level of education and hold a large number of elective political posts. However, they seldom hold high-paying management positions and earn on average only 80% of what men do.

Indigenous Sami (Lapps) receive government subsidies to enable them to maintain their traditional reindeer herding culture.

Healthcare

The entire population is covered by health insurance, which includes compensation for lost earnings and treatment cost. In 1994, Finland had 12,350 physicians (2.7 per 1,000 people). In 1990, there were an estimated 440 hospitals, with just over 67,000 total beds.

Although female health is good by international standards, male mortality in the over-25 age bracket is much higher in Finland than in most industrial countries, due mainly to heart disease. In addition, there has been an increase in suicide and alcohol-related problems among young men.

Life expectancy in 1995 was 77 years. Total health expenditures that year amounted to $26.9 million.

Housing

From 1974 through 1985, 558,000 new units were added to the housing stock. In 1991, 51,803 new dwellings were completed, down from 65,397 in 1990.

EDUCATION

The primary and lower secondary grades form a compulsory nine-year program. The upper secondary school (gymnasium) and vocational schools have both required and elective courses. Practically all adults are literate.

Entrance to the universities is through annual examinations. There were 13 universities and 12 colleges and institutes in 1991, with a total of 173,702 students. During 1986–97, the government allocated 13% of the total budget to education.

1999 KEY EVENTS TIMELINE

January

- The Euro in inter-bank and intra-European exchange replaces the Finnish markka.

- Finnish dockworkers continue their strike protesting the low wages of Estonian dockworkers.

- Pirjo Haeggman, one of the first women selected for the International Olympic Committee, was also one of the first IOC members to resign over the Salt Lake City corruption scandal.

- A scandal related to the privatization of Sonera, the state-owned telecommunications operator, resulted in the resignation of Finnish Communications Minister Matti Aura and the sacking of Sonera CEO Pekka Vennamo.

February

- Nokia, the Finnish mobile phone giant, agreed to buy the Petaluma, California, Diamond Lane Communications Corporation for $125 million in cash to increase its Internet business.

- Finnish air traffic controllers go on strike.

March

- Parliamentary elections return the ruling rainbow coalition of Social Democrats, the conservative Coalition party, the Greens, the ex-communist Left Party and the Swedish People's Party. The Social Democrats, while remaining the largest party in Parliament, suffer a loss of 12 seats in the 200-seat parliament.

- Tieto Oy, a Finnish computer services company, purchased Swedish rival Enator A. B. for $1 billion in stock to increase its competitiveness in a region with the highest per capita internet and telecom use.

April

- Speculation about Finnish neutrality was heightened when Defense Minister Anneli Taina remarked "Finland is engaged to NATO but no wedding has been set."

- Leaf, a unit of the Finnish Food packaging and candy company Huhtamaeki Oy, was sold to the Dutch candymaker CSM N.V. for 390 million euros ($423 million) in cash.

June

- Martti Ahtisaari, President of Finland, and Victor Chernomyrdin of Russia were successful in their mission to obtain Slobodan Milosevic's agreement to NATO's terms for ending the bombardment of Kosovo and Serbia.

- Pohjola announced a merger of its non-life operations with Sweden's Skandia and Norway's Storebrand.

July

- Finland assumed the Presidency of the European Union for the second half of 1999. The Finnish presidency will focus on employment, enlargement, transparency, and introducing a "Northern Dimension" into EU politics, which will focus on the improving and expanding relations with Russia.

- German culture and economic ministers boycott EU meetings in Finland in protest against the Finnish Presidency's decision not to use German as one of the working languages in informal meetings.

- Finland's Huhtamaeki Oy bought Dutch rival, Royal Packaging Industries Van Leer N.V. for 1.4 billion euros ($1.5 billion) in cash and debt, making it the world's largest maker of paper and plastic containers.

August

- Sonera, the most prominent Finnish telecom company, bought a 9.1 percent stake in Powertel Inc., a United States cellular phone operator,

from Swedish mobile phone competitor Ericsson A.B.

- BASF announced plans for a massive paper coating plant in Finland as part of its $275 million investment in production and R and D for paper chemicals in Central Europe.

October

- Sampo, Finland's largest insurer, proposed a merger with Leonia, the second largest Finnish Bank.

December

- Helsinki hosts one of the twice-yearly summit meetings of the European Union.

- Share prices on Finland's stock market have risen almost 140 percent in 1999, due in part to growth in electronics, especially by the mobile telephone manufacturer Nokia.

ANALYSIS OF EVENTS: 1999

BUSINESS AND THE ECONOMY

Finland began the year in the company of the eleven European Union countries embarking upon a single currency, and introduced the use of the euro in all non-cash transactions. The moved capped what has been a stunning economic performance by Finland of late. The economy is set to grow by 4 percent in 1999, down from 5.6 percent last year but well above the European average. Other economic indicators are sound, with inflation at about 1 percent and government debt levels continuing to fall. Only unemployment continues to be a problem, although its current level of about 10 percent is far less than the 18 percent peak in 1993. There exists the possibility for inflationary pressures in Finland. With monetary policy and interest rates now being set by the European Central Bank (the eurobor rate is currently about 3 percent, about half of the Helibor rate of 6.75 percent in 1995), one of the few macro-economic tools left to fight inflation is the centralized wage settlement. This settlement covers about 90 percent of wage-earners under negotiation in the autumn of 1999.

At the center of all this growth is Nokia, the telecommunications company which last year overtook the paper and pulp industry as the leading export sector. Nokia accounts for 26 percent of all Finnish exports; Nokia's growth continued apace in 1999 when its profits overtook their troubled Swedish competitor Ericsson. Nokia is now the world's largest mobile phone manufacturer, making one-quarter of the world's cellular phones. Concerns at the start of 1999 that Finland would be vulnerable to asymmetric shocks stemming from the move to the euro were put to rest as Finland's economy (thanks to Nokia) has diversified outside the euro-zone. Its economy is now able to weather the downturn in European demand for paper and pulp products.

Also emblematic of the Finnish economy is the continued merger-mania, particularly in banking and insurance sectors. Last year's merger between Finland's Merita and Sweden's Nordbanken created the largest Nordic banking entity, and has left other Finnish banks looking for cover. The state-owned Leonia entered talks with the largest Finnish insurance company, Sampo, to create a cross-industry alliance.

GOVERNMENT AND POLITICS

Finns were busy on the domestic, European, and international political stages in 1999. In the March parliamentary elections, voters seemed to approve of the performance of the Social Democratic-led "rainbow coalition." While the Social Democrats remained the largest party in the 200 member Eduskunta, they lost 12 of their 63 seats in the election, while the largest gain of seven seats was registered by the conservative National Coalition party. The members of the last coalition government—the Social Democrats, the National Coalition Party, the Greens, the ex-Communist Left Alliance and the Swedish People's Party—are set to form another government with limited changes of ministerial responsibility. There has been widespread public satisfaction with the consensus orientation and muted ideologies of the spectrum-spanning coalition, though necessary labor market reforms and a debate over nuclear power may introduce new strains to the coalition.

On the international stage, Finnish President Martti Ahtisaari was lauded for his shuttle diplomacy between Helsinki, Moscow, and Bonn in May and June as the EU Negotiator for resolving the conflict in Kosovo. In contrast to the EU's divisiveness in resolving the Bosnian conflict, it was the last-ditch mediation by Ahtisaari and Russian envoy Victor Chernomyrdin with Serbia's

Slobodan Milosevic that averted intensified air strikes and a possible ground war between NATO and Serbia. Ahtisaari's high profile success might have assured his re-election next year in the Presidential election had he not announced well in advance of his plan not to run again. The front-runner in the presidential race at the end of 1999 was Elisabeth Rehn, former Defense Minister and Senior United Nations Envoy to Bosnia.

Hard on the heels of Ahtisaari's success was Finland's turn to assume the EU presidency in the latter half of 1999. The Finns got off to an awkward start when several language rows erupted. The native Swedish speakers were upset when many documents were released first in English rather than one of the official languages of Finland. Germany boycotted several of the informal meetings of EU Ministerial Councils when Finland initially refused to use German as one of the working languages of these informal meetings. After this rocky start, the Finns hoped to focus their presidency on enlargement, employment, transparency, information technology, environment and intensified cooperation in European justice and home affairs. At a European Council held in Tampere in October, EU heads of state agreed on mutual recognition of member-states' legal systems which allows businessmen and travelers to pursue claims in the courts of other EU members. The centerpiece of the Finnish presidency is a program called the "Northern Dimension." This is an effort to create a northern EU border region to include EU members, Baltic EU applicants and some of the regions of northwest Russia in cross-border cooperation, trade, economic development, environmental protection, and promotion of energy resources such as pipelines, across the region.

CULTURE AND SOCIETY

It is little wonder that Nokia is so successful in the international telecoms industry. Finns have always embraced the information society; they were using telephones one year after Alexander Graham Bell first tested one in 1876. Fully 63 percent of Finns have a mobile phone, and cell-phone text messaging is the rage among Finnish teens. So pervasive is the mobile phone culture that some principals have banned cell phones within schools and 19 percent of Finnish families favor cellular phones over a landline telephone. Today Finns also have the highest per capita Internet connection of any nation in the world—35 percent are online—and the cheapest access in Europe. A barometer of this current embrace is that Mato Valtonen, for 24 years the lead singer of the band the Leningrad Cowboys, has abandoned music to lead a start-up of information services accessible from Nokia's "smart phones."

The largest social problem facing Finland is the demographic time bomb of an expanding population of the elderly and the extensive Finnish social security system. Eighty percent of the population opts for early retirement though the statutory age is 65. While the government encouraged early retirement during the economic recession of the early 1990s, others point to age discrimination in the move toward early retirement. While some have argued for raising the statutory retirement age, others argue that conditions must be created to encourage people to work until the current retirement age. Finland has the lowest labor-market activity rate for men aged 55–59 of any country in the OECD.

DIRECTORY

CENTRAL GOVERNMENT

Head of State

President
Martti Ahtisaari, Office of the President, Mariankatu 2, 00170 Helsinki, Finland
PHONE: +358 (9) 661133
FAX: +358 (9) 638247

Ministers

Prime Minister
Paavo Lipponen, Office of the Prime Minister, Snellmaninkatu 1 A, P.O. Box 275, 00171 Helsinki, Finland
PHONE: +358 (9) 1601
FAX: +358 (9) 1602225
E-MAIL: paavo.lipponen@vnk.vn.fi

Minister of Agriculture and Forestry
Kalevi Hemila, Ministry Of Agriculture And Forestry, Hallituskatu 3 A, P.O. Box 232, 00171 Helsinki, Finland
PHONE: +358 (9) 1601
FAX: +358 (9) 1602900
E-MAIL: kalevi.hemila@mmm.fi

Minister of Education
Suvi Linden, Ministry of Education, Meritullinkatu 10, P.O. Box 293, 00171 Helsinki, Finland
PHONE: +358 (9) 134171
FAX: +358 (9) 13416978
E-MAIL: suvi.linden@minedu.fi

Minister of Defense
Jan Erik Enestam, Ministry of Defense, Fabianinkatu 2, P.O. Box 31, 00131 Helsinki, Finland
PHONE: +358 (9) 1601
FAX: +358 (9) 16088274
E-MAIL: jan-erik.enestam@sm.intermin.fi

Minister of Education
Maija Rask, Ministry of Education, Meritullinkatu 10, P.O. Box 293, 00171 Helsinki, Finland
PHONE: +358 (9) 134171
FAX: +358 (9) 13417493
E-MAIL: maija.rask@minedu.fi

Minister of Environment
Satu Hassi, Ministry of The Environment, Kasarmikatu 25, P.O. Box 380, 00131 Helsinki, Finland
PHONE: +358 (9) 19911
FAX: +358 (9) 19919301
E-MAIL: satu.hassi@vyh.fi

Minister of Finance
Sauli Niinisto, Ministry of Finance, Snellmaninkatu 1 A, P.O. Box 286, 00171 Helsinki, Finland
PHONE: +358 (9) 1601
FAX: +358 (9) 1604856

Minister of Foreign Affairs
Tarja Halonen, Ministry of Foreign Affairs, Merikasarmi, Laivastokatu 22, 00161 Helsinki, Finland
PHONE: +358 (9) 134151
FAX: +358 (9) 13415002
E-MAIL: tarja.halonen@formin.fi

Minister of Trade and Industry
Kimmo Sasi, Ministry of Trade and Industry, Aleksanterinkatu 4, P.O. Box 230, 00171 Helsinki, Finland
FAX: +358 (9) 13416303
E-MAIL: kimmo.sasi@formin.fi

Minister of the Interior
Kari Hakamies, Ministry of the Interior, Kirkkokatu 12, P.O. Box 257, 00171 Helsinki, Finland
FAX: +358 (9) 1602887
E-MAIL: kari.hakamies@sm.intermin.fi

Minister of Justice

Johannes Koskinen, Ministry of Justice, Eteläesplanadi 10, P.O. Box 1, 00131 Helsinki, Finland

PHONE: +358 (9) 18251
FAX: +358 (9) 18257730
E-MAIL: johannes.koskinen@om.vn.fi

Minister of Labor

Sinikka Monkare, Ministry of Labor, Eteläesplanadi 4, P.O. Box 524, 00101 Helsinki, Finland

PHONE: +358 (9) 18561
FAX: +358 (9) 18257525
E-MAIL: sinikka.monkare@mol.fi

Minister of Local and Regional Affairs

Martti Korhonen, Ministry of Local and Regional Affairs, Kirkkokatu 12, P.O. Box 257, 00171 Helsinki, Finland

FAX: +358 (9) 1602887
E-MAIL: martti.korhonen@sm.intermin.fi

Minister of Social Affairs and Health

Maija Perho, Ministry of Social Affairs And Health, Meritullinkatu 8, P.O. Box 267, 00171 Helsinki, Finland

FAX: +358 (9) 1603810
E-MAIL: maija.perho@stm.vn.fi

Minister of Trade and Industry

Erkki Tuomioja, Ministry of Trade And Industry, Aleksanterinkatu 4, P.O. Box 230, 00171 Helsinki, Finland

FAX: +358 (9) 1602655
E-MAIL: erkki.tuomioja@ktm.vn.fi

Minister of Transport and Communications

Olli-Pekka Heinonen, Ministry of Transport And Communications, Eteläesplanadi 16, P.O. Box 235, 00131 Helsinki, Finland

FAX: +358 (9) 1602708
E-MAIL: olli-pekka.heinonen@mintc.fi

POLITICAL ORGANIZATIONS

Suomen Sosialidemokraattinen Poulue-SDP (Social Democratic Party)

Saariniemenkatu 6, 00530 Helsinki, Finland
PHONE: +358 (9) 478988
FAX: +358 (9) 712752
TITLE: President
NAME: Paavo Lipponen

Kansallinen Kokoomus (National Coalition Party)

Kansakoulukuja 3, 00100 Helsinki, Finland

PHONE: +358 (9) 69381
FAX: +358 (9) 6943736
E-MAIL: Sauli.Niinisto@vm.vn.mailnet.fi
TITLE: Chairman
NAME: Sauli Niinisto

Vasemmistoliitto (Leftist Alliance)

Siltasaarenkatu 6,7. Krs, 00530 Helsinki, Finland
PHONE: +358 (9) 774741
FAX: +358 (9) 77474200
E-MAIL: suvianne@vasemmistoliitto.fi
NAME: Suvi-Anne Siimes

Svenska Folkpartiet-SFP (Swedish People's Party)

Simonsgatan 8 A, PB 430, 00101 Helsingfors, Finland
PHONE: +358 (9) 693070
FAX: +358 (9) 6931968
E-MAIL: info@sfp.fi
NAME: Jan-Erik Enestam

Vihreä Liitto (Green League)

Runeberginkatu 5 B, 9. Krs, 00100 Helsinki, Finland
PHONE: +358 (9) 58604160
FAX: +358 (9) 58604161
E-MAIL: vihreat@vihrealiitto.fi
NAME: Pekka Haavisto

Suomen Keskusta (Center Party)

Pursimiehenkatu 15, 00150 Helsinki, Finland
PHONE: +358 (9) 172721
FAX: +358 (9) 653589
E-MAIL: olli.mattila@keskusta.fi
NAME: Esko Aho

Suomen Kristillinen Liitto (Finnish Christian League)

Mannerheimintie 40 D, 00100 Helsinki, Finland
PHONE: +358 (9) 34882200
FAX: +358 (9) 34882228
E-MAIL: skl@skl.fi
NAME: C. P. Bjarne Kallis

Liberaalinen Kansanpuolue-LKP (Liberal People's Party)

Fredrikinkatu 58 A, 00100 Helsinki, Finland
PHONE: +358 (9) 440227
FAX: +358 (9) 440771
E-MAIL: liberal@liberaalit.fi
TITLE: President

NAME: Altti Majava

Nuorsuomalainen Puolue (Young Finns)

Nuorsuomalaiset r.p., PL 267, 00101 Helsinki,
Finland
PHONE: +358 (09) 6856211
FAX: +358 (09) 6856233
E-MAIL: nuorsuom@nuorsuom.fi
NAME: Risto Penttila

DIPLOMATIC REPRESENTATION

Embassies in Finland

Canada
Pohjois Esplanadi 25B, P.O. Box 779, 00101
Helsinki 10, Finland

Denmark
Tanskan Suurlähetystö, Keskuskatu 1 A, PL
1042, 00101 Helsinki, Finland
PHONE: +358 (09) 6841050
FAX: +358 (09) 68410540
E-MAIL: danmark@kolumbus.fi

Indonesia
Kuusisaarentie 3, 00340, Helsinki, Finland
PHONE: +358 (9) 4582100
FAX: +358 (9) 4582882
E-MAIL: kbri.helsinki@indo-embassy.inet.fi

Japan
Eteläranta 8, 00130 Helsinki, Finland
PHONE: +358 (9) 6860200
FAX: +358 (9) 633012
TITLE: Ambassador
NAME: Yasuji Ishigaki

United Kingdom
Itäinen Puistotie 17, 00140 Helsinki, Finland
PHONE: +358 (9) 22865100
FAX: +358 (9) 22865284
E-MAIL: mailbox@ukembassy.fi
TITLE: Ambassador
NAME: Gavin Hewitt

United States
Itäinen Puistotie 14 B, FIN-00140, Helsinki,
Finland
PHONE: +358 (9) 171931
E-MAIL: webmaster@usembassy.fi
TITLE: Ambassador
NAME: Eric S. Edelman

JUDICIAL SYSTEM

Supreme Court
Pohjoisesplanadi 3, PL 301, 00171 Helsinki,
Finland
PHONE: +358 (09) 12381
FAX: +358 (09) 1238354
E-MAIL: korkein.oikeus@om.fi

Supreme Administrative Court
Postiosoite, PL 180, 00131 Helsinki, Finland

FURTHER READING

Articles

"'He Didn't Look Defeated.' (Finland's
President Martti ahtisaari)." *Newsweek
International*. June 21, 1999, p. 32.

Klee, Kenneth, and Jennifer Bensko. "The
Future is Finnish. (Finland Bets on High-
Technology)." *Newsweek International*. (May
24, 1999): 58.

"Photo Finish. (Politics and Government in
Finland)." *The Economist (US)*, March 27,
1999, vol. 350, no. 8112, p. 54.

Smiley, Xan. "Happy Family? A Survey of the
Nordic Countries" *The Economist*. January
23, 1999.

"Survey of Finland." *The Financial Times*. July
1, 1999.

Books

Central Intelligence Agency. *CIA World
Factbook*. Washington, D.C: GPO, 1999

Jutikkala, Eino, with Kauko Pirinen. *A History
of Finland*. Porvoo-Helsinki: Werner
Soederstroem OY, 1996.

Sundberg, Jan and Sten Berglund, eds. *Finnish
Democracy*. Jyväskylä: The Finnish Political
Science Association, 1990.

Internet

Embassy of Finland, Washington, D.C. Available
Online @ http://www.finland.org (November
11, 1999).

Ministry for Foreign Affairs. "Virtual Finland."
Available Online @ http://virtual.finland.fi
(November 11, 1999).

Statistics Finland. *The Statistical Yearbook of
Finland*. Available Online @ http://
www.etla.fi/english (November 11, 1999).

FINLAND: STATISTICAL DATA

For sources and notes see "Sources of Statistics" in the front of each volume.

GEOGRAPHY

Geography (1)

Area:

Total: 337,030 sq km.

Land: 305,470 sq km.

Water: 31,560 sq km.

Area—comparative: slightly smaller than Montana.

Land boundaries:

Total: 2,628 km.

Border countries: Norway 729 km, Sweden 586 km, Russia 1,313 km.

Coastline: 1,126 km (excludes islands and coastal indentations).

Climate: cold temperate; potentially subarctic, but comparatively mild because of moderating influence of the North Atlantic Current, Baltic Sea, and more than 60,000 lakes.

Terrain: mostly low, flat to rolling plains interspersed with lakes and low hills.

Natural resources: timber, copper, zinc, iron ore, silver.

Land use:

Arable land: 8%

Permanent crops: NA%

Permanent pastures: 0%

Forests and woodland: 76%

Other: 16% (1993 est.).

HUMAN FACTORS

Demographics (2A)

	1990	1995	1998	2000	2010	2020	2030	2040	2050
Population	4,986.4	5,105.3	5,149.2	5,164.8	5,169.9	5,092.7	4,886.0	4,545.9	4,170.1
Net migration rate (per 1,000 population)	NA	NA	NA	NA	NA	NA	NA	NA	NA
Births	NA	NA	NA	NA	NA	NA	NA	NA	NA
Deaths	50.1	NA	NA	NA	NA	NA	NA	NA	NA
Life expectancy - males	70.9	72.8	73.6	74.0	75.7	77.1	78.2	79.0	79.7
Life expectancy - females	78.9	80.3	80.8	81.1	82.5	83.6	84.4	85.2	85.7
Birth rate (per 1,000)	13.2	12.4	11.2	10.3	9.4	8.8	7.7	7.0	6.8
Death rate (per 1,000)	10.1	9.7	9.6	9.7	10.4	11.6	13.5	15.2	15.9
Women of reproductive age (15-49 yrs.)	1,258.2	1,269.6	1,237.8	1,217.3	1,145.3	1,061.5	987.8	888.2	765.6
of which are currently married	303.0	NA	NA	NA	NA	NA	NA	NA	NA
Fertility rate	1.8	1.8	1.7	1.6	1.5	1.4	1.4	1.3	1.3

Except as noted, values for vital statistics are in thousands; life expectancy is in years.

Health Personnel (3)

Total health expenditure as a percentage of GDP, 1990-1997[a]

Public sector 5.7

Private sector 1.7

Total[b] 7.4

Health expenditure per capita in U.S. dollars, 1990-1997[a]

Purchasing power parity 1,409

Total 1,666

Availability of health care facilities per 100,000 people

Hospital beds 1990-1997[a] 930

Doctors 1993[c] 269

Nurses 1993[c] 2,184

Health Indicators (4)

Life expectancy at birth

1980 73

1997 77

Daily per capita supply of calories (1996) 2,916

Total fertility rate births per woman (1997) 1.9

Maternal mortality ratio per 100,000 live births (1990-97) . . . . .11[c]

Safe water % of population with access (1995) 98

Sanitation % of population with access (1995) 100

Consumption of iodized salt % of households (1992-98)[a] . . . .

Smoking prevalence

Male % of adults (1985-95)[a] 27

Female % of adults (1985-95)[a] 19

Tuberculosis incidence per 100,000 people (1997) 13

Adult HIV prevalence % of population ages 15-49 (1997) 0.02

Infants and Malnutrition (5)

Under-5 mortality rate (1997) 4

% of infants with low birthweight (1990-97) 4

Births attended by skilled health staff % of total[a] . . .NA

% fully immunized (1995-97)

TB 100

DPT 100

Polio 100

Measles 98

Prevalence of child malnutrition under age 5 (1992-97)[b] . . . . .NA

Ethnic Division (6)

Finn 93%

Swede 6%

Lapp 0.11%

Gypsy 0.12%

Tatar 0.02%

Religions (7)

Evangelical Lutheran .89%

Greek Orthodox 1%

None 9%

Other 1%

Languages (8)

Finnish 93.5% (official), Swedish 6.3% (official), small Lapp- and Russian-speaking minorities.

EDUCATION

Public Education Expenditures (9)

Public expenditure on education (% of GNP)

1980 . . . . .5.3

1996 . . . . .7.6[1]

Expenditure per student

Primary % of GNP per capita

1980 . . . . .20.7

1996 . . . . .23.3[1]

Secondary % of GNP per capita

1980 . . . .

1996 . . . . .28.6[1]

Tertiary % of GNP per capita

1980 . . . . .37.4

1996 . . . . .49.4[1]

Expenditure on teaching materials

Primary % of total for level (1996) 6.2

Secondary % of total for level (1996) . . . .

Primary pupil-teacher ratio per teacher (1996) . . . .

Duration of primary education years (1995) 6

Educational Attainment (10)

Age group (1990) . . . . .25+

Total population 3,387,384

Highest level attained (%)

No schooling . . . . .NA

First level
  Not completed 49.4
  Completed .... .NA
Entered second level
  S-1 .... .35.3
  S-2 .... .NA
Postsecondary 15.4

GOVERNMENT & LAW

Political Parties (12)

Parliament	% of seats
Social Democratic Party 28.3	

Center Party 19.9
National Coalition (Conservative) Party 17.9
Leftist Alliance (Communist) 11.2
Green League 6.5
Swedish People's Party 5.1
Finnish Christian League 3.0
Young Finns 2.8
Rural 1.3
Liberal People's Party 0.6
Ecology Party 0.3

Military Affairs (14B)

	1990	1991	1992	1993	1994	1995
Military expenditures						
Current dollars (mil.)	1,965	2,421	2,510	2,439	2,559	2,381
1995 constant dollars (mil.)	2,259	2,675	2,699	2,557	2,623	2,381
Armed forces (000)	31	32	33	31	35	32
Gross national product (GNP)						
Current dollars (mil.)	120,700	115,700	113,700	114,200	121,300	119,400[e]
1995 constant dollars (mil.)	138,700	127,800	122,300	119,700	124,400	119,400[e]
Central government expenditures (CGE)						
1995 constant dollars (mil.)	45,140	51,860	62,210	60,310	59,400	46,600[e]
People (mil.)	5.0	5.0	5.0	5.1	5.1	5.1
Military expenditure as % of GNP	1.6	2.1	2.2	2.1	2.1	2.0
Military expenditure as % of CGE	5.0	5.2	4.3	4.3	4.4	5.1
Military expenditure per capita (1995 $)	453	534	535	505	516	467
Armed forces per 1,000 people (soldiers)	6.2	6.4	6.5	6.1	6.9	6.3
GNP per capita (1995 $)	27,820	25,500	24,270	23,630	24,450	23,410
Arms imports[6]						
Current dollars (mil.)	60	50	430	290	60	30
1995 constant dollars (mil.)	69	55	463	304	62	30
Arms exports[6]						
Current dollars (mil.)	5	10	0	10	20	0
1995 constant dollars (mil.)	6	11	0	10	21	0
Total imports[7]						
Current dollars (mil.)	27,000	21,810	21,210	18,030	23,210	28,110
1995 constant dollars (mil.)	31,030	24,100	22,810	18,900	23,800	28,110
Total exports[7]						
Current dollars (mil.)	26,570	23,080	23,980	23,450	29,660	39,570
1995 constant dollars (mil.)	30,540	25,500	25,800	24,580	30,400	39,570
Arms as percent of total imports[8]	.2	.2	2.0	1.6	.3	.1
Arms as percent of total exports[8]	0	0	0	0	.1	0

Government Budget (13A)

Year: 1996

Total Expenditures: 231,425 Millions of Markkaa

Expenditures as a percentage of the total by function:

General public services and public order 8.43
Defense 3.85
Education 10.13
Health 3.03
Social Security and Welfare 38.53
Housing and community amenities 2.98
Recreational, cultural, and religious affairs 1.01
Fuel and energy 33
Agriculture, forestry, fishing, and hunting 5.79
Mining, manufacturing, and construction 3.30
Transportation and communication 3.14
Other economic affairs and services 6.10

Crime (15)

Crime rate (for 1997)

Crimes reported 722,000
Total persons convicted 509,700
Crimes per 100,000 population 14,000

Persons responsible for offenses

Total number of suspects 564,400
Total number of female suspects 83,500
Total number of juvenile suspects 112,300

LABOR FORCE

Labor Force (16)

Total (million) 2.533
Public services 30.4%
Industry 20.9%
Commerce 15.0%
Finance, insurance, ...
    and business services .10.2%
Agriculture and forestry 8.6%
Transport and . . . .
    communications 7.7%
Construction 7.2%

Unemployment Rate (17)

14.6% (1997 est.)

PRODUCTION SECTOR

Electric Energy (18)

Capacity . . . . .14.143 million kW (1995)
Production . . . . .58.626 billion kWh (1995)
Consumption per capita . . . . .13,181 kWh (1995)

Transportation (19)

Highways:

total: 77,782 km

paved: 49,780 km (including 431 km of expressways)

unpaved: 28,002 km (1996 est.)

Waterways: 6,675 km total (including Saimaa Canal); 3,700 km suitable for steamers

Pipelines: natural gas 580 km

Merchant marine:

total: 93 ships (1,000 GRT or over) totaling 1,069,794 GRT/1,127,087 DWT ships by type: bulk 8, cargo 22, chemical tanker 5, oil tanker 11, passenger 1, railcar carrier 1, roll-on/roll-off cargo 34, short-sea passenger 11 (1997 est.)

Airports: 158 (1997 est.)

Airports—with paved runways:

total: 69

over 3,047 m: 3

2,438 to 3,047 m: 23

1,524 to 2,437 m: 13

914 to 1,523 m: 21

under 914 m: 9 (1997 est.)

Airports—with unpaved runways:

total: 89

914 to 1,523 m: 5

under 914 m: 84 (1997 est.)

Top Agricultural Products (20)

Cereals, sugar beets, potatoes; dairy cattle; annual fish catch about 160,000 metric tons.

MANUFACTURING SECTOR

GDP & Manufacturing Summary (21)

Detailed value added figures are listed by both International Standard Industry Code (ISIC) and product title.

	1980	1985	1990	1994
GDP ($-1990 mil.)[1]	98,701	113,888	134,788	125,113
Per capita ($-1990)[1]	20,649	23,233	27,033	24,614
Manufacturing share (%) (current prices)[1]	27.6	25.1	22.7	24.7
Manufacturing				
Value added ($-1990 mil.)[1]	20,708	24,192	27,558	29,713

	1980	1985	1990	1994
Industrial production index	100	112	131	142
Value added ($ mil.)	14,343	13,594	26,980	20,950
Gross output ($ mil.)	40,839	36,967	74,497	59,336
Employment (000)	531	496	432	341

Profitability (% of gross output)

	1980	1985	1990	1994
Intermediate input (%)	65	63	64	65
Wages and salaries inc. supplements (%)	19	20	21	*18*
Gross operating surplus	16	17	15	*18*

Productivity ($)

	1980	1985	1990	1994
Gross output per worker	76,435	74,030	171,573	173,801
Value added per worker	26,845	27,223	62,163	61,365
Average wage (inc. supplements)	14,694	14,599	36,741	*30,933*

Value added ($ mil.)

	1980	1985	1990	1994
311/2 Food products	1,402	1,413	2,576	1,935
313 Beverages	225	227	666	386
314 Tobacco products	46	57	177	100
321 Textiles	469	309	386	321
322 Wearing apparel	499	435	428	204
323 Leather and fur products	54	38	48	31
324 Footwear	134	106	93	60
331 Wood and wood products	1,196	652	1,578	1,367
332 Furniture and fixtures	257	215	515	238
341 Paper and paper products	2,088	1,845	3,603	3,672
342 Printing and publishing	1,080	1,222	2,113	1,357
351 Industrial chemicals	555	561	1,371	1,040
352 Other chemical products	349	371	707	607
353 Petroleum refineries	445	384	674	432
354 Miscellaneous petroleum and coal products	46	47	121	99
355 Rubber products	105	84	133	118
356 Plastic products	164	168	425	314
361 Pottery, china and earthenware	46	40	73	51
362 Glass and glass products	105	78	163	148
369 Other non-metal mineral products	434	434	1,053	455
371 Iron and steel	544	463	850	1,016
372 Non-ferrous metals	142	103	363	405
381 Metal products	756	768	1,759	1,145
382 Non-electrical machinery	469	1,618	3,355	2,129
383 Electrical machinery	694	764	1,832	1,703
384 Transport equipment	823	915	1,405	1,130
385 Professional and scientific equipment	110	166	344	337
390 Other manufacturing industries	107	112	168	151

FINANCE, ECONOMICS, & TRADE

Economic Indicators (22)

National product: GDP—purchasing power parity—$102.1 billion (1997 est.)

National product real growth rate: 4.6% (1997 est.)

National product per capita: $20,000 (1997 est.)

Inflation rate—consumer price index: 1.2% (1997 est.)

Exchange Rates (24)

Exchange rates:

Markkaa (FMk) per US$1

January 1998 . . . . .5.4948

1997 . . . . .5.1914

1996 . . . . .4.5936

1995 . . . . .4.3667

1994 . . . . .5.2235

1993 . . . . .5.7123

Top Import Origins (25)

$29.3 billion (c.i.f., 1996) Data are for 1995.

Origins	%
European Union	.44
Germany	.16.6
United Kingdom	.8.0
Sweden	.11.7
United States	.7.1
Russia	.7.1
Japan	.6.3

Top Export Destinations (26)

$38.4 billion (f.o.b., 1996) Data are for 1995.

Destinations	%
European Union	.46.5
Germany	.13.4
United Kingdom	.10.4
Sweden	.10.1
United States	.6.7
Japan	.2.6
Russia	.4.8

Economic Aid (27)

Donor: ODA, $355 million (1993).

Import Export Commodities (28)

Import Commodities	Export Commodities
Foodstuffs	Paper and pulp
Petroleum and	Machinery
petroleum products	Chemicals
Chemicals	Metals
Transport equipment	Timber Russia 4.8%
Iron and steel	
Machinery	
Textile yarn and fabrics	
Fodder grains Japan 6.3%	

Balance of Payments (23)

	1992	1993	1994	1995	1996
Exports of goods (f.o.b.)	23,942	23,478	29,731	40,515	40,539
Imports of goods (f.o.b.)	−20,165	−17,217	−22,241	−28,169	−29,457
Trade balance	3,777	6,261	7,490	12,346	11,082
Services - debits	−14,328	−12,544	−13,265	−16,938	−15,259
Services - credits	6,400	5,588	7,502	10,390	10,061
Private transfers (net)	−532	−350	−358	−401	−667
Government transfers (net)	−262	−78	−96	−196	−430
Overall balance	−4,945	−1,123	1,273	5,201	4,788

FRANCE

French Republic
République Française

INTRODUCTORY SURVEY

RECENT HISTORY

After World War II (1939–45), France still faced almost continuous fighting overseas. It lost control of Indochina in Asia in 1954. Later, Algeria was the scene of a nationalist rebellion by Muslims. After a rebellion by French settlers in Algeria in 1958, General de Gaulle, the only leader who could rally the nation, was installed as premier. He ended the threat in Algeria peaceably. In December 1958, he was officially named the first president of the Fifth Republic.

Algeria gained independence on 1 July 1962. Nearly all of France's former African territories were given their independence as well. France has continued to provide economic assistance, and its ties with most of the former colonies have remained close. During the mid-1960s, de Gaulle sought to distance France from the Anglo-American alliance. France developed its own atomic weapons and withdrew its forces from the NATO command.

In the spring of 1968, student riots and a month-long general strike severely weakened the Gaullist regime. In April 1969, General de Gaulle resigned. In June, Georges Pompidou, a former premier in de Gaulle's government, was elected the second president of the Fifth Republic. In 1974, after President Pompidou died in office, an Independent Republican, Valéry Giscard d'Estaing, became the third president of the Fifth Republic. Giscard strengthened relations with the United States but continued to follow a middle course be-

tween the superpowers (United States and Soviet Union) in world affairs.

A Socialist, François Mitterrand, was elected president in May 1981. Mitterrand launched a program of economic reforms, including government takeover of many industrial companies and most major banks. Mitterrand committed French troops to a peacekeeping force in Lebanon, and aided the Chadian government against domestic rebels and their Libyan backers.

In the March 1986 elections, the Socialists lost their majority in the National Assembly. In order to keep control of the government, Mitterrand had to appoint a conservative prime minister to head a new center-right cabinet. The new prime minister, Jacques Chirac, successfully began a program to denationalize sixty-five state-owned companies. This plan was opposed by Mitterrand. In 1988, Mitterand won a commanding 54% of the vote and a second seven-year term, and Chirac resigned.

By 1994, however, Mitterrand had grown ill and announced he would retire in May 1995. In the elections that followed, Chirac received 52% of the vote and gained the presidency. Chirac sought to limit government spending in order to meet certain monetary guidelines so that France would be ready to join the European Monetary Union (EMU) in 1999. The EMU would create one currency to replace member countries' individual currencies. Many of Chirac's policies to reduce public spending were met with resistance.

Chirac called for parliamentary elections in 1997, a year earlier than the constitution required. He believed that a majority of the population would support decreased government spending and restrained monetary policy. Chirac's plan backfired when the Socialists and Communists won the majority. Socialist leader Lionel Jospin was named prime minister and he pledged to protect the welfare state. By early 1998, however, unemployment was still high, and the jobless protested outside unemployment offices demanding more benefits.

GOVERNMENT

Under the constitution of the Fifth Republic (1958), as subsequently amended, the president of the republic is elected for a seven-year term by direct universal voting. The president appoints the premier and, on the premier's recommendation, the other members of the cabinet. The president has the power to dissolve the National Assembly. When this occurs, new elections must be held in twenty to forty days. The president executes laws approved by the legislature, has the right of pardon, and is commander of the armed forces.

The Parliament consists of two houses, the National Assembly and the Senate. The National Assembly is composed of 577 deputies, each representing an electoral district. The deputies' term of office, unless the Assembly is dissolved, is five years. The Senate consists of 321 members elected to nine-year terms, one-third being chosen every three years. All citizens aged 18 or over are eligible to vote.

Judiciary

There are two types of lower judicial courts in France, the civil courts and the criminal courts. The function of the civil courts is to judge conflicts arising between persons. The function of the criminal courts is to judge violations against the law. The most serious crimes, for which the penalties may range to life imprisonment, are tried in special courts periodically. Special administrative courts deal with disputes between individuals and government agencies.

From the lower courts, appeals may be taken to appeals courts. Judgments of the appeals courts are final, except that appeals on the interpretation of the constitution may be taken to the highest of the judicial courts, the Court of Cassation in Paris.

The Conseil Constitutionnel rules on whether or not laws are constitutional. The death penalty was abolished in 1981.

Political Parties

Since the late 1950s, French politics has been dominated by four political groups: the Gaullists; an independent center-right coalition; the Socialists; and the Communists.

The Gaullist party, called the Rally for the Republic (Rassemblement pour la République—RPR) was founded by Jacques Chirac in 1976. In the same year, the centrist parties formed the Union for French Democracy (Union pour la Démocratie Française—UDF).

DEFENSE

All French males between the ages of 18 and 45 must perform ten months of national service. The annual draft intake is around 200,000 a year. Women may volunteer, and 14,000 now serve.

In 1995, there were 398,900 regular personnel in the armed services, including 236,600 in the army, 88,600 in the air force, 63,300 in the navy, 92,400 in the Gendarmerie Nationale, and 14,000 in various other service organizations. Reserves totaled 1.2 million, including 915,200 army reserves. In 1996, the military budget was $38.3 billion.

France's Force Action Rapide (42,500) is an elite five-division force designed for rapid air deployment anywhere in the world. The French army uses weapons and equipment of French manufacture.

France began building its own independent nuclear force during the de Gaulle era and has conducted a number of atmospheric nuclear tests. France maintains substantial forces abroad. It has a composite air squadron in Turkey and almost 6,000 troops deployed on peacekeeping missions to seven different countries, including Croatia.

France is one of the world's leading makers and sellers of armaments, including the Mirage aircraft, Super Étendard fighter-bombers, and Exocet missiles, tanks, and armored vehicles. During 1981–91, French arms exports had a value of around $40 billion.

ECONOMIC AFFAIRS

France is one of the most richly endowed countries of Europe. The favorable climate, extensive areas of rich soil, and long-established tradition of skilled agriculture have created ideal conditions for a thriving farm economy. Large deposits of iron ore, a well-integrated network of power plants, important domestic reserves of natural gas, good transport, and high standards of industrial workmanship have made French industry one of the most modern in Europe.

Public Finance

Deficits have been commonplace, but in recent years, efforts have been made to cut back on the growth of taxes and government spending and, since 1986, to remove state enterprises from the expense of government ownership.

The French government had succeeded in progressively cutting the budget deficit until 1991, from 3.3% of GDP in 1985 to 1.9% in 1990. However, from 1991 to 1993, the sharp drop in economic growth led to a dramatic decline in revenues. The deficit climbed to 3.3% in 1992 and over 5% in 1993 and 1994, the highest amounts in over twenty years. In 1993, government revenues totaled approximately $220.5 billion and expenditures $249.1 billion, including capital expenditures of $47 billion. External debt totaled $300 billion. Deficit reduction became a top priority of the government when France committed to the European Monetary Union (EMU).

Income

In 1998, France's gross national product (GNP) was about $1.47 trillion at current prices, or $24,940 per person. For the period 1985–95, the average inflation rate was 2.8%, resulting in a real growth rate in GNP of 1.5% per person.

Industry

Industry has expanded considerably since World War II, with major progress in the electronics, transport, processing, and construction industries. France is the fourth-leading industrial power, after the United States, Japan, and Germany. In 1994, industry accounted for 27% of the gross domestic product (GDP) and over four-fifths of all exports.

The French automotive industry, which employed 350,000 workers in 1995, is one of the largest in the world. Some 3.1 million passenger cars and 423,000 commercial vehicles were produced in 1995. The French aircraft industry specializes in advanced design and experimental development.

Chemicals, one of the fastest-growing industries in France, range from perfume components to such industrial materials as sulfuric acid. The chemical industry ranks fourth in the world, employing 298,000 and generating $72 billion in revenues in 1995.

Other industries important to France's economy include pharmaceuticals, perfume and cosmetics, electronics, textiles, and food processing. In 1994, France produced 54.6 million hectoliters (1.4 billion gallons) of wine, making it the second-largest producer after Italy.

Banking and Finance

The Banque de France, founded in 1800, came completely under government control in 1945. It is the bank of issue, sets discount rates and maximum discounts for each bank, regulates public and private finance, and is the Treasury depository. In 1945, a provisional government headed by Gen. de Gaulle also nationalized France's four largest commercial banks, and the state thus came to control 55% of all deposits. In 1982, Socialist President François Mitterrand nationalized thirty-nine banks, bringing the state's control over deposits to 90%.

Measured by stock market capitalization, the Paris Bourse is the third largest in Europe after London and Frankfurt. The Lyon Bourse is the most active provincial stock exchange. MATIF (marché à terme des instruments financiers), the financial futures exchange, was opened in Paris in 1986 and has proved a success. The Société des Bourses Françaises (SBF), the operator of the French stock market, has been determinedly pursuing a policy of reform and modernization, and it expects to benefit from the liberalization of financial services brought about by the EU's Investment Services Directive (ISD). New French legislation, providing for the liberalization of financial services, has transposed the directive into national law.

Economic Development

Since World War II, France has implemented a series of economic plans, introduced to direct the postwar recovery period but later expanded to provide for generally increasing governmental direction of the economy.

French loans to its former African territories totaled CFA Fr50 billion by November 1972, when President Pompidou announced that France would cancel the entire amount (including all accrued interest) to lighten these countries' debt burdens. In 1993, France spent $7.9 billion on international aid.

SOCIAL WELFARE

By the early 1980s, virtually every person living in France was covered by some form of social assistance.

In addition to providing for the partial reimbursement of medical, pharmaceutical, and hospitalization expenses, health insurance guarantees the payment of cash benefits as partial compensation for loss of earnings during the period of disability. Maternity insurance provides for the payment of pharmaceutical, medical, surgical, and hospitalization expenses incurred during pregnancy, confinement, and postnatal treatment, as well as other benefits.

Unemployed workers receive daily payments not limited in time but reduced by 10% each consecutive year. Disability insurance pays a pension to compensate for the loss of earnings and costs of care. Old-age insurance guarantees payment of a pension when the insured reaches age 65, provided his or her contributions have been sufficient. Death insurance provides payment of a lump sum to the dependents of the insured.

Monthly benefits are paid to employed heads of families having at least two dependent children. Maternity and prenatal allowances are also paid. The growth of the feminist movement in the 1970s led to the creation in 1974 of a special cabinet office for women's rights. In 1992, the Penal Code was revised to include provisions stipulating up to one year in prison and up to the equivalent of $20,000 in fines for workplace sexual harassment.

Healthcare

Patients have the option of seeing a private doctor on a fee basis or going to a state-operated facility. During the 1980s, there was a trend away from inpatient and toward outpatient care, with a growing number of patients receiving care at home.

In 1993, the population per physician was 461. There are over 1,000 public hospitals and 2,700 private hospitals. There are also about 11,000 infants' and children's facilities of various kinds. Life expectancy in 1995 averaged 78 years for men and women. From 1985 to 1990, major causes of death were noncommunicable diseases (362 per 100,000) and injuries (76 per 100,000).

Housing

In 1984, there were over 24.2 million housing units in France. By 1991, the total number of housing units had risen to 26.1 million. More than six million new dwellings were completed between 1970 and 1986. In 1992, the total number of new dwellings completed was 248,400. Living standards are high. About 97% of all French households have a refrigerator, over 90% a television set, 84% a washing machine, 73% an automobile, 35% a freezer, and 23% a dishwasher.

EDUCATION

Education is compulsory for children from the age of 6 to 16 and is free in all state primary and secondary schools. Higher education is not free, but academic fees are low, and more than half of the students are excused from payment. Practically the entire adult population is literate.

In 1994, there were 4 million pupils in primary schools (ages 6–11); and 5.7 million in secondary schools. Choice of a lycée (or secondary school) depends on aptitude test results.

University enrollment was 2.1 million in 1993. There are seventy public universities. The former University of Paris, also referred to as the Sorbonne, is the oldest in France and one of the leading institutions of higher learning in the world.

1999 KEY EVENTS TIMELINE

January

- The French Franc is substituted by the euro in some non-cash transactions.

- Transportation workers strike at the Arc de Triomphe, halting public transport.

- France fails to support the United Nations oil embargo against Iraq, and asks for greater weapons control instead.

- The far-right National Front Party, led by Jean Marie Le Pen, splinters in two. Bruno Maigret leads the new far-right faction of the group.

- Lionel Jospin, socialist Prime Minister, deploys an additional 7,000 policemen and creates 50 new detention centers to combat juvenile delinquency.

February

- In Paris, 200,000 citizens protest gay marriages after the courts determine their legitimacy.

- Laurent Fabius, former Prime Minister, goes on trial for criminal negligence in a case of spreading AIDS through contaminated blood to 4,000 people in the mid 1980s.

- An avalanche in Grenoble kills 12 people.

- A Paris court upholds the French ban on ritual genital mutilation in the case of 48 African girls under the age of 10.

March

- Laurent Fabius and Former Social Affairs Minister Georgina Dufoix are acquitted of criminal negligence and manslaughter.

- Abdullah Senoussi, the brother-in-law of Libyan leader Colonel Muammar El-Qaddafi, and five others are convicted in the bombing of a French airliner that killed 171 people in 1989.

- An Air France plane carrying 75 passengers is hijacked. The terrorist surrenders at Charles de Gaulle airport in Paris.

- The French Banking Association, which allegedly profited from unclaimed accounts after the Holocaust, announces compensation for the heirs of French Jewish Holocaust victims.

April

- The Banque National de Paris (BNP) bids for Société Générale and Paribas, two national rivals.

- Philippe Séguin resigns from the leadership of the right-wing Gaullists Rally for the Republic.

May

- Bernard Bonnet, prefect of Corsica, is fined for mismanagement of the island, and is also under suspicion for arson.

June

- France allows New Caledonia's first semi-independent government.

- French Health Minister Bernard Kouchner classifies marijuana as the least dangerous drug, even compared to alcohol and tobacco, causing a controversy.

- Terrorists from the Corsican National Liberation Front threaten France with military action.

- Twenty-four terrorists from the Algerian Armed Islamic Group go on trial for 1995 bomb attacks which killed 12 and injured 200.

July

- TotalFina makes a bid for Elf Aquitaine, which could compete successfully in world oil production markets.

- French songbird hunting is extended for an extra month, angering birdwatchers in EU countries.

- Taxpayers hold a rally outside the French finance ministry because of exorbitant tax reforms.

August

- José Bové, leader of the Farm-workers Union is arrested for trashing a McDonald's construction site, protesting American cultural imperialism.

- French police break up tangoers on the Left Bank who have been dancing there illegally for ten years.

- French hunters ignore a recent ban on hunting the bunting.

- Germans pull French pork products off grocery shelves in allegations that the animals are fed sewage, in response to a French ban on German beef.

September

- Finance Minister Dominique Strauss-Kahn delivers a year 2000 budget with huge tax cuts on household property and rents.

October

- Students in secondary schools protest, demanding more professors, lower class fees and better preparation for employment.

- A French judge demands that Colonel Muammar El-Qaddafi, Libyan leader, be prosecuted for bombing a French airliner in 1989.

- Protests by French truckers disrupt traffic in Paris.

- French chefs throw eggs at police during riots over the high tax on restaurant dining.

November

- France's left-wing prime minister, Lionel Jospin, implicates Jacques Chirac, the right-wing president, in accusations about the management of the Paris city administration.

- The European Commission in Brussels gives France an eight-day deadline to end its ban on

British beef, indicating it will launch legal action unless the demand is met.

- A much-debated new law is publicized, granting France's homosexuals the right to sign a Pacte civil de solidarite (better known as Pacs), allowing them basically the same rights as conventional married couples.

- Christian Sautter is named as France's new Minister of Economy, Finances, and Industry, taking over for Dominique Strauss-Kahn.

December

- NATO members cautiously welcome an offer by France and Germany to revamp their joint Eurocorps force, so it could take over as the rotating headquarters of the peacekeeping force in Kosovo.

- *Euro-business* magazine reports Liliane Bettencourt, the French woman who controls the L'Oreal cosmetics empire, is the richest person in Europe with an estimated personal fortune of $14.58 billion.

- Michele Alliot-Marie becomes the first woman to head a large French political party after 63 percent of members of President Jacques Chirac's Gaulist RPR party vote for her.

- A Maltese tanker sinks off northwest France, leaking thousands of tons of oil into the ocean.

- Hurricane-force winds reaching 95 miles per hour strike northern France and surrounding areas in late December, resulting in dozens of deaths and injuries.

- A French court rules that Seita, the manufacturer of Galoise and Gitane brand cigarettes, is partially responsible for the lung and tongue cancer death of a smoker. This is the first time that a French court has ruled against a cigarette manufacturer in a health liability case.

- The government approves a regulation calling for a 35-hour work week.

ANALYSIS OF EVENTS: 1999

BUSINESS AND THE ECONOMY

The birth of the euro and other economic adjustments related to France's participation in the European Union introduced uncertainty in the public's expectation in the future performance of the French economy. But inflation hovered at a low 0.05% and foreign companies continued to invest in French enterprises. Preparation for the introduction of the Euro forced France to stabilize interest rates in order to converge economically with other EU countries. While leading economists in France forecasted a downturn in the financial arena early in the year, the results toward the close of 1999 point to a successful 2.3% growth factor, and perhaps even 3.0% by 2000. These positive figures and considerable taxpayer unrest prompted Finance Minister Dominique Strauss-Kahn to declare large tax cuts for 2000. Unemployment also declined during the year, which some linked to the advent of the thirty-five hour workweek, reduced from thirty-nine hours per week for the same pay. Some observers argued, though, that a number of companies sought out labor-saving technologies and part-time workers instead of investing further in the workforce.

European companies consolidated and merged this year en masse, within national boundaries, and French banks attempted to do the same. The Banque Nationale de Paris (BNP) made a controversial bid for both Société Générale (SocGen) and Paribas, which would have created French banking giant SBP. BNP won control of Paribas, but not SocGen, because the company had previously signed a deal with Paribas that was waylaid by the BNP takeover. The French government deplores the hostile takeovers prevalent in the U.S. market, but this capitalistic behavior has become more popular in France. TotalFina's bid for Elf Aquitaine in July is another example of a national merger that recent privatization of French companies has induced. This combination would create a French oil giant capable of shifting capital away from American oil investments. The French government still holds onto a majority stake in Renault, Air France, France Telecom, the Caisse des Dépôts et Consignations and Crédit Lyonnais, but many other French companies have been privatized since the second half of the 1980s.

GOVERNMENT AND POLITICS

A coalition between President Jacques Chirac of the right-wing Rally for the Republic Gaullist party and Prime Minister Lionel Jospin of the Socialist Party brought France through a year of political instabilities caused by the war in Kosovo and continuing European integration. Support for French intervention in Serbia waned during the first half of the year as refugees fled into major cities and American bombings brought back images of World War II. Philippe Séguin resigned as leader of the Gaullists' Rally for the Republic in part from opposition to the Balkan conflict and also in protest against the government coalition with a socialist Prime Minister. Mr. Jospin signed the so-called ''Third Way'' pact early in the year with British Prime Minister Tony Blair and Germany's Gerhard Schröder which supported leftist policies but somehow found it possible to accept considerable privatization of formerly state-owned sectors of the economy. The Prime Minister's economic policies came under considerable scrutiny for espousing leftist rhetoric while enacting further economic liberalism, but the country's finances benefited in the short term.

CULTURE AND SOCIETY

Social issues came to the fore during Lionel Jospin's government through the legalization of gay marriages and a proposed bill calling for equal access to political representation for women. Both issues were hotly debated around the country, for fear that gay marriages would increase the burden on the social welfare system and that the women's bill would start a French affirmative action program.

Problems off-shore also posed a challenge to the government, with Corsican terrorist activity and corruption of the prefecture. Bernard Bonnet, Corsica's prefect, was imprisoned on suspicion of ordering the military to light an illegally built restaurant on fire. Mismanagement of the island has been denounced by the Corsican National Liberation Front whose nationalist attacks disrupt the tourism, which remains the country's main source of income. In a reaction to native unrest in New Caledonia, though, France prepared to grant autonomy to the territory between 2000 and 2014, and its first government convened in June.

French culture took a beating from American cultural imperialism and in general, globalization. Despite efforts to retain the traditional French language and government regulation of business, the country is slowly becoming Europeanized and Americanized. The English language is creeping daily into everyday usage, and privatization and capitalism are the buzzwords for French business. One holdout against liberalization and privatization is the French civil service. Upholding a culinary tradition, French farmers continue to shoot more

game than any other European country in spite of the increasingly prevalent fast-food chains. French chefs do not take kindly to the McDonald's food chain restaurants either, claiming that indigenous restaurants must pay much higher taxes than fast-food restaurants. Finally, the love-hate relationship between France and Germany became more pronounced this year as Germany took control of the European Union's Presidency.

France experienced a rise in juvenile delinquency and crimes committed by suburban youths, which elicited a quick response from Prime Minister Jospin. As a result, France has become one of the most heavily policed countries in Europe, although this doesn't seem to be helping the problem much. Detention centers and counseling have been added to the list of services Mr. Jospin hopes to give to criminal youths. Minister of Health Bernard Kouchner put out a report on drugs trying to classify substances according to the harm they do to health, but the French were loathe to listen to the advice that alcohol and tobacco had the most harmful effects, compared to cocaine and heroin. Using medical studies and lawsuits in America involving tobacco companies this year, however, the Health Minister supported his claims.

DIRECTORY

CENTRAL GOVERNMENT
Head of State

President
Jacques Chirac, Office of the President

Prime Minister
Lionel Jospin, Office of the Prime Minister, 57, rue de Varenne, 75007 Paris, France
PHONE: +33 (01) 42758000
E-MAIL: premier-ministre@premier-ministre.gouv.fr

Ministers

Minister of Agriculture, Fisheries, and Urban Affairs
Jean Glavany, Ministry of Agriculture, Fisheries, and Urban Affairs, 78 rue de Varenne, 75349 Paris 07 SP, France
PHONE: +33 (01) 49554955
E-MAIL: webmaster@agriculture.gouv.fr

Minister of Civil Service, Administrative Reform, and Decentralization
Emile Zuccarelli, Ministry of Civil Service, Administrative Reform, and Decentralization

Minister of Culture and Communication
Catherine Trautmann, Ministry of Culture and Communication

Minister of Defense
Alain Richard, Ministry of Defense

Minister of European Affairs
Pierre Moscovici, Ministry of European Affairs

Minister of Schools
Segolene Royal, Ministry of Schools

Minister of Economy, Finance, and Industry
Christian Sautter, Ministry of Economy, Finance, and Industry

Minister of Employment and Solidarity
Martine Aubry, Ministry of Employment and Solidarity

Minister of Foreign Affairs
Hubert Védrine, Ministry of Foreign Affairs

Minister of Infrastructure, Transport, and Housing
Jean-Claude Gayssot, Ministry of Infrastructure, Transport, and Housing

Minister of the Interior
Jean-Pierre Chevenement, Ministry of the Interior

Minister of Justice
Elisabeth Guigou, Ministry of Justice

Minister of National Education, Research, and Technology
Claude Allegre, Ministry of National Education, Research, and Technology

Minister of Regional Development and Environment
Dominique Voynet, Ministry of Regional Development and Environment

Minister of Relations with Parliament
Daniel Vaillant, Ministry of Relations with Parliament

Minister of Youth and Sports
Marie-George Buffet, Ministry of Youth and Sports

POLITICAL ORGANIZATIONS

Parti Communiste Français-PCF (Communist Party)
NAME: Robert Hue

Front National-FN (National Front)
NAME: Jean-Marie Le Pen

Prassemblement pour la République-RPR (Rally for the Republic)
NAME: Philippe Seguin

Union pour la Démocratie Française-UDF (Union for French Democracy)
NAME: François Leotard

Parti Radical Socialiste-PRS (Radical Socialist Party)
NAME: Aymeri De Montesquieu

Lutte Ouvriere-LO (Worker's Fight)
Independent Republicans (RI)
Popular Republican Movement (MPR)
Reformists (REF)

DIPLOMATIC REPRESENTATION
Embassies in France

Afghanistan
32, avenue Raphael, 75116 Paris, France
PHONE: +33 (01) 45250529
FAX: +33 (01) 45244687

Albania
57, avenue Marceau, 75116 Paris, France
PHONE: +33 (01) 47243100
FAX: +33 (02) 99606527

Australia
4, rue Jean Rey, 75724 Paris Cedex 15, France
PHONE: +33 (04) 40593300
FAX: +33 (01) 40593310
E-MAIL: Information.Paris@dfat.gov.au

Austria
Commercial Section, 75116 Paris, France
PHONE: +33 (01) 53230505
FAX: +33 (01) 47202580
E-MAIL: paris@ahst.paris.wk.or.at

Canada
35, avenue Montaigne, 75008 Paris, France
PHONE: +33 (01) 44432900

FAX: +33 (01) 44432999

China
Service of Information, 78, street of the
University, 75007 Paris, France
PHONE: +33 (01) 44398843
FAX: +33 (01) 44398872
E-MAIL: giopar@imaginet.fr.

Côte d'Ivoire
Bureau Economique 24 Bd Suchet, 75016 Paris,
France
PHONE: +33 (01) 44149393
FAX: +33 (01) 45202160
E-MAIL: bureco-fr@cotedivoire.com

Denmark
77, avenue Marceau, 75116 Paris, France
PHONE: +33 (01) 44312121
FAX: +33 (01) 44312188

Finland
2, rue Fabert, 75007 Paris, France
PHONE: +33 (01) 44181920
FAX: +33 (01) 45555157

Germany
13-15, avenue Franklin D. Roosevelt, 75008
Paris, France
PHONE: +33 (01) 53834500
FAX: +33 (01) 43597418
E-MAIL: ambassade@amb-allemagne.fr

Greece
9, rue de la Liberté, 38000 Grenoble, France
PHONE: +33 (4) 76473923
FAX: +33 (4) 76473776
E-MAIL: consulat.grece.grenoble@wanadoo.fr

Israel
3, rue Rabelais, 75008 Paris, France
PHONE: +33 (01) 40765500
FAX: +33 (01) 40765555

Italy
Hotel of Galliffet, 50, street of Game preserve,
75007 Paris, France
PHONE: +33 (1) 44394939
FAX: +33 (1) 42223788

Japan
Chancellerie et Service Consulaire 7, avenue
Hoche, 75008 Paris, France
PHONE: +33 (1) 48886200
FAX: +33 (1) 42275081

Nicaragua
8, rue de Sfax, 75116 Paris, France
PHONE: +33 (01) 45004102; 45003542
FAX: +33 (01) 45009681

E-MAIL: 106115.464@compuserve.com

Poland
2, rue Geiler, F-67000 Strasbourg, France
PHONE: +33 (03) 88255072
FAX: +33 (03) 88362109

Portugal
3, street of Noisiel, 75116 Paris, France
PHONE: +33 (01) 47273529
FAX: +33 (01) 44059402; 47550040
E-MAIL: mailto@embaixada-Portugal-fr.org

Romania
5 Rue de l'Exposition, 75007 Paris, Cedex 07,
France
PHONE: +33 (1) 40622202; 40622204
FAX: +33 (1) 45569747

Singapore
12, Public garden of the Foch avenue, 75116
Paris, France
PHONE: +33 (01) 45003361
FAX: +33 (01) 45005875
E-MAIL: ambsing@club-internet.fr

South Africa
59, Quai d'Orsay, 75007 Paris, France
PHONE: +33 (01) 53592323
FAX: +33 (01) 47539970

Sweden
17, rue Barbet-de-Jouy, 75007 Paris, France
PHONE: +33 (01) 44188800
FAX: +33 (01) 44188840
E-MAIL: presseinfo@amb-suede.fr

United Kingdom
31, rue Boissy d'Anglas, 75008 Paris, France
PHONE: +33 (01) 53308132; 44513326;
44513327
FAX: +33 (01) 53308135; 44513234
E-MAIL: spresse@paris.mail.fco.gov.uk

United States
2, avenue Gabriel, 75008 Paris, France

JUDICIAL SYSTEM
Constitutional Council
2 rue de Montpensier, 75001 Paris, France
PHONE: +33 (01) 40153000
FAX: +33 (01) 40209327

High Court of Justice
Supreme Court of Appeals

High Council of the Judiciary

FURTHER READING
Government Publications

Central Intelligence Agency. *CIA World Factbook*. Washington, D.C.: GPO, 1999.

Articles

"A Civil Self-Service," *The Economist* (May 1, 1999): 49-50.

"French Dressing," *The Economist* (July 10, 1999): 53-54.

"The French Left Begins to Falter," *The Economist* (January 9, 1999): 45-46.

"Gigantisme, quand mjme," *The Economist* (February 6, 1999): 78-79.

"Indignant," *The Economist* (July 10, 1999): 45-46.

"Jospin's Way," *The Economist* (September 18, 1999): 55.

"Liberté, but not égalité," *The Economist* (February 27, 1999): 48-49.

"Out of the Cage," *The Economist* (April 24, 1999): 52-53.

"Pluprefect," *The Economist* (May 8, 1999): 53-54.

"The Politics of Procrastination," *The Economist* (June 26, 1999): 48.

"Rural France, Up in Arms," *The Economist* (September 11, 1999): 54.

"Still Divided," *The Economist* (September 25, 1999): 59-60.

"A Survey of France: The Grand Illusion," *The Economist* (June 5, 1999): 1-18.

"Two Into Three Won't Go," *The Economist* (April 10, 1999): 69.

"Unaccountable," *The Economist* (March 13, 1999): 62.

"Unintended Results," *The Economist* (April 3, 1999): 44.

"What's a Drug," *The Economist* (June 26, 1999): 60.

"Yes, But Who Won?," *The Economist* (August 21, 1999): 63-64.

"Young, Bored and Inclined to Crime," *The Economist* (February 6, 1999): 54.

Books

Jones, Colin. The Cambridge Illustrated History of France New York, NY: Cambridge University Press, 1999.

Lageux, Robert C. Let's Go France New York, NY: St. Martin's Press, 1999.

Wilson, Frank Lee. European Politics Today: The Democratic Experience Upper Saddle River, NJ: Prentice Hall, 1999.

FRANCE: STATISTICAL DATA

For sources and notes see "Sources of Statistics" in the front of each volume.

GEOGRAPHY

Geography (1)

Area:

Total: 547,030 sq km.

Land: 545,630 sq km.

Water: 1,400 sq km.

Note: includes only metropolitan France, but excludes the overseas administrative divisions.

Area—comparative: slightly less than twice the size of Colorado.

Land boundaries:

Total: 2,892.4 km.

Border countries: Andorra 60 km, Belgium 620 km, Germany 451 km, Italy 488 km, Luxembourg 73 km, Monaco 4.4 km, Spain 623 km, Switzerland 573 km.

Coastline: 3,427 km.

Climate: generally cool winters and mild summers, but mild winters and hot summers along the Mediterranean.

Terrain: mostly flat plains or gently rolling hills in north and west; remainder is mountainous, especially Pyrenees in south, Alps in east.

Natural resources: coal, iron ore, bauxite, fish, timber, zinc, potash.

Land use:

Arable land: 33%

Permanent crops: 2%

Permanent pastures: 20%

Forests and woodland: 27%

Other: 18% (1993 est.).

HUMAN FACTORS

Demographics (2A)

	1990	1995	1998	2000	2010	2020	2030	2040	2050
Population	56,735.2	58,149.4	58,804.9	59,128.2	59,653.4	58,710.4	56,550.0	52,838.1	48,219.5
Net migration rate (per 1,000 population)	NA	NA	NA	NA	NA	NA	NA	NA	NA
Births	NA	NA	NA	NA	NA	NA	NA	NA	NA
Deaths	526.2	NA	NA	NA	NA	NA	NA	NA	NA
Life expectancy - males	72.9	74.1	74.6	74.9	76.3	77.5	78.4	79.2	79.7
Life expectancy - females	81.3	82.4	82.6	82.8	83.6	84.3	84.9	85.4	85.8
Birth rate (per 1,000)	13.4	12.5	11.7	11.1	9.3	8.5	7.4	6.6	6.3
Death rate (per 1,000)	9.3	9.0	9.1	9.2	10.2	11.1	12.5	14.8	16.3
Women of reproductive age (15-49 yrs.)	14,175.9	14,615.9	14,566.6	14,429.7	13,780.6	12,686.1	11,423.1	10,044.7	8,601.8
of which are currently married	20,941.8	NA	NA	NA	NA	NA	NA	NA	NA
Fertility rate	1.8	1.7	1.6	1.6	1.5	1.4	1.3	1.3	1.3

Except as noted, values for vital statistics are in thousands; life expectancy is in years.

Health Personnel (3)

Total health expenditure as a percentage of GDP, 1990-1997[a]

Public sector 7.7

Private sector 2.1

Total[b] 9.8

Health expenditure per capita in U.S. dollars, 1990-1997[a]

Purchasing power parity 2,086

Total 2,349

Availability of health care facilities per 100,000 people

Hospital beds 1990-1997[a] 890

Doctors 1993[c] 280

Nurses 1993[c] 392

Health Indicators (4)

Life expectancy at birth

1980 74

1997 78

Daily per capita supply of calories (1996) 3,551

Total fertility rate births per woman (1997) 1.7

Maternal mortality ratio per 100,000 live births (1990-97) . . . . .15[c]

Safe water % of population with access (1995) 100

Sanitation % of population with access (1995) . . . .

Consumption of iodized salt % of households (1992-98)[a] . . . .

Smoking prevalence

Male % of adults (1985-95)[a] 40

Female % of adults (1985-95)[a] 27

Tuberculosis incidence per 100,000 people (1997) 19

Adult HIV prevalence % of population ages 15-49 (1997) 0.37

Infants and Malnutrition (5)

Under-5 mortality rate (1997) 5

% of infants with low birthweight (1990-97) 5

Births attended by skilled health staff % of total[a] . . .NA

% fully immunized (1995-97)

TB 83

DPT 96

Polio 97

Measles 97

Prevalence of child malnutrition under age 5 (1992-97)[b] . . . . .NA

Ethnic Division (6)

Celtic and Latin with Teutonic, Slavic, North African, Indochinese, Basque minorities.

Religions (7)

Roman Catholic 90%

Protestant 2%

Jewish 1%

Muslim (North African workers) 1%

Unaffiliated 6%

Languages (8)

French 100%, rapidly declining regional dialects and languages (Provencal, Breton, Alsatian, Corsican, Catalan, Basque, Flemish).

EDUCATION

Public Education Expenditures (9)

Public expenditure on education (% of GNP)

1980 . . . . .5.0

1996 . . . . .6.1[1]

Expenditure per student

Primary % of GNP per capita

1980 . . . . .12.0

1996 . . . . .15.8[1]

Secondary % of GNP per capita

1980 . . . . .20.2

1996 . . . . .26.9[1]

Tertiary % of GNP per capita

1980 . . . . .29.3

1996 . . . . .26.0[1]

Expenditure on teaching materials

Primary % of total for level (1996) . . . .

Secondary % of total for level (1996) . . . .

Primary pupil-teacher ratio per teacher (1996) . . . . .19[1]

Duration of primary education years (1995) 5

Educational Attainment (10)

Age group (1990) . . . . .25+

Total population 37,354,255

Highest level attained (%)

No schooling[24] . . . . .NA

First level

Not completed 51.1

Completed . . . . .NA

Entered second level

S-1 . . . . .36.9

S-2 . . . . .NA

Postsecondary 11.4

Literacy Rates (11B)

Adult literacy rate

1980

  Male .... .99x

  Female .... .98x

1995

  Male ....-

  Female ....-

GOVERNMENT & LAW

Political Parties (12)

National Assembly—	No. of seats
Socialist Party (PS)	.245
Rally for the Republic (RPR)	.140
Union for French Democracy (UDF)	.109
Communist Party (PCF)	.37
Radical Socialist Party (PRS)	.13
Ecologists	.8
Citizens Movement (MDC)	.7
Movement for France (LDI-MPF)	.1
National Front (FN)	.1
Various left	.9
Various right	.7

Government Budget (13B)

Revenues	.$222 billion
Expenditures	.$265 billion
Capital expenditures	.NA

Data for 1998 est. NA stands for not available.

Military Affairs (14B)

	1990	1991	1992	1993	1994	1995
Military expenditures						
Current dollars (mil.)	44,800	46,970	46,760	47,390	48,960	47,770
1995 constant dollars (mil.)	51,480	51,910	50,300	49,680	50,190	47,770
Armed forces (000)	550	542	522	506	506	504
Gross national product (GNP)						
Current dollars (bil.)	1,251,000	1,311,000	1,358,000	1,382,000	1,452,000	1,521,000[e]
1995 constant dollars (bil.)	1,438,000	1,449,000	1,461,000	1,449,000	1,488,000	1,521,000[e]
Central government expenditures (CGE)						
1995 constant dollars (mil.)	613,100	642,700	664,300	683,900	698,200	724,300
People (mil.)	56.5	56.8	57.1	57.4	57.7	57.9
Military expenditure as % of GNP	3.6	3.6	3.4	3.4	3.4	3.1
Military expenditure as % of CGE	8.4	8.1	7.6	7.3	7.2	6.6
Military expenditure per capita (1995 $)	911	914	881	865	870	826
Armed forces per 1,000 people (soldiers)	9.7	9.5	9.1	8.8	8.8	8.7
GNP per capita (1995 $)	25,460	25,510	25,570	25,240	25,810	26,290
Arms imports[6]						
Current dollars (mil.)	210	270	150	80	150	150
1995 constant dollars (mil.)	241	298	161	84	154	150
Arms exports[6]						
Current dollars (mil.)	5,200	2,100	1,800	1,100	1,500	2,200
1995 constant dollars (mil.)	5,976	2,321	1,936	1,153	1,538	2,200
Total imports[7]						
Current dollars (mil.)	234,400	231,800	239,600	201,800	230,200	275,300
1995 constant dollars (mil.)	269,400	256,100	257,800	211,600	236,000	275,300
Total exports[7]						
Current dollars (mil.)	216,600	217,100	235,900	209,300	235,900	286,700
1995 constant dollars (mil.)	248,900	239,900	253,700	219,500	241,800	286,700
Arms as percent of total imports[8]	.1	.1	.1	0	.1	.1
Arms as percent of total exports[8]	2.4	.8	.8	.5	.6	.8

Crime (15)

Crime rate (for 1997)

Crimes reported 3,493,400

Total persons convicted 1,030,600

Crimes per 100,000 population 5,950

Persons responsible for offenses

Total number of suspects 797,400

Total number of female suspects 110,800

Total number of juvenile suspects 154,700

LABOR FORCE

Labor Force (16)

Total (million) 25.5

Services 69%

Industry 26%

Agriculture 5%

Data for 1995.

Unemployment Rate (17)

12.4% (1997)

PRODUCTION SECTOR

Electric Energy (18)

Capacity ....102.94 million kW (1995)

Production ....467.541 billion kWh (1995)

Consumption per capita ....6,841 kWh (1995)

Transportation (19)

Highways:

total: 892,500 km

paved: 892,500 km (including 9,500 km of expressways)

unpaved: 0 km (1996 est.)

Waterways: 14,932 km; 6,969 km heavily traveled

Pipelines: crude oil 3,059 km; petroleum products 4,487 km; natural gas 24,746 km

Merchant marine:

total: 62 ships (1,000 GRT or over) totaling 1,528,107 GRT/2,354,235 DWT ships by type: bulk 5, cargo 5, chemical tanker 8, combination bulk 1, container 6, liquefied gas tanker 4, multi-function large load carrier 1, oil tanker 18, passenger 2, roll-on/roll-off cargo 5, short-sea passenger 6, specialized tanker 1 note: France also maintains a captive register for French-owned ships in Iles Kerguelen (French Southern and Antarctic Lands) (1997 est.)

Airports: 473 (1997 est.)

Airports—with paved runways:

total: 266

over 3,047 m: 13

2,438 to 3,047 m: 29

1,524 to 2,437 m: 95

914 to 1,523 m: 73

under 914 m: 56 (1997 est.)

Airports—with unpaved runways:

total: 207

1,524 to 2,437 m: 3

914 to 1,523 m: 75

under 914 m: 129 (1997 est.)

Top Agricultural Products (20)

Wheat, cereals, sugar beets, potatoes, wine grapes; beef, dairy products; fish catch of 850,000 metric tons ranks among world's top 20 countries and is all used domestically.

MANUFACTURING SECTOR

GDP & Manufacturing Summary (21)

Detailed value added figures are listed by both International Standard Industry Code (ISIC) and product title.

	1980	1985	1990	1994
GDP ($-1990 mil.)[1]	950,787	1,025,299	1,195,498	1,241,863
Per capita ($-1990)[1]	17,646	18,584	21,078	21,505
Manufacturing share (%) (current prices)[1]	25.5	23.1	22.3	*19.6*
Manufacturing				
Value added ($-1990 mil.)[1]	232,560	228,763	256,107	253,271
Industrial production index	100	95	109	106
Value added ($ mil.)	161,552	115,474	257,284	*268,611*
Gross output ($ mil.)	453,636	326,406	681,401	685,694
Employment (000)	5,103	4,579	4,389	*3,959*
Profitability (% of gross output)				
Intermediate input (%)	64	65	62	*61*

	1980	1985	1990	1994
Wages and salaries inc. supplements (%)	24	23	22	23
Gross operating surplus	11	12	16	17
Productivity ($)				
Gross output per worker	84,523	67,851	148,266	165,478
Value added per worker	30,101	24,004	56,000	65,118
Average wage (inc. supplements)	21,643	16,725	34,299	39,098
Value added ($ mil.)				
311/2 Food products	15,952	12,825	25,556	31,850
313 Beverages	3,486	2,268	5,382	7,000
314 Tobacco products	1,497	948	1,919	2,687
321 Textiles	6,130	4,239	7,666	6,128
322 Wearing apparel	4,742	3,104	5,807	5,878
323 Leather and fur products	757	527	1,130	946
324 Footwear	1,411	929	1,420	1,572
331 Wood and wood products	2,888	1,704	4,183	4,318
332 Furniture and fixtures	2,846	1,632	3,973	4,953
341 Paper and paper products	3,592	2,817	6,823	5,926
342 Printing and publishing	6,660	5,069	12,500	17,124
351 Industrial chemicals	6,462	4,669	10,873	8,330
352 Other chemical products	6,302	4,996	12,427	16,498
353 Petroleum refineries	9,973	8,127	15,129	17,966
354 Miscellaneous petroleum and coal products	118	83	177	197
355 Rubber products	2,483	1,544	3,341	3,729
356 Plastic products	3,083	2,415	6,663	7,374

	1980	1985	1990	1994
361 Pottery, china and earthenware	639	406	1,000	1,093
362 Glass and glass products	2,170	1,365	3,090	2,788
369 Other non-metal mineral products	5,653	3,153	7,523	7,538
371 Iron and steel	6,741	3,788	8,434	6,403
372 Non-ferrous metals	2,479	2,340	4,534	4,453
381 Metal products	12,119	7,792	20,097	19,783
382 Non-electrical machinery	16,245	11,998	24,821	18,792
383 Electrical machinery	14,411	11,491	25,771	26,923
384 Transport equipment	17,733	11,316	28,618	29,222
385 Professional and scientific equipment	2,206	1,752	4,109	4,141
390 Other manufacturing industries	2,772	2,178	4,319	5,000

FINANCE, ECONOMICS, & TRADE

Economic Indicators (22)

National product: GDP—purchasing power parity— $1.32 trillion (1997 est.)

National product real growth rate: 2.3% (1997 est.)

National product per capita: $22,700 (1997 est.)

Inflation rate—consumer price index: 2% (1996)

Exchange Rates (24)

Exchange rates:

French francs (F) per US$1

January 1998	6.0836
1997	5.8367
1996	5.1155
1995	4.9915
1994	5.5520
1993	5.6632

Top Import Origins (25)

$256 billion (f.o.b., 1997 est.) Data are for 1997 est.

Origins	%
Germany	.17
Italy	.10
United States	.9
Belgium-Luxembourg	.8
United Kingdom	.8
Spain	.7
Netherlands	.5
Japan	.3
China	.2

Top Export Destinations (26)

$275 billion (f.o.b., 1997 est.) Data are for 1996.

Destinations	%
Germany	.17
Italy	.9
United Kingdom	.9
Spain	.8
Belgium-Luxembourg	.8
United States	.6
Netherlands	.4.5
Japan	.2
Russia	.0.7

Economic Aid (27)

Donor: ODA, $7.915 billion (1993).

Import Export Commodities (28)

Import Commodities	Export Commodities
Crude oil	Machinery and transportation equipment
Machinery and equipment	Chemicals
Agricultural products	Foodstuffs
Chemicals	Agricultural products
Iron and steel products %	Iron and steel products
	Textiles and clothing

Balance of Payments (23)

	1992	1993	1994	1995	1996
Exports of goods (f.o.b.)	227,442	199,044	230,811	278,627	281,846
Imports of goods (f.o.b.)	−225,071	−191,528	−223,561	−267,629	−266,911
Trade balance	2,371	7,516	7,249	10,998	14,936
Services - debits	−168,857	−177,694	−105,992	−120,261	−117,529
Services - credits	179,361	185,369	117,082	129,270	131,079
Private transfers (net)	−5,655	−5,404	−10,201	−9,322	−7,054
Government transfers (net)	−3,327	−797	−725	155	−870
Overall balance	3,892	8,990	7,414	10,840	20,562

FRENCH GUIANA

Department of Guiana
Guyane

CAPITAL: Cayenne.

FLAG: The flag of France is used.

ANTHEM: *La Marseillaise.*

MONETARY UNIT: 1 French franc (F) = 100 centimes

WEIGHTS AND MEASURES: The metric system is used.

HOLIDAYS: Bastille Day, 14 July.

TIME: 8 AM = noon GMT.

LOCATION AND SIZE: Located on the northeast coast of South America, and extending from 1°30′ to 5°30′N and from 51°4′ to 54°3′W, French Guiana (Guyane Française) has an Atlantic shoreline of about 320 km (200 mi.) and a total area of some 91,000 sq. km (35,000 sq. mi.). It is separated from Brazil by the Oyapock River in the E and the Tumuc-Humac Mountains in the S (440 km/273 mi.); and from Suriname by the Maroni River (398 km/247 mi.) on the W. Its length is about 400 km (250 mi.) N–S, and its width is 300 km (190 mi.) E–W. Several islands offshore are part of French Guiana including the Îles du Salut (Devil's Island, Royale, and Saint-Joseph).

CLIMATE: The mean annual temperature along the coast is 26°C (80°F) year-round. There are two rainy seasons from November to January and from April to June. Annual rainfall has a range of 350–400 cm (140–160 in.). Average humidity is 85%. Trade winds keep the coastal climate more comfortable.

INTRODUCTORY SURVEY

RECENT HISTORY

French Guiana was used for many years as a penal colony by France, with the most notorious colony being Devil's Island. The brutality and inhumanity of the penal colonies was exposed in the 1930s and the last penal colony closed in 1953.

Guiana became a department of France (similar to a state or province) in 1946. France heavily subsidizes the country, keeping movements for independence in check. The European Space Agency built a Center at Kourou for the launching of unmanned space vehicles in 1968. This launch facility has brought a sizable technology workforce to the country. Adoption of the Plan Vert ("Green Plan") in the 1970s was designed to encourage development of agricultural and forestry resources.

GOVERNMENT

As a department of France, the government was established by the French Constitution of September 28, 1958. Also as a department, French Guiana sends three elected representatives to the French Parliament, two representatives to the National Assembly and one to the Senate. The chief of state is the French President, represented in Guiana by a Prefect. The chief executive Prefect is appointed by the French President on the advice of the French Ministry of Interior. The heads of the government in Guiana are the President of the General Council and the President of the Regional Council.

The General Council is a unicameral legislature of 19 seats, with all members elected to six year terms. The unicameral Regional Council is comprised of 31 seats, and members are also elected to six year terms. Suffrage is universal and the voting age is 18.

As an overseas department of France, the responsibility for international relations and defense rest with the French government in Paris. The French Ministry of Interior is the responsible authority in Paris.

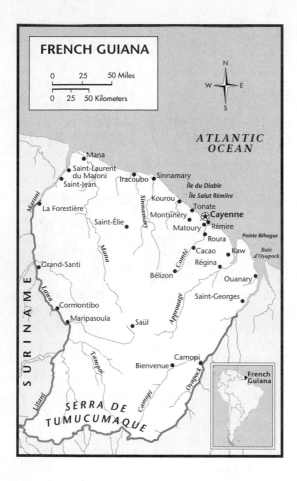

FRENCH GUIANA

ECONOMIC AFFAIRS

The French Guiana economy is a market economy, but it is still developing and is heavily subsidized by aid from France. The largest segments of the economy are the services, agriculture, forestry, and fishing industries. Agriculture represents 5% of the gross domestic product (GDP) and subsistence farming centers on cassava, dasheen (taro), sweet potatoes, rice corn, bananas and plantains. Cash crops include sugarcane, limes, bananas, and other tropical fruits. Most agricultural exports are to France. Timber is cut for industrial purposes, with 40% of the harvest exported. Livestock and dairy production is limited, and most of the country's needs for these are imported. Fisheries concentrate on shrimp.

Fuels and minerals are imported. Gold, gravel, and sand are extracted locally. Limited manufacturing concentrates on fish and meat processing, rum, and sawn-wood products. Labor is concentrated in the services and agricultural areas. Unemployment and inflation rates are high. Wages and benefits are mandated by law to match those in France. The rocket-launching base at Kourou is the major technology employer and contributes about 15% to the GDP.

There is a negative balance of payments. Exports include forest products and gold. Imports include food products, machinery, consumer goods, and refined petroleum products. The country has twelve radio stations and three broadcast television stations.

Public Finance

The government spent $332 million with only $191 million in revenues in 1996. The government carries $1.2 billion in external debt. The balance of payments reflects imports of $600 million in 1997 against exports of $148 million.

Income

Gross Domestic Product per capita was estimated by the CIA at $6,000 in 1998. The unemployment rate is high, estimated in 1997 at 25.7%. Nevertheless, French Guiana enjoys one of the better standards of living in South America.

Industry

Industries in French Guiana include agriculture, the rocket-launching facility at Kourou, fishing, forestry, gold mining, rum, and clothing.

Judiciary

The legal system replicates the French legal system. The courts include the Court of Appeals, which is based in the French department of Martinique, where it has jurisdiction over Martinique, Guadeloupe, and French Guiana.

Political Parties

Political parties in French Guiana include the Guianese Socialist Party, the Socialist Party, the Union of Social Democrats, the Union for French Democracy, the Guiana Democratic Forces, the Action Democrate Guiana, and the Democratic and European Rally of the Senate. One party, the violence-prone Front National Libere de la Guiana, is outlawed.

DEFENSE

Defense is the responsibility of the French Forces. Local police responsibilities belong to the Gendarmerie.

Banking and Finance

The currency is the French franc. Banking services and laws follow French norms.

Economic Development

Economic development involves promotion of tourism and the further development of technology associated with the rocket-launch facility at Kourou by the European Space Agency.

SOCIAL WELFARE

The social security system follows that of France, providing work injury, unemployment, maternity, old-age, disability, and survivor benefits. Unemployment is chronically high.

Healthcare

Healthcare is generally good and five government hospitals provide public health services. The Pasteur Institute in Cayenne is a research institute focusing on tropical and endemic local diseases, and it enjoys an excellent reputation throughout Latin America. Life expectancies are about 77 years.

EDUCATION

Education is compulsory for children from ages 6 to 16. The government operates 66 primary and 19 secondary schools. Private colleges and teacher training are available in the country, or students can pursue higher education either in France or in the French Antilles.

1999 KEY EVENTS TIMELINE

February

- Carnaval is observed for four days prior to Ash Wednesday and the traditional Christian season of Lent. Flamboyant parades and parties are staged everywhere, the largest and most elaborate of which are in the capital, Cayenne.

March

- A new satellite launch pad was tested in Hawaii, and could pose a threat to the launch station operated by a European consortium on French Guiana.

October

- Arianespace officials report the launch of the 120th Ariane rocket from the launch center in Kourou. The payload was Koreasat, a communications satellite owned by South Korea. Another launch of TELKOM-1, an Indonesian communications satellite, was also accomplished.

December

- The first commercial Ariane 5 rocket is successfully launched, carrying the European Space Agency's XMM satellite.

ANALYSIS OF EVENTS: 1999

BUSINESS AND THE ECONOMY

The March testing of a satellite launch pad in Hawaii was financed by a group of nations interested in finding a cost-effective means of launching their satellites. The location of the launch platform on the equator could make launching rockets less expensive. The new facility will charge $40 million per launch, whereas Europe's consortium Arianespace charges $55 million per launch from its station on French Guiana; until now, 70 percent of commercial rocket launches have been accomplished on French Guiana.

CULTURE AND SOCIETY

French Guiana was once best known for the island penal colony just off its shore known as Devil's Island and made famous by the novel and film, *Papillon*. Seventy thousand prisoners were sent there from France, and over 50,000 of them died there. Now the former penal colony is a rocket-tracking station.

DIRECTORY

CENTRAL GOVERNMENT

Head of State

President
Jacques Chirac, Office of the President, Palais de l'Elysée, 55, rue du faubourg Saint-Honoré, 75008 Paris, France

Prefect
Dominique Vian

Ministers

President of the General Council
Andre Lecante

POLITICAL ORGANIZATIONS

Guianese Socialist Party

NAME: Marie-Claude Verdan

Socialist Party

NAME: Jean Bart

Parti Nationaliste Populaire Guiana (Nationalist Popular Party of Guyana)

Union des Socialistes Democrates (Union of Social Democrats)

NAME: Leon Bertrand

Rally for the Republic

NAME: Leon Bertrand

Union for French Democracy

NAME: R. Chow-Chine

Guyana Democratic Forces

NAME: Georges Othily

Walwari Committee

NAME: Christine Taubira-Delanon

Action Democrate Guiana

NAME: Andre Lecante

Democratic and European Rally of the Senate

DIPLOMATIC REPRESENTATION

Embassies in French Guiana

United Kingdom
16 Ave. President Monnerville, Cayenne, French Guiana
PHONE: +594 311034
FAX: +594 304242

JUDICIAL SYSTEM

Court of Appeals

FURTHER READING

Books

Crane, Janet. *French Guiana: World Bibliographic Series.* San Diego: ABC-Clio, 1999.

FRENCH GUIANA: STATISTICAL DATA

For sources and notes see "Sources of Statistics" in the front of each volume.

GEOGRAPHY

Geography (1)

Area:

Total: 91,000 sq km.

Land: 89,150 sq km.

Water: 1,850 sq km.

Area—comparative: slightly smaller than Indiana.

Land boundaries:

Total: 1,183 km.

Border countries: Brazil 673 km, Suriname 510 km.

Coastline: 378 km.

Climate: tropical; hot, humid; little seasonal temperature variation.

Terrain: low-lying coastal plains rising to hills and small mountains.

Natural resources: bauxite, timber, gold (widely scattered), cinnabar, kaolin, fish.

Land use:

Arable land: 0%

Permanent crops: 0%

Permanent pastures: 0%

Forests and woodland: 83%

Other: 17% (1993 est.).

HUMAN FACTORS

Ethnic Division (6)

Black or mulatto 66%

White 12%

East Indian, Chinese, Amerindian 12%

Other 10%

Demographics (2A)

	1990	1995	1998	2000	2010	2020	2030	2040	2050
Population	115.9	145.3	162.5	173.2	216.3	250.7	283.2	312.3	338.8
Net migration rate (per 1,000 population)	NA	NA	NA	NA	NA	NA	NA	NA	NA
Births	NA	NA	NA	NA	NA	NA	NA	NA	NA
Deaths	NA	NA	NA	NA	NA	NA	NA	NA	NA
Life expectancy - males	70.6	72.3	73.1	73.7	76.0	77.6	78.7	79.5	80.0
Life expectancy - females	77.4	78.9	79.7	80.2	82.3	83.8	84.8	85.5	86.0
Birth rate (per 1,000)	28.4	25.2	23.7	22.8	20.5	19.0	17.5	16.3	15.3
Death rate (per 1,000)	4.9	4.6	4.5	4.5	4.7	5.5	6.6	7.5	7.8
Women of reproductive age (15-49 yrs.)	28.9	35.5	39.3	41.5	50.1	56.8	65.3	72.8	78.1
of which are currently married	17.3	NA	NA	NA	NA	NA	NA	NA	NA
Fertility rate	3.7	3.5	3.3	3.3	2.9	2.7	2.5	2.3	2.2

Except as noted, values for vital statistics are in thousands; life expectancy is in years.

Religions (7)

Roman Catholic.

Languages (8)

French.

EDUCATION

Educational Attainment (10)

Age group (1982) . . . . .25+

Total population 34,145

Highest level attained (%)

No schooling 20.8

First level

  Not completed 40.5

  Completed . . . . .NA

Entered second level

  S-1 . . . . .32.4

  S-2 . . . . .NA

Postsecondary 6.4

GOVERNMENT & LAW

Political Parties (12)

General Council	No. of seats
Guianese Socialist Party (PSG)	8
Guyana Democratic Forces (FDG)	4
Rally for the Republic (RPR)	1
Other left	2
Other right	2
Other	2

Government Budget (13B)

Revenues . . . .$176 million

Expenditures . . . .$350 million

  Capital expenditures . . . .$92 million

Data for 1994.

Military Affairs (14A)

Availability of manpower

  Males age 15-49 (1998 est.) 46,136

Fit for military service

  Males (1998 est.) 29,878

Total expenditures . . . .$NA

Expenditures as % of GDP . . . . .NA%

Defense is the responsibility of France. NA stands for not available.

LABOR FORCE

Labor Force (16)

Total 46,300

Services, government, and commerce 60.6%

Industry 21.2%

Agriculture 18.2%

Data for 1993. Percent distribution for 1980.

Unemployment Rate (17)

24.1% (1993 est.)

PRODUCTION SECTOR

Electric Energy (18)

Capacity .165,000 kW (1995)

Production . . . . .420 million kWh (1995)

Consumption per capita . . . . .2,890 kWh (1995)

Transportation (19)

Highways:

total: 1,817 km (national 432 km, departmental 385 km, community 1,000 km)

Waterways: 460 km, navigable by small oceangoing vessels and river and coastal steamers; 3,300 km navigable by native craft

Merchant marine: none

Airports: 11 (1997 est.)

Airports—with paved runways:

total: 4

over 3,047 m: 1

914 to 1,523 m: 2

under 914 m: 1 (1997 est.)

Airports—with unpaved runways:

total: 7

914 to 1,523 m: 3

under 914 m: 4 (1997 est.)

Top Agricultural Products (20)

Rice, corn, manioc, cocoa, vegetables, bananas, sugar; cattle, pigs, poultry.

MANUFACTURING SECTOR

GDP & Manufacturing Summary (21)

	1980	1985	1990	1992	1993	1994
Gross Domestic Product						
Millions of 1990 dollars	922	987	1,103	1,129	*1,126*	*1,135*
Growth rate in percent	0.00	3.00	2.20	1.28	*-0.26*	*0.82*
Per capita (in 1990 dollars)	13,565.7	10,845.5	9,427.3	8,821.0	*8,404.4*	*8,110.1*
Manufacturing Value Added						
Millions of 1990 dollars	11	10	11	12	12	*12*
Growth rate in percent	4.52	2.81	0.43	0.00	1.67	*2.44*
Manufacturing share in percent of current prices	NA	NA	NA	NA	NA	NA

FINANCE, ECONOMICS, & TRADE

Economic Indicators (22)

National product: GDP—purchasing power parity—$800 million (1993 est.)

National product real growth rate: NA%

National product per capita: $6,000 (1993 est.)

Inflation rate—consumer price index: 2.5% (1992)

Exchange Rates (24)

Exchange rates:

French francs (F) per US$1

January 1998	6.0836
1997	5.8367
1996	5.1155
1995	4.9915
1994	5.5520
1993	5.6632

Top Import Origins (25)

$605 million (c.i.f., 1994)

Origins	%
France	.62
Germany	.4
Belgium-Luxembourg	.4
United States	.2

Top Export Destinations (26)

$81 million (f.o.b., 1994).

Destinations	%
France	.60
European Union	.7

Economic Aid (27)

Recipient: ODA, $NA. NA stands for not available.

Import Export Commodities (28)

Import Commodities	Export Commodities
Food (grains	Shrimp
Processed meat)	Timber
Machinery and transport equipment	Gold
	Rum
Fuels and chemicals	Rosewood essence
	Clothing

FRENCH POLYNESIA

Territory of French Polynesia
Territoiré de la Polynésie Française
Polynésie Française

INTRODUCTORY SURVEY

CAPITAL: Papeete.

FLAG: The flag of French Polynesia has two narrow horizontal bands that encase a wide white band; centered on the white band is a disk with blue and white wave pattern on the lower half and gold and white ray pattern on the upper half; a stylized red, black and white ship rides on the wave pattern; the French flag is used for official occassions.

ANTHEM: *La Marseillaise.*

MONETARY UNIT: 1 CFP franc (CFPF) = 100 centimes.

WEIGHTS AND MEASURES: The metric system is used.

HOLIDAYS: New Year's Day, 1 January; Anniversary day of the bringing of the Gospel, 5 March; Easter Monday; Labor Day, 1 May; Ascension, 39 days after Easter Sunday; Monday after Pentecost, about 10 days after the Ascension; Bastille Day, 14 July; Assumption, 15 August; All Saints Day, 1 November; Armistice Day, 11 November; and Christmas Day.

TIME: 2 PM = noon GMT.

LOCATION AND SIZE: The overseas territory of French Polynesia (Polynésie Française) in the South Pacific Ocean includes five island groups: (1) The Society Islands (Îles de la Société) are the most important. They include Tahiti (at 17°40′S and about 149°20′W), with an area of 1,042 sq. km (402 sq. mi.); Moorea; and Raiatea. (2) The Marquesas Islands (Îles Marquises, between 8° and 11°S and 138° and 141°W), about 1,500 km (930 mi.) NE of Tahiti. (3) The Tuamotu Islands, about 480 km (300 mi.) S and SW of the Marquesas over an area of 800 sq. km (310 sq. mi.). (4) The Gambier Islands, SE of the Tuamotus. (5) The Tubuai or Austral Islands (Îles Australes), S of the Society Islands. Clipperton Island (10°18′N and 109°12′W), an uninhabited atoll SW of Mexico and about 2,900 km (1,800 mi.) W of Panama. Total area of the territory is between 3,600 and 4,200 sq. km (1,400 and 1,600 sq. mi.).

CLIMATE: The climate is warm and humid with little temperature change throughout the year. The annual average temperature is 25°C (78°F).

RECENT HISTORY

The five island groups that comprise French Polynesia were originally settled by the Polynesian people around AD 300, then later "discovered" by French, Spanish, and English explorers. The five groups were consolidated under French control in the 1800s. One island, Clipperton Island, was also claimed by Mexico, but that claim was relinquished in 1932; Clipperton was placed under direct French control in 1979. After World War II, the islands became an overseas territory of France titled French Polynesia.

In 1953 and 1957, a political party dedicated to autonomy, the People's Democratic Assembly, won majorities in the Territorial Assembly. The autonomy movement continued into the 1960s and 1970s until France granted partial autonomy to the islands in 1977. More local control was added in 1984. France moved significant military forces to French Polynesia in 1962. It began the testing of nuclear weapons on two outlying atolls in 1966. Those atolls were later ceded directly to France. Among the impacts of the testing are a large influx of income to the islands from the efforts of the French military, and the movement of many residents from the outlying islands to the larger islands. This consolidation of the population has altered cultural life styles as well as impacted the economy.

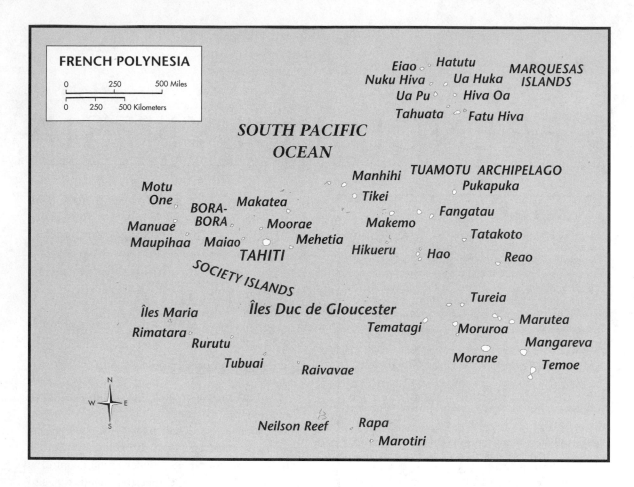

GOVERNMENT

As an overseas territory of France, the government was established by the French Constitution of September 28, 1958. As a territory, French Polynesia sends three elected representatives to the French Parliament: two representatives to the National Assembly and one to the Senate. The chief of state is the French President, represented in French Polynesia by the High Commissioner of the Republic. The chief executives of the government are the President of the Territorial Government and the President of the Territorial Assembly. The Council of Ministers are appointed by the president and ratified by the Territorial Assembly.

The legislative branch is comprised of the unicameral Territorial Assembly, whose 41 members are elected by an electorate based upon universal suffrage and an age of 18. Members are elected to five-year terms.

As an overseas territory of France, the responsibility for international relations and defense rests with the French government. The French Ministry of Interior is the responsible authority in Paris.

Judiciary

The legal system replicates the French legal system. The courts include the Court of Appeal, the Court of the First Instance, and the Court of Administrative Law.

Political Parties

Political parties in the islands include the People's Rally for the Republic, the Polynesian Union Party, the Independent Front for the Liberation of Polynesia, the New Fatherland Party, the Independent Party, Te Aratia Ote Nunaa, Haere i Mua, Te e'a No Maohi Nui, Pupu Taina, Entente Polynesian, and the Centrist Union.

DEFENSE

Defense is the responsibility of the French Forces. Local police responsibilities belong with the Gendarmerie.

ECONOMIC AFFAIRS

The economy in French Polynesia moved away from a subsistence economy in 1962 with the stationing of 5,000 military personnel. Another

4,000 jobs were created by the nuclear weapons testing in the 1960s and 1970s. The industry on the rise during this period of time was the tourism industry, and many French Polynesians have moved into that industry. Tourism now accounts for 20% of the islands' gross domestic product (GDP) and is its major source of hard currency earnings.

The islands have a small manufacturing sector which is primarily engaged in processing agricultural products. Manufacturing consist of coconut oil, processed foods, beer, construction materials, printed cloth, sandals, copper wares, and publications. Agriculture is small and cannot provide all necessary foodstuffs, so much of these products are imported. Agricultural products include coconuts, tropical fruits, vanilla, vegetables, poultry, beef, and dairy products. Fishing is a solid industry, along with the related oyster and shrimp farming and cultured pearls. Handicraft efforts are prevalent throughout the islands.

Major imports include fuels, foodstuffs, fuel, and equipment; major exports include coconut products, mother-of-pearl, vanilla, and shark meat. France and the United States dominate trade. The islands have seven radio stations and seven broadcast television stations.

Public Finance

The government spent $613 million in 1996 while $652 million was collected in revenue. French Polynesia was the recipient of $450.4 million in economic aid in 1995. The balance of payments was not favorable, reflecting $212 million in exports in 1996 and $860 million in imports.

Income

Gross Domestic Product in 1997 was estimated by the CIA at $2.6 billion, for a per capita income of $10,800. The unemployment rate is high, reaching 15% in 1992.

Industry

Industries in French Polynesia include tourism, pearls, agricultural processing, and handicrafts. There is a significant service industry in French Polynesia, including a segment that provides support to the French Military and weapons testing organizations.

Banking and Finance

The currency is the Comptoirs Francais du Pacifique franc, which is tied to the French franc. Banking services follow French norms.

Economic Development

Economic development is focused on the tourist trade and the fishing industries. Services to the French Military and the nuclear weapons testing organizations are slipping with the ban on nuclear testing that was instituted in the 1980s.

SOCIAL WELFARE

French Polynesia maintains a relatively high standard of living which is maintained through French financial aid. French social-security systems are in place. Unemployment is chronically high.

Healthcare

Government supplied healthcare is good. One general hospital is supplemented by seven secondary hospitals and twelve medical centers. Regular doctor visits are provided to outlying islands and atolls. Life expectancy is over 73 years.

EDUCATION

Education is compulsory for children through the end of primary school. The government provides 161 public primary schools, four secondary schools, and eighteen colleges. Private schools account for fifteen primary and three secondary schools. The literacy rate among those over the age of fourteen is about 98%.

1999 KEY EVENTS TIMELINE

January

- In France, the Ministry of Finance announces that 1,000 Pacific Francs, the currency of French Polynesia, New Caledonia, and Wallis and Futuna (all French Pacific territories) will buy 8.38 euros when the new currency goes into effect.

September

- The French Assistant Overseas Minister appoints union leader Pierre Frébaut to a five-year term on the French Economic and Social Council (Conseil Economique et Social-CES). Frébaut chairs the French Polynesian main trade union, CSTPFO.

November

- A French court convicts President Gaston Flosse of corruption for accepting thousands of dollars in bribes to allow illegal gambling in Tahiti. He is banned from holding public office for one year, and his two-year prison sentence is suspended.

ANALYSIS OF EVENTS: 1999

BUSINESS AND THE ECONOMY

French Polynesians enjoy one of the highest standards of living in their region. France has invested heavily in the territory since the 1960s, so the infrastructure is relatively modern by regional standards. Still, French Polynesia's remote location is the single greatest impediment to expanding trade with France and other European nations. Cooperation with its sister island nations by forming regional consortiums to share shipping and other transportation resources will help the economy to progress.

Beginning in 1993, France fostered an economic development program (Contrat de Développement). Under this program France budgeted an investment in the territory of about 26 billion F CFP ($300 million), which is to be matched by an equal investment by French Polynesia, for the 1993–2003 period. A much larger post-nuclear testing program for the 1996–2006 period is also still in place. Expansion of tourism accounted for much of the economy's gowth during the 1990s, supported on a smaller scale by an increase in the export of goods such as pearls. The goal is for the French Polynesian economy to be self-sufficient by 2003. Other sources of income are agriculture and fishing. In addition to pearls, export products are copra and vanilla. Other crops and animals are raised for local consumption.

GOVERNMENT AND POLITICS

French Polynesia is a semi-autonomous territory. French Polynesians have full French citizenship and may vote in French elections. Only about six percent support independence from France, an action the territory could take at any time. The government of France assumes responsibility for foreign affairs, justice, defense, and secondary education.

DIRECTORY

CENTRAL GOVERNMENT

Head of State

President
Jacques Chirac, Office of the President

High Commissioner
Jean Aribaud, Office of the High Commissioner

President of the Territorial Assembly
Justin Arapari, Territorial Assembly

POLITICAL ORGANIZATIONS

Tahoeraa Huiraatira-RPR (People's Rally for the Republic)

NAME: Gaston Flosse

Te Tiarama and Pupu Here Ai'a Party (Polynesian Union Party)

NAME: Jean Juventin

Tavini Huiraatira (Independent Front for the Liberation of Polynesia)

NAME: Oscar Temaru

Ai'a Api-NF (New Fatherland Party)

NAME: Emile Vernaudon

Ia Mana Te Nunaa-IP (Independent Party)

NAME: Jacques Drollet

Te Aratia Ote Nunaa

NAME: Tinomana Ebb

Haere i Mua (HM)

NAME: Alexandre Leontieff

Te e'a No Maohi Nui

NAME: Jean-Marius Raapoto

Pupu Taina

NAME: Michel Law

Entente Polynesian

NAME: Arthur Chung

Centrist Union

DIPLOMATIC REPRESENTATION

None (Territory of France)

JUDICIAL SYSTEM

Court of Appeal

Papeete, French Polynesia

Court of the First Instance

Papeete, French Polynesia

Court of Administrative Law

FURTHER READING

French Embassy in Suva. Available Online @ www.ambafrance.org.fj (November 15, 1999).

FRENCH POLYNESIA: STATISTICAL DATA

For sources and notes see "Sources of Statistics" in the front of each volume.

GEOGRAPHY

Geography (1)

Area:

Total: 4,167 sq km (118 islands and atolls).

Land: 3,660 sq km.

Water: 507 sq km.

Area—comparative: slightly less than one-third the size of Connecticut.

Land boundaries: 0 km.

Coastline: 2,525 km.

Climate: tropical, but moderate.

Terrain: mixture of rugged high islands and low islands with reefs.

Natural resources: timber, fish, cobalt.

Land use:

Arable land: 1%

Permanent crops: 6%

Permanent pastures: 5%

Forests and woodland: 31%

Other: 57% (1993 est.).

HUMAN FACTORS

Ethnic Division (6)

Polynesian 78%

Chinese 12%

Local French 6%

Metropolitan French 4%

Demographics (2A)

	1990	1995	1998	2000	2010	2020	2030	2040	2050
Population	200.7	224.4	237.8	246.2	284.6	319.8	349.3	372.1	388.6
Net migration rate (per 1,000 population)	NA	NA	NA	NA	NA	NA	NA	NA	NA
Births	NA	NA	NA	NA	NA	NA	NA	NA	NA
Deaths	NA	NA	NA	NA	NA	NA	NA	NA	NA
Life expectancy - males	68.6	69.7	69.9	70.0	71.6	73.0	74.3	75.3	76.3
Life expectancy - females	73.2	74.4	74.8	75.0	76.9	78.6	80.0	81.3	82.3
Birth rate (per 1,000)	27.7	24.4	22.7	21.5	18.6	16.6	14.7	13.7	13.0
Death rate (per 1,000)	4.9	4.8	5.0	5.1	5.6	6.3	7.2	8.4	9.6
Women of reproductive age (15-49 yrs.)	49.7	56.5	60.4	63.2	75.8	82.8	87.0	88.0	87.2
of which are currently married	NA	NA	NA	NA	NA	NA	NA	NA	NA
Fertility rate	3.3	2.9	2.7	2.6	2.3	2.1	2.0	2.0	2.0

Except as noted, values for vital statistics are in thousands; life expectancy is in years.

Religions (7)

Protestant 54%

Roman Catholic 30%

Other 16%

Languages (8)

French (official), Tahitian (official).

GOVERNMENT & LAW

Political Parties (12)

Territorial Assembly	No. of seats
People's Rally for the Republic (Gaullist) 22	
Polynesian Liberation Front 10	
New Fatherland Party 5	
Other 4	

Government Budget (13B)

Revenues . . . .$636 million

Expenditures . . . .$643 million

  Capital expenditures . . . . .NA

Data for 1994. NA stands for not available.

Military Affairs (14A)

Defense is the responsibility of France.

LABOR FORCE

Labor Force (16)

Total 118,744

Agriculture . . . . : .13%

Industry 19%

Services 68%

Data for 1992 est. Of the labor force, 70,044 are employed (1988).

Unemployment Rate (17)

15% (1992 est.)

PRODUCTION SECTOR

Electric Energy (18)

Capacity . . . . .79,000 kW (1995)

Production . . . . .330 million kWh (1995)

Consumption per capita . . . . .1,500 kWh (1995)

Transportation (19)

Highways:

total: 792 km

paved: 792 km (1995 est.)

Merchant marine:

total: 3 ships (1,000 GRT or over) totaling 4,127 GRT/6,710 DWT ships by type: passenger-cargo 2, refrigerated cargo 1 (1997 est.)

Airports: 43 (1997 est.)

Airports—with paved runways:

total: 25

over 3,047 m: 2

1,524 to 2,437 m: 5

914 to 1,523 m: 14

under 914 m: 4 (1997 est.)

Airports—with unpaved runways:

total: 18

914 to 1,523 m: 7

under 914 m: 11 (1997 est.)

MANUFACTURING SECTOR

GDP & Manufacturing Summary (21)

	1980	1985	1990	1992	1993	1994
Gross Domestic Product						
Millions of 1990 dollars	1,684	2,361	3,007	3,250	*3,431*	*3,614*
Growth rate in percent	0.48	5.35	3.97	4.00	*5.57*	*5.33*
Per capita (in 1990 dollars)	11,151.2	13,570.9	15,266.3	15,778.0	*16,262.4*	*16,810.4*
Manufacturing Value Added						
Millions of 1990 dollars	120	202	219	236	*249*	*263*
Growth rate in percent	1.77	8.27	5.22	3.84	*5.62*	*5.34*
Manufacturing share in percent of current prices	6.6	8.5	7.3	NA	NA	NA

PRODUCTION SECTOR

Top Agricultural Products (20)

Coconuts, vanilla, vegetables, fruits; poultry, beef, dairy products.

FINANCE, ECONOMICS, & TRADE

Economic Indicators (22)

National product: GDP—purchasing power parity—$1.76 billion (1995 est.)

National product real growth rate: NA%

National product per capita: $8,000 (1995 est.)

Inflation rate—consumer price index: 1.5% (1994)

Exchange Rates (24)

Exchange rates:

Comptoirs Francais du Pacifique francs (CFPF) per US$1

January 1998	110.60
1997	106.11
1996	93.00
1995	90.75
1994	100.94
1993	102.96

Linked at the rate of 18.18 to the French franc

Top Import Origins (25)

$967 million (c.i.f., 1994) Data are for 1994.

Origins	%
France	44.7
United States	13.9

Top Export Destinations (26)

$245 million (f.o.b., 1994) Data are for 1994.

Destinations	%
France	33
United States	8.5

Economic Aid (27)

Recipient: ODA, $NA. NA stands for not available.

Import Export Commodities (28)

Import Commodities	Export Commodities
Fuels	Cultured pearls 53.8%
Foodstuffs	Coconut products
Equipment	Mother-of-pearl
	Vanilla
	Shark meat

GABON

Gabonese Republic
République Gabonaise

CAPITAL: Libreville.

FLAG: The flag is a tricolor of green, golden yellow, and royal blue horizontal stripes.

ANTHEM: *La Concorde (Harmony).*

MONETARY UNIT: The Communauté Financière Africaine franc (CFA Fr) is a paper currency. There are coins of 1, 2, 5, 10, 25, 50, 100, and 500 CFA francs, and notes of 50, 100, 500, 1,000, 5,000, and 10,000 CFA francs. CFA Fr1 = $0.00196 (or $1 = CFA Fr510.65).

WEIGHTS AND MEASURES: The metric system is the legal standard.

HOLIDAYS: New Year's Day, 1 January; Day of Renewal, 12 March; Labor Day, 1 May; Africa Freedom Day, 25 May; Assumption, 15 August; Independence Day, 17 August; All Saints' Day, 1 November; Christmas, 25 December. Movable religious holidays include Easter Monday, Ascension, Pentecost Monday, 'Id al-Fitr, and 'Id al-'Adha'.

TIME: 1 PM = noon GMT.

LOCATION AND SIZE: Situated on the west coast of Africa and centered on the Equator, Gabon has an area of 267,670 square kilometers (103,348 square miles), extending 717 kilometers (446 miles) north-northeast to south-southwest and 644 kilometers (400 miles) east-southeast to west-northwest. Comparatively, the area occupied by Gabon is slightly smaller than the state of Colorado. Gabon's capital city, Libreville, is located on the country's northwestern coast.

CLIMATE: Gabon has the moist, hot climate typical of tropical regions. The hottest month is January, with an average high at Libreville of 31°C (88°F) and an average low of 23°C (73°F). From June to September there is almost no rain but high humidity. There is occasional rain in December and January. During the remaining months, rainfall is heavy.

INTRODUCTORY SURVEY

RECENT HISTORY

On 28 September 1958, the territory of Gabon voted to become a self-governing republic within the French Community. Independence was formally proclaimed on 17 August 1960. On 12 February 1961, Léon Mba was elected president of the republic, heading a government of national union in which Jean-Hilaire Aubame served as foreign minister. Friction developed between Mba and Aubame, however, and after several years of political maneuvering, Aubame led a successful takeover on 18 February 1964. Mba was reinstated on the very next day through French military intervention, as provided for by a treaty signed between the Mba government and the French in 1960.

Mba created the post of vice-president in February 1967. At his death on 28 November of that year, power was transferred peacefully to his vice-president, Albert-Bernard Bongo. On 12 March 1968, Bongo announced the formal institution of a one-party system and the creation of the Gabon Democratic Party (PDG). He was reelected without opposition in 1973, 1979, and 1986. (It was announced in 1973 that Bongo had taken the name of Omar and converted to Islam.)

However, depressed oil prices in the late 1980s damaged the economy and caused unrest among the population. After months of pro-democracy rallies and strikes, Bongo ended twenty-two years of one-party rule in 1990. In January 1991, the Assembly passed by unanimous vote a law legalizing opposition parties. On 5 December 1993,

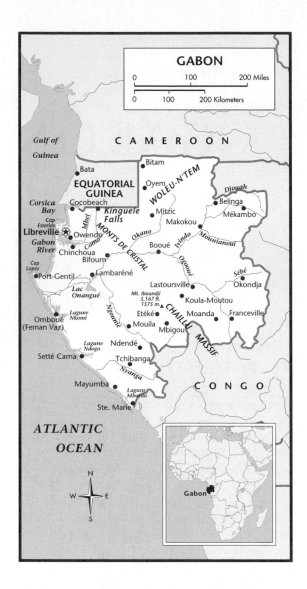

In July 1996, the people of Gabon approved a new constitution that called for a ninety-one-member senate.

GOVERNMENT

In 1990, a national political conference discussed the political system. The conference approved sweeping reforms, including the creation of a national senate, decentralization of the budgetary process, and freedom of assembly and press.

A new constitution came into force in March 1991 and was approved by voters in July 1996. It provided for a basic bill of rights and an independent judiciary, but retained a strong presidency.

Judiciary

The civil court system consists of three tiers: the trial court, the appellate court, and the Supreme Court. The 1991 constitution, which established many basic freedoms and fundamental rights, also created a Constitutional Court, a body that considers only constitutional issues.

Political Parties

On 12 March 1968, the Democratic Party of Gabon (Parti Démocratique Gabonais–PDG) became the sole political party. The Movement for National Reform (Mouvement de Redressement National–MORENA), an opposition group, emerged in 1981 and formed a government in exile in 1985.

In the National Assembly elections of December 1996, the PDG won a majority, with 85 of 120 seats. Elections for the newly created Senate in early 1997 also gave a majority to the PDG, with fifty-four of ninety-one seats.

DEFENSE

In 1995, Gabon had an army of 3,200 personnel; a navy of 500; and an air force of 1,000. Paramilitary forces of coast guards and police totaled 4,800.

ECONOMIC AFFAIRS

Rich in resources, Gabon realized a growth rate of 9.5% before succumbing to oil-price instability and the laws of international borrowing. High inflation did not last long, however, as the country's tight monetary policies helped reduce inflation to 5% in 1996.

Gabon is not self-sufficient in food although 65% of its population gain their livelihood in the

multiparty presidential elections confirmed Bongo, running as an independent, as president with 51% of the vote, against Paul Mba Abessole. Opposition parties protested the result. Abessole announced the formation of a rival government dedicated to new presidential elections, restoring peace, and maintaining national unity.

Civil unrest continued in 1994, as the economy suffered from the devaluation of the currency, the CFA franc. In September 1994, the Organization for African Unity sponsored talks in Paris that resulted in a power-sharing agreement between the government and the main opposition parties. The agreement fell apart when the opposition received few leadership positions in Bongo's government. By mid-1995, the functioning Bongo government included some opposition representation.

agricultural sector. The staple food crops are cassava, plantains, and yams.

Public Finance

The oil sector brings in nearly 50% of government revenues. The CIA estimates that, in 1993, government revenues totaled approximately $1.3 billion and expenditures $1.6 billion, including capital expenditures of $311 million. External debt totaled $3.8 billion. Government finances are generally poorly managed. Large deficits have required borrowing from foreign creditors, although the government's failure to privatize state-owned enterprises and to fully account for oil revenues has soiled its reputation with international financial institutions.

Income

In 1998, Gabon's gross national product (GNP) was $4.66 billion at current prices, or $3,950 per person. For the period 1985–95 the average inflation rate was 4.8%, resulting in a decline in GNP of 1.6% per person.

Industry

Gabon's industry is centered on petroleum, mining, and timber processing. Timber-related concerns include five veneer plants and one of the world's largest plywood factories, located in Port-Gentil. In 1995, Gabon produced 2 million cubic meters of sawlogs and veneer logs and 25,000 cubic meters (32,700 cubic yards) of plywood.

Banking and Finance

The bank of issue is the Bank of the Central African States (Banque des Etats de l'Afrique Centrale–BEAC), the central bank for UDEAC members.

Commercial banking in Gabon is largely controlled by French and other foreign interests. The Gabonese Bank of Development, 69% Gabonese-owned, is the nation's development bank.

There is no securities market in Gabon.

Economic Development

Economic liberalism tempered by planning is the basic policy of the Gabonese government, which seeks to make the most of the country's rich natural resources. Priority is being given to the agricultural sector, to reduce imports, and to diversify the economy.

SOCIAL WELFARE

Family allowances are paid to all salaried workers. Other benefits include workers' compensation, old-age insurance, medicine and hospitalization, and housing assistance. Contributions are made by employers and employees at a fixed percentage of the employee's wage.

Women have many legal protections, but face discrimination in practice.

Healthcare

Gabon's medical system is considered one of the best in West Africa. Records indicate that from 1985 to 1995, 90% of the population had access to health care services. A comprehensive government health program treats such diseases as leprosy, sleeping sickness, malaria, filariasis, intestinal worms, and tuberculosis. Life expectancy averages 55 years.

Housing

Credit institutions make small loans for the repair of existing houses and larger loans (amounting to almost the total cost of the house) for the construction of new houses. The government has established a national habitation fund, and there have been a number of urban renewal projects.

EDUCATION

Education is free and compulsory between the ages of 6 and 16. In 1991, there were 1,024 primary schools with 210,000 pupils and 4,782 teachers. At the secondary level, general schools had 42,871 pupils and vocational schools had 8,477 pupils. The adult illiteracy rate was estimated at 37% in 1995.

At Omar Bongo University, and other equivalent institutions, there were 3,000 students in 1991.

1999 KEY EVENTS TIMELINE

February

- On February 10, President Albert-Bernard Bongo, amid considerable public pressure to enact social and economic change through the instrument of the ministries, announces his new cabinet. Key posts—such as Prime Minister, the Minister of Foreign Affairs and the Minister of Planning and Development—are filled by the previous ministers of other posts. The practice of switching ministers around to suggest a change in government is a tactic Bongo has used in the past.

April

- President Bongo, his wife, and an entourage of approximately forty-five, arrive in Washington, D.C., on April 18, 1999. They hold meetings with officials at the U.S. Department of State, the International Monetary Fund, and the World Bank. To the chagrin of his government, Bongo does not secure a meeting with U.S. President Bill Clinton, and continues on to New York, Houston, Los Angeles, and Canada for further meetings.

May

- The government announces that it will begin to pursue opportunities for mineral mining, since the depressed world market for oil is having a negative effect on the economy. Only three of the available thirteen offshore oil exploration licenses have been leased.

June

- South African Mike Horn heads west from the coast of Gabon on June 2 on a 40,000 km solo journey along the equator, by foot and catamaran. He expects the trip to take him approximately 18 months.

- Retired South African President Nelson Mandela arrives in Gabon on June 18 for a short vacation. When asked by the press why he chose Gabon, Mandela answered that he had visited the country shortly after his release from prison in 1990, and had always remembered its beauty and tranquility.

- Gabon's national soccer team, Azingo, beats Angola in a home-field victory on June 22 to reach the final qualifying round of the 2000 Africa Cup of Nations. Gabon has made it this far only twice before; in 1991, and 1997.

July

- A corporal serving in the first parachute regiment of the Gabonese Army is found stabbed to death in a Libreville neighborhood on July 5. Two days later, violence erupts in the area, reported by some to involve soldiers bent on revenge. Two people are killed and eleven wounded. The army issues a statement denying any involvement in the incident.

August

- After three years of exploration, Marathon Oil gives up on drilling prospects in Gabon's deepwater coastal basin.

- The United Nations High Commission for Refugees sends reinforcements to southern Gabon on August 25. Some 10,000 refugees are camped on both sides of the Gabon-Congo border after fleeing civil war in Republic of the Congo. France has responded to the crisis by sending ten tons of food and equipment. Earlier in August, Gabon hosted a summit of central African heads of state to address the issue of populations displaced by armed conflict around the region.

September

- The Gabonese legislature opens its second session of the year on September 1. Senators' and Deputies' debate centers around the physical degradation of the capital, Libreville, national security issues, particularly in regards to illegal immigrants and refugees, and the continuing fall of local purchasing power caused by the worsening financial crisis.

- The Seventh All-African Games open in Johannesburg, South Africa, on September 9. Gabon goes on to win medals in karate and judo.

October

- Participation is confirmed on October 1 for fifteen Western donor and African nations in ''Gabon 2000,'' a series of military exercises scheduled to take place in January 2000 near the town of Lambaréné. These exercises are intended to test a regional interventionist force whose mission will be to restore peace and respond to humanitarian crises in neighboring countries divided by internal conflict.

December

- President Omar Bongo announces that he has cut the government budget by eliminating eleven of 42 ministers in his cabinet.

- A network of Central African journalists covering the environment meets in Gabon to exchange ideas.

ANALYSIS OF EVENTS: 1999

BUSINESS AND THE ECONOMY

It is difficult to separate government and business in the case of Gabon; the nation's primary source of wealth—oil and minerals—is controlled by the government. Exploitation rights are sold or leased to foreign businesses, mostly French-owned. There was a continuing effort in 1999 to privatize state-owned industries in other sectors, such as transportation and utilities, although in the case of agribusiness, privatization was stymied because the parastatal enterprise Agripog found no interested investors.

Gabon's oil production grew substantially in the late 1990s, and several new North American companies signed contracts with the government to begin new exploration in 1999, despite low '97-'98 oil prices. However, ten licenses for exploration were not leased as of late 1999, and the government began to investigate options in mineral mining to offset the possible decline in revenue from oil if either exploration or oil prices don't improve.

Two 1999 events may portend a growth in diversified business for Gabon in the future. While on a trip to New York in April, President Bongo spoke with banking and finance leaders about the possibility of opening a Gabonese Stock Exchange. In July, telecommunications choices were expanded by the granting of operating licenses to two mobile phone networks, promising to offer cellular service up to international standards in both rural and urban areas.

Despite fears of destabilization, the CFA, Gabon's currency, was officially tied to the Euro in 1999.

GOVERNMENT AND POLITICS

On December 6, 1998, Gabon held a peaceful general election, the results of which gave President El Hadj Omar Bongo another seven-year mandate after 31 years in power. Although international observers claimed serious irregularities in voter registration and balloting, few suggested that Bongo was not the likely choice of the electorate, which has continuously chosen stability over change. But the hope of stability was soon dashed for most Gabonese citizens with the advent of 1999. The year opened with the same low oil prices seen in 1998, shrinking the GDP of a country that depends on petroleum revenue to survive. By August, even the president was admitting a full-fledged financial crisis in his public addresses, and offering to cut his own salary, and those of many senior government officials, to ease the burden on the treasury.

In international relations, Gabon concentrated on sustaining bilateral relationships through presidential visits to the United States and Canada, and receiving high-level delegations from Côte d'Ivoire and Morocco. Morocco and Gabon have long been security partners, the former providing soldiers for Bongo's private security detail for years. In African politics, Bongo played the role once again of regional peacemaker in 1999, hosting meetings on conflict resolution in the central African region. Particular attention was paid to Gabon's neighbor to the east and south, the Republic of the Congo (also known as Congo-Brazzaville), which has sent thousands of refugees fleeing towards Gabonese territory since 1997.

CULTURE AND SOCIETY

With over forty-five different languages and ethnic groups, Gabon is not a country of one culture, but many. There is nothing that brings Gabonese together, however, like sports. Gabon showed very well in two important 1999 athletic events. Beating Angola to make it to the final rounds of the All-Africa Cup of Nations, to be played in 2000, and winning medals in men's and women's martial arts at the All-Africa games in Johannesburg, are a great source of pride in the country.

In the music world, the Union of Gabonese Artists demanded a ban on the broadcast of all Gabonese recordings from local radio and television stations in September 1999, in an attempt to protest copyright infringement and press for royalty payments. One of the country's most well known artists, Patience Dabany, ex-First Lady of Gabon, spoke out against the ban, and privately owned media outlets continued to play the popular local music.

DIRECTORY

CENTRAL GOVERNMENT
Head of State

President
El Hadj Omar Bongo, Presidency of the Republic, BP 546, Libreville, Gabon
PHONE: +241 727600

Vice President
Didjob Divungi Di Ndinge, Office of the Vice President

Ministers

Prime Minister
Jean-Francois Ntoutoume-Emane, Office of the Prime Minister, BP 91, Libreville, Gabon
PHONE: +241 724284; 778958

Minister of Agriculture, Livestock, and Rural Economy
Emmanuel Ondo Methogo, Ministry of Agriculture, Livestock, and Rural Economy, BP 551, Libreville, Gabon
PHONE: +241 720960; 720917

Minister of Civil Services and Administrative Reforms
Patrice Nziengui, Ministry of Public Services and Administrative Reforms, BP 496, Libreville, Gabon
PHONE: +241 763886

Minister of Trade, Industry, Medium and Small Companies and Handicrafts
Martin Fidele Magnaga, Ministry for Trade, Industry, Medium and Small Companies and Handicrafts, BP 3096 et 561, Libreville, Gabon
PHONE: +241 745921; 745922, Ministry for Communication, Culture, and Mass Education, BP 2280, Libreville, Gabon
PHONE: +241 766183

Minister of Equipment and Construction
Zacharie Myboto, Ministry of Equipment and Construction

Minister of Finance, Economy, Budget, and Privatization
Emile Doumba, Ministry of Finance, Economy, Budget, and Privatization, BP 165, Libreville, Gabon
PHONE: +241 761210

Minister of Foreign Affairs and Cooperation
Jean Ping, Ministry of Foreign Affairs and Cooperation
PHONE: +241 739465

Minister of Health, Population, and Social Affairs
Paulin Obame-Nguema, Ministry of Health, Population, and Social Affairs, BP 50, Libreville, Gabon
PHONE: +241 763611

Minister of Higher Education and Scientific Research
Gaston Ovono, Ministry for Higher Education and Scientific Research, BP 2217, Libreville, Gabon

PHONE: +241 724108

Minister of Housing, Zoning, and Urban Affairs
Jean-Francois Ntoutoume-Emane, Ministry of Housing, Zoning, and Urban Affairs

Minister of Interior
Antoine Mboumbou Miyakou, Ministry of Interior

Minister of Justice
Pierre-Louis Okawe, Ministry of Justice, BP 547, Libreville, Gabon
PHONE: +241 746628

Minister of Labor and Human Resources
Paulette Missambo, Ministry of Labor and Human Resources
PHONE: +241 763925

Minister of Mines, Energy, and Water Resources
Paul Toungui, Ministry of Mines, Energy, and Water Resources, BP 576-874, Libreville, Gabon
PHONE: +241 772239; 772240

Minister of National Defense, Security and Immigration
Idriss Ngari, Ministry for National Defense, Security and Immigration, BP 13493, Libreville, Gabon
PHONE: +241 778694

Minister of National Education and Women's Affairs
Paulette Missambo, Ministry for National Education and Women's Affairs, BP 6, Libreville, Gabon
PHONE: +241 724461

Minister of Planning
Casimir Oye-Mba, Ministry of Planning
PHONE: +241 740462

Minister of Social Affairs and National Solidarity
Zeng Emome, Ministry for Social Services and National Solidarity, BP 5684, Libreville, Gabon
PHONE: +241 775032

Minister of Tourism and Environment
Jacques Adiahenot, Ministry of Tourism and Environment, BP 3974, Libreville, Gabon
PHONE: +241 763905

Minister of Transport and Merchant Marine
Idriss Ngari, Ministry of Transport and Merchant Marine, BP 803, Libreville, Gabon
PHONE: +241 747197

Minister of Water and Forests
Andre Berre, Minister of Water and Forests

Minister of Youth and Sports
Alexandre Sambat, Ministry for Youth and Sports, BP 6, Libreville, Gabon

POLITICAL ORGANIZATIONS

Convention des Libéraux Réformateurs (Circle of Liberal Reformists)

NAME: Jean Boniface Assele

Parti Démocratique Gabonais (Gabonese Democratic Party)

TITLE: Secretary General
NAME: Simplice Guedet Manzela

Parti gabonais du progrès (Gabonese Party for Progress)

TITLE: President
NAME: Pierre-Louis Agondho-Okawe

Union du Peuple Gabonais (Gabonese People's Union)

NAME: Pierre Mamboundou

Union pour le socialisme au Gabon (Gabonese Socialist Union)

NAME: Serge Mba Bekale

Rassemblement National des Bûcherons (National Lumberjacks Rally)

NAME: Paul M'ba-Abessole

Rassemblement pour la Démocratie et le Progrès (Rally for Democracy and Progress)

TITLE: President
NAME: Akexandre Sambat

Alliance Démocratique et Réplicaine (Republican and Democratic Alliance)

DIPLOMATIC REPRESENTATION

Embassies in Gabon

Algeria
BP 4008, Libreville, Gabon
PHONE: +241 732318

Angola
BP 4884, Libreville, Gabon
PHONE: +241 730426

Belgium
BP 4079, Libreville, Gabon
PHONE: +241 732992

Benin
BP 3851, Libreville, Gabon
PHONE: +241 737692

Brazil
BP 3899, Libreville, Gabon
PHONE: +241 760535

Cameroon
BP 14001, Libreville, Gabon
PHONE: +241 732800

Canada
BP 4037, Libreville, Gabon
PHONE: +241 743464
FAX: +241 743466

China
BP 3914, Libreville, Gabon
PHONE: +241 743207

Congo
BP 269, Libreville, Gabon
PHONE: +241 732906

Côte d'Ivoire
BP 3861, Libreville, Gabon
PHONE: +241 738268

Ecuador
BP 3708, Libreville, Gabon
PHONE: +241 734665

Egypt
BP 4240, Libreville, Gabon
PHONE: +241 732538

Equatorial Guinea
BP 1462, Libreville, Gabon
PHONE: +241 751056

France
BP 2125, Libreville, Gabon
PHONE: +241 761064

Germany
BP 229, Libreville, Gabon
PHONE: +241 760188

Greece
BP 2178, Libreville, Gabon
PHONE: +241 732454

Guinea
BP 4046, Libreville, Gabon
PHONE: +241 738509

Iran
BP 2158, Libreville, Gabon

PHONE: +241 730533

Italy
BP 2251, Libreville, Gabon
PHONE: +241 742892

Japan
BP 3341, Libreville, Gabon
PHONE: +241 732297

South Korea
BP 2620, Libreville, Gabon
PHONE: +241 734000

Libya
BP 3341, Libreville, Gabon
PHONE: +241 739645

Mali
BP 4007, Libreville, Gabon
PHONE: +241 737382

Mauritania
BP 3917, Libreville, Gabon
PHONE: +241 743165

Morocco
BP 3983, Libreville, Gabon
PHONE: +241 774151

Romania
BP 557, Libreville, Gabon
PHONE: +241 774225

Russia
BP 3963, Libreville, Gabon
PHONE: +241 724868

Sao Tome
BP 489, Libreville, Gabon
PHONE: +241 720994

Senegal
BP 3856, Libreville, Gabon
PHONE: +241 774267

South Africa
BP 4063, Libreville, Gabon
PHONE: +241 774530

Spain
BP 1157, Libreville, Gabon

PHONE: +241 721264

Togo
BP 14160, Libreville, Gabon
PHONE: +241 732904

United States
BP 4000, Boulevard de la Mer, Libreville, Gabon
PHONE: +241 3762003; 743492
FAX: +241 745507

Zaire
BP 2257, Libreville, Gabon
PHONE: +241 743253

JUDICIAL SYSTEM
Supreme Court

BP 198, Libreville, Gabon
PHONE: +241 773202

Constitutional Court

PHONE: +241 725717

FURTHER READING
Articles

Akanni, Fred. ''Gabon: Marathon Lets Go of Akoumba Marin.'' *Offshore* 59 (August 1999): 22.

''Gabon.'' *The Oil and Gas Journal* 97 (April 12, 1999): 75.

''Gabon Is Trying to Compensate for Lost Oil Revenues.'' *Offshore* 59 (May 1999): 11.

Simons, Marlise. ''Eau de Rain Forest.'' *The New York Times Magazine* (May 2, 1999): 56.

Internet

''Gabon.'' *Africa News.* Available Online @ www.africanews.org/central/gabon/stories (October 25, 1999).

L'Union. Available Online @ www.internetgabon.com/gabon/actu, 1997 (October 19, 1999).

GABON:
STATISTICAL DATA

For sources and notes see "Sources of Statistics" in the front of each volume.

GEOGRAPHY

Geography (1)

Area:

Total: 267,670 sq km.

Land: 257,670 sq km.

Water: 10,000 sq km.

Area—comparative: slightly smaller than Colorado.

Land boundaries:

Total: 2,551 km.

Border countries: Cameroon 298 km, Republic of the Congo 1,903 km, Equatorial Guinea 350 km.

Coastline: 885 km.

Climate: tropical; always hot, humid.

Terrain: narrow coastal plain; hilly interior; savanna in east and south.

Natural resources: petroleum, manganese, uranium, gold, timber, iron orc.

Land use:

Arable land: 1%

Permanent crops: 1%

Permanent pastures: 18%

Forests and woodland: 77%

Other: 3% (1993 est.).

HUMAN FACTORS

Demographics (2A)

	1990	1995	1998	2000	2010	2020	2030	2040	2050
Population	1,077.7	1,155.7	1,207.8	1,244.2	1,445.2	1,674.6	1,932.7	2,220.5	2,517.9
Net migration rate (per 1,000 population)	NA	NA	NA	NA	NA	NA	NA	NA	NA
Births	NA	NA	NA	NA	NA	NA	NA	NA	NA
Deaths	NA	NA	NA	NA	NA	NA	NA	NA	NA
Life expectancy - males	50.2	52.3	53.5	54.4	58.5	62.4	65.9	69.0	71.6
Life expectancy - females	55.5	58.1	59.6	60.6	65.5	69.9	73.7	76.8	79.3
Birth rate (per 1,000)	29.3	28.3	28.0	27.8	26.2	24.2	22.3	20.3	18.5
Death rate (per 1,000)	14.7	13.7	13.2	12.9	11.3	9.7	8.1	6.9	6.8
Women of reproductive age (15-49 yrs.)	258.8	271.0	280.4	288.2	351.1	428.1	500.3	572.2	638.7
of which arc currently married	NA	NA	NA	NA	NA	NA	NA	NA	NA
Fertility rate	4.1	3.9	3.8	3.7	3.4	3.0	2.8	2.6	2.4

Except as noted, values for vital statistics are in thousands; life expectancy is in years.

Health Personnel (3)

Total health expenditure as a percentage of GDP, 1990-1997[a]

Public sector 0.6

Private sector . . . . .NA

Total[b] . . . . .NA

Health expenditure per capita in U.S. dollars, 1990-1997[a]

Purchasing power parity . . . . .NA

Total . . . . .NA

Availability of health care facilities per 100,000 people

Hospital beds 1990-1997[a] 320

Doctors 1993[c] 19

Nurses 1993[c] 56

Health Indicators (4)

Life expectancy at birth

1980 48

1997 52

Daily per capita supply of calories (1996) 2,517

Total fertility rate births per woman (1997) 5.2

Maternal mortality ratio per 100,000 live births (1990-97) . . . . .500[c]

Safe water % of population with access (1995) 67

Sanitation % of population with access (1995) 76

Consumption of iodized salt % of households (1992-98)[a] . . . .

Smoking prevalence

Male % of adults (1985-95)[a] . . . .

Female % of adults (1985-95)[a] . . . .

Tuberculosis incidence per 100,000 people (1997) 174

Adult HIV prevalence % of population ages 15-49 (1997) 4.25

Infants and Malnutrition (5)

Under-5 mortality rate (1997) 145

% of infants with low birthweight (1990-97) . . . . . .NA

Births attended by skilled health staff % of total[a] . . .80

% fully immunized (1995-97)

TB 72

DPT 54

Polio 54

Measles 32

Prevalence of child malnutrition under age 5 (1992-97)[b] . . . . .NA

Ethnic Division (6)

Bantu tribes including four major tribal groupings (Fang, Eshira, Bapounou, Bateke), other Africans and Europeans 154,000, including 6,000 French and 11,000 persons of dual nationality.

Religions (7)

Christian 55%-75%

Muslim . . . .<1%

Animist . . . . .NA

Languages (8)

French (official), Fang, Myene, Bateke, Bapounou/Eschira, Bandjabi.

EDUCATION

Public Education Expenditures (9)

Public expenditure on education (% of GNP)

1980 . . . . .2.7

1996 . . . . .2.8[1]

Expenditure per student

Primary % of GNP per capita

1980 . . . .

1996 . . . .

Secondary % of GNP per capita

1980 . . . .

1996 . . . .

Tertiary % of GNP per capita

1980 . . . .

1996 . . . .

Expenditure on teaching materials

Primary % of total for level (1996) . . . .

Secondary % of total for level (1996) . . . .

Primary pupil-teacher ratio per teacher (1996) . . . . .51[1]

Duration of primary education years (1995) 6

Literacy Rates (11A)

In thousands and percent[1]	1990	1995	2000	2010
Illiterate population (15+ yrs.)	320	295	263	193
Literacy rate - total adult pop. (%)	55.9	63.2	70.7	83.1
Literacy rate - males (%)	67.7	73.7	79.7	88.7
Literacy rate - females (%)	44.8	53.3	62.1	77.7

GOVERNMENT & LAW

Political Parties (12)

National Assembly	No. of seats
Gabonese Party for Progress (PGP) 100	
National Recovery Movement—Lumberjacks (Morena-Bucherons/RNB) .8	
People's Unity Party (PUP) 3	
Circle of Liberal Reformers (CLR) 3	
Action Forum for Renewal (FAR) 1	
Gabonese People's Union (UPG) 1	
Gabonese Socialist Union (USG) 2	
Gabonese Democratic Party (PDG) 2	

Government Budget (13B)

Revenues . . . .$1.5 billion
Expenditures . . . .$1.3 billion
   Capital expenditures . . . .$302 million

Data for 1996 est.

Military Affairs (14B)

	1990	1991	1992	1993	1994	1995
Military expenditures						
Current dollars (mil.)	110[e]	NA	112[e]	123[e]	89[e]	104[e]
1995 constant dollars (mil.)	126[e]	NA	120[e]	129[e]	91[e]	104[e]
Armed forces (000)	9	10	7	7	6	10[e]
Gross national product (GNP)						
Current dollars (mil.)	3,209	3,540	3,550	3,815	3,855	4,024
1995 constant dollars (mil.)	3,687	3,911	3,818	3,999	3,952	4,024
Central government expenditures (CGE)						
1995 constant dollars (mil.)	922	1,353	1,188[e]	1,345[e]	NA	NA
People (mil.)	1.1	1.1	1.1	1.1	1.1	1.2
Military expenditure as % of GNP	3.4	NA	3.1	3.2	2.3	2.6
Military expenditure as % of CGE	13.7	NA	10.1	9.6	NA	NA
Military expenditure per capita (1995 $)	117	NA	109	115	80	90
Armed forces per 1,000 people (soldiers)	8.4	9.2	6.3	6.2	5.3	8.2
GNP per capita (1995 $)	3,422	3,587	3,451	3,563	3,470	3,482
Arms imports[6]						
Current dollars (mil.)	0	0	0	0	0	0
1995 constant dollars (mil.)	0	0	0	0	0	0
Arms exports[6]						
Current dollars (mil.)	0	0	0	0	0	0
1995 constant dollars (mil.)	0	0	0	0	0	0
Total imports[7]						
Current dollars (mil.)	772	772	834	700	756	882
1995 constant dollars (mil.)	887	887	922	753	775	882
Total exports[7]						
Current dollars (mil.)	2,464	2,464	2,243	2,082	2,350	2,713
1995 constant dollars (mil.)	2,832	2,832	2,479	2,239	2,409	2,713
Arms as percent of total imports[8]	0	0	0	0	0	0
Arms as percent of total exports[8]	0	0	0	0	0	0

LABOR FORCE

Labor Force (16)

Agriculture 65%; idustry and commerce, services.

Unemployment Rate (17)

10%-14% (1993 est.)

PRODUCTION SECTOR

Electric Energy (18)

Capacity . . . . .310,000 kW (1995)

Production . . . . .925 million kWh (1995)

Consumption per capita . . . . .800 kWh (1995)

Transportation (19)

Highways:

total: 7,670 km

paved: 629 km (including 30 km of expressways)

unpaved: 7,041 km (1996 est.)

Waterways: 1,600 km perennially navigable

Pipelines: crude oil 270 km; petroleum products 14 km

Merchant marine:

total: 3 bulk (1,000 GRT or over) totaling 37,003 GRT/60,663 DWT (1997 est.)

Airports: 64 (1997 est.)

Airports—with paved runways:

total: 10

over 3,047 m: 1

2,438 to 3,047 m: 1

1,524 to 2,437 m: 7

914 to 1,523 m: 1 (1997 est.)

Airports—with unpaved runways:

total: 54

1,524 to 2,437 m: 10

914 to 1,523 m: 18

under 914 m: 26 (1997 est.)

Top Agricultural Products (20)

Cocoa, coffee, sugar, palm oil; rubber; okoume (a tropical softwood); cattle; small fishing operations (provide a catch of about 30,000 metric tons).

MANUFACTURING SECTOR

GDP & Manufacturing Summary (21)

Detailed value added figures are listed by both International Standard Industry Code (ISIC) and product title.

	1980	1985	1990	1994
GDP ($-1990 mil.)[1]	7,369	7,484	5,456	5,637
Per capita ($-1990)[1]	9,142	7,598	4,761	4,394
Manufacturing share (%) (current prices)[1]	5.1	5.6	12.2	*11.3*
Manufacturing				
Value added ($-1990 mil.)[1]	740	825	631	722
Industrial production index	100	127	123	*140*
Value added ($ mil.)	224	*188*	*281*	*174*
Gross output ($ mil.)	690	*630*	*935*	*592*
Employment (000)	*18*	*18*	*16*	*16*
Profitability (% of gross output)				
Intermediate input (%)	*68*	*70*	*70*	*71*
Wages and salaries inc. supplements (%)	*16*	*17*	*19*	*20*
Gross operating surplus	*16*	*13*	*11*	*10*
Productivity ($)				
Gross output per worker	*38,481*	*35,477*	*59,531*	*35,912*
Value added per worker	*12,470*	*10,852*	*18,130*	*10,804*
Average wage (inc. supplements)	*6,283*	*6,107*	*11,669*	*7,243*
Value added ($ mil.)				
311/2 Food products	*18*	*17*	*26*	*16*
313 Beverages	19	*13*	*20*	*12*
314 Tobacco products	17	*12*	*17*	*10*
321 Textiles	3	*2*	*3*	*2*
322 Wearing apparel	5	*3*	*5*	*3*
323 Leather and fur products	1	—	*1*	—
324 Footwear	1	—	*1*	—
331 Wood and wood products	64	*35*	*51*	*31*
332 Furniture and fixtures	9	*5*	*7*	*4*
341 Paper and paper products	2	*1*	*3*	*2*
342 Printing and publishing	3	*3*	*5*	*3*

	1980	1985	1990	1994
351 Industrial chemicals	6	6	10	6
352 Other chemical products	3	3	4	3
353 Petroleum refineries	18	18	28	18
354 Miscellaneous petroleum and coal products	—	—	—	—
355 Rubber products	—	—	—	—
356 Plastic products	—	—	—	—
361 Pottery, china and earthenware	—		—	—
362 Glass and glass products	1	2	2	1
369 Other non-metal mineral products	8	14	17	10
371 Iron and steel	3	3	5	3
372 Non-ferrous metals	3	3	5	3
381 Metal products	13	15	24	16
382 Non-electrical machinery	2	2	3	2
383 Electrical machinery	8	9	14	9
384 Transport equipment	11	13	20	13
385 Professional and scientific equipment	1	1	1	1
390 Other manufacturing industries	5	6	9	6

FINANCE, ECONOMICS, & TRADE

Economic Indicators (22)

National product: GDP—purchasing power parity—$6 billion (1996 est.)

National product real growth rate: 3% (1996 est.)

National product per capita: $5,000 (1996 est.)

Inflation rate—consumer price index: 6.2% (1996 est.)

Exchange Rates (24)

Exchange rates:

CFA francs (CFAF) per US$1

January 1998	608.36
1997	583.67
1996	511.55
1995	499.15
1994	555.20
1993	283.16

Beginning 12 January 1994, the CFA franc was devalued to CFAF 100 per French franc from CFAF 50 at which it had been fixed since 1948

Top Import Origins (25)

$969 million (f.o.b., 1996 est.)

Origins	%
France	39
Cote d'Ivoire	13
United States	6
Netherlands	5
Japan	NA

NA stands for not available.

Balance of Payments (23)

	1991	1992	1993	1994	1995
Exports of goods (f.o.b.)	2,228	2,259	2,326	2,365	2,643
Imports of goods (f.o.b.)	−861	−886	−845	−777	−898
Trade balance	1,367	1,373	1,481	1,589	1,744
Services - debits	−1,524	−1,794	−1,681	−1,337	−1,733
Services - credits	352	395	343	232	286
Private transfers (net)	23	29	16	−3	—
Government transfers (net)	−143	−171	−209	−163	−198
Overall balance	75	−168	−49	317	100

Top Export Destinations (26)

$3.1 billion (f.o.b., 1996 est.) Data are for 1996.

Destinations	%
United States	.50
France	.16
Japan	.8
China	.NA
Spain	.NA
Germany	.NA

NA stands for not available.

Economic Aid (27)

$NA. NA stands for not available.

Import Export Commodities (28)

Import Commodities	Export Commodities
Machinery and equipment	Crude oil 81%
	Timber 12%
Foodstuffs	Manganese 5%
Chemicals	Uranium
Petroleum products	
Construction materials	

THE GAMBIA

Republic of The Gambia

CAPITAL: Banjul (formerly Bathurst).

FLAG: The flag is a tricolor of red, blue, and green horizontal bands, separated by narrow white stripes.

ANTHEM: *For The Gambia, Our Homeland.*

MONETARY UNIT: In 1971, the dalasi (D), a paper currency of 100 butut, replaced the Gambian pound. There are coins of 1, 5, 10, 25, and 50 butut and 1 dalasi, and notes of 1, 5, 10, 25, and 50 dalasi. D1 = $0.10194 (or $1 = D9.81).

WEIGHTS AND MEASURES: Both British and metric weights and measures are in use.

HOLIDAYS: New Year's Day, 1 January; Confederation Day, 1 February; Independence Day, 18 February; Labor Day, 1 May; Assumption, 15 August; Christmas, 25 December. Movable religious holidays include Good Friday, Easter Monday, 'Id al-Fitr, 'Id al-'Adha', and Milad an-Nabi.

TIME: GMT.

LOCATION AND SIZE: Located on the west coast of Africa, the Republic of The Gambia (commonly known as "The Gambia") has an area of 11,300 square kilometers (4,363 square miles), slightly more than twice the size of the state of Delaware.

The Gambia's capital city, Banjul, is located on the Atlantic coast.

CLIMATE: The Gambia has a subtropical climate with distinct cool and hot seasons. From November to mid-May there is uninterrupted dry weather, with temperatures as low as 16°C (61°F) in Banjul and surrounding areas. Hot, humid weather predominates the rest of the year, with a rainy season from June to October.

INTRODUCTORY SURVEY

RECENT HISTORY

The Gambia attained full internal self-government on 4 October 1963, with Dr. (later Sir) Dawda Kairaba Jawara as prime minister. An independence constitution, which came into force in February 1965, established The Gambia as a constitutional monarchy within the British Commonwealth.

On 23 April 1970, The Gambia became a republic with Jawara as the first president. He and the ruling PPP (People's Progressive Party) remained in power into the 1980s, weathering an attempted left-wing takeover and a rebellion in July 1981. He was reelected in 1982, 1987, and 1992. Jawara was expected to retire in mid-term, but on 22 July, 1994, he was overthrown in a bloodless military takeover led by Lieutenant Yahya Jammeh.

President Jawara took shelter in an American warship which, at the time, had been on a courtesy call. The junta of junior officers and a few civilians suspended the constitution, banned all political activity, detained its superior officers, and placed ministers of the former government under house arrest. The European Union and the United States suspended aid and pressed for a quick return to civilian rule.

Jammeh won 56% of the vote in the presidential elections of September 1996. Jammeh dissolved the provisional council and called for legislative elections in January 1997. Although the

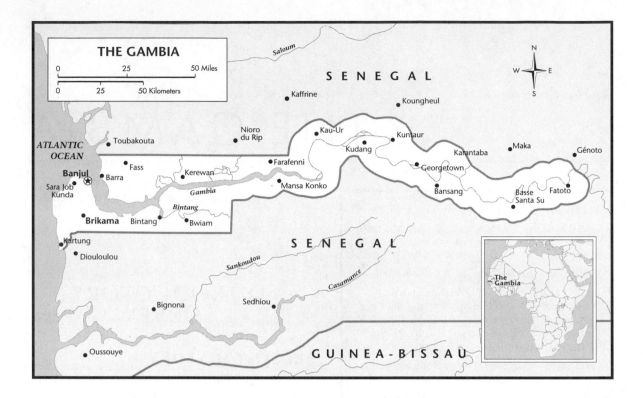

elections were considered fair, opposition candidates were harassed and there was no media exposure of any but the ruling party.

GOVERNMENT

Under the republican constitution of 24 April 1970, the president, popularly elected for a five-year term, was the head of state. Presidential powers included designating a vice-president, who exercised the functions of a prime minister, and appointing cabinet members. The House of Representatives had thirty-six members elected by universal adult voting (at age 18). The military government suspended the constitution on 22 July 1994, and instituted a new National Assembly in 1996. The National Assembly has forty-nine members, four of which are appointed by the president and the rest are elected.

Judiciary

The Supreme Court, presided over by a chief justice, has both civil and criminal jurisdiction. Appeals from any decision of the Supreme Court go before the Court of Appeals, whose judgments may then be taken to the United Kingdom's Privy Council.

A new constitution in 1997 reorganized the court system. The Supreme Court replaced the Privy Council.

Political Parties

In January 1997, the newly formed Alliance for Patriotic Reorientation and Construction won thirty-two of forty-five seats up for election in the National Assembly. The United Democratic Party took seven seats, and two smaller parties split the remaining three seats.

DEFENSE

The Gambia's armed forces had 800 members in 1995.

ECONOMIC AFFAIRS

The Gambia's light sandy soil is well suited to the cultivation of peanuts, which is The Gambia's principal agricultural export. However, in 1990, tourism overtook peanut exports as the nation's number-one export earner. The military takeover in 1994 caused The Gambia to lose $50 million in aid. Tourism declined steeply, and Senegal closed the border because of smuggling.

Public Finance

In the 1980s, expansionary fiscal policies exacerbated a weakening economy; by 1985, the budget deficit reached 30% of GDP. An economic recovery program was initiated to reduce public expenditures, diversify the agricultural sector, and privatize the parastatal sector. This step preceded the 1988 agreement with the IMF for a structural adjustment program that helped the economy grow at an annual rate of 4% between 1990 and 1993. The U.S. CIA estimates that, in 1995, government revenues totaled approximately $91.4 million and expenditures $90 million. External debt totaled $386 million.

Income

In 1998, The Gambia's gross national product (GNP) was $413 million at current prices, or $340 per person. For the period 1985–95 the average inflation rate was 10.3%.

Industry

Industries include peanut processing, building and repair of river craft, village handicrafts, and clothing manufacture.

Banking and Finance

The Central Bank of Gambia (CBG), the bank of issue, was established in 1971. The largest commercial bank is Standard Chartered Bank Gambia, which is incorporated locally. The government no longer has an equity interest in the bank, in which the parent company holds 75% and Gambian shareholders 25%. The Gambia Commercial and Development Bank (GCDB) was wholly owned by the government but now has been sold to private interests, and the International Bank for Commerce and Industry (BICI), is, as of 1997, also privately owned.

Economic Development

Development goals have been focused on transport and communications improvements, increases in rice and groundnut yields, and production diversity.

The historical importance of Great Britain to the Gambia has declined, as Gambia has turned increasingly to the IDA and the European Development Fund, France, Germany, Switzerland, Japan, and Arab donors for aid.

SOCIAL WELFARE

Under tribal organization, the individual's basic welfare needs are traditionally met by the group. Women play little part in the public life of this conservative Islamic country.

Healthcare

Health conditions in The Gambia are poor. Average life expectancy was estimated at 53 years. Nearly half of all children die by age five, primarily because of malaria and diarrheal diseases. Malaria, tuberculosis, trypanosomiasis, and schistosomiasis are widespread. In 1992, there were 12 doctors per 100,000 inhabitants.

Housing

A Housing Finance Fund provides low-cost housing and related assistance.

EDUCATION

Primary school is free but not compulsory and lasts for six years. Secondary schooling is in two stages of five plus two years. In 1992, primary schools had an enrollment of 97,262 students, while secondary schools had 25,929 students. There were nine higher-level schools, including a teachers' training college. The overall adult illiteracy rate was estimated at 61% in 1995.

1999 KEY EVENTS TIMELINE

January

- Amid accusations of embezzlement, the government takes over the privately held peanut processing and marketing company, Gambian Groundnut Corporation (GGC).

February

- February marked the one-year anniversary of the government's closing of the popular private radio station, Citizen FM. Citizen FM's license has since been suspended, while the station owner and news editor, temporarily arrested, were released shortly after.

- Augustin Diamacoune, leader of the Casamance MFDC, receives an official invitation from President Jammeh to come to Banjul for talks.

- Gambian troops leave for Bissau.

- A company of 140 Gambian soldiers leaves Banjul for Dakar, Senegal, where they will join a French warship taking them on peacekeeping duties in Guinea-Bissau.

- General Abdulsalami Abubukar arrives in the Gambia for a two-day official visit and talks with President Yahya Jammeh on technical assistance and regional conflict.

- The first graduates of the University of the Gambia are awarded their degrees. In a ceremony in Banjul, which is broadcast on television, sixty-two students received their diplomas in the first university graduation to be held in the Gambia.

March

• The Gambia National Ballet Troupe tours the United States.

• The United Nations World Food Program (WFP) approves U.S. $23-million in emergency food aid for people facing severe food shortages in Cape Verde, the Gambia, Mauritania and Senegal. The six-month operation will provide 40,000 tons of food to more than a million people living in areas consistently affected by drought and below-average harvests.

April

• President Jammeh extends invitations to the Casamance separatists to meet in Banjul.

May

• The Gambia's leading independent newspaper, *The Daily Observer*, is bought by a pro-Jammeh businessman, Amadou Samba.

• Shyngle Nyassi, youth leader of the opposition United Democratic Party (UDP), disappears from his home.

June

• President Jammeh, his wife, and several ministers go on the annual "meet the people" tour.

• High waters and coastal erosion threaten to engulf the capital city of Banjul.

• Casamance separatists representing the MFDC meet in Banjul.

• Cuba sends 150 doctors to serve three-year tours in the Gambia.

• The FAO is expected to send Bangladeshi experts under the FAO program.

• The cornerstone is laid for the African Human Rights Center.

• Shyngle Nyassi, youth leader of the opposition United Democratic Party (UDP), is imprisoned. The High Court orders the National Intelligence Agency (NIA) to release Mr. Nyassi.

• Guinea-Bissau's interim president, Malam Baci Sanha, pays his first visit to the Gambia.

• The European Union announces plans to disburse $22 million for three major poverty eradication projects over 4-5 years.

July

• Colonel Jammeh marks the fifth anniversary of his coup d'état that brought down the Gambia's first and long-ruling president, Sir David Jawara Dauda.

• The African Development Fund (ADF) approves loans for the Gambia, Ghana and Cameroon. The Gambia will receive some U.S. $770,730 to finance a livestock development study that aims to "identify and prepare two priority bankable projects in the livestock subsector."

August

• Directors general of national agricultural research institutions in nine Sahelian countries pledge to modernize agriculture over the next three years.

• Close to 3,000 homes are reported swept away in the Central and Upper River districts by heavy rains. Parts of Banjul are also reported under water.

September

• Rains continue over the Gambia making this season among the wettest in recent years.

• U.N. agencies in coordination with national and local authorities distribute foodstuffs and drugs to victims of flooding. A fact-finding team reports that heavy rainfall between June and August caused heavy flooding, affecting 27,000 people and damaging roads and bridges in the Central and Upper River divisions.

October

• Satellite photos for the first ten days of October show cloud cover over most of the producing areas of the Sahel.

• The FAO reports that the Gambia is among five West African Sahelian countries with the largest reductions in undernourishment worldwide during the 1990s.

ANALYSIS OF EVENTS: 1999

BUSINESS AND THE ECONOMY

In 1995, the United Nations Human Development Index ranked the Gambia as the 14th least developed country in the world. Tourism (64 percent) and agriculture (23 percent) are the mainstays of the economy, while industry provides just 13 percent of the GDP. The European Union is spending $20 million for poverty alleviation, and a cellular phone network is in the works. An African Development Bank $1 million rehabilitation program will give fish exports a boost.

The Gambia turned in a good economic performance in 1999, reducing the debt to $430 million, and increasing the real GDP by 4 percent (projected). Despite the flooding, food supplies should be higher than average. However, the International Monetary Fund (IMF) gave it average marks owing to delays in reforming government finances and the parastatals. The IMF is expected to press the government to launch privatization before the end of the year, or withhold further disbursement under the three-year enhanced structural adjustment facility (ESAF) dating from 1998. Besides its hotels, the country will have to sell off the telecommunication, water and electricity utility. The peanut corporation (GGC), taken over by the government in January, is a more immediate target of the IMF. Charges of embezzlement are rife, and if the next harvest is smuggled to Senegal, balance of payments will suffer greatly.

GOVERNMENT AND POLITICS

In 1994, the Gambia joined the ranks of sub-Saharan African countries run by soldiers in mufti when Sir David Jawara Dauda was overthrown in a coup by Colonel Jahyah Jammeh. Presumably elected in September 1996, Jammeh maintains a tight grip on the key levers of power, and holds the defense ministry portfolio himself. His ties to Libya have not endeared him to the West.

The key issues of 1999 had to do with President Jammeh's harassment of the opposition and his desire to play a greater regional role. Security forces arrested the leader of the youth wing of the opposition UDP, and released him only after protests from the EU. During his annual tour, Jammeh lashed at the opposition, referring to them as a "gang of alcoholics." An outspoken independent newspaper, *The Daily Observer*, was sold to a pro-Jammeh businessman, who sacked the deputy managing director. Resignations from key editors followed.

Jammeh's regional credibility grew on two counts. First, he succeeded in holding the Casamance rebels' MFCD conference in Banjul. Jammeh is from the Diola ethnic minority in Casamance, and General Ansumane Mane of Guinea-Bissau, is of Gambian parentage. Thus, he is uniquely positioned to play a peace-brokering role in the immediate region at the present. Second, although not his doing, the cornerstone of the African Center for Democracy and Human Rights Studies in Banjul was laid. The Center's cost, estimated at $275,000, is to promote human rights, values, and democratic principles in Africa. Banjul has been home to the Center for Democracy and Human Rights for several years, thus earning the Gambia a place in Africa's quest for institutionalizing democratic values.

CULTURE AND SOCIETY

Gambians are a highly rural people who depend on the land for their livelihoods. Gambia's extremely unpredictable rainfall, however, makes life precarious. Early in 1999, the WFP asked for extra stocks of food to prepare for drought conditions and famine. But by August, Vice President Isatou Njie-Saidy had to appeal for assistance from international donors and the local business community to help up to 10,000 people in the countryside displaced by floods. They needed food, shelter, clothing and medicines. The worst hit areas were the Central River, Upper River and Western administrative divisions where close to 3,000 homes, and many schools and roads were washed away. Parts of Banjul and outlying towns were also flooded.

One of this year's cultural highlights was the third U.S. tour of Gambia's national folkloric dance ensemble. Formed in April 1995, the Gambian folkloric dance and music ensemble consists of 26 members. It received rave reviews from its performance at the Atlanta Summer Olympic Games in 1996. Among its repertoire is the epic story of Sundiata Keita, the founder of the Mali Empire. The troupe also performs masked dances of rice harvests by moonlight, rituals, and rites of passage such as circumcision, forced marriage, funeral ceremonies for village elders, and the Wolof lion dance.

DIRECTORY

CENTRAL GOVERNMENT
Head of State

President
Yahya Jammeh, Office of the President, State House, Banjul, The Gambia

PHONE: +220 227881
FAX: +220 227034

Vice President

Isatou Njie Saidy, Office of the Vice President
and Department of State for Defense, State
House, Banjul, The Gambia
PHONE: +220 227822; 228552
FAX: +220 227034

Cabinet

Secretary of State for Agriculture and Natural Resources

Fa Sainey Dumbuya, Department of State for
Agriculture and Natural Resources, The
Quadrangle, Banjul, The Gambia
PHONE: +220 228291; 228292; 229469
FAX: +220 228230

Secretary of State for Education

Ann-Therese Ndong-Jatta, Department of State
for Education, Bedford Place Building, Banjul,
The Gambia
PHONE: +220 228231; 227236
FAX: +220 223578

Secretary of State for External Affairs

Momodou Lamin Sedat Jobe, Department of
State for External Affairs, 4 Marina Parade,
Banjul, The Gambia
PHONE: +220 225654
FAX: +220 223578

Secretary of State for Finance and Economic Affairs

Famara Jatta, Department of State for Finance
and Economic Affairs, The Quadrangle, Banjul,
The Gambia
PHONE: +220 228291
FAX: +220 227954; 227122

Secretary of State for Health, Social Welfare and Women's Affairs

Isatou Njie Saidy, Department of State for
Health, Social Welfare and Women's Affairs,
The Quadrangle, Banjul, The Gambia
PHONE: +220 227605; 228291, 227881
FAX: +220 229325; 225066; 228505

Secretary of State for Tourism and Culture

Susan Wafa-Ogoo, Department of State for
Tourism and Culture, The Quadrangle, Banjul,
The Gambia
PHONE: +220 228496; 227881
FAX: +220 227753

Secretary of State for Interior

Lamin Bajo, Department of State for the Interior,
71 Dobson St., Banjul, The Gambia
PHONE: +220 228511; 228611
FAX: +220 223063; 226453

Secretary of State for Justice and Attorney General

Fatou Bensouda, Department State for Justice
and Attorney General, Buckle Street, Banjul,
The Gambia
PHONE: +220 227743; 227388

Secretary of State for Local Government and Lands

Lamine Bajo, Department of State for Local
Government and Lands, The Quadrangle, Banjul,
The Gambia
PHONE: +220 227881; 228291; 227674
FAX: +220 225261

Secretary of State for Public Works and Communications

Momodou Sarjo Jallow, Department of State for
Public Works and Communications, Half-Die,
Banjul, The Gambia
PHONE: +220 227449; 227668; 228259
FAX: +220 226655

Secretary of State for Trade, Industry, and Employment

Musa Sillah, Department of State for Trade,
Industry, and Employment, Independence Drive,
Banjul, The Gambia
PHONE: +220 228370; 228398; 226600
FAX: +220 227756

Secretary of State for Youth, Sports, and Culture

Yankuba Touray, Department of State for Youth
and Sports, The Quadrangle, Banjul, The
Gambia
PHONE: +220 225266; 227881
FAX: +220 225267; 225066

POLITICAL ORGANIZATIONS

Alliance for Patriotic Reorientation and Construction (APRC)

NAME: Yahya Jammeh

United Democratic Party (UDP)

NAME: Ousainou Darboe

Peoples Democratic Organization for Independence and Socialism (PDOIS)

NAME: Sidia Jatta

National Reconciliation Party (NRP)

NAME: Hamat Bah

People's Progressive Party (PPP)

NAME: Dawda K. Jawara

National Convention Party (NCP)

NAME: Sheriff Dibba

Gambian People's Party (GPP)

NAME: Hassan Musa Camira

DIPLOMATIC REPRESENTATION

Embassies in the Gambia

China
6A Marina Parade, Banjul, The Gambia
PHONE: +220 227351; 228385

Germany
Independence Drive, P.O. Box 833, Banjul, The
Gambia
PHONE: +220 227783

Guinea-Bissau
Wellington Street, Banjul, The Gambia
PHONE: +220 228134

Liberia
Garba Jahumpa Road, Fajara, Banjul, The
Gambia
PHONE: +220 496775

Mali
VM Company Ltd., Cotton Street, Banjul, The
Gambia
PHONE: +220 226947

Mauritania
PHONE: +220 496518

Palestine
Kairaba Avenue, Serrekunda, Banjul, The
Gambia
PHONE: +220 393394

Russia
7 Buckle Street, Banjul, The Gambia
PHONE: +220 228282

Senegal
Corner of Nelson Mandela and Buckle Streets,
Banjul, The Gambia
PHONE: +220 227469

United Kingdom
P.O. Box 507, 48 Atlantic Road, Fajara, Banjul,
The Gambia

PHONE: +220 495133
FAX: +220 496134

United States
White House, Kairaba Avenue, P.O. Box 596,
Fajara, Banjul, The Gambia
PHONE: +220 392358; 392856
FAX: +220 392475

JUDICIAL SYSTEM

Supreme Court

Buckle Street, Banjul, The Gambia
PHONE: +220 227743; 227388

Court of Appeals

FURTHER READING

Articles

Schofield, John. "Independence Day: Launching a First in the Gambia." *Maclean's* (March 8, 1999): 60.

Webb, Patrick. "Guests of the Crown: Convicts and Liberated Slaves on McCarthy Island, the Gambia." *The Geographical Journal* 160 (July 1994): 136-7.

Willis-Jones, Matthew. "That-hell-hole-of-yours." *American Heritage* 46 (October 1995): 47.

Books

Gailey, Harry A. *Historical Dictionary of the Gambia.* Second Edition. Metuchen, N.J. and London: The Scarecrow Press, Inc., 1987.

Vollmer, Jurgen. *Black Genesis, African Roots: A Voyage from Juffure, the Gambia, to Mandingo Country to the Slave Port of Dakar, Senegal.* New York: St. Martin's Press, 1980.

Wright, Donald R. "The World and a Very Small Place in Africa (History of Niumi)." *Sources and Studies in World History Series.* New York: M.E. Sharpe, Armonk, 1997.

Internet

Africa News Online. Available Online @ http://www.africanews.org/west/stories/1999_feat1.html (October 28, 1999).

Africa Online. Available Online @ http://www.africaonline.com (November 3, 1999).

BBC Online. Available Online @ http://www.bbc.co.uk/ (November 3, 1999).

THE GAMBIA: STATISTICAL DATA

For sources and notes see "Sources of Statistics" in the front of each volume.

GEOGRAPHY

Geography (1)

Area:

Total: 11,300 sq km.

Land: 10,000 sq km.

Water: 1,300 sq km.

Area—comparative: slightly less than twice the size of Delaware.

Land boundaries:

Total: 740 km.

Border countries: Senegal 740 km.

Coastline: 80 km.

Climate: tropical; hot, rainy season (June to November); cooler, dry season (November to May).

Terrain: flood plain of the Gambia River flanked by some low hills.

Natural resources: fish.

Land use:

Arable land: 18%

Permanent crops: 0%

Permanent pastures: 9%

Forests and woodland: 28%

Other: 45% (1993 est.).

HUMAN FACTORS

Ethnic Division (6)

African 99% (Mandinka 42%, Fula 18%, Wolof 16%, Jola 10%, Serahuli 9%, other 4%); Non-African 1%.

Religions (7)

Muslim 90%

Christian 9%

Indigenous beliefs 1%

Demographics (2A)

	1990	1995	1998	2000	2010	2020	2030	2040	2050
Population	963.8	1,162.5	1,291.9	1,381.5	1,864.2	2,398.9	2,958.3	3,510.6	4,037.6
Net migration rate (per 1,000 population)	NA	NA	NA	NA	NA	NA	NA	NA	NA
Births	NA	NA	NA	NA	NA	NA	NA	NA	NA
Deaths	NA	NA	NA	NA	NA	NA	NA	NA	NA
Life expectancy - males	48.2	50.3	51.6	52.5	56.8	60.9	64.6	68.0	70.8
Life expectancy - females	52.1	54.7	56.3	57.4	62.6	67.4	71.7	75.3	78.2
Birth rate (per 1,000)	47.4	45.0	43.3	42.2	36.5	30.5	25.0	21.1	18.2
Death rate (per 1,000)	16.1	14.0	12.9	12.2	9.3	7.3	6.2	5.6	5.6
Women of reproductive age (15-49 yrs.)	220.7	265.7	294.6	315.1	439.3	600.4	787.9	968.5	1,103.1
of which are currently married	NA	NA	NA	NA	NA	NA	NA	NA	NA
Fertility rate	6.4	6.1	5.9	5.8	4.8	3.7	2.9	2.4	2.2

Except as noted, values for vital statistics are in thousands; life expectancy is in years.

Languages (8)

English (official), Mandinka, Wolof, Fula, other indigenous vernaculars.

EDUCATION

Literacy Rates (11A)

In thousands and percent[1]	1990	1995	2000	2010
Illiterate population (15+ yrs.)	355	403	429	457
Literacy rate - total adult pop. (%)	33.7	38.6	43.4	53.3
Literacy rate - males (%)	47.6	52.8	57.5	66.6
Literacy rate - females (%)	20.3	24.9	29.7	40.6

GOVERNMENT & LAW

Political Parties (12)

National Assembly	No. of seats
Alliance for Patriotic Reorientation and Construction (APRC)	33
United Democratic Party (UDP)	7
National Reconciliation Party (NRP)	2
People's Democratic Organization for Independence and Socialism (PDOIS)	1
Independents	2

Government Budget (13B)

Revenues	$88.6 million
Expenditures	$98.2 million
Capital expenditures	NA

Data for FY96/97 est. NA stands for not available.

Military Affairs (14B)

	1990	1991	1992	1993	1994	1995
Military expenditures						
Current dollars (mil.)	2	NA	10[e]	11[e]	12[e]	15
1995 constant dollars (mil.)	3	NA	11[e]	11[e]	12[e]	15
Armed forces (000)	2	2	1	1[e]	1	1[e]
Gross national product (GNP)						
Current dollars (mil.)	243	285	299	309	301	314[e]
1995 constant dollars (mil.)	279	315	322	324	308	314[e]
Central government expenditures (CGE)						
1995 constant dollars (mil.)	58	73	55[e]	65[e]	NA	90[e]
People (mil.)	1.0	1.0	1.0	1.1	1.1	1.2
Military expenditure as % of GNP	.9	NA	3.4	3.5	3.9	4.6
Military expenditure as % of CGE	4.5	NA	19.7	17.4	NA	16.2
Military expenditure per capita (1995 $)	3	NA	11	11	11	13
Armed forces per 1,000 people (soldiers)	2.1	2.0	1.0	.9	.9	.9
GNP per capita (1995 $)	290	314	309	300	275	270
Arms imports[6]						
Current dollars (mil.)	0	5	5	0	0	0
1995 constant dollars (mil.)	0	6	5	0	0	0
Arms exports[6]						
Current dollars (mil.)	0	0	0	0	0	0
1995 constant dollars (mil.)	0	0	0	0	0	0
Total imports[7]						
Current dollars (mil.)	200	222	234	243	209	140
1995 constant dollars (mil.)	229	245	252	255	214	140
Total exports[7]						
Current dollars (mil.)	40	42	63	52	32	16
1995 constant dollars (mil.)	46	46	68	55	33	16
Arms as percent of total imports[8]	0	2.3	2.1	0	0	0
Arms as percent of total exports[8]	0	0	0	0	0	0

LABOR FORCE

Labor Force (16)

Total ....NA

Agriculture 75.0%

Industry, commerce, and services 18.9%

Government 6.1%

NA stands for not available.

Unemployment Rate (17)

Rate not available.

PRODUCTION SECTOR

Electric Energy (18)

Capacity ....29,000 kW (1995)

Production ....73 million kWh (1995)

Consumption per capita ....74 kWh (1995)

Transportation (19)

Highways:

total: 2,700 km

paved: 956 km

unpaved: 1,744 km (1996 est.)

Waterways: 400 km

Merchant marine: none

Airports: 1 (1997 est.)

Airports—with paved runways:

total: 1

over 3,047 m: 1 (1997 est.)

Top Agricultural Products (20)

Peanuts, millet, sorghum, rice, corn, cassava (tapioca), palm kernels; cattle, sheep, goats; forest and fishing resources not fully exploited.

FINANCE, ECONOMICS, & TRADE

Economic Indicators (22)

National product: GDP—purchasing power parity—$1.23 billion (1997 est.)

National product real growth rate: 2.1% (1997 est.)

National product per capita: $1,000 (1997 est.)

MANUFACTURING SECTOR

GDP & Manufacturing Summary (21)

Detailed value added figures are listed by both International Standard Industry Code (ISIC) and product title.

	1980	1985	1990	1994
GDP ($-1990 mil.)[1]	212	251	300	321
Per capita ($-1990)[1]	331	338	325	297
Manufacturing share (%) (current prices)[1]	3.6	8.9	5.4	6.3
Manufacturing				
Value added ($-1990 mil.)[1]	10	13	17	18
Industrial production index	100	104	133	141
Value added ($ mil.)	11	9	16	21
Gross output ($ mil.)	30	41	57	69
Employment (000)	2	3	4	4
Profitability (% of gross output)				
Intermediate input (%)	62	77	71	70
Wages and salaries inc. supplements (%)	10	7	8	8
Gross operating surplus	28	16	21	22

GDP & Manufacturing Summary (21)

	1980	1985	1990	1994
Productivity ($)				
Gross output per worker	16,115	14,058	16,890	18,681
Value added per worker	6,094	3,309	5,278	8,373
Average wage (inc. supplements)	1,566	1,007	1,330	1,468
Value added ($ mil.)				
311/2 Food products	3	4	5	6
313 Beverages	1	1	2	3
314 Tobacco products	—	—	—	—
321 Textiles	—	—	—	1
322 Wearing apparel	—	—	—	—
323 Leather and fur products	—	—	—	—
324 Footwear	—	—	—	—
331 Wood and wood products	—	—	—	—
332 Furniture and fixtures	1	1	1	1
341 Paper and paper products	—	—	—	—
342 Printing and publishing	—	—	—	1
351 Industrial chemicals	—	—	—	—
352 Other chemical products	—	—	—	—
353 Petroleum refineries	—	—	—	—
354 Miscellaneous petroleum and coal products	—	—	—	—
355 Rubber products	—	—	—	—
356 Plastic products	—	—	—	—
361 Pottery, china and earthenware	—	—	—	—
362 Glass and glass products	—	—	—	—
369 Other non-metal mineral products	—	—	—	—
371 Iron and steel	—	—	—	—
372 Non-ferrous metals	—	—	—	—
381 Metal products	—	—	—	1
382 Non-electrical machinery	—	—	—	—
383 Electrical machinery	—	—	—	—
384 Transport equipment	—	—	—	—
385 Professional and scientific equipment	—	—	—	—
390 Other manufacturing industries	6	2	6	8

Inflation rate—consumer price index: 2.2% (1997)

Exchange Rates (24)

Exchange rates:

Dalasi (D) per US$1

December 1997	10.513
1997	10.200
1996	9.789
1995	9.546
1994	9.576
1993	9.129

Top Import Origins (25)

$140 million (c.i.f., 1995)

Origins	%
China	NA
Cote d'Ivoire	NA
Hong Kong	NA
United Kingdom	NA
Germany	NA

NA stands for not available.

Top Export Destinations (26)

$160 million (f.o.b., 1995).

Destinations	%
Japan	NA
Senegal	NA
Hong Kong	NA
France	NA
Switzerland	NA
United Kingdom	NA
Indonesia	NA

NA stands for not available.

Economic Aid (27)

Recipient: bilateral $36.1 million; multilateral $34.7 million (1994).

Import Export Commodities (28)

Import Commodities	Export Commodities
Foodstuffs	Peanuts and peanut products 70%
Manufactures	
Raw materials	Fish
Fuel	Cotton lint
Machinery and transport equipment	Palm kernels

Balance of Payments (23)

	1992	1993	1994	1995	1996
Exports of goods (f.o.b.)	147	157	125	123	119
Imports of goods (f.o.b.)	−178	−214	−182	−163	−217
Trade balance	−31	−57	−57	−40	−98
Services - debits	−74	−80	−72	−79	−86
Services - credits	86	85	95	58	107
Private transfers (net)	43	33	28	29	15
Government transfers (net)	13	14	13	23	15
Overall balance	37	−5	8	−8	−48

GEORGIA

Republic of Georgia
Sakartveld Respublika

INTRODUCTORY SURVEY

RECENT HISTORY

Georgia's first multiparty elections were held in October 1990, during the liberal era of Mikhail Gorbachev's perestroika in the Soviet Union. On 31 March 1991, the people voted for independence from the Soviet Union, and former dissident Zviad Gamsakhurdia was elected president in May 1991. After being removed from office in December 1991, Gamsakhurdia was replaced by former Soviet Foreign Minister Eduard Shevardnadze.

Since the beginning of 1992, Georgia has experienced secessionist movements, civil war, and economic collapse. During the fall of 1993, Georgian forces were forced out of the region of Abkhazia, whose Muslim minority fought to secede from the country. On 1 December, both sides signed a peace agreement. Since 1994, Abkhazia has been run as an autonomous (self-governing) state. About 1,500 Russian peacekeepers and 100 observers from the United Nations were stationed in the area to help foster a peaceful settlement between Georgia and Abkhazia. Georgian forces have also battled separatists in South Ossetia. They want to join the region with North Ossetia, which is inside the Russian Federation. Ajaria, in the southwest, is another self-governing area.

During the latter part of 1993, former President Gamsakhurdia and his supporters launched a rebellion in western Georgia. It was defeated when Russia came to Shevardnadze's aid after he agreed to join the Commonwealth of Independent States (CIS).

By 1994, the economy was failing and hyperinflation caused the government's coupons to become worthless. In 1995, the government introduced a new currency, the lari. Together with monetary reforms, the annual inflation rate was brought down to about 15%.

In early 1998, President Shevardnadze narrowly escaped an assassination attempt. In May 1998, after two years of relative calm, fighting

broke out between Abkhazian separatists and Georgian troops.

GOVERNMENT

Until 1995, Georgia had been governed according to a constitution dating back to 1921. The new constitution provided for an executive branch that reports to the president, a legislature, and an independent judiciary. The president appoints ministers with the approval of the 223-member parliament.

As of the late 1990s, the regions of South Ossetia, Abkhazia, and Ajaria were self-governing and were not under the control of the Georgian government.

Judiciary

The 1995 constitution provides for an independent judiciary. However, the judiciary is subject to executive pressure. Courts include district courts, a Tiblisi city court, and the Supreme Court of the Republic. A Constitutional Court was created in 1996.

Political Parties

The most influential parties are the Citizens Union of Georgia, the National Democratic Party, and the All Georgia Revival Union.

DEFENSE

Although there are armed communal militias and over 500,000 men with military experience, Georgia has no national army. It plans to have an army of 20,000, supported by a national guard of 13,000.

ECONOMIC AFFAIRS

Georgia's mild climate makes it an important agricultural producer. A growing range of sub-tropical crops flourish in the coastal region. Georgia exports them to its northern neighbors in return for manufactured goods. Georgia supplied almost all the former Soviet Union's citrus fruits and tea, and much of its grape crop. The country has deposits of manganese, coal, iron ore, and lead, and a number of oil refineries operate in Batumi.

The economy, based largely on the country's mineral deposits and agricultural resources, has been slowed by political unrest.

Public Finance

The government budget of 1995 resulted in a deficit of 8.5%, down from 17% in 1994. Runaway inflation, revenue shortfalls, and civil conflict all exacerbated the deficit, which was largely financed by bank credit. Revenues were up in 1996 and expenditures had been cut sharply through the elimination of almost all price and enterprise subsidies. Government employment was reduced by one-third in 1995.

Income

In 1998, the gross national product (GNP) was about $5.0 billion, or $850 per person. For the period 1985–95, the average inflation rate was 310.0% and the average decline in the GNP per person was 7.0%.

Industry

Heavy industry dominates, and includes metallurgy, construction materials, and machine building. Light industry includes food processing, beverage production, garments, and oil processing. In 1996, less than 20% of Georgia's industries were operating, most at less than 15% of capacity.

Banking and Finance

The National Bank of Georgia (NBG), the state's central bank, was founded in 1991. The NBG has the functions of a central bank, namely, issuing currency, managing the exchange rate, controlling monetary and credit aggregates, and regulating the activities of the banking sector. A central bank directive in May 1995 raised the minimum capital requirement, which in 1994 had fallen to a low of coupon equivalent to $385, to coupon equivalent to $100,000.

In September 1995, Georgia introduced a new currency, the Lari, to replace its interim currency, the coupon, at the rate of Lari 1:coupon 1,000,000. The coupon had been introduced in May 1993 after the collapse of the ruble zone in response to a severe cash shortage in the republic. The coupon experienced one of the steepest devaluations of any currencies in the former Soviet Union.

The government has since had more success with the Lari. The new currency was introduced at Lari 1.3:US $1, and given the dramatic success in reducing inflation, by the end of November 1996 it had appreciated in nominal terms slightly to trade around 1.28 = $1.

At the time of independence there were, in addition to the NBG, five specialized commercial banks, about 200 small domestic commercial banks, and the former Georgian branches of the Soviet Savings Bank and Vneshekonombank.

Economic Development

In late 1992, the government inaugurated its Medium-Term Program of Macroeconomic Stabilization and Systemic Change focusing on price and trade liberalization, budget constraints for public enterprises, and privatization. As part of a small enterprise privatization program, the first auction of small-scale assets was held in Tiblisi in March 1993. Practically all housing has been privatized, as well as 60% of agricultural land. Privatization was progressing as of 1996, although at a slow pace.

SOCIAL WELFARE

Georgians experienced a significant decline in their standard of living in 1996, and unemployment remained high. Women mostly work in low-paying, traditional occupations, often on a part-time basis.

Healthcare

In 1993, there was 1 physician per 182 people. Infant mortality was 27 per 1,000 live births in 1994. Life expectancy averages 73 years.

Housing

Georgia has a severe housing shortage. Over 128,000 households were on waiting lists for housing in urban areas during the early 1990s.

EDUCATION

Adult literacy was estimated at 99.0% in 1990. Georgian students are taught in a number of languages, including Georgian, Russian, Armenian, Azerbaijani, Abkhazian, and Ossetian. Several colleges and universities are located in Georgia.

1999 KEY EVENTS TIMELINE

January

- A malfunction in the electricity distribution system causes a blackout throughout much of the country.

- A bus returning from near the Russian border crashes and kills all 38 people aboard.

- Defense ministers from Georgia, Ukraine, and Azerbaijan meet in Baku to discuss establishing a joint peacekeeping battalion to protect oil pipelines running from Azerbaijan through Georgia.

- Georgia gets conditional approval to join the Council of Europe.

February

- President Shevardnadze indicates that Georgia is considering ending its collective security treaty obligations with the Commonwealth of Independent States.

March

- Georgia signs a five-year military cooperation agreement with Turkey.

April

- A new pipeline from Azerbaijan delivers oil to the Georgian port of Supsa, where Georgian oil tankers have access to Western markets via the Black Sea. It is the first Azeri crude oil from the Caspian Sea region to be exported by a pipeline that does not cross Russia, thus threatening Russia's monopoly over the shipment of Azerbaijani oil to the Black Sea.

- Georgia officially joins the Council of Europe as its 41st member.

May

- The 54th annual Victory Day procession takes place in Georgia to commemorate the anniversary of the Soviet Union's victory over Nazi Germany.

- A powerful bomb explodes near the parliament building in Sukhumi, the capital of the breakaway region of Abkhazia. There are no injuries.

- President Shevardnadze pardons and releases 99 prisoners to mark Georgia's independence day.

- Officials arrest several people suspected of conspiring to assassinate President Shevardnadze and others in the government's leadership. Shevardnadze believes that the plotters are receiving support from the Russian government.

- Georgia signs an agreement with the United States, which will train helicopter pilots and technicians and supply ten helicopter gunships.

June

- Georgia and Abkhazia agree to a prisoner exchange.

- The European Union completes its new partnership and cooperation pacts with Armenia, Azerbaijan and Georgia on political, trade and investment issues.

July

- Seventeen officials and journalists are taken hostage by an unknown armed group in Abkhazia. The gunmen later release all the hostages unharmed.

- The United Nations Security Council decides to extend its military observer mission in Abkhazia for six more months.

- U.S. Defense Secretary William Cohen visits President Shevardnadze in Tbilisi to discuss joint planning to guard against arms proliferation in the southern Caucasus area.

August

- Abkhazian leader Vladislav Ardzinba meets with Russian Prime Minister Sergey Stepashin in Moscow to discuss a possible peace settlement between Georgia and Abkhazia.

- Stalin's grandson, Yevgeny Dzhugashvili, is prohibited from running in the upcoming October parliamentary election by the electoral commission because he is not a Georgian citizen.

- Two unidentified military aircraft violate Georgian airspace and bomb a village in the Tusheti region of eastern Georgia, injuring three people and causing a forest fire. Russia later apologizes for the mistake, which occurred when the aircraft strayed into Georgian airspace in pursuit of rebels in Dagestan.

- Georgian government condemns Abkhazia's plans to hold its own presidential elections and a referendum on independence.

September

- An ambush in the Abkhazian village of Tagiloni kills a customs official and wounds three others. Abkhazian security officials blame Georgian saboteurs.

- The main political opposition bloc nominates Aslan Abashidze, chairman of the provincial parliament in the southern region of Adjaria, as its candidate for the 2000 presidential elections against President Shevardnadze, who will run for reelection.

- President Shevarnadze visits Ukraine to discuss political and economic relations between the two countries.

October

- President Shevardnadze denounces the presidential elections in Abkhazia as illegal and undemocratic. Abkhazian President Vladislav Ardzinba is re-elected with a landslide majority.

- Abkhazia's parliament declares independence from Georgia and urges the international community to recognize Abkhazia's sovereignty.

- Gunmen kidnap several U.N. military observers in Abkhazia and demand ransom. They free the hostages within a week.

- The Russian-U.S. gas firm ITERA cuts off supplies to Georgia's Gardabani power station and several other Georgian users because of nonpayment problems.

- President Shevardnadze announces that Georgia will accept Chechen refugees after Russia seals off its border with Chechnya.

- President Eduard Shevardnadze's Citizens' Union of Georgia (CUG) party wins the parliamentary elections.

November

- President Shevardnadze refuses Russia's request to allow Russian troops to pass through Georgia on their way to Chechnya.

- Ten thousand people, including President Shevardnadze, attend a mass celebrated by Pope John Paul II, who is on his first visit to Georgia.

- Georgia issues a formal complaint to the United Nations Security Council that Russian military aircraft are violating Georgian airspace as they attack Chechnya.

December

- President Shevardnadze asks the United Nations to help with the flow of thousands of refugees into Georgia from neighboring Chechnya.

ANALYSIS OF EVENTS: 1999

BUSINESS AND THE ECONOMY

Georgia was reminded of its continuing tenuous economic situation early in 1999, when an accident to the electricity system cut power to much of the country. Residences and businesses went without power for a few hours and Tbilisi's subway stopped running.

However, in April, Georgia completed a major accomplishment in its ongoing quest for economic self-determination—the first pipeline to carry Caspian Sea oil directly to world markets without going through Russian territory was officially opened. The pipeline runs through Georgia and links the oil fields of Azerbaijan to a transfer terminal at the Georgian Black Sea port of Supsa, providing a cheaper route to world markets for Azeri oil companies. Before the pipeline opened, the only available Russian pipeline was often inoperative because of technical problems or from disputes with Chechnya, across whose territory it runs. The new oil pipeline caused Russia to lose its regional monopoly over the shipment of Azerbaijani oil to the Black Sea. The pipeline also benefits Ukraine by reducing its reliance on Russian oil. Georgia and Ukraine also initiated a rail ferry service across the Black Sea, completing unbroken rail service between Europe and Central Asia.

Georgia's economic ties with Russia also soured when the Russian-U.S. gas firm ITERA cut off supplies to several major Georgian users, including a power station. ITERA, which is affiliated with the Russian gas monopoly Gazprom and has been Georgia's main supplier since 1996, cut off supplies because Georgia owed it a total of $60 million.

GOVERNMENT AND POLITICS

Georgia's political stability was frequently challenged in 1999, both externally and internally. With political turmoil already occurring in the northern Caucasus, Russia's conflict with its breakaway republic of Chechnya and the subsequent flight of refugees threatened to spread into the southern Caucasus region as well, endangering Georgia's stability. Meanwhile, Georgia's own breakaway province, Abkhazia, stepped up its efforts for total independence from Georgia. The province, although technically still a part of Georgia, has essentially been autonomous since its war with Georgia ended in 1993, but the Georgian government has refused to acknowledge the province's ultimate objective of secession.

In January, the defense ministers of Georgia, Ukraine, and Azerbaijan met at Baku to discuss creating a joint peacekeeping force that would also include Moldova. The group would protect oil pipelines running from Azerbaijan to Turkey and Georgia. The four-nation organization could also be used to maintain stability within its members' own troubled breakaway regions.

In a move for greater autonomy from Russia's influence, President Shevardnadze also contemplated ending Georgia's cooperation in the collective security treaty with the Commonwealth of Independent States (CIS), the group of twelve states formed after the break-up of the Soviet Union. The administration believed that the CIS was no longer an effective security group and not relevant to Georgia's interests, and that it had failed to help negotiate a solution to Georgia's ongoing problem with its breakaway province of Abkhazia. Georgia's assessment of the CIS treaty was not unique—Uzbekistan and Azerbaijan had already indicated that they would abandon the treaty. Moreover, Russia announced that it would begin installing anti-aircraft missiles in its bases in neighboring Armenia, which Georgia perceived as destabilizing for the entire southern Caucasus. In March, Georgia signed a five-year military cooperation agreement with Turkey, a NATO member country. Turkey will help train Georgian officers and will supply medical equipment, transport vehicles, and other supplies to the Georgian military.

In April, Georgia officially joined the Council of Europe, becoming its 41st member. With its membership in the Council, Georgia has one year to ratify European conventions on human rights and the protection of minorities. The Council is also requiring that by April 2001, Georgia must have set up the legal framework to guarantee autonomy to the breakaway territories of Abkhazia and Ossetia. In July, the European Union (EU) began implementing new partnership and cooperation agreements with Armenia, Azerbaijan and Georgia concerning political, trade, and investment issues. EU leaders believe that as the organization eventually expands into Eastern Europe, the Black Sea and Caucasian countries will become more regionally significant.

In May, Shevardnadze ordered the release of 99 prisoners to commemorate Georgia's Independence Day. That month also, several people were arrested for conspiring to assassinate President Shevardnadze. The group allegedly had ties to former security chief Igor Giogadze, who had been involved in two earlier assassination attempts on Shevardnadze. The administration indicated that it believed Giogadze had received Russian backing, which was vehemently denied by the Russian government. The Georgian government believed that the latest assassination conspiracy was different than those before because unlike the previous attempts in 1995 and 1998, the intent this time was to liquidate all of Georgia's main political leaders in order to create the instability necessary to overthrow the government. Shevardnadze believed that the motivation behind the plot was to prevent Georgia's integration with Europe.

At breakthrough United Nations-sponsored talks in Istanbul, Turkey in June, representatives from Georgia and its breakaway province of Abkhazia agreed to a prisoner exchange and worked on the coordination of returning refugees. Their agreement also included organized joint economic development projects such as constructing dams and power plants. The two sides also promised to help create a security zone at the border and agreed to hold a future session of talks in Yalta, Ukraine at an unspecified date.

In August, Vladislav Ardzinba, the leader of Abkhazia, met with Russian Prime Minister Sergey Stepashin in Moscow to discuss a possible peace settlement between Georgia and Abkhazia. Stepashin also met separately with Georgian state minister Vazha Lortkipanidze. These meetings came a week after the United Nations Security Council voted for a half-year extension of its military observer mission in Abkhazia. Russia's increased mediating effort to negotiate a deal between Georgia and Abkhazia came after Georgia offered increased security cooperation with the United States. In July, U.S. Defense Secretary William Cohen met with President Shevardnadze to plan joint measures to guard against arms proliferation in the southern Caucasus.

Later in August, the Georgian government protested Abkhazia's plans to hold its own presidential election and referendum regarding independence on October 3. The only candidate for the presidency was the province's current leader, Vladislav Ardzinba, who went on to win the election with a landslide majority. Some 98 percent of voters supported the independence referendum and agreed to reinstate the 1929 constitution that recognized Abkhazia as an independent state. Georgian officials believed that the referendum was in violation of international law because some 60–80 percent of the province's population had been expelled during the 1992–93 civil war between Abkhazia and Georgia. After the October election, the Abkhazian parliament declared its independence from Georgia, urging the United Nations and other international organizations to acknowledge Abkhazia's independence. Russia, fearing the escalation of secessionist movements within its own borders, refused to endorse Abkhazia's declaration of independence.

Meanwhile, the main political opposition alliance in Georgia nominated Aslan Abashidze as its candidate for the 2000 presidential election against incumbent President Shevardnadze, who will run for reelection. Abashidze is the chairman of the provincial parliament in the southern region of Adjaria.

CULTURE AND SOCIETY

Several violent incidents of social conflict occurred in 1999, stemming primarily from the animosity between Georgia and its breakaway region of Abkhazia. Most of Abkhazia is under the control of separatists, who forcibly expelled the Georgian army and thousands of Georgians from the area during the 1992–93 war, which killed about 10,000 people.

In May, a bomb exploded near the parliament building in Sukhumi, the capital of Abkhazia, but no one was injured. In July, 17 senior officials and journalists were abducted by an unknown armed group while visiting the Kodorskoye gorge, the only part of Abkhazia under Georgian control. After a standoff of several hours involving talks between the kidnappers and a special envoy of President Shevardnadze, the gunmen released all the hostages unharmed. In September, a customs official in Abkhazia was killed and three others wounded during an ambush in Tagiloni. Abkhazian officials blamed Georgian saboteurs. In October, gunmen kidnapped seven people in the village of Azhara, demanding a ransom of $250,000. The hostages included two United Nations military observers and their Abkhazian translator. Later that week, the gunmen freed all the hostages.

Georgian authorities released evidence to the International Tribunal in the Hague regarding acts of ethnic cleansing allegedly committed by Abkhazian rebels. The rebels were accused of killing some 6,000 Georgians living in Abkhazia. The evidence consisted of hundreds of documents, including videotapes and eyewitness testimonies.

Social unrest in Chechnya also spilled over into Georgia. In August, two unidentified warplanes flew over eastern Georgia and bombed a village in the Tusheti region bordering Dagestan, where Russian forces were fighting Islamist militants. President Shevardnadze was outraged by the bombing and wrote to Russian President Yeltsin, demanding justice. The Russian Defense Ministry initially denied responsibility, but nine days later the Russian government apologized to Georgia, claiming that its aircraft mistakenly bombed the village with anti-personnel mines while in pursuit of rebels moving from Chechnya to Dagestan. Russia agreed to compensate any Georgians who were injured or had property loss from the incident. In October, President Shevardnadze announced that Georgia would admit refugees fleeing from Chechnya after Russia closed the Chechen border.

DIRECTORY

CENTRAL GOVERNMENT
Head of State

President
Eduard Shevardnadze, Office of the President, 7 Ingorokea Street, 380034 Tbilisi, Georgia
FAX: +995 (320) 997256

Ministers

Minister of Agriculture and Food Industry
Bakur Gulua, Ministry of Agriculture And Food Industry, 41 Kostava Str., 380023 Tbilisi, Georgia
PHONE: +995 (32) 931997
FAX: +955 (32) 933300

Minister of Communications and Posts
Sergo Esakia, Ministry of Communications and Posts, 29 April Str., 380008 Tbilisi, Georgia
PHONE: +995 (32) 999528
FAX: +995 (32) 991111

Minister of Culture
Valeri Asatiani, Ministry of Culture, 37 Rustaveli Ave., 380008 Tbilisi, Georgia

PHONE: +995 (32) 932255; 987430
FAX: +995 (32) 999037

Minister of Defense
David Tevzadze, Ministry of Defense, 2a
University Str., 380114 Tbilisi, Georgia
PHONE: +995 (32) 983930; 300027
FAX: +995 (32) 983925

Minister of Economics
Vladimer Papava, Ministry of Economics, 12
Chanturia Str., 380008 Tbilisi, Georgia
PHONE: +995 (32) 230925; 989467
FAX: +995 (32) 982743

Minister of Education
Aleksandre Kartozia, Ministry of Education, 52
Uznadze Str., 380002 Tbilisi, Georgia
PHONE: +995 (32) 958886; 953213
FAX: +995 (32) 770073

Minister of Environmental Protection and Natural Resources
Nino Chkhobadze, Ministry of Environmental
Protection and Natural Resources, 68 a Kostava
Street, 380015 Tbilisi, Georgia
PHONE: +995 (32) 230664; 334729
FAX: +995 (32) 943670; 334729

Minister of Finance
David Onoprishvili, Ministry of Finance, 70
Abashidze Str., 380062 Tbilisi, Georgia
PHONE: +995 (32) 226805; 290778
FAX: +995 (32) 931922
E-MAIL: tege@access.sanet.ge

Minister of Foreign Affairs
Irakli Menagharishvili, Ministry of Foreign
Affairs, 4 Chitadze Str., 380018 Tbilisi, Georgia
PHONE: +995 (32) 989377; 989388; 989391
FAX: +995 (32) 997249

Minister of Fuel and Energy
Teimuraz Giorgadze, Ministry of Fuel and
Energy, 10 Lermontov Str., Tbilisi, Georgia
PHONE: +995 (32) 931384; 989814; 996098
FAX: +995 (32) 933542

Minister of Health
Avtandil Jorbenadze, Ministry of Health, 30
Gamsakhurdia Ave., 380113 Tbilisi, Georgia
PHONE: +995 (32) 387071
FAX: +995 (32) 389802

Minister of Industry
Badri Shoshitaishvili, Ministry of Industry, 28
Gamsakhurdia Ave., 380060 Tbilisi, Georgia
PHONE: +995 (32) 380704; 931045

Minister of Internal Affairs
Kakha Targamadze, Ministry of Internal Affairs,
10 Gulua Str., 380014 Tbilisi, Georgia
PHONE: +995 (32) 996298; 996233; 991049

Minister of Justice
Johnny Khetsuriani, Ministry of Justice, 19
Griboedov Str., 380046 Tbilisi, Georgia
PHONE: +995 (32) 935049
FAX: +995 (32) 990225

Minister of Refugee and Resettlement Issues
Valerian Vashakidze, Ministry of Refugee And
Resettlement Issues, 28 Rustaveli Ave., 380008
Tbilisi, Georgia
PHONE: +995 (32) 941611; 921427; 920543

Minister of Security
Vakhtang Kutateladze, Ministry of Security, 49
April Str., 380018 Tbilisi, Georgia
PHONE: +995 (32) 932791; 935060; 931903

Minister of Social Security, Labor, And Employment
Tengiz Gazdeliani, Ministry of Social Security,
Labor, And Employment, 2 Leonidze Str.,
380007 Tbilisi, Georgia
PHONE: +995 (32) 936236; 936622
FAX: +995 (32) 936151

Minister of State Property
Mikheil Ukleba, Ministry of State Property, 64
Chavchavadze Ave., 380062 Tbilisi, Georgia
PHONE: +995 (32) 294875; 225209; 292793

Minister of Trade and Foreign Economic Relations
Tamriko Beruchashvili, Ministry of Trade and
Foreign Economic Relations, 42 Kazbegi Ave.,
380077 Tbilisi, Georgia
PHONE: +995 (32) 389612; 225186
FAX: +995 (32) 234134

Minister of Transport
Merab Adeishvili, Ministry of Transport, 12
Kazbegi Str., 380060 Tbilisi, Georgia
PHONE: +995 (32) 932846; 367956

Minister of Urban Affairs and Construction
Merab Chkhenkeli, Ministry of Urban Affairs
and Construction, 16 V. Pshavela Ave., 380060
Tbilisi, Georgia
PHONE: +995 (32) 374276; 379491
FAX: +995 (32) 220541

POLITICAL ORGANIZATIONS

Sruliad Sakartvelos Aghordzinesis Kavshiri (All Georgia Union for Revival)

NAME: Alsan Abashidze

Sakartvelos Mokalaketa Kavshiri (Citizens Union of Georgia)

TITLE: General Secretary
NAME: Eduard Shevardnadze

Sakartvelos Mtsvaneta Partia (Greens Party of Georgia)

NAME: Giorgi Gachechiladze

Sakartvelos Komunisturi Partia (Communist Party of Georgia)

Erovnul Demokratiuli Partia (National Democratic Party)

NAME: Irina Sarishvili-Chantaria

Sakartvelos Sotsialisturi Partia (Socialist Party of Georgia)

NAME: Vakhtang Rcheulishvili

DIPLOMATIC REPRESENTATION

Embassies in Georgia

Armenia
4 Tetelashvili St., Tbilisi, Georgia
PHONE: +995 (32) 959443; 957866; 964290
FAX: +995 (32) 990126
TITLE: Ambassador
NAME: Levon Khachatrian

Azerbaijan
4 Mukhadze St., Tbilisi, Georgia
PHONE: +995 (32) 234037
FAX: +995 (32) 234037
TITLE: Ambassador
NAME: Hajan Hajiev

China
52 Barnov St., Tbilisi, Georgia
PHONE: +995 (32) 998011; 291093; 983953
FAX: +995 (32) 931276
TITLE: Ambassador
NAME: Zhang Youg Quan

France
15 Gogebashvili St., Tbilisi, Georgia
PHONE: +995 (32) 934210; 999976; 953375
FAX: +995 (32) 953375
TITLE: Ambassador

NAME: Mireille Musso

Germany
166 Agmashenebeli Av., Tbilisi, Georgia
PHONE: +995 (32) 950936; 953326
TITLE: Ambassador
NAME: Norbert Baas

Greece
5 Arakishvili Lane II, Tbilisi, Georgia
PHONE: +995 (32) 938981
FAX: +995 (32) 938981
TITLE: Ambassador
NAME: Tassos Kriekoukis

Iran
16 Zovrety St., Tbilisi, Georgia
PHONE: +995 (32) 294695; 294502
FAX: +995 (32) 986993
TITLE: Ambassador
NAME: Akbar Aminian

Israel
61 David Agmashenebeli Av., Tbilisi, Georgia
PHONE: +995 (32) 964457; 951709; 960213
FAX: +995 (32) 951709
TITLE: Charge d'Affairs
NAME: Ran Giddor

Poland
19 Zubalashvili St., Tbilisi, Georgia
PHONE: +995 (32) 920398; 367086
FAX: +995 (32) 920397
TITLE: Ambassador
NAME: Piotr Boravski

Romania
9 Shatbcrashvili st, Tbilisi, Georgia
PHONE: +995 (32) 381575; 224755
TITLE: Ambassador
NAME: Constantin Girbea

Russian Federation
61 David Agmashenebeli Av., Tbilisi, Georgia
PHONE: +995 (32) 955911; 951754; 955353
FAX: +995 (32) 955233
TITLE: Ambassador
NAME: Felix Stanevski

Turkey
61 David Agmashenebeli Av., Tbilisi, Georgia
PHONE: +995 (32) 292319; 952014; 951810
FAX: +995 (32) 951810
TITLE: Ambassador
NAME: Tevfik Ufuk Okiayuz

Ukraine
75 Oniashvili St., Tbilisi, Georgia
PHONE: +995 (32) 989362; 941043; 237145

FAX: +995 (32) 237145
TITLE: Ambassador
NAME: Stephane Volkovetski

United Kingdom
''Sheraton Palace'' Hotel, Tbilisi, Georgia
PHONE: +995 (32) 955497
FAX: +995 (32) 955497
TITLE: Ambassador
NAME: Richard Jankins

United States
25 Atoneli St., Tbilisi, Georgia
PHONE: +995 (32) 989967; 989968; 933803
FAX: +995 (32) 933759
TITLE: Charge d'Affairs
NAME: Laurence Kerr

Vatican City
40 Jgenty St., Tbilisi, Georgia
PHONE: +995 (32) 941305
FAX: +995 (32) 293944
NAME: Ambros Madta

JUDICIAL SYSTEM
Supreme Court of Georgia
Constitutional Court of Georgia

29 Rustaveli, Tbilisi, Georgia
E-MAIL: court@conSt.gov.ge

FURTHER READING
Articles
''Black Sea Mischief.'' *The Economist* 352,
8128 (July 17, 1999): 46.

Steavenson, Wendell. ''Trapped Between War
and Peace: Ethnic Conflict Has Polarized the
People of Georgia and Abkhazia'' *Time
International* 154, 1 (July 12, 1999): 27.

Books

Atal, Yogesh, ed. *Poverty in Transition and
Transition in Poverty: Studies of Poverty in
Countries-in-transition: Hungary, Bulgaria,
Romania, Georgia, Russia, Mongolia.* Paris:
United Nations Educational, Scientific and
Cultural Organization; New York: Berghahn
Books, 1998.

Gachechiladze, Revaz Givievich. *The New
Georgia: Space, Society, Politics.* College
Station: Texas A and M University Press,
1995.

Schwartz, Donald V. and Razmik Panossian, eds.
*Nationalism and History: the Politics of
Nation Building in Post-Soviet Armenia,
Azerbaijan and Georgia.* Toronto: University
of Toronto Centre for Russian and East
European Studies, 1994.

Internet

*Embassy of Georgia in the United States of
America.* Available Online @ http://
www.georgiaemb.org/ (November 15, 1999).

*Institute for the Study of Conflict, Ideology and
Policy at Boston University.* Available Online
@ http://www.bu.edu/iscip (November 12,
1999).

GEORGIA: STATISTICAL DATA

For sources and notes see "Sources of Statistics" in the front of each volume.

GEOGRAPHY

Geography (1)

Area:

Total: 69,700 sq km.

Land: 69,700 sq km.

Water: 0 sq km.

Area—comparative: slightly smaller than South Carolina.

Land boundaries:

Total: 1,461 km.

Border countries: Armenia 164 km, Azerbaijan 322 km, Russia 723 km, Turkey 252 km.

Coastline: 310 km.

Climate. warm and pleasant; Mediterranean-like on Black Sea coast.

Terrain: largely mountainous with Great Caucasus Mountains in the north and Lesser Caucasus Mountains in the south; Kolkhida Lowland opens to the Black Sea in the west; Mtkvari River Basin in the east; good soils in river valley flood plains, foothills of Kolkhida Lowland.

Natural resources: forests, hydropower, manganese deposits, iron ore, copper, minor coal and oil deposits; coastal climate and soils allow for important tea and citrus growth.

Land use:

Arable land: 9%

Permanent crops: 4%

Permanent pastures: 25%

Forests and woodland: 34%

Other: 28% (1993 est.).

HUMAN FACTORS

Demographics (2A)

	1990	1995	1998	2000	2010	2020	2030	2040	2050
Population	5,457.2	5,290.1	5,108.5	5,034.1	4,850.1	4,766.7	4,676.5	4,569.2	4,364.9
Net migration rate (per 1,000 population)	NA	NA	NA	NA	NA	NA	NA	NA	NA
Births	NA	NA	NA	NA	NA	NA	NA	NA	NA
Deaths	NA	NA	NA	NA	NA	NA	NA	NA	NA
Life expectancy - males	68.6	62.3	61.4	60.9	64.1	68.5	72.1	74.9	77.0
Life expectancy - females	76.1	68.8	68.4	68.2	70.9	75.1	78.6	81.2	83.1
Birth rate (per 1,000)	17.3	12.2	11.7	11.6	14.0	10.4	9.8	8.9	8.0
Death rate (per 1,000)	8.6	13.4	14.1	14.5	13.8	11.9	11.4	12.3	13.5
Women of reproductive age (15-49 yrs.)	1,350.0	1,349.5	1,339.0	1,339.6	1,289.2	1,163.2	1,093.1	947.7	880.8
of which are currently married	NA	NA	NA	NA	NA	NA	NA	NA	NA
Fertility rate	2.2	1.6	1.5	1.5	1.8	1.7	1.6	1.5	1.5

Except as noted, values for vital statistics are in thousands; life expectancy is in years.

Health Personnel (3)

Total health expenditure as a percentage of GDP, 1990-1997[a]

Public sector 0.6

Private sector . . . . .NA

Total[b] . . . . .NA

Health expenditure per capita in U.S. dollars, 1990-1997[a]

Purchasing power parity . . . . .NA

Total . . . . .NA

Availability of health care facilities per 100,000 people

Hospital beds 1990-1997[a] 480

Doctors 1993[c] 436

Nurses 1993[c] 863

Health Indicators (4)

Life expectancy at birth

1980 71

1997 73

Daily per capita supply of calories (1996) 2,184

Total fertility rate births per woman (1997) 1.5

Maternal mortality ratio per 100,000 live births (1990-97) . . . . .19[b]

Safe water % of population with access (1995) . . . . . .

Sanitation % of population with access (1995) . . . . . .

Consumption of iodized salt % of households (1992-98)[a] . . . .

Smoking prevalence

Male % of adults (1985-95)[a] . . . .

Female % of adults (1985-95)[a] . . . .

Tuberculosis incidence per 100,000 people (1997) 67

Adult HIV prevalence % of population ages 15-49 (1997) . . . .<0.005

Infants and Malnutrition (5)

Under-5 mortality rate (1997) 29

% of infants with low birthweight (1990-97) . . . . . .NA

Births attended by skilled health staff % of total[a] . . .95

% fully immunized (1995-97)

TB 76

DPT 92

Polio 98

Measles 95

Prevalence of child malnutrition under age 5 (1992-97)[b] . . . . .NA

Ethnic Division (6)

Georgian 70.1%

Armenian 8.1%

Russian 6.3%

Azeri 5.7%

Ossetian 3%

Abkhaz 1.8%

Other 5%

Religions (7)

Christian Orthodox 75%

Georgian Orthodox 65%

Russian Orthodox 10%

Muslim 11%

Armenian Apostolic 8%

Unknown 6%

Languages (8)

Armenian 7%, Azeri 6%, Georgian 71% (official), Russian 9%, other 7%.

EDUCATION

Public Education Expenditures (9)

Public expenditure on education (% of GNP)

1980 . . . .

1996 . . . . .5.2[1]

Expenditure per student

Primary % of GNP per capita

1980 . . . .

1996 . . . .

Secondary % of GNP per capita

1980 . . . .

1996 . . . . .25.0[1]

Tertiary % of GNP per capita

1980 . . . .

1996 . . . . .25.5[1]

Expenditure on teaching materials

Primary % of total for level (1996) . . . .

Secondary % of total for level (1996) . . . .

Primary pupil-teacher ratio per teacher (1996) 18

Duration of primary education years (1995) 4

Literacy Rates (11B)

Adult literacy rate

1980

Male . . . .-

Female . . . .-

1995

Male 100%

Female 99%

GOVERNMENT & LAW

Political Parties (12)

Supreme Council	No. of seats
Citizen's Union of Georgia (CUG) 107	
National Democratic Party (NDP) 34	
Union for "Revival" Party (AGUR) 32	
Progress Bloc 4	
Socialist Party (SPG) 4	
Others 9	
Abkazian deputies 12	
Independents 29	
Not filled 4	

Government Budget (13A)

Year: 1997

Total Expenditures: 662.1 Millions of Lari

Expenditures as a percentage of the total by function:

General public services and public order 26.54	
Defense 10.19	
Education 5.74	
Health 3.87	
Social Security and Welfare 17.63	
Housing and community amenities 88	
Recreational, cultural, and religious affairs 5.45	
Fuel and energy 1.77	
Agriculture, forestry, fishing, and hunting 2.48	
Mining, manufacturing, and construction 41	
Transportation and communication 1.95	
Other economic affairs and services 51	

Military Affairs (14B)

	1992	1993	1994	1995
Military expenditures				
Current dollars (mil.)	85	94	106	194
1995 constant dollars (mil.)	91	99	109	194
Armed forces (000)	NA	35	7	5
Gross national product (GNP)				
Current dollars (mil.)	10,160	7,693	8,220	7,938
1995 constant dollars (mil.)	10,930	8,065	8,426	7,938

Central government expenditures (CGE)				
1995 constant dollars (mil.)	3,826	NA	NA	NA
People (mil.)	5.5	5.4	5.3	5.3
Military expenditure as % of GNP	0.8	1.2	1.3	2.4
Military expenditure as % of CGE	2.4	NA	NA	NA
Military expenditure per capita (1995 $)	17	18	20	37
Armed forces per 1,000 people (soldiers)	NA	6.5	1.3	.9
GNP per capita (1995 $)	2,001	1,489	1,575	1,503
Arms imports[6]				
Current dollars (mil.)	0	0	0	10
1995 constant dollars (mil.)	0	0	0	10
Arms exports[6]				
Current dollars (mil.)	0	0	0	0
1995 constant dollars (mil.)	0	0	0	0
Total imports[7]				
Current dollars (mil.)	NA	63	800	250[e]
1995 constant dollars (mil.)	NA	66	820	250[e]
Total exports[7]				
Current dollars (mil.)	NA	39	500	140[e]
1995 constant dollars (mil.)	NA	41	513	140[e]
Arms as percent of total imports[8]	NA	0	0	0
Arms as percent of total exports[8]	NA	0	0	0

Crime (15)

Crime rate (for 1997)

Crimes reported 13,900	
Total persons convicted 12,000	
Crimes per 100,000 population 250	
Persons responsible for offenses	
Total number of suspects 7,500	
Total number of female suspects 45	
Total number of juvenile suspects 5,700	

LABOR FORCE

Labor Force (16)

Total (million) 2.2

Industry and construction 31%

Agriculture and forestry .25%

Other 44%

Data for 1996. Percent distribution for 1990.

Unemployment Rate (17)

16% (1996 est.)

PRODUCTION SECTOR

Electric Energy (18)

Capacity . . . . .4.558 million kW (1995)

Production . . . . .7.1 billion kWh (1996)

Consumption per capita . . . . .1,175 kWh (1995)

Transportation (19)

Highways:

total: 20,700 km

paved: 19,354 km

unpaved: 1,346 km (1996 est.)

Pipelines: crude oil 370 km; refined products 300 km; natural gas 440 km (1992)

Merchant marine:

total: 9 ships (1,000 GRT or over) totaling 87,730 GRT/122,769 DWT ships by type: cargo 3, oil tanker 5, short-sea passenger 1 (1997 est.)

Airports: 28 (1994 est.)

Airports—with paved runways:

total: 14

over 3,047 m: 1

2,438 to 3,047 m: 7

1,524 to 2,437 m: 4

914 to 1,523 m: 1

under 914 m: 1 (1994 est.)

Airports—with unpaved runways:

total: 14

over 3,047 m: 1

2,438 to 3,047 m: 1

1,524 to 2,437 m: 1

914 to 1,523 m: 5

under 914 m: 6 (1994 est.)

Top Agricultural Products (20)

Citrus, grapes, tea, vegetables, potatoes; small livestock sector.

FINANCE, ECONOMICS, & TRADE

Economic Indicators (22)

National product: GDP—purchasing power parity—$8.1 billion (1997 est.)

National product real growth rate: 11.8% (1997 est.)

National product per capita: $1,570 (1997 est.)

Inflation rate—consumer price index: 7.1% (1997 est.)

MANUFACTURING SECTOR

GDP & Manufacturing Summary (21)

	1980	1985	1990	1992	1993	1994
Gross Domestic Product						
Millions of 1990 dollars	8,417	12,416	12,167	5,489	3,294	2,365
Growth rate in percent	4.56	12.66	−0.34	−43.40	−40.00	−28.20
Per capita (in 1990 dollars)	1,667.3	2,364.1	2,245.8	1,008.7	604.8	433.9
Manufacturing Value Added						
Millions of 1990 dollars	NA	NA	2,330	1,193	*713*	*463*
Growth rate in percent	NA	NA	NA	−42.22	*-40.22*	*-35.01*
Manufacturing share in percent of current prices	21.0	22.4	*19.2*	*14.9*	*11.0*	*11.0*

FINANCE, ECONOMICS, & TRADE

Balance of Payments (23)

	1989	1990	1991	1992[1]	1993
Exports of goods (f.o.b.)	NA	NA	NA	266	362
Imports of goods (f.o.b.)	NA	NA	NA	−644	−702
Trade balance	NA	NA	NA	−378	−340
Services - debits	NA	NA	NA	−79	−72
Services - credits	NA	NA	NA	137	116
Private transfers (net)	NA	NA	NA	71	127
Government transfers (net)	NA	NA	NA	NA	NA
Long-term capital (net)	NA	NA	NA	65	159
Short-term capital (net)	NA	NA	NA	NA	NA
Errors and omissions	NA	NA	NA	408	NA
Overall balance	NA	NA	NA	224	−10

Exchange Rates (24)

Exchange rates:

Lari per US$1 (end of period)

December 1997 . . . . .1.32

December 1996 . . . . .1.28

December 1995 . . . . .1.24

Top Import Origins (25)

$733 million (c.i.f., 1996 est.)

Origins	%
France	.39
Cote d'Ivoire	.13
United States	.6
Netherlands	.5
Japan	.NA

NA stands for not available.

Top Export Destinations (26)

$400 million (f.o.b., 1996 est.) Data are for 1996.

Destinations	%
United States	.50
France	.16
Japan	.8
China	.NA
Spain	.NA
Germany	.NA

NA stands for not available.

Economic Aid (27)

Recipient: ODA, $28 million (1993). Note: commitments, 1992-95, $1,200 million ($675 million disbursements).

Import Export Commodities (28)

Import Commodities	Export Commodities
Fuel	Citrus fruits
Grain and other foods	Tea
Machinery and parts	Wine
Transport equipment	Other agricultural products; diverse types of machinery; ferrous and nonferrous metals; textiles; chemicals; fuel re-exports

GERMANY

Federal Republic of Germany
Bundesrepublik Deutschland

INTRODUCTORY SURVEY

CAPITAL: Berlin.

FLAG: The flag is a tricolor of black, red, and gold horizontal stripes—the flag of the German (Weimar) Republic from 1919 until 1933.

ANTHEM: *Einigkeit und Recht und Freiheit (Unity and Justice and Liberty).*

MONETARY UNIT: The deutsche mark (DM) is a paper currency of 100 pfennigs. There are coins of 1, 2, 5, 10, and 50 pfennigs and 1, 2, 5, and 10 deutsche marks, and notes of 5, 10, 20, 50, 100, 200, 500, and 1,000 deutsche marks. DM1 = $0.66.094 (or $1 = DM1.513).

WEIGHTS AND MEASURES: The metric system is the legal standard.

HOLIDAYS: New Year's Day, 1 January; Labor Day, 1 May; German Unity Day, 3 October; Repentance Day, Wednesday before the 3rd Sunday in November (except Bavaria); Christmas, 25–26 December. Movable religious holidays include Good Friday, Easter Monday, Ascension, and Whitmonday. In addition, the movable Carnival/Rose Monday holiday and various provincial holidays are also celebrated.

TIME: 1 PM = noon GMT.

LOCATION AND SIZE: Germany is located in western Europe, bordering the North Sea between France and Poland. Germany has a total area of 356,910 square kilometers (137,804 square miles). Its boundary length totals 6,010 kilometers (3,734 miles).

Germany's capital city, Berlin, is located in the northeastern part of the country.

CLIMATE: The climate is temperate. Rapid changes in temperature are rare. Average temperatures in January, the coldest month of the year, range from 1.5°c (35°F) in the lowlands to −6°c (21°F) in the mountains. July is the warmest month of the year, with average temperatures between 18°c (64°F) in low-lying areas to 20°c (68°F) in the sheltered valleys of the south.

Precipitation occurs throughout the year: in the northern lowlands, from 51 to 71 centimeters (20–28 inches); in the central uplands, from 69 to 152 centimeters (27–60 inches); in the Bavarian Alps, to more than 200 centimeters (80 inches).

RECENT HISTORY

After the surrender in 1945, Germany was divided into West Germany (controlled by the United Kingdom, France, and the United States) and East Germany (controlled by the Soviet Union). The capital city of Berlin, although totally in East Germany, was also divided in half.

West Germany's first chancellor (1949–63), Konrad Adenauer, the leader of the Christian Democratic Union (CDU), followed a policy of "peace through strength." During his administration, West Germany joined the North Atlantic Treaty Organization (NATO) in 1955 and became a founding member of the European Community in 1957. A treaty of cooperation between France and Germany, signed on 22 January 1963, provided for coordination of policies in foreign affairs, defense, information, and cultural affairs.

The cost of this program of cooperation with the West was further separation from East Germany and abandonment, for the foreseeable future, of the goal of German reunification. During this time, many skilled and highly educated East Germans had been secretly emigrating through Berlin to the West. To stop the flow, East Germany sealed East Berlin off from West Berlin by a wall of concrete and barbed wire. The Western Allies refused to accept the legality of the partition.

Throughout the late 1960s and early 1970s, tensions over the Berlin division generally eased, as did pressures over the issue of reunification. On

GERMANY

21 December 1972, the two Germanys signed a basic treaty and agreed to cooperate culturally and economically.

The economy of Democratic West Germany became one of the strongest in Europe, whereas that of socialist East Germany failed to live up to western standards.

The mass movement of East Germans through Hungary in the summer of 1989 as well as mass demonstrations in several East German cities led to the collapse of the German Democratic Republic in the fall of 1989 and the fall of the Berlin Wall. Helmut Kohl, who had been West Germany's chancellor since 1983, outlined a ten-point plan for peaceful reunification, including continued membership in NATO and free elections in March 1990. Following these elections, the two Germanys peacefully evolved into a single state.

However, unification has not been easy. Rising unemployment and other problems have raised concerns that the costs of unification were underestimated. Many in the western part of the country resent the costs of absorbing the east, while many in the east are unhappy about the painful change to a market economy. By 1997, the government had given more than $600 billion to eastern Germany through business subsidies, special tax breaks, and support payments to individuals.

In October 1998 elections, Gerhard Schroder was elected chancellor, defeating Helmut Kohl. Kohl became the first incumbent chancellor since 1945 to be defeated.

GOVERNMENT

On 3 October 1990, the Federal Republic of Germany (FRG) and the German Democratic Republic (GDR) were unified in accordance with Article 23 of the Basic Law (Grundgesetz) that serves as Germany's constitution.

The two-chamber legislature (the federal parliament) consists of a federal council (Bundesrat) and a federal assembly (Bundestag). Following unification, Bundestag membership was raised to 662 deputies. The Bundesrat consists of sixty-eight representatives appointed by the provincial governments.

The chancellor, the leader of the executive branch, is elected by a majority of the Bundestag. The president, who is chief of state, performs largely ceremonial functions.

Judiciary

Cases receive their first hearing in local courts (Landkreis) and the superior courts in each of the states. The Federal Courts of Justice in the cities of Karlsruhe and Berlin are the courts of last resort in regular civil and criminal cases. The Federal Constitutional Court, the highest court in the land, rules on problems concerning the Basic Law and to test the constitutionality of laws.

Political Parties

The Social Democratic Party (Sozialdemokratische Partei Deutschlands—SPD) is the oldest and best organized of all German parties. In recent decades, it has modified its traditional Marxist program and made an appeal not only to industrial workers but also to farmers, youth, and professional people.

The Christian Democratic Union (Christlich-Demokratische Union—CDU) and its Bavarian affiliate, the Christian Social Union (Christlich-Soziale Union—CSU) emphasize Christian principles but are not linked to specific religious denominations. They favor free enterprise and are supported by small business, professional groups, farmers, and Christian-oriented labor unions.

The Free Democratic Party (Freie Demokratische Partei—FDP) is a more varied organization, consisting of both liberals and strongly nationalistic groups. It rejects socialism in principle.

The Greens (Die Grünen), Germany's newest political party, is a coalition of environmentalists and antinuclear activists. In elections in October 1998, the Greens won 6.7% of the vote and entered the national government for the first time.

DEFENSE

The German armed forces in 1995 numbered 358,400, about half of whom were draftees performing twelve months of required service.

The army (252,800) is divided into the field army and the territorial army. The navy (Bundesmarine) of 28,500 absorbed about 2,000 East German sailors and some of their vessels. The air force (Luftwaffe) has 77,100 officers and airmen, including about 9,000 former East Germans. In 1995, Germany spent $41.8 billion for defense.

ECONOMIC AFFAIRS

Germany has the world's third largest economy and the largest in Europe. Germany's unit of currency, the mark, is one of the strongest in the world.

The former German Democratic Republic was the wealthiest nation in the Soviet bloc. However, the unification of Germany in October 1990 proved a heavy economic burden on the West. Subsidies for the East resulted in a large public deficit.

Public Finance

Germany's unification in 1990 raised special problems with regard to economic and financial assimilation. The Unification Treaty provided that the new states should be incorporated in the financial system established by the Basic Law as much as possible from the onset. Therefore, since 1991, the new states have basically been subject to the same regulations with regard to budgetary management and tax distribution as the western states. A "German Unity Fund" was initiated to provide financial support for the new states (and their municipalities); it is jointly financed by the western states, with most of the money being raised in the capital market.

The CIA estimates that, in 1995, government revenues totaled approximately $690 billion and expenditures $780 billion, including capital expenditures of $96.5 billion. The Maastricht treaty, which stipulates conditions for a single European currency (the Euro) by 1999, requires Germany to limit its budget deficit to 3% of GDP by 1997. In 1996, however, the deficit reached 3.9%. A surge in unemployment threatened to raise it to 4% in 1997 due to a resulting decrease in tax revenues and raise in unemployment benefits. The export-led economic recovery, together with inefficiencies in the present tax system, has limited the ability of the government to boost revenues to offset spending. In the meantime, the government is trying to cut pension and health care programs, but faces stiff resistance from the political opposition.

Income

In 1998, Germany's gross national product (GNP) was $2.12 trillion at current prices, or about $25,850 per person. There is a big difference in income between western and eastern Germany. In 1995, the gross domestic product (GDP) per person in the eastern states was only one-third of the amount in the western states.

Industry

Since reunification, German industry has been struggling with high labor costs, international competition, and high business taxes.

Germany produced 2.2 million passenger cars and 318,858 trucks and commercial vehicles in 1995. Germany produced 40.8 million tons of crude steel in 1994, along with 32.1 million tons of semi-manufactured steel. Cement production totaled 40.2 million tons; gasoline, 225 million barrels; and distillate fuel oil, 355 million barrels.

Banking and Finance

The central banking system of Germany consists of the German Federal Bank (Deutsche Bundesbank). Although the Federal Bank is an independent institution, the federal government holds the bank's capital and appoints the presidents as well as the board of directors; the Central Bank Council acts as overseer. All German banks are subject to supervision by the German Federal Banking Supervisory Authority (Bundesaufsichtsamt für das Kreditwesen) in Berlin.

The Federal Bank is the sole bank of issue. It determines credit and open market transactions, sets interest and discount rates, and is authorized to fix minimum reserve rations for the commercial banks and to grant credit to the federal government as well as to the provincial governments. The largest commercial banks are the Deutsche Bank, Dresdner Bank, and Commerzbank.

In 1996 Moody's Investments Service capped an extremely poor year for Deutsche Bank by reducing its triple A rating to Aa1. This reflects the fact that elite banks are finding it harder to retain the triple A rating as banking becomes internationally more competitive. Deutsche Bank announced that it hopes to shed 1,300 employees through attrition by 2000.

Under the constitution, the governments of the Länder regulate the operations of stock exchanges and produce exchanges. Eight stock exchanges operate in Berlin, Bremen, Düsseldorf, Frankfurt, Hamburg, Hannover, Munich, and Stuttgart.

Economic Development

Outside of transportation, communications, and certain utilities, the government has remained on the sidelines of entrepreneurship. It has at the same time upheld its role as social arbiter and economic adviser. Overall economic priorities are set by the federal and land governments pursuant to the 1967 Stability and Growth Act, which demands stability of prices, a high level of employment, steady growth, and equilibrium in foreign trade. In addition to the state, the independent German Federal Bank (Bundesbank), trade unions, and employers' associations bear responsibility for the nation's economic health.

SOCIAL WELFARE

The social security systems of the FRG and the GDR were combined as of 2 January 1992. Unified Germany's social insurance system provides for illness, workers' compensation, unemployment, and old-age insurance. Special pension funds provide restitution to Nazi-era victims for physical, emotional, and material damage suffered during World War II.

Children's allowances, established in 1955, are granted to all families. Women enjoy full legal equality with men. However, women tend to be concentrated in low-pay and low-status jobs and can have trouble obtaining training in traditionally male fields.

Healthcare

In 1993, health insurance in Germany was available to everyone. In 1992, there was 1 physician for every 356 people. The average life expectancy is 77 years.

Housing

Nearly 2.8 million of the country's 12 million dwellings were destroyed or made uninhabitable as a result of World War II. From 1949 to 1972, 12.8 million housing units were built. The reunited Germany had roughly 33.9 million dwellings in 1992.

Housing in the western states and that in the states of the former East Germany differs considerably. In western Germany, each individual has about 36 square meters of living space, significantly more than is found in the eastern states.

EDUCATION

Most German schools are state run. Each of the Länder (states), including the six new ones, is responsible for its own system. Attendance at all public schools and universities is free.

Children start school after their sixth birthday and are required to attend until they are 18 years of age. After four years of primary or elementary school (*Grundschule*), students choose from three types of secondary school: the *Gymnasium,* which prepares them for university admissions; the *Realschule,* which leads to technical job training and middle management employment; and the *Hauptschule,* or general school.

In 1993 there were 3.5 million pupils in primary schools, 7.8 million students in secondary schools, and 2.3 million pupils enrolled in vocational education. There were 1.9 million students enrolled at universities and other institutions of higher education.

1999 KEY EVENTS TIMELINE

January

- The German mark is replaced by the euro in some non-cash transactions, tying the German economy further into Europe.

- Germany begins a six-month presidency of the European Union.

- Albanian refugees from Kosovo flood German cities.

- Gerhard Schröder, German Chancellor, changes 1913 citizenship laws which used to be determined by blood, so that inhabitants for eight years or longer may apply.

- The Green Party gains power in Parliament.

February

- A fund is set up to aid Nazi victims, supported by German banks.

- The Greens lose the majority in the upper house of Parliament.

- Four Kurdish protesters are shot to death by Israeli guards in Berlin.

- One thousand Neo-Nazi's protest in Magdeburg against lax immigration laws.

March

- Oskar Lafontaine, blamed for a looming German recession, resigns as finance minister and chairman of the Social Democrat's Party (SPD).

- Gerhard Schröder names himself SPD chairman and replaces Oskar Lafontaine with Hans Eichel.

- The cabinet approves a proposal to give German-born foreigners citizenship.

- Bonn tax reform plans threaten investment from big industry, including utilities giant RWE and insurance company Allianz.

April

- The Reichstag's name is changed to the "Deutscher Bundestag-Plenarbereich Reichstagsgebäude" (German Federal Assembly-Plenary Area, Imperial Assembly Building).

- Parliament and the rest of the German government moves from Bonn back to Berlin, convening in the restored Reichstag, which also has a new glass bubble surrounding it.

May

- The Green Party votes against further NATO airstrikes against Serbia.

- The SPD and Green coalition argue on vital issues such as NATO bombing of Serbia and ecology taxes.

June

- The Social Democrats win elections in the city-state of Bremen.

- The biggest reform package in German history drastically cuts state spending and gives tax breaks to businesses.

- The German Parliament agrees to build a monument to Jewish victims of the Holocaust in central Berlin, which attracts some controversy.

- The resurrected German army debuts.

- Germany heads the Group of 7 annual meeting.

July

- Johannes Rau, the first Social Democratic President for 30 years, takes over as head of state.

August

- Germans decide to open shops on Sundays.

- Germany refuses to lift the ban on British beef, saying that United Kingdom export laws are not strict enough, and fearing the spread of Mad Cow's disease.

September

- A book by former Finance Minister Oskar Lafontaine slanders Gerhard Schröder's government, claiming that the leader broke election promises.

- The Social Democrat Party experiences unpopularity in elections despite Chancellor Gerhard Schröder's leadership because of a large budget deficit.

October

- Günter Grass, who wrote *The Tin Drum,* is awarded the Nobel Prize in literature.

- German officials ask the American Central Intelligence Agency to leave the country and scale back espionage operations.

- More than a hundred headstones are desecrated by Neo-Nazi's at the Weissenssee Jewish cemetery.

November

- Latin American countries lobby against the candidacy of Caio Koch-Weser, the German deputy finance minister, to succeed Michel Camdessus as managing director of the International Monetary Fund.

December

- Former German chancellor Helmut Kohl admits he used secret bank accounts to handle undeclared party contributions.

- NATO members accept an offer by France and Germany to restructure their joint military forces to enable them to assume the rotating headquarters of the peacekeeping force in Kosovo.

- German Chancellor Gerhard Schroder wins re-election as chairman of the Social Democratic Party.

- Officials from industry and government agree to establish a $5.1 billion fund to compensate those who were forced into slave labor during the Nazi era.

ANALYSIS OF EVENTS: 1999

BUSINESS AND THE ECONOMY

Although the German economy is strong, many companies failed to invest in the country this year because of high corporate taxes, an outdated educational system, and the high cost of employing German workers. The negative ramifications of a unified Germany have just begun to be felt in the western portion of the country, while the East has enjoyed a steady influx of investment from the West since the fall of the Berlin wall in 1989. In March, Oskar Lafontaine resigned as Finance Minister surrounded by allegations that he was causing a recession. Citizens argued that his economic plan penalized big business, driving investment away, and failed to help the common man. Later in the year, Chancellor Schröder and his policies suffered the same negative publicity, this time for an ever-increasing debt which threatened retirement benefits. It is simply a fact that reunification with the former East Germany has drained Germany's resources, leaving an 11 percent unemployment rate, and an extremely high tax burden for both businesses and workers. Nevertheless, the long-term benefits of an emerging free market after decades of communist occupation promise to make the slow start worthwhile.

Investment in the European Union, highest among all European countries, also takes a big chunk out of the German budget. Farm subsidy programs, development aid and other European government services demand a high price from Germany, but these programs help support people in the underdeveloped areas of the East. In this leadership role, Germany has the clout to determine how and where its money is spent through the EU, which also increases its political power. As the main proponent of the Euro, Germany has put much expense into forging the success of the currency, but the nation itself has suffered some losses as a result. The Deutsche Mark is completely intertwined with the Euro, and that currency, as an experiment in regional integration, still has to gain the confidence of foreign investors. The conservative nature, though, of German banks has given some weight to the value of the Euro, which fluctuates around traditional European rates.

GOVERNMENT AND POLITICS

Germany's position in Europe dominated the politics and economies of the region in 1999, putting added stress on a land already divided by geographical and cultural disparities. The six-month presidency of the EU, leadership of the Western European Union (WEU) and chair of the Group of Seven annual meeting in June, gave Germany's national politics an international flavor that reflected the country's lingering fears of purely national power wielded so blatantly during World War II. Despite reparations and memorials made to Holocaust victims, Neo-Nazi protests against lax immigration laws and Jewish grave desecrations caused unrest. Partly as a result of the cultural embarrassment stemming from the Holocaust, Chancellor Gerhard Schröder pushed through policies changing citizenship laws to help integrate the many Turkish "guest-workers" in Germany. No doubt, the political advantages of creating thousands of new, voting citizens sympathetic to his cause were not lost on Mr. Schröder and his party. Albanian refugees put a further strain on the population, flooding Germany's cities from the war in Kosovo, which some citizens saw as a way to make reparations for previous abuses of minorities.

The powerful Social Democrat-Green coalition led by the SPD's Gerhard Schröder and the Green's Foreign Minister Joschka Fischer disagreed over NATO airstrikes in Kosovo and environmental taxation, but for the most part the parties agreed on environmental issues. It was a question of degree, of balancing the interests of industry and nature so that Germans and their environment could coexist. The closing of nuclear power plants was a favorite issue for the Green Party to champion this year, but these power plants provided the majority of Germany's, and for that matter Europe's, power supply, eliciting opposition from the SPD. Although the SPD-Green coalition experienced some strife, there was also a healthy competition. This kind of issue-based politics would not have been seen in Germany before reunification, and certainly not during foreign occupation. In September, the triumphant final move of Parliament back to Berlin was tinged with symbolic significance, putting a cap on the Cold War. The debut of the new German army and indignation at Central Intelligence Agency intelligence activities in Germany also signaled a break with the country's former occupation.

CULTURE AND SOCIETY

German society is trying desperately to get beyond the atrocities of World War II, and now that the population of veterans is shrinking rapidly, this is becoming more possible. Still, the author Günter Grass won the Nobel Prize for literature for his book "The Tin Drum" which dealt with the responsibility for the Holocaust, while in some ways asking the world community for permission to move on culturally. New immigration laws go part of the way towards accepting non Germanic cultures into the society, but Turkish immigrants are still expected to give up their roots and Muslim religion in order to assimilate, and they are still widely discriminated against by employers. The Neo-Nazi movement is actually smaller than news reports may claim, but sensitivity to anything resembling Nazi activity causes some overreactions, including the negative response to the resurrected German army.

Although it is only supposed to be used under the auspices of the WEU and NATO, neighboring countries feel threatened by the antagonistic move. This is understandable considering the history of two World Wars on German soil. Germany is not only rebuilding its cities, but its culture as well. Despite the feeling from many groups that a monument to Holocaust victims could never express the reality of those horrors, the nation must recover and take its place in Europe as a cultural, economic and political giant, as it already has through participation in the European Union. Some politicians would say under their breath that the European rule from Berlin this year was the start of a new German empire. Ironically, the creation of this European identity is vital to the full acceptance of Germany's recovery from World War II, and the acknowledgment of European interdependence.

DIRECTORY

CENTRAL GOVERNMENT
Head of State

President
Roman Herzog, Office of the President

Chancellor
Gerhard Schröeder, Chancellor's Office

Ministers

Minister of Agriculture
Karl-Heinze Funke, Ministry of Agriculture

Minister of Defense
Rudolf Scharping, Ministry of Defense

Minister of Economic Cooperation
Heidemarie Wieczorek-Zeul, Ministry of
Economic Cooperation

Minister of Economics
Werner Muller, Ministry of Economics

Minister of Education, Science and Research
Edelgard Bulmahn, Ministry of Education,
Science, and Research, Heinemannstr. 2, Bad
Godesberg, 53175 Bonn, Germany
FAX: +49 573601
E-MAIL: information@bmbf.bund400.de

Minister of the Environment
Juergen Trittin, Ministry of the Environment,
Referat Öffentlichkeitsarbeit, Alexanderplatz 6,
D-10178 Berlin
FAX: +49 (01888) 3054375
E-MAIL: oea-1000@bmu.de

Minister of Families
Christine Bergmann, Ministry of Families

Minister of Finance
Werner Muller, Ministry of Finance

Minister of Foreign Affairs
Joschka Fischer, Ministry of Foreign Affairs

Minister of Health
Andrea Fischer, Ministry of Health

Minister of the Interior
Otto Schily, Ministry of the Interior

Minister of Justice
Herta Daeubler-Gmelin, Ministry of Justice

Minister of Labor and Social Affairs
Walter Riester, Ministry of Labor and Social
Affairs

Minister of Overseas Development
Heidemarie Wieczorek-Zeul, Ministry of
Overseas Development

Minister of Transport and Construction
Franz Muentefering, Ministry of Transport and
Construction, P.O. Box 10 01 50, D-51401
Bergisch Gladbach, Germany
FAX: +49 (22) 0443673
E-MAIL: info@bast.de

POLITICAL ORGANIZATIONS

Bündnis 90 (Alliance '90)

Bundesgeschäftsstelle, Platz vor dem Neuen Tor
1, D-10115 Berlin, Germany
PHONE: +49 (030) 28442110
E-MAIL: info@gruene.de
NAME: Christa Nickels

Christlich-Demokratische Union-CDU (Christian Democratic Union)

TITLE: Chairman
NAME: Helmut Kohl

Christlich Soziale Union in Bayern-CSU (Christian Social Union)

Franz Josef Bunch House, Nymphenburger Str
64, D-80335 Munich, Germany
PHONE: +49 (089) 1243204
FAX: +49 (089) 1243258
E-MAIL: Landesleitung@csu bayern.de
TITLE: Chairman
NAME: Theo Waigel

Freie Demokratische Partei-FDP (Free Democratic Party)

FDP Bayern, Agnestrase 47, D-80798 München,
Germany
PHONE: +49 (089) 1260960
E-MAIL: mail@fdp-bayern.de
TITLE: Chairman
NAME: Wolfgang Gerhardt

Partei des Demokratischen Sozialismus-PDS (Party of Democratic Socialism)

Parteivorstand der PDS, Kleine Alexanderstraße
28, D-10178 Berlin, Germany
E-MAIL: parteivorstand@pds-online.de
TITLE: Chairman
NAME: Lothar Bisky

Sozialdemokratische Partei Deutschlands-SPD (Social Democratic Party)

SPD Party Headquarter, Ollenhauerstrase 1, D-
53113 Bonn, Germany
FAX: +49 (228) 532410
E-MAIL: parteivorstand@spd.de
TITLE: Chairman
NAME: Oskar La Fontaine

CDU-CSU Coalition

DIPLOMATIC REPRESENTATION

Embassies in Germany

Argentina
All 50-52, D-53113 Bonn, Germany
PHONE: +49 (0228) 228010
FAX: +49 (0228) 2280130

Australia
Friedrichstrasse 200, D-10117 Berlin, Germany
PHONE: +49 (030) 8800880
E-MAIL: presse@australian-embassy.bn.uunet.de

Belgium
Rheinweg 31, D-53113 Bonn, Germany
PHONE: +49 (228) 213903
FAX: +49 (228) 214757
E-MAIL: jlekeu@metronet.de

Canada
Friedrichstraße 95, D-10117 Berlin, Germany
PHONE: +49 (30) 203120

Denmark
Rauchstraße 1, D-10787 Berlin, Germany
PHONE: +49 (030) 50502000
FAX: +49 (030) 50502050
E-MAIL: berlin@daenemark.org

Finland
Rauchstraße 1, D-10787 Berlin, Germany
PHONE: +49 (030) 505030
FAX: +49 (030) 505033

Greece
Consulate of Greece, Wittenbergplatz 3A, D-10789 Berlin, Germany
PHONE: +49 (030) 2137033
FAX: +49 (030) 2182663
E-MAIL: grconsul@aol.com

Iceland
Rauchstrasse 1, D-10787 Berlin, Germany
PHONE: +49 (030) 50504000
FAX: +49 (030) 50504300

India
Adenauerallee 262-264, D-53113 Bonn, Germany
PHONE: +49 (228) 5405109
FAX: +49 (228) 5405154
E-MAIL: hoc@indembassy.bn.shuttle.de

Indonesia
Dottendorferstr. 86, D-53129 Bonn, Germany
PHONE: +49 (228) 230120
FAX: +49 (228) 236131
E-MAIL: Bidikbud@aol.com

Israel
Schinkelstrasse 10, D-14193 Berlin, Germany
PHONE: +49 (030) 8932203
FAX: +49 (030) 8928908

Italy
Hildebrandtstr. 1, D-10785 Berlin, Germany
PHONE: +49 (030) 2699410
FAX: +49 (030) 26994126

Japan
Kleiststr. 23-26, D-10787 Berlin, Germany
PHONE: +49 (030) 210940
E-MAIL: info@embjapan.de

Madagascar
Rolandstr. 48, D-53179 Bonn, Germany
PHONE: +49 (228) 953590
FAX: +49 (228) 334628

Mexico
Kurfürstendamm 72, D-10709 Berlín, Germany
PHONE: +49 (030) 3277110
FAX: +49 (030) 3277121
E-MAIL: ofber@aol.com

Norway
Rauchstr. 1, D-10787 Berlin, Germany
PHONE: +49 (030) 505050
FAX: +49 (030) 505055

Paraguay
Linprunstraße 2 Ecke Sandstraße, D-80335 München, Germany
PHONE: +49 (089) 5231112
FAX: +49 (089) 524635
E-MAIL: paraguay@i-dial.de

Poland
Leyboldstr. 74, D-50968 Koln, Germany
PHONE: +49 (0221) 937300
FAX: +49 (0221) 385074

Russia
Waldstrasse 42, D-53177 Bonn, Germany
PHONE: +49 (0228) 312083; 312089; 312575

Sudan
Koblenzer Strasse 107, D-53177 Bonn, Germany
PHONE: +49 (0228) 933700
FAX: +49 (0228) 335123
E-MAIL: Sudan-Embassy.Bonn@t-online.de

Tanzania
Theaterplatz 26, D-53177 Bonn, Germany
E-MAIL: info@tanzania-gov.de

Thailand
Lepsiusstrasse 64/66, D-12163 Berlin, Germany
PHONE: +49 (30) 7912266; 7912268

FAX: +49 (30) 7912229
E-MAIL: thaiber@berlin.snafu.de

United Kingdom

Unter den Linden 32/34, D-10117 Berlin,
Germany
PHONE: +49 (030) 201840

United States

Neustädtische Kirchstr. 4-5, D-10117 Berlin,
Germany
PHONE: +49(030) 8329233

Uzbekistan

PHONE: +49 (228) 953570
FAX: +49 (228) 9535799
E-MAIL: botschaft@uzbekistan.de

JUDICIAL SYSTEM

Federal Constitutional Court

Federal High Court, D-76125 Karlsruhe,
Germany
FAX: +49 (721) 159830

Federal Court of Justice
Federal Administrative Court
Federal Finance Court
Federal Labor Court
Federal Social Court

FURTHER READING

Government Publications

*The Educational System in Germany: Case Study
Findings.* Washington, D.C.: National Institute
on Student Achievement, Curriculum and
Assessment, Office of Educational Research
and Assessment, U.S. Department of
Education, 1999.

The Week in Germany. Weekly newsletter by the
German Foreign Ministry and the Federal
Press and Information Office. New York, NY:
German Information Center, 1999.

Sources of Statistical Information

Country Finance: Germany. New York, NY:
The Economic Intelligence Unit (EIU), 1999.

Articles

"The Berlin Republic." *The Economist*
(February 6, 1999): A Survey of Germany,
insert.

"Berlin's Blues." *The Economist* (April 3,
1999): 58.

"The Climb-Back of Schröder." *The Economist*
(April 10, 1999): 47–48.

"Germany Comes out of its Post-War Shell."
The Economist (July 10, 1999): 43.

"Germany's Awkwardly Historic Town." *The
Economist* (September 4, 1999): 52.

"Germany's Other Captain Walks." *The
Economist* (March 20, 1999): 53–54.

"Germany's Reform Battle." *The Economist*
(September 18, 1999): 53–55.

"Germany's Struggle in Europe." *The
Economist* (March 6, 1999): 47–48.

"Hans Eichel, Stodgy but Safe." *The Economist*
(March 20, 1999): 58.

"The Home Front." *The Economist* (May 8,
1999): 54.

"Ode to Bremen." *The Economist* (June 12,
1999): 48.

"Rivalry on the Right." *The Economist* (May 1,
1999): 49.

"The Sick Man of the Euro." *The Economist*
(June 5, 1999): 21–23.

"To the Polls." *The Economist* (May 22, 1999):
57.

"Towards the New Middle, At Last." *The
Economist* (June 26, 1999): 59–60.

"What's in a Name." *The Economist* (April 17,
1999): 55.

Books

Bynner, John and Rainer K. Silbereisen, eds.
*Adversity and Challenge in Life in the New
Germany and in England.* New York: St.
Martin's Press, 1999.

*The Heads of Government of the 16 Constituent
States in Germany.* Bonn, Germany: Inter
Nations Press, 1999.

Lippert, Barbara. *Britain, Germany, and EU
Enlargement: Partners or Competitors?.* New
York: Pinter, 1999.

Max-Stephan, Schulze, ed. *Western Europe:
Economic and Social Change Since 1945.*
New York: Longman, 1999.

Merkl, Peter H. *The Federal Republic of
Germany at Fifty: The End of a Century of
Turmoil.* New York: NYU Press, 1999.

GERMANY: STATISTICAL DATA

For sources and notes see "Sources of Statistics" in the front of each volume.

GEOGRAPHY

Geography (1)

Area:

Total: 356,910 sq km.

Land: 349,520 sq km.

Water: 7,390 sq km.

Note: includes the formerly separate Federal Republic of Germany, the German Democratic Republic, and Berlin, following formal unification on 3 October 1990.

Area—comparative: slightly smaller than Montana.

Land boundaries:

Total: 3,621 km.

Border countries: Austria 784 km, Belgium 167 km, Czech Republic 646 km, Denmark 68 km, France 451 km, Luxembourg 138 km, Netherlands 577 km, Poland 456 km, Switzerland 334 km.

Coastline: 2,389 km.

Climate: temperate and marine; cool, cloudy, wet winters and summers; occasional warm, tropical foehn wind; high relative humidity.

Terrain: lowlands in north, uplands in center, Bavarian Alps in south.

Natural resources: iron ore, coal, potash, timber, lignite, uranium, copper, natural gas, salt, nickel.

Land use:

Arable land: 33%

Permanent crops: 1%

Permanent pastures: 15%

Forests and woodland: 31%

Other: 20% (1993 est.).

HUMAN FACTORS

Demographics (2A)

	1990	1995	1998	2000	2010	2020	2030	2040	2050
Population	79,357.3	81,859.6	82,079.5	82,081.4	81,012.1	77,847.9	72,375.1	65,402.3	57,428.5
Net migration rate (per 1,000 population)	NA	NA	NA	NA	NA	NA	NA	NA	NA
Births	NA	NA	NA	NA	NA	NA	NA	NA	NA
Deaths	713.3	NA	NA	NA	NA	NA	NA	NA	NA
Life expectancy - males	72.0	73.3	73.8	74.2	75.8	77.2	78.2	79.1	79.7
Life expectancy - females	78.5	79.8	80.3	80.7	82.1	83.4	84.3	85.1	85.7
Birth rate (per 1,000)	11.4	9.4	8.8	8.5	7.3	7.0	6.0	5.6	5.6
Death rate (per 1,000)	11.6	10.9	10.8	10.8	11.7	13.1	14.8	17.2	19.7
Women of reproductive age (15-49 yrs.)	19,398.8	19,541.5	19,711.8	19,568.3	18,404.1	15,182.9	13,329.7	11,195.8	9,293.2
of which are currently married	NA	NA	NA	NA	NA	NA	NA	NA	NA
Fertility rate	1.5	1.2	1.2	1.3	1.3	1.3	1.3	1.3	1.3

Except as noted, values for vital statistics are in thousands; life expectancy is in years.

Health Personnel (3)

Total health expenditure as a percentage of GDP, 1990-1997[a]

Public sector 8.1

Private sector 2.4

Total[b] 10.4

Health expenditure per capita in U.S. dollars, 1990-1997[a]

Purchasing power parity 2,235

Total 2,677

Availability of health care facilities per 100,000 people

Hospital beds 1990-1997[a] 970

Doctors 1993[c] 319

Nurses 1993[c] . . . . .NA

Health Indicators (4)

Life expectancy at birth

1980 73

1997 77

Daily per capita supply of calories (1996) 3,330

Total fertility rate births per woman (1997) 1.4

Maternal mortality ratio per 100,000 live births (1990-97) . . . . .22[c]

Safe water % of population with access (1995) . . . .

Sanitation % of population with access (1995) . . . .

Consumption of iodized salt % of households (1992-98)[a] . . . .

Smoking prevalence

Male % of adults (1985-95)[a] 37

Female % of adults (1985-95)[a] 22

Tuberculosis incidence per 100,000 people (1997) 15

Adult HIV prevalence % of population ages 15-49 (1997) 0.08

Infants and Malnutrition (5)

Under-5 mortality rate (1997) 5

% of infants with low birthweight (1990-97) . . . . . .NA

Births attended by skilled health staff % of total[a] . . .NA

% fully immunized (1995-97)

TB . . . . .NA

DPT 45

Polio 80

Measles 75

Prevalence of child malnutrition under age 5 (1992-97)[b] . . . . .NA

Ethnic Division (6)

German 91.5%

Turkish 2.4%

Italians 0.7%

Greeks 0.4%

Poles 0.4%

Other 4.6%

Other is made up largely of people fleeing the war in the former Yugoslavia.

Religions (7)

Protestant 38%

Roman Catholic 34%

Muslim 1.7%

Unaffiliated or other 26.3%

Languages (8)

German.

EDUCATION

Public Education Expenditures (9)

Public expenditure on education (% of GNP)

1980 . . . .

1996 . . . . .4.8[1]

Expenditure per student

Primary % of GNP per capita

1980 . . . .

1996 . . . .

Secondary % of GNP per capita

1980 . . . .

1996 . . . . .30.7[1]

Tertiary % of GNP per capita

1980 . . . .

1996 . . . . .37.3[1]

Expenditure on teaching materials

Primary % of total for level (1996) . . . .

Secondary % of total for level (1996) . . . .

Primary pupil-teacher ratio per teacher (1996) . . . . .17[1]

Duration of primary education years (1995) 4

Educational Attainment (10)

Age group (1981)[25] . . . . .25+

Total population .10,714,841

Highest level attained (%)

No schooling . . . .-

First level

Not completed 30.1

Completed . . . . .NA

Entered second level

S-1 . . . . .52.6

S-2 . . . . .NA

Postsecondary 17.3

GOVERNMENT & LAW

Political Parties (12)

Federal Assembly (Bundestag)	% of seats
Christian Democratic Union (CDU)	.34.2
Social Democratic Party (SPD)	.36.4
Alliance 90/Greens	.7.3
Christian Social Union (CSU)	.7.3
Free Democratic Party (FDP)	.6.9
Party of Democratic Socialism (PDS)	.4.4
Republicans	.1.9

Crime (15)

Crime rate (for 1997)

Crimes reported 6,586,200

Total persons convicted 3,335,200

Crimes per 100,000 population 8,050

Persons responsible for offenses

Total number of suspects 2,273,600

Total number of female suspects 518,600

Total number of juvenile suspects 292,600

Government Budget (13B)

Revenues . . . .$755 billion

Expenditures . . . .$832.1 billion

Capital expenditures . . . . .NA

Data for 1995. NA stands for not available.

Military Affairs (14B)

	1990	1991[4]	1992	1993	1994	1995
Military expenditures						
Current dollars (mil.)	48,540	46,590	45,800	42,750	41,020	41,160
1995 constant dollars (mil.)	55,790	51,480	49,260	44,820	42,050	41,160
Armed forces (000)	545	457	442	398	362	352
Gross national product (GNP)						
Current dollars (bil.)	1,738,000	1,895,000	1,971,000	1,975,000	2,079,000	2,172,000
1995 constant dollars (bil.)	1,998,000	2,095,000	2,120,000	2,071,000	2,131,000	2,172,000
Central government expenditures (CGE)						
1995 constant dollars (mil.)	592,300	685,100	780,200	783,400	812,700	820,900
People (mil.)	79.4	80.1	80.7	81.5	82.3	82.9
Military expenditure as % of GNP	2.8	2.5	2.3	2.2	2.0	1.9
Military expenditure as % of CGE	9.4	7.5	6.3	5.7	5.2	5.0
Military expenditure per capita (1995 $)	703	643	610	550	511	496
Armed forces per 1,000 people (soldiers)	6.9	5.7	5.5	4.9	4.4	4.2
GNP per capita (1995 $)	25,170	26,140	26,260	25,400	25,890	46,190
Arms imports[6]						
Current dollars (mil.)	900	800	1,000	650	300	310
1995 constant dollars (mil.)	1,034	884	1,076	681	308	310
Arms exports[6]						
Current dollars (mil.)	1,700	2,400	1,000	1,700	1,400	1,200
1995 constant dollars (mil.)	1,954	2,652	1,076	1,782	1,435	1,200
Total imports[7]						
Current dollars (mil.)	346,200	389,900	402,400	346,000	385,400	444,500
1995 constant dollars (mil.)	397,800	430,900	432,900	362,800	395,000	444,500
Total exports[7]						
Current dollars (mil.)	410,100	402,800	422,300	382,500	429,700	508,300
1995 constant dollars (mil.)	471,300	445,100	454,200	401,000	440,500	508,300
Arms as percent of total imports[8]	.3	.2	.2	.2	.1	.1
Arms as percent of total exports[8]	.4	.6	.2	.4	.3	.2

LABOR FORCE

Labor Force (16)

Total (million) 38.7

Industry 41%

Agriculture 3%

Services 56%

Data for 1995.

Unemployment Rate (17)

12% (1997 est.)

PRODUCTION SECTOR

Electric Energy (18)

Capacity . . . . .109.727 million kW (1995)

Production . . . . .495.875 billion kWh (1995)

Consumption per capita . . . . . . .6,154 kWh (1995 est.)

Transportation (19)

Highways:

total: 633,000 km

paved: 627,303 km (including 11,300 km of expressways)

unpaved: 5,697 km all-weather (1996 est.)

Waterways: western—5,222 km, of which almost 70% are usable by craft of 1,000-metric-ton capacity or larger; major rivers include the Rhine and Elbe; Kiel Canal is an important connection between the Baltic Sea and North Sea; eastern—2,319 km (1988)

Pipelines: crude oil 3,644 km; petroleum products 3,946 km; natural gas 97,564 km (1988)

Merchant marine:

total: 515 ships (1,000 GRT or over) totaling 6,448,105 GRT/7,940,824 DWT ships by type: cargo 202, chemical tanker 10, combination bulk 2, container 253, liquefied gas tanker 6, multifunction large-load carrier 6, oil tanker 9, passenger 4, railcar carrier 2, refrigerated cargo 2, roll-on/roll-off cargo 12, short-sea passenger 7 note: includes ships from the former East Germany and West Germany; Germany owns 460 additional ships (1,000 GRT or over) that operate under the registries of Antigua and Barbuda, The Bahamas, Cyprus, Hong Kong, Liberia, Malta, Norway, Netherlands Antilles, Panama, Marshall Islands, Singapore, and Saint Vincent and the Grenadines (1997 est.)

Airports: 620 (1997 est.)

Airports—with paved runways:

total: 321

over 3,047 m: 14

2,438 to 3,047 m: 61

1,524 to 2,437 m: 70

914 to 1,523 m: 53

under 914 m: 123 (1997 est.)

Airports—with unpaved runways:

total: 299

over 3,047 m: 2

2,438 to 3,047 m: 6

1,524 to 2,437 m: 6

914 to 1,523 m: 57

under 914 m: 228 (1997 est.)

Top Agricultural Products (20)

Western: potatoes, wheat, barley, sugar beets, fruit, cabbage; cattle, pigs, poultry; eastern: wheat, rye, barley, potatoes, sugar beets, fruit; pork, beef, chicken, milk, hides.

MANUFACTURING SECTOR

GDP & Manufacturing Summary (21)

Detailed value added figures are listed by both International Standard Industry Code (ISIC) and product title.

	1980	1985	1990	1994
GDP[3] ($-1990 mil.)	1,217,500	1,284,926	1,501,516	1,593,771
Per capita ($-1990)	19,775	21,056	23,747	23,987
Manufacturing share (%) (current prices)	33.6	32.6	31.6	27.7
Manufacturing				
Value added ($-1990 mil.)	402,545	415,035	458,965	439,420
Industrial production index	100	105	125	119
Value added ($ mil.)	265,588	223,253	535,541	583,065
Gross output ($ mil.)	632,161	489,414	1,098,621	1,210,439
Employment (000)	7,229	6,616	7,120	6,768
Profitability (% of gross output)				
Intermediate input (%)	58	54	51	52[1]

GDP & Manufacturing Summary (21)

	1980	1985	1990	1994
Wages and salaries inc. supplements (%)	26	24	25	26
Gross operating surplus	16	22	24	22
Productivity ($)				
Gross output per worker	87,448	73,973	154,301	176,114
Value added per worker	36,739	33,744	75,216	88,680
Average wage (inc. supplements)	22,606	17,563	38,487	46,740
Value added ($ mil.)				
311/2 Food products	18,570	10,830	28,590	35,360
313 Beverages	6,452	5,047	11,911	14,056
314 Tobacco products	6,909	5,720	12,633	13,760
321 Textiles	6,964	5,526	11,849	10,950
322 Wearing apparel	4,934	2,803	5,887	5,550
323 Leather and fur products	935	501	944	844
324 Footwear	1,205	726	1,152	1,225
331 Wood and wood products	4,485	2,431	6,179	8,447
332 Furniture and fixtures	5,548	3,084	7,885	9,923
341 Paper and paper products	5,099	5,221	13,490	14,675
342 Printing and publishing	6,150	4,139	10,255	11,708
351 Industrial chemicals	13,944	16,570	35,537	33,831
352 Other chemical products	8,003	11,597	27,942	35,768
353 Petroleum refineries	14,637	9,580	19,130	25,759
354 Miscellaneous petroleum and coal products	990	546	528	453
355 Rubber products	3,201	2,880	6,414	6,587
356 Plastic products	6,095	5,638	17,313	20,615
361 Pottery china and earthenware	1,304	671	1,555	1,446
362 Glass and glass products	2,492	1,917	4,791	5,164
369 Other non-metal mineral products	7,937	4,876	12,031	16,171
371 Iron and steel	18,872	9,538	19,205	13,254
372 Non-ferrous metals	2,508	3,412	7,733	7,505
381 Metal products	14,455	14,162	39,181	43,835
382 Non-electrical machinery	34,263	33,812	82,544	79,701
383 Electrical machinery	30,501	28,329	72,567	81,957
384 Transport equipment	31,232	29,078	67,434	72,597
385 Professional and scientific equipment	6,205	3,446	8,011	8,950
390 Other manufacturing industries	1,700	1,175	2,849	2,934

FINANCE, ECONOMICS, & TRADE

Economic Indicators (22)

National product: GDP—purchasing power parity—$1.74 trillion (western $1.60 trillion; eastern: $144 billion) (1997 est.)

National product real growth rate: 2.4% (western 2.5%, eastern 1.7%) (1997 est.)

National product per capita: $20,800 (western: $23,600; eastern: $9,100) (1997 est.)

Inflation rate—consumer price index: 1.8% (1997)

Balance of Payments (23)

	1992	1993	1994	1995	1996
Exports of goods (f.o.b.)	430,480	382,680	430,580	523,600	519,440
Imports of goods (f.o.b.)	−402,280	−341,490	−379,650	−458,520	−448,220
Trade balance	28,200	41,190	50,930	65,080	71,210
Services - debits	−162,150	−161,610	−167,300	−213,340	−209,330
Services - credits	149,220	141,590	134,040	165,770	161,440
Private transfers (net)	−25,130	−25,860	−28,800	−29,560	−24,950
Government transfers (net)	−9,530	−9,430	−10,100	−11,490	−11,450
Overall balance	−19,400	−14,120	−21,230	−23,530	−13,080

Exchange Rates (24)

Exchange rates:

Deutsche marks (DM) per US$1

January 1998	.1.8167
1997	.1.7341
1996	.1.5048
1995	.1.4331
1994	.1.6228
1993	.1.6533

Top Import Origins (25)

$455.7 billion (f.o.b., 1996) Data are for 1995.

Origins	%
European Union	.55.5
France	.10.8
Netherlands	.8.6
Italy	.8.4
Belgium-Luxembourg	.6.6
United Kingdom	.6.4
Austria	.3.9
Eastern Europe	.8.7
Other W. Europe	.7.2
United States	.6.8
Japan	.5.3
NICs	.5.3
China	.2.4
OPEC	.1.7
other	.7.1

Top Export Destinations (26)

$521.1 billion (f.o.b., 1996) Data are for 1996 est.

Destinations	%
European Union	.57.7
France	.11.7
United Kingdom	.8.1
Italy	.7.6
Netherlands	.7.5
Belgium-Luxembourg	.6.5
Austria	.5.5
Eastern Europe	.8.0
Other Western Europe	.7.5
United States	.7.3
NICs	.5.6
Japan	.2.5
OPEC	.2.2
China	.1.4

Economic Aid (27)

Donor: ODA, $9 billion (1996 est.).

Import Export Commodities (28)

Import Commodities	Export Commodities
Manufactures 74.2% 9.9%	Manufactures 88.2%
Fuels 6.4%	Agricultural products 5.0%
Raw materials 5.9%	Raw materials 2.3%
Other 3.6%	Fuels 1.0%

GHANA

Republic of Ghana

INTRODUCTORY SURVEY

RECENT HISTORY

On 6 March 1957, the Gold Coast, including Ashanti, the Northern Territories Protectorate, and the Trust Territory of British Togoland, attained full independent membership in the Commonwealth of Nations under the name of Ghana. The nation became a republic on 1 July 1960.

During the period 1960–65, Ghana's first president, Kwame Nkrumah, steadily gained control over all aspects of Ghana's economic, political, cultural, and military affairs. A referendum in January 1964 established a one-party state and empowered the president to dismiss Supreme Court and High Court judges. In February 1966, Nkrumah was overthrown. A military government calling itself the National Liberation Council (NLC) established rule by decree, dismissing the civilian government and suspending the constitution. A three-year ban on political activities was lifted 1 May 1969, but Ghana's worsening economic condition resulted in another military takeover in January 1972 led by Lieutenant Colonel Ignatius Kutu Acheampong, who formed the National Redemption Council (NRC). Unlike the military rulers who came to power in 1966, however, the NRC made no plans for a rapid return to civilian rule.

The NRC was restructured as the Supreme Military Council in 1976. Two more military takeovers occurred in 1978 and 1979, the second led by a young flight lieutenant, Jerry Rawlings. The new government handed over power to civilians on 24

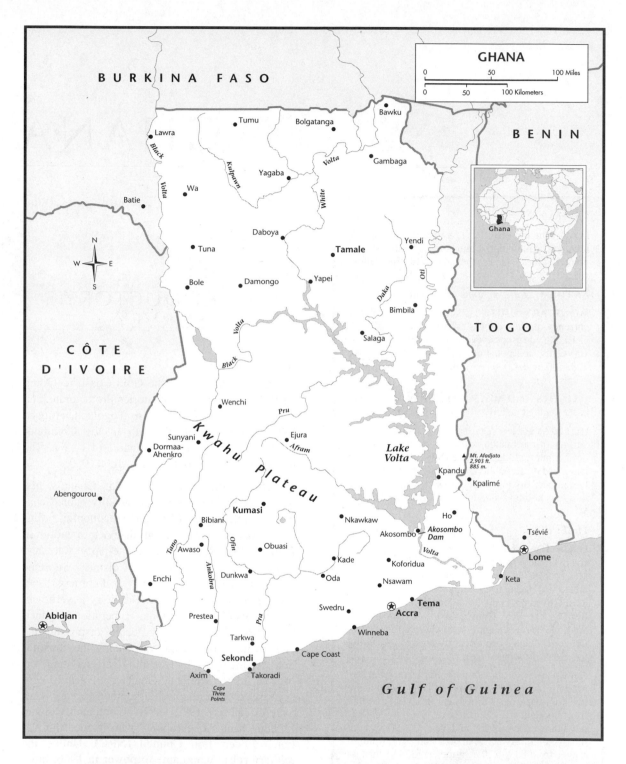

September 1979, following nationwide elections. The Nkrumah-style People's National Party (PNP) won 71 of 140 parliamentary seats in the balloting, and PNP candidate Hilla Limann was elected president. However, Ghana's economic condition deteriorated, and on 31 December 1981 a new takeover led by Rawlings overthrew the civilian regime. The constitution was suspended, all political parties were banned, and about 100 business leaders and government officials were arrested. Rawlings became chairman of the ruling Provisional National Defense Council. In the following twenty-seven months, there were at least five more real or alleged takeover attempts.

A new constitution was approved by referendum on 28 April 1992, and Rawlings was elected in a sharply contested multiparty election on 3 November 1993. On 4 January 1993, the Fourth Republic was proclaimed, and Rawlings was inaugurated as president. Opposition parties, assembled as the Inter-Party Coordinating Committee (ICC), issued a joint statement announcing their acceptance of the "present institutional arrangements" on 7 January, yet still refused to accept the election results.

Legislative elections were again held in 1996. By maintaining power throughout his elected term (1992–96), the Rawlings administration became the first Ghanaian government to serve a full term without being overthrown. Rawlings was reelected to a second four-year term in late 1996.

GOVERNMENT

A Consultative Assembly, convened late in 1991 to draw up a new constitution, completed its work in March 1992. In April 1992, the constitution was approved by 92.5% of voters in a low turnout (58% of those eligible). It provides for a presidential system and a legislature (National Assembly) of 200 members. The Cabinet has over ninety officials of ministerial rank, a major contribution to popular unhappiness with government. The 1996 democratic elections were proclaimed as being fair by international observers.

Judiciary

The 1993 Constitution established an independent judiciary and a number of institutions such as the Commission for Human Rights to investigate and take actions to remedy alleged violations of human rights. The new court system consists of two levels: superior courts and lower courts. The superior courts include the Supreme Court, the Appeals Court, the High Court, and regional tribunals. Parliament has the authority to create a system of lower courts.

Political Parties

With the adoption of a new constitution in April 1992, the long-standing ban on political activity was lifted. The parties that emerged could be grouped into three clusters. The center-right group formed the New Patriotic Party (NPP) and chose Adu Boaheu as their presidential candidate. The center-left group was Nkrumahists. Ideological and leadership differences kept them divided into five separate parties, of which the People's National Convention was best organized. PNDC supporters comprised the third grouping. They favored continuity and, after forming the National Democratic Congress (NDC), were able to draft Rawlings as their candidate. In the parliamentary elections of December 1996, the ruling NDC maintained its majority but fell from 190 to 133 seats out of a possible 200.

DEFENSE

In 1995, Ghana's defense forces consisted of units of the army (5,000), navy (1,000), and air force (1,000) as well as a presidential guard of 500 men and the People's Militia (5,000 part-time police).

ECONOMIC AFFAIRS

Ghana's economic history is one of the most interesting of the post-independence period. In a modern-day riches-to-rags story, the cocoa wealth of 1958 gave way to the food crisis of 1983 before Ghanaian leaders turned to the International Monetary Fund (IMF) for advice and financial relief. Since 1983, the economy has made measured progress toward recovery.

Ghana's economy is led by the agricultural sector, which employs two-thirds of the labor force. Cocoa is the dominant export crop. Ghana has significant deposits of gold. In 1992, earnings from gold exports exceeded those of cocoa for the first time.

Public Finance

Ghana turned to the IMF as the economy approached bankruptcy in 1983. The IMF-sponsored stabilization program, known as the ERP (Economic Recovery Program), has been pursued vigorously through its several phases, and borrowing from the IMF came to an end in 1992.

Ghana's budgets have habitually been in deficit, financed mainly through the domestic banking system, with consequent rapid increases in the money supply and the rate of inflation.

The CIA estimates that, in 1993, government revenues totaled approximately $1.05 billion and expenditures $1.2 billion. External debt totaled $4.6 billion.

Income

In 1998, Ghana's gross national product (GNP) was $7.2 billion at current prices, or $390 per person. For the period 1985–95, the average inflation rate was 28.4%, resulting in a real growth rate in GNP of 1.5% per person.

Industry

Industry represents only about 16% of the domestic economy. The Tema industrial estate includes the Tema Food Complex, made up of a fish cannery, flour and feed mills, a tin can factory, and other facilities. The aluminum smelter at Tema is owned by Kaiser Aluminum and is Ghana's largest manufacturing enterprise.

Banking and Finance

The Bank of Ghana, established in 1957, is the central bank. Commercial banking services are rendered mainly by the government-owned Commercial Bank of Ghana; the government-owned Agricultural Development Bank, which is concerned with agricultural credit and cooperatives; and two British banks, Barclays Bank of Ghana Ltd. and the Standard Chartered Bank of Ghana Africa Ltd.

Following a survey by the IDA, a National Investment Bank was established in 1963 to finance capital investment in private and state-owned industries and corporations.

A stock exchange was opened in Accra in 1987. By 1994, the tiny exchange was up nearly 300%.

Economic Development

Recent economic policy has aimed at correcting basic problems in every phase of the economy. The country relies heavily on financial assistance from international lenders, including the World Bank and the IMF.

The government's recently launched Vision 2020 plan aims at making Ghana a middle-income country through free-market reforms over the course of the next twenty-five years.

SOCIAL WELFARE

The Social Security and National Insurance Trust, established in 1972, covers wage employees. The secretariat of Mobilization and Productivity and the secretariat of Local Government and Rural Development deal with both urban and rural problems, including literacy, child welfare, and occupational safety. Women play a prominent role in agriculture and domestic trade, and are represented at the highest levels of political life. Among the Ewe, a criminal may only be forgiven by the community if his or her young daughter is given as a slave to a local priest. There may be as many as 10,000 Ewe girls kept in ritual slavery.

Healthcare

Waterborne parasitic diseases are a widespread health hazard, and the creation of Lake Volta and related irrigation systems has led to an increase in malaria, sleeping sickness, and schistosomiasis. In 1993, Ghana had 1 doctor for every 22,970 people, and 1 hospital bed per 685 inhabitants. The average life expectancy is 59 years.

Housing

Ghana's housing needs have been increasing as the main towns grow in population. In 1982, the government established the State Housing Construction Co. to help supply new low-cost dwelling units.

EDUCATION

By 1995, an estimated 36% of the population were illiterate: 24.1% of the men and 46.5% of the women. Primary education has been free since 1952 and compulsory since 1961. Lasting six years, it is followed by seven years of secondary schooling. In 1990, Ghana had 11,165 primary schools with 66,946 teachers and 1.9 million pupils. General secondary schools had 768,603 pupils and 39,903 teachers. Ghana has three universities with a combined 1990 enrollment of 9,609.

1999 KEY EVENTS TIMELINE

January

- Real Gross Domestic Product (GFP) growth for 1998 is reported at 4.6 percent by the Bank of Ghana. However, the Center for Economic Policy Analysis (CEPA), an independent research institute, estimates that growth was closer to 2.9 percent.

February

- President Rawlings visits the United States. In a joint news conference with Rawlings, President Clinton announces a three-day U.S.-Africa ministerial meeting in Washington for foreign, finance, and trade ministers from some 46 African countries.

- CMS Energy Corporation and its Ghanaian partner, the Volta River Authority (VRA), sign a $44 million contract.

- Four Ghanaians are sentenced to death for conspiracy, treason, and charges of attempting to overthrow President Rawlings in August 1994.
- Congestion in the shipment pipeline leaves cocoa rotting at Takoradi Harbour, costing billions of Cedis.

March

- Ghanaian and U.S. forces stage peacekeeping and humanitarian training exercises.
- Rawlings says he will step down when his term of office ends in 2000.
- The opposition New Patriotic Party, retains its parliamentary seat in a by-election.
- Within three weeks of each other, the king of Asante and the king of Akyem Abuakwa die.

April

- Ghana launches second Emancipation Day to call on Africans to fulfill the vision of Africa's martyrs in their struggles against slavery and colonialism.
- The Ghana News Agency reports an increase of 22% in exports.
- After six weeks of mourning for Otumfuo Opoku Ware II, his successor is installed at the Kumasi Sports Stadium. The new Asantehene is the 16th occupant of the Golden Stool.

May

- Rawlings appeals to Muslims to help Kosovo refugees.
- Speaking at the World Tourism Organization conference in Accra, the first lady asks for more attention to women's roles in tourism.

June

- Japan donates $16.5 million to support Ghana's structural adjustment program, specifically the importation of spare parts, machinery and industrial materials. The announcement is made during the Japanese former Prime Minister's visit to Accra.
- Higher import prices result in a 15 percent increase in fuel prices in Ghana.
- The government bans Belgian poultry products.
- The Accra-based All-Africa Students Union calls on the Ivorian government to exercise maximum restraint in dealing with student unrest in that country.

- Rawlings marks 20 years in power, admitting to excesses early on, but calling for futuristic rather than retroactive vision.
- A new minimum wage is set, increasing workers' wages by 45 percent from $.80 to $1.16.
- A new political party, Traditional Congress Party (TCP) is formed, increasing the number of Ghanaian parties to eight.
- Ghanaian and Ivorian officials meet to resolve the cocoa crisis associated with pricing and market liberalization.
- Ghana receives high marks from the UNDP with regard to industrial development.

July

- The national Population Council in Ghana announces that women's empowerment, the education of girls, and elimination of unsafe abortion will be at the heart of its program in the next millennium.
- Some 2,000 employees of Ashanti Goldfields are to be laid off, perhaps permanently.
- Flooding occurs in Ofankor.
- Ghana signs a loan agreement with the World Bank for $180 million to deepen economic reforms, mainly in cocoa privatization, energy, and the financial sectors.
- Ghana and South Africa announce their cooperation along with other gold producing countries in Africa to oppose the IMF's and the British gold sale, which is bringing down gold prices to a 20-year low.

August

- Representatives of Shell and Chevron sign a memorandum of understanding with representatives of Nigeria, Benin, Togo, and Ghana specifying that the gas pipeline from Nigeria will be ready by 2002.
- Ghana Civil Aviation Authority receives the 1999 African Aviation Award for civil aviation management, safety, security, and air navigation service.
- Internal fissures within the ruling National Democratic Council (NDC) spawn the National Reform Movement, threatening the NDC's traditional power base.
- Ghana and the EU sign two agreements worth 66 million euros to finance the government's trans-

port infrastructure program. Ten million euros of this sum are to be used on rural electrification.

- Border problems between Togo and Ghana persist.

September

- African experts establish an arms register and database for the continent in a two-day workshop held in Accra.

October

- Kwabena Duffour, governor of the Bank of Ghana, calls upon ECOWAS countries to combine their resources to improve transportation networks in the region.

- Floods along the Benue River in northern Cameroon render many people homeless and destroy farmland.

November

- Queen Elizabeth and Prince Philip of Britain arrive in Ghana for a visit forty years after the British monarch was removed as head of state in Ghana.

- General Seth Kofi Obeng of Ghana is named to command the United Nations peacekeeping force in Lebanon.

December

- The All-Share Index on the Accra bourse (stock exchange) has lost over 15 percent over the year.

ANALYSIS OF EVENTS: 1999

BUSINESS AND THE ECONOMY

Economic performance for 1999 was mixed. Real GDP growth for 1998 was reported at 4.6 percent by the Bank of Ghana, but the Center for Economic Policy Analysis (CEPA), an independent source, estimated growth closer to 2.9 percent. It is expected to rise to 5 percent in 1999. Resumption of energy will favor manufacturing, and the abundant rains should boost agriculture. The lackluster stock market performance and depressed gold prices held the economy down, but a modest recovery is expected. Average annual inflation was forecasted at 14 percent for 1999. Inflation combined with falling world prices for gold and cocoa suggest a further fall of the Cedi to C 3,050: $1.

With an election year on the horizon, the temptation will be to raise civil service wages, maintain the 25 percent price supports in cocoa, leading to budget deficits of 5 percent to 10 percent. Nontraditional exports in agriculture, and semi-processed products and handicrafts increased 22 percent in 1998 over the previous year, and are again expected to rise.

Despite this mixed picture, donors and foreign business partners remained bullish on Ghana. In May, at the Accra Economic Summit, the Reverend Leon Sullivan, business, and public sector leaders gathered for an African-American summit in Accra to explore business links. In June, Japan announced the donation of $16.5 million for importing machinery, spare parts, and industrial materials. The EU provided financing for rural roads and electrification in the amount of 66 million Euros. The U.S. firm CMS Energy Corporation announced that its subsidiary, CMS Generation, and its Ghanaian partner, the Volta River Authority (VRA), signed a $44 million engineering, procurement, and constructions contract with Black and Veatch to build a 110 megawatt electric generating unit in Ghana.

Ghana also concluded a number of important deals regionally. It joined forces with South Africa to oppose the IMF and Britain's gold sales, which will severely depress the sector in both countries. With a high powered delegation from neighbor Côte d'Ivoire, it established an ad-hoc technical committee to develop strategies for cocoa marketing. The privatization of the cocoa trade is being supported by the World Bank through a $180 million loan, the largest of its kind Ghana has received. The government also signed a memo of understanding with Nigeria, Benin, Togo and Chevron and Shell on the $400 million Nigerian gas pipeline. Issues of cost, security, and possible tie-in from a similar project in Côte d'Ivoire may still need to be resolved.

GOVERNMENT AND POLITICS

In February, Rawlings made a state visit to Washington, possibly his last as president. He has promised not to run for office again as stipulated in the constitution. His imminent departure raises the succession issue as the 2000 elections approach. Internal fissures within the ruling National Democratic Council (NDC) spawned the National Reform Movement, threatening the NDC's traditional power base. This fracture is preoccupying the NDC because the very people who transformed it to a viable party in the early 1990s are leading the movement. The breakaway was precipitated by Rawlings' appointment in June of vice-president John Atta Mills to be his heir apparent. Mills is capable, but not charismatic. He is expected to run strong in urban areas where Rawlings was weak.

The reform movement could beat the NDC candidate in a close and bitter campaign if it ignites voters and overcomes regionalism. However, a fair election may hinge on how the government handles a growing demand for truth and reconciliation of the country's bloody past. At issue for NDC members is their immunity against prosecution for executions of eight senior military officers 20 years ago and the murder of three high court judges in 1983. Unrest is also expected among labor where the loss of 2,000 jobs in mining is pressuring government to create more employment opportunities.

In September, Africans from 20 countries, U.N. representatives, and researchers meeting in Accra took a step toward enhancing regional stability by establishing an arms register and database to stem the illicit flow of small arms in the region. The workshop was organized by the U.N. Regional Center for Peace and Disarmament in Africa. The uncontrolled spread of small arms has contributed to banditry and insecurity in West Africa.

CULTURE AND SOCIETY

Ghanaian culture is unusual in having maintained ceremonial customary rule. This reality was made poignant when the kings of Asante and Akyem Abuakwa died within three weeks of each other in March. After six weeks of mourning for Otumfuo Opoku Ware II, Ghanaians witnessed the installation of the 16th occupant of the Golden Stool at the Kumasi Sports Stadium. Otumfuo Osei Tutu II was nominated by his mother, Nana Afua Kobi Ampem, the Asantehemaa, and unanimously approved by the Kumasi Traditional Council. Chiefs in full regalia attended the event.

Although issues of crime, drug abuse, and HIV/AIDS occupied decision-makers, leaders increasingly focused on women's issues. The first lady highlighted the need to involve women more fully in society when she called for them to assume their place in tourism. Through government and NGO partnerships, the National Population Council is attempting to empower women, educate girls, and eliminate unsafe abortion practices. Fertility rates declined from 6.5 percent in 1960 to 4.5 percent in 1998, while the use of modern contraceptives stands at 13 percent today. Ghana appears to have one of the lower HIV/AIDS adult infection rates in Africa at 2.4 percent (1997) where the average for the subcontinent is 8 percent of the adult population.

DIRECTORY

CENTRAL GOVERNMENT

Head of State

President
Jerry John Rawlings, Office of the President, Castle, P.O. Box 1627, Osu Accra, Ghana
PHONE: +233 (21) 665415

Vice President
John Evans Atta Mills, Office of the Vice President

Ministers

Minister of Communications
John Mahama, Ministry of Communications

Minister of Defense
Enoch Donkoh, Ministry of Defense

Minister of Education
Ekwow Spio-Garbrah, Ministry of Education

Minister of Employment and Social Welfare
Mohammed Alhaji Mumuni, Ministry of Employment and Social Welfare

Minister of Environment, Science, and Technology
Cletus Apul Avoka, Ministry of Environment, Science, and Technology

Minister of Finance and Economic Planning
Richard Kwame Peprah, Ministry of Finance and Economic Planning, P.O. Box M40, Accra, Ghana
PHONE: +233 (21) 665441
FAX: +233 (21) 667069; 663854

Minister of Food and Agriculture
J. H. Owusu-Acheampong, Ministry of Food and Agriculture

Minister of Foreign Affairs
James Victor Gbeho, Ministry of Foreign Affairs

Minister of Health
Eunice Brookman-Amissah, Ministry of Health

Minister of Interior
Nii Okaidja Adamafio, Ministry of Interior

Minister of Justice
Obed Asamoah, Ministry of Justice, P.O. Box
M60, Accra, Ghana
PHONE: +233 (21) 665421

Minister of Lands and Forestry
Christine Amoako-Nuamah, Ministry of Lands
and Forestry

**Minister of Local Government and Rural
Development**
Kwamena Ahwoi, Ministry of Local Government
and Rural Development

Minister of Mines and Energy
Fred Ohene Kena, Ministry of Mines and Energy

Minister of Parliamentary Affairs
Kwabena Adjei, Ministry of Parliamentary
Affairs

Minister of Roads and Transport
Edward Salia, Ministry of Roads and Transport

Minister of Tourism
Michael Gizo, Ministry of Tourism

Minister of Trade and Industry
John Abu, Ministry of Trade and Industry
PHONE: +233 (21) 663188
FAX: +233 (21) 664776; 662428
E-MAIL: dfdt-moti@africaonline.com.gh

Minister of Works and Housing
Isaac Adjei-Mensah, Ministry of Works and
Housing

Minister of Youth and Sports
Enoch T. Mensah, Ministry of Youth and Sports

Ashanti Regional Minister
Kojo Yankah, Office of the Ashanti Regional
Minister

Brong Ahafo Regional Minister
Donald Adabre, Office of the Brong Ahafo
Regional Minister

Central Regional Minister
Charles Agbenaza, Office of the Central
Regional Minister

Greater Accra Regional Minister
Daniel Ohene-Agyekum, Office of the Greater
Accra Regional Minister

Northern Regional Minister
Joshua Alabi, Office of the Northern Regional
Minister

Upper East Regional Minister
Amidu Alhaji Suleimana, Office of the Upper
East Regional Minister

Upper West Regional Minister
David Osei-Wusu, Office of the Upper West
Regional Minister

Volta Regional Minister
Gilbert Seidu Iddi, Office of the Volta Regional
Minister

Western Regional Minister
Esther Lily Nkansah, Office of the Western
Regional Minister

POLITICAL ORGANIZATIONS

People's National Convention (PNC)

Kokomlemle, near Sadisco, Accra, Ghana
PHONE: +233 (21) 226528
NAME: Edward Mahama

People's Convention Party

H/No. 825/3 Mango Tree Ave. Asylum Down,
P.O. Box 10939, Accra, Ghana
PHONE: +233 (21) 221776
TITLE: Interim Chairman
NAME: Asuma Banda

National Convention Party

H/No. B.314/4, Johannesville, Adabraka Official
Town, Accra, Ghana
TITLE: Interim Chairman
NAME: Atta-Kesson

Every Ghanaian Living Everywhere Party

Isaac Ashong, Kokomlemle, Accra, Ghana
NAME: Nana Yaw Boakye Ofori Atta

New Patriotic Party

H/No. C. 912/2, Duade Street, Kokomlemle,
Accra, Ghana
PHONE: +233 (21) 220864; 227951
E-MAIL: NPP@africaonline.com.gh
TITLE: Chairman
NAME: Samuel Odoi-Sykes

National Democratic Congress

H/No. 641/4 Ringway Close, Kokomlemle,
Accra. P.O. Box 5825, Accra North, Ghana
PHONE: +233 (21) 224905; 223195
TITLE: General Secretary
NAME: Huudu Yahaya

DIPLOMATIC REPRESENTATION

Embassies in Ghana

Afghanistan
Bole Road, H-17, K-19, N-102, P.O. Box 2308, Addis Ababa, Ghana
PHONE: +233 (21) 187637

Algeria
82 Tito Avenue, P.O. Box 2747, Accra, Ghana
PHONE: +233 (21) 776719

Benin
19 Volta Street, 2nd Close, Airport Residential Area, P.O. Box 7871, Accra North, Ghana
PHONE: +233 (21) 774860; 774889

Brazil
5 Volta Street, Airport Residential Area, P.O. Box 2918, Accra, Ghana
PHONE: +233 (21) 774908

Bulgaria
3 Kakramadu Rd., East Cantonments, P.O. Box 3193, Accra, Ghana
PHONE: +233 (21) 772404

Burkina Faso
House No. 772/3, Asylum Down, P.O. Box 651, Accra, Ghana
PHONE: 233 (21) 221988

Canada
46 Independence Avenue, P.O. Box 1639, Accra, Ghana
PHONE: +233 (21) 228555; 228556
FAX: +233 (21) 773792

China
6 Agostino Neto Road, Airport Residential Area, P.O. Box 3356, Accra, Ghana
PHONE: +233 (21) 774527

Cuba
20 Amilcar Cabral Road, Airport Junction, P.O. Box 9163, Accra, Ghana
PHONE: +233 (21) 775868

Czech Republic
Kanda High Road, No. 2, House No. C260/5, P.O. Box 5226, Accra North, Ghana
PHONE: +233 (21) 223540; 229738

Denmark
67 Dr. Isert Road North Ridge, P.O. Box C596, Accra, Ghana
PHONE: +233 (21) 226972
FAX: +233 (21) 228061
NAME: Ole Blicher-Olsen

Egypt
House No. 27, Fetreke Street, Ambassadorial Estate, Roman Ridge, P.O. Box 2508, Accra, Ghana
PHONE: +233 (21) 776925

Ethiopia
6 Adiembra Road, East Cantonments, P.O. Box 1646, Accra, Ghana
PHONE: +233 (21) 775928; 775470

France
12th Road, P.O. Box 187, Accra, Ghana
PHONE: +233 (21) 228571; 228504

Germany
Valdemosa Lodge, North Ridge, P.O. Box 1757, Accra, Ghana
PHONE: +233 (21) 221311; 221326; 221347

Ivory Coast
9 Eighteenth Lane, Christiansborg, P.O. Box 3445, Accra, Ghana
PHONE: +233 (21) 774611; 774612

Spain
Lamptey Avenue Extension, Airport Residential Area, P.O. Box 1218, Accra, Ghana
PHONE: +233 (21) 774004; 774005

Switzerland
9 Water Road, North Ridge Area, P.O. Box 359, Accra, Ghana
PHONE: +233 (21) 228125

United Kingdom
Osu Link, off Gamel Abdul Nasser Avenue, P.O. Box 296, Accra, Ghana
PHONE: +233 (21) 221665; 221715

United States
Ring Road East, East of Danquah Circle, P. O. Box 194, Accra, Ghana
PHONE: +233 (21) 775348; 775349; 775295
FAX: +233 (21) 776008
TITLE: Ambassador
NAME: Kathryn Dee Robinson

JUDICIAL SYSTEM

Supreme Court

P.O. Box M60, Accra, Ghana
PHONE: +233 (21) 665421

Appeals Court

High Court

FURTHER READING
Books

Aidoo, Ama Ata. *The Dilemma of a Ghost.* Harlow, UK: Longman, 1970.

Ardayfio-Schandorf, Elizabeth and Kate Kwafo-Akoto. *Women in Ghana: An Annotated Bibliography.* Accra: Woeli Publishing Services, 1990.

Armah, Ayi Kwei. *The Beautyful Ones Have Not Been Born.* Boston: Houghton Mifflin, 1968.

——. *Fragments.* Boston: Houghton Mifflin, 1970.

Awoonor, Kofi. *Rediscovery and Other Poems.* Ibadan, Nigeria: Mbari, 1964.

Berry, LaVerle. *Ghana: A Country Study.* Third Edition. Washington, DC: Federal Research Division, Library of Congress, 1995.

Davidson, Basil. *Black Star: A View of the Life and Times of Kwame Nkrumah.* Boulder: Westview Press, 1989.

Glickman, Harvey, ed. *Political Leaders of Contemporary Africa South of the Sahara: A Biographical Dictionary.* New York: Greenwood Press, 1992.

Pinkney, Robert. *Democracy and Dictatorship in Ghana and Tanzania.* New York: St. Martin's Press, 1977.

Tendler, Judith. *Good Government in the Tropics.* Baltimore: Johns Hopkins University Press, 1997.

Internet

Africa News Online. Available Online @ http://www.africanews.org/west/stories/1999_feat1.html (October 28, 1999).

Africaonline. Available Online @ http://www.africaonline.com (October 28, 1999).

Integrated Regional Information Network (IRIN). Available Online @ http://www.reliefweb.int/IRIN (October 28, 1999).

GHANA:
STATISTICAL DATA

For sources and notes see "Sources of Statistics" in the front of each volume.

GEOGRAPHY

Geography (1)

Area:

Total: 238,540 sq km.

Land: 230,020 sq km.

Water: 8,520 sq km.

Area—comparative: slightly smaller than Oregon.

Land boundaries:

Total: 2,093 km.

Border countries: Burkina Faso 548 km, Cote d'Ivoire 668 km, Togo 877 km.

Coastline: 539 km.

Climate: tropical; warm and comparatively dry along southeast coast; hot and humid in southwest; hot and dry in north.

Terrain: mostly low plains with dissected plateau in south-central area.

Natural resources: gold, timber, industrial diamonds, bauxite, manganese, fish, rubber.

Land use:

Arable land: 12%

Permanent crops: 7%

Permanent pastures: 22%

Forests and woodland: 35%

Other: 24% (1993 est.).

HUMAN FACTORS

Demographics (2A)

	1990	1995	1998	2000	2010	2020	2030	2040	2050
Population	15,189.9	17,290.8	18,497.2	19,271.7	22,929.5	26,516.2	29,706.2	32,277.0	34,324.0
Net migration rate (per 1,000 population)	NA	NA	NA	NA	NA	NA	NA	NA	NA
Births	NA	NA	NA	NA	NA	NA	NA	NA	NA
Deaths	NA	NA	NA	NA	NA	NA	NA	NA	NA
Life expectancy - males	52.4	53.9	54.8	55.4	58.3	61.2	63.8	66.3	68.5
Life expectancy - females	56.1	57.9	58.9	59.6	63.0	66.3	69.3	72.0	74.4
Birth rate (per 1,000)	41.8	36.1	32.8	30.8	24.6	21.1	17.6	15.7	14.5
Death rate (per 1,000)	12.8	11.4	10.6	10.2	8.7	8.0	7.9	8.6	9.4
Women of reproductive age (15-49 yrs.)	3,565.0	4,096.7	4,457.3	4,751.4	6,307.8	7,488.3	8,331.1	8,656.7	8,540.8
of which are currently married	NA	NA	NA	NA	NA	NA	NA	NA	NA
Fertility rate	5.7	4.8	4.3	4.0	2.8	2.3	2.1	2.0	2.0

Except as noted, values for vital statistics are in thousands; life expectancy is in years.

Health Indicators (4)

Life expectancy at birth

1980 53

1997 60

Daily per capita supply of calories (1996) 2,560

Total fertility rate births per woman (1997) 4.9

Maternal mortality ratio per 100,000 live births (1990-97) . . . . .740[c]

Safe water % of population with access (1995) 65

Sanitation % of population with access (1995) 32

Consumption of iodized salt % of households (1992-98)[a] 10

Smoking prevalence

Male % of adults (1985-95)[a] . . . .

Female % of adults (1985-95)[a] . . . .

Tuberculosis incidence per 100,000 people (1997) 214

Adult HIV prevalence % of population ages 15-49 (1997) 2.38

Infants and Malnutrition (5)

Under-5 mortality rate (1997) 107

% of infants with low birthweight (1990-97) 8

Births attended by skilled health staff % of total[a] . . .44

% fully immunized (1995-97)

TB 72

DPT 60

Polio 61

Measles 59

Prevalence of child malnutrition under age 5 (1992-97)[b] 27

Ethnic Division (6)

Black African 99.8%

Major tribes

Akan 44%

Moshi-Dagomba 16%

Ewe 13%

Ga 8%

European and other 0.2%

Religions (7)

Indigenous beliefs 38%

Muslim 30%

Christian 24%

Other 8%

Languages (8)

English (official), African languages (including Akan, Moshi- Dagomba, Ewe, and Ga).

EDUCATION

Public Education Expenditures (9)

Public expenditure on education (% of GNP)

1980 . . . . .3.1

1996 . . . .

Expenditure per student

Primary % of GNP per capita

1980 . . . . .3.7

1996 . . . .

Secondary % of GNP per capita

1980 . . . .

1996 . . . .

Tertiary % of GNP per capita

1980 . . . . .26.7[1]

1996 . . . .

Expenditure on teaching materials

Primary % of total for level (1996) . . . . .1.6[1]

Secondary % of total for level (1996) . . . .

Primary pupil-teacher ratio per teacher (1996) . . . .

Duration of primary education years (1995) 6

Literacy Rates (11A)

In thousands and percent[1]	1990	1995	2000	2010
Illiterate population (15+ yrs.)	3,434	3,387	3,300	2,985
Literacy rate - total adult pop. (%)	58.2	64.5	70.7	80.9
Literacy rate - males (%)	70.8	75.9	80.5	87.7
Literacy rate - females (%)	45.9	53.5	61.2	74.2

GOVERNMENT & LAW

Political Parties (12)

Parliament	No. of seats
National Democratic Congress (NDC)	133
New Patriotic Party (NPP)	61
Peoples Convention Party (PCP)	5
Peoples National Convention (PNC)	1

Government Budget (13A)

Year: 1993

Total Expenditures: 813,526 Millions of Cedis

Expenditures as a percentage of the total by function:

General public services and public order 14.11

Defense 4.85

Education 22.03

Health 6.96

Social Security and Welfare 7.10

Housing and community amenities 2.76

Recreational, cultural, and religious affairs . . . .-

Fuel and energy 86

Agriculture, forestry, fishing, and hunting 3.50

Mining, manufacturing, and construction 1.36

Transportation and communication 9.77

Other economic affairs and services 46

Crime (15)

Crime rate (for 1997)

Crimes reported 184,400

Total persons convicted .NA

Crimes per 100,000 population 1,000

Persons responsible for offenses

Total number of suspects . . . . .NA

Total number of female suspects . . . . .NA

Total number of juvenile suspects . . . . .NA

Military Affairs (14B)

	1990	1991	1992	1993	1994	1995
Military expenditures						
Current dollars (mil.)	20	29	40	67[e]	113[e]	87[e]
1995 constant dollars (mil.)	23	32	43	70[e]	115[e]	87[e]
Armed forces (000)	9	9	7	7	7	7
Gross national product (GNP)						
Current dollars (mil.)	4,362	4,775	5,095	5,467	5,778	6,176
1995 constant dollars (mil.)	5,013	5,276	5,480	5,732	5,922	6,176
Central government expenditures (CGE)						
1995 constant dollars (mil.)	663	733	945	1,215	NA	NA
People (mil.)	15.2	15.6	16.0	16.5	16.9	17.3
Military expenditure as % of GNP	.5	.6	.8	1.2	1.9	1.4
Military expenditure as % of CGE	3.4	4.3	4.6	5.6	NA	NA
Military expenditure per capita (1995 $)	1	2	3	4	7	5
Armed forces per 1,000 people (soldiers)	.6	.6	.4	.4	.4	.4
GNP per capita (1995 $)	330	338	342	348	351	357
Arms imports[6]						
Current dollars (mil.)	5	0	0	0	0	0
1995 constant dollars (mil.)	6	0	0	0	0	0
Arms exports[6]						
Current dollars (mil.)	0	0	0	0	0	0
1995 constant dollars (mil.)	0	0	0	0	0	0
Total imports[7]						
Current dollars (mil.)	1,614[e]	1,611[e]	1,743[e]	1,700[e]	NA	NA
1995 constant dollars (mil.)	1,855[e]	1,780[e]	1,875[e]	1,782[e]	NA	NA
Total exports[7]						
Current dollars (mil.)	925[e]	861[e]	676[e]	623[e]	NA	NA
1995 constant dollars (mil.)	1,063[e]	951[e]	727[e]	653[e]	NA	NA
Arms as percent of total imports[8]	.3	0	0	0	NA	NA
Arms as percent of total exports[8]	0	0	0	0	NA	NA

LABOR FORCE

Labor Force (16)

Total . . . . .NA
Agriculture and fishing .61%
Industry 10%
Services 29%

Data for 1996 est. NA stands for not available.

Unemployment Rate (17)

20% (1997 est.)

PRODUCTION SECTOR

Electric Energy (18)

Capacity . . . . .1.3 million kW (1997)
Production . . . . .600 million kWh (1996)
Consumption per capita . . . . .373 kWh (1996)

Transportation (19)

Highways:

total: 39,409 km

paved: 11,653 km (including 30 km of expressways)

unpaved: 27,756 km (1997 est.)

Waterways: Volta, Ankobra, and Tano Rivers provide 168 km of perennial navigation for launches and lighters; Lake Volta provides 1,125 km of arterial and feeder waterways

Pipelines: 0 km

Merchant marine:

total: 4 ships (1,000 GRT or over) totaling 17,037 GRT/22,747 DWT ships by type: cargo 1, oil tanker 1, refrigerated cargo 2 (1997 est.)

Airports: 12 (1997 est.)

Airports—with paved runways:

total: 6

2,438 to 3,047 m: 1

1,524 to 2,437 m: 3

914 to 1,523 m: 2 (1997 est.)

Airports—with unpaved runways:

total: 6

1,524 to 2,437 m: 1

914 to 1,523 m: 3

under 914 m: 2 (1997 est.)

Top Agricultural Products (20)

Cocoa, rice, coffee, cassava (tapioca), peanuts, corn, shea nuts, bananas; timber.

FINANCE, ECONOMICS, & TRADE

Economic Indicators (22)

National product: GDP—purchasing power parity—$36.2 billion (1997 est.)

National product real growth rate: 3% (1997 est.)

National product per capita: $2,000 (1997 est.)

Inflation rate—consumer price index: 27.7% (1997 est.)

Exchange Rates (24)

Exchange rates:

New cedis per US$1

January 1998 . . . . .2,271.70
1997 . . . . .2,050.17
1996 . . . . .1,637.23
1995 . . . . .1,200.43
1994 . . . . .956.71
1993 . . . . .649.06

MANUFACTURING SECTOR

GDP & Manufacturing Summary (21)

	1980	1985	1990	1992	1993	1994
Gross Domestic Product						
Millions of 1990 dollars	4,988	4,881	6,226	6,713	7,046	7,313
Growth rate in percent	0.46	5.08	2.66	3.88	4.95	3.80
Per capita (in 1990 dollars)	464.6	380.2	414.5	420.7	428.4	431.6
Manufacturing Value Added						
Millions of 1990 dollars	536	429	575	553	565	582
Growth rate in percent	−1.44	24.29	−4.47	2.71	2.19	3.04
Manufacturing share in percent of current prices	7.8	11.5	9.3	8.7	8.8	8.8

FINANCE, ECONOMICS, & TRADE

Top Import Origins (25)

$1.84 billion (c.i.f., 1995)

Origins	%
France	.39
Cote d'Ivoire	.13
United States	.6
Netherlands	.5
Japan	.NA

NA stands for not available.

Top Export Destinations (26)

$1.57 billion (f.o.b., 1996 est.).

Destinations	%
United Kingdom	.NA
Germany	.NA
United States	.NA
Netherlands	.NA
Japan	.NA
Nigeria	.NA

NA stands for not available.

Economic Aid (27)

Recipient: ODA, $472 million (1993).

Import Export Commodities (28)

Import Commodities	Export Commodities
Capital equipment	Gold 39%
Petroleum	Cocoa 35%
Consumer goods	Timber 9.4%
Foods	Tuna
Intermediate goods	Bauxite
	Aluminum
	Manganese ore
	Diamonds

Balance of Payments (23)

	1992	1993	1994	1995	1996
Exports of goods (f.o.b.)	986	1,064	1,238	1,431	1,571
Imports of goods (f.o.b.)	−1,456	−1,728	−1,580	−1,688	−1,937
Trade balance	−470	−664	−342	−257	−366
Services - debits	−506	−569	−543	−575	−620
Services - credits	129	156	159	164	180
Private transfers (net)	215	256	201	260	206
Government transfers (net)	225	262	271	263	276
Overall balance	−377	−560	−255	−145	−324

GIBRALTAR

CAPITAL: Gibraltar.

FLAG: The flag of Gibraltar has two horizontal bands of white (top, double width) and red with a three-towered red castle in the center of the white band; hanging from the castle gate is a gold key centered in the red band.

ANTHEM: God Save the Queen.

MONETARY UNIT: 1 Gibraltar pound (£G) = 100 pence.

WEIGHTS AND MEASURES: The imperial system is used.

HOLIDAYS: New Year's Day, 1 January; Commonwealth Day, 10 March; Easter, 28 and 31 March; May Day, 1 May; Spring Bank Holiday, 26 May; The Queen's Official Birthday, 14 June; Late Summer Bank Holiday, 25 August; Referendum Day, 12 September; Christmas, 25 and 26 December.

TIME: 1 PM = noon GMT.

LOCATION AND SIZE: The colony of Gibraltar (5.83 sq. km/2.25 sq. mi. in area), the smallest UK dependency, is a narrow peninsula connected to the southwest coast of Spain. From a low, sandy plain in the north, it rises sharply in the 430 m (1,400 ft.) Rock of Gibraltar, a shrub-covered mass of limestone with huge caves.

CLIMATE: Gibraltar has a pleasantly temperate climate, except for occasional hot summers. Average annual rainfall is 89 cm (35 in.). There is a rainy season from December to May.

INTRODUCTORY SURVEY

RECENT HISTORY

Although ceded to England "for ever" in 1713, the small Iberian peninsula at the mouth to the Mediterranean has never been very far away from the question of sovereignty. Spain has been trying to recover Gibraltar for most of the twentieth century, however, the strategic location of the peninsula has been fortified with financial incentives for the United Kingdom and Gibraltar to maintain the status quo. Gibraltar was evacuated for most of World War II and the military occupied the UK dependency. Following the war and with the civilian population restored, Gibraltarians moved for autonomy and a measure of it was granted. The original Association for the Advancement of Civil Rights led to a reconstituted and elected City Council in 1945.

In 1950, the Legislative Council was formed and legislative authority was vested in the council. The next several years saw the establishment of many economic and financial institutions, and medical, educational, housing, and social security services were established. Then in 1963, the question of sovereignty was raised by Spain in the United Nations.

The United Kingdom eventually held a referendum on the issue in 1967, but the residents of Gibraltar voted 12,138 to 44 to retain their status with the UK. Interestingly, the residents of Gibraltar are primarily of Spanish descent and speak Spanish as their primary language although they hold British citizenship. To put pressure on the Gibraltarians following the vote, Spain closed the land frontier connecting the peninsula to the Spanish mainland. This closure would last until 1985, but the Gibraltarians did not change their minds.

Gibraltar entered the European Community along with the United Kingdom. The free movement of persons, capital, and services of the European Community apply to Gibraltar and serve to solidify the populations attitude towards changing allegiances. A constitution was established in 1969

GIBRALTAR

structuring the government and establishing the rights of Gibraltarians within the United Kingdom.

GOVERNMENT

As a self-governing dependency of the United Kingdom, the head of state for Gibraltar is the British monarch, represented by an appointed governor. Eight full time ministers are responsible for defined domestic matters. The legislature is a fifteen member unicameral House of Assembly, democratically elected.

Judiciary

The legal system in Gibraltar is based upon English common law as amended by local legislation. It is this ability to self-rule that is establishing the necessary independence to take advantage of European Community financial services opportunities. The Supreme Court oversees the courts and consists of a Chief Justice and an Associate Justice appointed by the governor. The Court of Appeal and the Court of the First Instance, Coroner's Court and Magistrates' Court round out the court structure.

Political Parties

There are no formal political parties in Gibraltar.

DEFENSE

Defense of Gibraltar is the responsibility of the United Kingdom as represented by the governor. A naval station is permanently manned. A small police force is present in the dependency.

ECONOMIC AFFAIRS

Gibraltar is the smallest of the United Kingdom's dependencies and has few natural resources. Virtually all food, fuel, machinery, and commodities must be imported. The only exports of the dependency are re-exports of tobacco, wine, and fuels. Government services are the principle industry of the dependency (70% of Gross Domestic Product) and United Kingdom subsidies and government expenditures determine the health of the economy. There is a small ship repair facility that is a privatized Royal Navy shipyard. Local industry does include some tobacco and coffee processing. Income is also derived from a ship refueling station.

A growing financial services industry is developing within the dependency due to favorable tax, duty, and tariff regulations established by the United Kingdom's European Community treaty. Corporate registrations and "offshore" financial services had already accounted for 15% of GDP by 1992.

Public Finance

The currency of Gibraltar is the Gibraltar pound. It is directly tied to the British pound and can be exchanged one for one. The British pound is therefore accepted currency throughout the dependency. In 1993, government expenditures totaled $124 million with revenues of $116 million. Gross Domestic Product in 1997 was estimated at $500 million, Also in 1997, exports were listed at $83.7 million and imports were listed at $778 million.

Income

Per capita income in 1997 was estimated at $17,500-one of the higher per capita values in the world. There is little unemployment.

Industry

Industry in the dependency of Gibraltar is heavily weighted towards governmental services. Ship refueling and the re-exporting of goods provides some income. Financial services are prominent. Some ship repair, and tobacco and coffee processing is established.

Economic Development

Economic development efforts are focused on the financial services to be offered as an offshore finance center. The infrastructure is in place for this industry to become very significant. Gibraltar's referendum on attachments to Spain, it's relationship with the United Kingdom and the constitution, as well as the United Kingdom's agreement with the European Community have all be geared towards establishing Gibraltar for this service.

SOCIAL WELFARE

Medical, educational, housing, and social security services are provided by the government to the citizens.

Healthcare

Healthcare is provided through government programs.

Housing

There is a serious housing shortage on Gibraltar.

EDUCATION

Education is free and compulsory between the ages of 5 and 15. There are twelve primary schools, a secondary school for each sex, and the College of Further Education. Military children attend military run schools. The populace is considered fully literate.

1999 KEY EVENTS TIMELINE

January

- Gibraltar authorities detain fourteen Spanish fishermen who were catching fish with nets in a prohibited area; hundreds of fishermen stop pedestrian and vehicle traffic between Spain and Gibraltar to protest the arrests.

February

- Under official orders from Madrid, Spain tightens border controls with Gibraltar in response to the arrests.

- Britain appeals to the European Union to resolve the flare-up between Gibraltar and Spain.

- British Foreign Secretary Robin Cook urges Spanish officials to rescind new restrictions on travelers from Gibraltar.

- The European Court of Human Rights in Strasbourg rules that the British government has violated the rights of citizens of Gibraltar by not allowing them to vote in European elections.

March

- Spain claims it has evidence of drug trafficking and money laundering in Gibraltar and will forward the report to British authorities.

- British authorities say they will seek voting rights for Gibraltar residents in European Parliament elections; the request is expected to worsen its dispute with Spain.

April

- Raymond Benson, the latest Bond author, says James Bond's next villain will be an embittered ex-bullfighter bent on recovering Gibraltar for Spain.

June

- Gibraltar authorities say the famous population of apes on the Rock of Gibraltar is growing out of control and may have to be put on a contraceptive pill.

August

- Spain and Gibraltar cut a deal to allow the British colony's one-man team at the IAAF championships in Seville to run, but not carry a flag.

ANALYSIS OF EVENTS: 1999

BUSINESS AND THE ECONOMY

In October, the British government announced a crackdown on the use of British dependent territories as tax havens by United Kingdom firms. Chancellor Gordon Brown was seeking to close tax loopholes that have cost the country millions of dollars. He also wanted to show British support for international initiatives against what are seen as unfair tax regimes. Gibraltar was mentioned as a major culprit.

Earlier in the year, Ladbrokes, Britain's largest bookmaker, unveiled plans to expand its Gibraltar operations and offer tax-free phone and internet betting to United Kingdom customers.

GOVERNMENT AND POLITICS

Gibraltar authorities detained fourteen Spanish fishermen for allegedly violating fishing restrictions in disputed waters off the British colony. Within hours, the detention had become an international incident. Spain quickly clamped down on its border, and began to conduct meticulous immigration control checks, forcing travelers to wait as much as four hours.

English tabloids responded faster than the British government, and fanned the dispute. Some conservative members of Parliament demanded the immediate dispatch of warships. The dispute reminded Gibraltar residents of the late Spanish dictator Gen. Francisco Franco, who shut the border for thirteen years beginning in 1969, splitting families and creating economic problems for Gibraltar.

Spain after Franco has not been much friendlier to Gibraltar. The Spaniards have occasionally imposed tough border controls and refused official cooperation with Gibraltar, also known as the Rock. In March, the Spaniards claimed they had evidence showing that Gibraltar had become a haven for money laundering and drug traffickers. Spanish President José María Aznar gave the detailed report to his British colleague Tony Blair during a meeting in Germany. By April, with more pressing issues on their agendas, Britain and Spanish leaders diplomatically sidestepped the Gibraltar dispute. Kosovo took precedence, and Gibraltar issues would be discussed privately.

CULTURE AND SOCIETY

In February, the European Court of Human Rights in Strasbourg ruled that the British government had violated the rights of citizens of Gibraltar by not allowing them to vote in European elections. The government was ordered to pay compensation and legal fees to Denise Matthews, a 23-year-old Gibraltar resident. She filed her case in 1994. The decision meant Britain would have to seek unanimous approval from all European Union members, including Spain, to amend the treaty on elections to the European Parliament to allow Gibraltar residents to vote. But getting Spain to agree will be difficult. While Gibraltar is considered part of the EU, Spain regards the Rock as a British colony, and has repeatedly blocked attempts to allow the 30,000 residents who live there the same rights enjoyed by other EU member states.

In Britain, Sir William Jackson was known as a military historian, and the first British officer to meet the German army in battle in World War II. In Gibraltar, he was regarded as one of its greatest supporters, a governor who championed the Rock's right of self-determination. Jackson died in March 12 at age 81. The Guardian of London wrote that Jackson, governor of the Rock between 1978–82, was a tireless supporter of Gibraltar.

Gibraltar is not only known for the "Rock." Its apes are just as famous. But authorities said the ape population on the Rock of Gibraltar was growing out of control, with numbers soaring from 70 or 80 to as many as 250. Authorities culled more than 20, and sent 20 others to a German zoo, but the population has continued to grow. Legend claims that the colony would cease to be British if the apes disappear, which is why Winston Churchill reportedly imported extra apes to Gibraltar during World War II. But the apes have become a problem, attacking people and destroying property. Gibraltar authorities said a researcher at Zurich University is working on their behalf to see if the population could be controlled with contraceptive drugs.

DIRECTORY

CENTRAL GOVERNMENT
Head of State

Queen
Elizabeth II, Monarch, Buckingham Palace, London SW1, England

Governor
Richard Luce, Office of the Governor

Ministers

Chief Minister
Peter Caruana, Office of the Chief Minister, 6 Convent Place, Gibraltar

POLITICAL ORGANIZATIONS
Gibraltar Socialist Labor Party

NAME: Joe Bossano

Gibraltar Social Democrats

NAME: Peter Caruana

Gibraltar National Party

NAME: Joe Garcia

Liberal Party

JUDICIAL SYSTEM
Supreme Court

Law Courts, 277 Main St., Gibraltar
PHONE: +350 78808

FAX: +350 77118

Court of Appeals

Law Courts, 277 Main St., Gibraltar
PHONE: +350 78808
FAX: +350 77118

Court of the First Instance
Coroner's Court
Magistrate's Court

FURTHER READING
Articles

"Britain Will Seek European Voting Rights for Gibraltar Residents." *Associated Press,* 3 March 1999.

"Gibraltar Cut Off as Spanish Fishermen Stage Border Protest." *Associated Press,* 29 January 1999.

"Gibraltar Says It Isn't Spain's to Claim or Britain's to Give Away." *Associated Press,* 6 October 1999.

"Spain and Britain Carrying Gibraltar Dispute Into 21st Century." *Associated Press,* 4 March 1999.

"Spain Nixes Gibraltar Runner from Track Ceremony." *Associated Press,* 19 August 1999.

"Spain Seeks to Support Charges Gibraltar is Hotbed of Crime." *Associated Press,* 3 March 1999.

Internet

"Choppy Waters Round Rock: Gibraltar Row Is Ratcheted Up." *The Guardian of London,* 12 February 1999. Available Online @ http://www.guardianunlimited.co.uk/Archive/Article/0,4273,3820762,00.html (December 14, 1999)

"EU acts on Gibraltar bottleneck." *BBC Online Network,* 1 July 1999. Available Online @ http://news2.thls.bbc.co.uk/hi/english/world/europe/newsid%5F382000/382574.stm (December 14, 1999)

"Gibraltar fears Franco-style siege as Spain blocks traffic," *The Guardian of London,* 11 February 1999 http://www.guardianunlimited.co.uk/Archive/Article/0,4273,3820499,00.html

"Gibraltar resident wins Euro vote." *BBC Online Network,* 18 February 1999. Available Online @ http://news2.thls.bbc.co.uk/hi/english/uk/newsid%5F281000/281935.stm (December 14, 1999)

"NI drug buster for Gibraltar Straits." *BBC Online Network,* 11 June 1999. Available Online @ http://news2.thls.bbc.co.uk/hi/english/uk/newsid%5F366000/366644.stm (December 14, 1999)

"No more monkey business for Rock apes." *BBC Online Network,* 6 June 1999. Available Online @ http://news2.thls.bbc.co.uk/hi/english/uk/newsid%5F362000/362366.stm (December 14, 1999)

"A simple and easy way for the Spanish to win back Gibraltar." *The Guardian of London,* 4 July 1999. Available Online @ http://www.guardianunlimited.co.uk/Archive/Article/0,4273,3880430,00.html (December 14, 1999)

"007 fights for the Rock." *BBC Online Network,* 14 April 1999. Available Online @ http://news2.thls.bbc.co.uk/hi/english/entertainment/newsid%5F319000/319033.stm (December 14, 1999)

GIBRALTAR:
STATISTICAL DATA

For sources and notes see "Sources of Statistics" in the front of each volume.

GEOGRAPHY

Geography (1)

Area:

Total: 6.5 sq km.

Land: 6.5 sq km.

Water: 0 sq km.

Area—comparative: about 11 times the size of The Mall in Washington, DC.

Land boundaries:

Total: 1.2 km.

Border countries: Spain 1.2 km.

Coastline: 12 km.

Climate: Mediterranean with mild winters and warm summers.

Terrain: a narrow coastal lowland borders the Rock of Gibraltar.

Natural resources: negligible.

Land use:

Arable land: NA%

Permanent crops: NA%

Permanent pastures: NA%

Forests and woodland: NA%

Other: NA%

GOVERNMENT & LAW

Crime (15)

Crime rate (for 1997)

Crimes reported 2,000

Total persons convicted 875

Crimes per 100,000 population 6,700

Persons responsible for offenses

Total number of suspects 1,050

Total number of female suspects . . . . .NA

Total number of juvenile suspects . . . . .NA

HUMAN FACTORS

Demographics (2A)

	1990	1995	1998	2000	2010	2020	2030	2040	2050
Population	31.1	28.6	29.0	29.3	29.9	30.0	29.9	29.1	28.0
Net migration rate (per 1,000 population)	NA	NA	NA	NA	NA	NA	NA	NA	NA
Births	NA	NA	NA	NA	NA	NA	NA	NA	NA
Deaths	NA	NA	NA	NA	NA	NA	NA	NA	NA
Life expectancy - males	72.4	74.3	74.9	75.3	76.9	78.1	79.0	79.6	80.0
Life expectancy - females	78.1	81.2	81.6	82.0	83.3	84.3	85.1	85.6	86.0
Birth rate (per 1,000)	17.1	14.6	13.0	12.3	10.5	11.2	10.1	9.3	9.6
Death rate (per 1,000)	9.0	8.6	8.8	8.9	9.7	10.7	11.8	13.0	13.6
Women of reproductive age (15-49 yrs.)	7.3	6.4	6.1	6.1	6.1	6.0	5.9	6.0	5.5
of which are currently married	NA	NA	NA	NA	NA	NA	NA	NA	NA
Fertility rate	2.5	2.3	2.2	2.1	1.9	1.8	1.8	1.7	1.7

Except as noted, values for vital statistics are in thousands; life expectancy is in years.

GREECE

Hellenic Republic
Elliniki Dhimokratia

INTRODUCTORY SURVEY

RECENT HISTORY

After World War II, Greece became involved in a five-year civil war (1944–49) between the government and the communist-supported National Liberation Front. U.S. aid under the Truman Doctrine played a significant role in defeating the rebellion. A new constitution took effect in 1952, the same year Greece joined NATO.

On 21 April 1967, a successful takeover of the government was staged by a right-wing military group. This group was to rule Greece for the next eight years. Leftists were rounded up, press censorship was imposed, and political liberties were suspended. Colonel George Papadopoulos was made premier. In 1973, Greece was declared a republic, and Papadopoulos became president, only to be overthrown by a group of officers. The military government fell from power in July 1974. Constantine Karamanlis, a former prime minister and moderate, returned from exile to form a civilian government that effectively ended eight years of dictatorial rule. Prime Minister Karamanlis brought Greece into the European Community in January 1981.

With the victory of the Pan-Hellenic Socialist Movement (Panellinio Socialistikou Kinema—PASOK) in the elections of October 1981, Greece installed its first Socialist government. The new prime minister, Andreas Papandreou, was the son of former Prime Minister George Papandreou.

Tensions arose between Greece and the former Yugoslav republic of Macedonia. After the breakup of Yugoslavia, the territory known within Yugoslavia as Macedonia took steps to declare itself an independent country.

The elections of September 1996 returned PASOK to power, giving them a commanding majority over parliament. Under Prime Minister Costas Simitis, Greece has continued with a program of economic modernization.

The outbreak of the NATO-Yugoslav conflict in March 1999 brought new concerns for Greece.

The country feared a new and uncontrolled movement of Albanian refugees into Greece. As a result, the Greek government provided aid for Kosovar Albanians forced from their homes and offered to accept 5,000 refugees.

GOVERNMENT

The 1975 constitution abolished the 146-year-old Greek monarchy. The president, who is head of state, appoints the prime minister, who is head of government and requires the support of the 300-seat parliament to remain in power.

Judiciary

The 1975 constitution designates the Supreme Court (Areios Pagos), made up of eleven judges, as the highest court of appeal. It consists of two penal and four civil sections. A Council of State does not hear cases but decides on administrative disputes, administrative violations of laws, and disciplinary procedures affecting civil servants.

Political Parties

Postwar political parties in Greece centered more on leaders than issues. On 28 September 1974, Constantine Karamanlis formed the New Democracy Party (Nea Dimokratia—ND), advocating a middle course between left and right, and promoting closer ties with Western Europe. Groups that emerged after 1981 included the Pan-Hellenic Socialist Movement (Panellinio Socialistikou Kinema—PASOK). In May 1986, the Communist Party changed its name to the New Hellenic Left Party.

In the parliamentary elections of September 1996, PASOK won 170 seats, and the ND took 108 seats. The remaining seats were split among three smaller parties.

DEFENSE

The Hellenic (Greek) armed forces belong to NATO. All able-bodied men of 21 years of age are obliged to fulfill 19–23 months of military service, plus reserve service to age 50. The total reserves number 406,000. In 1995, there were 122,000 in the army (95,000 male conscripts and 2,900 female volunteers); 19,500 in the navy; and 26,800 in the air force.

ECONOMIC AFFAIRS

The Greek economy suffers from a lack of profitable natural resources and a low level of industrial development relative to the rest of Western Europe. By 1992, it had fallen behind Portugal to become the poorest European Community member. The country still depends on many imports to meet its food needs.

Greece has stimulated foreign investments in the development of its mineral resources by constitutionally providing guarantees for capital and profits. The government has encouraged tourism, which has developed into a major source of revenue. Greece continues to play a major role in the international shipping industry.

Public Finance

In 1995, Greece's government debt exceeded 120% of GDP, requiring annual interest payments of almost 9% of GDP.

The U.S. CIA estimates that, in 1995, government revenues totaled approximately $43.2 billion and expenditures $47 billion. External debt totaled $31.2 billion, approximately 21% of which was financed abroad.

Helped by a sharp decline in inflation that reduced the cost of the government's monthly borrowing, the public debt stabilized in 1996 at 110% GDP.

Income

In 1998, Greece's gross national product (GNP) was about $122.8 billion, or $11,650 per person. For the period 1985–92 the average inflation rate was 16.5%, resulting in a real growth rate in GNP of 1.1% per person.

Industry

Manufacturing, which now ranks ahead of agriculture as an income earner, has increased rapidly owing to a strong policy of industrialization. However, Greek industry must rely on imports for its raw materials, machinery, parts, and fuel.

Banking and Finance

The government-controlled Bank of Greece (founded in 1927) is the central bank and the bank of issue, and it also engages in other banking activities. Its foreign exchange reserve in 1996 totaled US$ 19,116 million.

There are 21 Greek commercial banks, which are dominated by two massive, state-controlled banking groups, the National Bank and the Commercial Bank.

The Athens Stock Exchange (Chrimatisterion) was founded by royal decree in 1876.

Economic Development

Until the mid-1970s, Greek governments devoted themselves principally to expanding agricultural and industrial production, controlling prices and inflation, improving state finances, developing natural resources, and creating basic industries.

The Socialist government that took office in 1981 promised more equal distribution of income and wealth through "democratic planning" and measures to control inflation and increase productivity.

The conservative government that came to power in 1990 adopted a 1991–93 "adjustment program" that called for reduction of price and wage increases and a reduction in the public-sector deficit from 13% to 3% of GDP.

Greece received $1.2 billion in foreign aid in 1995.

SOCIAL WELFARE

The Social Insurance Foundation, the national social security system, provides for medical treatment; pays old-age pensions, disability pensions, and benefits to widows, orphans, and parents of deceased pensioners; and offers cash benefits for sickness, tuberculosis, accidents, maternity, and funeral expenses.

In January 1983, Greece's family law was changed by parliament to guarantee equality between marriage partners, make divorce easier, and abolish the traditional dowry as a legal requirement for marriage.

Healthcare

Pulmonary tuberculosis, dysentery, and malaria have been controlled. The incidence of typhoid dropped to only 149 cases in 1985 following the application of U.S. aid to improving sanitary conditions in more than 700 villages. In 1993, life expectancy averaged 78 years.

Housing

Construction of new dwellings reached 88,477 units in 1985 and rose to 120,240 in 1990. In 1991, the total number of housing units was 3.4 million. Most new construction is in Athens or Thessaloníki, indicating the emphasis on urban development.

EDUCATION

Adult illiteracy in 1995 was estimated at 5%. Education is free and compulsory for nine years beginning at age 6. In 1993 there were 7,193 primary schools with 723,701 pupils. Secondary schools (gymnasiums) had 851,294 pupils.

Greece has several major universities. Together, all institutions of higher education, including technical schools, enrolled 198,988 students in 1995.

1999 KEY EVENTS TIMELINE

January

- Russian-built S-300 surface-to-air-missiles purchased by Cyprus are based in Crete following Turkish threats to bomb the missiles if they are based in Cyprus.

February

- Tensions with Turkey heighten following the capture of Kurdish terrorist leader Abdullah Ocalan at the Greek embassy in Nairobi, Kenya.
- Prime Minister Costas Simitis reshuffles his cabinet.

March

- NATO begins its air war against Yugoslavia. Greek public opinion is overwhelmingly opposed, but the Greek government provides limited aid for its allies.

May

- Former New Democracy minister Stefanos Manos founds the Liberal Party.

June

- The Kosovo war ends. NATO peacekeepers land in the Greek port of Thessaloniki.

July

- A Greek-Turkish dialogue begins at the ministerial level. Talks focus on economic issues.

August

- Following a devastating earthquake in Turkey, Greece is the first country to provide humanitarian assistance.

September

- Turkey reciprocates the previous month's gesture following an earthquake in Athens.

October

- An air tragedy over Romania takes the life of Deputy Foreign Minister Yiannos Kranidiotis.

November

- Two people on a motorcycle fire at least six shots at the central Athens offices of the Hellenic-American Union, causing minor damage but no injuries.

- U.S. president Bill Clinton's visit is met by destructive protests in Athens, but the audience for Clinton's speech cheers when he acknowledges that U.S. policy has wronged Greece in the past.

- Clinton urges Greece and Turkey to solve their two main sources of discord: a boundary dispute in the Aegean, and the division of Cyprus.

December

- Greece deports to the U.S. 18 cult members Washington accuses of planning violence to hasten the return of Jesus as the millennium approaches.

ANALYSIS OF EVENTS: 1999

BUSINESS AND THE ECONOMY

Greece entered 1999 with an economic program aiming to meet EU criteria for convergence into the euro zone by the end of the year with an eye toward adopting the euro in 2001. Initially, the Kosovo war threatened to jeopardize the country's continued progress. By year's end, however, the Greek economy had rebounded and is among the most robust in Europe.

Signs of the government's continued commitment to monetary union appeared at the beginning of the year with the divestment of Greece's telecommunications company, OTE. During the course of the year, the Athens bourse index doubled while the Greek bond market was the best in Europe. Forecasts predicted a continued drop in inflation to 1.9 percent by 2000, GDP growth would reach 3.9 percent, while the deficit as a percent of GDP would drop to 1.7 percent, well within the range for monetary union.

Although these figures are impressive, large sectors of Greek society oppose Simitis's austerity program. A wave of strikes by trade unions, plagued the country.

GOVERNMENT AND POLITICS

Greek politics underwent a roller coaster ride in 1999 as the country began the year embroiled in a major diplomatic dispute with arch-rival (and NATO ally) Turkey, and found itself trying to keep a lid on popular pro-Serb passions during the Kosovo war. By last summer and into fall, however, the situation had changed markedly. Relations with Turkey were improving and the country appeared on the road toward the euro and emerged as a major player in the Balkans.

Relations with Turkey reached a low point in February when Turkey's most wanted man, Kurdish separatist terrorist leader Abdullah Ocalan was found hiding in the Greek embassy in Nairobi, Kenya. Turkish agents abducted Ocalan while en route to the airport in search of a new sanctuary. Turkish Prime Minister Bullet Ecevit accused Greece of sponsoring terrorism. The episode led his Greek counterpart, Costas Simitis, to reshuffle his cabinet. His chief change was the ouster of Minister of Foreign Affairs Theodoros Pangalos, who was blamed for the Ocalan fiasco, and his replacement with the U.S.-born and educated George Papandreou (son of the late Andreas Papandreou, Simitis's predecessor). Under George Papandreou, Greece provided grudging, limited, but important support to the NATO air campaign against Yugoslavia at a time when Greek public opinion ran over ninety percent against the war. Although refusing overflight of NATO strike aircraft, Greece did provide its port of Thessaloniki as a point of disembarkation for NATO peacekeepers assigned to Kosovo once the war ended.

Following the Kosovo war, Greek diplomatic initiatives aimed at improving relations with Turkey. In July, Papandreou and his Turkish counterpart, Ismail Cem, began a series of low-level talks aimed at fostering improved economic ties. The two men developed a good rapport and talks continued. Then tragedy struck. In August, an earthquake measuring 7.1 on the Richter scale struck Turkey and killed over 20,000. Greece was the first country to provide aid to the victims. This act of neighborly goodwill further improved the atmosphere between the two adversaries. When Athens was struck by a smaller quake the next month, Turkey returned the favor by rushing aid to Greece. In the aftermath of the earthquakes, Greece has softened its stance on Turkish entry into the European Union (EU) and has allowed the release of funds it had previously vetoed due to concerns over human rights protection.

Domestically, Simitis's pro-EU policies, particularly economic austerity measures designed to secure entry into the second round of monetary union, have cost the socialist prime minister support in public opinion. In European elections, center-right New Democracy (ND) pulled even with

Simitis's PASOK (Panhellenic Socialist Movement). ND has succeeded in drawing away moderate voters disgruntled with Simitis's slashing on social expenditures. However, it is unclear how much this newly-gained support will have in parliamentary elections (to be held by next spring at the latest). Former ND deputy and cabinet minister Stefanos Manos formed a reformist Liberal Party and may draw strength away from ND.

CULTURE AND SOCIETY

The events of 1999, particularly the Kosovo war, indicate the continuing position of Greece as a cultural crossroads between Western and Eastern Europe—politically and economically tied to the West, historically bound both to the East and West. Indeed, the Greek experience in dealing with its desire to be integrated into Western Europe—while continuing to display its Eastern European heritage—may serve as a preview of what is yet to come as the former communist states of the Balkans desire to join Western Europe's political and economic structures. The staunchly pro-Orthodox, pro-Serb, and anti-NATO reaction expressed by Archbishop Christodoulos, is held by many at all levels and age groups of Greek society.

Yet if the Eastern attitudes taken by Greece during the Kosovo war represent one-half of the Greek cultural heritage, the idea of a four-year "Cultural Olympiad" represents the Western half, the half admired by the West as the basis of its civilization. Put forward by Minister of Culture Evangelos Venizelos, and inspired by the ancient Greeks, the "Cultural Olympiad" seeks to revive the ancient ideal of the Olympics as an expression of all aspects of culture, of which athletics is a small part.

DIRECTORY

CENTRAL GOVERNMENT

Head of State

President
Constantinos Stephanopoulos, Office of the President, 7 Vas. Georgiou St., GR-106 74 Athens, Greece

Ministers

Prime Minister
Constantine Simitis, Office of the Prime Minister, Irodou Attikou 19, GR-10 674 Athens, Greece
PHONE: +30 (1) 6717059
FAX: +30 (1) 6716183
E-MAIL: mail@primeminister.gr

Minister of Interior, Public Administration, and Decentralization
Vaso Papandreou, Ministry of Interior, Public Administration, and Decentralization, 27 Stadiou St., GR-101 83 Athens, Greece
PHONE: +30 (1) 3223521; 3235610
E-MAIL: dhes@gspa.gr

Minister of National Defense
Apostolos-Athanasios Tsohatzopoulos, Ministry of National Defense, Mesogion 151, GR-155 00 Holargos, Athens, Greece
PHONE: +30 (1) 6555911
E-MAIL: minister@mod.gr

Minister of Foreign Affairs
Georgios A. Papandreou, Jr., Ministry of Foreign Affairs, 1, Acadimias St., GR-106 71 Athens, Greece
PHONE: +30 (1) 3681000
E-MAIL: gap@mfa.gr; mfa@mfa.gr

Minister of National Economy
Ioannis Papantoniou, Ministry of National Economy, Nikis 5-7, GR-101 80 Athens, Greece
PHONE: +30 (1) 3332000
FAX: +30 (1) 3332130
E-MAIL: info@ypetho.gr

Minister of Finance
Giannos Papantoniou, Ministry of Finance, Karageorgi Servias 10, Athens, Greece
PHONE: +30 (1) 3477166; 3478706; 3479109
E-MAIL: gsis@di.uoa.gr

Minister of Education and Religious Affairs
Gerassimos D. Arsenis, Ministry of Education and Religious Affairs, Mitropoleos 15, GR-101 85 Athens, Greece
PHONE: +30 (1) 3230461; 3252001
E-MAIL: edu_ref@ypepth.gr

Minister of Development
Evangelos Venizelos, Ministry of Development, Michalacopoulou 80, GR-101 92 Athens, Greece
PHONE: +30 (1) 7482770

Minister of Environment, Physical Planning and Public Works
Costas Laliotis, Ministry of Environment, Physical Planning and Public Works, Amaliados 17, GR-115 23 Athens, Greece
PHONE: +30 (1) 6431641
E-MAIL: minister@minenv.gr

Minister of Agriculture
Georgios Anomeritis, Ministry of Agriculture, Acharnon 5, GR-104 32 Athens, Greece
PHONE: +30 (1) 5291111

Minister of Labor and Social Affairs
Miltiadis Papaioannou, Ministry of Labor and Social Affairs, Pireos 40, Athens, Greece
PHONE: +30 (1) 5295000
E-MAIL: postmaster@www.labor-ministry.gr

Minister of Health and Welfare
Lambros Papadhimas, Ministry of Health and Welfare, Aristotelous 17, Athens, Greece
PHONE: +30 (1) 5232820; 5249010
E-MAIL: info@ypyp.gr

Minister of Justice
Evangelos Giannopoulos, Ministry of Justice, Mesogeion 96, GR-115 27 Athens, Greece
PHONE: +30 (1) 7711019

Minister of Culture
Elisavet Papazoi, Ministry of Culture, Bouboulinas 20-22, GR-106 82 Athens, Greece
PHONE: +30 (1) 8201100
E-MAIL: w3admin@culture.gr

Minister of Merchant Marine
Stavros Aristidi Soumakis, Ministry of Merchant Marine, Grigori Lambraki 150, GR-185 18 Pireus, Greece
PHONE: +30 (1) 4121211
E-MAIL: yen@yen.gr

Minister of Public Order
Michalis Chryssochoidis, Ministry of Public Order, Kanelopoulou 4, GR-101 77 Athens, Greece
PHONE: +30 (1) 6928510
E-MAIL: webmaster@mopo.gr

Minister of Macedonia-Thrace
Ioannis Mangriotis, Ministry of Macedonia-Thrace, Administration Building, GR-541 23 Thessaloniki, Greece
PHONE: +30 (1) 31264321
E-MAIL: minister@mathra.gr

Minister of the Aegean
Stavros Benos, Ministry of the Aegean, Filellinon 9, Athens, Greece
PHONE: +30 (1) 3311714

Minister of Transport and Communications
Anastassios Mantelis, Ministry of Transport and Communications, Xenofontos 13, GR-101 91 Athens, Greece
PHONE: +30 (1) 3251211

Minister of Press and Mass Media
Dimitrios Reppas, Ministry of Press and Mass Media, 10, Zalocosta St., GR-101 63 Athens, Greece
PHONE: +30 (1) 3696000
FAX: +30 (1) 3606969; 3609682; 3632639
E-MAIL: press01@otenet.gr

POLITICAL ORGANIZATIONS
Nea Dimocratia-ND (New Democracy)
18 Rigillis Street, GR-106 74 Athens, Greece
PHONE: +30 (1) 7252209; 7252221
TITLE: President
NAME: Konstandinos Karamanlis

Panellino Socialistiko Kinima-PASOK (Pan-Hellenic Socialist Movement)
Charilaou Trikoupi 50, GR-106 80 Athens, Greece
PHONE: +30 (1) 3247141
FAX: +30 (1) 3247596
E-MAIL: pasok@pasok.gr
TITLE: President
NAME: Kostantinos Georgiou (Kostas) Simitis

Vinozhito (Rainbow)
Stefanou Dragoumi 11, P.O. Box 51, GR-531 00 Florina, Greece
PHONE: +30 (1) 546548
FAX: +30 545044
E-MAIL: rainbow@florina.org
NAME: Pavlos Voskopoulos

Dimokratiki Kinoniku Kinima-DIKKI (Democratic Social Movement)
9 Halkokondili Street, GR-106 77 Athens, Greece
PHONE: +30 (1) 3801712; 3304430; 3829051
FAX: +30 (1) 3839047
E-MAIL: dikki@otenet.gr
TITLE: President
NAME: Dimitris Tsovolas

Synaspismos (Coalition of the Left and Progress)

1 Eleftherias Square, GR-105 53 Athens, Greece
PHONE: +30 (1) 3378400
FAX: +30 (01) 3219914; 3217003
E-MAIL: nak@syn.gr
TITLE: President
NAME: Nicos A. Constantopoulos

Komounistiko Komma Elladas-KKE (Communist Party of Greece)

145 Leof.Irakliou, GR-142 31 Nea Ionia-Athens, Greece
PHONE: +30 (1) 2592111
FAX: +30 (1) 2592298
E-MAIL: cpg@kke.gr
NAME: Aleka Papariga

Politiki Anixi (Political Spring)

PHONE: +30 (1) 3254355
FAX: +30 (1) 3249429
E-MAIL: anixi@otenet.gr
NAME: Andonis Samaras

DIPLOMATIC REPRESENTATION

Embassies in Greece

Italy
Odos Sekeri, GR-106 74 Athens, Greece
PHONE: +30 (1) 3617260; 3617273
FAX: +30 (1) 3617330
E-MAIL: ambaten@hol.gr
TITLE: Ambassador
NAME: Agostino Mathis

The Netherlands
Leof. Vass. Konstantinou 5-7, GR-106 74 Athens, Greece
PHONE: +30 (1) 7239701
FAX: +30 (1) 7248900
E-MAIL: nlgovath@dutchembassy.gr
TITLE: Ambassador
NAME: Paul R. Brouwer

South Africa
P.O. Box 61152, GR-151 10 Athens, Greece
PHONE: +30 (1) 6806645; 6806646; 6806647
FAX: +30 (1) 6806640; 6806655
E-MAIL: embassy@southafrica.gr
TITLE: Ambassador
NAME: David Jacobs

United Kingdom
1 Ploutarchou Street, GR-106 75 Athens, Greece
PHONE: +30 (1) 7272600
FAX: +30 (1) 7272743; 7272722; 7272743
E-MAIL: info@athens.mail.fco.gov.uk; britania@hol.gr
TITLE: Ambassador
NAME: David C. A. Madden

United States
91 Vasilissis Sophias, GR-101 60 Athens, Greece
PHONE: +30 (1) 7212951
FAX: +30 (1) 6456282
TITLE: Ambassador
NAME: R. Nicholas Burns

JUDICIAL SYSTEM

Supreme Judicial Court

Special Supreme Tribunal

FURTHER READING

Articles

"Greece." *Current History* 98, 627 (April 1999): 188.

"Greece: Euroland Ahoy!" *The Economist* (January 23, 1999): 49.

"Greece: Return of the Minotaurs." *The Economist* (May 15, 1999): 58.

"The Ocalan Crisis." *The Economist* (February 20, 1999): 48.

Books

Curtis, Glenn E., ed. *Greece, a Country.* 4th ed. Washington, D.C.: U.S. G.P.O., 1995.

Speake, Graham, ed. *Encyclopedia of Greece and the Hellenic Tradition.* London: Fitzroy Dearborn, 1999.

Internet

Embassy of Greece in Washington, D.C. Available Online @ http://www.greekembassy.org/ (November 3, 1999).

GREECE: STATISTICAL DATA

For sources and notes see "Sources of Statistics" in the front of each volume.

GEOGRAPHY

Geography (1)

Area:

Total: 131,940 sq km.

Land: 130,800 sq km.

Water: 1,140 sq km.

Area—comparative: slightly smaller than Alabama.

Land boundaries:

Total: 1,210 km.

Border countries: Albania 282 km, Bulgaria 494 km, Turkey 206 km, The Former Yugoslav Republic of Macedonia 228 km.

Coastline: 13,676 km.

Climate: temperate; mild, wet winters; hot, dry summers.

Terrain: mostly mountains with ranges extending into sea as peninsulas or chains of islands.

Natural resources: bauxite, lignite, magnesite, petroleum, marble.

Land use:

Arable land: 19%

Permanent crops: 8%

Permanent pastures: 41%

Forests and woodland: 20%

Other: 12% (1993 est.).

HUMAN FACTORS

Demographics (2A)

	1990	1995	1998	2000	2010	2020	2030	2040	2050
Population	10,123.5	10,519.1	10,662.1	10,750.7	10,982.9	10,739.8	10,149.6	9,356.0	8,361.6
Net migration rate (per 1,000 population)	NA	NA	NA	NA	NA	NA	NA	NA	NA
Births	NA	NA	NA	NA	NA	NA	NA	NA	NA
Deaths	54.0	NA	NA	NA	NA	NA	NA	NA	NA
Life expectancy - males	74.5	75.4	75.8	76.0	77.1	77.9	78.7	79.3	79.8
Life expectancy - females	79.4	80.6	81.0	81.3	82.6	83.6	84.5	85.2	85.8
Birth rate (per 1,000)	10.0	9.9	9.6	9.4	8.2	6.9	6.3	5.7	5.2
Death rate (per 1,000)	9.5	9.2	9.4	9.5	10.7	11.9	13.1	15.3	18.0
Women of reproductive age (15-49 yrs.)	2,397.4	2,587.3	2,630.3	2,645.2	2,571.0	2,320.1	1,948.3	1,619.3	1,367.4
of which are currently married	NA	NA	NA	NA	NA	NA	NA	NA	NA
Fertility rate	1.4	1.4	1.3	1.3	1.3	1.3	1.3	1.3	1.3

Except as noted, values for vital statistics are in thousands; life expectancy is in years.

Health Personnel (3)

Total health expenditure as a percentage of GDP, 1990-1997[a]

Public sector 5.3

Private sector 1.8

Total[b] 7.1

Health expenditure per capita in U.S. dollars, 1990-1997[a]

Purchasing power parity 843

Total 803

Availability of health care facilities per 100,000 people

Hospital beds 1990-1997[a] 500

Doctors 1993[c] 387

Nurses 1993[c] 278

Health Indicators (4)

Life expectancy at birth

1980 74

1997 78

Daily per capita supply of calories (1996) 3,575

Total fertility rate births per woman (1997) 1.3

Maternal mortality ratio per 100,000 live births (1990-97) . . . . .10[c]

Safe water % of population with access (1995) . . . .

Sanitation % of population with access (1995) . . . .

Consumption of iodized salt % of households (1992-98)[a] . . . .

Smoking prevalence

Male % of adults (1985-95)[a] 46

Female % of adults (1985-95)[a] 82

Tuberculosis incidence per 100,000 people (1997) 29

Adult HIV prevalence % of population ages 15-49 (1997) 0.14

Infants and Malnutrition (5)

Under-5 mortality rate (1997) 8

% of infants with low birthweight (1990-97) 6

Births attended by skilled health staff % of total[a] . . .NA

% fully immunized (1995-97)

TB 70

DPT 85

Polio 95

Measles 90

Prevalence of child malnutrition under age 5 (1992-97)[b] . . . . .NA

Ethnic Division (6)

Greek 98%

Other 2%

Note: the Greek Government states there are no ethnic divisions in Greece.

Religions (7)

Greek Orthodox 98%

Muslim 1.3%

Other 0.7%

Languages (8)

Greek (official), English, French.

EDUCATION

Public Education Expenditures (9)

Public expenditure on education (% of GNP)

1980 . . . . .2.0[1]

1996 . . . . .3.0

Expenditure per student

Primary % of GNP per capita

1980 . . . . .7.0[1]

1996 . . . . .16.0[1]

Secondary % of GNP per capita

1980 . . . . .9.6[1]

1996 . . . . .14.7[1]

Tertiary % of GNP per capita

1980 . . . . .30.1[1]

1996 . . . . .20.7[1]

Expenditure on teaching materials

Primary % of total for level (1996) . . . . .2.4[1]

Secondary % of total for level (1996) . . . .

Primary pupil-teacher ratio per teacher (1996) . . . . .15[1]

Duration of primary education years (1995) 6

Educational Attainment (10)

Age group (1991) . . . . .25+

Total population 6,738,566

Highest level attained (%)

No schooling 5.7

First level

Not completed 12.7

Completed 44.2

Entered second level

S-1 . . . . .6.7

S-2 . . . . .22.0

Postsecondary 8.7

Literacy Rates (11B)

Adult literacy rate

1980

  Male 93x

  Female 76x

1995

  Male 98

  Female 95

GOVERNMENT & LAW

Political Parties (12)

Parliament	% of seats
Socialist Movement (PASOK)	41.5
New Democracy (ND)	38.1
Communist Party (KKE)	5.6
Coalition of the Left and Progress	5.1
Democratic Social Movement (DIKKI)	4.4
Political Spring	2.9

Military Affairs (14B)

	1990	1991	1992	1993	1994	1995
Military expenditures						
Current dollars (mil.)	4,182	4,185	4,539	4,621	4,811	5,056
1995 constant dollars (mil.)	4,806	4,625	4,882	4,845	4,932	5,056
Armed forces (000)	201	205	208	213	206	213
Gross national product (GNP)						
Current dollars (mil.)	71,740	77,440	80,300	83,480	86,660	91,250[e]
1995 constant dollars (mil.)	82,450	85,580	86,380	87,520	88,830	91,250[e]
Central government expenditures (CGE)						
1995 constant dollars (mil.)	54,650	38,850	36,120	40,050	52,670	47,000[e]
People (mil.)	10.1	10.3	10.3	10.4	10.4	10.5
Military expenditure as % of GNP	5.8	5.4	5.7	5.5	5.6	5.5
Military expenditure as % of CGE	8.8	11.9	13.5	12.1	9.4	10.8
Military expenditure per capita (1995 $)	475	450	472	466	472	482
Armed forces per 1,000 people (soldiers)	19.9	19.9	20.1	20.5	19.7	20.3
GNP per capita (1995 $)	8,144	8,328	8,351	8,414	8,501	8,696
Arms imports[6]						
Current dollars (mil.)	440	260	725	850	470	825
1995 constant dollars (mil.)	506	287	780	891	482	825
Arms exports[6]						
Current dollars (mil.)	20	0	20	10	5	0
1995 constant dollars (mil.)	23	0	22	10	5	0
Total imports[7]						
Current dollars (mil.)	19,780	21,580	23,220	22,010	21,470	NA
1995 constant dollars (mil.)	22,730	23,850	24,980	23,080	22,000	NA
Total exports[7]						
Current dollars (mil.)	8,105	8,666	9,509	8,434	9,384	NA
1995 constant dollars (mil.)	9,315	9,576	10,230	8,842	9,619	NA
Arms as percent of total imports[8]	2.2	1.2	3.1	3.9	2.2	NA

Government Budget (13A)

Year: 1996

Total Expenditures: 10,943 Billions of Drachmas

Expenditures as a percentage of the total by function:

General public services and public order 6.77

Defense 7.33

Education 9.58

Health 6.71

Social Security and Welfare 18.44

Housing and community amenities 2.05

Recreational, cultural, and religious affairs 1.02

Fuel and energy . . . .-

Agriculture, forestry, fishing, and hunting 3.19

Mining, manufacturing, and construction 1.50

Transportation and communication 3.94

Other economic affairs and services 84

Crime (15)

Crime rate (for 1994)

Crimes reported 303,311

Total persons convicted 83,818

Crimes per 100,000 population 2,909

Persons responsible for offenses

Total number of suspects 273,840

Total number of female suspects 32,910

Total number of juvenile suspects . . . . .NA

LABOR FORCE

Labor Force (16)

Total (million) 4.21

Services 52%

Agriculture 23%

Industry 25%

Data for 1995.

Unemployment Rate (17)

10% (1997 est.)

PRODUCTION SECTOR

Electric Energy (18)

Capacity . . . . .8.606 million kW (1995)

Production . . . . .38.814 billion kWh (1995)

Consumption per capita . . . . .3,720 kWh (1995)

Transportation (19)

Highways:

total: 117,000 km

paved: 107,406 km (including 470 km of expressways)

unpaved: 9,594 km (1996 est.)

Waterways: 80 km; system consists of three coastal canals; including the Corinth Canal (6 km) which crosses the Isthmus of Corinth connecting the Gulf of Corinth with the Saronic Gulf and shortens the sea voyage from the Adriatic to Peiraiefs (Piraeus) by 325 km; and three unconnected rivers

Pipelines: crude oil 26 km; petroleum products 547 km

Merchant marine:

total: 875 ships (1,000 GRT or over) totaling 25,264,916 GRT/45,188,813 DWT

Airports: 78 (1997 est.)

Airports—with paved runways:

total: 63

over 3,047 m: 5

2,438 to 3,047 m: 16

1,524 to 2,437 m: 16

914 to 1,523 m: 17

under 914 m: 9 (1997 est.)

Airports—with unpaved runways:

total: 15

1,524 to 2,437 m: 1

914 to 1,523 m: 3

under 914 m: 11 (1997 est.)

Top Agricultural Products (20)

Wheat, corn, barley, sugar beets, olives, tomatoes, wine, tobacco, potatoes; meat, dairy products.

MANUFACTURING SECTOR

GDP & Manufacturing Summary (21)

Detailed value added figures are listed by both International Standard Industry Code (ISIC) and product title.

	1980	1985	1990	1994
GDP ($-1990 mil.)[1]	57,305	61,238	66,532	68,402
Per capita ($-1990)[1]	5,943	6,164	6,499	6,567
Manufacturing share (%) (current prices)[1]	19.5	18.2	16.4	*15.1*
Manufacturing				

	1980	1985	1990	1994
Value added ($-1990 mil.)[1]	9,362	9,405	9,534	9,067
Industrial production index	100	98	99	94
Value added ($ mil.)	6,129	4,644	9,293	10,412
Gross output ($ mil.)	20,906	16,937	29,649	29,836
Employment (000)	378	352	346	312
Profitability (% of gross output)				
Intermediate input (%)	71	73	69	65
Wages and salaries inc. supplements (%)	14	15	17	17
Gross operating surplus	15	12	15	18
Productivity ($)				
Gross output per worker	55,275	48,081	85,619	95,485
Value added per worker	16,204	13,184	26,837	33,368
Average wage (inc. supplements)	7,964	7,281	14,319	16,381
Value added ($ mil.)				
311/2 Food products	731	631	1,349	1,787
313 Beverages	233	217	474	635
314 Tobacco products	138	114	280	394
321 Textiles	987	762	1,109	990
322 Wearing apparel	283	235	552	558
323 Leather and fur products	46	38	68	74
324 Footwear	76	61	100	100
331 Wood and wood products	138	65	176	183
332 Furniture and fixtures	54	34	93	102
341 Paper and paper products	118	94	272	315
342 Printing and publishing	155	99	289	332
351 Industrial chemicals	180	192	290	224
352 Other chemical products	314	223	628	808
353 Petroleum refineries	152	140	217	538
354 Miscellaneous petroleum and coal products	31	19	27	47
355 Rubber products	58	44	84	72
356 Plastic products	186	109	276	343
361 Pottery, china and earthenware	61	43	73	68
362 Glass and glass products	49	23	49	45
369 Other non-metal mineral products	414	276	641	633
371 Iron and steel	200	153	280	162
372 Non-ferrous metals	245	184	347	294
381 Metal products	365	276	449	451
382 Non-electrical machinery	125	81	178	168
383 Electrical machinery	295	219	441	525
384 Transport equipment	453	268	488	503
385 Professional and scientific equipment	8	5	16	18
390 Other manufacturing industries	31	39	47	43

FINANCE, ECONOMICS, & TRADE

Economic Indicators (22)

National product: GDP—purchasing power parity—$137.4 billion (1997 est.)

National product real growth rate: 3.7% (1997 est.)

National product per capita: $13,000 (1997 est.)

Inflation rate—consumer price index: 6% (1997 est.)

Exchange Rates (24)

Exchange rates:

Drachmae (Dr) per US$1

January 1998	.286.99
1997	.273.06
1996	.240.71
1995	.231.66
1994	.242.60
1993	.229.26

Top Import Origins (25)

$27 billion (c.i.f., 1997 est.) Data are for 1995.

Origins	%
European Union	.70
Italy	.18
Germany	.16
France	.8
United Kingdom	.6%
United States	.4

Top Export Destinations (26)

$9.8 billion (f.o.b., 1997 est.) Data are for 1995.

Destinations	%
European Union	.60
Germany	.22
Italy	.14
France	.6
United Kingdom	.6
United States	.3

Economic Aid (27)

Recipient: EU, $5.4 billion (1997 est.).

Import Export Commodities (28)

Import Commodities	Export Commodities
Manufactured goods 72%	Manufactured goods 53%
Foodstuffs 15%	Foodstuffs 34%
Fuels 10%	Fuels 5%

Balance of Payments (23)

	1992	1993	1994	1995	1996
Exports of goods (f.o.b.)	6,076	5,112	5,338	5,918	5,890
Imports of goods (f.o.b.)	−17,637	−15,611	−16,611	−20,343	−21,395
Trade balance	−11,561	−10,499	−11,273	−14,425	−15,505
Services - debits	−6,306	−5,888	−6,121	−7,364	−7,575
Services - credits	9,252	9,141	10,312	10,917	10,504
Private transfers (net)	4,058	4,085	4,307	4,968	5,057
Government transfers (net)	2,417	2,414	2,629	3,040	2,965
Overall balance	−2,140	−747	−146	−2,864	−4,554

GREENLAND

INTRODUCTORY SURVEY

RECENT HISTORY

The Inuit (Eskimo) peoples inhabited Greenland, the world's largest island, for several thousand years prior to arrival of Norwegian Erik the Red in 982. Erik the Red inspired settlement several years later by Icelandic immigrants who established farming communities. Following introduction of Christianity by Leif Ericksson in the eleventh century, a bishop's seat was established in 1126. A cooling climate soon led to abandonment of Greenlandic settlements by the Norse in the fifteenth century.

Not until 1721 did European settlement return. Hans Egede from the United Kingdom of Denmark and Norway established a trading post and Lutheran mission. By 1776 Denmark banned foreign access to the island and monopolized trade with Greenland. However, in the early 1940s during World War II the United States temporarily assumed protection of Greenland while Germany occupied Denmark. Following the return of Greenland to Denmark in 1945 local pressure mounted for greater political freedom. By 1951 Denmark's Royal Greenland Trading Company's monopoly was terminated. Greenland became a county of the Kingdom of Denmark under a new Danish constitution adopted in 1953. An increased emphasis on expanding Greenland's economy, educational system, and transportation system was initiated. In 1979 Greenland achieved greater independence under Home Rule but with Greenlanders maintaining Danish citizenship. By the 1990s

GREENLAND

0   200 Miles

0   200 Kilometers

almost 80% of Greenlanders were still predominately of mixed Inuit and early European immigrant descent living in broadly dispersed small coastal settlements.

GOVERNMENT

Based on the 1953 Danish constitution, Greenland's chief of state is the monarch of the Kingdom of Denmark. Queen Margrethe II has reigned in that position since 1972. Since 1979 Greenland is a self-governing overseas administrative division of Denmark, known as the Greenland Home Rule Government (GHRG). The monarch appoints a High Commissioner to represent her in Greenland's governmental affairs.

Greenland's legislative branch is a thirty-one-seat unicameral parliament, known as the Landsting. Members are elected to four year terms through popular vote by all residents above eighteen years of age.

Parliament elects Greenland's head of government, the prime minister, who normally is the majority party's leader. A seven-member cabinet, the Landsstyre, carries out Greenland's executive responsibilities, and is formed from the parliament based on relative political party strength. Greenland's voting public also elects two representatives to the Danish parliament. Greenland is divided into three administrative districts, Avannaa, Tunu, and Kitaa, and eighteen municipalities for which town councils are elected to four-year terms.

Judiciary

Integrated with the Danish legal system, Greenland has a High Court in the town of Nuuk composed of one professional judge and two lay magistrates, and eighteen district courts presided by lay assessors. Appeals may be heard at the Danish High Court in Copenhagen. A unique Greenlandic penal system does not include imprisonment but instead applies fines, counseling, or stays at minimal security reform centers.

Political Parties

Greenland's political parties include the Siumut, the Inuit Ataqatigiit (IA), Atassut Party, Akulliit Party, Issituup, and the Candidates' League. The Siumut, founded in 1971, is a moderate socialist party supporting increased autonomy from Denmark. The IA, founded in 1978, is a socialist organization favoring Greenland independence from Denmark. Also founded in 1978, the Atassut is a more conservative party, seeking to maintain close links with Denmark.

DEFENSE

Denmark is responsible for Greenland's defense and foreign affairs. The Greenland Command, stationed in southwest Greenland, primarily patrols for fishing violations and performs sea rescues. Greenlanders are not obligated to military service. Given its far Northern Atlantic location, Greenland also is home to the North Atlantic Treaty Organization's (NATO) military communication network and the North American radar defense system.

ECONOMIC AFFAIRS

Two-thirds of the expansive island lies north of the Arctic Circle. Approximately 700,000 of the 840,000 square miles of land mass is covered by an ice sheet up to 5,000 feet thick. With the rugged coastal areas and much permafrost, only 1% of Greenland is capable of supporting agriculture. Most ice-free regions provide pasture for reindeer and sheep. Consequently, fishing and mining are the basic components of the Greenlandic economy.

An early dominant activity of seal hunting gave way in the early 20th century to fishing, canning, and freezing of cod, prawns and other marine foods. Economically important saltwater fish are halibut, cod, flounder, and salmon while trout and salmon are found in the rivers.

General economic growth in the 1970s and 1980s gave way to financial difficulties in 1990 with closure of a key lead and zinc mine and depletion of the cod fisheries. The economy began recovery by 1994, but totally reliant on fisheries and consequently vulnerable to fluctuating international fish prices. Fish and fish products constituted 95% of Greenland's exports in 1995. Exports totaled U.S. $363 million in 1995 with U.S. $421 million of imports.

Whaling is still a subsistence tradition of the Inuit. Greenlanders caught 169 whales in 1997 while operating under the International Whaling Commission regulations. A subsistence barter economy is still prevalent in many areas. Greenland is also active in the Inuit Circumpolar Conference (ICC) supporting Inuit cultural tradition and economy.

Public Finance

Following a decline in economic growth in the early 1990s, the economy has improved since 1993. Denmark provides annual aid, U.S. $427 million in 1995, to balance Greenland's budget. The Greenland budget involved U.S. $706 million in revenue in 1995 with an expenditure of U.S. $697 million. Approximately 58% of the 1996 revenue came from aid and 38% from direct and indirect taxes. Primary government expenditures in 1996 included social security and welfare services (22%), economic services (17%), education and research (17%), general governmental administration including law enforcement (14%), and health (11%). Economic services included subsidies for trade, fishing, agriculture, manufacturing, roads and other transportation, and electricity and water.

Income

The estimated gross domestic product (GDP) for 1997 was U.S. $945 million, representing a growth rate of 0.6%. The per capita GDP for 1997 was U.S. $16,100.

Industry

The fishing industry provides Greenland's principal exports consisting of tinned, dried, frozen, and smoked fish. Shrimp alone accounted for almost 65% of the island's economy in 1997. The last lead and zinc mines closed in 1989. Other mineral resources of value identified on the island include iron ore coal, gold, molybdenum, uranium, and platinum but any development is difficult in the arctic conditions. Offshore petroleum and natural gas discoveries in the 1990s raised economic hopes for the future. Wool exports, small shipyards that repair and maintain ships and manufacture other industrial metal products, and handicraft industries also add to the economy. A short season and high costs hamper development of a tourism industry. Some 15,000 tourists came to Greenland in 1995.

Banking and Finance

A private bank, The Bank of Greenland or Grønlandsbanken, was founded in 1967 and located in Nuuk.

SOCIAL WELFARE

With the social welfare system based on the Scandinavian model, annual economic subsidies from Denmark fund a wide range of social welfare services, including free health care. Old-age pensions are granted to Greenlanders over sixty years of age and cash benefits for periods of unemployment or illness are available to all Greenlanders. Members of the National Workers' Union also have an unemployment insurance system.

Healthcare

All Greenlanders receive free medical and dental services. In 1997 a central hospital was located in Nuuk with fifteen smaller district health centers in the other communities. Approximately 16% of the 1996 government budget was allocated to health services. High rates of venereal disease and tuberculosis were reported in 1997.

Life expectancy at birth was estimated in 1999 at 70.1 years for the total population; 66.0 years for males and 72.2 years for females. The most common non-natural cause of death was suicide in 1996, accounting for ten percent of all deaths.

Housing

Housing financial benefits are available from the government for Greenlanders in need. Approximately 9% of the 1996 expenditures were allocated to housing.

EDUCATION

Similar to Denmark, the literacy rate on the islands is high, as 99% of those over age fifteen can read and write. Greenland had eighty-eight primary schools and three secondary schools in 1998. Education is compulsory for youth from age six to fifteen and an additional three years is optional. Instruction is primarily in Greenlandic language despite wide use of Danish. A teacher training college and business college are located in Nuuk as is the University of Greenland, founded in 1987. In 1996 education constituted almost 12% of the Greenlandic budget.

1999 KEY EVENTS TIMELINE

February

- About 75 percent of Greenland's eligible voters turn out for parliamentary elections. Government coalition parties lose three seats.

March

- The vast ice sheet covering Greenland, the world's second largest after Antarctica, is thinning by up to a meter a year, according to some scientific research.

June

- The Premier of Nunavut visits Greenland to help celebrate the twentieth anniversary of the introduction of home rule to the Arctic Island. Greenland and Nunavut sign a cooperation agreement.

September

- Danish Prime Minister Poul Nyrup Rasmussen apologizes to a group of Greenland Inuits who were evicted from their homes and hunting grounds more than forty years ago to allow for the expansion of an American air base.

November

- Greenland chooses the Sprint Corporation to wire its automatic teller machines network.

- Greenland sets tough terms for allowing the United States to use its northwestern Thule air base for a planned missile defense system. Greenland officials say radar installation can proceed only with Russian approval; Russia opposes the plan.

- Scientists report that the ocean current in the sea off Greenland, known as the North Atlantic Drift, is changing. The current brings warm water north from the gulf stream and is currently shifting because of an increase in freshwater

flowing into the ocean, possibly due to melting ice.

ANALYSIS OF EVENTS: 1999

BUSINESS AND THE ECONOMY

On June 21, the Premier of Greenland, Jonathan Motzfeldt, gave a long speech to celebrate Greenland's twentieth anniversary of Home Rule. Part of the speech dealt with the economy, which, he said, was being managed very tightly.

"We are still very dependent on our export of shrimp and fish, but the efforts being done in this field is indeed very good and praiseworthy work. It is a hard and professional task, which have to be carried out for the benefit of all of us," he said. Motzfeldt said Greenland had mineral wealth that needed to be extracted, but without hurting its delicate environment.

"A well-managed and healthy economy is a prerequisite for our working towards a greater ability to act. We are responsible in finding new ways and get even with old ways of managing the economy. This is a task, which is already well underway," he said.

GOVERNMENT AND POLITICS

In the seventh election since the introduction of Home Rule, the number of women delegates in Parliament increased from one to six. The government coalition parties Siumut (social democrat), and the Atassut (liberal), lost three seats, but still maintained a majority with 19 seats in parliament in the February 16 elections.

The Inuit Ataqatigiit (the Socialist party) increased its representation by one seat, to seven.

In November, Greenland's government risked conflict with Denmark by insisting that the United States must meet tough terms before it can install a planned missile defense system at Thule air base.

Greenland has limited home rule under Danish Administration. Denmark oversees the Arctic island's security, and conducts its foreign policy. But Greenland Prime Minister Jonathan Motzfeldt said the U.S. could upgrade its radar installation only with the approval of Russia, which is opposed to the project. Motzfeldt also demanded the presence of Greenland representatives at any negotiations between Denmark and the United States that deal with the radar installation issue. Denmark has not allowed Greenland to have any say on security and defense concerns.

CULTURE AND SOCIETY

In September, Danish Prime Minister Poul Nyrup Rasmussen apologized to a group of Greenland Inuits who were evicted from their homes and hunting-grounds more than forty years ago to make room for the expansion of an American air force base. In August, a Copenhagen court awarded the Inuits more than $70,000 in collective damages, saying the eviction had infringed on their rights. The Inuits were pushed out of the way when NATO expanded its radar surveillance base at Thule, in northwestern Greenland.

DIRECTORY

CENTRAL GOVERNMENT

Head of State

Premier
Jonathan Motzfeldt, Office of the Premier, P.O. Box 1015, Nuuk 3900, Greenland
PHONE: +299 345000
FAX: +299 325002

Ministers

Minister of Economy and Trade
Josef Motzfeldt, Ministry of Economy and Trade, P.O. Box 1037, Nuuk 3900, Greenland
PHONE: +299 345000
FAX: +299 324614

Minister of Housing and Infrastructure
Steffen Ulrich-Lynge, Ministry of Housing and Infrastructure, P.O. Box 909, Nuuk 3900, Greenland
PHONE: +299 345000
FAX: +299 324319

Minister of Business
Simon Olsen, Ministry of Business, P.O. Box 269, Nuuk 3900, Greenland
PHONE: +299 345000
FAX: +299 324704

Minister of Health, Environment, and Church
Alfred Jakobs, Ministry of Health, Environment, and Church

Minister of Health and Church
Martha Abelsen, Ministry of Health and Church, P.O. Box 1160, Nuuk 3900, Greenland
PHONE: +299 345000
FAX: +299 325505

Minister of Environment and Nature
Ministry of Environment and Nature, P.O. Box 1614, Nuuk 3900, Greenland
PHONE: +299 345000
FAX: +299 325286

Minister of Culture, Education, and Research
Lise Skifte Lennert, Ministry of Culture, Education, and Research, P.O. Box 1029, Nuuk 3900, Greenland
PHONE: +299 345000
FAX: +299 322073

Minister of Social Affairs and Labor Market
Mikael Petersen, Ministry of Social Affairs and Labor Market, P.O. Box 260, Nuuk 3900, Greenland
PHONE: +299 345000
FAX: +299 324547

Minister of Taxation
Kaare Hagemann, Ministry of Taxation, P.O. Box 1605, Nuuk 3900, Greenland
PHONE: +299 345000
FAX: +299 322042

Minister of Industry
Simon Olsen, Ministry of Industry, P.O. Box 269, Nuuk 3900, Greenland
PHONE: +299 345000
FAX: +299 324704

POLITICAL ORGANIZATIONS

Atassut

PHONE: +299 323366; 323366
FAX: +299 325840
E-MAIL: atassut@greennet.gl
NAME: Finn Karlsen

Inuit Ataqatigiit

NAME: Johan Lund Olsen

Siumut

NAME: Lars Karl Jensen

Kandidatforbundet

NAME: Anthon Frederiksen

DIPLOMATIC REPRESENTATION

Embassies in Greenland

Canada
P.O. Box 1012, Nuuk 3900, Greenland
PHONE: +299 328888
FAX: +299 327288
TITLE: Honorary Consul
NAME: Lars-Peter Danielsen

Finland
Dr. Ingridsvej, P.O. Box 200, Nuuk 3900, Greenland
PHONE: +299 321385
FAX: +299 321003
TITLE: Consulate-General
NAME: Henning Edvard Madsen

Germany
Greenland Tours, Kussangajaannguaq 18, 3952 Ilulissat, Greenland
PHONE: +299 944411
FAX: +299 944511
TITLE: Honorary Consul
NAME: Elke Meissner

Iceland
P.O. Box 1616, Nuuk 3900, Greenland
PHONE: +299 324411
FAX: +299 324460
TITLE: Consulate-General
NAME: Anders Brøns

Norway
P.O. Box 1033, Nuuk 3900, Greenland
PHONE: +299 347700
FAX: +299 347720
TITLE: Consulate-General
NAME: Svend-Erik Danielsen

Sweden
P.O. Box 1616, Nuuk 3900, Greenland
PHONE: +299 324411
FAX: +299 324460
TITLE: Honorary Consul
NAME: Hans-Pavia Egede

JUDICIAL SYSTEM

Grønlands Landsret

P.O. Box 1040, Nuuk 3900, Greenland
PHONE: +299 324200
FAX: +299 323975

FURTHER READING

Articles

"Greenland Corporation Announces Partnership with Sprint and Cisco Systems." Reuters, 8 Nov 1999.

"Greenland Says Russia Must Back U.S. Missile Plan." Reuters, 3 November 1999.

Internet

"Caught in Their Tracks: How a Theropod Would Have Left a Deep Track." *BBC Online Network*, 18 May 1999. Available Online @ http://news2.thls.bbc.co.uk/hi/english/sci/tech/newsid%5F342000/342352.stm (December 14, 1999).

"Denmark Apologizes to Evicted Inuit." *BBC Online Network*, 2 October 1999. Available Online @ http://news2.thls.bbc.co.uk/hi/english/world/europe/newsid%5F437000/437003.stm (December 14, 1999).

"Greenland Ice Warning." *BBC Online Network*, 19 March 1999. Available Online @ http://news2.thls.bbc.co.uk/hi/english/sci/tech/newsid%5F291000/291120.stm (December 14, 1999).

"Greenland Takes Up the Fight for Inuit Hunters: Fairness of Trade Bans on Export of Seal Parts to Be Challenged." *The Guardian of London*, 13 October 1999. Available Online @ http://www.guardianunlimited.co.uk/Archive/Article/0,4273,3911756,00.html (December 14, 1999).

"How's the Film Industry in Greenland? On an Arctic Roll." *The Guardian of London*, 25 April 1999. Available Online @ http://www.guardianunlimited.co.uk/Archive/Article/0,4273,3857853,00.html (December 14, 1999).

"Land Where Killers Are Free to Go Hunting: The Traditional Inuit Belief That Criminals Should Not Be Imprisoned Lives on in Greenland." *The Guardian of London*. Available Online @ http://www.guardianunlimited.co.uk/Archive/Article/0,4273,3901135,00.html (December 14, 1999).

"Smiling Lessons End Service with a Scowl in Greenland." *The Guardian of London*, 23 October 1999. Available Online @ http://www.guardianunlimited.co.uk/Archive/Article/0,4273,3917191,00.html (December 14, 1999).

GREENLAND: STATISTICAL DATA

For sources and notes see "Sources of Statistics" in the front of each volume.

GEOGRAPHY

Geography (1)

Area:

Total: 2,175,600 sq km.

Land: 2,175,600 sq km (341,600 sq km ice-free, 1,834,000 sq km ice-covered) (est.).

Area—comparative: slightly more than three times the size of Texas.

Land boundaries: 0 km.

Coastline: 44,087 km.

Climate: arctic to subarctic; cool summers, cold winters.

Terrain: flat to gradually sloping icecap covers all but a narrow, mountainous, barren, rocky coast.

Natural resources: zinc, lead, iron ore, coal, molybdcnum, gold, platinum, uranium, fish, seals, whales.

Land use:

Arable land: 0%

Permanent crops: 0%

Permanent pastures: 1%

Forests and woodland: 0%

Other: 99% (1993 est.).

HUMAN FACTORS

Ethnic Division (6)

Greenlander 87%

Danish and others 13%

Greenlander includes Eskimos and Greenland-born whites.

Demographics (2A)

	1990	1995	1998	2000	2010	2020	2030	2040	2050
Population	55.5	57.6	59.3	60.3	64.9	69.0	71.4	71.8	70.9
Net migration rate (per 1,000 population)	NA	NA	NA	NA	NA	NA	NA	NA	NA
Births	NA	NA	NA	NA	NA	NA	NA	NA	NA
Deaths	NA	NA	NA	NA	NA	NA	NA	NA	NA
Life expectancy - males	59.6	63.3	65.3	66.7	72.0	75.6	77.9	79.2	80.0
Life expectancy - females	68.6	72.0	73.6	74.8	79.3	82.3	84.1	85.3	86.0
Birth rate (per 1,000)	22.6	17.7	15.8	14.8	13.9	12.8	11.0	10.5	10.0
Death rate (per 1,000)	8.4	7.2	6.9	6.7	6.8	7.7	9.1	10.9	12.1
Women of reproductive age (15-49 yrs.)	14.7	14.7	15.2	15.5	16.6	15.5	16.4	15.8	14.7
of which are currently married	NA	NA	NA	NA	NA	NA	NA	NA	NA
Fertility rate	2.4	2.3	2.2	2.1	1.9	1.8	1.8	1.7	1.7

Except as noted, values for vital statistics are in thousands; life expectancy is in years.

Religions (7)

Evangelical Lutheran

Languages (8)

Eskimo dialects, Danish, Greenlandic (an Inuit dialect).

GOVERNMENT & LAW

Political Parties (12)

Parliament	% of seats
Siumut	.38.4
Inuit Ataqatigiit	.20.3
Atassut Party	.30.1

Government Budget (13B)

Revenues	.$706 million
Expenditures	.$697 million
Capital expenditures	.NA

Data for 1995. NA stands for not available.

Military Affairs (14A)

Defense is the responsibility of Denmark.

LABOR FORCE

Labor Force (16)

Total 24,500. Data for 1995 est.

Unemployment Rate (17)

10.5% (1995 est.)

PRODUCTION SECTOR

Electric Energy (18)

Capacity	.106,000 kW (1995)
Production	.245 million kWh (1995)
Consumption per capita	.4,253 kWh (1995)

Transportation (19)

Highways:

total: 150 km

paved: 60 km

unpaved: 90 km

Merchant marine: none

Airports: 10 (1997 est.)

Airports—with paved runways:

total: 7

over 3,047 m: 1

2,438 to 3,047 m: 1

1,524 to 2,437 m: 1

914 to 1,523 m: 2

under 914 m: 2 (1997 est.)

Airports—with unpaved runways:

total: 3

1,524 to 2,437 m: 1

914 to 1,523 m: 2 (1997 est.)

Top Agricultural Products (20)

Forage crops, small garden vegetables; sheep, fish.

FINANCE, ECONOMICS, & TRADE

Economic Indicators (22)

National product: GDP—purchasing power parity— $945 million (1997 est.)

National product real growth rate: 0.6% (1997 est.)

National product per capita: $16,100 (1997 est.)

Inflation rate—consumer price index: 0.6% (1997 est.)

Exchange Rates (24)

Exchange rates:

Danish kroner (DKr) per US$1

January 1998	.6.916
1997	.6.604
1996	.5.799
1995	.5.602
1994	.6.361
1993	.6.484

Top Import Origins (25)

$421 million (c.i.f., 1995)

Origins	%
Denmark	.7.5
Iceland	.3.8
Japan	.3.3
Norway	.3.1
United States	.2.4
Germany	.2.4
Sweden	.1.8

Top Export Destinations (26)

$363.4 million (f.o.b., 1995).

Destinations	%
Denmark	.89
Japan	.5
United Kingdom	.5

Economic Aid (27)

Substantial annual subsidy from Denmark—$427 million (1995).

Import Export Commodities (28)

Import Commodities	Export Commodities
Machinery and transport equipment 25%	Fish and fish products 95%
Manufactured goods 18%	
Food and live animals 11%	
Petroleum products 6%	

GRENADA

CAPITAL: St. George's.

FLAG: The national flag consists of a red border surrounding a rectangle divided into two gold and two green triangles. There are seven yellow stars—three on the upper and three on the lower red border, and one large star at the apex of the four triangles—representing the six parishes and the island of Carriacou. A yellow nutmeg is represented on the hoist triangle.

ANTHEM: National anthem beginning "Hail Grenada, land of ours, we pledge ourselves to thee."

MONETARY UNIT: The East Caribbean dollar (EC $) is a paper currency of 100 cents. There are coins of 1, 2, 5, 10, 25, and 50 cents, and 1 dollar, and notes of 5, 10, 20, and 100 East Caribbean dollars. EC $1 = US $0.3704 (or US $1 = EC $2.70).

WEIGHTS AND MEASURES: The metric system is in use.

HOLIDAYS: New Year, 1–2 January; Independence Day, 7 February; Labor Day, 1 May; Thanksgiving, 25 October; Christmas, 25 December; Boxing Day, 26 December. Movable holidays include Good Friday, Easter Monday, and Emancipation Day, 1st Monday in August.

TIME: 8 AM = noon GMT.

LOCATION AND SIZE: Grenada has an area of 340 square kilometers (131 square miles), slightly less than twice the size of Washington, D.C. Grenada's capital city, St. George's, is located on the island's southwestern coast.

CLIMATE: Temperatures range from 21° to 29°C (70–84°F). Annual rainfall varies from about 150 centimeters (60 inches) to 380 centimeters (150 inches). There is a wet season from June to December.

INTRODUCTORY SURVEY

RECENT HISTORY

Grenada's colonial status ended in 1958 when it joined the short-lived Federation of the West Indies. In 1962, the federation dissolved, and in 1967, Grenada became an associated state of the United Kingdom. Independence came on 7 February 1974 despite widespread strikes and demonstrations protesting against the secret police of Prime Minister Eric Matthew Gairy.

On 13 March 1979, the opposition party, the New Jewel Movement, seized power, and Maurice Bishop became prime minister of the People's Revolutionary Government (PRG). Bishop suspended the constitution, jailed opposition leaders, and shut down independent newspapers. The PRG was drawn toward Cuba and its allies in the Caribbean region, as relations with the United States and some of Grenada's Caribbean neighbors deteriorated. Cuban advisors and troops supported the PRG in Grenada.

On 19 October 1983, Bishop and several followers were shot to death as the result of a power struggle within the PRG. A staunch Marxist military council, headed by General Hudson Austin, took over. Six days later, thousands of United States troops, accompanied by token forces from seven other Caribbean nations, invaded the island. Nearly all the 700 Cubans then in Grenada were captured and expelled. General Austin was placed in detention, and the governor-general, Sir Paul Scoon, formed an interim government that ruled until the 1984 elections.

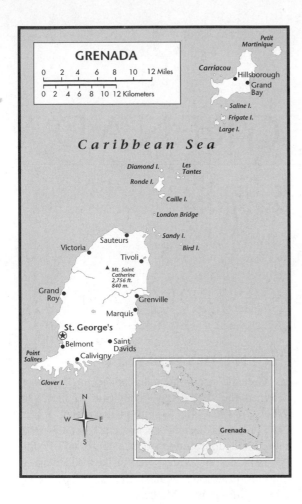

The elections of 1990 elevated the National Democratic Congress (NDC) to majority status, and Nicholas Brathwaite became prime minister. Brathwaite reintroduced the personal income tax in 1994, which had been abolished since 1986. The unpopular tax helped carry the opposing New National Party to power in the 1995 elections, and Keith Mitchell became the new prime minister.

GOVERNMENT

The constitution provides for a governor-general appointed by the British crown and a parliamentary government with independent executive, legislative, and judicial branches. The bicameral legislature consists of a thirteen-member Senate and a fifteen-seat House of Representatives. The main island is divided into six parishes and one dependency.

Judiciary

The Grenada Supreme Court, in St. George's, consists of a High Court of Justice and a two-tier Court of Appeals.

Political Parties

There are six political parties in Grenada. The National Democratic Congress (NDC), a moderate party, gained control of the government in the 1990 elections. The New National Party won eight of fifteen seats in the 1995 elections, and Keith Mitchell became the prime minister.

DEFENSE

The 550-man Royal Grenada Police and Coast Guard provides internal defense.

ECONOMIC AFFAIRS

Since 1983, Grenada's economy has been highly dependent on international trade. Exports of nutmeg, cocoa, spices, and bananas are the main sources of income from abroad. The tourism industry continues to expand. Grenada receives aid from the United States, the European Communities, the United Kingdom, and Canada.

Public Finance

Main sources of revenue are export and import duties, income tax, estate duties, and various internal rates, licenses, and taxes. The 1986 Fiscal Reform Program replaced a number of taxes, including a personal income tax, with a VAT of 20% on certain consumer goods.

The U.S. CIA estimates that, in 1995, government revenues totaled approximately $75.7 million and expenditures $126.7 million, including capital expenditures of $51 million. External debt totaled $89.1 million.

Income

In 1998, Grenada's gross national product (GNP) was U.S. $305 million at current prices, or U.S. $3,170 per person.

Industry

Industry is small scale, mainly producing consumer products for local use. Local firms produce beer, oils, soap (from copra), furniture, mattresses, clothing, and a number of other items.

Banking and Securities

Local financial institutions include the National Commercial Bank of Grenada, the Grenada Bank of Commerce, the Grenada Development Bank, and the Grenada Cooperative Bank. There is no stock exchange.

At the end of 1996, foreign exchange reserves totaled US$37.3 million.

Economic Development

Government policy has aimed toward sustained development of agriculture and tourism as the prime sectors of the economy, with respect to both employment and foreign exchange earnings. Import substitution has been the focal point of the agricultural development plan. The PRG is committed to nationalizing agriculture and turned the large estates that had belonged to former Prime Minister Gairy into cooperative farms.

Economic growth is expected to remain at around 4%, based on a recovery of world commodity prices as well as new foreign investment. Tourism is expected to pick up as new hotels are being built. The government is expanding its cargo ports to handle the growing volume of containerized cargo.

SOCIAL WELFARE

A National Insurance Scheme, introduced on 4 April 1983, provides old-age, disability, survivor, health, and maternity benefits to workers. There is also a funeral grant. Women's rights advocates claim that many cases of rape and abuse go unreported. The law requires harsh penalties for both child and spousal abuse.

Healthcare

Grenada General Hospital and two other general hospitals have a combined total of 409 beds. Life expectancy averaged 71 years for both women and men.

Housing

The Grenada Housing Authority acquires land and constructs low-income housing projects. All main population centers have been supplied with sewerage and piped-water facilities.

EDUCATION

Education is provided by the government and compulsory for twelve years. In 1992, there were 22,345 primary school students with 963 teachers. Secondary schools had an enrollment of 12,213 students that year. Postsecondary institutions include the Technical and Vocational Institute and the Teacher Training College. The adult illiteracy rate in the mid-1990s was an estimated 2%.

1999 KEY EVENTS TIMELINE

January

- Prime Minister Keith Mitchell's New National Party wins all fifteen parliamentary seats only seven weeks after his government collapses; Mitchell promises to clean up his image after an election that focused on corruption allegations in his government.

February

- Grenada celebrates the 25th anniversary of independence.

May

- The prime ministers of Grenada, Barbados and other Caribbean officials travel to Washington to meet with Secretary of State Madeleine Albright and other U.S. officials for high-level talks to find a solution to the banana trade dispute.

- The International Whaling Commission meets in Grenada, where Japan denounces plans to expand whale sanctuaries.

June

- Justice ministers from more than a dozen countries meet in Grenada to discuss the creation of a Caribbean court to replace Britain's Privy Council, a colonial vestige that still has final say on legal appeals.

July

- Prime Minister Mitchell visits the U.S. Virgin Islands and encourages people from Grenada to return home to help the tiny nation.

October

- Grenada police arrest a journalist on sedition charges for reportedly alleging in a radio broadcast that the prime minister plotted to kill a former minister.

- Dead fish, including snapper, parrotfish, and angelfish among others, are washing up on beaches around the Caribbean, especially in Barbados, St. Vincent and the Grenadines, Grenada, and Trinidad and Tobago. Health inspectors and scientists are searching for an explanation.

ANALYSIS OF EVENTS: 1999

BUSINESS AND THE ECONOMY

Tourism industry leaders were not expecting 1999 to be a good year in the Caribbean. Most island nations expected no growth or a decline in tourism. Grenada, one of the nations affected by the downturn, braced for another major impact after the Carnival cruise line announced its ships would no longer stop at Port St. George, ending a decade-long relationship. Industry officials said vendors and taxi operators could face a 40 percent drop in income.

GOVERNMENT AND POLITICS

In January, Prime Minister Keith Mitchell's ruling New National Party became the first in Grenada to win two successive terms since 1984, when parliamentary democracy was restored in the three southern Caribbean islands which make up the nation.

The party, which held a slim 8-7 majority in Parliament, captured all 15 seats in the January elections despite defections by two of Mitchell's top aides and accusations of corruption in his government. Mitchell was accused of irregularities in awarding public works contracts, and negotiating with foreign investors with questionable credentials. He was forced to call elections 18 months ahead of schedule when a member of his party and parliament resigned, leaving his government in the minority. Turnout was low, with only 56.4 percent of registered voters casting ballots. In the 1995 elections, there was a 61.7 percent turnout. Opponents complained that they only had six weeks to campaign, which gave Mitchell an advantage. Mitchell has been credited with stimulating the economy, and attracting investment. After being sworn in, he was conciliatory to the opposition.

The Organization of American States (OAS), which monitored the elections and pronounced them fair, later said Grenada should consider campaign finance reform. Opponents said they could not compete against the better-funded NNP.

In other developments, the government persecuted Grenadian journalists for reporting allegations of government corruption. The London-based International Center for the Legal Protection of Human Rights offered legal assistance to news-paper editor George Worme and radio journalist Stanley Charles. Both were facing criminal charges for their reports. Worme was charged with criminal libel for publishing a letter accusing Prime Minister Mitchell of bribing voters in the January election. Charles was charged with sedition for statements made on a radio talk show. He was arrested in connection with a statement made about an alleged plot to kill the former Foreign Affairs Minister, Raphael Fletcher. The court was expected to hear his case in January 2000.

CULTURE AND SOCIETY

Prime Minister Keith Mitchell said battling poverty was among the goals of his administration. A poverty assessment survey released in 1999 determined that nearly one-third of Grenada's population lives below the poverty line.

The Poverty Assessment Survey, commissioned in 1998, found that 48 percent of those below the poverty line were under the age of 20, and that unemployment was high in all communities. The survey also found that 21.5 percent of Grenada's citizens were extremely poor and indigent, and unable to obtain the minimum daily food requirements.

DIRECTORY

CENTRAL GOVERNMENT

Head of State

Queen

Elizabeth II, Monarch, Buckingham Palace, London SW1A 1AA, England
PHONE: +44 (171) 8391377
FAX: +44 (171) 9309625

Prime Minister

Keith Mitchell, Office of the Prime Minister, Botanical Gardens, St. George's, Grenada
PHONE: +(809) 4402255
FAX: +(809) 4404116

Governor-General
Daniel Williams

Ministers

Minister of Tourism, Civil Aviation, Co-operatives, and Social Security
Joslyn Whiteman, Ministry of Tourism, Civil Aviation, Co-operatives, and Social Security

Minister of National Security
Keith Mitchell, Ministry of National Security

Minister of Legal Affairs and Local
Government
Elvin Nimrod, Ministry of Legal Affairs and
Local Government

Minister of Information
Keith Mitchell, Ministry of Information

Minister of Housing, and Social Security and
Women's Affairs
Laurina Waldron, Ministry of Housing, and
Social Security and Women's Affairs

Minister of Health and Environment
Modeste Clarise, Ministry of Health and
Environment, The Carenage, St. George's,
Grenada
PHONE: +(809) 4402649; 4402962
FAX: +(809) 4404127

Minister of Foreign Affairs
Mark Isaac, Ministry of Foreign Affairs,
Botanical Gardens, St. George's, Grenada
PHONE: +(809) 4402255
FAX: +(809) 4404116

Minister of Fisheries
Michael Baptiste, Ministry of Fisheries

Minister of Finance, Trade, and Industry
Patrick Bubb, Ministry of Finance, Trade, and
Industry

Minister of Education and Labor
Lawrence Joseph, Ministry of Education and
Labor

Minister of Communications, Works, and
Public Utilities
Gregory Bowen, Ministry of Communications,
Works, and Public Utilities

Minister of Carriacou and Petit Martinique
Affairs
Keith Mitchell, Ministry of Carriacou and Petit
Martinique Affairs

Minister of Agriculture, Forestry, and Lands
Mark Isaac, Ministry of Agriculture, Forestry,
and Lands

Minister of Youth, Sports, Culture, and
Community Development
Adrian Mitchell, Ministry of Youth, Sports,
Culture, and Community

POLITICAL ORGANIZATIONS

The National Party (TNP)

Democratic Labor Party

New National Party (NNP)

NAME: Keith Mitchell

National Democratic Congress (NDC)

NAME: George Brizan

Grenada United Labor Party (GULP)

NAME: Jerry Seales

DIPLOMATIC REPRESENTATION

Embassies in Grenada

China
PHONE: +(809) 4403054
TITLE: Ambassador
NAME: Jeanette W. Hyde

France
TITLE: Ambassador
NAME: Sylvie Alvarez

Netherlands
PHONE: +(809) 4402031

Sweden
P.O. Box 325, St George's, Grenada
PHONE: +(809) 4402765
FAX: +(809) 4404183
NAME: Hugh Dennie

Trinidad and Tobago
High Commission for Grenada, c/o Ministry of
External Affairs, Botanical Gardens, Tanteen, St.
George's, Grenada

United States
Point Salines, P.O. Box 54, St. George's,
Grenada
PHONE: +(809) 4441173
FAX: +(809) 4444820
TITLE: Ambassador
NAME: Dennis G. Antoine

Venezuela
PHONE: +(809) 4401721

JUDICIAL SYSTEM
West Indies Associate States Supreme Court

FURTHER READING
Articles

"Banana Wars Could Slip Up U.S.-Europe Trade Relations." *The Miami Herald*, 7 February 1999.

"Grenada's Premier Promises to Clean Up Corruption Image." *The Miami Herald*, 20 January 1999.

"Grenadian Journalist Arrested on Charges of Sedition." The Associated Press, 3 October 1999.

"Grenadians Oppose Release of Coup Leaders." The Associated Press, 13 October 1999.

"Judge Upholds Monopoly of Cable and Wireless Grenada." The Associated Press, 25 June 1999.

"Offshore Banking Raises Concerns: Laundering Made Too Easy." *The Washington Post*, 31 October 1999.

Internet

"Banana Players." *The Guardian of London*, 5 March 1999. Available Online @ http://www.guardianunlimited.co.uk/Archive/Article/0,4273,3832162,00.html (December 14, 1999).

GRENADA: STATISTICAL DATA

For sources and notes see "Sources of Statistics" in the front of each volume.

GEOGRAPHY

Geography (1)

Area:

Total: 340 sq km.

Land: 340 sq km.

Water: 0 sq km.

Area—comparative: twice the size of Washington, DC.

Land boundaries: 0 km.

Coastline: 121 km.

Climate: tropical; tempered by northeast trade winds.

Terrain: volcanic in origin with central mountains.

Natural resources: timber, tropical fruit, deepwater harbors.

Land use:

Arable land: 15%

Permanent crops: 18%

Permanent pastures: 3%

Forests and woodland: 9%

Other: 55% (1993 est.).

HUMAN FACTORS

Infants and Malnutrition (5)

Under-5 mortality rate (1997) 29

% of infants with low birthweight (1990-97) 9

Births attended by skilled health staff % of total[a] . . .NA

% fully immunized (1995-97)

   TB . . . . .NA

   DPT 95

   Polio 95

   Measles 92

Prevalence of child malnutrition under age 5
(1992-97)[b] . . . . .NA

Demographics (2A)

	1990	1995	1998	2000	2010	2020	2030	2040	2050
Population	93.6	94.5	96.2	97.9	114.8	141.3	166.8	189.9	210.2
Net migration rate (per 1,000 population)	NA	NA	NA	NA	NA	NA	NA	NA	NA
Births	NA	NA	NA	NA	NA	NA	NA	NA	NA
Deaths	NA	NA	NA	NA	NA	NA	NA	NA	NA
Life expectancy - males	67.2	68.2	68.8	69.2	70.9	72.5	73.8	75.0	76.0
Life expectancy - females	71.7	73.2	74.0	74.6	77.1	79.1	80.8	82.2	83.3
Birth rate (per 1,000)	32.3	29.7	28.1	27.2	25.7	22.4	18.4	16.8	15.2
Death rate (per 1,000)	7.3	5.9	5.3	5.0	3.9	3.5	3.9	5.2	6.4
Women of reproductive age (15-49 yrs.)	20.5	20.7	21.3	22.4	30.4	38.0	44.9	49.1	51.3
of which are currently married	NA	NA	NA	NA	NA	NA	NA	NA	NA
Fertility rate	4.2	3.8	3.6	3.5	2.9	2.5	2.3	2.2	2.1

Except as noted, values for vital statistics are in thousands; life expectancy is in years.

Ethnic Division (6)

Black.

Religions (7)

Roman Catholic 53%

Anglican 13.8%

Other Protestant sects 33.2%

Languages (8)

English (official), French patois.

EDUCATION

Educational Attainment (10)

Age group (1981) . . . . .25+

Total population 33,401

Highest level attained (%)

No schooling 2.2

First level

Not completed 87.8

Completed . . . . .NA

Entered second level

S-1 . . . . .8.5

S-2 . . . . .NA

Postsecondary 1.5

GOVERNMENT & LAW

Political Parties (12)

House of Representatives	No. of seats
New National Party (NNP)	8
National Democratic Congress (NDC)	5
Grenada United Labor Party (GULP)	2

Government Budget (13A)

Year: 1995

Total Expenditures: 209.69 Millions of Dollars

Expenditures as a percentage of the total by function:

General public services and public order 22.37

Defense . . . .-

Education 16.85

Health 10.44

Social Security and Welfare 8.64

Housing and community amenities 2.06

Recreational, cultural, and religious affairs 2.14

Fuel and energy . . . .-

Agriculture, forestry, fishing, and hunting 9.65

Mining, manufacturing, and construction 1.26

Transportation and communication 14.08

Other economic affairs and services 3.41

Military Affairs (14A)

Total expenditures . . . .$NA

Expenditures as % of GDP . . . . .NA%

NA stands for not available.

Crime (15)

Crime rate (for 1997)

Crimes reported 9,650

Total persons convicted 6,700

Crimes per 100,000 population 10,200

Persons responsible for offenses

Total number of suspects . . . . .NA

Total number of female suspects . . . . .NA

Total number of juvenile suspects . . . . .NA

LABOR FORCE

Labor Force (16)

Total 36,000

Services 31%

Agriculture 24%

Construction 8%

Manufacturing 5%

Other 32%

Data for 1985.

Unemployment Rate (17)

20% (1 October 1996)

PRODUCTION SECTOR

Electric Energy (18)

Capacity . . . . .9,000 kW (1995)

Production . . . . .70 million kWh (1995)

Consumption per capita . . . . .741 kWh (1995)

Transportation (19)

Highways:

total: 1,040 km

paved: 638 km

unpaved: 402 km (1996 est.)

Merchant marine: none

Airports: 3 (1997 est.)

Airports—with paved runways:

Transportation (19)

total: 2

2,438 to 3,047 m: 1

914 to 1,523 m: 1 (1997 est.)

Airports—with unpaved runways:

total: 1

under 914 m: 1 (1997 est.)

Top Agricultural Products (20)

Bananas, cocoa, nutmeg, mace, citrus, avocados, root crops, sugarcane, corn, vegetables.

FINANCE, ECONOMICS, & TRADE

Economic Indicators (22)

National product: GDP—purchasing power parity—$300 million (1996 est.)

National product real growth rate: 3.1% (1996 est.)

National product per capita: $3,200 (1996 est.)

Inflation rate—consumer price index: 3.2% (1996 est.)

Exchange Rates (24)

Exchange rates: East Caribbean dollars (EC$) per US$1—2.7000 (fixed rate since 1976)

Top Import Origins (25)

$128 million (f.o.b., 1996 est.) Data are for 1991.

Origins	%
United States	.31.2
Caricom	.23.6
United Kingdom	.13.8
Japan	.7.1

Top Export Destinations (26)

$24 million (f.o.b., 1996 est.) Data are for 1991.

Destinations	%
Caricom	.32.3
United Kingdom	.20
United States	.13
Netherlands	.8.8

Economic Aid (27)

Recipient: ODA, $NA. NA stands for not available.

Import Export Commodities (28)

Import Commodities	Export Commodities
Food 25%	Bananas
Manufactured goods 22%	Nutmeg
	Cocoa
Machinery 20%	Fruit and vegetables
Chemicals 10%	Clothing
Fuel 6%	Mace

Balance of Payments (23)

	1990	1991	1992	1993	1994
Exports of goods (f.o.b.)	29	27	23	23	26
Imports of goods (f.o.b.)	−106	−114	−103	−118	−125
Trade balance	−77	−87	−80	−96	−99
Services - debits	−47	−45	−44	−52	−55
Services - credits	66	74	79	91	106
Private transfers (net)	1	−0	1	3	4
Government transfers (net)	10	11	11	10	13
Overall balance	−46	−47	−33	−44	−33

GUADELOUPE

Department of Guadeloupe

INTRODUCTORY SURVEY

RECENT HISTORY

Guadeloupe for many years was the richest of the Caribbean colonies of European powers, and as is the case for several of the islands, sovereignty was contested between France, Spain, and England for many years. France finally took control of Guadeloupe in 1635. In 1946, France granted Guadeloupe the status of a full Department (similar to a state or province). Black or mulatto persons predominate the islands' population as a result of early slavery to establish and maintain sugar cane plantations.

A secessionist movement has been kept alive on the islands, and occasional acts of violence and terrorism occur. The volcano on the island Basse-Terre, La Soufriere, has been active. It erupted twice in the 1970s, and still belches sulfurous fumes.

GOVERNMENT

As a department of France, the government is established by the French Constitution of September 28, 1958. Also as a department, Guadeloupe sends four elected representatives to the French Parliament, three representatives to the National Assembly and one to the Senate. The chief of state is the French President, represented in Guadeloupe by an appointed Commissioner.

The elected General Council is a 41 seat legislature, with all members elected by universal suffrage. A Regional Council is also elected by universal suffrage. The voting age is 18.

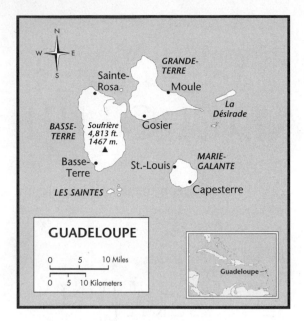

GUADELOUPE

```
0     5     10 Miles
0     5     10 Kilometers
```

Guadeloupe

As an overseas department of France, the responsibility for international relations and defense rest with the French government in Paris. The French Ministry of Interior is the responsible authority in Paris.

Judiciary

The legal system replicates the French legal system. The courts include the Court of Appeals, which is based in the French department of Martinique, where it has jurisdiction over Martinique, Guadeloupe, and French Guiana.

Political Parties

The political parties and system are not satisfying to all on the island, as the occasional violence and terrorism in the name of secession attests.

DEFENSE

Defense is the responsibility of the French military. Local police responsibilities belong to the Gendarmerie.

ECONOMIC AFFAIRS

Guadeloupe is a market economy, but the previously strong plantation system is giving way to tourism as the major source of income. Agriculture includes sugar cane, bananas, tropical fruits, vegetables, cattle, pigs, and goats. Food production is limited on the islands, however, as most of the country's needs for these are imported. Fishing is a major source of income. Cement and natural pumice are produced for local construction needs.

Light industries include tourism, fishing, agriculture, construction, cement, rum, and sugar refining. Exports to France (at 60% of exports, the major trading partner), the United States, Martinique, Japan, and others, include bananas, sugar, and rum. Fuels, minerals, and machinery are all imported. Tourism produces in excess of 350,000 visitors per year.

Public Finance

The balance of payments reflects imports of $1.6 billion in 1994 and exports of $145 million. The difference is made up from cash infusions from tourism and from French aid. Government expenditures and revenues were not available.

Income

Gross domestic product was estimated in 1995 at $3.7 billion, or $9,200 per capita. The unemployment rate is high, estimated in 1995 at 31.3%.

Industry

The sugar plantations that have been the mainstay of Guadeloupe's economy are slowly giving way to tourism as the major force driving employment and income.

Banking and Finance

The currency is the French franc. Banking services and laws follow French norms.

Economic Development

The government is taking steps to promote tourism and increase the infusion of money it represents.

SOCIAL WELFARE

The social-security system of France, providing work injury, unemployment, maternity, old-age, disability, and survivor benefits is present in the islands. Unemployment is chronically high.

Healthcare

Healthcare is generally good and government hospital facilities are provided. The infant mortality rate dropped by half between 1985 and 1996 to 8.3 per 1,000 live births.

EDUCATION

Education is compulsory for children. In the 1994/1995 school year, over 38,000 students were enrolled in elementary schools and more than 41,000 in secondary school. Higher education is available at the Universite Antilles-Guyane in Pointe-a-Pitre. Scholarships are provided for study in French universities. The literacy rate is about 91%.

1999 KEY EVENTS TIMELINE

March

- The European Union and the United States decide to abolish protective tariffs on imported liquors such as rum, which is a staple of Guadeloupe's economy as well as that of other Caribbean islands.

April

- The inhabitants of Guadeloupe celebrate the 100th anniversary of the abolition of slavery on the island.

September

- Labor unions protest the embargo of English beef products. France claims that beef products from Great Britain may contain the mad cow virus. Riots break out in the capital city.

October

- Sixty-one Chinese refugees arrive in Guadeloupe seeking political asylum. They are placed in a refugee center at the airport.

- Hurricane Jose threatens the island of Guadeloupe.

November

- Dockworkers strike to protest the visit of French Prime Minister Lionel Jospin. They are dissatisfied with France's casual treatment of the poor economic conditions in Guadeloupe and the imbalance of trade.

- Lucette Michaux-Chevry, Regional Council President, is accused of misappropriating government funds for hurricane victims. She denies these claims.

ANALYSIS OF EVENTS: 1999

BUSINESS AND THE ECONOMY

Guadeloupe is the poorest of all the overseas departments of France. Currently the banana and sugarcane industries are in crisis. The government is instituting a "Plan 2000-2006" which is supposed to address these economic conditions. Also, the government of Guadeloupe accuses France of not helping more. Trade for Guadeloupe is limited to Martinique and Guyane, other French dependencies. There is a twenty-five percent unemployment rate, which mainly affects the young.

GOVERNMENT AND POLITICS

Guadeloupe remains an overseas department of France, which means all central government is controlled by France. Guadeloupe sends delegates to the French legislature. The local government is headed at present by Marcellin Lubeth and the regional government is headed by Lucette Michaux-Chevry. As of November 1999, Michaux-Chevry is under investigation for the misappropriation of government funds that were supposed to go to hurricane victims. Michaux-Chevry denies these charges but lawyers have asked for a fine of 150,000 francs and a six months prison term. She was previously accused of similar charges in February 1998.

CULTURE AND SOCIETY

Although France is the parent country of Guadeloupe, the culture is reflected in the cuisine and language of the Creole culture. Creole is a mixture of African and European influences and the Creole language is French-based, but of a pidgin variety. In 1999, the citizens of Guadeloupe celebrated 100 years of the abolition of slavery.

DIRECTORY

CENTRAL GOVERNMENT

Head of State

President of France
Jacques Chirac, Office of the President, Palais de l'Elysée, 55 rue du faubourg Saint-Honoré, F-75008 Paris, France

Prefect
Michel Diefenbacher, Office of the Prefect

President of the General Council
Marcellin Lubeth, Office of the President of the General Council

President of the Regional Council
Lucette Michaux-Chevry, Conseil Regional
Guadeloupe, rue Paul Lacave, Petit Paris, 97109
Basse-Terre Cedex, Guadeloupe
PHONE: +590 804040
FAX: +590 813419

POLITICAL ORGANIZATIONS
Christian Movement for the Liberation of Guadeloupe
NAME: Jacques Gillot

Communist Party of Guadeloupe
NAME: Mona Cadoce

FGPS Dissidents
NAME: Dominique Larifla

Movement for an Independent Guadeloupe
NAME: Luc Reiette

Popular Union for the Liberation of Guadeloupe
NAME: Claude Makouke

Progressive Democratic Party
NAME: Henri Bangou

Rally for the Republic
TITLE: President
NAME: Lucette Michaux-Chevry

Socialist Party
NAME: Georges Louisor

Union for French Democracy
NAME: Marcel Esdras

JUDICIAL SYSTEM
Cour d'Appel (Court of Appeal)

FURTHER READING
Books
Guadeloupe. 2nd ed. Montreal: Ulysses Travel Publications, 1996.

Internet
Arapaho Services Internet. Available Online @ http://www.outremer.com (November 12, 1999).

Expatriate Resources on the Internet. "Guadeloupe Antilles Francaises." Available Online @ http://www.escapeartist.com/guadeloupe/guadeloupe.html (November 12, 1999).

GUADELOUPE: STATISTICAL DATA

For sources and notes see "Sources of Statistics" in the front of each volume.

GEOGRAPHY

Geography (1)

Area:

Total: 1,780 sq km.

Land: 1,706 sq km.

Water: 74 sq km.

Note: Guadeloupe is an archipelago of nine inhabited islands, including Basse-Terre, Grande-Terre, Marie-Galante, La Desirade, Iles des Saintes, Saint Barthelemy, and part of Saint Martin.

Area—comparative: 10 times the size of Washington, DC.

Land boundaries:

Total: 10.2 km.

Border countries: Netherlands Antilles (Sint Maarten) 10.2 km.

Coastline: 306 km.

Climate: subtropical tempered by trade winds; moderately high humidity.

Terrain: Basse-Terre is volcanic in origin with interior mountains; Grande-Terre is low limestone formation; most of the seven other islands are volcanic in origin.

Natural resources: cultivable land, beaches and climate that foster tourism.

Land use:

Arable land: 14%

Permanent crops: 4%

Permanent pastures: 14%

Forests and woodland: 39%

Other: 29% (1993 est.).

HUMAN FACTORS

Demographics (2A)

	1990	1995	1998	2000	2010	2020	2030	2040	2050
Population	377.7	402.3	416.4	425.3	462.0	489.5	507.6	511.1	498.5
Net migration rate (per 1,000 population)	NA	NA	NA	NA	NA	NA	NA	NA	NA
Births	NA	NA	NA	NA	NA	NA	NA	NA	NA
Deaths	NA	NA	NA	NA	NA	NA	NA	NA	NA
Life expectancy - males	71.6	74.2	74.8	75.2	76.9	78.1	78.9	79.6	80.0
Life expectancy - females	78.0	80.4	81.0	81.4	83.0	84.1	85.0	85.6	86.0
Birth rate (per 1,000)	20.0	17.7	16.7	15.9	12.9	11.7	10.5	9.6	9.3
Death rate (per 1,000)	6.2	5.6	5.6	5.6	6.0	6.8	8.2	10.3	13.1
Women of reproductive age (15-49 yrs.)	103.5	111.5	115.0	117.0	126.2	119.4	111.0	105.6	97.3
of which are currently married	86.2	NA	NA	NA	NA	NA	NA	NA	NA
Fertility rate	2.2	1.9	1.8	1.8	1.7	1.7	1.7	1.7	1.7

Except as noted, values for vital statistics are in thousands; life expectancy is in years.

Ethnic Division (6)

Black or mulatto 90%

White 5%

East Indian, Lebanese, Chinese . . . .<5%

Religions (7)

Roman Catholic 95%

Hindu and pagan . . . .

   African 4%

Protestant sects 1%

Languages (8)

French (official) 99%, Creole patois.

EDUCATION

Educational Attainment (10)

Age group (1982) . . . . .25+

Total population 150,253

Highest level attained (%)

No schooling 10.7

First level

   Not completed 54.6

   Completed . . . . .NA

Entered second level

   S-1 . . . . .29.5

   S-2 . . . . .NA

Postsecondary 5.2

GOVERNMENT & LAW

Political Parties (12)

General Council	No. of seats
Dissidents (FRUI.G)	13
Rally for the Republic (RPR)	13
Progressive Democratic Party (PPDG)	8
FGPS	3
Communist Party of Guadeloupe (PCG)	3
Popular Union for the Liberation of Guadeloupe (UPLG)	1
PSG	1
Independent	1

Government Budget (13B)

Revenues . . . .$300 million

Expenditures . . . .$460 million

   Capital expenditures . . . .$90 million

Data for 1995.

Military Affairs (14A)

Defense is the responsibility of France.

LABOR FORCE

Labor Force (16)

Total 128,000

Agriculture 15%

Industry 20%

Services 65%

Data for 1993.

Unemployment Rate (17)

31.3% (1995)

PRODUCTION SECTOR

Electric Energy (18)

Capacity .388,000 kW (1995)

Production . . . . .1 billion kWh (1995)

Consumption per capita . . . . .2,483 kWh (1995)

Transportation (19)

Highways:

total: 2,082 km (national 329 km, regional 582 km, community/local 1,171 km)

Merchant marine: none

Airports: 9 (1997 est.)

Airports—with paved runways:

total: 8

over 3,047 m: 1

914 to 1,523 m: 2

under 914 m: 5 (1997 est.)

Airports—with unpaved runways:

total: 1

under 914 m: 1 (1997 est.)

Top Agricultural Products (20)

Bananas, sugarcane, tropical fruits and vegetables; cattle, pigs, goats.

FINANCE, ECONOMICS, & TRADE

Economic Indicators (22)

National product: GDP—purchasing power parity—$3.7 billion (1995 est.)

National product real growth rate: NA%

National product per capita: $9,200 (1995 est.)

Inflation rate—consumer price index: 3.7% (1990)

Exchange Rates (24)

Exchange rates:

French francs (F) per US$1

January 1998 . . . . .6.0836
1997 . . . . .5.8367
1996 . . . . .5.1155
1995 . . . . .4.9915
1994 . . . . .5.5520
1993 . . . . .5.6632

Top Import Origins (25)

$1.6 billion (c.i.f., 1994) Data are for 1994.

Origins	%
France	.64
European Union	.13
Martinique	.4
United States	.NA
Japan	.NA

NA stands for not available.

Top Export Destinations (26)

$145 million (f.o.b., 1994) Data are for 1994.

Destinations	%
France	.75
Martinique	.13

Economic Aid (27)

Recipient: ODA, $NA. Note: substantial annual French subsidies. NA stands for not available.

Import Export Commodities (28)

Import Commodities	Export Commodities
Foodstuffs	Bananas
Fuels	Sugar
Vehicles	Rum
Clothing and other consumer goods	
Construction materials	

MANUFACTURING SECTOR

GDP & Manufacturing Summary (21)

	1980	1985	1990	1992	1993	1994
Gross Domestic Product						
Millions of 1990 dollars	1,676	1,706	2,200	2,172	2,273	2,340
Growth rate in percent	4.66	−0.76	3.14	2.78	4.69	2.94
Per capita (in 1990 dollars)	5,125.0	4,805.6	5,626.6	5,348.8	5,504.6	5,558.6
Manufacturing Value Added						
Millions of 1990 dollars	113	89	129	126	131	134
Growth rate in percent	−5.16	11.54	3.22	1.84	3.83	2.45
Manufacturing share in percent of current prices	6.3	4.9	5.4	NA	NA	NA

GUAM

Territory of Guam

INTRODUCTORY SURVEY

RECENT HISTORY

The earliest known settlers on Guam were the original Chamorro, who migrated from the Malay Peninsula to the Pacific around 1500 BC. When Ferdinand Magellan landed on Guam in 1521, it is believed that as many as 100,000 Chamorro lived on the island; by 1741, their numbers had been reduced to 5,000. Most of the population either had fled the island or been killed through disease or war with the Spanish. A Spanish fort was established in 1565, and from 1696 until 1898, Guam was under Spanish rule.

Under the Treaty of Paris that ended the Spanish-American War in 1898, the island was ceded to the United States and placed under the jurisdiction of the Department of the Navy. During World War II, Guam was occupied by Japanese forces; the United States recaptured the island in 1944 after 54 days of fighting. In 1950, the island's administration was transferred from the Navy to the U.S. Department of the Interior. Under the 1950 Organic Act of Guam, passed by the U.S. Congress, the island was established as an unincorporated territory of the United States; Guamanians were granted U.S. citizenship, and internal self-government was introduced.

GOVERNMENT

The governor and lieutenant governor have been elected directly since 1970. A 21-member unicameral legislature elected for two years by adult suffrage is empowered to legislate on all local

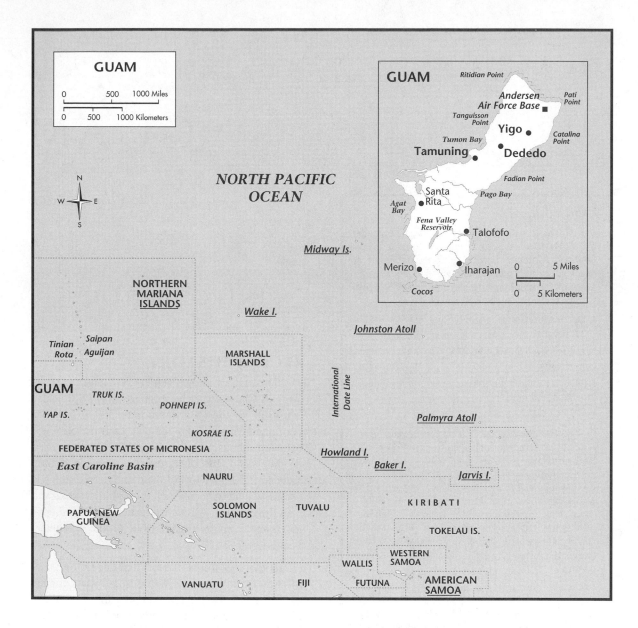

matters, including taxation and appropriations. The U.S. Congress reserves the right to annul any law passed by the Guam legislature, but must do so within a year of the date it receives the text of any such law.

Judiciary

Judicial authority is vested in the district court of Guam, and appeals may be taken to the regular U.S. courts of appeal and ultimately to the U.S. Supreme Court. An island superior court and other specialized courts have jurisdiction over certain cases arising under the laws of Guam. The judge of the district court is appointed by the U.S. president; the judges of the other courts are appointed by the governor. Guam's laws were codified in 1953.

ECONOMIC AFFAIRS

Guam is one of the most important U.S. military bases in the Pacific, and the island's economy has been profoundly affected by the large sums of money spent by the U.S. defense establishment. During the late 1960s and early 1970s, when the U.S. took the role of a major combatant in the Vietnam conflict, Guam served as a base for long-range U.S. bombers on sorties over Indochina. In 1995–96, there were 4,508 active-duty U.S. military personnel stationed on the island.

Income

U.S. income tax laws are applicable in Guam; all internal revenue taxes derived by the United States from Guam are paid into the territory's treasury. U.S. customs duties, however, are not levied. Guam is a duty-free port. In its trade with the U.S. mainland, Guam is required to use U.S. shipping.

Industry

Prior to World War II, agriculture and animal husbandry were the primary activities. By 1947, most adults were wage earners employed by the U.S. armed forces, although many continued to cultivate small plots to supplement their earnings. Since World War II, agriculture has generally contributed less than 1% of the GNP, partly because a considerable amount of arable land is taken up by military installations. Fruits and vegetables are grown and pigs and poultry are raised for local consumption, but most food is imported. Current fish catches are insufficient to meet local demand.

Tourism has become a major industry and sparked a boom in the construction industry in the mid-1980s. The number of visitors grew rapidly from 6,600 in 1967 to over 900,000 in 1992 and provided $600 million in revenues to the economy. The stagnation in the Japanese economy since the early 1990s has slowed the growth of Guam's tourism sector.

Economic Development

The Guam Rehabilitation Act of 1963 has funded the territory's capital improvement program. Further allocations in 1969 and 1977 provided over $120 million for additional capital improvements and development of the island's power installations. More than $200 million of federal funds were authorized for typhoon relief in 1977–78. Total expenditures by the government of Guam were $395 million in 1991; revenues were $525 million. Total grants from the U.S. federal government in 1996/97 amounted to $134 million.

Guam had 1,955 business establishments (including 886 retail) in 1992, with sales of over $3 billion. Guam's foreign trade usually shows large deficits. The bulk of Guam's trade is with the United States, Micronesia, and Japan.

SOCIAL WELFARE
Healthcare

Typical tropical diseases are practically unknown today in Guam. Tuberculosis, long the principal killer, was brought under control by the mid-1950s. The Guam Memorial Hospital has a capacity of 147 beds. Village dispensaries serve both as public health units and first-aid stations. In addition, there are a number of physicians in private practice. Specialists from the U.S. Naval Hospital in Guam, assisting on a part-time basis, have made possible a complete program of curative medicine.

EDUCATION

School attendance is compulsory from the age of 6 through 16. In 1995–96, 33,502 pupils were enrolled in public elementary and secondary schools. The University of Guam and Guam Community College enrolled 6,449 students in 1994–95.

1999 KEY EVENTS TIMELINE

January

- Two fishing vessels carrying some 60 undocumented Chinese migrants are intercepted off the coast of Guam. The island may have become a new outpost for human traffickers, according to United States law-enforcement officials.

- Guam Governor Carl Gutierrez is quietly sworn into his second term of office. His political opponent claims that thousands of voters may have cast fraudulent ballots. A legal challenge to the election remains undecided.

February

- Hawaii fears Guam's brown tree snake. A legislator suggests that agriculture personnel should inspect departing aircraft on Guam.

April

- President Bill Clinton authorizes Attorney General Janet Reno to maintain custody of undocumented Chinese migrants found in boats off the Northern Mariana Islands, easing concerns in Guam that they would seek asylum there.

July

- The Outrigger Hotel opens a 600-room resort in Guam, on the beach at Tumn Bay.

September

- Guam, which bills itself as "Where America's Day Begins," is expected to give federal officials a 15-hour advance notice of what the rest of the nation may experience with the Y2K computer bug.

October

- Congressman Robert A. Underwood said Guam is being treated unfairly in tax treaties with some nations, and called for U.S. treaty negotiators to include Guam in the definition of ''United States'' in future treaties.

- President Bill Clinton says the government will honor its commitment to provide millions of dollars in badly-needed funding for Guam and other Pacific territories for assisting federal authorities in detaining, housing and repatriating illegal Chinese immigrants.

December

- On December 19, an earthquake measuring 6.1 on the Richter scale hits Guam, although there are no reported casualties or property damage.

- Guam is the first U.S. territory to welcome 2000.

ANALYSIS OF EVENTS: 1999

BUSINESS AND THE ECONOMY

In May, Standard and Poor's downgraded the rating for $330 million in Guam bonds, citing the island's continued weak economy and the local government's inability to stick to an austerity plan.

The island's bond rating of BBB was lowered to BBB- and was not likely to improve in the near future. Guam was suffering from a decline in tourism, and was increasingly more dependent on Japanese visitors. Visitor arrivals fell by 18 percent in 1998, down to 1.12 million people. S and P also warned Guam to implement austerity measures to eliminate a budget deficit that is expected to grow to $146.5 million in 1999. A growing deficit could bring a lower bond rating.

GOVERNMENT AND POLITICS

In January, U.S. law enforcement officials intercepted two fishing vessels off the coast of Guam that were carrying about 60 undocumented Chinese migrants. Officials believe Guam had become the latest target for human traffickers. Officials said undocumented migrants by the hundreds have already entered Guam illegally to continue travel to the U.S. mainland. By March, authorities had captured 450 migrants and seized four vessels. Many more eluded capture. The U.S. Coast Guard

planned to supplement its regular two-ship fleet patrolling Guam with several more ships and aircraft.

The media reported that Guam residents are angry at the illegal immigration. So far, Guam had spent more than $1 million feeding, housing and providing medical care for the undocumented Chinese migrants. In October, President Bill Clinton reiterated his support to reimburse Guam for sheltering the illegal immigrants.

Many residents reported that the Chinese arrive at their doors asking for water or to use the phone. The local newspaper began running an information box with phone numbers to report illegal immigrants. Guam is a U.S. territory and operates under U.S. immigration laws. Some migrants have declared political asylum once they arrive on the island. But some obtain false documents in Guam and travel by plane to the U.S. mainland, officials said.

In January, Guam Gov. Carl Gutierrez took office. However, Joe Ada, a former two-time Guam governor and political opponent, continued to insist Gutierrez may have won with fraudulent ballots. As sides traded political accusations, Ada formally challenged the ballot results. A federal district judge decided there should be a run-off election between Ada and Gutierrez. But a federal appeals court in San Francisco granted Gutierrez's motion for a temporary restraining order to prevent a run-off election until his appeal was decided.

Guam was one of nine locations outside the U.S. mainland where nuclear weapons or components for nuclear weapons were kept during the Cold War, according to declassified Pentagon history. In Guam, there were non-nuclear bombs, bombs, depth bombs, Regulus missiles, ''Honest John'' rockets, atomic demolition munitions, 8-inch howitzers, and other weapons. They were deployed between July 1950 and June 1968, and withdrawn between April-June 1964 and March 1974.

CULTURE AND SOCIETY

The U.S. Department of Health and Human Services in October announced that the number of births to teenagers fell for a seventh straight time in 1998, with the rate of births to those of high school age hitting a 40-year low. But in Guam, birth rates actually rose, from 95.7 per 1,000 teenage girls 15 to 19 to 106.3, an 11.1 percent change. For girls 15 to 17, it rose from 55 to 61.4. per 1,000 teen-age girls, an 11.6 percent change.

DIRECTORY

CENTRAL GOVERNMENT

Head of State

Governor of Guam
Carl T.C. Guiterrez, Office of the Governor, P.O. Box 2950, Hagatna, Guam 96932
PHONE: +671 4728931
FAX: +671 4774826
E-MAIL: magalahi@ns.gov.gu

Departments

Acting Director of Administration
Rodney C. Webb, Department of Administration, P.O. Box 884, Hagatna, Guam 96932
PHONE: +671 4751101; 4751136
FAX: 671 4756788
E-MAIL: doa@ns.gov.gu

Acting Director of Agriculture
Juan Taijito, Department of Agriculture, 192 Dairy Road, Mangialo, Guam 96923
PHONE: +671 7343942; 7343943
FAX: 7346569
E-MAIL: agr@ns.gov.gu

Director of Commerce
Isabel D.S.A. Lujan, Department of Commerce, 102 M Street, Tiyan, Guam 96913
PHONE: +671 4750321; 4750322
FAX: +671 4779031
E-MAIL: commerce@ns.gov.gu

Director of Corrections
Angel Sablan, Department of Corrections, P.O. Box 3236, Hagatna, Guam 96932
PHONE: +671 7344668; 7343126
FAX: +671 7344990
E-MAIL: doc@ns.gov.gu

Director of Customs and Quarantine
John M. Quinata, Department of Customs and Quarantine, 1503 Central Avenue Tiyan, Barrigada, Guam 96921
PHONE: +671 4756202; 4756203
FAX: +671 4756227

Director of Education
Michael J. Reidy, Department of Education, P.O. Box DE, Agana, Guam 96932
PHONE: +671 4750457; 4750462

Director of Integrated Services for Individuals with Disabilities
Joseph Arter-Cameron, Department of Integrated Services for Individuals with Disabilities, 1313 Central Avenue, Tiyan, Guam 96913
PHONE: +671 4754646; 4754647
FAX: +671 4772892
E-MAIL: disid@ns.gov.gu

Director of Labor
Jim Underwood, Department of Labor, P.O. Box 9970, Tamuning, Guam 96931
PHONE: +671 6476400
FAX: +671 4772988
E-MAIL: labor@ns.gov.gu

Director of Land Management
Carl J.C. Aguon, Department of Land Management, P.O. Box 2950, Hagatna, Guam 96932
PHONE: +671 4755252; 4755278
FAX: +671 4770083
E-MAIL: dlm@ns.gov.gu

Director of Mental Health and Substance Abuse
John W. Leon Guerrero, Department of Mental Health and Substance Abuse, 790 Gov. Carlos G. Camacho Rd., Tamuning, Guam 96911
PHONE: +671 6475330; 6475303
FAX: +671 6496948
E-MAIL: mhsa@ns.gov.gu

Director of Parks and Recreation
Austing J. Shelton, Department of Parks and Recreation, P.O. Box 2950, Hagatna, Guam 96932
PHONE: +671 4756296
FAX: +671 4729626
E-MAIL: dpr@ns.gov.gu

Director of Public Works
Daniel Lizama, Department of Public Works, 542 N. Marine Drive, Tamuning, Guam 96911
PHONE: +671 6463131; 6474388
FAX: +671 6496178
E-MAIL: dpw@ns.gov.gu

Director of Revenue and Taxation
Joseph T. Duenas, Department of Revenue and Taxation, P.O. Box 23607, GMF, Guam 96921
PHONE: +671 4751817; 4751819
FAX: +671 4722643
E-MAIL: revtax@ns.gov.gu

Director of Youth Affairs
David M. Dell'Isola, Department of Youth Affairs, P.O. Box 23672, GMF, Guam 96921

PHONE: +671 7342597; 7343911; 7343915
FAX: +671 7347536
E-MAIL: ddell@ns.gov.gu

POLITICAL ORGANIZATIONS
Guam Democratic Party

P.O. Box 2950, Agana, Guam 96910
PHONE: +671 4728931
FAX: +671 4776425

Guam Republican Party

DIPLOMATIC REPRESENTATION
Embassies in Guam

Marshall Islands
111 Chalan Santo Papa, Suite 701, Agana, Guam 96910
PHONE: +671 4722922
TITLE: Honorary Consul
NAME: Daniel A. Roland

Micronesia
Old Hakubotan Building, 973, S. Marine Dr., Suite 201, Tamuning, Guam 96911
PHONE: +671 6469154
FAX: +671 6496320
TITLE: Consul General
NAME: Wilton Jaboar Mackwelung

Nauru
Ada Professional Bldg., Marine Dr., lst Floor, Agana, Guam 96910
TITLE: Consul
NAME: Manfred R. Depaune

New Zealand
290 Salas St., P.O. Box 8196, Tamuning, Guam 96931
PHONE: +671 6467662
FAX: +671 6461061
TITLE: Honorary Consul
NAME: John W. Scragg

Phillipines
Guam International Center, Marine Dr., Suite 406, Tamuning, Guam 96911
PHONE: +671 6464620
TITLE: Consul General
NAME: Antonio Pascual Villamor

JUDICIAL SYSTEM
Supreme Court
3rd Floor, Judicial Center Bldg., 120 West O'Brien Drive, Hagåtña, Guam 96910

Superior Court
Judiciary Center, 120 West O'Brien Drive, Agana, Guam 96910
PHONE: +671 4753250

FURTHER READING
Articles
"Guam, Other Pacific Islands Will Provide Early Warnings for Y2K." Associated Press, 16 September 1999.

"Radar Faulted in Plane Crashes." Associated Press, 18 October 1999.

Internet
"Chinese Migrants Caught Near Guam." The Seattle Times news services, 13 January 1999. Available Online @ http://archives.seattletimes.com/cgi-bin/texis.mummy/web/vortex/display?storyID=36d4b74d37 (December 15, 1999).

"FAA Hit in KAL Crash in Guam." The Honolulu Star-Bulletin, 22 October 1999. Available Online @ http://starbulletin.com/1999/10/22/news/story8.html (December 15, 1999).

"Guam Governor Begins Second Term Amid Allegations by Opponent of Fraud." The Honolulu Star-Bulletin, 8 January 1999. Available Online @ http://starbulletin.com/1999/01/08/news/story11.html (December 15, 1999).

"Hawaii Tries to Prevent Guam's Brown Tree Snake from Reaching Shore." The Honolulu Star-Bulletin, 4 February 1999. Available Online @ http://starbulletin.com/1999/02/04/news/story9.html (December 15, 1999).

"Illegal Immigrants from China Invade Resentful Guam." The Honolulu Star-Bulletin, 10 May 1999. Available Online @ http://starbulletin.com/1999/05/10/news/story8.html (December 15, 1999).

GUAM: STATISTICAL DATA

For sources and notes see "Sources of Statistics" in the front of each volume.

GEOGRAPHY

Geography (1)

Area:

Total: 541.3 sq km.

Land: 541.3 sq km.

Water: 0 sq km.

Area—comparative: three times the size of Washington, DC.

Land boundaries: 0 km.

Coastline: 125.5 km.

Climate: tropical marine; generally warm and humid, moderated by northeast trade winds; dry season from January to June, rainy season from July to December; little seasonal temperature variation.

Terrain: volcanic origin, surrounded by coral reefs; relatively flat coralline limestone plateau (source of most fresh water) with steep coastal cliffs and narrow coastal plains in north, low-rising hills in center, mountains in south.

Natural resources: fishing (largely undeveloped), tourism (especially from Japan).

Land use:

Arable land: 11%

Permanent crops: 11%

Permanent pastures: 15%

Forests and woodland: 18%

Other: 45% (1993 est.).

HUMAN FACTORS

Demographics (2A)

	1990	1995	1998	2000	2010	2020	2030	2040	2050
Population	134.1	143.9	149.1	154.2	182.8	210.5	235.7	255.0	271.3
Net migration rate (per 1,000 population)	NA	NA	NA	NA	NA	NA	NA	NA	NA
Births	NA	NA	NA	NA	NA	NA	NA	NA	NA
Deaths	NA	NA	NA	NA	NA	NA	NA	NA	NA
Life expectancy - males	71.0	73.4	74.4	74.8	76.6	77.9	78.9	79.5	80.0
Life expectancy - females	77.9	78.6	81.1	81.5	83.0	84.2	85.0	85.6	86.0
Birth rate (per 1,000)	28.7	29.1	27.9	25.2	19.9	18.6	15.7	14.1	13.3
Death rate (per 1,000)	4.2	4.3	4.3	4.4	4.9	5.6	6.4	7.3	7.7
Women of reproductive age (15-49 yrs.)	34.3	35.7	35.2	35.6	41.8	49.8	57.1	62.6	61.5
of which are currently married	NA	NA	NA	NA	NA	NA	NA	NA	NA
Fertility rate	3.3	3.8	4.0	3.8	2.9	2.3	2.1	2.0	2.0

Except as noted, values for vital statistics are in thousands; life expectancy is in years.

Ethnic Division (6)

Chamorro 47%

Filipino 25%

White 10%

Chinese, Japanese, Korean, and other 18%

Religions (7)

Roman Catholic 98%

Other 2%

Languages (8)

English, Chamorro, Japanese.

EDUCATION

Educational Attainment (10)

Age group (1990)[13] . . . . .25+

Total population 66,700

Highest level attained (%)

No schooling[2] . . . . .NA

First level

  Not completed 13.9

  Completed . . . . .NA

Entered second level

  S-1 . . . . .46.2

  S-2 . . . . .NA

Postsecondary 39.9

GOVERNMENT & LAW

Political Parties (12)

Legislative branch is a unicameral Legislature (21 seats; members are elected by popular vote to serve two-year terms). The Republican Party controls the legislature. The Democratic Party is the party of the Governor.

Government Budget (13B)

Revenues . . . .$524.3 million

Expenditures . . . .$361.4 million

  Capital expenditures . . . . .NA

Data for 1995. NA stands for not available.

Military Affairs (14A)

Defense is the responsibility of the US.

LABOR FORCE

Labor Force (16)

Total 65,660

Federal and territorial . . . .

  government 31%

Private 69%

  Trade 21%

  Services 33%

  Construction 12%

  Other 3%

Data for 1995.

Unemployment Rate (17)

2% (1992 est.)

PRODUCTION SECTOR

Electric Energy (18)

Capacity . . . . .302,000 kW (1995)

Production . . . . .755 million kWh (1995)

Consumption per capita . . . . .4,925 kWh (1995)

Transportation (19)

Highways:

total: 885 km

paved: 675 km

unpaved: 210 km note: there is another 685 km of roads classified non-public, including roads located on federal government installations

Merchant marine: none

Airports: 5 (1997 est.)

Airports—with paved runways:

total: 4

over 3,047 m: 2

2,438 to 3,047 m: 1

914 to 1,523 m: 1 (1997 est.)

Airports—with unpaved runways:

total: 1

under 914 m: 1 (1997 est.)

Top Agricultural Products (20)

Fruits, copra, vegetables; total value: $86.1 million (f.o.b., 1992) commodities: mostly transshipments of refined petroleum products, construction materials, fish, food and beverage products partners: US 25%, former Trust Territory of the Pacific Islands 63%, other 12%.

FINANCE, ECONOMICS, & TRADE

Economic Indicators (22)

National product: GDP—purchasing power parity—$3 billion (1996 est.)

National product real growth rate: NA%

National product per capita: $19,000 (1996 est.)

Inflation rate—consumer price index: 4% (1992 est.)

Exchange Rates (24)

Exchange rates: US currency is used

Top Import Origins (25)

$202.4 million (c.i.f., 1992)

Origins	%
United States	23
Japan	19
other	58

Economic Aid (27)

Recipient: although Guam receives no foreign aid, it does receive large transfer payments from the general revenues of the US Federal Treasury into which Guamanians pay no income or excise taxes; under the provisions of a special law of Congress, the Guamanian Treasury, rather than the US Treasury, receives federal income taxes paid by military and civilian Federal employees stationed in Guam.

Import Export Commodities (28)

Import Commodities	Export Commodities
Petroleum and petroleum products	Bananas
	Sugar
Food	Rum
Manufactured goods	

GUATEMALA

Republic of Guatemala
República de Guatemala

INTRODUCTORY SURVEY

RECENT HISTORY

In the 1950s, the government of president Jacobo Árbenz Guzmán took over the holdings of the United Fruit Co., a U.S. firm, as part of a land reform program. In the summer of 1954, Colonel Carlos Castillo Armas and an army of Guatemalan exiles, backed by the U.S. CIA, invaded Guatemala from Honduras and toppled the government. Castillo took over, restored the U.S. properties, and ruled by decree until 1957. General Miguel Ydígoras Fuentes, who became president in 1958, allowed Guatemala to be used as a training area for Cuban exiles in the abortive U.S. invasion of the Bay of Pigs in April 1961.

Dr. Julio César Méndez Montenegro, elected in 1966, was the first civilian president since Árbenz and the last for twenty years. After several years of violence between the army and left-wing guerrilla forces, Guatemala returned to military rule with the election of Colonel Carlos Arana Osorio as president in 1970. Political violence by the military, the left, and right-wing death squads continued for over twenty years, with a succession of governments unable to contain it. In 1993, the military intervened and Ramior de León Carpio was appointed president on 5 June. De León, a human rights advocate, promised to bring to justice those responsible for the dismal state of human rights in Guatemala.

On 29 December 1996, under the government of Alvaro Arzu, the Guatemalan government signed a peace accord with the guerilla Guatemalan

National Revolutionary Unity. The agreement marked the end of Central America's longest-running guerilla war.

GOVERNMENT

In theory, Guatemala is a republic. The president is elected by direct vote for a five-year term and may not be reelected. Each district elects at least two deputies to the single-chamber National Congress. In 1994, there were eighty seats in the interim congress.

Judiciary

Courts include the nine-member Supreme Court, courts of appeals, civil courts of first instance, and penal courts. As of July 1994, a new criminal code gave more emphasis to due process protection.

Political Parties

The main political parties during the elections of November 1995 and January 1996 were the National Advancement Party (Partido de Avanzada Nacional—PAN), the Guatemalan Republican Front (Frente Republicano Guatemalteco—FRG), the Christian Democrats (Union del Centro Nacional Democracía Cristiana Partido Social Democrata—DCG), and the New Guatemalan Democratic Front (Frente Democratico Nueva Guatemala—FDNG).

DEFENSE

In 1995, the armed forces numbered 42,000 in the army, 1,500 in the navy, and 700 in the air force. Defense expenditures amounted to $140 million in 1995.

ECONOMIC AFFAIRS

In the 1980s, the chief exports in order of value were coffee, bananas, sugar, and cotton. During 1991–95, the Guatemalan economy—the largest in Central America—grew at a healthy pace of about 3.5–5% per year. In 1996, the growth rate decreased to 3%.

Public Finance

Fiscal policy loosened after the 1985 elections, but tax reforms in 1987 failed to generate additional income, and governmental expenditures continued to grow. By 1990, the public sector deficit was 4.7% of GDP. The Serrano administration transformed the deficit of 1990 to a slight surplus in 1991 and a virtually balanced budget in 1992.

The U.S. CIA estimates that, in 1995, government revenues totaled approximately $1.6 billion and expenditures $1.88 billion. External debt totaled $3.1 billion.

Income

In 1998, Guatemala's gross national product (GNP) was $17.7 billion at current prices, or about $1,640 per person.

Industry

Industry represents about 20% of the domestic economy. Most manufacturing is devoted to light assembly and food processing operations. Products include food, clothing and textiles, construction materials, tires, and pharmaceuticals.

Banking and Finance

The Bank of Guatemala (BANGUAT) is the central bank and the bank of issue. The Monetary Board, an independent body, determines the monetary policy of the country.

In March-April 1995, Congress approved financial sector reforms, which tightened supervisory standards and brought Guatemala into line with the Basle convention on minimum capital requirements for banks.

The National Stock Exchange of Guatemala (the Bolsa Nacional de Valores-BNV) opened in 1989 where shares from private companies in the country and other securities are traded. It is the largest of Guatemala's stock exchanges.

Economic Development

Guatemala's economic development policy is to create rural employment through the provision of investment incentives. Such enticements include inexpensive financing by government institutions, free assistance and technical support, and preferential treatment to use government facilities and institutions for guidance.

The government has initiated a number of programs aimed at liberalizing the economy and improving the investment climate. After the signing of the final peace accord in December 1996, Guatemala is well-positioned for rapid economic growth over the next several years.

The country's economy is commanded by the private sector which generates about 85% of GDP. The public sector is small and shrinking, with its business activities limited to public utilities (now being privatized) and several development oriented institutions.

Problems hindering economic growth include illiteracy and low levels of education; inadequate and underdeveloped capital markets; and lack of infrastructure, particularly in the transportation, communications and electricity sectors. The distribution of income and wealth remains skewed. The wealthiest 10% of the population receives almost one half of all income, the top 20% receives two-thirds of all income.

SOCIAL WELFARE

Social security provides maternity benefits, general medical insurance, and pensions for the disabled, aged, widows, and minors. Despite legal equality, women are paid significantly less than their male counterparts.

An estimated 100,000 people died during the civil war, and 40,000 more disappeared. An amnesty law was passed in late 1996 so that those responsible for human rights violations in the past are unlikely to be punished.

Healthcare

Only 40% of the population has access to health care services. Among the chief causes of death are heart disease, intestinal parasites, bronchitis, influenza, and tuberculosis. Malnutrition, alcoholism, and inadequate sanitation and housing also pose serious health problems. The average life expectancy is 66 years.

Housing

Many of the nation's urban housing units and most of its rural dwellings are poorly built and lack electricity and drinkable water. In 1983, only 48% of the urban population and 28% of the rural population had sewer service.

EDUCATION

In 1995, the adult illiteracy rate was estimated at 44% (males, 37.5%; females, 51.4%). Elementary education is free and compulsory for six years. In 1991, there were 9,362 primary schools with 1.3 million pupils and 36,757 teachers. The general secondary schools had 294,907 pupils. The University of San Carlos of Guatemala, in Guatemala City, is the most important center of higher learning.

1999 KEY EVENTS TIMELINE

February

- The Historical Clarification Commission, referred to as the "truth commission" issues a report blaming the army for more than 90 percent of human rights violations. According to the report, the United States, despite knowing "acts of genocide" were being committed against Guatemalan Indians, continued to aid the military.

- Rigoberta Menchu, winner of the Nobel Peace prize, admits discrepancies in her memoir, *I, Rigoberta Menchu.* She says she mixed the testimony of other victims of Guatemala's civil war with her own life story.

- Three Guatemalans are each sentenced to 28 years in prison for the rapes and robberies of five American students in 1998.

March

- U.S. President Bill Clinton apologizes to Guatemalans for United States support of right-wing governments.

May

- Guatemalan and Salvadoran immigrants are allowed to stay in the United States.

- Guatemalan voters reject a ballot measure to give Amerindian groups a greater voice in public affairs.

July

- A United Nations commission travels to Guatemala to investigate the sale of Guatemalan children to childless couples in the developed world.

August

- An American archeologist returns a 1,000 year-old stolen Mayan artifact.

- The U.S. government donates $2.5 million to preserve a Guatemalan nature reserve.

September

- Presidential candidate Alfonso Portillo admits killing two men. Portillo claims he acted in self-defense outside a party in Mexico in 1982.

October

- Excavations begin in the former police headquarters. Prosecutors expect to find the remains of suspected leftist guerrilla sympathizers.

November

- Opposition candidate Alfonso Portillo narrowly misses an outright win in the presidential election, sending the contest into a second round.

December

- Second round of voting takes place December 27 and Alfonso Portillo is declared the winner.

ANALYSIS OF EVENTS: 1999

BUSINESS AND THE ECONOMY

Guatemala, in 1999, was still trying to recover from Hurricane Mitch, which hit the nation in late October 1998. The hurricane left 258 dead, 150 missing and thousands homeless. U.S. Embassy officials said Guatemalans had lost 20 to 60 percent of their corn, bean, coffee, and sugar crops. Nearly all the banana crops were damaged.

During his visit to Central America in March, U.S. President Bill Clinton vowed to reduce tariffs on some exports, and said he would press for nearly $1 billion in aid for hurricane victims. He also pledged $8 million for the region's schools.

Leaders from Guatemala and other Central American countries wanted Clinton to stop or slow the deportation of undocumented workers from the United States. The president would not budge on the issue, saying the United States will continue to discourage illegal immigration. Impoverished Guatemala depends on the money these immigrants send back home. In May, the Clinton administration said it would implement guidelines to give legal residency to more than 500,000 Guatemalans and Salvadorans already living in the United States.

GOVERNMENT AND POLITICS

Many Amerindian leaders believed the peace process would lead to more rights, but they suffered a serious setback in May, when voters rejected some 50 proposals to change the constitution. Indigenous people make up nearly two-thirds of the country's 11 million people, yet few of them bothered to vote. In fact, less than one-fifth of the electorate voted. The ballot measure would have given official recognition to Guatemala's 24 indigenous groups. Also in the defeated ballot were proposed changes in the army. A key proposal would have removed the army's responsibility for internal security, as well as placing the army more firmly under civilian control.

Amerindian leaders were at a loss to explain the defeat, considering the ballot's importance to their people. Some pointed to poverty, illiteracy, weak political organizations, and divisions left by the civil war. Others said Amerindians were simply afraid to vote within a system they have long distrusted.

Amerindian leaders came to the defense of the 1992 Nobel Prize winner Rigoberta Menchu after a U.S. anthropologist claimed she used the experiences of other people during the civil war to construct her own story for the book ''I, Rigoberta Menchu.'' She said the book was an accurate testimonial of what happened to her people.

On the political front, the presidential election proved to many Guatemalans that real change is elusive, and many members of the old guard held on to power. One of them is former Gen. Efrain Rios Montt, who was considered a despot during his dictatorship of 1982–83. Montt, a member of the right-wing Republican Front, was a candidate for Congress in the November 7 general elections.

In September, the party's presidential candidate, Alfonso Portillo, admitted he killed two men in Mexico in 1982, and fled the country to avoid prosecution. Portillo, who was leading the polls in August, said he shot the men in self-defense.

CULTURE AND SOCIETY

Guatemala's Historical Clarification Commission, commonly referred to as the ''truth commission'' released the report of the results of an eighteen-month study in February that accused the military of genocide during a thirty-six-year war that ended in 1996. The three-member Historical Clarification Commission spared no single segment of Guatemalan society in its report, but placed most of the blame on the army for the deaths or disappearances of more than 200,000 people during the conflict. Most of the casualties were Amerindian Mayas.

The commission used the term genocide in its 3,600-page report. Guatemalan soldiers ''blindly pursued the anti-Communist struggle, without respect for any legal principles or the most elemental ethical and religious values and, in this way, completely lost any semblance of human morals,'' they determined.

Based on testimony from 9,200 people on all sides of the conflict, the report said the military and death squads committed 93 percent of the 42,275 documented violations. Guerrillas committed 3 percent of the atrocities

The powerful document reached beyond borders, blaming the United States for supporting the right-wing governments of Guatemala despite knowing that atrocities were being committed by Guatemalan troops. The Central Intelligence Agency lent direct and indirect support to some illegal state activities, according to the report.

''It is with profound sadness,'' said commission member Christian Tomuschat on the day the report was released, ''that the commission learned of the extreme cruelty with which many of the violations were committed. Of the large number of girls and boys who were victims of violent cruelty and murder; and of the special brutality directed against women, especially against Mayan women, who were tortured, raped and murdered.'' (The Chicago Tribune, February 26, 1999).

Nearly two months before its release, President Alvaro Arzu appealed for national reconciliation, asking Guatemalans to forgive the state for its role in the 36-year war. "In the name of the state, I ask forgiveness," he said. Following the report, the country's former leftist guerilla army apologized for its abuses in the conflict. "We ask for forgiveness from the memory of the victims, their families and communities for any kind of excesses," Jorge Ismael, former rebel leader, said.

One of the most unexpected statements came from U.S. President Bill Clinton during a short visit to Guatemala in March. Clinton expressed regret for the U.S. role, saying his country "was wrong" for supporting security forces.

"It is important that I state clearly that support for military forces or intelligence units which engaged in violent and widespread repression of the kind described in the report was wrong," Clinton said. "And the United States must not repeat that mistake. We must, and we will, instead continue to support the peace and reconciliation process in Guatemala."

The Guatemalan army remained silent and no apologies came from their ranks, but some of its members are being charged for the atrocities. The truth commission was not allowed to name individuals responsible for crimes. It was powerless to bring anyone to trial as well, but it recommended investigations, and reforms in the police and army. It also urged the government to continue looking for hundreds of clandestine mass graves throughout the country, and proposed a compensation plan for families of the victims.

In August, a court convicted 25 soldiers on homicide charges in the first trial of military personnel accused of massacring civilians during Guatemala's civil war. And in October, authorities looked for the remains of disappeared citizens in the grounds of a former military police headquarters. Two prominent human rights workers were killed in what appeared to be attempts to stop the probes.

DIRECTORY

CENTRAL GOVERNMENT

Head of State

President
Alfonso Portillo, Office of the President, Palacio Nacional, Guatemala City, Guatemala
PHONE: +502 (2) 393339
FAX: +502 (2) 519702

Ministers

Minister of Agriculture
Mariano Ventura, Ministry of Agriculture

Minister of Defense
Héctor Mario Barrios Celada, Ministry of Defense, Palacio Nacional, Guatemala City, Guatemala
FAX: +502 (2) 321906
E-MAIL: webmaster@mindef.mil.gt

Minister of Education
Arabella Castro, Ministry of Education, Avenida la Reforma y 6a. Calle, Zona 10, Guatemala City, Guatemala
PHONE: +502 (3) 600911
E-MAIL: infouconime@mineduc.gob.gt

Minister of Energy and Mines
Leonel López Rodas, Ministry of Energy and Mines
PHONE: +502 (4) 760680

Minister of Public Finance
Pedro Miguel Lamport, Ministry of Public Finance, 21 Calle y 8a. Avenida Esquina, Centro Civico, Zona 01, Guatemala City, Guatemala
E-MAIL: dti@minfin.gob.gt

Minister of the Interior
Rodolfo Mendoza, Ministry of the Interior, Despacho Ministerial, Of. No. 8, Palacio Nacional, 6ª Calle y 7ª Avda, Zona 1, Guatemala City, Guatemala
PHONE: +502 (2) 515368

Minister of Foreign Affairs
Eduardo Stein Barillas, Ministry of Foreign Affairs

Minister of Health and Welfare
Marco Tulio Sosa Ramírez, Ministry of Health and Welfare

Minister of Labor and Social Security
Luis Filipe Linares Lopez, Ministry of Labor and Social Security

Minister of Communications, Transportation, and Public Works
Fritz García Gallont, Ministry of Communications, Transportation, and Public Works

Minister of Culture and Sports
Augusto Vela, Ministry of Culture and Sports

POLITICAL ORGANIZATIONS

Frente de Unidad Nacional-FUN (National Unity Front)

7a Avenida Sta. Cecilia 27-51, Zona 8,
Guatemala City, Guatemala
PHONE: +502 (2) 714048
NAME: Gabriel Girón Ortiz

Fuerza Democrática Popular-FDP (Democratic Popular Force)

11a Calle 4-13, Zona 1, Guatemala City,
Guatemala
NAME: Francisco Reyes Ixcamey

Movimiento de Liberación Nacional-MLN (National Liberation Movement)

5a Calle 1-20, Zona 1, Guatemala City,
Guatemala
NAME: Mario Sandóval Alarcón

Partido Democracia Cristiana Guatemalteca-PDCG (Guatemalan Christian Democracy Party)

8a Avda 14-53, Zona 1, Guatemala City,
Guatemala
NAME: Alfonso Cabrera Hidalgo

Partido Institucional Democrático-PID (Democratic Institutional Party)

2a Calle 10-73, Zona 1, Guatemala City,
Guatemala
NAME: Óscar Humberto Rivas García

Unidad Revolucionaria Nacional Guatemalteca-URNG (National Revolutionary Union of Guatemala)

11 Avenida 11-56, Zona 2, 001002 Ciudad
Nueva, Guatemala
PHONE: +502 (2) 540572
E-MAIL: sedeurng@quik.guate.com

DIPLOMATIC REPRESENTATION

Embassies in Guatemala

Belgium
15 Calle A 14-44, Zona 10, Guatemala City,
Guatemala
PHONE: +502 (2) 313505
FAX: +502 (2) 335659

France
11 Calle 0-69, Zona 14, Apartado Postal 162 A,
01909 Guatemala City, Guatemala
PHONE: +502 (3) 336157; 374851
FAX: +502 (3) 681616; 336156
E-MAIL: guatemala@dree.org

Israel
13 Avenida 14-07, Zona 10, Guatemala City,
Guatemala
PHONE: +502 (2) 334624; 371305
FAX: +502 (2) 336950

Italy
5 Avenida 8-59, Zona 14, Guatemala City,
Guatemala
PHONE: +502 (2) 374557
FAX: +502 (2) 374538

United Kingdom
Edificio Centro Financiero, Tower Two, 7th
Floor, 7a Avenida 5-10, Zona 4, Guatemala City,
Guatemala
PHONE: +502 (2) 321601; 321602; 321604
FAX: +502 (2) 341904

United States
Avenida la Reforma 7-01, Zone 10, Guatemala
City, Guatemala
PHONE: +502 (3) 311541, 318904
FAX: +502 (3) 310564
TITLE: Ambassador
NAME: Donald J. Planty

JUDICIAL SYSTEM
Supreme Court of Justice
Court of Constitutionality

FURTHER READING
Articles

"Buried On a Hillside Clues To Terror;
Scientists Uncover Evidence of a Massacre."
The New York Times, 23 February 1999.

"Clinton Offers His Apologies to Guatemala."
The New York Times, 11 March 1999.

"Fear and Cynicism in Guatemala." *The Economist* (May 22, 1999): 36

"Guatemala Human Rights Activist Is Reported
Murdered." *The Miami Herald,* 27 June
1999.

"Guatemalans Deny Changes for Indians and the
Army." *The New York Times,* 17 May 1999.

"Guatemala: Pending Justice." *The Economist*
(March 13, 1999): 46

"Rigoberta Menchu Admits Inaccuracies in Her Book," The Associated Press, 12 February 1999.

"Unsolved Murder Weakens Faith in Guatemalan Justice System." *Los Angeles Times,* 30 May 1999.

"U.S. Donate $2.5 Million to Preserve Guatemalan Nature Reserve," *The Miami Herald,* 22 August 1999.

"The World: The C.I.A. and Guatemala; The Spies Who Never Came In From the Cold War." *The New York Times,* 7 March 1999.

GUATEMALA: STATISTICAL DATA

For sources and notes see "Sources of Statistics" in the front of each volume.

GEOGRAPHY

Geography (1)

Area:

Total: 108,890 sq km.

Land: 108,430 sq km.

Water: 460 sq km.

Area—comparative: slightly smaller than Tennessee.

Land boundaries:

Total: 1,687 km.

Border countries: Belize 266 km, El Salvador 203 km, Honduras 256 km, Mexico 962 km.

Coastline: 400 km.

Climate: tropical; hot, humid in lowlands; cooler in highlands.

Terrain: mostly mountains with narrow coastal plains and rolling limestone plateau (Peten).

Natural resources: petroleum, nickel, rare woods, fish, chicle.

Land use:

Arable land: 12%

Permanent crops: 5%

Permanent pastures: 24%

Forests and woodland: 54%

Other: 5% (1993 est.).

HUMAN FACTORS

Demographics (2A)

	1990	1995	1998	2000	2010	2020	2030	2040	2050
Population	9,630.8	11,060.7	12,007.6	12,669.6	16,295.0	20,282.8	24,412.1	28,444.9	32,184.8
Net migration rate (per 1,000 population)	NA	NA	NA	NA	NA	NA	NA	NA	NA
Births	NA	NA	NA	NA	NA	NA	NA	NA	NA
Deaths	NA	NA	NA	NA	NA	NA	NA	NA	NA
Life expectancy - males	60.3	62.3	63.4	64.2	67.6	70.5	72.9	74.9	76.4
Life expectancy - females	65.3	67.6	68.8	69.7	73.4	76.6	79.1	81.1	82.6
Birth rate (per 1,000)	38.5	37.3	36.0	35.1	30.5	26.0	22.3	19.3	17.0
Death rate (per 1,000)	8.4	7.4	7.0	6.6	5.4	4.7	4.6	4.8	5.4
Women of reproductive age (15-49 yrs.)	2,175.1	2,558.9	2,809.3	2,979.7	3,965.5	5,148.9	6,329.2	7,375.8	8,166.1
of which are currently married	1,745.4	NA	NA	NA	NA	NA	NA	NA	NA
Fertility rate	5.3	5.0	4.8	4.7	3.9	3.3	2.8	2.5	2.3

Except as noted, values for vital statistics are in thousands; life expectancy is in years.

Health Personnel (3)

Total health expenditure as a percentage of GDP, 1990-1997[a]

Public sector 1.7

Private sector 1.5

Total[b] 3.2

Health expenditure per capita in U.S. dollars, 1990-1997[a]

Purchasing power parity 111

Total 41

Availability of health care facilities per 100,000 people

Hospital beds 1990-1997[a] 120

Doctors 1993[c] 90

Nurses 1993[c] 30

Health Indicators (4)

Life expectancy at birth

1980 57

1997 64

Daily per capita supply of calories (1996) 2,191

Total fertility rate births per woman (1997) 4.5

Maternal mortality ratio per 100,000 live births (1990-97) ....190[d]

Safe water % of population with access (1995) 67

Sanitation % of population with access (1995) 67

Consumption of iodized salt % of households (1992-98)[a] 64

Smoking prevalence

Male % of adults (1985-95)[a] 38

Female % of adults (1985-95)[a] 18

Tuberculosis incidence per 100,000 people (1997) 85

Adult HIV prevalence % of population ages 15-49 (1997) 0.52

Infants and Malnutrition (5)

Under-5 mortality rate (1997) 55

% of infants with low birthweight (1990-97) 15

Births attended by skilled health staff % of total[a] ...35

% fully immunized (1995-97)

TB 87

DPT 83

Polio 83

Measles 74

Prevalence of child malnutrition under age 5 (1992-97)[b] 27

Ethnic Division (6)

Mestizo (mixed Amerindian-Spanish—in local Spanish called Ladino) 56%

Amerindian or predominantly Amerindian 44%

Religions (7)

Roman Catholic, Protestant, traditional Mayan.

Languages (8)

Spanish 60%, Amerindian languages 40% (23 Amerindian languages, including Quiche, Cakchiquel, Kekchi).

EDUCATION

Public Education Expenditures (9)

Public expenditure on education (% of GNP)

1980 ....1.8

1996 ....1.7[1]

Expenditure per student

Primary % of GNP per capita

1980 ....4.8[1]

1996 ....6.1[1]

Secondary % of GNP per capita

1980 ....10.4[1]

1996 ....

Tertiary % of GNP per capita

1980 ....44.8[1]

1996 ....31.1[1]

Expenditure on teaching materials

Primary % of total for level (1996) ....

Secondary % of total for level (1996) ....

Primary pupil-teacher ratio per teacher (1996) 35

Duration of primary education years (1995) 6

Educational Attainment (10)

Age group (1981) ....25+

Total population 2,060,399

Highest level attained (%)

No schooling 55.0

First level

Not completed 27.3

Completed 8.6

Entered second level

S-1 ....2.9

S-2 ....4.0

Postsecondary 2.2

Literacy Rates (11A)

In thousands and percent[1]	1990	1995	2000	2010
Illiterate population (15+ yrs.)	3,638	2,346	2,627	2,939
Literacy rate - total adult pop. (%)	53.3	55.6	57.9	62.1
Literacy rate - males (%)	60.5	62.5	64.5	68.1
Literacy rate - females (%)	46.0	48.6	51.2	56.2

GOVERNMENT & LAW

Political Parties (12)

Congress of the Republic	No. of seats
National Advancement Party (PAN)	43
Guatemalan Republican Front (FRG)	21
New Guatemalan Democratic Front (FDNG)	6
Christian Democratic Party (DCG)	4
National Centrist Union (UCN)	3
Democratic Union (UD)	2
National Liberation Movement (MLN)	1

Military Affairs (14B)

	1990	1991	1992	1993	1994	1995
Military expenditures						
Current dollars (mil.)	162	167	187	173	182	191[e]
1995 constant dollars (mil.)	186	185	201	181	187	191[e]
Armed forces (000)	43	43	44	44	34	36
Gross national product (GNP)						
Current dollars (mil.)	10,780	11,740	12,690	12,610	13,470	14,710
1995 constant dollars (mil.)	12,390	12,970	13,650	13,220	13,810	14,710
Central government expenditures (CGE)						
1995 constant dollars (mil.)	1,180	1,134	1,326	1,399	1,265	1,347
People (mil.)	9.6	9.9	10.2	10.4	10.7	11.0
Military expenditure as % of GNP	1.5	1.4	1.5	1.4	1.4	1.3
Military expenditure as % of CGE	15.8	16.3	15.2	13.0	14.8	14.2
Military expenditure per capita (1995 $)	19	19	20	17	17	17
Armed forces per 1,000 people (soldiers)	4.5	4.5	4.3	4.2	3.2	3.3
GNP per capita (1995 $)	1,287	1,287	1,342	1,266	1,288	1,337
Arms imports[6]						
Current dollars (mil.)	20	10	0	5	5	5
1995 constant dollars (mil.)	23	11	0	5	5	5
Arms exports[6]						
Current dollars (mil.)	0	0	0	0	0	0
1995 constant dollars (mil.)	0	0	0	0	0	0
Total imports[7]						
Current dollars (mil.)	1,649	1,851	2,532	2,599	2,604	3,293
1995 constant dollars (mil.)	1,895	2,045	2,724	2,725	2,669	3,293
Total exports[7]						
Current dollars (mil.)	1,163	1,202	1,295	1,340	1,522	2,156
1995 constant dollars (mil.)	1,337	1,328	1,393	1,405	1,560	2,156
Arms as percent of total imports[8]	1.2	.5	.0	.2	.2	.2
Arms as percent of total exports[8]	0	0	0	0	0	0

Government Budget (13B)

Revenues . . . . .NA

Expenditures . . . . .NA

NA stands for not available.

LABOR FORCE

Labor Force (16)

Total (million) 3.32

Agriculture 58%

Services 14%

Manufacturing 14%

Commerce 7%

Construction 4%

Transport 2.6%

Utilities 0.3%

Mining 0.1%

Data for 1997 est. Percent distribution for 1995.

Unemployment Rate (17)

5.2% (1997 est.)

PRODUCTION SECTOR

Electric Energy (18)

Capacity . . . . .766,000 kW (1995)

Production . . . . .3.1 billion kWh (1995)

Consumption per capita . . . . .282 kWh (1995)

Transportation (19)

Highways:

total: 13,100 km

paved: 3,616 km (including 140 km of expressways)

unpaved: 9,484 km (1996 est.)

Waterways: 260 km navigable year round; additional
730 km navigable during high-water season

Pipelines: crude oil 275 km

Merchant marine: none

Airports: 479 (1997 est.)

Airports—with paved runways:

total: 12

over 3,047 m: 1

2,438 to 3,047 m: 1

1,524 to 2,437 m: 2

914 to 1,523 m: 6

under 914 m: 2 (1997 est.)

Airports—with unpaved runways:

total: 467

2,438 to 3,047 m: 1

1,524 to 2,437 m: 9

914 to 1,523 m: 124

under 914 m: 333 (1997 est.)

Top Agricultural Products (20)

Sugarcane, corn, bananas, coffee, beans, cardamom;
cattle, sheep, pigs, chickens.

MANUFACTURING SECTOR

GDP & Manufacturing Summary (21)

Detailed value added figures are listed by both International
Standard Industry Code (ISIC) and product title.

	1980	1985	1990	1994
GDP ($-1990 mil.)[1]	7,012	6,627	7,650	8,951
Per capita ($-1990)[1]	1,014	832	832	867
Manufacturing share (%) (current prices)[1]	11.6	11.1	9.9	NA
Manufacturing				
Value added ($-1990 mil.)[1]	772	694	761	*853*
Industrial production index	100	97	106	*118*
Value added ($ mil.)	794	907	851	*1,325*
Gross output ($ mil.)	1,968	2,195	*2,067*	*3,183*
Employment (000)	82	73	93	*103*
Profitability (% of gross output)				
Intermediate input (%)	60	59	*59*	*58*
Wages and salaries inc. supplements (%)	*10*	*10*	8	8
Gross operating surplus	*30*	*31*	*33*	*33*
Productivity ($)				
Gross output per worker	23,189	28,305	*20,481*	*28,378*
Value added per worker	9,359	11,690	*8,429*	*11,813*

	1980	1985	1990	1994
Average wage (inc. supplements)	2,477	3,079	1,874	2,579
Value added ($ mil.)				
311/2 Food products	204	276	254	378
313 Beverages	91	89	50	81
314 Tobacco products	14	15	24	42
321 Textiles	45	71	53	77
322 Wearing apparel	19	13	24	34
323 Leather and fur products	3	3	3	5
324 Footwear	15	13	8	12
331 Wood and wood products	10	7	8	12
432 Furniture and fixtures	4	3	5	7
341 Paper and paper products	19	21	15	21
342 Printing and publishing	34	34	38	59
351 Industrial chemicals	28	28	29	45
352 Other chemical products	110	121	130	214
353 Petroleum refineries	14	8	8	13
354 Miscellaneous petroleum and coal products	2	—	—	1
355 Rubber products	21	24	22	33
356 Plastic products	19	37	30	50
361 Pottery, china and earthenware	2	8	6	10
362 Glass and glass products	22	17	14	23
369 Other non-metal mineral products	34	41	38	62
371 Iron and steel	16	21	24	36
372 Non-ferrous metals	1	—	—	1
381 Metal products	23	23	25	47
382 Non-electrical machinery	6	4	6	9
383 Electrical machinery	25	19	27	41
384 Transport equipment	8	5	3	5
385 Professional and scientific equipment	1	1	2	3
390 Other manufacturing industries	4	3	4	6

FINANCE, ECONOMICS, & TRADE

Economic Indicators (22)

National product: GDP—purchasing power parity—$45.8 billion (1997 est.)

National product real growth rate: 4.1% (1997 est.)

National product per capita: $4,000 (1997 est.)

Inflation rate—consumer price index: 9% (1997 est.)

Balance of Payments (23)

	1992	1993	1994	1995	1996
Exports of goods (f.o.b.)	1,284	1,363	1,550	2,157	2,237
Imports of goods (f.o.b.)	−2,328	−2,384	−2,547	−3,033	−2,880
Trade balance	−1,044	−1,021	−996	−875	−643
Services - debits	−735	−766	−838	−901	−930
Services - credits	683	721	761	712	599
Private transfers (net)	52	1	12	—	—
Government transfers (net)	339	362	436	491	522
Overall balance	−706	−702	−625	−572	−451

Exchange Rates (24)

Exchange rates:

Free market quetzales (Q) per US$1

January 1998	.6.2580
1997	.6.0653
1996	.6.0495
1995	.5.8103
1994	.5.7512
1993	.5.6354

Top Import Origins (25)

$3.3 billion (c.i.f., 1997 est.) Data are for 1995.

Origins	%
European Union	.70
Italy	.18
Germany	.16
France	.8
United Kingdom	.6
United States	.4

Top Export Destinations (26)

$2.9 billion (f.o.b., 1997 est.).

Destinations	%
United States	.37
El Salvador	.13
Honduras	.7
Costa Rica	.5
Germany	.5

Economic Aid (27)

Recipient: ODA, $274 million (1994).

Import Export Commodities (28)

Import Commodities	Export Commodities
Fuel and petroleum products	Coffee
	Bananas
Machinery	Sugar
Grain	Cardamom
Fertilizers	Petroleum
Motor vehicles	

GUERNSEY

CAPITAL: St. Peter Port.

FLAG: White with red cross of Saint George (patron saint of England) extending to the edges of the flag.

ANTHEM: God Save the Queen.

MONETARY UNIT: 1 Guernsey pound (£G) = 100 pence.

WEIGHTS AND MEASURES: The imperial system is standard, but the metric and historic local measurement units are used as well.

HOLIDAYS: Liberation Day, 9 May.

TIME: Noon = noon GMT.

LOCATION AND SIZE: Guernsey, a territory of England, lies about 32 km (20 miles) off the coast of France in the English Channel. 49°28′N, 2°35′W; Area: 194 sq. km. Total land includes Alderney, Guernsey, Herm, Sark, and some other smaller islands.

CLIMATE: Guernsey is temperate with mild winters and cool summers, with an average rainfall of 84 cm (33 inches). February temperatures average 6°C (43°F) and August temperatures range between 16–17°C (60–63°F). About 50% of the days are overcast.

INTRODUCTORY SURVEY

RECENT HISTORY

Guernsey, one of a group of islands known as the Channel Islands, lies off the northwest coast of France. Once a part of the Duchy of Normandy, the Crown of England has possessed the island since the twelfth century. Although a British Crown dependency, it is not part of the United Kingdom, which includes England, Wales, Scotland, and Northern Ireland. The island operates under its own individual legislative, legal, and administrative systems.

By the fifteenth century Guernsey had its own administrator called a captain. The captain's position later became known as the governor and in the nineteenth century the lieutenant-governor.

Judicial responsibilities historically fell to a bailiff. Guernsey's Royal Court, presided over by the bailiff, handed down judgements and declared law. The bailiff would often refer difficult points of law to local leaders. From this practice, Guernsey's legislative assembly, the States of Deliberation, evolved in the nineteenth century. The lieutenant-governor, Royal Court, and States of Deliberation all continue to function into the twenty-first century.

Though Guernsey is self-ruling, the British government remains responsible for its international relations and defense. As were all the Channel Islands, during World War II Guernsey was left undefended from 1940 to 1945 and fell briefly to the Germans. Many of Guernsey's inhabitants evacuated to England before the German take-over.

The Guernsey dairy cattle, a pure breed, originating on Guernsey, has been exported extensively in the nineteenth and twentieth centuries to the United States, England, Australia, and Canada.

GOVERNMENT

Guernsey, along with the Isle of Man and Jersey, have unique relations with the United Kingdom. Neither sovereign states nor part of the United Kingdom, they are dependencies of the Crown. The chief of state is the British monarch. The monarch's personal representative and channel for communication between the Crown and island government is the lieutenant-governor who also serves as commander-in-chief of Guernsey.

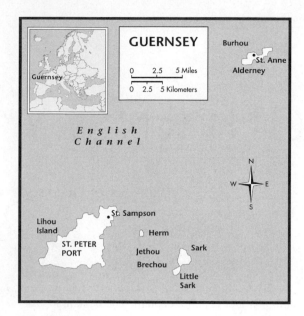

Appointed by the Crown, the lieutenant-governor may attend and speak in Guernsey's legislative body, the States of Deliberation, but has no vote.

Guernsey's unicameral legislative branch, the States of Deliberation, is composed of the bailiff, twelve Conseillers elected by local popular vote, the HM Procureur (attorney-general), the HM Comptroller (solicitor-general), thirty-three People's Deputies elected by general popular vote, ten Douzaine Representatives elected by their respective Parochial Douzaines, and two Alderney Representatives elected by the States of Alderney. Appointed by the Crown, the bailiff is president of the States and has a casting vote. Also appointed by the Crown, the Procureur and the Comptroller are the law officers of the Crown and may sit and speak in the States, but not vote. The Advisory and Finance Committee, appointed by the States, conducts the government's business.

Judiciary

Guernsey's justice system is administered by the Royal Court that is comprised of the bailiff and the twelve jurats, and permanent jurors; they are elected by the States of Election. Appeals proceed to the Guernsey Court of Appeal. In certain cases final appeal may be made to the Judicial Committee of the Privy Council in England. Minor civil and criminal cases fall to a Stipendiary Magistrate.

Political Parties

No political parties exist. All elected officials are independents.

DEFENSE

The defense of Guernsey is the responsibility of the United Kingdom.

ECONOMIC AFFAIRS

Financial services including banking, fund management, and insurance are mainstays of Guernsey's economy. Guernsey's ability to set low taxation rates encourage merchant banks, especially subsidiaries of London banks, to locate on the island. Financial services account for approximately 55% of the gross domestic product (GDP).

Agriculture also contributes to the island's economy. Dairy farming with the famous Guernsey cattle is found in the southern portions of Guernsey. Market gardening produces predominately greenhouse tomatoes and flowers for export to England.

Tourism, an important part of the twentieth century economy, is overseen by the Guernsey Tourist Board. The house occupied by the French author Victor Hugo from 1855 to 1870 is now a museum and popular tourist attraction. A total of 398,000 tourists visited the island in 1998.

Guernsey's chief exports included tomatoes, flowers, and ferns, and other vegetables. Exports are protected by British tariff barriers. Major imports are coal, gasoline, oil, machinery, and equipment. Imports are free of British purchase tax. The inflation rate was 7% in 1998.

Public Finance

Revenue is predominately raised by taxation. In 1996 revenue amounted to 233 million pounds and expenditures were 212 million pounds.

Income

Financial services account for about 55% of Guernsey's total income, the rest coming from tourism, agriculture, and light manufacturing.

Industry

Principle industrial activities in addition to the financial service industry, agriculture, and tourism, include light manufacturing. Several trade fairs are held each year. The Transport and General Worker's Union is a trade union located on Guernsey.

Banking and Finance

The Guernsey Financial Services Commission regulates banking, investment, insurance, and trust activities. In 1996, seventy-eight financial institutions were licensed on Guernsey and 380 insurance companies maintained offices on the island. Concerns over investment fraud and tax evasion under the lax enforcement of banking regulations drew considerable attention of the British government through the 1990s.

SOCIAL WELFARE

The States of Guernsey Insurance Authority and Board of Health oversee public health. Implemented by the States in 1996, a private medical insurance scheme provides specialist cover for all residents.

Healthcare

Life expectancy for the total population by 1999 estimations is 78.7 years with males 76 years and females 82 years.

EDUCATION

Modern primary and secondary schools are located on Guernsey and a College of Further Education provides higher education. Facilities are also available for the study of art, science, and many technical subjects.

1999 KEY EVENTS TIMELINE

January

- When the European Union launches its currency, the euro, the banking system of the Channel Islands, of which Guernsey is one, comes under fire. Several prominent European politicians, including the commissioner for the single market, Mario Monti, call for banking in the Channel Islands to be closed down to end its status as a tax haven.

- Two people die in a in a plane crash as a Fokker 27 turbo prop plane, operated by Channel Express Ltd., bursts into flames on its approach to Guernsey Airport.

February

- The former head of the Russian Central Bank, Sergei Dubinin, defends his role in hiding state funds in the accounts of a company called Financial Management Company (FIMACO), based in the Channel Islands.

March

- Special anniversary stamps are issued in the Channel Islands to celebrate the United King-

dom's Royal National Lifeboat Institution's 175 years of saving lives at sea.

- Computer millionaire Christopher Dawes is one of three people killed in a car crash. Dawes was arrested on Boxing Day (December 26) in the first crack cocaine seizure in the Channel Islands and due to appear in court later this year charged with possession of a Class A drug.

May

- United Kingdom Tory leader William Hague attacks Prime Minister Tony Blair over a proposal for a Europe-wide withholding tax aimed at stopping EU citizens from using tax havens such as the Channel Islands.

- While the Marine Conservation Society reports sewage problems on the U.K.'s northern beaches are becoming worse, its Good Beach Guide 1999 praises the south of England and Channel Island beaches for their clean-up efforts.

August

- Authorities suspect Russian mobsters may have been involved in the diversion of International Monetary Fund (IMF) loans made to Russia; investigators focus on $200 million that ended up in a Channel Islands account held by a Russian commercial bank.

October

- Britain's Treasury and Internal Revenue announces it will take immediate action to crack down on the use of favorable corporate tax rates in the U.K. dependencies. The legislation, to be officially introduced in the government's next finance bill, is expected to affect the Channel Islands of Jersey and Guernsey.

- European Union talks stall over proposals for a minimum EU-wide withholding tax and how it would apply to offshore territories like the Channel Islands; EU finance ministers agree to hold emergency talks in an attempt to unblock a controversial package of measures designed to eliminate tax evasion in the EU ahead of the looming December deadline.

December

- A new British Irish Council is formed to provide a forum for regional debate. The council includes representatives from the U.K., Ireland, Northern Ireland, Jersey, Guernsey, and the Isle of Man.

ANALYSIS OF EVENTS: 1999

BUSINESS AND THE ECONOMY

Launch of the euro and the issue of tax harmonization within the European Union sparked controversy as 1999 opened. Several prominent European politicians, including then-commissioner of the EU, Mario Monti, called for the Channel Islands' banking business to be closed down and its status as a tax haven to end. Under pressure, British foreign secretary Robin Cook called upon the islands to police banking activity; however, chief executive of the Channel Islands Stock Exchange, Tamara Mentashvili, claimed that island regulation is already comparable to British mainland banking law. Focus on a proposal for a European withholding tax designed to stop EU citizens from using Channel Island banks as a tax haven caused year-long strife within the British government. While the Islands may be territories of the U.K., they have been self-governing for 800 years, and any attempt at control by the U.K. could potentially incite rebellion. Nonetheless, by October Britain's Treasury and Inland Revenue announced it was cracking down on "designer tax regimes" in its dependent territories, with legislation aimed at the Channel Islands of Jersey and Guernsey. Guernsey and the other Channel Islands claimed that Gordon Brown, U.K. Chancellor of the Exchequer, was responding to pressure from the EU in introducing new tax legislation. The Guernsey government does not need to increase tax revenues, since the 59,000 residents don't require increased social and government services. The banking business, marketed to the international community since the 1960s, provides work for a large portion of the population. In 1999, the Guernsey government reported that just over 100 people were unemployed.

The year also found Channel Island banks amidst another international scandal. The Russian prosecutor's office accused its own bank officials of hiding over $50 billion in the offshore accounts of the little-known Financial Management Company (FIMACO), registered in the Channel Islands. The former head of the Russian Central Bank, Sergei Dubinin, defended his role in hiding state funds, claiming it was necessary to keep it away from foreign creditors trying to seize it.

Channel Island beaches were praised in the Marine Conservation Society's Good Beach Guide 1999 for improved sewage treatment. Other causes for celebration included the 175th anniversary of the Royal National Lifeboat Institution in March, for which the Channel Islands issued special anniversary stamps. The British Royal Mint also issued special gold and silver proof coins for the Channel Island of Alderney, which scientists declared as one of the best places in the world to observe August's total eclipse of the Sun.

DIRECTORY

CENTRAL GOVERNMENT

Head of State

Lieutenant Governor
John Coward, Office of the Lieutenant Governor

H.M. Procureur and Receiver General
A.C.K. Day, Office of H.M. Procureur and Receiver General, Q.C. St James Chambers, St. Peter Port, Guernsey

H.M. Comptroller
G.R. Rowland, Office of H.M. Comptroller, Q.C. St. James Chambers, St. Peter Port, Guernsey

Ministers

Minister of Finance
I.C. Morgan, Ministry of Finance, Sir Charles Frossard House, La Charroterie, St. Peter Port, Guernsey
PHONE: 717000

Minister of Agricultural and Milk Marketing
C.R.W. Best, Ministry of Agricultural and Milk Marketing, States Dairy, La Brigade Rd., St. Andrew's, Guernsey
PHONE: 37777

Minister of Administration
R.C. Berry, Ministry of Administration, Sir Charles Frossard House, La Charroterie, St. Peter Port, Guernsey
PHONE: 717000

Minister of Health
B. Russell, Ministry of Health, Le Vauquiedor, St. Martin's, Guernsey
PHONE: 725214

Minister of Industry
P.T.R. Ferhrache, Ministry of Industry, Burnt Lane, St. Martin's, Guernsey

PHONE: 35741

Minister of Education

M.A. Ozanne, Ministry of Education, Grange Road, St. Peter's Port, Guernsey
PHONE: 710821

Minister of Social Security

O.D. Le Tissier, Ministry of Social Security, Edward T. Wheadon House, Le Truchot, St. Peter's Port, Guernsey
PHONE: 720500

Minister of Horticulture

P.A.C. Falla, Ministry of Horticulture, Burnt Lane, St. Martin's, Guernsey
PHONE: 35741

Minister of Housing

J.E. Langtons, Ministry of Housing, Fountain Street, St. Peter Port, Guernsey
PHONE: 710631

Minister of Income Tax

J. Kitts, Ministry of Income Tax, 2 Cornet Street, St. Peter Port, Guernsey
PHONE: 724711

Minister of Island Development

W.M. Bell, Ministry of Island Development, Sir Charles Frossard House, La Charroterie, St. Peter Port, Guernsey
PHONE: 717000

Minister of Tourism

G.J. Norman, Ministry of Tourism, North Esplanade, St. Peter Port, Guernsey
PHONE: 726611

JUDICIAL SYSTEM
Royal Court

FURTHER READING
Articles

Barraclough, Colin. "Taxing Times for Money Havens." *Institutional Investor* 33 (May 1999): 137.

"Hapoalim Opens Jersey Trust Company." *Israel Business Today* 11 (July 15, 1997): 12.

Books

Channel Islands in Your Pocket. Clermont-Ferrand, France: Manufacture Francaise des Pneumatiques Michelin, 1999.

Internet

Guernsey Tourist Board. "The Islands of Guernsey." Available Online @ http://www.guernseymap.com/ (October 25, 1999).

Visit Guernsey. Available Online @ http://www.visitguernsey.com/ (October 24, 1999).

GUERNSEY: STATISTICAL DATA

For sources and notes see "Sources of Statistics" in the front of each volume.

GEOGRAPHY

Geography (1)

Area:

Total: 194 sq km.

Land: 194 sq km.

Water: 0 sq km.

Note: includes Alderney, Guernsey, Herm, Sark, and some other smaller islands.

Area—comparative: slightly larger than Washington, DC.

Land boundaries: 0 km.

Coastline: 50 km.

Climate: temperate with mild winters and cool summers; about 50% of days are overcast.

Terrain: mostly level with low hills in southwest.

Natural resources: cropland.

Land use:

Arable land: NA%

Permanent crops: NA%

Permanent pastures: NA%

Forests and woodland: NA%

Other: NA%

HUMAN FACTORS

Ethnic Division (6)

UK and Norman-French descent.

Religions (7)

Anglican, Roman Catholic, Presbyterian, Baptist, Congregational, Methodist.

Demographics (2A)

	1990	1995	1998	2000	2010	2020	2030	2040	2050
Population	61.1	62.1	64.6	66.2	73.8	78.7	80.1	79.4	77.0
Net migration rate (per 1,000 population)	NA	NA	NA	NA	NA	NA	NA	NA	NA
Births	NA	NA	NA	NA	NA	NA	NA	NA	NA
Deaths	NA	NA	NA	NA	NA	NA	NA	NA	NA
Life expectancy - males	74.8	75.1	75.6	75.9	77.3	78.3	79.1	79.6	80.0
Life expectancy - females	80.1	81.1	81.6	81.9	83.3	84.3	85.1	85.6	86.0
Birth rate (per 1,000)	12.4	12.5	13.9	14.4	11.3	11.0	10.8	9.6	9.4
Death rate (per 1,000)	10.4	9.8	9.5	9.4	8.9	9.2	10.3	11.8	13.3
Women of reproductive age (15-49 yrs.)	15.7	16.4	16.6	16.8	18.0	17.8	16.9	16.2	15.3
of which are currently married	NA	NA	NA	NA	NA	NA	NA	NA	NA
Fertility rate	1.6	1.5	1.7	1.8	1.8	1.8	1.7	1.7	1.7

Except as noted, values for vital statistics are in thousands; life expectancy is in years.

Languages (8)

English, French, Norman-French dialect spoken in country districts.

GOVERNMENT & LAW

Political Parties (12)

The legislative branch is a unicameral Assembly of the States (60 seats, 33 popularly elected members serve six-year terms). There are no political parties. All seats held by independents.

Government Budget (13B)

Revenues . . . .$277.9 million

Expenditures . . . .$248.8 million

  Capital expenditures . . . . .NA

Data for 1995 est. NA stands for not available.

Military Affairs (14A)

Defense is the responsibility of the UK.

LABOR FORCE

Unemployment Rate (17)

3%-4% (1994 est.)

PRODUCTION SECTOR

Electric Energy (18)

No data available.

Transportation (19)

Highways:

total: NA km

paved: NA km

unpaved: NA km

Merchant marine: none

Airports: 2 (1997 est.)

Airports—with paved runways:

total: 2

914 to 1,523 m: 1

under 914 m: 1 (1997 est.)

Top Agricultural Products (20)

Tomatoes, greenhouse flowers, sweet peppers, eggplant, other vegetables, fruit; Guernsey cattle.

FINANCE, ECONOMICS, & TRADE

Economic Indicators (22)

Inflation rate—consumer price index: 7% (1988)

Exchange Rates (24)

Exchange rates:

Guernsey pounds (£G) per US$1

January 1998	.0.6115
1997	.0.6106
1996	.0.6403
1995	.0.6335
1994	.0.6529
1993 . . . . :	.0.6658

The Guernsey pound is at par with the British pound

Economic Aid (27)

None.

Import Export Commodities (28)

Import Commodities	Export Commodities
Coal	Tomatoes
Gasoline	Flowers and ferns
Oil	Sweet peppers
Machinery and equipment	Eggplant
	Other vegetables

GUINEA

Republic of Guinea
République de Guinée

CAPITAL: Conakry.

FLAG: The national flag is a tricolor of red, yellow, and green vertical stripes.

ANTHEM: *Liberté (Liberty)*.

MONETARY UNIT: A new currency, the syli (s), of 100 cauris, was introduced in October 1972; s1 = 10 old Guinea francs. The Guinea franc (GFr) of 100 centimes was restored in January 1986 on a one-to-one basis with the syli. There are notes of 25, 50, 100, 500, 1,000, and 5,000 GFr. GFr1 = $0.001 (or $1 = GFr999.979).

WEIGHTS AND MEASURES: The metric system is the legal standard.

HOLIDAYS: New Year's Day, 1 January; Labor Day, 1 May; Anniversary of Women's Revolt, 27 August; Referendum Day, 28 September; Independence Day, 2 October; Armed Forces Day, 1 November; Day of 1970 Invasion, 22 November; Christmas, 25 December. Movable religious holidays include 'Id al-Fitr, 'Id al-'Adha', and Easter Monday.

TIME: GMT.

LOCATION AND SIZE: Guinea, on the west coast of Africa, has an area of 245,860 square kilometers (94,927 square miles), extending 831 kilometers (516 miles) southeast–northwest and 493 kilometers (306 miles) northeast-southwest. Comparatively, the area occupied by Guinea is slightly smaller than the state of Oregon.

Guinea's capital city, Conakry, is located on the country's Atlantic coast.

CLIMATE: The coastal region and much of the inland area have a tropical climate with a long rainy season of six months, a relatively high and uniform annual temperature, and high humidity. Conakry's year-round average high is 29°C (84°F), and the low is 23°C (73°F). Its average rainfall is 430 centimeters (169 inches) per year. April is the hottest month. July and August are the wettest.

INTRODUCTORY SURVEY

RECENT HISTORY

Guinea became an independent state on 2 October 1958, with Ahmed Sékou Touré, leader of Guinea's strongest labor union, as president. During its first three decades of independence, Guinea developed into a militant Socialist state, with nearly complete government control over the country's economic and political life. Guinea expelled the U.S. Peace Corps in 1966 because of supposed involvement in a plot to overthrow President Touré. Similar charges were directed against France. Diplomatic relations were ended in 1965 and did not resume until 1975. An ongoing source of tension between Guinea and its French-speaking neighbors was the estimated half-million Guineans in Senegal and Côte d'Ivoire, some of them active dissidents who, in 1966, formed the National Liberation Front of Guinea (Front de Libération Nationale de Guinée—FLNG). Between 1969 and 1976, according to Amnesty International, Guinea detained 4,000 persons for political reasons, with the fate of 2,900 unknown.

In 1977, protests against the government's economic policy led to riots in which three regional governors were killed. Touré responded by relaxing restrictions, offering amnesty to exiles (thousands of whom returned), and releasing hundreds of political prisoners. Ties were loosened with the Soviet bloc, as Touré sought increased Western aid and private investment for Guinea's sagging economy. Touré was elected unopposed to a fourth seven-year term as president on 9 May 1982. Ac-

cording to the government radio station, he received 100% of the vote. A new constitution was adopted that month, and during the summer Touré visited the United States as part of an economic policy reversal that found Guinea seeking Western investment to develop its huge mineral reserves. Measures announced in 1983 brought further economic liberalization.

Touré died on 26 March 1984 while undergoing cardiac treatment at the Cleveland Clinic, where he had been rushed after being stricken in Sa'udi Arabia the previous day. On 3 April, however, just as the Political Bureau of the ruling Guinea Democratic Party (PDG) was about to name its choice as Touré's successor, the armed forces seized power, denouncing the last years of Touré's rule as a "bloody and ruthless dictatorship." The constitution was suspended, the Na-

tional Assembly dissolved, and the PDG abolished. The leader of the takeover, Colonel Lansana Conté, assumed the presidency on 5 April, heading the Military Committee for National Recovery (Comité Militaire de Redressement National— CMRN). About 1,000 political prisoners were freed.

Conté suppressed an attempted military takeover led by Colonel Diarra Traoré on 4 July 1985. Almost two years later, it was announced that fifty-eight persons, including both takeover leaders and members of Touré's government, had been sentenced to death. However, it was believed that many of them, as well as Traoré, had actually been shot days after the takeover attempt. All were identified with the Malinké, who were closely identified with the Touré regime. The military government adopted free-market policies in an effort to revive the economy. Under local pressure and from abroad, Guinea embarked on a transition to multi-party democracy. The military-dominated government has not been entirely supportive of the process. It legalized parties in April 1992, but did not really allow them to function freely. It postponed presidential elections for over a year (until 19 December 1993) and then verified the results (Conté was elected by a narrow margin) after international monitors had rejected them as fraudulent. The legislative elections were delayed until 11 June 1995. In February 1996, a minor coup was staged against Conté to raise soldiers' pay and to remove the acting defense minister. Conté gave into the mutineers' demands by doubling soldiers' pay and taking over the defense department himself.

GOVERNMENT

In practice, under the Touré regime, the legislature, the cabinet, and the national administration were subordinate to the PDG (the ruling party) in the direction and control of the nation. The assembly and the cabinet (appointed by Touré) carried out the decisions and orders of the party arrived at by the party congress, national conference, and the Political Bureau.

The armed forces leaders who seized power after Touré's death ruled Guinea through the Military Committee for National Recovery (CMRN), followed by a transitional Committee of National Recovery (CTRN) set up in February 1991. In 1993, the government created a 114-member National Assembly and held elections—viewed as deeply flawed—in 1995.

Judiciary

There are district courts, two Courts of Appeal, and a Supreme Court. There is also a State Security Court and a military tribunal. A traditional system of dispute resolution exists alongside the court system at the village and neighborhood level. Although the 1990 constitution created an independent judiciary, judges are susceptible to influence by the executive branch.

Political Parties

Political parties were legalized in April 1992. By late 1993, over forty political parties were legally registered. The most significant national opposition parties are the Rally for the Guinean People (Rassemblement du Peuple Guinéen–RPG), the Union for a New Republic (UNR), and the Party for Renewal and Progress (Parti de l'Unité et du Progrès–PUP). Following the elections of June 1995, the PUP held a majority, with seventy-one seats. The elections were denounced as unfair and the opposition briefly held a boycott of the assembly afterwards.

DEFENSE

The armed forces numbered about 9,700 in 1995, including 8,500 in the army, 400 in the navy, and 800 in the air force. There was a People's Militia of 7,000 and 2,600 in the police force and Republican Guard. Defense spending in 1995 was estimated at $52 million.

ECONOMIC AFFAIRS

After two decades of socialist-style economic management, a major reform movement gained political power in 1984. Of the more than 100 state enterprises, most were closed. Food prices were decontrolled, private trade reestablished, and the government began to seek foreign investment for sectors other than mining and energy. Monetary reform was enacted in early 1986, with a 93% currency devaluation. Although the reforms were successful, the economy has been restrained by poor transportation and communication systems.

Public Finance

Guinea did not have a formal government budget until 1989. Since then, overly optimistic revenue projections, increasing civil service salaries, and falling world market prices for bauxite have resulted in deficits. The U.S. CIA estimates that, in 1994, government revenues totaled approximately $449 million and expenditures $708 million, including capital expenditures of $361 million. External debt totaled $3.02 billion. Government expenditures were expected to increase again in 1996 and 1997.

Income

In 1998, Guinea's gross national product (GNP) was $3.82 billion at current prices, or $540 per person. For the period 1985–95 the average inflation rate was 16.8%, resulting in a real growth rate in GNP of 1.4% per person.

Industry

Manufacturing in Guinea consists of three elements: public enterprises with large staffs; approximately 360 small private businesses; and around 10,000 small non-industrial units employing some 25,000 persons. The alumina smelter at Fria operates at over 90% capacity, and produced 660,000 tons in 1994.

Banking and Finance

At independence, central banking functions were carried out by the Central Bank of the West African States (Banque Centrale des États de l'Afrique de l'Ouest—BCEAO), and commercial banking by branches of five French banks. On 1 March 1960, Guinea withdrew from the franc zone. The Guinean branch of the BCEAO was abolished, and the Central Bank of Guinea was established. All banking activities were taken over by the Central Bank, but by 1962, its functions were decentralized and three new state-owned banks were added.

As of 1997, the government was considering making obligatory the direct transfer of public-sector wages and salaries to designated accounts within the commercial banks. While this measure has been welcomed by the banks, government employees are less enamored of it, saying that the banking system is still too fragile to cope with the sudden opening of thousands of new accounts.

Local currency may not be exported or imported. There are no securities exchanges in Guinea.

Economic Development

The 1981–85 development plan entailed spending of $32 billion and gave priority to rural development. The 1987–91 recovery program called for $670 million in spending through 1989, with 42% for infrastructure and 24% for rural development. A major aim was to diversify the economy and reduce the heavy reliance on bauxite. By 1990, the government had privatized the majority of its 180 public enterprises and closed over 300 state farms. Since then, however, the pace of structural reform has slowed.

SOCIAL WELFARE

There was a decline in social services during the Touré years (1958–84). In 1994, social security legislation was updated, providing pensions at age 55 and cash sickness benefits for employed persons. Violence against women is common, but courts rarely intervene in domestic disputes.

Healthcare

In 1992 there were about 20 physicians, per 100,000 people. It is estimated that 75% of the population had access to health care services. Malaria, yaws, leprosy, and sleeping sickness have been the major tropical diseases. Also widespread are schistosomiasis, tuberculosis, and venereal diseases. Life expectancy is estimated at 46 years.

Housing

The most common rural dwelling is round, windowless, and made of wattle and daub or sun-dried mud bricks, with a floor of packed earth and a conical thatched roof. Urban dwellings are usually one-story rectangular frame or mud-brick buildings, generally without electricity or indoor plumbing.

EDUCATION

Education is free and compulsory between the ages of 7 and 13. In 1995, the estimated adult illiteracy rate was 64%; for males 50.1% and 78.1% for females. Children go through six years of primary and seven years of secondary school.

In 1993, there were 471,792 primary-level pupils. Secondary schools served 116,377 pupils.

1999 KEY EVENTS TIMELINE

January

- Four RPG parliamentarians with immunity detained, and some 70 RPG militants arrested and subjected to torture.

- Alpha Condé remains under house arrest. The U.S., Canadian, German, and EU ambassadors visit him.

- Lansana Conté is sworn in as president for the second time after officially winning the December 14, 1998 election.

February

- Alpha Condé gives an interview to *Jeune Afrique* explaining his side of the story.

March

- President Conté reshuffles the cabinet.

- President Conté removes the prime minister and replaces him with a party loyalist.

April

- The Sierra Leone People's Army (SPA) attacks villages in the Forécariah area.

- UNHCR begins moving refugees in the Forest Region inland, away from the Sierra Leonean border.

May

- World Food Program (WFP) announces a $1 million Food For Work program to clean up Conakry.

- Human Rights Watch (HRW) appeals for protection of refugees against rebel attacks and abuses.

- Representatives of gendarmerie and police meet in Conakry to discuss more effective implementation of their mandates.

June

- A major reshuffle among senior army officers occurs.

- The defense minister authorizes punitive attacks against the SPA.

- Municipal elections scheduled for June, postponed until December.

- Contract to build wide-band fiber-optic network awarded to Société Télécommunications de Guinée (STG).

- Internet gateway opened in Labé as part of the Leland Initiative.

July

- President Jacques Chirac of France visits Guinea on a four-country African tour.

- Alpha Condé's defense team holds a press conference.

- Trial of RPG militants opens in Faranah.

- HRW repeats charges against the UNHCR despite heavy rains preventing the relocation of refugee camps.

- Reporteurs sans Frontières (RSF) deplores lack of media freedom in Guinea.

- Guinea and Morocco sign fisheries pact.

- President Conté travels to Morocco to attend King Hussein's funeral.

August

- ENTAG, the Franco-Guinean cigarette manufacturer, closes its operations, laying off 150 employees.

- Government announces that local elections will be held before the end of the year.

September

- IMF Mission scheduled to arrive in Guinea to review existing ESAF.

- President Conté visits the United States.

- The Alpha Condé trial is delayed.

October

- The United States Agency for International Development (USAID) pledges to provide $250,000 for conflict management in the Forest Region.

- The Alpha Condé trial is rescheduled.

- The Presidential palace is inaugurated, and named for Sékou Touré.

December

- Early in December, the weekly Guinea newspaper *L'Independant Plus* publishes an inquiry on corruption which implicates the Guinean government. The French organization, Reporteurs sans Frontières (RSF-Reporters Without Borders) reports that Saliou Samb, editor-in-chief of the weekly Guinea newspaper *L'Independant Plus* was expelled to Ghana and the newspaper's owner, Aboubacar Sylla, was arrested by twelve armed men and detained for two days.

ANALYSIS OF EVENTS: 1999

BUSINESS AND THE ECONOMY

Guinean forecasters predicting double-digit growth for 1999 far underestimated the negative effects of the souring relationship between the government and multilaterals. Real GDP growth in 1999 was robust at 4.5 percent, but much less than expected. The government announced its decision to privatize the bauxite sector, but its insistence on 15 percent shareholding raised fears that, as in the past, it would use its votes to distribute patronage. Production of Guinea's main mineral commodities was improved, and the first of two planned Garafiri hydro-electric dams opened ahead of schedule, more than doubling Guinea's electric capacity, which relies on thermal generators.

Much of the gloominess in the economic picture has to do with Guinea's failure to meet the IMF's ESAF policy and performance targets. While some of the blame may be placed on defense and security expenditures, widespread diversion of public funds has siphoned off millions of dollars of bauxite revenue. In 1999, bauxite provided more than one-third of the nation's export earnings.

President Conté's visit to Washington in September included talks with the IMF. While the talks were beneficial, the failure to meet ESAF guidelines has scared off investors, and reduced foreign aid inflows. Consequently, foreign reserves have fallen to dangerous levels. Guinea is ineligible for debt relief from the World Bank-sponsored heavily indebted poor countries (HIPC) initiative without IMF support. The introduction of new bank notes in August encouraged speculation that inflation was likely to rise, while the exchange rate was expected to slip.

GOVERNMENT AND POLITICS

Democracy, good governance, and human rights in Guinea suffered during 1999. The fall-out from the December 1998 presidential election set the tone. The opposition submitted a detailed report documenting fraudulent and illegal practices by the ruling party in the election and campaign. The government angered the Malinké opposition by imprisoning RPG leader Alpha Condé, four RPG parliamentarians, and some 70 RPG militants after the elections. The Guinean Human Rights Organization and Amnesty International accused the government of routine torture—stripping, tying up, and beating opposition militants. The Condé trial has been repeatedly delayed and rescheduled.

Despite laws guaranteeing freedom of the press, the government refuses to liberalize the broadcast media. President Conté seems to be using regional insecurity as a pretext to maintain repressive policies, while his critics accuse him of nepotism and ethnic favoritism.

Other signs indicate backsliding on political reforms. The local CRD elections, four years beyond their mandate, will be held in December, but without party affiliation. This decision was taken without consulting the opposition, and prevents opposition parties from capitalizing on their regional constituencies. The naming of the new presidential palace for Sékou Touré, whom many remember as a repressive dictator, has angered Guineans whose relatives were persecuted or died for political reasons under his regime.

In sum, the political climate is intolerant toward a loyal opposition, shows failure to establish an impartial elections commission, and suffers from Executive heavy-handed control over the key levers of power. Lack of opportunity to challenge the incumbent could push the opposition to boycott the legislative elections scheduled for next year.

The President of the National Assembly, Boubacar Biro Diallo, a founding member of the president's ruling party, described the intransigence of the regime to create a more viable political environment "preoccupying."

International politics in 1999 offer mixed blessings for Guinea. The peace accords in Guinea-Bissau and Sierra Leone have returned Guinean troops home, but the troops must be reintegrated to the barracks where deep tensions exist. The peace accord in Sierra Leone has not prevented dissident rebels, offshoots of the RUF, from marauding Guinean border villages, completely destroying two of them. Rebels have had access to refugee camps where they have murdered and mutilated dozens of people. UNHCR has been unable to sufficiently protect women and girls from rape and abduction. But rather than flee, some 500,000 refugees are waiting for signs that it is safe for them to return to their villages in Liberia and Sierra Leone.

President Conté attempted to find a place in the sun, hosting President Jacques Chirac and travelling to the United States. Chirac calmed tensions, but then aggravated reformists by suggesting that donors had to let Africans find their own rhythm for democracy. President Conté visited Washington, D.C., but was not received by President Clinton. In Pittsburgh, he visited Halco Mining, the international bauxite consortium partner for CBG in Kamsar. His advance people elected to visit Allegheny County Hospital when they learned that the University of Pittsburgh was not offering the president a second honorary doctorate degree from a U.S. institution of higher learning.

CULTURE AND SOCIETY

The Guinean music scene in 1999 was made livelier by the return of the Amazones, a women's band founded in 1960 as the women's brigade of the National Gendarmerie. The name changed to the Gendarmerie Female Orchestra in 1961, and to "The Amazones of Guinea" in 1965. Whereas their concerts were mapped out for them in the socialist First Republic, under free enterprise, they now make their own bookings. They have nicknames like "tigresses of the stage," and "music goddesses." Salimata Diallo is the band leader, and their CD is called, "Les Amazones de Guinée, au coeur de Paris," released by Editions Bolibana.

DIRECTORY

CENTRAL GOVERNMENT
Head of State

President
Lansana Conte, Office of the President, State House, Conakry, Guinea

Ministers

Prime Minister and Coordinator of Government Actions
Lamine Sidime, Office of the Prime Minister
PHONE: +224 411070; 415283

Minister of Agriculture and Animal Husbandry
Jean-Paul Sarr, Ministry of Agriculture and Animal Husbandry

Minister of Commerce, Industry, and Small and Medium-Scale Enterprise
Madikaba Camara, Ministry of Commerce, Industry, and Small and Medium-Scale Enterprise, Boulevard du Commerce, Conarky, Guinea
PHONE: +224 444920; 444921

Minister of Communication
Ibrahima Mongo Diallo, Ministry of Communication, Boulbinet, Conakry, Guinea
PHONE: +224 415001

Minister of Defense
Dorank Assifat Diasseny, Ministry of Defense, Camp Samory, Toure, Guinea
PHONE: +224 441154; 451154; 411638

Minister of Economy and Finance
Ibrahima Kassory Fofana, Ministry of Economy and Finance, Boulevard du Commerce, Conakry, Guinea
PHONE: +224 414987; 442693

Minister of Employment and Public Administration
Lamine Kamara, Ministry of Employment and Public Administration

Minister of Energy
Facinet Fofana, Ministry of Energy

Minister of Fishing and Aquaculture
Mansa Moussa Sidibe, Ministry of Fishing and Aquaculture

Minister at the Presidency in charge of Foreign Affairs
Zainoul Abidine Sanoussy, Ministry of Foreign Affairs, Boulevard du Commerce, Conarky, Guinea
PHONE: +224 441602; 451270

Minister of Justice and Keeper of the Seals
Maurice Zogbelemou Togba, Ministry of Justice and Keeper of the Seals

Minister of Mining, Geology, and Environment
Facinet Fofana, Ministry of Mining, Geology, and Environment

Minister of National Education and Scientific Research
Eugene Camara, Ministry of National Education and Scientific Research, Boulevard du Commerce, Conarky, Guinea
PHONE: +224 411901

Minister of Planning and Cooperation
Elhadj Thierno Mamadou Cellou Diallo, Ministry of Planning and Cooperation
PHONE: +224 414987; 452693

Minister of Pre-University and Civic Education
Germain Doualamou, Ministry of Pre-University and Civic Education

Minister of Public Health
Kandjoura Drame, Ministry of Public Health, Boulevard du Commerce, Conarky, Guinea
PHONE: +224 412032

Minister of Public Works and Transport
Cellou Dalein Diallo, Ministry of Public Works and Transport

Minister of Security
Sekou Koureissy Conde, Ministry of Security

Minister of Social Affairs and Promotion of Women and Children
Mariama Aribot, Ministry of Social Affairs and Promotion of Women and Children, Corniche-Ouest, Conarky, Guinea
PHONE: +224 412015
FAX: +224 414660

Minister of Technical Teaching and Professional Training
Almamy Fode Sylla, Ministry of Technical Teaching and Professional Training

Minister of Territorial Administration and Decentralization

Moussa Solano, Ministry of Territorial Administration and Decentralization

Minister of Tourism, Hotels and Handicrafts

Kozo Zoumanigui, Ministry of Tourism, Hotels and Handicrafts

Minister of University Education and Scientific Research

Eugene Camara, Ministry of University Education and Scientific Research

Minister of Urban Planning and Housing

Alpha Ousmane Diallo, Ministry of Urban Planning and Housing

Minister of Water Power and Energy

Fassou Niancoye, Ministry of Water Power and Energy

Minister of Youth, Sports, and Culture

Sylla Koumba Diakite, Ministry of Youth, Sports, and Culture, Avenue du Port, Conarky, Guinea
PHONE: +224 441959; 441926; 444956
FAX: +224 411926

POLITICAL ORGANIZATIONS

Union National pour la Prosperité de la Guinée-UNPG (National Union for the Prosperity of Guinea)

TITLE: Leader
NAME: Facine Toure

Parti du Renouveau et du Progrès-PRP (Party for Renewal and Progress)

NAME: Siradiou Diallo

Parti de l'Unité et du Progrès-PUP (Party for Unity and Progress)

NAME: Lansana Conte

Rassemblement du Peuple Guinéen-RPG (Rally for the Guinean People)

NAME: Alpha Conde

Union pour le Progrès et le Renouveau-UPR (Union for Progress and Renewal)

NAME: Mamadou Bah

DIPLOMATIC REPRESENTATION

Embassies in Guinea

United States
BP 603, 2d Blvd. and 9th Avenue, Conakry, Guinea
PHONE: +224 411520
FAX: +224 411522
TITLE: Ambassador
NAME: Tibor P. Nagy, Jr.

JUDICIAL SYSTEM

Court of Appeal

FURTHER READING

Articles

Kaba, Lansine. "Guinean Politics: A Critical Historical Overview." *Journal of Modern African Studies* 15 (1997): 25-46.

"Lansana Conté's Stormy Weekend." *West Africa.* (February 1996): 12-18.

Books

Ajayi, J.F.A., and Michael Crowder, eds. *History of West Africa.* Vol. 1. New York: Columbia University Press, 1976.

Derman, William. *Serfs, Peasants, and Socialists: A Former Serf Village in the Republic of Guinea.* Berkeley: University of California Press, 1973.

Harris, Joseph Earl. *The Kingdom of Fouta Diallon.* Ph.D. diss., Northwestern University, 1965.

Laye, Camara. *The Dark Child.* Trans. Eva Thoby-Marcelin. New York: Farrar, Straus and Giroux, 1954.

Mouser, Bruce L., ed. *Guinea Journals: Journeys into Guinea—Conakry during the Sierra Leone Phase, 1800-1821.* Washington, D.C.: University Press of America, 1979.

Nelson, Harold D. et al, eds. *Area Handbook for Guinea.* Foreign Area Studies. Washington, DC.: American University, 1975.

Niane, Djibril Tamsir. *Sundiata: An Epic of Old Mali.* Trans. G.D. Pickett. Essex: Longman, 1965.

O'Toole, Thomas. *Historical Dictionary of Guinea.* Third Edition. Lanham, Md., and London: The Scarecrow Press, 1994.

Rivière, Claude. *Guinea: The Mobilization of a People.* Translated from the French by Virginia Thompson and Richard Adloff. Ithaca and London: Cornell University Press, 1977.

Suret-Canale, Jean. *French Colonialism in Tropical Africa: 1900–1945.* Trans. Till Gottheiner. London: C. Hurst and Company, 1971.

Internet

Africaonline. Available Online @ http://www.africaonline.com (October 28, 1999).

Africa News Online. Available Online @ http://www.africanews.org/west/stories/1999_feat1.html (October 28, 1999).

Integrated Regional Information Network (IRIN). Available Online @ http://www.reliefweb.int/IRIN (October 28, 1999).

GUINEA: STATISTICAL DATA

For sources and notes see "Sources of Statistics" in the front of each volume.

GEOGRAPHY

Geography (1)

Area:

Total: 245,860 sq km.

Land: 245,860 sq km.

Water: 0 sq km.

Area—comparative: slightly smaller than Oregon.

Land boundaries:

Total: 3,399 km.

Border countries: Guinea-Bissau 386 km, Cote d'Ivoire 610 km, Liberia 563 km, Mali 858 km, Senegal 330 km, Sierra Leone 652 km.

Coastline: 320 km.

Climate: generally hot and humid; monsoonal-type rainy season (June to November) with southwesterly winds; dry season (December to May) with northeasterly harmattan winds.

Terrain: generally flat coastal plain, hilly to mountainous interior.

Natural resources: bauxite, iron ore, diamonds, gold, uranium, hydropower, fish.

Land use:

Arable land: 2%

Permanent crops: 0%

Permanent pastures: 22%

Forests and woodland: 59%

Other: 17% (1993 est.).

HUMAN FACTORS

Demographics (2A)

	1990	1995	1998	2000	2010	2020	2030	2040	2050
Population	5,936.4	7,164.6	7,477.1	7,610.9	9,439.9	11,835.8	14,474.5	17,240.3	20,034.4
Net migration rate (per 1,000 population)	NA	NA	NA	NA	NA	NA	NA	NA	NA
Births	NA	NA	NA	NA	NA	NA	NA	NA	NA
Deaths	NA	NA	NA	NA	NA	NA	NA	NA	NA
Life expectancy - males	40.3	42.3	43.6	44.4	49.1	53.9	58.7	63.1	67.1
Life expectancy - females	44.4	46.9	48.5	49.6	55.1	60.8	66.1	70.8	74.8
Birth rate (per 1,000)	46.8	43.3	41.3	40.0	36.7	32.0	27.0	23.3	20.2
Death rate (per 1,000)	21.6	19.2	17.8	16.9	13.4	10.5	8.3	7.1	6.5
Women of reproductive age (15-49 yrs.)	1,387.8	1,670.3	1,756.1	1,801.1	2,346.1	3,023.2	3,835.9	4,663.6	5,408.7
of which are currently married	NA	NA	NA	NA	NA	NA	NA	NA	NA
Fertility rate	6.1	5.8	5.6	5.5	4.7	3.9	3.2	2.7	2.4

Except as noted, values for vital statistics are in thousands; life expectancy is in years.

Health Personnel (3)

Total health expenditure as a percentage of GDP, 1990-1997[a]

Public sector 1.2

Private sector . . . . .NA

Total[b] . . . . .NA

Health expenditure per capita in U.S. dollars, 1990-1997[a]

Purchasing power parity . . . . .NA

Total . . . . .NA

Availability of health care facilities per 100,000 people

Hospital beds 1990-1997[a] 60

Doctors 1993[c] 15

Nurses 1993[c] 3

Health Indicators (4)

Life expectancy at birth

1980 40

1997 46

Daily per capita supply of calories (1996) 2,099

Total fertility rate births per woman (1997) 5.5

Maternal mortality ratio per 100,000 live births (1990-97) . . . . .880[d]

Safe water % of population with access (1995) 55

Sanitation % of population with access (1995) 14

Consumption of iodized salt % of households (1992-98)[a] . . . .

Smoking prevalence

Male % of adults (1985-95)[a] . . . .

Female % of adults (1985-95)[a] . . . .

Tuberculosis incidence per 100,000 people (1997) 171

Adult HIV prevalence % of population ages 15-49 (1997) 2.09

Infants and Malnutrition (5)

Under-5 mortality rate (1997) 201

% of infants with low birthweight (1990-97) 13

Births attended by skilled health staff % of total[a] . . .31

% fully immunized (1995-97)

TB 69

DPT 53

Polio 53

Measles 56

Prevalence of child malnutrition under age 5 (1992-97)[b] 24

Ethnic Division (6)

Peuhl 40%

Malinke 30%

Soussou 20%

Smaller tribes 10%

Religions (7)

Muslim 85%

Christian 8%

Indigenous beliefs 7%

Languages (8)

French (official), each tribe has its own language.

EDUCATION

Public Education Expenditures (9)

Public expenditure on education (% of GNP)

1980 . . . .

1996 . . . .

Expenditure per student

Primary % of GNP per capita

1980 . . . .

1996 . . . . .7.8[1]

Secondary % of GNP per capita

1980 . . . .

1996 . . . .

Tertiary % of GNP per capita

1980 . . . .

1996 . . . . .260.2[1]

Expenditure on teaching materials

Primary % of total for level (1996) . . . .

Secondary % of total for level (1996) . . . .

Primary pupil-teacher ratio per teacher (1996) . . . . .49[1]

Duration of primary education years (1995) 6

Literacy Rates (11A)

In thousands and percent[1]	1990	1995	2000	2010
Illiterate population (15+ yrs.)	2,116	2,272	2,432	2,751
Literacy rate - total adult pop. (%)	31.0	35.9	41.0	51.6
Literacy rate - males (%)	44.7	49.9	55.1	64.9
Literacy rate - females (%)	17.5	21.9	26.9	38.2

GOVERNMENT & LAW

Political Parties (12)

People's National Assembly	No. of seats
Party for Unity and Progress (PUP)	71
Rally for the Guinean People (RPG)	19
Party for Renewal and Progress (PRP)	9
Union for a New Republic (UNR)	9
Union for Progress of Guinea (UPG)	2
Democratic Party of Guinea (PDG-AST)	1
National Union for the Prosperity of Guinea (UNPG)	1
Democratic Party of Guinea-African Democratic Rally (PDG-RDA)	1
Other	1

Government Budget (13B)

Revenues	$553 million
Expenditures	$652 million
Capital expenditures	$317 million

Data for 1995 est.

Military Affairs (14B)

	1990	1991	1992	1993	1994	1995
Military expenditures						
Current dollars (mil.)	30	33	44	NA	51	51[e]
1995 constant dollars (mil.)	35	37	47	NA	52	51[e]
Armed forces (000)	15	15	15	15	12	12
Gross national product (GNP)						
Current dollars (mil.)	2,450	2,658	2,848	3,092	3,303	3,540
1995 constant dollars (mil.)	2,816	2,937	3,063	3,242	3,386	3,540
Central government expenditures (CGE)						
1995 constant dollars (mil.)	699	675	671	NA	NA	NA
People (mil.)	5.9	6.3	6.6	6.9	7.0	7.2
Military expenditure as % of GNP	1.2	1.3	1.5	NA	1.5	1.5
Military expenditure as % of CGE	5.0	5.4	7.0	NA	NA	NA
Military expenditure per capita (1995 $)	6	6	7	NA	7	7
Armed forces per 1,000 people (soldiers)	2.5	2.4	2.3	2.2	1.7	1.7
GNP per capita (1995 $)	474	467	464	473	485	492
Arms imports[6]						
Current dollars (mil.)	20	5	0	0	0	5
1995 constant dollars (mil.)	23	6	0	0	0	5
Arms exports[6]						
Current dollars (mil.)	0	0	0	0	0	0
1995 constant dollars (mil.)	0	0	0	0	0	0
Total imports[7]						
Current dollars (mil.)	600	732	768	798	688	NA
1995 constant dollars (mil.)	690	809	826	837	705	NA
Total exports[7]						
Current dollars (mil.)	605	653	622	NA	562	NA
1995 constant dollars (mil.)	695	722	669	NA	576	NA
Arms as percent of total imports[8]	3.3	.7	0	0	0	NA
Arms as percent of total exports[8]	0	0	0	NA	0	NA

LABOR FORCE

Labor Force (16)

Total (million) 2.4

Agriculture 80.0%

Industry and commerce 11.0%

Services 5.4%

Civil Service 3.6%

Data for 1983.

Unemployment Rate (17)

Rate not available.

PRODUCTION SECTOR

Electric Energy (18)

Capacity .176,000 kW (1995)

Production . . . . .500 million kWh (1995)

Consumption per capita . . . . .76 kWh (1995)

Transportation (19)

Highways:

total: 30,500 km

paved: 5,033 km

unpaved: 25,467 km (1996 est.)

Waterways: 1,295 km navigable by shallow-draft native craft

Merchant marine:

total: 1 cargo ship (1,000 GRT or over) totaling 4,722 GRT/6,226 DWT (1997 est.)

Airports: 15 (1997 est.)

Airports—with paved runways:

total: 5

over 3,047 m: 1

2,438 to 3,047 m: 1

1,524 to 2,437 m: 3 (1997 est.)

Airports—with unpaved runways:

total: 10

1,524 to 2,437 m: 5

914 to 1,523 m: 4

under 914 m: 1 (1997 est.)

Top Agricultural Products (20)

Rice, coffee, pineapples, palm kernels, cassava (tapioca), bananas, sweet potatoes; cattle, sheep, goats; timber.

FINANCE, ECONOMICS, & TRADE

Economic Indicators (22)

National product: GDP—purchasing power parity— $8.3 billion (1997 est.)

National product real growth rate: 4.8% (1997 est.)

National product per capita: $1,100 (1997 est.)

Inflation rate—consumer price index: 3.5% (1996 est.)

MANUFACTURING SECTOR

GDP & Manufacturing Summary (21)

	1980	1985	1990	1992	1993	1994
Gross Domestic Product						
Millions of 1990 dollars	2,296	2,188	2,818	3,045	3,183	3,310
Growth rate in percent	5.60	3.89	4.69	3.23	4.51	4.00
Per capita (in 1990 dollars)	514.8	438.7	489.7	497.9	504.7	509.2
Manufacturing Value Added						
Millions of 1990 dollars	61	62	100	110	116	*122*
Growth rate in percent	2.70	3.33	5.07	3.83	5.03	*5.90*
Manufacturing share in						
percent of current prices	1.5	1.1	3.6	4.6	4.7	*4.6*

Exchange Rates (24)

Exchange rates:

Guinean francs (FG) per US$1

January 1997	1,004.0
1997	1,004.0
1995	991.4
1994	976.6
1993	955.5
1992	902.0

The official exchange rate of the Guinean franc was set and quoted weekly against the US dollar until the end of October 1993; since 1 November 1994, the exchange rate is determined in the interbank market for foreign exchange.

Top Import Origins (25)

$809 million (1995 est.) Data are for 1995.

Origins	%
France	35
Cote d'Ivoire	31
United States	14
Belgium-Luxembourg	10
Hong Kong	10

Top Export Destinations (26)

$748 million (1995 est.).

Destinations	%
United States	37
El Salvador	13
Honduras	7
Costa Rica	5
Germany	5

Economic Aid (27)

Recipient: ODA, $NA. NA stands for not available.

Import Export Commodities (28)

Import Commodities	Export Commodities
Petroleum products	Bauxite
Metals	Alumina
Machinery	Diamonds
Transport equipment	Gold
Textiles	Coffee
Grain and other foodstuffs	Fish
	Agricultural products

Balance of Payments (23)

	1992	1993	1994	1995	1996
Exports of goods (f.o.b.)	517	561	516	583	636
Imports of goods (f.o.b.)	−608	−583	685	622	525
Trade balance	−91	−22	−170	−39	111
Services - debits	−471	−427	−446	−490	−528
Services - credits	168	196	159	130	137
Private transfers (net)	131	124	207	147	127
Government transfers (net)	1	72	1	32	−25
Overall balance	−263	−57	−248	−219	−177

GUINEA-BISSAU

CAPITAL: Bissau.

FLAG: The flag has equal horizontal stripes of yellow over green, with a red vertical stripe at the hoist bearing a black star.

ANTHEM: *Esta é a Nossa Pátria Bem Amada (This Is Our Well-Beloved Land).*

MONETARY UNIT: The Guinean peso (PG) of 100 centavos replaced the Guinean escudo (GE) on 2 February 1976. There are coins of 50 centavos and 1, 2, 5, and 20 pesos, and notes of 50, 100, 500, and 1,000 pesos. PG1 = $0.0808 (or $1 = PG12.369).

WEIGHTS AND MEASURES: The metric system is used.

HOLIDAYS: New Year's Day, 1 January; Death of Amilcar Cabral, 20 January; Labor Day, 1 May; Anniversary of the Killing of Pidjiguiti, 3 August; National Day, 24 September; Anniversary of the Movement of Readjustment, 14 November; Christmas Day, 25 December. Movable religious holidays include Korité (end of Ramadan) and Tabaski (Feast of the Sacrifice).

TIME: 11 AM = noon GMT.

LOCATION AND SIZE: Situated on the west coast of Africa, Guinea-Bissau, formerly Portuguese Guinea, has a total area of 36,120 square kilometers (13,946 square miles). Comparatively, the area occupied by Guinea-Bissau is slightly less than three times the size of the state of Connecticut. Besides its mainland territory, it includes the Bijagós Archipelago (Archipélago dos Bijagós) and various coastal islands.

The capital city, Bissau, is located on the country's Atlantic coast.

CLIMATE: Guinea-Bissau has a hot, humid climate, with a rainy season from mid-May to mid-November and a cooler dry season the rest of the year. During the dry season, the harmattan (dust-laden wind) blows from the Sahara.

Republic of Guinea-Bissau
República da Guiné-Bissau

INTRODUCTORY SURVEY

RECENT HISTORY

In 1951, Guinea-Bissau was made a Portuguese overseas province. In September 1956, a group of dissatisfied Cape Verdeans founded an underground movement aimed at achieving independence from Portugal. It was named the African Party for the Independence of Guinea and Cape Verde (Partido Africano de Independência da Guiné e Cabo Verde—PAIGC), and Amilcar Cabral became its secretary-general. By 1963, large-scale guerrilla warfare had broken out in the territory.

During the following years, PAIGC soldiers, fighting a Portuguese force of about 30,000, increased their hold on the countryside. When Cabral was assassinated on 20 January 1973, Aristides Pereira took over the leadership of the movement, which on 24 September 1973 proclaimed the independence of the Republic of Guinea-Bissau. On 26 August 1974, the Portuguese government (under new leadership following a takeover earlier that year) and the PAIGC signed an agreement in Algiers providing for the independence of Guinea-Bissau effective 10 September.

The new government, under President Luis de Almeida Cabral, had to deal with extensive economic turmoil brought about by the war. On 14 November 1980, President Cabral, who was of mixed European and American Indian ancestry with close ties to Cape Verde, was overthrown by a group of Guinean blacks under João Bernardo Vieira's command. Vieira and the PAIGC ruled

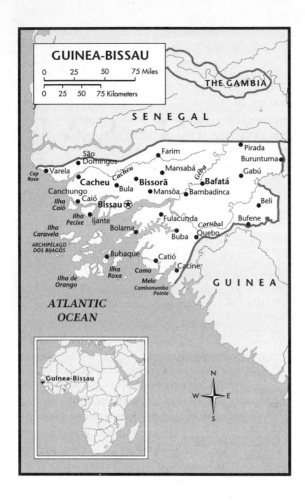

former army official whom President Vieira had dismissed on suspicion of arming separatist rebels in southern Senegal. Senegal and Guinea sent 2,000 soldiers to help put down the rebellion. However, Mane agreed to negotiate with the government only if all the foreign troops leave Guinea-Bissau.

GOVERNMENT

A new constitution was adopted in April 1991, and opposition political parties were permitted. Government continues to control the pace of political reform, which remains very slow. In 1993, it formed a National Elections Commission charged with organizing legislative and presidential elections that were conducted in 1994.

Judiciary

The Supreme Court has jurisdiction over serious crimes and serves as an appeals court for the regional military courts. In rural areas, persons are often tried outside the formal system by traditional law.

Political Parties

Formerly, the ruling African Party for the Independence of Guinea and Cape Verde (Partido Africano de Independência da Guiné e Cabo Verde—PAIGC) was the sole legal party. However, opposition parties were legalized by a new constitution adopted in April 1991. The most important opposition party is Bafata, the Guinea-Bissau Resistance-Bafata Movement.

DEFENSE

The People's Revolutionary Armed Forces (FARP) in 1995 numbered 9,250, of whom 6,800 were soldiers, 350 sailors, and 100 airmen, all considered part of a single service army.

ECONOMIC AFFAIRS

About 90% of the population relies on agriculture and fishing. The government is firmly committed to market-style economic policies after an initial decade of socialist central planning.

Public Finance

The IMF-sponsored structural adjustment program in Bissau began in 1987 and projected the achievement of a 3.5% growth rate, reforms to the economy and public administration.

The currency was devalued in May 1987. In January 1990, Guinea-Bissau agreed with Portugal to adopt the escudo. Reform of the national banking system has been underway since 1989.

Guinea-Bissau as a one-party state for ten years. However, in 1990, he denounced single-party rule, and in April 1991, Guinea-Bissau formally began a multiparty system and adopted a new constitution.

After several postponements, legislative and presidential elections were finally held in July 1994, the first multiparty elections in the country's history. The PAIGC won a decisive majority in the Assembly. Vieira was elected president.

Since 1989, Guinea-Bissau and neighboring Senegal have disputed over their border, which had been determined by Portugal and France in 1960. In 1992, the dispute erupted into violence as Senegalese bombers attacked the bases of Senegalese separatists located in Guinea-Bissau. In 1995, Senegal again bombed Guinea-Bissau, although it claimed the bombing was done in error. In March 1996, the two governments reached an agreement to end the hostilities.

In June 1998, tens of thousands fled north to Senegal as civil war broke out in Bissau. The rebellion was led by Brigadier Ansumane Mane, a

Failure to meet IMF targets translated into a suspension of international financing when the IMF decided not to renew the structural adjustment program. Negotiations resumed with the World Bank and led to a resumption of World Bank funding in July 1993.

Income

In 1998, Guinea-Bissau's gross national product (GNP) was $186 million at current prices, or $160 per person. Inflation during 1985–95 averaged 62.8% per year. During the same period, the average annual real growth rate of the GNP per person was 1.8%.

Industry

Manufacturing constitutes a very minor part of Guinea-Bissau's economy. Industries include a sugar refinery, and a rice and groundnut (peanut) processing plant. Brewing, urban construction, and vehicle assembly are also represented.

Banking and Finance

A savings and loan bank and a postal savings bank, both domestically owned, operate in Bissau. There are no securities exchanges in Guinea-Bissau.

The first investment bank in Guinea-Bissau, Banco de Africa Ocidental (BAO), was established in the first quarter of 1997 with joint Portuguese and Guinea-Bissau capital.

Economic Development

A main objective of the Guinea-Bissau government is the development of agriculture and infrastructure. The first development plan (1983–88) called for self-sufficiency in food supplies, with 25% of a $403.3 million investment going for construction and public works, 18% for rural development, and 14% for transport.

The second development plan (1988–91) was to be totally financed by foreign aid. Numerous countries and intergovernmental organizations have provided food aid, technical assistance, and balance-of-payments support.

SOCIAL WELFARE

Provision of health services, sanitation, and basic education is the principal social goal of the Guinea-Bissau government. As of 1995, no national social security system was in place. Women play an active part in government at all levels. Domestic abuse of women remains a problem and certain ethnic groups prohibit women from owning property.

Healthcare

In 1992, there were an estimated 12 physicians per 100,000 people. The average life expectancy was 44 years in 1995.

Housing

As of 1979, 44% of all housing units were adobe, 32% were mud, and 20% were mud and/or quirinton, a combination of woven branches and straw.

EDUCATION

In 1988, there were 79,035 students enrolled in primary schools and 6,630 students enrolled in secondary schools. Education is compulsory between the ages of 7 and 13, but only about 55% of all children in this age group actually attend school. Of the adult population, 45% is estimated to be illiterate.

1999 KEY EVENTS TIMELINE

January

- General Ansumane Mané, whom observers expected to stage a coup, continues to cooperate with President Joao Bernardo Vieira's government.

February

- Intensive fighting breaks out between government forces and rebels trying to overthrow President Joao Bernardo Vieira. At least 50 people are killed, 220 wounded, and thousands are forced to flee the capital, Bissau.

- President Vieira and rebel leader Brigadier General Ansumane Mané agree to end hostilities, disarm, and demobilize troops.

March

- Senegalese and Guinean peacekeeping troops pull out of Bissau according to agreements reached under ECOWAS/ECOMOG negotiations last November.

- Some 600 unarmed West African peacemakers replace Senegalese and Guinean peacekeeping troops.

- The deadline for presidential and legislative elections, prescribed by the Abuja Accord in November 1998, is not respected.

April

- The European Union ships $700,000 worth of vaccines to stem the meningitis epidemic hitting the interior of the country.

May

- Rebels mount a final assault on Bissau, storming the presidential palace, and forcing a surrender by President Vieira's special forces commander.

- The former head of parliament, Malan Bacai Sanha, is sworn in as president following the military coup. Vieira seeks asylum in the Portuguese Embassy.

- Coup leaders demand that the Portuguese Embassy hand over Vieira for trial.

- General Mané announces elections for November, and declares that he will not be a candidate.

- U.N. Secretary General Kofi Annan condemns Vieira's overthrow as unconstitutional.

- The OAU condemns the coup and deplores the undermining of ECOWAS's efforts.

June

- The Observatory for the Protection of Human Rights Defenders condemns military threats to suppress criticism of its activities.

- Médecins sans Frontières (MSF) concludes its emergency operations.

July

- Parliament approves an amended constitution. Prime Minister Francisco Fadul, whose family is of Lebanese origin, calls for its veto because of language stating that the positions of president, speaker of the parliament, chief justice, prime minister, attorney-general and armed forces chief be held only by native-born citizens whose parents are also native-born citizens.

- The Guinea-Bissau human rights league condemns the "native born" requirement as a violation of the Universal Declaration of Human Rights and says it will fight against it with all legal means.

- The U.N. sets up a trust fund to support peace-building with the participation of civil society and the armed forces in Guinea-Bissau.

August

- Former minister of justice, attorney-general and home affairs minister in deposed President Vieira's cabinet, Nicanda Barreto, is found dead in his home—gagged and with signs of blows on his body. His death appears to be a political killing.

September

- The IMF approves post-conflict aid for Guinea-Bissau.

- Tens of thousands in the capital city register to vote in the upcoming presidential elections.

- The PAIGC chooses a new chairman, and expels Vieira.

- Interim President Sanha announces his candidacy for the presidential elections.

October

- U.N. Secretary General Kofi Annan announces that large numbers of refugees are returning to Guinea-Bissau, as well as internally displaced persons, to settle at least temporarily with host families. Some $4.4 million will be needed to help them resettle permanently.

- The Supreme Court approves the applications of 12 candidates running for president. The Court begins examination of applications of some 2,600 candidates for parliamentary seats.

December

- Two opposition parties combined to win 64 of the 102 seats in Parliament in elections completed December 5. Kumba Yalla is ahead in presidential voting and will face the interim president Malam Bacai Sanha in a runoff election.

ANALYSIS OF EVENTS: 1999

BUSINESS AND THE ECONOMY

The amazing news in Guinea-Bissau is that somehow, in spite of widespread corruption, civil war, a coup d'etat, destruction of the capital city, and more than 250,000 refugees and displaced persons, the real GDP continued to grow in 1999 by 3–4 percent. The strength of this growth derives mainly from an anticipated record cashew crop of $50 million. Prices are fairly stable, although some prices rose sharply for staples in short supply such as rice.

Guinea-Bissau's interim and successor governments will find themselves relying on foreign aid, and rebuilding for years to come. Prime Minister Fadul's European tour netted several millions of U.S. dollars with Portugal contributing $4 million, and Sweden offering $2.3 million for external debt financing. At a roundtable in May, the UNDP estimated that some $20 million would be necessary for peace consolidation and national reconstruction. Additionally, the transitional government estimated that $138 million would be required for investments in the public and private sectors, including housing, electricity, health, and education. The donor community's commitments exceeded estimated need by $60 million.

Despite this show of compassion and confidence, three executives at the Central Bank have been accused of embezzling $4.3 million since Guinea-Bissau joined the Franc Zone in 1997. But that has not stopped markets, restaurants, bars, and shops from reopening in Bissau. The city now looks forward to the resumption of electricity, postal service, and other amenities it has gone without for the past year.

GOVERNMENT AND POLITICS

Politically, 1999 was a tumultuous year. The 11-month civil war came to end in May when troops loyal to deposed General Ansumane Mané stormed the presidential palace. President Vieira took refuge at the French Cultural Center, and later sought asylum at the Portuguese Embassy after being escorted there by a member of the junta. He was allowed to leave the country for Lisbon only after signing a declaration that he had renounced the presidency, and that he would return for trial in Guinea-Bissau.

At issue was Vieira's and several of his senior military officials' involvement in arms deals and illegal arms trafficking to secessionist rebels in the southern Casamance Province of Senegal. His unilateral appeal to bring in foreign troops to quell General Ansumane Mané's insurrection in June 1998 was extremely unpopular. Then, in violation of the 1998 Abuja accords, Vieira tried to nominate an attorney general sympathetic to his cause without consulting the transitional government. Fortunately for Vieira, Prime Minister Fadul recommended that he not be put on trial despite overwhelming, and vehement public opinion against him.

If the upheaval gave the ruling party, PAIGC, cause to reassess its internal cohesion and ideology, it also seems to have furthered political development. The Assembleia Nacional (parliament) announced political reforms regarding excessive Executive power, and the abuse of power for personal gain. Specifically, it has an anti-corruption agenda to add constitutional guidelines that would require politicians to declare possessions. It also voted for peer-election of the Supreme Court president, instead of appointment by the Executive. The abusive National Security police, which acted under presidential orders, has been disbanded.

However, language in the July amendment to the constitution limiting key senior-level offices to ''native-born'' Bissauens, has run into stiff opposition from influential quarters. The issue reflects a deep-seated animosity toward foreign-born or foreign-descended elites who practically ran the country since the Portuguese located the seat of government in Cape Verde.

Guinea-Bissau will have to mend relations with Senegal, Guinea, Portugal, and international organizations as a result of the arms-smuggling, the civil war, the coup, and Vieira's asylum. It is clear that Bissauen support for the separatist Mouvement des Forces Démocratiques de Casamance (MFDC) came from contending factions both within the Vieira government and General Mané's forces. The interim government will have to move swiftly and deliberately toward elections, which are scheduled next year, in order to restore a climate for rebuilding and investment.

CULTURE AND SOCIETY

The social priorities in Guinea-Bissau are the reunification and reintegration into society of the armed forces, and the return of refugees and displaced persons who must rebuild homes and their lives. The defense minister, director of the National Security police, and senior military officers accused of corruption and arms smuggling must receive fair trials so that ethnic groups such as the Balanta, and the rest of the country may reconcile and move ahead with rebuilding.

Amnesty International has approved of the way the transitional government has handled human rights, and it has recommended foreign aid to reform the justice system and law-enforcement agencies. The international community has promised and is delivering aid to remove landmines, deactivate anti-personnel mines, and for other humanitarian purposes. The FAO and the World Food Program distributed seeds and agricultural inputs in Bafata and Gabu. In October, U.N. General Secretary Kofi Annan announced that $4.4 million would be needed for rehabilitation and resettlement of displaced persons and refugees, indicating that 50,000 internally displaced persons had agreed to settle at least temporarily with host families.

DIRECTORY

CENTRAL GOVERNMENT

Head of State

President
Malan Bacai Sanha, Office of the President, Conselho de Estado, Bissau, Guinea-Bissau

Ministers

Prime Minister
Francisco Fadul, Office of the Prime Minister

Minister of Agriculture, Fisheries, Energy and Industry
Pinho Brandao, Ministry of Agriculture, Fisheries, Energy and Industry

Minister of Defense and Freedom Fighters
Francisco Benante, Ministry of Defense and Freedom Fighters

Minister of Economy and Finances
Abubacar Demba Dahaba, Ministry of Economy and Finances

Minister of Education
Califa Seidi, Ministry of Education

Minister of Foreign Affairs and International Cooperation
Jose Pereira Baptista, Ministry of Foreign Affairs and International Cooperation

Minister of Health and Social Affairs
Justino Fadia, Ministry of Health and Social Affairs

Minister of Interior
Caetan N'Tchama, Ministry of Interior

Minister of Justice and Labor
Carlos Domingos Gomes, Ministry of Justice and Labor

Minister of Social Communication and Parliamentary Affairs
Armando Procel, Ministry of Social Communication and Parliamentary Affairs

Minister of Social Equipment
Silvestre Alves, Ministry of Social Equipment

POLITICAL ORGANIZATIONS

Partido Africano da Independência de Guiné e Cabo Verde-PAIGC (African Party for the Independence of Guinea-Bissau)

TITLE: Secretary General
NAME: Manuel Saturnino da Costa

Frente para a Libertaçao e a Independência Nacional da Gunié-FLING (Front for the Liberation and Independence of Guinea)

NAME: Jose Katengul M. Endes

Resistência da Guiné-Bissau-RGB (Guinea-Bissau Resistance)

TITLE: Leader
NAME: Helder Jorge Vaz Gomes Lopes

Movimento Bafatá-MB (Bafata Movement)

TITLE: Leader
NAME: Domingos Fernandes Gomes

Partido para a Renova ao Social-PRS (Social Renovation Party)

TITLE: Leader
NAME: Koumba Yalla

União para a Mudança-UM (Union for Change Coalition)

TITLE: President
NAME: Jorge Mandinga

JUDICIAL SYSTEM
Supreme Court

FURTHER READING
Books

Forrest, Joshua. *Guinea-Bissau: Power, Conflict, and Renewal in a West African Nation.* Boulder: Westview Press, 1992.

Lopes, Carlos. *Guinea-Bissau: From Liberation Struggle to Independent Statehood*. Boulder: Westview Press, 1987.

Pedlar, Frederick. *Main Currents of West African History, 1940–1978*. London: The Macmillan Press, Ltd., 1979.

Swedish International Development Authority. *Guinea-Bissau: Economic Difficulties and Prospects for Structural Adjustment*. Sweden: Studies in Macroeconomic Management, 1989.

Internet

Africaonline. Available Online @ http://www.africaonline.com (October 28, 1999).

Africa News Online. Available Online @ http://www.africanews.org/west/stories/1999_feat1.html (October 28, 1999).

Integrated Regional Information Network (IRIN). Available Online @ http://www.reliefweb.int/IRIN (October 28, 1999).

GUINEA-BISSAU: STATISTICAL DATA

For sources and notes see "Sources of Statistics" in the front of each volume.

GEOGRAPHY

Geography (1)

Area:

Total: 36,120 sq km.

Land: 28,000 sq km.

Water: 8,120 sq km.

Area—comparative: slightly less than three times the size of Connecticut.

Land boundaries:

Total: 724 km.

Border countries: Guinea 386 km, Senegal 338 km.

Coastline: 350 km.

Climate: tropical; generally hot and humid; monsoonal-type rainy season (June to November) with southwesterly winds; dry season (December to May) with northeasterly harmattan winds.

Terrain: mostly low coastal plain rising to savanna in east.

Natural resources: fish, timber, phosphates, bauxite, unexploited deposits of petroleum.

Land use:

Arable land: 11%

Permanent crops: 1%

Permanent pastures: 38%

Forests and woodland: 38%

Other: 12% (1993 est.).

HUMAN FACTORS

Demographics (2A)

	1990	1995	1998	2000	2010	2020	2030	2040	2050
Population	997.8	1,124.5	1,206.3	1,263.3	1,578.8	1,925.2	2,280.3	2,633.6	2,970.2
Net migration rate (per 1,000 population)	NA	NA	NA	NA	NA	NA	NA	NA	NA
Births	NA	NA	NA	NA	NA	NA	NA	NA	NA
Deaths	NA	NA	NA	NA	NA	NA	NA	NA	NA
Life expectancy - males	44.2	46.2	47.5	48.3	52.7	57.1	61.3	65.2	68.5
Life expectancy - females	47.5	49.6	50.8	51.7	56.1	60.5	64.7	68.6	72.1
Birth rate (per 1,000)	43.2	40.2	38.7	37.8	33.3	28.2	24.1	20.9	18.4
Death rate (per 1,000)	18.8	16.6	15.5	14.8	12.0	9.9	8.5	7.8	7.5
Women of reproductive age (15-49 yrs.)	243.9	276.4	298.1	312.4	392.7	502.0	606.3	701.4	779.6
of which are currently married	NA	NA	NA	NA	NA	NA	NA	NA	NA
Fertility rate	5.8	5.4	5.2	5.0	4.2	3.4	2.9	2.5	2.3

Except as noted, values for vital statistics are in thousands; life expectancy is in years.

Health Indicators (4)

Life expectancy at birth

1980 39

1997 44

Daily per capita supply of calories (1996) 2,381

Total fertility rate births per woman (1997) 5.8

Maternal mortality ratio per 100,000 live births
(1990-97) . . . . .910[c]

Safe water % of population with access (1995) 53

Sanitation % of population with access (1995) 21

Consumption of iodized salt % of households
(1992-98)[a] 37

Smoking prevalence

Male % of adults (1985-95)[a] . . . .

Female % of adults (1985-95)[a] . . . .

Tuberculosis incidence per 100,000 people
(1997) 181

Adult HIV prevalence % of population ages
15-49 (1997) 2.25

Infants and Malnutrition (5)

Under-5 mortality rate (1997) 220

% of infants with low birthweight (1990-97) 20

Births attended by skilled health staff % of total[a] . . .25

% fully immunized (1995-97)

TB 22

DPT 63

Polio 60

Measles 51

Prevalence of child malnutrition under age 5
(1992-97)[b] . . . . .NA

Ethnic Division (6)

African 99%

Balanta 30%

Fula 20%

Manjaca 14%

Mandinga 13%

Papel 7%

European and mulatto . . . .<1%

Religions (7)

Indigenous beliefs 50%

Muslim 45%

Christian 5%

Languages (8)

Portuguese (official), Crioulo, African languages.

EDUCATION

Public Education Expenditures (9)

Public expenditure on education (% of GNP)

1980 . . . .

1996 . . . .

Expenditure per student

Primary % of GNP per capita

1980 . . . . .32.1

1996 . . . .

Secondary % of GNP per capita

1980 . . . . .107.5

1996 . . . .

Tertiary % of GNP per capita

1980 . . . .

1996 . . . .

Expenditure on teaching materials

Primary % of total for level (1996) . . . .

Secondary % of total for level (1996) . . . .

Primary pupil-teacher ratio per teacher (1996) . . . .

Duration of primary education years (1995) 6

Educational Attainment (10)

Age group (1979)[3] . . . . .7+

Total population 483,336

Highest level attained (%)

No schooling 91.1

First level

Not completed 8.0

Completed . . . . .NA

Entered second level

S-1 . . . . .0.6

S-2 . . . . .0.2

Postsecondary 0.1

Literacy Rates (11A)

In thousands and percent[1]	1990	1995	2000	2010
Illiterate population (15+ yrs.)	287	282	277	264
Literacy rate - total adult pop. (%)	49.5	54.9	60.2	70.0
Literacy rate - males (%)	63.3	68.0	72.4	79.8
Literacy rate - females (%)	36.5	42.5	48.7	60.7

GOVERNMENT & LAW

Political Parties (12)

National People's Assembly	% of seats
African Party for the Independence of Guinea-Bissau and Cape Verde (PAIGC) 46.0	
Guinea-Bissau Resistance-Ba Fata Movement (RGB-MB) 19.2	
Social Renovation Party (PRS) 10.3	
Union for Change (UM) .12.8	

Front for the Liberation and Independence of
    Guinea (FLING) 2.5
Party for Democratic Convergence (PCD) 5.3
United Social Democratic Party (PUSD) 2.9
Guinean Civic Forum (FCG) 0.2
Others 0.8

LABOR FORCE

Unemployment Rate (17)

Rate not available.

Military Affairs (14B)

	1990	1991	1992	1993	1994	1995
Military expenditures						
Current dollars (mil.)	NA	NA	7[e]	8[e]	8	7[e]
1995 constant dollars (mil.)	NA	NA	7[e]	8[e]	8	7[e]
Armed forces (000)	12	12	11	11	7	7
Gross national product (GNP)						
Current dollars (mil.)	197	198	212	220	236	253
1995 constant dollars (mil.)	227	219	229	230	242	253
Central government expenditures (CGE)						
1995 constant dollars (mil.)	111	96	92	NA	NA	NA
People (mil.)	1.0	1.0	1.0	1.1	1.1	1.1
Military expenditure as % of GNP	NA	NA	3.1	3.6	3.4	2.8
Military expenditure as % of CGE	NA	NA	7.6	NA	NA	NA
Military expenditure per capita (1995 $)	NA	NA	7	8	8	6
Armed forces per 1,000 people (soldiers)	12.0	11.7	10.5	10.3	6.4	6.2
GNP per capita (1995 $)	227	214	218	215	220	225
Arms imports[6]						
Current dollars (mil.)	5	5	0	0	0	0
1995 constant dollars (mil.)	6	6	0	0	0	0
Arms exports[6]						
Current dollars (mil.)	0	0	0	0	0	0
1995 constant dollars (mil.)	0	0	0	0	0	0
Total imports[7]						
Current dollars (mil.)	68	67	84	62	17	70
1995 constant dollars (mil.)	78	74	90	65	17	70
Total exports[7]						
Current dollars (mil.)	19	20	6	16	32	23
1995 constant dollars (mil.)	22	22	6	17	33	23
Arms as percent of total imports[8]	7.4	7.5	0	0	0	0
Arms as percent of total exports[8]	0	0	0	0	0	0

PRODUCTION SECTOR

Electric Energy (18)

Capacity . . . . .11,000 kW (1995)

Production . . . . .45 million kWh (1995)

Consumption per capita . . . . .40 kWh (1995)

Transportation (19)

Highways:

total: 4,400 km

paved: 453 km

unpaved: 3,947 km (1996 est.)

Waterways: several rivers are accessible to coastal shipping

Merchant marine: none

Airports: 30 (1997 est.)

Airports—with paved runways:

total: 3

over 3,047 m: 1

1,524 to 2,437 m: 1

914 to 1,523 m: 1 (1997 est.)

Airports—with unpaved runways:

total: 27

1,524 to 2,437 m: 1

914 to 1,523 m: 4

under 914 m: 22 (1997 est.)

Top Agricultural Products (20)

Rice, corn, beans, cassava (tapioca), cashew nuts, peanuts, palm kernels, cotton; fishing and forest potential not fully exploited.

MANUFACTURING SECTOR

GDP & Manufacturing Summary (21)

	1980	1985	1990	1992	1993	1994
Gross Domestic Product						
Millions of 1990 dollars	168	186	236	250	258	276
Growth rate in percent	−4.19	−2.30	3.30	2.80	3.00	6.90
Per capita (in 1990 dollars)	210.7	213.0	245.3	248.9	250.8	262.5
Manufacturing Value Added						
Millions of 1990 dollars	25	24	17	16	16	*16*
Growth rate in percent	−5.09	−5.95	−1.54	−1.40	1.21	*-1.35*
Manufacturing share in percent of current prices	7.3	7.1	7.0	8.4	8.0	*8.0*

FINANCE, ECONOMICS, & TRADE

Balance of Payments (23)

	1991	1992	1993	1994	1995
Exports of goods (f.o.b.)	20	6	16	33	24
Imports of goods (f.o.b.)	−67	−84	−54	−54	−59
Trade balance	−47	−77	−38	−21	−35
Services - debits	−47	−44	−40	−51	−36
Services - credits	—	—	—	—	—
Private transfers (net)	23	24	18	23	47
Government transfers (net)	−4	−1	−2	−1	−1
Overall balance	−75	−97	−62	−49	−26

Economic Indicators (22)

National product: GDP—purchasing power parity—$1.15 billion (1997 est.)

National product real growth rate: 5% (1997 est.)

National product per capita: $975 (1997 est.)

Inflation rate—consumer price index: 65% (1996)

Exchange Rates (24)

Exchange rates:

CFA francs (CFAF) per US$1

January 1998	.608.36
1997	.583.67

Guinea-Bissauan pesos (PG) per US$1

1996	.26,373
1995	.18,073
1994	.12,892
1993	.10,082

As of 2 May 1997, Guinea-Bissau has adopted the CFA franc as the national currency following its membership in BCEAO

Top Import Origins (25)

$63 million (f.o.b., 1996 est.) Data are for 1995.

Origins	%
Thailand	.27
Portugal	.23
Japan	.6
Cote d'Ivoire	.7

Top Export Destinations (26)

$25.8 million (f.o.b., 1996 est.) Data are for 1995.

Destinations	%
Spain	.35
India	.30
Thailand	.10
Italy	.10

Economic Aid (27)

Recipient: ODA, $NA. NA stands for not available.

Import Export Commodities (28)

Import Commodities	Export Commodities
Foodstuffs	Cashews 95%
Transport equipment	Fish
Petroleum products	Peanuts
Machinery and equipment	Palm kernels
	Sawn lumber

GUYANA

Cooperative Republic of Guyana

INTRODUCTORY SURVEY

RECENT HISTORY

British imperial policy changed after World War II (1939–45), and British Guiana received a new constitution providing for a two-chamber legislature and universal adult vote. The colony was granted full internal self-government in 1961 and became a sovereign and independent nation on 26 May 1966.

Guyana was proclaimed a cooperative republic on 23 February 1970, the 207th anniversary of a Guyanese slave revolt. The People's National Congress (PNC) ruled as the majority party between 1968–92.

Desmond Hoyte, president from 1985–92, sought to improve Guyana's relations with non-socialist nations. By 1992, the country had grown tired of the PNC, and elected Cheddi Jagan of the People's Progressive Party to the presidency. Jagan served effectively as president until his death in March 1997. Under Jagan's administration, Guyana was able to consolidate its massive foreign debts and begin to enjoy sustained economic growth. Prime Minister Samuel Hinds was appointed interim president. In December 1997, Janet Jagan, long-time political activist and widow of Cheddi Jagan, was elected president.

GOVERNMENT

As of 23 February 1970, Guyana became a cooperative republic. Under a new constitution approved in 1980, the single-chamber National Assembly consisted of fifty-three members. The office

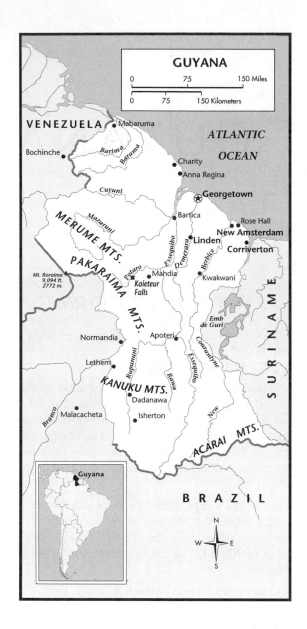

GUYANA

of executive president, created by the 1980 constitution, is filled by the leader of the majority party as both chief of state and head of government. The president appoints a cabinet, including a prime minister, who also holds the title of first vice-president.

Judiciary

The Supreme Court has two divisions: the high court and the court of appeal. Magistrates' courts have jurisdiction over less serious civil and criminal matters.

Political Parties

The People's National Congress (PNC) dominated Guyana's politics from independence in 1968 until 1992. It draws its members primarily from urban blacks. Guyana's other major party is the People's Progressive Party (PPP), which gained the majority position in 1992. Appealing to Asian Indian rice farmers and sugar workers, the PPP has usually taken a traditional socialist position along the lines of international communism.

DEFENSE

The Combined Guyana Defense Force numbered 1,600 full-time officers and troops (including a women's army corps) in 1995. Reserves and paramilitary forces numbered 1,500. Defense expenditures in 1995 were US $7 million.

ECONOMIC AFFAIRS

The bulk of the population is engaged in agriculture, either as laborers on sugar plantations or as peasant cultivators of rice. Although sugar and rice continued to be important export earners, bauxite's share of national exports grew from 25% in 1970 to 48% in 1985.

In recent years, Guyana's economy has improved dramatically under the Economic Recovery Program (ERP) launched by the government in April 1989 to steer the country towards a more open free market system. Inflation has dropped from a 1989–91 annual average of 60–100% to only 14% in 1992. Real growth of 7.3% in 1996 marked the sixth consecutive year of strong economic recovery.

Public Finance

Taxes finance the current account budget, with net surpluses or deficits being added to or subtracted from a general revenue balance. At the end of 1985, the IMF declared Guyana ineligible to receive further loans. In 1988, the government began an economic recovery program, adopting a free market. Nevertheless, in 1991, Guyana's debt exceeded 600% of GDP and total debt service was two-thirds as large as export revenue. The U.S. CIA estimates that, in 1995, government revenues totaled approximately $209 million and expenditures $303 million, including capital expenditures of $109 million. External debt totaled $2.2 billion.

Income

In 1998, Guyana's gross national product (GNP) was U.S. $660 million at current prices, or U.S. $770 per person. For the period 1985–95, the average inflation rate was 51.1%, resulting in a real growth rate in GNP of 0.8% per person.

Industry

Industry is limited chiefly to processing bauxite, sugar, and rice for export and food and beverages for the local market. Industry accounts for 28% of the domestic economy.

Banking and Finance

The Bank of Guyana is the central bank. In April 1995, Parliament approved the Financial Institutions Act of 1995. The new legislation aimed to tighten the supervisory and regulatory framework of the financial system.

While a number of firms with publicly issued share capital are active, no large-scale securities market has developed.

Economic Development

A continuing theme of Guyanese economic development policy has been the attempt, without great success, to expand agriculture and to diversify the economy.

In the late 1990s, primarily as a result of economic reforms, agricultural output is expected to continue growing at an stable rate. Manufacturing output is also likely to grow because of expected improvements in electricity generation and distribution and improved incentives for private investments. These factors combined should make attaining continued recovery with real growth rates in excess of 5% per year possible in the medium term.

The continuation of sound macroeconomic policies and public sector reform, together with multilateral and bilateral assistance, is crucial to sustaining these recovery efforts. The fiscal situation is expected to continue improving in the short and medium term, largely as a result of increased current revenues.

SOCIAL WELFARE

Social welfare benefits include workers' compensation, maternity and health insurance, death benefits, disability, and old-age pensions.

The 1990 Equal Rights Act, which was intended to end sex discrimination, has been difficult to enforce.

Healthcare

In 1990, there were 200 doctors, and 96% of the population had access to health care services. In 1995, the average life expectancy was about 64 years. Public health measures had virtually eliminated malaria as a major problem. Filariasis, enteric fever, helminthiasis, nutritional deficiencies, and venereal diseases all still pose significant health risks. Yellow fever remains a constant threat.

Housing

Housing is a critical problem, as is the lack of adequate water supplies and of effective waste disposal and sewage systems. Urban development plans have been prepared for Georgetown and New Amsterdam.

EDUCATION

The adult illiteracy rate in 1995 was 2%, among the highest in South America. School attendance is free and compulsory for children between the ages of 6 and 14. The University of Guyana was established in 1963. There were 497 teachers and 8,257 students enrolled at universities and all higher level institutions in 1993.

1999 KEY EVENTS TIMELINE

January

- Government and opposition parliamentarians vote unanimously for a bill to reform Guyana's constitution.

- Guyana lifts restrictions on sex-related Internet content.

June

- The privatized new national airline, Guyana Airways 2000, has troubles getting off the ground. Its inaugural flight to Toronto is cancelled.

- Rioters damage a store with a hand grenade, smash windows and overturn cars to protest the shooting of a boy. The nation is shaken by strike-related violence. Riot police fire tear gas to break up the crowd in Georgetown

July

- President Janet Jagan travels to the United States for medical checkup. She is discharged from Akron City Hospital in Ohio after tests for a heart condition.

August

- President Janet Jagan says she will step down because of health problems at the age of 78.

- Guyana and the United States come closer to formalizing a treaty to set up an electronic anti-narcotics eavesdropping center.

September

- An independent tribunal stuns Guyanese officials by awarding public workers a large pay raise in the wake of a bitter 57-day strike.

- Guyana is declared one of several nations eligible for U.S. debt relief.

October

- Venezuela reiterates claim to territory in Guyana. The claim covers two-thirds of Guyana's territory, an area that is sparsely populated and believed to be rich in minerals.

- The new president of Guyana, Bharrat Jagdeo, steps in for Janet Jagan. President Jagdeo is from the governing People's Progressive Party, which is dominated by people of Indian descent. He served under Jagan as finance minister.

- Venezuela claims military activities near Guyana were part of an operative against drug traffickers, and not an attempt to enter the Essequibo, a large disputed area that Venezuela claims as its own.

- The High Court bans all weapons from courtrooms, in response to a clash between lawyers in a death row case over the attorney general's right to carry a gun in court.

November

- The industrialized nations of the world reach agreement on debt relief for the world's poorest nations. The Heavily Indebted Poor Countries (HIPC) initiative, launched in 1996, will provide cancellation of about $70 billion of debt for nations that qualify. Guyana is one of four nations (Bolivia, Uganda, and Mozambique are the others) that has received debt relief under this program.

ANALYSIS OF EVENTS: 1999

BUSINESS AND THE ECONOMY

The United States announced in September that Guyana is one of 36 heavily indebted countries eligible for U.S. debt relief. That same month, England announced that Guyana could soon qualify for additional debt relief under the Poor Indebted Countries (HIPC) initiative. Guyana owes its creditors about $1.4 billion, and became only the third country to qualify for $256 million in debt relief under the HIPC program.

A drop in world prices for sugar, rice and gold hurt Guyana in 1999. In March, Jagdeo presented a budget based on 1.8 percent growth, with inflation targeted at 5.5 percent. Political observers said Jagdeo, who is considered the architect of the country's debt relief plan, will continue to shape the economy as president.

GOVERNMENT AND POLITICS

Janet Jagan, the American expatriate who fought for Guyana's independence and became one of the nation's most powerful politicians, resigned the presidency due to health reasons. Her finance minister, Bharrat Jagdeo, stepped in for the 78-year-old Jagan in August.

Jagan made her decision after undergoing medical tests in the United States, ending a long and distinguished political career that began in the early 1940s, when she moved with her husband Cheddi Jagan to what was then known as British Guiana.

Janet voted in the 1947 elections in the colony, effectively renouncing her U.S. citizenship. She quickly established herself as her husband's chief political partner and adviser. By 1950, the Jagans had founded the People's Progressive Party (PPP), the colony's first political party, and still one of the most powerful in the country. The Jagans embarked on a civil disobedience campaign modeled on the one led by Mohandas K. Gandhi against British rule in India. They were arrested and jailed for six months. They emerged from prison as heroes, both winning Cabinet posts in the 1957 elections.

In the early 1960s, the Jagans became victims of Cold War politics. With U.S. aid being sent to his foes, Cheddi was unable to return to power. Finally in 1992, Cheddi was elected president but died in 1997 before completing his term. His wife Janet won the elections that year, taking office in December. Cheddi Jagan had attempted to minimize the racial divisions that have plagued his nation for most of its young history by diversifying his cabinet. His wife promised to do the same, but selecting Bharrat Jagdeo as her successor met with criticism from the mainly-black opposition People's National Congress. Jagdeo, a member of the governing PPP, promised to work with the opposition.

At 35, Jagdeo is one of the world's youngest heads of state. "Being young is not a disadvantage, it is an opportunity," the Moscow-educated economist told the press at the swearing-in ceremony.

Historically, Guyana has had an uneasy relationship with its neighbors. Already one of the smallest nations in South America, it would be even smaller if Suriname and Venezuela had their way. In 1999, the larger and wealthier Venezuela again made claims to two-thirds of Guyana, a sparsely populated area known as the Essequibo. Venezuela revived its claim in October, 100 years after an international tribunal of arbitration set the existing border with what was then British Guiana.

Guyana has rejected the claims, but Venezuelan President Hugo Chavez said his country would seek a "peaceful solution" to the dispute, and would not abandon its claims. The Venezuelans claim the 100-year old deal is invalid because it was the result of a secret deal to favor British Guiana. Few people live in the Essequibo, a 61,500 square mile region believed to be rich in gold, diamond, and bauxite.

CULTURE AND SOCIETY

In January, Guyana lifted Internet restrictions that blocked on-line information about sex, racism, and explosives. Guyana's Minister of Information, Moses Nagamootoo, said the government was removing all restrictions on access to the Internet.

Nagamootoo said the government didn't believe the indiscriminate restricting of specific sites was useful, even though many of the sites were pornographic. The decision, he said, was consistent with the government's stance on freedom of expression and free access to information. Former President Cheddi Jagan ordered the controls in place in 1995, when local companies began to offer high-speed Internet access. At the time, the country's leaders were uneasy about Guyana's reputation for international sex chat lines. They said they wanted to prevent the transmission of "immoral" material over a new medium. According to some estimates, about one-third of the Guyana Telephone and Telegraph's Co.'s income comes from international sex lines.

Cricket is a national pastime in Guyana, but the small nation could be banned from hosting international events because of rowdy crowds. During a tournament in April, the Australian delegation complained that bottles were thrown at them during a game. During a match, fans invaded the playing field, and jostled with players. The Australians said they would not return to Guyana until the country improves security measures.

DIRECTORY

CENTRAL GOVERNMENT

Head of State

President
Bharrat Jagdeo, Office of the President, New Garden Street, Bourda, Georgetown, Guyana
PHONE: +592 (02) 51330

Second Vice President; Minister of Agriculture and Parliamentary Affairs
Reepu Daman Persaud, Office of the Vice President
E-MAIL: guyagri@hotmail.com

Prime Minister; Minister of Public Works
Samuel A. Hinds, Office of the Prime Minister, Wights Lane, Bourda, Georgetown, Guyana
PHONE: +592 (02) 73101; 73102; 66955
FAX: +592 (02) 67563

Ministers

Minister of Home Affairs
Ronald Gajraj, Ministry of Home Affairs, Brickdam, Stabroek, Georgetown, Guyana
PHONE: +592 (02) 63454; 57270

Minister of Finance
Bharrat Jagdeo, Ministry of Finance, Main Street, Kingston, Georgetown, Guyana
PHONE: +592 (02) 73991; 56088; 71114
FAX: +592 (02) 61284

Minister of Foreign Affairs
Clement Rohee, Ministry of Foreign Affairs, 254 South Road and New Garden Street, Georgetown, Guyana
PHONE: +592 (02) 61607; 56467
FAX: +592 (02) 59192
E-MAIL: minfor@sdnp.org.gy

Minister of Information
Moses Nagamootoo, Ministry of Information, Area B Homestretch Avenue, Georgetown, Guyana
PHONE: +592 (02) 68849
FAX: +592 (02) 68853

Minister of Public Service
George Fung-On, Ministry of Public Service

Minister of Education
Dale Bisnauth, Ministry of Education, 26
Brickdam, Georgetown, Guyana
PHONE: +592 (22) 63094
FAX: +592 (22) 55570

Minister of Amerindian Affairs
Vibert De Souza, Ministry of Amerindian
Affairs

Minister of Environmental Protection
Ministry of Environmental Protection, IAST
Building, U.G. Campus, Turkeyen, Greater
Georgetown, Guyana
E-MAIL: epa@sdnp.org.gy

Minister of Local Government
Harripersaud Nokta, Ministry of Local
Government, Fort Street, Kingston, Georgetown,
Guyana
PHONE: +592 (02) 58621; 54878; 63959
FAX: +592 (02) 65070

Minister of Local Government
Clinton Collymore, Ministry of Local
Government

Minister of Trade, Industry, and Tourism
Michael Shree Chan, Ministry of Trade,
Industry, and Tourism, 229 South Road,
Lacytown, Georgetown, Guyana
PHONE: +592 (02) 68695; 62392; 63182
FAX: +592 (02) 59898

Minister of Transport and Hydraulics
Anthony Xavier, Ministry of Transport and
Hydraulics

Minister of Labor and Health
Henry Jeffrey, Ministry of Labor and Health, 18
Brickdam, Stabroek, Georgetown, Guyana
PHONE: +592 (02) 65861; 61560
FAX: +592 (02) 54505
E-MAIL: moh@sdnp.org.gy

**Minister of Human Service and Social
Security**
Indranie Chandarpal, Minister of Human Service
and Social Security, 1 Water Street, Stabroek,
Georgetown, Guyana
PHONE: +592 (02) 68996; 66115
FAX: +592 (02) 71308

Minister of Culture, Youth, and Sports
Gail Teixeira, Ministry of Culture, Youth, and
Sports, 71 Main Street, North Cummingsburg,
Georgetown, Guyana

PHONE: +592 (02) 60142; 73576; 77860
FAX: +592 (02) 65067

Minister of Fisheries, Crops, and Livestock
Satyadeow Sawh, Ministry of Fisheries, Crops,
and Livestock, Regent Road, Bourda,
Georgetown, Guyana
PHONE: +592 (02) 61565; 56768
FAX: +592 (02) 72978

Minister of Housing and Water
Shaik Baksh, Ministry of Housing and Water,
Homestretch Avenue, Durban Park, Georgetown,
Guyana
PHONE: +592 (02) 61809; 54991

**Minister of Public Works and
Communications**
Samuel Hinds, Ministry of Public Works and
Communications, Wights Lane, Kingston,
Georgetown, Guyana
PHONE: +592 (02) 61875
FAX: +592 (02) 56954

POLITICAL ORGANIZATIONS
People's Progressive Party

Freedom House, 41 Robb Street, Georgetown,
Guyana
PHONE: +592 (02) 72095; 74301; 74302
FAX: +592 (02) 72096
E-MAIL: pppcivic@pppcivic.org
TITLE: President
NAME: Donald Ramotar

People's National Congress

Congress Place, Sophia, Georgetown, Guyana
PHONE: +59 (02) 57852
FAX: +592 (02) 50696; 56055
TITLE: General Secretary
NAME: Oscar Eleazer Clarke

Working People's Alliance

Rodney House, 80 Croal Street, Georgetown,
Guyana
PHONE: +592 (02) 56624
NAME: Rupert Roopnaraine

DIPLOMATIC
REPRESENTATION
Embassies in Guyana

Canada
Young and High Streets, Georgetown, Guyana
TITLE: High Commissioner
NAME: Alan Bowker

China
Duke Street, Georgetown, Guyana
TITLE: Ambassador
NAME: Wang Fuyuan

India
10 Avenue of the Republic, Georgetown, Guyana
TITLE: High Commissioner
NAME: Prakash V. Joshi

Russian Federation
Public Road, Kitty Avant, Georgetown, Guyana
TITLE: Ambassador
NAME: Tahir Byashimovich Durdiyev

United Kingdom
44 Main Street, Georgetown, Guyana
TITLE: High Commissioner
NAME: Edward Charles Glover

United States
Young and Duke Street, Georgetown, Guyana
TITLE: Ambassador
NAME: James F. Mack

JUDICIAL SYSTEM

Supreme Court of Judicature

Guyana Court of Appeal

60 High Street, Kingston, Georgetown, Guyana

PHONE: +592 (02) 57383

FURTHER READING

Articles

"Changes in Guyana Bring Uncertainty." *The Miami Herald*, 8 August 1999.

"The Cricketers Are a Joke. The Bananas Aren't Selling. Can My Country Survive on Drugs and Tourists Alone?" *The Guardian*, 14 March 1999.

"Guyana Grenade Attacks Aimed at Supporters of Jagan," *The Miami Herald*, 14 June 1999.

"Guyana parrots among vulnerable species around the world." *The Guardian*, 6 August 1999.

"Guyana's New Generation." *The Economist* (August 14, 1999): 30.

"How Britain Betrayed Its Black Soldiers." *The Guardian*, 7 October 1999.

"No Weapons in Court, Guyana's High Court Rules." Associated Press, 22 October 1999.

"Raise Granted to Public Workers." *The Miami Herald*, 2 September 1999.

"Venezuela Claims Most of Guyana as Its Own." *The Economist* (October 9, 1999): 36.

GUYANA: STATISTICAL DATA

For sources and notes see "Sources of Statistics" in the front of each volume.

GEOGRAPHY

Geography (1)

Area:

Total: 214,970 sq km.

Land: 196,850 sq km.

Water: 18,120 sq km.

Area—comparative: slightly smaller than Idaho.

Land boundaries:

Total: 2,462 km.

Border countries: Brazil 1,119 km, Suriname 600 km, Venezuela 743 km.

Coastline: 459 km.

Climate: tropical; hot, humid, moderated by northeast trade winds; two rainy seasons (May to mid-August, mid-November to mid-January).

Terrain: mostly rolling highlands; low coastal plain; savanna in south.

Natural resources: bauxite, gold, diamonds, hardwood timber, shrimp, fish.

Land use:

Arable land: 2%

Permanent crops: 0%

Permanent pastures: 6%

Forests and woodland: 84%

Other: 8% (1993 est.).

HUMAN FACTORS

Demographics (2A)

	1990	1995	1998	2000	2010	2020	2030	2040	2050
Population	747.5	722.3	708.0	703.4	717.9	714.2	709.1	717.7	726.4
Net migration rate (per 1,000 population)	NA	NA	NA	NA	NA	NA	NA	NA	NA
Births	NA	NA	NA	NA	NA	NA	NA	NA	NA
Deaths	NA	NA	NA	NA	NA	NA	NA	NA	NA
Life expectancy - males	60.4	60.6	59.5	58.8	49.9	52.9	60.4	67.9	70.9
Life expectancy - females	67.3	67.5	65.3	63.9	52.5	55.9	64.9	73.9	77.3
Birth rate (per 1,000)	22.0	19.4	18.5	18.0	17.3	15.0	13.6	12.9	11.6
Death rate (per 1,000)	7.6	7.8	8.7	9.4	16.9	16.2	13.3	11.1	11.2
Women of reproductive age (15-49 yrs.)	195.3	195.3	195.9	196.8	199.3	188.9	184.2	175.6	168.8
of which are currently married	NA	NA	NA	NA	NA	NA	NA	NA	NA
Fertility rate	2.5	2.2	2.1	2.0	1.9	1.8	1.8	1.8	1.8

Except as noted, values for vital statistics are in thousands; life expectancy is in years.

Infants and Malnutrition (5)

Under-5 mortality rate (1997) 82

% of infants with low birthweight (1990-97) 15

Births attended by skilled health staff % of total[a] . . .NA

% fully immunized (1995-97)

TB 94

DPT 88

Polio 89

Measles 82

Prevalence of child malnutrition under age 5
(1992-97)[b] . . . . .NA

Ethnic Division (6)

East Indian 49%

Black 32%

Mixed 12%

Amerindian 6%

White and Chinese 1%

Religions (7)

Christian 57%

Hindu 33%

Muslim 9%

Other 1%

GOVERNMENT & LAW

Military Affairs (14B)

	1990	1991	1992	1993	1994	1995
Military expenditures						
Current dollars (mil.)	5	4	7	8	8	7
1995 constant dollars (mil.)	6	5	8	8	8	7
Armed forces (000)	4	4	2	2	2	2
Gross national product (GNP)						
Current dollars (mil.)	311	305	391	492	539	560
1995 constant dollars (mil.)	358	337	421	516	552	560
Central government expenditures (CGE)						
1995 constant dollars (mil.)	360	320	272	273	255	238
People (mil.)	.7	.7	.7	.7	.7	.7
Military expenditure as % of GNP	1.7	1.4	1.8	1.6	1.4	1.3
Military expenditure as % of CGE	1.7	1.4	2.8	3.1	3.1	3.0
Military expenditure per capita (1995 $)	8	6	10	12	11	10
Armed forces per 1,000 people (soldiers)	4.7	4.7	2.7	2.7	2.8	2.8
GNP per capita (1995 $)	479	453	570	705	761	779
Arms imports[6]						
Current dollars (mil.)	0	0	0	0	0	0
1995 constant dollars (mil.)	0	0	0	0	0	0
Arms exports[6]						
Current dollars (mi0.)	0	0	0	0	0	0
1995 constant dollars (mil.)	0	0	0	0	0	0
Total imports[7]						
Current dollars (mil.)	311	307	443	484	456[e]	NA
1995 constant dollars (mil.)	357	339	477	507	467[e]	NA
Total exports[7]						
Current dollars (mil.)	251	248	302	423	439	467
1995 constant dollars (mil.)	288	274	325	443	450	467
Arms as percent of total imports[8]	0	0	0	0	0	NA
Arms as percent of total exports[8]	0	0	0	0	0	0

Languages (8)

English, Amerindian dialects.

EDUCATION

Educational Attainment (10)

Age group (1980) ....25+
Total population 270,849
Highest level attained (%)
No schooling 8.1
First level
Not completed 72.9
Completed ....NA
Entered second level
S-1 ....17.3
S-2 ....NA
Postsecondary 1.8

Literacy Rates (11A)

In thousands and percent[1]	1990	1995	2000	2010
Illiterate population (15+ yrs.)	15	11	9	5
Literacy rate - total adult pop. (%)	97.2	98.1	98.6	99.3
Literacy rate - males (%)	98.1	98.6	99.0	99.4
Literacy rate - females (%)	96.3	97.5	98.2	99.2

GOVERNMENT & LAW

Political Parties (12)

National Assembly	% of seats
People's Progressive Party (PPP)	54
People's National Congress (PNC)	41

Alliance for Guyana (AFG) 1
The United Force (TUF) 1

Government Budget (13B)

Revenues ....$278 million
Expenditures ....$299 million
Capital expenditures ....$133 million
Data for 1996 est.

Crime (15)

Crime rate (for 1997)
Crimes reported 10,500
Total persons convicted 4,300
Crimes per 100,000 population 1,350
Persons responsible for offenses
Total number of suspects 5,850
Total number of female suspects 400
Total number of juvenile suspects 41

LABOR FORCE

Unemployment Rate (17)

12% (1992 est.)

PRODUCTION SECTOR

Electric Energy (18)

Capacity ....114,000 kW (1995)
Production ....230 million kWh (1995)
Consumption per capita ....339 kWh (1995)

MANUFACTURING SECTOR

GDP & Manufacturing Summary (21)

	1980	1985	1990	1992	1993	1994
Gross Domestic Product						
Millions of 1990 dollars	561	469	396	453	490	531
Growth rate in percent	1.66	1.02	−10.09	7.75	8.23	8.50
Per capita (in 1990 dollars)	739.6	593.3	497.8	560.1	600.3	644.2
Manufacturing Value Added						
Millions of 1990 dollars	40	28	18	24	25	*27*
Growth rate in percent	0.76	−3.13	−16.67	19.32	3.07	*12.06*
Manufacturing share in percent of current prices	12.1	9.8	5.2	4.4	*3.8*	NA

Transportation (19)

Highways:

total: 7,970 km

paved: 590 km

unpaved: 7,380 km (1996 est.)

Waterways: 6,000 km total of navigable waterways; Berbice, Demerara, and Essequibo Rivers are navigable by oceangoing vessels for 150 km, 100 km, and 80 km, respectively

Merchant marine:

total: 2 cargo ship (1,000 GRT or over) totaling 2,340 GRT/4,530 DWT (1997 est.)

Airports: 50 (1997 est.)

Airports—with paved runways:

total: 5

1,524 to 2,437 m: 3

914 to 1,523 m: 1

under 914 m: 1 (1997 est.)

Airports—with unpaved runways:

total: 45

1,524 to 2,437 m: 1

914 to 1,523 m: 10

under 914 m: 34 (1997 est.)

Top Agricultural Products (20)

Sugar, rice, wheat, vegetable oils; beef, pork, poultry, dairy products; development potential exists for fishing and forestry.

FINANCE, ECONOMICS, & TRADE

Economic Indicators (22)

National product: GDP—purchasing power parity—$1.8 billion (1997 est.)

National product real growth rate: 5% (1997 est.)

National product per capita: $2,500 (1997 est.)

Inflation rate—consumer price index: 4.5% (1997 est.)

Balance of Payments (23)

Exchange Rates (24)

Exchange rates:

Guyanese dollars (G$) per US$1

January 1998	144.2
1997	142.4
1996	140.4
1995	142.0
1994	138.3
1993	126.7

Top Import Origins (25)

$589 million (c.i.f., 1996 est.) Data are for 1994 est.

Origins	%
United States	29
Trinidad and Tobago	17
Netherlands Antilles	17
United Kingdom	11

Top Export Destinations (26)

$546 million (f.o.b., 1996) Data are for 1994 est.

Destinations	%
Canada	33
United States	24
United Kingdom	22

Economic Aid (27)

Recipient: ODA, $NA. NA stands for not available.

Import Export Commodities (28)

Import Commodities	Export Commodities
Manufactures	Sugar
Machinery	Gold
Petroleum	Bauxite/alumina
Food est.	Rice
	Shrimp
	Molasses

	1985	1992	1993	1994	1995
Exports of goods (f.o.b.)	214	382	415	463	496
Imports of goods (f.o.b.)	−209	−443	−484	−504	−536
Trade balance	5	−61	−68	−41	−41
Services - debits	−144	−241	−255	−276	−302
Services - credits	48	111	120	129	146
Private transfers (net)	−3	12	14	11	3
Government transfers (net)	−2	41	48	51	59
Overall balance	−97	−139	−140	−125	−135

HAITI

CAPITAL: Port-au-Prince.

FLAG: The upper half is blue, the lower half red; superimposed in the center is the national coat of arms with the motto *L'Union Fait la Force* ("Union makes strength").

ANTHEM: *La Dessalinienne (Song of Dessalines)*.

MONETARY UNIT: The gourde (G) is a paper currency of 100 centimes. There are coins of 5, 10, 20, and 50 centimes and notes of 1, 2, 5, 10, 50, 100, 250, and 500 gourdes. Silver (5, 10, and 25 gourdes) and gold (20, 50, 100, 200, 1,000 gourdes) coins have also been minted. G1 = $0.20 (or $1 = G5).

WEIGHTS AND MEASURES: The metric system is official for customs purposes.

HOLIDAYS: Independence and New Year's Day, 1 January; Forefathers Day, 2 January; Pan American Day, 14 April; Labor Day, 1 May; Flag and University Day, 18 May; National Sovereignty Day, 22 May; Assumption, 15 August; Anniversary of the Death of Dessalines, 17 October; UN Day, 24 October; All Saints' Day, 1 November; Commemoration of the Battle of Vertières and Armed Forces Day, 18 November; Discovery of Haiti, 5 December; Christmas, 25 December. Movable religious holidays include Carnival (three days before Ash Wednesday) and Good Friday.

TIME: 7 AM = noon GMT.

LOCATION AND SIZE: Haiti occupies the western third of the island of Hispaniola (the Dominican Republic occupies the eastern two thirds). Haiti has an area of 27,750 square kilometers (10,714 square miles) including the islands of Tortuga, Gonâve (Ile de la Gonâve), Les Cayemites, and Vache (Ile Á Vache). Haiti has a total boundary length of 2,046 kilometers (1,269 miles). Haiti's capital city, Port-au-Prince.

CLIMATE: The climate is tropical, with some variation depending on altitude. Temperatures in Port-au-Prince range from 20°–31°C (68°–88°F) in January to an average maximum of 23–34°C (73–93°F) in July. Port-au-Prince receives an average annual rainfall of 137 centimeters (54 inches).

INTRODUCTORY SURVEY

RECENT HISTORY

After World War II (1939–45), a period of instability led to a coup d'etat in 1950 that brought General Paul Magloire to power. Magloire's economic policies led to a serious depression, and he was forced from office in 1956.

In a September 1957 election, François Duvalier, a middle-class black physician known to his followers as Papa Doc, became president. He began to rule by decree in 1958, and on 22 June 1964, he had himself formally elected president for life. Despite several attempted revolts, he strengthened his position, ruling largely through his security force, the Tontons Macoutes.

Political opposition was ruthlessly suppressed, and thousands of suspected dissidents "disappeared." Opposition leaders went into hiding or exile. Haitian exiles in New York, Montreal, Chicago, and Washington mounted an anti-Duvalier campaign during the 1960s.

Papa Doc died on 21 April 1971, and his son Jean-Claude Duvalier, at the age of 19, became president for life the following day. The younger Duvalier (known as Baby Doc) tried to ease political tensions and contributed to the beginnings of an economic revival. However, political arrests did not wholly cease, and there were severe economic problems in the mid- and late 1970s.

Tensions mounted and civil disorder broke out in the mid-1980s. In February 1986, Jean-Claude and his family fled to France. The National Gov-

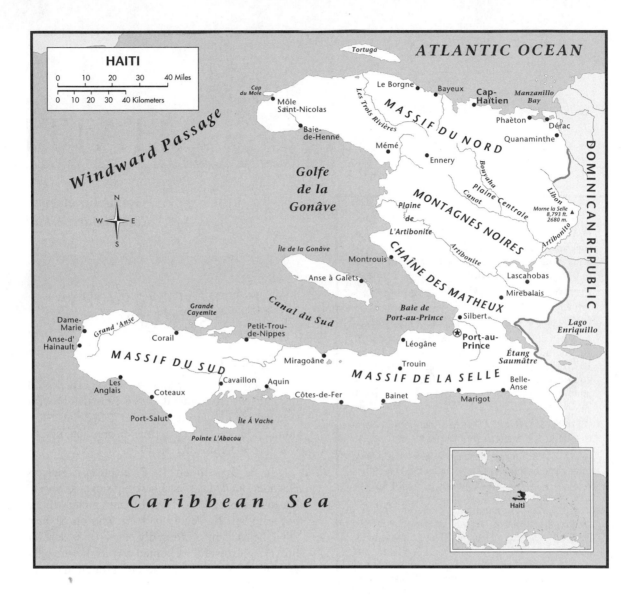

erning Council (Conseil National de Gouvernement—CNG), led by Lieutenant-General Henri Namphy, seized power.

Political prisoners were released. The dreaded Tontons Macoute, Duvalier's secret police, were disbanded. A national assembly convened in October 1986 and drafted a new constitution that was approved by referendum in March 1987. In December 1990, a Roman Catholic priest, Jean-Bertrand Aristide, was elected president with 67.5% of the votes cast.

Upset by Aristide's popularity and his foreign policy, the military, under General Raoul Cédras, ousted him in October 1991. The UN and the Organization of American States (OAS) forged an agreement between Cédras and Aristide that was to return Aristide to the presidency in October 1993,

but the military stalled and remained in power. Aristide appealed to the United States, and the administration of President Bill Clinton responded with sanctions against the Haitian regime in May and June of 1994.

In September 1994, as a last resort, the Clinton administration secured international support for a military invasion of Haiti to force Cédras from power. A U.S. invasion force was assembled and war seemed imminent. However, Clinton sent a special delegation, headed by former U.S. president Jimmy Carter, to negotiate a peaceful solution to the crisis.

As U.S. fighter planes were about to take off for Haiti, the Carter team reached an agreement with Cédras and war was averted. American forces peacefully took control of the country and, in October 1994, restored Aristide to power. Aristide was constitutionally limited to one term in office, even though most of his term had been taken over by military rule. In December 1995, René Préval was elected to the presidency with 90% of the vote.

GOVERNMENT

The constitution adopted in March 1987 established a president elected to a five-year term as head of state. The legislature is made up of a Senate and a House of Representatives.

Judiciary

The judiciary consists of four levels: the Court of Cassation, courts of appeal, civil courts, and magistrates' courts. There are also land, labor, and children's courts. The 1987 constitution was put into force in 1995. All judges have been appointed and removed at the will of the government since 1986, even though the constitution calls for an independent judiciary.

Political Parties

Dozens of parties emerged after the National Governing Council (Conseil National de Gouvernement—CNG) ousted Jean-Claude Duvalier in February 1986. The most prominent has been the National Front for Change and Democracy (FNCD) led by Jean-Bertrand Aristide, a political coalition of fifteen parties, including the National Cooperative Action Movement (MKN) and the National Congress of Democratic Movements (CONACOM).

By 1995, the dominant political force was the Lavalas Political Organization, an alliance of Aristide's Lavalas Political Organization and the Movement for the Organization of the Country. Backed by Aristide, René Préval was elected president in December 1995. In the mid-1995 legislative elections, Lavalas candidates won the majority in both houses.

DEFENSE

In 1994, a civilian administration replaced the military government. That year, the military government's armed forces and police of 7,400 personnel were disbanded and replaced with a security force of 3,000 personnel. The air force was disbanded in 1995. The defense budget was estimated at $35 million in 1994.

ECONOMIC AFFAIRS

Haiti is one of the world's poorest countries. About three-quarters of the population work in farming. Coffee, sugar, sisal, cotton, castor beans, cacao, plantains, and essential oils are the main products.

Public Finance

The U.S. CIA estimates that, in 1995, government revenues totaled approximately $242 million and expenditures $299.4 million. External debt totaled $827 million.

Income

In 1998, Haiti's gross national product (GNP) was $3.13 billion at current prices, or about $410 per person. For the period 1985–95, the average inflation rate was 14.7%, resulting in a real growth rate in GNP of −5.2% per person.

Industry

Industry is primarily devoted to the processing of agricultural and forestry products. Other industries produce aluminum, enamelware, garments and hats, essential oils, plastics, soap, pharmaceuticals, and paint. Haitian plants also assemble U.S.-made components to create electronic devices, toys, and leather goods.

Banking and Finance

The national bank of the Republic of Haiti (Banque Nationale de la République d'Haïti–BRH), the sole bank of issue and government depository, was founded in 1880 and acquired from U.S. interests in 1934 and became the fiscal agent of Haiti in 1947.

The first private Haitian bank, the Bank of the Haitian Union, opened in 1973. Money supply, as measured by M2, was G14,722.3 million as of 1995. Foreign exchange reserves, excluding gold, totaled $107.9 million at the end of 1996.

There is no securities exchange in Haiti.

Economic Development

Although its annual national revenue covers basic necessities, the government supports development programs by encouraging loans and by requiring private enterprises to finance development projects. Aided by the U.S. and various international aid organizations, the government has supported the construction of tourist facilities, public works, and irrigation and the creation of monopolies in cement, sugar marketing, tobacco and lumbering.

Macroeconomic stability, structural and institutional reforms, and poverty alleviation are still the main objectives in Haiti's agenda for the future.

SOCIAL WELFARE

Public social insurance programs are limited, but there is a widespread tradition of self-help and personal charity. The national lottery is the principal source of welfare funds, while an employer tax provides workers' compensation for occupational accidents to the relatively small number of industrial workers. Old-age, disability, and survivor benefits are funded by taxes on employees and employers.

Healthcare

In general, sanitation facilities in Haiti are among the poorest in Latin America. In 1995, only 24% of Haiti's population had access to adequate sanitation. Only half the population had access to health care services in 1992. Life expectancy for women and men is 55 years.

Tuberculosis has long been a serious health problem, and in 1990, there were about 333 reported cases of tuberculosis per 100,000 inhabitants. Malnutrition and gastrointestinal diseases are responsible for more than half of all deaths. In the early 1980s, Haitians were named among the groups that had high risk factors for contracting acquired immune deficiency syndrome (AIDS). In 1994, the frequency of HIV infection was 4.4 cases per 100 adults.

Housing

Although housing projects have been constructed in cities such as Port-au-Prince and in Cap-Haïtien, there is an increasing shortage of low-cost housing. Outside the capital and some other cities, housing facilities are generally primitive and almost universally without sanitation.

EDUCATION

The adult literacy rate is estimated at 55%. In 1990, Haiti had 7,306 primary schools, with 555,433 pupils and 26,208 teachers. In general secondary schools, there were 184,968 students and 9,470 teachers. The sole university, the Université d'État d'Haïti, is at Port-au-Prince.

1999 KEY EVENTS TIMELINE

January

- President Rene Preval announces installation by decree of former Education Minister Jacques-Edouard Alexis as Prime Minister, bypassing parliamentary approval. The announcement provokes street violence.

- President Preval's sister, Marie-Claude Calvin, is wounded when unknown gunmen fire upon her car, killing her driver.

- Preval begins replacing mayors and other officials because the political situation has prevented elections.

- Preval announces that most legislative terms have expired, and dissolves Parliament.

February

- President Rene Preval fails to meet the deadline to name an election council.

- The Supreme Court refuses to rule in a dispute between legislators and Preval over length of legislative terms.

March

- The United States general in command of forces in Latin America and Caribbean recommends withdrawal of American troops from Haiti, due to increasing political unrest.

- Thirteen people die in a crash of a United Nations helicopter; the passengers were on a mercy mission in remote mountains.

- President Preval creates new fifteen-member cabinet by decree.

- Opposition politician, OPL Sen. Jean-Yvon Toussaint is shot to death.

June

- An orphanage run by former President Jean-Bertrand Aristide is seized by youths demanding jobs and better conditions for the children inside the center. They surrender after a twelve hour standoff, following police tear gas assault.

July

- Twice a week during market days, Haitians are permitted to cross the boundary separating the Dominican Republic from Haiti.

- Election offices in two different towns are set on fire.

August

- The United States appropriates $3.5 million to Haiti for the creation of voter registration cards, a step towards Haiti's first legislative elections since 1997.

- Protegés of former President Jean-Bertrand Aristide fear for their lives after leader of June protest against Aristide's orphanage is murdered. Violence escalates as elections approach.

- Haiti announces it will return all deportees who arrived in the country without proof of Haitian citizenship.

- Former President Aristide announces his party will participate in upcoming elections.

- Defense officials announce the withdrawal of remaining U.S. troops in coming months, as the U.S. closes permanent camp there. A series of humanitarian visits will begin as part of a "New Horizons" program in Caribbean region

September

- A grenade attack damages the headquarters of the Haitian Chamber of Commerce; gunmen fire on car of Sauveur Pierre-Etienne, secretary-general of the Organization of People in Struggle (OPL) party. He and his family are unhurt in the third attack on leaders of the OPL in one month.

- Haiti's provisional electoral council sets March 19 as the date for legislative and municipal elections, the first since 1997.

- Violent demonstrations follow reports that President Preval will replace telephone company director Julio Cadet.

- Teleco, one of seven state-owned companies set to be privatized, pulls the plug on Haiti's largest Internet provider, Alpha Communications Network, charging them with violating Teleco's monopoly.

- Officials announce the visit of President Preval to Washington; he will meet with the Congressional Black Caucus to discuss Haiti's upcoming elections.

- Police officers are suspected of stealing a cargo of cocaine headed for Miami as part of a network of drug traffic from Colombia through Haiti.

December

- With parliamentary and local elections deferred to March 19, 2000, suspicions are growing that President Preval may be seeking ways to keep postponing polling day just long enough to ensure the parliamentary and local polls coincide with the presidential poll due in December 2000.

ANALYSIS OF EVENTS: 1999

BUSINESS AND THE ECONOMY

Haitians, already the poorest people in the Americas, have seen their economy suffer from the forces of nature, as well as their own politicians. The hurricane season of 1998 devastated the economy, damaging rice crops and leaving hundreds dead. The United States and the European Union offered recovery assistance, but most other foreign aid has been suspended, since the country has lacked a government and a budget since 1997. Seven state owned companies, including Teleco, the telephone company, are set to be privatized soon. The Presidential Palace and many businesses found themselves without Internet access in September, when Telecom closed down Alpha Communications Network (ACN), the country's largest Internet service provider. Teleco and the government communications regulator (Conatel) charged ACN with having violated the Teleco monopoly by providing international phone service and telephone cards. The State University of Haiti and the United Nations office were among the many schools, banks, and other organizations that were cut off from the Internet.

Although Haiti is burdened with an unemployment rate of 70% and an annual per capita income of only $250, the Internet has provided an important international communications tool because Teleco provides less than one phone line per 100 residents. Earlier in September, Teleco was the focus of bloody demonstrations by protesters angered by President Rene Preval's announcement that he would replace telephone company director Julio Cadet. Critics say the company is overstaffed, plagued by nepotism and inefficient.

GOVERNMENT AND POLITICS

Haiti's prime minister, Rosny Smarth, resigned in 1997 to protest electoral fraud. Elections, last held, have been repeatedly postponed, and with no budget and no functioning parliament the country has lacked a government for the last two years. President Rene Preval installed by decree former Education Minister Jacques-Eduard Alexis as Prime Minister, in January, when he also dissolved parliament by declaring legislative terms expired. Since there had been no new elections, he also began replacing many mayors and other officials. The Haitian Supreme Court refused to rule in the dispute between Preval and legislators over the length of legislative terms. In March, Preval created a new fifteen-member cabinet by decree. The United States released $3.5 million to Haiti for the creation of voter registration cards, as a step towards less fraudulent elections. Former President Jean-Bertrand Aristide announced that his party would participate in the elections, the date for which was finally set as March 19, 2000. The U.S. Congressional Black Caucus has invited President Preval to Washington, to discuss the coming elections.

Haiti announced it would return all persons who had been deported there without proof of Haitian citizenship, but that citizens are now allowed to cross the border into the Dominican Republic twice a week, on market days. Political unrest has grown and violence escalated throughout the year. President Preval's sister was wounded and members of the opposition party, Organization of People in Struggle (OPL), have been repeatedly attacked, and some killed. Election offices have been burned, and street violence and demonstrations have increased. Defense officials announced the closing of the United States' permanent camp in Haiti and the gradual withdrawal of U.S. troops. A series of humanitarian visits will begin, part of the ''New Horizons'' program in the Caribbean region.

CULTURE AND SOCIETY

The atmosphere of turmoil in Haiti has increased the number of refugees seeking to escape poverty and violence. Hundreds have died in inadequate vessels attempting to reach Florida. Drug-running, too, has grown. Haitian police have been attempting to close down a network that carries drugs from Colombia through Haiti to the United States and other destinations. Six of the police themselves were detained on suspicion of theft.

They were believed to have stolen the majority of a haul of cocaine that was discovered in a boat headed for Miami. U.S. government officials estimate twenty percent of drugs now reaching its borders pass through Haiti. The national police of Haiti decided to intensify the fight on drug trafficking as a means of lowering crime in general, in hopes of improving the environment for the upcoming elections. The U.S. military presence will be reduced to specific humanitarian missions in the future. They are already engaged in road building and repair and medical care. In March, thirteen people died in the crash of a United Nations helicopter on a mercy mission in remote mountains.

DIRECTORY

CENTRAL GOVERNMENT

Head of State

President

René G. Préval, Office of the President, National Palace, Champ de Mars, Port-au-Prince, Haiti
PHONE: +509 2223024; 2231646; 2232923

Prime Minister

Jacques Edouard Alexis, Office of the Prime Minister, Villa d'Accueil, Delmas 60, Musseau, Port-au-Prince, Haiti
PHONE: +509 2450007; 2450025
FAX: +509 2451624

Ministers

Minister of Agriculture, Natural Resources and Rural Development

François Séverin, Ministry of Agriculture, Natural Resources and Rural Development, Rte. Nationale 1, Damien, Haiti
PHONE: +509 2223595; 2223594; 2223596

Minister of Commerce and Industry

Gérald Germain, Ministry of Commerce and Industry, 26 Rue Légitime, Port-au-Prince, Haiti
PHONE: +509 2225674; 2231628; 2224152

Minister of Culture

Jean-Robert Vaval, Ministry of Culture, 31, Rue Roy, Port-au-Prince, Haiti
PHONE: +509 2228603; 2232382; 2227357

Minister of the Environment

Yves Cadet, Ministry of the Environment, Haut Turgeau, Port-au-Prince, Haiti
PHONE: +509 2457572; 2492737; 2228231

Minister of Finance and Economy

Fred Joseph, Ministry of Finance and Economy, Palais des Ministères, Port-au-Prince, Haiti
PHONE: +509 2220724; 2222822; 2223436

Minister of Foreign Affairs and Worship

Fritz Longchamp, Ministry of Foreign Affairs and Worship, Blvd. Harry Truman, Cité de l'Exposition, Port-au-Prince, Haiti
PHONE: +509 2221243; 2229937; 2228482

Minister of Haitians Living Abroad

Jean Généus, Ministry of Haitians Living Abroad, 37, Rue Duncombe, Port-au-Prince, Haiti
PHONE: +509 2450287; 2457006; 2451116

Minister of the Interior

Jacques Edouard Alexis, Ministry of the Interior, Palais des Ministères, Port-au-Prince, Haiti
PHONE: +509 2226490; 2225533; 2228603

Minister of Justice and Public Safety

Camille Leblanc, Ministry of Justice and Public Safety, 19 Ave. Charles Sumner, Port-au-Prince, Haiti
PHONE: +509 2455856; 2451646; 2451626

Minister of National Education, Youth and Sports

Paul Antoine Bien-Aimé, Ministry of National Education, Youth and Sports, Rue Dr. Audain, Port-au-Prince, Haiti
PHONE: +509 2221037; 2221036; 2342100

Minister of Planning and External Cooperation

Anthony Dessources, Ministry of Planning and External Cooperation, Palais des Ministères, Port-au-Prince, Haiti
PHONE: +509 2234222; 2220700; 2224148

Minister of Public Health

Michaëlle Amédée Gédéon, Ministry of Public Health, Palais des Ministères, Port-au-Prince, Haiti
PHONE: +509 2222725; 2221583; 2222728

POLITICAL ORGANIZATIONS

Front National pour le Changement et la Démocratie-FNCD (National Front for Change and Democracy)

NAME: Evans Paul

Initiatives Démocratiques (Democratic Initiatives)

NAME: Guy Alexandre; Françoise Boucard

Konfederasyon Inite Demokratik-KID (Democratic Unity Confederation)

NAME: Evans Paul

Mobilisation pour le Devellopement National (Mobilization for National Development)

NAME: Hubert DeRonceray

Mouvement Démocratique pour la Libération d'Haïti-MODELH (Democratic Movement for the Liberation of Haiti)

NAME: François Latortue

Mouvement pour l'Instauration de la Démocratie en Haïti-MIDH (Movement for the Instauration of Democracy in Haiti)

NAME: Marc Bazin

Mouvman Konbit Nasyonal-MKN (National Cooperative Action Movement)

NAME: Volvick Rémy Joseph

Mouvement Nationale et Patriotique du 28 Novembre-MNP-28 (National Patriotic Movement of November 28)

NAME: Déjean Bélizaire

Mouvement pour l'Organisation du Pays-MOP (Movement for the Organization of the Country)

NAME: Gesner Comeau, Jean Molière

Mouvement de la Reconstruction Nationale-MRN (Movement for National Reconstruction)

NAME: René Théodore

Organisation du Peuple en Lutte-OPL (Organization of the People in Struggle)

NAME: Gérard Pierre-Charles

PARADIS (Haitian Party of God)

NAME: Vladimir Jeanty

Parti Agricole et Industrie National-PAIN (National Agricultural and Industrial Party)

NAME: Louis Dejoie II

Parti des Démocrates Haïtiens-PADEMH (Party of Haitian Democrats)

NAME: Jean-Jacques Clark Parent

Parti Démocratique et Chrétien d'Haïti-PDCH (Haitian Christian Democratic Party)

NAME: Joachin Pierre

Parti pour un Développement Alternatif-PADH (Alternative Party for Development)

NAME: Gérard Dalvius

Parti National Progressiste et Révolutionnaire-PANPRA (National Progressive Revolutionary Party)

NAME: Serge Gilles

Parti National des Travailleurs-PNT (National Labor Party)

NAME: Thomas Desulmé

Parti Social Chrétien d'Haïti-PSCH (Haitian Social Christian Party)

NAME: Grégoire Eugène

Pati Louvri Barye-PLB (Open the Gate Party)

NAME: Renaud Bernardin

Rassemblement des Démocrates Chrétiens-RDC (Assembly of Christian Democrats)

NAME: Eddy Volel

Rassemblement des Démocrates Nationalistes et Progressistes-RDNP (Assembly of Progressive National Democrats)

NAME: Leslie Manigat

Pouvoir Rassemblement des Organisations Populaires-PROP (Powerful Assembly of Popular Organizations)

Union des Démocrates Patriotiques-UDP (Union of Patriotic Democrats)

NAME: Rockefeller Guerre

DIPLOMATIC REPRESENTATION

Embassies in Haiti

United States
5 Harry Truman Boulevard, Port-au-Prince, Haiti
PHONE: +509 220354; 220368; 220200
FAX: +509 231641

JUDICIAL SYSTEM

Court of Cassation

FURTHER READING

Articles

"13 Dead in U.N. Helicopter Crash in Haiti." *New York Times*, 16 March 1999.

"Haiti." *Current History* (May 1999): 238.

"Haiti." *Current History* (March 1999): 141.

"Haiti." *The Economist* (January 23-29, 1999): 32.

"Haiti." *The Economist* (April 3-9, 1999): 30.

"Haiti Gunmen Confront Police At Orphanage." *New York Times*, 25 June 1999.

"Haitian Leader Fails to Meet Deadline to Name Election Board." *New York Times*, 4 February 1999.

Holmes, Steven A. "U.S. General Recommends Pullout from Haiti." *New York Times*, 14 March 1999.

"A Legal Impasse in Haiti." *New York Times*, 27 February 1999.

Navarro, Mireya. "At Last on Hispaniola, Hands Across the Border." *New York Times*, 11 July 1999.

Books

Brune, Lester H. *The United States and Post-Cold War Interventions: Bush and Clinton in Somalia, Haiti, and Bosnia, 1992–1998.* Claremont, California: Regina Books, 1999.

Catanese, Anthony V. *Haitians: Migration and Diaspora.* Boulder, Colorado: Westview Press, 1999.

Wucker, Michele. *Why the Cocks Fight: Dominicans, Haitians, and the Struggle for Hispaniola.* New York: Hill and Wang, 1999.

Internet

Library of Congress Federal Research Division—Country Study. "Haiti: A Country Study." Available Online @ http://lcweb2.loc.gov./frd/cs/httoc.html (October 25, 1999).

National Coalition for Haitian Rights. "Haiti Insight Online." Available Online @ http://www.nchr.org/hrp/unreport.htm (October 25, 1999).

Our World: Haiti. Available Online @ http://www.rosro.com/ourworld.htm (October 24, 1999).

Windows on Haiti. Available Online @ http://windowsonhaiti.com (October 24, 1999).

HAITI: STATISTICAL DATA

For sources and notes see "Sources of Statistics" in the front of each volume.

GEOGRAPHY

Geography (1)

Area:

Total: 27,750 sq km.

Land: 27,560 sq km.

Water: 190 sq km.

Area—comparative: slightly smaller than Maryland.

Land boundaries:

Total: 275 km.

Border countries: Dominican Republic 275 km.

Coastline: 1,771 km.

Climate: tropical; semiarid where mountains in east cut off trade winds.

Terrain: mostly rough and mountainous.

Natural resources: none.

Land use:

Arable land: 20%

Permanent crops: 13%

Permanent pastures: 18%

Forests and woodland: 5%

Other: 44% (1993 est.).

HUMAN FACTORS

Demographics (2A)

	1990	1995	1998	2000	2010	2020	2030	2040	2050
Population	6,048.0	6,487.9	6,780.5	6,991.6	8,265.9	9,599.7	10,718.0	11,809.3	12,745.7
Net migration rate (per 1,000 population)	NA	NA	NA	NA	NA	NA	NA	NA	NA
Births	NA	NA	NA	NA	NA	NA	NA	NA	NA
Deaths	NA	NA	NA	NA	NA	NA	NA	NA	NA
Life expectancy - males	47.8	48.7	49.3	49.7	51.7	53.9	58.3	62.6	64.8
Life expectancy - females	51.6	52.7	53.6	54.2	57.1	59.5	64.7	69.9	72.3
Birth rate (per 1,000)	40.0	34.0	32.8	32.3	29.8	23.7	19.8	17.6	15.3
Death rate (per 1,000)	17.0	14.9	14.2	13.8	12.5	11.4	9.6	8.7	9.2
Women of reproductive age (15-49 yrs.)	1,380.3	1,483.6	1,605.1	1,703.9	2,173.2	2,610.8	3,053.0	3,212.2	3,322.8
of which are currently married	NA	NA	NA	NA	NA	NA	NA	NA	NA
Fertility rate	5.7	4.9	4.7	4.5	3.5	2.7	2.3	2.1	2.0

Except as noted, values for vital statistics are in thousands; life expectancy is in years.

Health Personnel (3)

Total health expenditure as a percentage of GDP, 1990-1997[a]

Public sector 1.2

Private sector 2.3

Total[b] 3.6

Health expenditure per capita in U.S. dollars, 1990-1997[a]

Purchasing power parity 44

Total 14

Availability of health care facilities per 100,000 people

Hospital beds 1990-1997[a] 80

Doctors 1993[c] 16

Nurses 1993[c] 13

Health Indicators (4)

Life expectancy at birth

1980 51

1997 54

Daily per capita supply of calories (1996) 1,855

Total fertility rate births per woman (1997) 4.4

Maternal mortality ratio per 100,000 live births (1990-97) ....600[d]

Safe water % of population with access (1995) 39

Sanitation % of population with access (1995) 26

Consumption of iodized salt % of households (1992-98)[a] 10

Smoking prevalence

Male % of adults (1985-95)[a] ....

Female % of adults (1985-95)[a] ....

Tuberculosis incidence per 100,000 people (1997) 385

Adult HIV prevalence % of population ages 15-49 (1997) 5.17

Infants and Malnutrition (5)

Under-5 mortality rate (1997) 132

% of infants with low birthweight (1990-97) 15

Births attended by skilled health staff % of total[a] ...20

% fully immunized (1995-97)

TB 40

DPT 35

Polio 32

Measles 30

Prevalence of child malnutrition under age 5 (1992-97)[b] 28

Ethnic Division (6)

Black 95%

Mulatto plus white 5%

Religions (7)

Roman Catholic 80%

Protestant 16%

Baptist 10%

Pentecostal 4%

Adventist 1%

Other 1%

None 1%

Other 3% (1982)

Roughly one-half of the population also practices Voodoo.

Languages (8)

French (official) 20%, Creole.

EDUCATION

Public Education Expenditures (9)

Public expenditure on education (% of GNP)

1980 ....1.5

1996 ....

Expenditure per student

Primary % of GNP per capita

1980 ....5.9

1996 ....

Secondary % of GNP per capita

1980 ....

1996 ....

Tertiary % of GNP per capita

1980 ....130.0

1996 ....

Expenditure on teaching materials

Primary % of total for level (1996) 1.5

Secondary % of total for level (1996) ....

Primary pupil-teacher ratio per teacher (1996) ....

Duration of primary education years (1995) 6

Educational Attainment (10)

Age group (1986) ....25+

Total population 2,229,501

Highest level attained (%)

No schooling 59.5

First level

Not completed 30.5

Completed ....NA

Entered second level

S-1 . . . . .9.3

S-2 . . . . .NA

Postsecondary 0.7

Literacy Rates (11A)

In thousands and percent[1]	1990	1995	2000	2010
Illiterate population (15+ yrs.)	2,289	2,360	2,422	2,553
Literacy rate - total adult pop. (%)	41.0	45.0	49.4	57.7

Literacy rate - males (%)	44.2	48.0	52.1	59.7
Literacy rate - females (%)	37.9	42.2	46.9	55.7

GOVERNMENT & LAW

Political Parties (12)

Chamber of Deputies	No. of seats
Lavalas Political Organization 7	
Lavalas family-leaning 7	
Independent 2	
Non-active members 2	
Vacant 9	

Military Affairs (14B)

	1990	1991	1992	1993	1994	1995
Military expenditures						
Current dollars (mil.)	39[e]	36[e]	33[e]	39[e]	44[e]	59[e]
1995 constant dollars (mil.)	45[e]	40[e]	36[e]	40[e]	45[e]	59[e]
Armed forces (000)	8	8	8	8	0	0
Gross national product (GNP)						
Current dollars (mil.)	2,325	2,346	2,058	2,054	1,878	2,011
1995 constant dollars (mil.)	2,672	2,592	2,213	2,153	1,925	2,011
Central government expenditures (CGE)						
1995 constant dollars (mil.)	326	262	244	201	149	274
People (mil.)	6.1	6.2	6.3	6.4	6.5	6.6
Military expenditure as % of GNP	1.7	1.5	1.6	1.9	2.3	2.9
Military expenditure as % of CGE	13.8	15.3	14.7	20.1	30.2	21.6
Military expenditure per capita (1995 $)	7	6	6	6	7	9
Armed forces per 1,000 people (soldiers)	1.3	1.3	1.3	1.3	0	0
GNP per capita (1995 $)	441	441	338	338	338	304
Arms imports[6]						
Current dollars (mil.)	0	0	0	0	0	0
1995 constant dollars (mil.)	0	0	0	0	0	0
Arms exports[6]						
Current dollars (mil.)	0	0	0	0	0	0
1995 constant dollars (mil.)	0	0	0	0	0	0
Total imports[7]						
Current dollars (mil.)	279	400	278	355	252	653
1995 constant dollars (mil.)	321	442	299	372	258	653
Total exports[7]						
Current dollars (mil.)	158	167	73	80	82	110
1995 constant dollars (mil.)	182	185	79	84	84	110
Arms as percent of total imports[8]	0	0	0	0	0	0
Arms as percent of total exports[8]	0	0	0	0	0	0

Government Budget (13B)

Revenues . . . .$284 million

Expenditures . . . .$308 million

  Capital expenditures . . . . .NA

Data for FY96/97 est. NA stands for not available.

LABOR FORCE

Labor Force (16)

Total (million) 3.6

Agriculture 66%

Services 25%

Industry 9%

Shortage of skilled labor, unskilled labor abundant. Data for
1995. Percent distribution for 1982.

Unemployment Rate (17)

60% (1996 est.)

PRODUCTION SECTOR

Electric Energy (18)

Capacity .153,000 kW (1995)

Production . . . . .315 million kWh (1995)

Consumption per capita . . . . .48 kWh (1995)

Transportation (19)

Highways:

total: 4,160 km

paved: 1,011 km

unpaved: 3,149 km (1996 est.)

Waterways: NEGL; less than 100 km navigable

Merchant marine: none

Airports: 14 (1997 est.)

Airports—with paved runways:

total: 3

2,438 to 3,047 m: 1

1,524 to 2,437 m: 1

914 to 1,523 m: 1 (1997 est.)

Airports—with unpaved runways:

total: 11

914 to 1,523 m: 5

under 914 m: 6 (1997 est.)

Top Agricultural Products (20)

Coffee, mangoes, sugarcane, rice, corn, sorghum; wood.

FINANCE, ECONOMICS, & TRADE

Economic Indicators (22)

National product: GDP—purchasing power parity—
$7.1 billion (1997 est.)

National product real growth rate: 1.1% (1997 est.)

National product per capita: $1,070 (1997 est.)

Inflation rate—consumer price index: 17% (1997
est.)

MANUFACTURING SECTOR

GDP & Manufacturing Summary (21)

	1980	1985	1990	1992	1993	1994
Gross Domestic Product						
Millions of 1990 dollars	2,380	2,270	2,281	1,955	1,853	1,609
Growth rate in percent	7.39	0.59	−0.14	−14.85	−5.24	−13.19
Per capita (in 1990 dollars)	444.7	387.1	351.6	289.5	268.8	228.7
Manufacturing Value Added						
Millions of 1990 dollars	506	429	417	271	269	*217*
Growth rate in percent	14.81	−0.84	2.41	−21.42	−0.77	*−19.30*
Manufacturing share in percent of current prices	19.1	17.6	19.5	16.8	13.1	*13.1*

FINANCE, ECONOMICS, & TRADE

Exchange Rates (24)

Exchange rates:

Gourdes (G) per US$1 (end of period)

December 1997 . . . . .17.311
1997 . . . . .17.311
1996 . . . . .15.093
1995 . . . . .16.160
1994 . . . . .12.947
1993 . . . . .12.805

Top Import Origins (25)

$665 million (f.o.b., 1996) Data are for 1995.

Origins	%
United States	.65.0
European Union	.13.9

Top Export Destinations (26)

$90 million (f.o.b., 1996) Data are for 1996.

Destinations	%
United States	.76.3
European Union	.19.8

Economic Aid (27)

Recipient: ODA, $NA. NA stands for not available.

Import Export Commodities (28)

Import Commodities	Export Commodities
Machines and manufactures 34%	Light manufactures 53%
Food and beverages 22%	Coffee 17%
Petroleum products 14%	Other agriculture 17%
Chemicals 10%	
Fats and oils 9%	

Balance of Payments (23)

	1990	1991	1992	1993	1994
Exports of goods (f.o.b.)	266	202	76	82	57
Imports of goods (f.o.b.)	−443	−449	−214	−267	−141
Trade balance	−177	−247	−139	−185	84
Services - debits	−97	−103	−48	−43	−75
Services - credits	59	60	40	38	7
Private transfers (net)	132	165	85	100	113
Government transfers (net)	61	70	70	73	43
Overall balance	−22	−56	8	−17	4

HONDURAS

Republic of Honduras
República de Honduras

CAPITAL: Tegucigalpa.

FLAG: The national flag consists of a white horizontal stripe between two blue horizontal stripes, with five blue stars on the white stripe representing the five members of the former union of Central American provinces.

ANTHEM: *Himno Nacional,* beginning "Tu bandera es un lampo de cielo" ("Thy flag is a heavenly light").

MONETARY UNIT: The lempira (L), also known as the peso, is a paper currency of 100 centavos. There are coins of 1, 2, 5, 10, 20, and 50 centavos, and notes of 1, 2, 5, 10, 20, 50, and 100 lempiras. L1 = $0.10638 (or $1 = L9.4).

WEIGHTS AND MEASURES: The metric system is the legal standard; some old Spanish measures are still used.

HOLIDAYS: New Year's Day, 1 January; Day of the Americas, 14 April; Labor Day, 1 May; Independence Day, 15 September; Birthday of Francisco Morazán, 3 October; Columbus Day, 12 October; Army Day, 21 October; Christmas, 25 December. Movable religious holidays include Holy Thursday, Good Friday, and Holy Saturday.

TIME: 6 AM = noon GMT.

LOCATION AND SIZE: Situated in Central America, Honduras has a total area of 112,090 square kilometers (43,278 square miles), slightly larger than the state of Tennessee. It has a total boundary length of 2,170 kilometers (1,349 miles).

The capital city of Honduras, Tegucigalpa, is located in the south central part of the country.

CLIMATE: The northern Caribbean area and the southern coastal plain have a wet, tropical climate, but the interior is drier and cooler. Temperatures vary from a mean of 31°C (88°F) in the coastal lowlands to 23°C (73°F) at the highest altitudes. Average annual rainfall varies from over 240 centimeters (95 inches) along the northern coast to about 84 centimeters (33 inches) in the south. The northwest coast is vulnerable to hurricanes.

INTRODUCTORY SURVEY

RECENT HISTORY

U.S. corporate interests, especially the United Fruit Co. (now United Brands), and military dictators dominated Honduran political and economic life during the first half of the twentieth century. Elected politics was dominated by the conservative General Tiburcio Carías Andino (1932–48). In the 1950s and early 1960s, there were several different governments, with military coups in 1956 and 1963, when power was seized by a conservative coalition of military, Nationalist Party, and Liberal Party leaders under an air force officer, Colonel Oswaldo López Arellano.

This government was legalized almost two years later by an elected national assembly, which adopted a new constitution and proclaimed López president in June 1965. During López's second term, a bitter and destructive four-day war broke out in July 1969 between Honduras and El Salvador.

Although the immediate cause of the war was hostility arising from a World Cup elimination-round soccer match between the two countries, the underlying causes were a long-standing border dispute and the long-term migration of some 300,000 Salvadorans in search of land, which the Honduran government made it illegal for Salvadoran immigrants to own. With the help of the OAS, a compromise cease-fire was arranged. In June 1970, the two nations accepted a seven-point peace plan, creating a demilitarized zone along their common frontier.

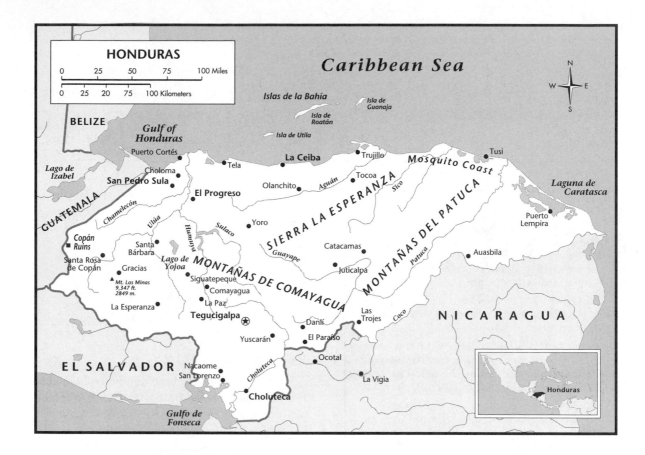

Map of HONDURAS with scale 0–100 Miles / 0–100 Kilometers. Caribbean Sea. Labels include: Islas de la Bahía, Isla de Guanaja, Isla de Roatán, Isla de Utila, BELIZE, Gulf of Honduras, Puerto Cortés, Tela, La Ceiba, Trujillo, Tusi, Mosquito Coast, Lago de Izabal, Choloma, San Pedro Sula, El Progreso, Olanchito, Aguán, Tocoa, Sico, Laguna de Caratasca, GUATEMALA, Chamelecón, Ulúa, Humuya, Sulaco, Yoro, SIERRA LA ESPERANZA, Puerto Lempira, Copán Ruins, Santa Bárbara, Lago de Yojoa, Guayape, Catacamas, MONTAÑAS DEL PATUCA, Auasbila, Santa Rosa de Copán, Gracias, MONTAÑAS DE COMAYAGUA, Juticalpa, Patuca, Mt. Las Minas 9,347 ft. 2849 m., Siguatepeque, Comayagua, La Paz, La Esperanza, Tegucigalpa, Danlí, Las Trojes, Coco, NICARAGUA, Yuscarán, El Paraíso, Ocotal, EL SALVADOR, Nacaome, San Lorenzo, Choluteca, La Vigia, Gulfo de Fonseca, Honduras (inset).

López and the military continued to dominate Honduran politics until López was overthrown in April 1974 by a group of lieutenant colonels. Two more military governments followed between 1975 and 1983. This period saw strong economic growth and, at the same time, a gradual movement toward democracy.

Under a new constitution in 1982, Roberto Suazo Córdova of the Liberal Party became president, and the military continued to grow in response to domestic unrest and the fighting in neighboring Nicaragua and El Salvador.

By 1983, several thousand anti-Sandinista guerrillas (popularly known as ''contras'') in Honduras were working for the overthrow of Nicaragua's Sandinista government, while the Honduran army, backed by the United States, was helping Salvadoran government forces in their fight against leftist guerrillas. The CIA used Honduras during that time as a base for covert activities against the Sandinista regime. In exchange, the United States sent large amounts of economic aid to Honduras.

In November 1985, Hondurans elected José Simón Azcona Hoyo to the presidency in the first peaceful transfer of power between elected executives in half a century. Azcona signed the Central American peace plan outlined by President Oscar Arias Sánchez of Costa Rica, but did not move to close down contra bases as promised.

In 1989, Rafael Leonardo Callejas of the National (conservative) Party was elected. Callejas focused on domestic issues, especially reducing the deficit. In November 1993, the Liberal Party returned to power in the person of Carlos Roberto Reina. The struggle to improve economic conditions continued through 1996, with the government caught in the middle. The international financial community demanded tough structural reforms which the Honduran population resisted.

GOVERNMENT

The constitution of 1982 defines Honduras as a democratic republic headed by a president who must be a native-born citizen. The president is elected by direct popular vote for a four-year term. The executive branch also includes a cabinet of twelve ministers. The 1982 constitution provides for the popular election of deputies to the single-chamber National Assembly, consisting of 128 deputies. All men and women 18 years of age and older are eligible to vote.

Judiciary

Judicial power is exercised by the nine-member Supreme Court and five courts of appeal, as well as by lower-level courts and local judges. The Supreme Court has the power to declare laws unconstitutional. Owing to the lack of funds and corruption, the outcome of legal disputes in courts is often the product of influence and political pressure.

Political Parties

The two major parties in Honduras are the Liberal Party (Partido Liberal—PL) and the National Party (Partido Nacional—PN). The National Party is generally the more conservative.

Two minor parties occupy mildly leftist positions: the Christian Democratic Party, and the National Innovation and Unity Party. Neither takes more than a couple of seats in the Assembly.

DEFENSE

The regular forces consisted of 18,800 personnel in 1995; there were 16,000 in the army, 1,800 in the air force, and 1,000 in the navy. Police forces numbered 5,500 personnel. Two years of compulsory peacetime military service may be required of all males between the ages of 18 and 55. The defense budget in 1996 was $49 million.

ECONOMIC AFFAIRS

Honduras is one of the three largest exporters of bananas in the world. It is, nevertheless, by most measures, the poorest nation on the mainland of the Americas.

With its economy heavily dependent on banana production, the country is vulnerable to crop and world market price variations. The vast majority of banana holdings are controlled by two United States companies—United Brands and Standard Fruit. Bananas and coffee accounted for half of all exports in 1995.

Honduras has extensive forest, marine, and mineral resources. Unemployment is officially estimated at 15%, and combined unemployment and underemployment is 45%.

Public Finance

The U.S. CIA estimates that, in 1994, government revenues totaled approximately $527 million and expenditures $668 million, including capital expenditures of $166 million. External debt totaled $3.7 billion.

Income

In 1998, Honduras' gross national product (GNP) was $4.49 billion at current prices, or about $730 per person. For the period 1985–95, the average inflation rate was 14.2%, resulting in a real growth rate in GNP of 0.2% per person.

Industry

The largest firms are found in the cement, cotton, sugar, and wood products industries, and these companies are also active exporters.

Manufacturing grew by 5.5% in 1995 and 4.6% in 1996. Growth was greatest among the electric, gas, and water sectors. Food and tobacco products, wood and paper products, and basic metalworking and metal products have also grown in recent years. The country has a well-established clothing assembly industry.

Banking and Finance

In 1950, the Central Bank of Honduras (Banco Central de Honduras), the sole bank of issue, was established to centralize national financial operations and to replace foreign currencies then in circulation. As of 1994, money supply, as measured by M2, was L8,407 million.

The government-controlled banks, including the National Development Bank, the National Agricultural Development Bank, and the Municipal Bank, provide credit for development projects. The National Development Bank extends agricultural and other credit—mainly to the tobacco, coffee, and livestock industries—and furnishes technical and financial assistance and other services to national economic interests. The Municipal Bank gives assistance at the local level.

In 1990, a stock exchange opened in San Pedro Sula to raise short-term bond finance for local businesses.

Economic Development

The November 1993 elections gave birth to a new political era in Honduras. President Reina of the Liberal Party was expected to slow down the pace of market-oriented reforms. Continued strong growth in nontraditional exports and the prospects for moderate improvement in coffee prices brought an improvement in the current account deficit. For this reason, the continuation of official aid and the promotion of foreign investment are expected to play an increasing role in financing Honduras external gap. The Central Bank plans to rely increasingly on open market operations to regulate credit conditions.

SOCIAL WELFARE

The present Honduran Social Insurance Law covers accidents, illness, maternity, old age, occupational disease, unemployment, disability, death, and other circumstances affecting the capacity to work and maintain oneself and one's family. Actual coverage, however, has been limited mainly to maternity, sickness, and workers' compensation. In 1995, 30% of the government's budget went for education and health care.

Traditional attitudes prevent women from obtaining full access to educational and economic opportunities guaranteed by the law.

Healthcare

Health conditions in Honduras are among the worst in the Western Hemisphere, and health care remains inadequate. In 1992, there were 2,326 people per physician. In 1993, 62% of the population had access to health care services.

Major causes of illness are diseases of the digestive tract, intestinal parasites, influenza, pneumonia, cancer, and infant diseases. Malnutrition, impure water, poor sewage disposal, and inadequate housing are the major causes of health problems. Life expectancy is an average of 67 years.

Housing

Many urban dwellings and most rural dwellings lack running water, electricity, and indoor plumbing. Estimates of the shortage in housing units grew to 500,000 in 1985.

EDUCATION

The rate of illiteracy among adults in 1995 was estimated at 27%. Public education is free and compulsory for children between the ages of 7 and 15. In 1993, 90% of primary-school-age children were actually in school. There are about 7,600 primary and elementary schools, with 900,000 students and 23,000 teachers. Secondary and normal schools had 194,083 pupils and 8,507 teachers.

In 1994, total university enrollment was 50,323, with 4,078 teaching staff. The major university is the National Autonomous University of Honduras.

1999 KEY EVENTS TIMELINE

January

- The Honduran military yields control to a civilian president.

February

- Honduran coffee growers suffer double jolt when low international coffee prices follow Hurricane Mitch.

May

- A United States-built base is suspected to have graves and cells, which may have been used to kill and torture suspected leftist guerrillas.

June

- A Honduran boy claims he traveled 3,200 miles from Honduras to New York City to find his father, but the story turns out to be an elaborate hoax.

- The government attempts to stop cattle ranchers and hired henchmen from killing criminals.

July

- In the aftermath of Hurricane Mitch, ancient artifacts are discovered in Honduras.

August

- The Honduran president fires top military officials amid coup rumors.

- Six Central American countries support Taiwan's efforts to rejoin the United Nations. Honduras, a recipient of Taiwanese aid, is among the supporters.

September

- President Clinton expands the U.S. debt-relief plan for poor nations. Honduras is a strong candidate among countries that may see their debts forgiven.

- Torrential rains threaten Honduras' major dam. Less than one year after Hurricane Mitch, thousands of people are forced to evacuate.

- The military pledges an open-door policy to help human rights groups investigating the disappearance of 184 people in the 1980s and 1990s.

October

- The government announces it will take five years to eliminate Chagas disease. It affects 300,000 of the country's 6.3 million people.

December

- Honduras and Nicaragua meet for talks at the Organization of American States to seek a solution to a new territorial dispute relating to their sea borders.

ANALYSIS OF EVENTS: 1999

BUSINESS AND THE ECONOMY

Hurricane Mitch washed away fertile soil, and agriculture officials in Honduras said it could take five years before farms recover. For coffee planters, the loss of land was only one problem. Coffee prices fell in 1999, a blow for Honduran growers already facing smaller crops. In 1998, Honduras was the world's 10th largest explorer, with revenues of about $430 million. But exports were expected to bring only $217 million in 1999.

In March, during a visit to Central America, U.S. President Bill Clinton pledged about $300 million in aid to Honduras. Later, he announced the United States was prepared to forgive debts from poor nations, including Honduras, as long as these countries used the windfall to finance basic human needs. While most of the debt was considered uncollectable, the president's announcement was seen as a signal to developed nations to forgive large debts from poor countries. In June, leaders of the world's seven wealthiest nations met in Germany, and pledged to slash the debt burdens of the neediest countries by $70 billion or more. The International Monetary Fund said the plan would bring some debt relief to Honduras. In October, Clinton said the United States was prepared to forgive $122 million dollars owed by Honduras.

To raise more revenues, the Honduran government announced it was prepared to privatize the nation's four airports, and was searching for international investors. The 20-year lease to operate the airports was expected to bring $125 million.

GOVERNMENT AND POLITICS

In January, the Honduran legislature voted unanimously to end more than 41 years of military autonomy and put the nation's armed forces under civilian control. The following day, the military commander in chief turned over control of the armed forces to President Carlos Flores. In August, Flores fired four top military officials in an attempt to quell a power struggle in the military. Flores denied media reports of an attempted coup. Brig. Gen. Roberto Lazarus, the deputy defense minister, and Col. Eugenio Romero, chief of the joint chiefs of staff were among the fired officials.

Honduran officials in August said they discovered cramped metal cells that may have been used to torture and kill political prisoners at a military base built by the United States in 1983. They also found dozens of possible graves at the *El Aguacate* air base in eastern Honduras. The United States built the base for Nicaraguan Contra rebels fighting the leftist government of that country. Forensic experts from the United States and Germany were expected to examine the site, which may contain the remains of some of the 184 people who disappeared under Honduran military custody in the past decade.

CULTURE AND SOCIETY

For Hondurans, 1999 was supposed to be a year of recovery after Hurricane Mitch devastated the country in October 1998. The hurricane killed approximately 7,000 Hondurans, and left more than 400,000 homeless. The rains and mudslides destroyed nearly 70 percent of all roads, and caused $800 million in damages to crops.

Life was anything but normal for most of the country's citizens after the hurricane. The schools were an example of the daunting problems facing the small nation. Most school buildings were destroyed or heavily damaged. So was the education ministry building in Tegucigalpa, where educators were supposed to plan the school year for more than 1.75 million students. School started on time for most students on March 1, but 150,000 students were expected to start late, and would have to attend schools on Saturdays to catch up. Administrators also expected to spend more than $3 million to replace textbooks damaged by the hurricane. The capital city of Tegucigalpa was devastated, with frequent electrical outages, mountains of trash, and a sewage system so heavily damaged that citizens faced a serous contamination problem. Yet, with forcign aid pouring into the country, Hondurans were rebuilding their live—and their lost homes. Yet full recovery is not expected for many years. Many people remained in shelters in 1999. To add to the misery, torrential rains in September forced thousands to flee to higher ground.

In other developments, Honduran authorities announced a plan to stop the illegal migration of children to other Central American countries. According to some government and non-government sources, the number of Honduran children leaving the country jumped by 200 percent after Hurricane Mitch. The government also announced a plan to repatriate children living in the streets of Guatemala and El Salvador towns. According to unofficial figures, about 10 percent of street children in these countries are from Honduras. The government may face problems stopping the flow. Most children do not cross border checkpoints to escape into neighboring countries.

A plan to fund a government office for the protection of men was scrapped after several women organizations complained. Some government officials claimed they were simply seeking equality, since an office for protection of women already exists. Women organizations said men don't need protection. It is the other way around, with women making up 97 percent of victims of sexual assault and aggression. They also suffer inequalities in society, including the work place. As long as these inequalities exist, it is not possible to create an office for the protection of men, they said. The government agreed, saying it is committed to upholding women's rights under international law.

In September, Honduras announced it was prepared to "sell" oxygen to developed countries by protecting its forests and planting more trees. Hondurans said they were close to reaching an agreement with Canada. The Hondurans did not release details of their plan.

DIRECTORY

CENTRAL GOVERNMENT
Head of State

President
Carlos Roberto Flores Facussé, Office of the President
PHONE: +504 2344922
FAX: +504 2378521

Ministers

Minister of Agriculture and Livestock
Pedro Arturo Sevilla, Ministry of Agriculture and Livestock, Avenida La Paz, Edificio Atala, Tegucigalpa, M.D.C., Honduras, C.A.
PHONE: +504 2328851
FAX: +504 2325375

Minister of Culture, Arts, and Sports
Herman Allan Padgett, Ministry of Culture, Arts, and Sports, Avenida La Paz, Edificio Atala, Tegucigalpa, M.C.D., Honduras, C.A.
PHONE: +504 2369643
FAX: +504 2369532

Minister of Defense
Cristobal Corrales Calix, Ministry of Defense

Minister of Education
Ramon Calix Figueroa, Ministry of Education, 1era Calle, 2-3 Avenida, Comayaguela, M.D.C., Honduras, C.A.
PHONE: +504 2228571
FAX: +504 2374192

Minister of Finance
Gabriela Nunez, Ministry of Finance

Minister of Foreign Relations
Roberto Flores Bermúdez, Ministry of Foreign Relations, Antigua Casa Presidencial Boulevard Fuerzas Armadas, Tegucigalpa, Honduras C.A.
PHONE: +504 2341922; 2345411; 2341178
FAX: +504 2341484
E-MAIL: rfloresb@sre.hn

Ministers

Minister of Government and Justice
Delmer Urbizo Panting, Ministry of Government and Justice

Minister of Industry and Commerce
Reginaldo Panting Penalba, Ministry of Industry and Commerce

Minister of Labor
Andres Victor Artiles, Ministry of Labor

Minister of Natural Resources and Environment
Elvin Ernesto Santos, Ministry of Natural Resources and Environment
PHONE: +504 2327718
FAX: +504 2375725

Minister of Presidency
Gustavo Adolfo Alfaro Zelaya, Ministry of Presidency

Minister of Public Health
Marco Antonio Rosa, Ministry of Public Health

Minister of Public Works, Transportation, and Housing
Tomas Lozano Reyes, Ministry of Public Works, Transportation, and Housing, Barrio La Bolsa, Apartado Postal No 976, Comayaguela, M.D.C., Honduras, C.A.
PHONE: +504 2337690
FAX: +504 2339227

Minister of Tourism
Norman Garcia Paz, Ministry of Tourism

POLITICAL ORGANIZATIONS

Partido de Inovación y Unidad-Social Democracia (National Innovation and Unity Party)

Apdo 105, 29 Avenida de Comayagüela 912, Tegucigalpa, Honduras
PHONE: +504 371357; 371178
FAX: +504 374245
TITLE: President
NAME: Olban Valladares

Partido Liberal de Honduras (Liberal Party of Honduras)

Colonia Miramonte Atrás del Supermercado La Colonia No.1, Tegucigalpa, Honduras
PHONE: +504 320520; 324850
FAX: +504 320797
TITLE: President
NAME: Carlos Roberto Flores Facuseé

Partido Nacional (National Party)

Paseo el Obelisco, Comayagüela M.D.C., Tegucigalpa, Honduras
PHONE: +504 377310; 377413
FAX: +504 377365
TITLE: President
NAME: Oswaldo Ramos Soto

DIPLOMATIC REPRESENTATION

Embassies in Honduras

Peru
Reformation Colony, Stroll The Reformation 2618, Tegucigalpa, Honduras, P.O. Box 3171
PHONE: +504 2210596; 2210604
FAX: +504 2366070
E-MAIL: embaperu@netsys.hn
TITLE: Ambassador
NAME: Víctor Yamamoto Miyakawa

United States
Avenido La Paz, Apartado Postal No. 3453, AMEMB Honduras, APO AA 34022
PHONE: +504 385114
FAX: +504 369037

JUDICIAL SYSTEM

Supreme Court of Justice

FURTHER READING

Articles

"Ancient Site in Honduras." *The New York Times,* 8 July 1999.

"Clinton Expands Debt-Relief Plan for Poor Nations." *The Seattle Times,* 30 September 1999.

"A Fruitless Confrontation About More Than Bananas." *The Seattle Times,* 16 March 1999.

"Giving Aid Where It Counts Can Be Tricky." *The Seattle Times,* 11 March 1999.

"Honduras and Nicaragua. Farming After the Hurricane." *The Economist* (February 20, 1999): 35.

"Honduras: Making Do." *The Economist* (July 3, 1999): 28.

"Honduras Retreats from Estimate of Storm Deaths." *The New York Times,* 1 January 1999.

"Months After Mitch, Half-Light in Honduras." *The Miami Herald,* 14 January 1999.

"Story of Boy's Trek to Find Father in Big Apple a Hoax." *The Seattle Times,* 30 June 1999.

"U.S.-Built Base May Have Graves, Cells." *Los Angeles Times,* 13 August 1999.

HONDURAS: STATISTICAL DATA

For sources and notes see "Sources of Statistics" in the front of each volume.

GEOGRAPHY

Geography (1)

Area:

Total: 112,090 sq km.

Land: 111,890 sq km.

Water: 200 sq km.

Area—comparative: slightly larger than Tennessee.

Land boundaries:

Total: 1,520 km.

Border countries: Guatemala 256 km, El Salvador 342 km, Nicaragua 922 km.

Coastline: 820 km.

Climate: subtropical in lowlands, temperate in mountains.

Terrain: mostly mountains in interior, narrow coastal plains.

Natural resources: timber, gold, silver, copper, lead, zinc, iron ore, antimony, coal, fish.

Land use:

Arable land: 15%

Permanent crops: 3%

Permanent pastures: 14%

Forests and woodland: 54%

Other: 14% (1993 est.).

HUMAN FACTORS

Demographics (2A)

	1990	1995	1998	2000	2010	2020	2030	2040	2050
Population	4,739.9	5,445.3	5,862.0	6,130.1	7,280.2	8,182.0	9,056.6	10,020.4	11,001.3
Net migration rate (per 1,000 population)	NA	NA	NA	NA	NA	NA	NA	NA	NA
Births	NA	NA	NA	NA	NA	NA	NA	NA	NA
Deaths	NA	NA	NA	NA	NA	NA	NA	NA	NA
Life expectancy - males	62.9	63.8	63.3	63.0	57.3	60.3	67.7	75.0	78.1
Life expectancy - females	67.9	68.5	66.8	65.7	62.3	65.4	73.2	80.9	84.1
Birth rate (per 1,000)	37.6	34.1	31.8	30.1	24.1	21.0	18.2	16.0	14.4
Death rate (per 1,000)	7.3	6.7	7.0	7.3	9.7	9.3	7.2	5.5	5.8
Women of reproductive age (15-49 yrs.)	1,076.9	1,285.8	1,419.3	1,504.8	1,907.8	2,242.2	2,485.2	2,661.0	2,711.7
of which are currently married	NA	NA	NA	NA	NA	NA	NA	NA	NA
Fertility rate	5.2	4.6	4.1	3.8	2.8	2.3	2.1	2.0	2.0

Except as noted, values for vital statistics are in thousands; life expectancy is in years.

Health Personnel (3)

Total health expenditure as a percentage of GDP, 1990-1997[a]

Public sector 2.8

Private sector 2.8

Total[b] 5.6

Health expenditure per capita in U.S. dollars, 1990-1997[a]

Purchasing power parity 106

Total 33

Availability of health care facilities per 100,000 people

Hospital beds 1990-1997[a] 110

Doctors 1993[c] 22

Nurses 1993[c] 17

Health Indicators (4)

Life expectancy at birth

1980 60

1997 69

Daily per capita supply of calories (1996) 2,368

Total fertility rate births per woman (1997) 4.3

Maternal mortality ratio per 100,000 live births (1990-97) ....220[c]

Safe water % of population with access (1995) 77

Sanitation % of population with access (1995) 82

Consumption of iodized salt % of households (1992-98)[a] 85

Smoking prevalence

Male % of adults (1985-95)[a] 36

Female % of adults (1985-95)[a] 11

Tuberculosis incidence per 100,000 people (1997) 96

Adult HIV prevalence % of population ages 15-49 (1997) 1.46

Infants and Malnutrition (5)

Under-5 mortality rate (1997) 45

% of infants with low birthweight (1990-97) 9

Births attended by skilled health staff % of total[a] ...55

% fully immunized (1995-97)

TB 98

DPT 94

Polio 93

Measles 89

Prevalence of child malnutrition under age 5 (1992-97)[b] 18

Ethnic Division (6)

Mestizo (mixed Amerindian and European) 90%

Amerindian 7%

Black 2%

White 1%

Religions (7)

Roman Catholic 97%; Protestant minority.

Languages (8)

Spanish, Amerindian dialects.

EDUCATION

Public Education Expenditures (9)

Public expenditure on education (% of GNP)

1980 ....3.2

1996 ....3.6[1]

Expenditure per student

Primary % of GNP per capita

1980 ....10.7

1996 ....9.0[1]

Secondary % of GNP per capita

1980 ....

1996 ....

Tertiary % of GNP per capita

1980 ....77.4

1996 ....68.8[1]

Expenditure on teaching materials

Primary % of total for level (1996) 3.6

Secondary % of total for level (1996) ....0.3[1]

Primary pupil-teacher ratio per teacher (1996) .....35[1]

Duration of primary education years (1995) 6

Educational Attainment (10)

Age group (1983)[9] ....25+

Total population ....NA

Highest level attained (%)

No schooling 33.5

First level

Not completed 51.3

Completed ....NA

Entered second level

S-1 ....4.3

S-2 ....7.6

Postsecondary 3.3

Literacy Rates (11A)

In thousands and percent[1]	1990	1995	2000	2010
Illiterate population (15+ yrs.)	817	869	925	1,013
Literacy rate - total adult pop. (%)	69.4	72.7	75.6	80.7
Literacy rate - males (%)	69.9	72.6	75.1	79.4
Literacy rate - females (%)	68.9	72.7	76.0	82.0

GOVERNMENT & LAW

Political Parties (12)

National Assembly	% of seats
Liberal Party (PLH)	.50
National Party of Honduras (PNH)	.42
National Innovation and Unity Party-Social Democratic Party (PINU-SD)	.4
Christian Democratic Party (PDCH)	.2
Other	.2

Military Affairs (14B)

	1990	1991	1992	1993	1994	1995
Military expenditures						
Current dollars (mil.)	57	47	45	53[e]	50[e]	51
1995 constant dollars (mil.)	66	52	49	55[e]	51[e]	51
Armed forces (000)	18	17	17	17	17	18
Gross national product (GNP)						
Current dollars (mil.)	2,652	2,801	3,025	3,423	3,443	3,668
1995 constant dollars (mil.)	3,048	3,096	3,254	3,588	3,530	3,668
Central government expenditures (CGE)						
1995 constant dollars (mil.)	600	570	597	669	623	590
People (mil.)	4.7	4.9	5.0	5.2	5.3	5.5
Military expenditure as % of GNP	2.2	1.7	1.5	1.5	1.4	1.4
Military expenditure as % of CGE	11.0	9.1	8.1	8.2	8.1	8.7
Military expenditure per capita (1995 $)	14	11	10	11	10	9
Armed forces per 1,000 people (soldiers)	3.8	3.5	3.4	3.3	3.2	3.3
GNP per capita (1995 $)	643	635	647	694	664	672
Arms imports[6]						
Current dollars (mil.)	30	30	30	20	10	10
1995 constant dollars (mil.)	34	33	32	21	10	10
Arms exports[6]						
Current dollars (mil.)	0	0	0	0	0	0
1995 constant dollars (mil.)	0	0	0	0	0	0
Total imports[7]						
Current dollars (mil.)	935	955	1,037	1,130	1,056	1,219
1995 constant dollars (mil.)	1,075	1,055	1,115	1,185	1,082	1,219
Total exports[7]						
Current dollars (mil.)	831	792	802	814	843	1,061
1995 constant dollars (mil.)	955	875	863	853	864	1,061
Arms as percent of total imports[8]	3.2	3.1	2.9	1.8	.9	.8
Arms as percent of total exports[8]	0	0	0	0	0	0

Government Budget (13B)

Revenues . . . .$655 million

Expenditures . . . .$850 million

  Capital expenditures . . . .$150 million

Data for 1997 est.

LABOR FORCE

Labor Force (16)

Total (million) 1.3

Agriculture 62%

Services 20%

Manufacturing 9%

Construction 3%

Other 6%

Data for 1997 est. Percent distribution for 1985.

Unemployment Rate (17)

6.3% (1997); underemployed 30% (1997 est.)

PRODUCTION SECTOR

Electric Energy (18)

Capacity .305,000 kW (1995)

Production . . . . .2.8 billion kWh (1995)

Consumption per capita . . . . .516 kWh (1995)

Transportation (19)

Highways:

total: 15,400 km

paved: 3,126 km

unpaved: 12,274 km (1996 est.)

Waterways: 465 km navigable by small craft

Merchant marine:

total: 219 ships (1,000 GRT or over) totaling 545,829 GRT/801,456 DWT ships by type: bulk 25, cargo 131, chemical tanker 3, container 7, liquefied gas tanker 1, livestock carrier 2, oil tanker 19, passenger 1, passenger-cargo 3, refrigerated cargo 18, roll-on/roll-off cargo 5, short-sea passenger 3, vehicle carrier 1 note: a flag of convenience registry; Russia owns 7 ships, Vietnam 2, Singapore 2, North Korea 1, Brazil 1, Japan 1, Iran 1 (1997 est.)

Airports: 122 (1997 est.)

Airports—with paved runways:

total: 12

2,438 to 3,047 m: 3

1,524 to 2,437 m: 2

914 to 1,523 m: 5

under 914 m: 2 (1997 est.)

Airports—with unpaved runways:

total: 110

2,438 to 3,047 m: 1

1,524 to 2,437 m: 2

914 to 1,523 m: 20

under 914 m: 87 (1997 est.)

Top Agricultural Products (20)

Bananas, coffee, citrus; beef; timber; shrimp.

MANUFACTURING SECTOR

GDP & Manufacturing Summary (21)

Detailed value added figures are listed by both International Standard Industry Code (ISIC) and product title.

	1980	1985	1990	1994
GDP ($-1990 mil.)[1]	2,476	2,617	3,049	3,472
Per capita ($-1990)[1]	694	625	625	632
Manufacturing share (%) (current prices)[1]	15.1	15.1	16.3	*17.0*
Manufacturing				
Value added ($-1990 mil.)[1]	308	326	443	*499*
Industrial production index	100	140	219	*353*
Value added ($ mil.)	*296*	498	466	470
Gross output ($ mil.)	*1,021*	1,618	1,651	1,663
Employment (000)	58	64	79	133
Profitability (% of gross output)				
Intermediate input (%)	*71*	69	72	72
Wages and salaries inc. supplements (%)	*12*	13	11	12
Gross operating surplus	*17*	18	18	17
Productivity ($)				
Gross output per worker	*16,728*	*25,279*	20,996	12,553
Value added per worker	*4,961*	7,785	5,926	3,550
Average wage (inc. supplements)	*2,039*	3,219	2,239	1,477
Value added ($ mil.)				
311/2 Food products	*75*	130	128	133
313 Beverages	*58*	78	59	80

	1980	1985	1990	1994
314 Tobacco products	*20*	42	34	26
321 Textiles	*13*	14	16	10
322 Wearing apparel	*9*	17	20	61
323 Leather and fur products	*3*	2	3	3
324 Footwear	*3*	2	2	2
331 Wood and wood products	*22*	30	20	23
332 Furniture and fixtures	*5*	8	8	7
341 Paper and paper products	*5*	9	12	13
342 Printing and publishing	*7*	13	10	10
351 Industrial chemicals	*1*	2	2	2
352 Other chemical products	*12*	20	20	18
353 Petroleum refineries	*13*	38	39	1
354 Miscellaneous petroleum and coal products	—	—	—	—
355 Rubber products	*5*	8	7	5
356 Plastic products	*9*	18	16	13
361 Pottery, china and earthenware	—	—	1	—
362 Glass and glass products	—	—	—	—
369 Other non-metal mineral products	*15*	24	26	31
371 Iron and steel	*1*	2	4	2
372 Non-ferrous metals	*1*	1	1	1
381 Metal products	*13*	21	21	16
382 Non-electrical machinery	*1*	3	4	3
383 Electrical machinery	*4*	8	7	5
384 Transport equipment	—	2	2	1
385 Professional and scientific equipment	—	1	1	—
390 Other manufacturing industries	*2*	5	6	3

FINANCE, ECONOMICS, & TRADE

Economic Indicators (22)

National product: GDP—purchasing power parity—$12.7 billion (1997 est.)

National product real growth rate: 4.5% (1997 est.)

National product per capita: $2,200 (1997 est.)

Inflation rate—consumer price index: 15% (1997 est.)

Exchange Rates (24)

Exchange rates:

Lempiras (L) per US$1 (end of period)

January 1998	13.1332
1997	13.0942
1996	12.8694
1995	10.3432
1994	9.4001
1993	7.2600

Balance of Payments (23)

	1991	1992	1993	1994	1995
Exports of goods (f.o.b.)	841	839	1,000	1,101	1,377
Imports of goods (f.o.b.)	−912	−990	−1,203	−1,351	−1,519
Trade balance	−72	−151	−204	−250	−141
Services - debits	−513	−587	−510	−549	−592
Services - credits	215	263	241	266	290
Private transfers (net)	144	155	96	96	115
Government transfers (net)	53	61	68	93	128
Overall balance	−172	−258	−309	−343	−201

Top Import Origins (25)

$1.8 billion (c.i.f. 1996) Data are for 1995.

Origins	%
United States	.43
Guatemala	.5
Japan	.5
Germany	.4
Mexico	.3
El Salvador	.3

Top Export Destinations (26)

$1.3 billion (f.o.b., 1996) Data are for 1995.

Destinations	%
United States	.54
Germany	.7
Belgium	.5
Japan	.4
Spain	.3

Economic Aid (27)

Recipient: ODA, $NA. NA stands for not available.

Import Export Commodities (28)

Import Commodities	Export Commodities
Machinery and transport equipment	Bananas
	Coffee
Industrial raw materials	Shrimp
Chemical products	Lobster
Manufactured goods	Minerals
Fuel and oil	Meat
Foodstuffs	Lumber

HUNGARY

Republic of Hungary

Magyar Népköztársaság

INTRODUCTORY SURVEY

RECENT HISTORY

In 1946, a republican constitution was adopted, and a coalition government was established. The Hungarian Workers (Communist) Party seized power in 1948. Hungarian foreign trade was oriented toward the Soviet bloc, and industry and land were taken over by the government. Resentment to Soviet influence led to a popular uprising in October 1956 that was quickly put down by Soviet military force after a few days' success. Many people fled the country, and many others were executed.

From 1956, Hungary was a firm ally of the Soviet Union. In 1968, the New Economic Mechanism was introduced in order to make the economy more competitive and open to market forces. Reform measures beginning in 1979 further encouraged private enterprise. The movement toward relaxation of tensions in Europe in the 1970s was reflected in the improvement of Hungary's relations with Western countries, including reestablishment of diplomatic relations with the Federal Republic of Germany in 1973.

The energy crisis of the late 1970s, aggravated by the abandonment of the New Economic Mechanism at Soviet insistence, led to growing foreign debt. By the late 1980s the country owed $18 billion, the highest rate of debt in Europe.

This debt and other social factors spurred political change. In October 1989 the state constitution was amended to create a multiparty political

system. After the 1990 general election, the first major free election to be held in more than four decades, a coalition government was formed.

Under prime minister Jozsef Antall, Hungary began to transform its economy with the goal of transferring 30–35% of state assets to private control by the end of 1993. Hungary's liberal investment laws and comparatively well-developed industries permitted the nation to become an early leader in attracting Western investors. However, many found the pace of transition too slow, especially since the government did not keep to its own time schedule.

In addition, nationalistic intolerance of Hungary's ethnic minorities began to increase. Approximately 10% of the Hungarian population is non-Hungarian, including large populations of Jews and Roma (Gypsies).

In the parliamentary elections of May 1994, voters turned overwhelmingly to the Hungarian Socialist Party (the former Communist Party), giving it an absolute majority of 54%.

Hungary's international debt remains very high—the country ran a $936 million trade deficit for the first two months of 1994 alone—forcing new Prime Minister Gyula Horn to continue most of the same economic reform programs which the previous government began. There was concern, however, that the Socialists' victory could lead to reversal of some of the important democratic gains of the recent past.

In January 1994, Hungary formally accepted the offer of a compromise on NATO membership. In July 1997, NATO agreed to grant Hungary full membership to the organization by 1999. Hungary, along with the Czech Republic and Poland, formally joined NATO on March 12, 1999. In September 1996, Hungary and Romania signed a treaty ending a centuries-old dispute over the status of Romania's 1.6 million ethnic Hungarians and the integrity of its borders.

GOVERNMENT

Hungary's constitution remains based upon the 1949 Soviet-style constitution, with major changes made in 1972 and 1988. The lack of a new constitution has left Hungary with a number of remnants of the communist era.

The present system is a multiparty republic, with a parliamentary government. There is one legislative house, with 386 seats. The president is head of state, elected by the parliament for a five-year term. The head of the government is the prime minister, leader of the largest party seated in the parliament.

Judiciary

Cases usually receive their first hearing before provincial city courts or Budapest district courts. Appeals can be submitted to county courts or the Budapest Metropolitan Court. The Supreme Court is basically a court of appeal, although it may also hear important cases in the first instance. A Constitutional Law Council was established in April 1984 to verify the constitutionality of proposed laws.

Political Parties

Each of the last two parliaments has seated representatives of the same six political parties. However, the relative numbers of seats shifted dramatically between 1990 and 1994.

The dominant party is the Hungarian Socialist Party (HSP)—the former Communist Party—which took 209 of the legislature's 386 seats in the 1994 elections. Although it supports a market economy system, the HSP, like the communists of the past, stresses a high amount of government spending.

The Alliance of Free Democrats (AFD) favors closer integration with Europe and cooperation with Hungary's neighbors. With its right wing purged in 1993, the Hungarian Democratic Forum (HDF) is a party of strong support for the ethnic minorities within Hungary. The Independent Smallholders' Party (ISP) is a center-right party that seeks to ensure Hungarian interests in the context of European integration.

The Christian Democratic People's Party (CDPP) is a center-right group with a religious dimension. The Alliance of Young Democrats (AYD) is similar in program to the AFD, but with narrower appeal. The final parliamentary party is the Agrarian Alliance, which is primarily concerned with issues affecting the nation's farmers.

Hungary also has a noticeable "skinhead" movement, which has provoked fights and other disturbances, especially with Gypsies.

DEFENSE

Military service is compulsory. All males aged 18 to 55 are eligible for induction for twelve months' service. In 1995, Hungary had an army of 48,000 men and an air force of 16,300 men. Security forces, consisting of frontier and border guards under the direction of the Ministry of the Interior, number about 13,800. The defense budget was estimated at $520 million in 1996.

ECONOMIC AFFAIRS

After the fall of communism in 1989, Hungary began a painful transition to a market economy. Freed to reach their own level, consumer prices rose 162% between 1989 and 1993. The rate of unemployment was 12.2% at the end of 1992. By late 1993, the private sector accounted for 35–40% of the domestic economy.

By 1994, Hungary was in an economic slump unknown since the reforms toward capitalism began, with high rates of inflation and unemployment. In March 1995, the government began a program that reduced its expenditures and devalued the currency in order to control inflation.

Public Finance

The growing budget deficit is a crucial problem. State spending has been held in check, but unexpectedly large drops in GDP have depressed tax revenues. The budget problem is expected to persist without better tax collection and a restructuring of overly generous social benefits. In 1995, the general government deficit amounted to approximately 280 billion forints, with a deficit/GDP ratio of 6.5%, an improvement over the 8.1% ratio of 1994.

Hungary has the heaviest per capita debt burden of Eastern Europe. Gross foreign debt reportedly fell from $31.6 billion in 1995 to an estimated $27 billion in 1996.

The U.S. CIA estimates that, in 1995, government revenues totaled approximately $12.6 billion and expenditures $13.8 billion. External debt totaled $32.7 billion.

Income

In 1998, the gross national product (GNP) was $45.6 billion, or $4,510 per person. For the period 1985–95, the average inflation rate was 19.9%, resulting in a decline in GNP of 1.0% per person.

Industry

Industry has expanded rapidly since 1948 and provides the bulk of exports. Hungary's industries produce steel, machine tools, buses, diesel engines and locomotives, televisions, radios, electric light bulbs and fluorescent lamps, telecommunications equipment, refrigerators, washing machines, medical and other precision engineering equipment, pharmaceuticals, and petrochemical products. Chemicals became a leading industry in the early 1990s. In 1992, Suzuki and Opel began to produce the first automobiles manufactured in Hungary since before World War II.

Banking and Finance

Banking was nationalized in 1948, when the National Bank of Hungary was installed as the bank of issue, with a monopoly on credit and foreign exchange operations.

Following the 1987 reform of the banking system, the National Bank retained its central position as a bank of issue and its foreign exchange monopoly, but its credit functions were transferred to commercial banks. The main bank for the general public is the National Savings Bank. The Central Corporation of Banking Companies handles state property, performs international property transactions for individuals, and deals with the liquidation of bankrupt companies. The State Development Institution manages and controls development projects. Upon joining the OECD in 1996, Hungary agreed to cease its ban on the establishment of foreign bank branches by the beginning of 1998.

At the end of 1995, total foreign reserves, excluding gold, totaled $12,052 million. The central bank changed the official currency basket in January 1997. In keeping with an earlier government decision, the bank replaced the Ecn with the D-mark in the exchange rate fixing. The new daily fixing will be based on a 70 D-mark: U.S. $30 basket instead of the present 70 Ecn: U.S. $30 basket.

In Budapest, an authentic commodity and stock exchange functioned from 1867 until 1948, when it was closed down as the country transformed into a centralized socialist economy. The reorganization of the Hungarian securities market, after a pause of some forty years, started at the beginning of the 1980s. The Exchange was founded on 21 June 1990.

Economic Development

Far-reaching economic reforms, called the New Economic Mechanism (NEM), were introduced on 1 January 1968. In order to create a competitive consumers' market, some prices were no longer fixed administratively, but were to be determined by market forces. Central planning was restricted to essential materials, and managers of state enterprises were expected to plan and carry out all the tasks necessary to ensure profitable production. Beginning in 1979, the government introduced a program of price reform, aimed at aligning domestic with world prices; changes in wage setting, intended to encourage productivity; and decentralization of industry, including the breakup of certain large enterprises and the creation of small-scale private ones, especially in services. New measures introduced in 1985 and 1986 included the lifting of government subsidies for retail prices (which led to sharp price increases) and the imposition of management reform, including the election of managers in 80% of all enterprises. The 1991–95 economic program aimed to fully integrate Hungary into the world economy on a competitive basis. The program's main features were to accelerate privatization, control inflation, and institute measures to prepare the way for the convertibility of the forint.

In 1994, the Development Assistance Committee of the OECD distributed $68.3 million in aid to Hungary. Net concessional flows from mulitlateral institutions that year amounted to $132 million.

SOCIAL WELFARE

By 1974, 99% of the population enjoyed the benefits of social insurance. Coverage includes relief for sickness, accidents, unemployment, and old age and incapacity, and provides maternity allowances for working women, allowances for children, and payment of funeral expenses.

Women receive their monthly average earnings during maternity leave, which lasts twenty-four weeks. An employed woman or a father raising his child alone is entitled to unpaid leave until the child is 3 years old.

Women have the same legal rights as men, including inheritance and property rights. They hold a large number of the positions in teaching, medicine, and the judiciary, which are all relatively low-paid professions. In 1995, 43 of 386 deputies in parliament were female.

Healthcare

By the end of 1974, 99% of the population was covered by social insurance and enjoyed free medical services. Free professional assistance is given to insured pregnant women and to the mothers of newborn children. Limited private medical practice is permitted. In 1993, there was 1 physician for every 312 people.

Hungary has a declining population which is aging rapidly. Arteriosclerosis is a major cause of death, and there is a high incidence of cardiovascular disease. Contributing factors include work-related stress, together with smoking and dietary factors. Average life expectancy is 70 years.

Housing

Although the housing stock increased from 3.1 million units in 1970 to 3.8 million in 1986, construction has not kept pace with the needs of Hungary's growing urban population.

EDUCATION

Practically the entire adult population is literate. Eight years of primary and four years of secondary education are free. The state also pays most of the costs for higher education.

In 1994, there were 3,814 general elementary schools, with 89,939 teachers and 985,291 pupils, and general secondary schools, with 140,352 students. Institutions of higher education had 133,956 students and 18,687 professors and lecturers in 1993. Although there are university fees, many students are excused from payment or pay reduced fees.

1999 KEY EVENTS TIMELINE

January

- Gasko Istvan leads a five-day strike by rail workers. The strike is the longest in Hungary since World War II and the goal is to obtain a 21 percent wage increase, compared to the 16 percent offered by the government. The strike is declared illegal and the workers return to their jobs.

- Government officials announce an agreement to support the Hungarian Language Department at Ain Shams University in Egypt. In related talks, the two states agree to extend a cultural cooperation accord for an additional three-year period.

- A university in Szeged announces a breakthrough method for decomposing soil pollutants by means of solar energy. As a result of their discovery, the colloid chemistry department at Attila Jozsef University of Arts and Sciences is granted an award of fifty million forints. The method is considered best suited for the decomposition of oil and its byproducts, positive news in regards to worldwide incidences of oil spills.

February

- Health care reform leads to increasing price levels for prescription drugs. In a move designed to improve competition and market freedom, Hungarian drug manufacturers are allowed to raise their prices by ten percent. Imported drugs are granted a three percent increase. The National Health Fund Association, the government agency which subsidized drug costs to the consumer, is limited to 123 billion forints nationwide in total annual subsidy, signaling a reduction in public support for medical costs.

- A European Union Manual is translated into Hungarian. It is the first translation of its kind among the fourteen applicant states. Ten thousand copies are printed and made available to the public, free of charge.

- A gathering in Budapest of hundreds of neo-Nazis from around Europe leads to violence, resulting in the injury of eight policemen and the arrest of 34 protestors.

March

- Estonia, in a gesture of solidarity, marks Hungary's national day with performances of Liszt compositions and exhibitions of Hungarian art and literature. March 15 marks the date of Hungary's most important festival, a commemoration of the 1848 democratic revolution.

- The first enlargement of NATO since the fall of the Berlin Wall accepts Hungary, Poland, and the Czech Republic, all former members of the Warsaw Pact.

- University of Pecs officials announce the establishment of the world's first postgraduate curriculum in migrational medicine. Hungary serves as a haven for many refugees from conflicts in neighboring Balkan states, the former Soviet republics, Africa, and elsewhere. The Medical School at the University of Pecs is combining efforts with the International Organization for Migration (Geneva, Switzerland) to develop a training program for doctors who intend to work with refugee populations and their unique concerns.

April

- President Arpad Goncz is honored at the White House by United States President Clinton. President Goncz's work in the translation of western literature is recognized. Goncz is also an author whose works have been translated into and published in English.

May

- An exhibition honoring architect Lipot Baumhorn concludes. Baumhorn was active around the turn-of-the-century designing banks, houses, and many synagogues in Hungary and neighboring states such as Romania, Slovakia and the former Yugoslav states. Baumhorn's masterpiece is the Great Synagogue in Szeged, and was restored in 1989. His style developed under the tutelage of Odon Lechner, the founder of the national Art Nouveau. The exhibit is a collaboration of the Museum of Architecture and the Jewish Museum.

- An appeal by fifty professionals and politicians to suspend bombings in Yugoslavia is issued. The group, called the For Peace in the Balkans Movement, is composed of well-known figures including George Konrad, writer and President of the Berlin-Brandenburg Academy of Arts; Magda Kosa-Kovacs, senior politician of the Hungarian Socialist Party; and economist Maria Zita Petschnig. The appeal calls negotiations and a cessation of hostilities.

June

- Parliament passes a law to merge and consolidate universities. The current eighty-five small and medium-sized institutions will be reduced to twenty-five by early 2001. The intention is to provide every city and major town to have one large state university, and to obtain cost savings to the public through increased efficiency.

July

- Ethnic Hungarian lecturers in a Romanian university ask for the establishment of Hungarian-language faculties. In accordance with a new Romanian law, the ethnic Hungarian minority in Romania is to be served by specifically Hungarian-language facilities. The lecturers at the Babes-Bolyai University in western Romania also hope for faculties to be set up in other universities.

- The Foreign Minister comments on an autonomy plan for Vojvodina. The region of Yugoslavia nearest to Hungary, Vojvodina has a significant ethnic Hungarian populace. Ethnic political organizations developed a plan for a return to autonomy for the region within the Yugoslav federal system.

August

- Work nears completion on the conversion of the former headquarters of Budapest Police Department into a five-star hotel. The building dates back to 1918, but has been a control center for the police under Communist rule since 1948. The cells and the bomb shelter in the basement will be converted to banquet and meeting rooms.

September

- Judit Polgar of Hungary is the first woman to advance as far as the semi-finals of the International Chess Federation's World Championship.

October

- The Frankfurt Book Fair spotlights Hungary. The fair is considered the world book industry's central locale for trade in rights for publication and distribution. The content of the exhibition was debated by politicians and intellectuals, with the original emphasis on "urbanite" culture tempered by the inclusion of nationalist historical figures. Hungary reserved a part of the budget to promote translations of Hungarian works into German, deemed by many a positive move towards wider circulation of Hungary's native arts.

- The first of several electronics plants to be built by Japanese concern Sanshin is completed. The plant currently employs 150, and will supply manufacturers including BMW, Mercedes, and Renault. Sanshin has plans to build three additional plants of the same size.

- The Hungarian-Russian Economic Cooperation Committee convenes for the first time in two years. Hungary's Economics Minister (and university professor) Attila Chikan makes clear that no future deals between the two states will be bartered, but rather free-market business arrangements.

- Energy company MOL restarts natural gas shipments to Yugoslavia. Hungary had been voluntarily complying with an oil and oil-derivatives embargo implemented as a part of NATO's campaign against Yugoslavia. In addition to oil, Hungary also withheld shipments of natural gas. The re-commencement of sales to Yugoslavia are based on approval by the government of shipments for the humanitarian needs of the coming winter.

- The European Union releases the second Enlargement Report on Hungary. The report awards high marks for economic, legal, and judicial reform. Agricultural and social policies, particularly the absence of any law providing minority representation in Parliament for Roma (Gypsies) are criticized.

December

- The Hungarian issue bank recalls the old 5,000-forint bills and replaces them with newer versions that have a metal strip.

ANALYSIS OF EVENTS: 1999

BUSINESS AND THE ECONOMY

In 1999, Hungary focused on preparations for the coming half-century, in the arenas of business and economics, politics and government, and culture and society.

The major news in business and economics involved Hungary's orientation towards the competitive economic model of the European Union (EU). Although many of the post-communist era's reforms were long hoped-for under the shadow of Soviet domination, they are coming to fruition with the specific goal of Hungary's entry into the EU.

Annual inflation has consistently fallen, reaching a new low of 10.9 percent in October. Growth of gross domestic product (GDP) was slightly under four in 1999, the leading rate among regional states. The government has successfully streamlined most of its enterprises in order to reduce expense and centralization. Previously state-owned banks have reached a level of almost 70% foreign ownership, tying Hungary's economy and credit system into the European system. In preparation for its entrance into NATO, the Hungarian Army has been reduced from its previous 160,000 under communism to only 60,000, more professional soldiers.

Tourism has continued to rise with Hungary's economic ascent. New hotels are being built and older ones are refurbished to accommodate the influx. Tourism-related income has increased six percent in the first quarter of 1999 over the first quarter of 1998.

Reforms have not been without problems. A massive sale of natural gas distribution assets in 1995 was challenged in 1999 by a group composed of local authorities and towns, who argue that the sale was outside the government's authority and as such has removed rights and income from the towns. Industry observers note that the government has conceded some error in the 1995 sale, but the settlement will likely be much smaller than the towns' demand.

Price reforms have generated some opposition in 1999. The government's reduction of drug subsidies and lifting of price controls have led to as much as a 30 percent increase in price. Water prices since privatization have increased threefold (1991 to 1999). Water authorities have become more efficient, even yielding (in some cases) profits for investors; on the other hand, prices have risen slightly faster than inflation.

The downside of the improved status of major lending markets in Hungary has been that small and medium-sized enterprises (SMEs) have found it difficult to grow and develop. Several large banks, including giant Citigroup's Hungarian operations, have begun to serve the interests of SMEs. In addition, the government has established the Hungarian Development Bank to provide credit and has encouraged local firms to develop supply relationships with the multinational corporations doing business in Hungary. It remains to be seen whether the trend for SMEs will be positive or negative.

Hungary stands as leading candidate for EU admission, although not likely to enter until 2004. The October EU Report on enlargement places Hungary as the model for the other applicants to emulate, but still points out that the country must yet improve its issues with the Roma minority.

Admission to NATO was the biggest story for Hungarian politics and government in 1999. After four decades in the Warsaw Pact, ostensibly developed in opposition to NATO, Hungary was accepted into the Western military alliance in March. Improvements in equipment and communications facilities were necessary following Hungary's admittance, and are still being completed. Several days after the admission, Hungary was allowing NATO planes to use its airspace for bombing missions in Yugoslavia. Although not directly involved, Hungary's official policy was allied with the rest of NATO. Some high profile public figures united in opposition to the war, including George Konrad and several Socialist Party officials.

The Fidesz-Hungarian Civic Party coalition retained control of government. Early in its tenure, the administration appointed several well-qualified officials to posts in major ministries and institutions. Zsigmond Jarai, former chairman of the Budapest Stock Exchange is currently the Finance Minister, and Attila Chikan, economics professor Attila Chikan now heads the Economic Affairs Ministry. In 1999, these officials continued to guide Hungary's economic policies more in the direction of the competitive model of the EU.

The legacy of World War II arose in relation to the seizure of art works from Hungarian Jews and others as war loot. Hungarian Jews filed claims against the international community, including the Hungarian government, for illegal seizures. The Hungarian government debated with Russia their right to retain art works seized by Red Army during and after the war.

Hungarian literature received acclaim as a result of the high profile exhibition at the Frankfurt Book Fair. The Frankfurt Fair afforded Hungary an opportunity to prove its mettle, although translations into English and German will be necessary for major growth in sales.

Hungarian scientists developed breakthrough techniques in chemistry and technology. Increasingly, cooperation with outside institutions yields results and publicity. The anti-pollution method from Attila Jozsef University of Arts and Sciences was funded in part through the NATO "Science for Peace" initiative, and should yield positive results in ecology.

Ethnic Hungarians form minorities in several regions of neighboring states. It is a common characteristic of central European nationalities for members of the ethnic group to be minority citizens of other states, and Hungary is no exception. The Vojvodina region of Yugoslavia and western Romania are main examples. In both places, efforts were made either at the Foreign Ministry level (Vojvodina) or the local level (western Romania) to guarantee civil rights and security of ethnic Hungarians outside the borders of Hungary.

Hungary's own major minority, the Roma (Gypsies) have not fared so well under the recent government. European Union observers have criticized the government for its failure to establish a parliamentary voice for the Roma. Foreign Minister Janos Martonyi has commented that the lack of education among Roma is the cause for their poverty, whereas pro-Roma activists have judged that systematic, culture-wide discrimination against Roma has created the lack of education that Martonyi laments. The normal method of treating Roma discrimination has been to ignore it; thus the Minister's comments have been interpreted as a small, but significant step towards equality for them.

DIRECTORY

CENTRAL GOVERNMENT
Head of State

President
Árpad Goncz, Office of the President, V. Kossuth L.ter 1-3, 1055 Budapest, Hungary
PHONE: +36 (1) 2684000
FAX: +36 (1) 2684800

Ministers

Prime Minister
Viktor Orban, Office of the Prime Minister, V. Kossuth L.ter 1/3, 1055 Budapest, Hungary
PHONE: +36 (1) 2683000
FAX: +36 (1) 1533322
E-MAIL: horn@mehp.meh.hu

Minister Without Portfolio in Charge of Prime Minister's Office
Istvan Stumpf, Ministry Without Portfolio in Charge of Prime Minister's Office

Minister Without Portfolio in Charge of Civilian National Security Services
Laszlo Kover, Ministry Without Portfolio in Charge of Civilian National Security Services

Minister of Transport, Communications, and Water Management
Kalman Katona, Ministry of Transport, Communications, and Water Management

Minister of Social and Family Affairs
Peter Harrach, Ministry of Social and Family Affairs

Minister for National Cultural Heritage
Jozsef Hamori, Ministry for National Cultural
Heritage

Minister of Justice
David Ibolya, Ministry of Justice

Minister of Interior
Sandor Pinter, Ministry of Interior

Minister of Health
Arpad Gogl, Ministry of Health

Minister of Finance
Zsigmond Jarai, Ministry of Finance

Minister of Environmental Protection
Pal Pepo, Ministry of Environmental Protection

Minister of Education
Zoltan Pokorni, Ministry of Education

**Minister of Agriculture and Regional
Development**
Jozsef Torgyan, Ministry of Agriculture and
Regional Development

Minister of Sports and Youth
Tamas Deutsch, Ministry of Sports and Youth

Minister of Economic Affairs
Attila Chikan, Ministry of Economic Affairs, V.
Honved utca 13-15, H-1880 Budapest, Hungary
PHONE: +36 (1) 3022355
FAX: +36 (1) 3022394
E-MAIL: webmaster@gm.hu

Minister of Defense
Janos Szabo, Ministry of Defense, V. ker.,
Balaton u. 7-11, 1055 Budapest, Hungary
PHONE: +36 (1) 2365111
FAX: +36 (1) 4741110
E-MAIL: modpress@hm.gov.hu

Minister of Foreign Affairs
Janos Martonyi, Ministry of Foreign Affairs,
Bem rkp. 47, 1027 Budapest, Hungary
PHONE: +36 (1) 4581000

POLITICAL ORGANIZATIONS

Munkaspart-MP (Workers' Party)

**Magyar Demokrata Neppart-MDNP
(Hungarian Democratic People's Party)**

**Nemzeti Demokrata Part-NDP (National
Democratic Party)**

**Fuggetlen Kisgazda, Foldmunkas es
Polgari Part-FKgP (Independent
Smallholders, Argarian Workers and
Citizens)**
TITLE: President
NAME: Jozsef Torgyan

**Magyar Igazsag es Elet Partja-MIEP
(Hungarian Justice and Life Party)**
TITLE: Chairman
NAME: Istvan Csurka

**Magyar Demokrata Forum-MDF
(Hungarian Democratic Forum)**
TITLE: Chairman
NAME: Sandor Lezsak

**Fiatal Demokratak Szovetsege-FiDeSz
(Federation of Young Democrats)**
TITLE: Chairman
NAME: Viktor Orban

**Keresztenydemokrata Neppart-KDNP
(Christian Democratic People's Party)**
TITLE: President
NAME: Gyorgy Giczy

**Szabad Demokratak Szovetsege (Alliance
of Free Democrats)**
Gizella ut 36, 1143 Budapest, Hungary
PHONE: +36 (1) 2232050
E-MAIL: szdsz@szdsz.hu
TITLE: Chairman
NAME: Ivan Peto

**Magyar Szocialista Part-MSZP (Hungarian
Socialist Party)**
Koztarsasag ter 26, 1081 Budapest, Hungary
PHONE: +36 (1) 2100046; 2100078
FAX: +36 (1) 2100081
E-MAIL: info@mszp.hu
TITLE: Chairman
NAME: Laszlo Kovacs

DIPLOMATIC REPRESENTATION

Embassies in Hungary

Egypt
1016 Bp. Berc u. 16, Budapest, Hungary
PHONE: +36 (1) 4665080; 4668060
FAX: +36 (1) 2092638

Japan
1125 Zalai ut 7, Budapest, Hungary
PHONE: +36 (1) 2751275
FAX: +36 (1) 2751281
E-MAIL: infocons@japan-embassy.hu

United States
V. 1054 Szabadsag ter 12, Budapest, Hungary
PHONE: +36 (1) 2674400; 2699331; 2699339
FAX: +36 (1) 2699326
TITLE: Ambassador
NAME: Peter F. Tufo

JUDICIAL SYSTEM
Supreme Court of the Republic of Hungary

FURTHER READING
Articles

"As Farmers Sell Out in Secret . . . Budapest Asks for a Break." *Business Week* (July 12, 1999): 4.

Glass, Nigel. "Infanticide in Hungary Faces Stiffer Penalties." *The Lancet* (February 13, 1999): 570.

Olivier, Charles. "Investors Converge on Hungary." *Euromoney* (March 1999): 90.

Books

Adam, Jan. *Why Did the Socialist System Collapse in Central and Eastern European Countries?: The Case of Poland, the Former Czechoslovakia, and Hungary.* New York: St. Martin's Press, 1995.

Gero, Andras. *Modern Hungarian Society in the Making: The Unfinished Experience.* London: Central European University Press, 1995.

Stephan, Johannes. *Economic Transition in Hungary and East Germany: Gradualism and Shock Therapy in Catch-up Development.* New York: St. Martin's Press, 1999.

Wu, Yu-Shan. *Comparative Economic Transformations: Mainland China, Hungary, the Soviet Union.* Stanford, Calif.: Stanford University Press, 1994.

Internet

Budapest Sun. Available Online @ http://www.budapestsun.com/archive.asp (November 1, 1999).

HUNGARY: STATISTICAL DATA

For sources and notes see "Sources of Statistics" in the front of each volume.

GEOGRAPHY

Geography (1)

Area:

Total: 93,030 sq km.

Land: 92,340 sq km.

Water: 690 sq km.

Area—comparative: slightly smaller than Indiana.

Land boundaries:

Total: 2,009 km.

Border countries: Austria 366 km, Croatia 329 km, Romania 443 km, Serbia and Montenegro 151 km (all with Serbia), Slovakia 515 km, Slovenia 102 km, Ukraine 103 km.

Coastline: 0 km (landlocked).

Climate: temperate; cold, cloudy, humid winters; warm summers.

Terrain: mostly flat to rolling plains; hills and low mountains on the Slovakian border.

Natural resources: bauxite, coal, natural gas, fertile soils.

Land use:

Arable land: 51%

Permanent crops: 2%

Permanent pastures: 13%

HUMAN FACTORS

Demographics (2A)

	1990	1995	1998	2000	2010	2020	2030	2040	2050
Population	10,352.3	10,285.0	10,208.1	10,167.2	9,962.6	9,604.3	9,107.3	8,450.8	7,683.7
Net migration rate (per 1,000 population)	NA	NA	NA	NA	NA	NA	NA	NA	NA
Births	NA	NA	NA	NA	NA	NA	NA	NA	NA
Deaths	145.7	NA	NA	NA	NA	NA	NA	NA	NA
Life expectancy - males	65.1	65.2	66.5	67.2	70.7	73.5	75.8	77.4	78.7
Life expectancy - females	73.8	74.5	75.4	76.0	78.7	80.9	82.6	83.9	84.9
Birth rate (per 1,000)	12.1	11.0	10.7	10.9	9.1	7.8	7.1	6.2	5.7
Death rate (per 1,000)	14.1	14.2	13.5	13.1	12.4	12.4	13.4	14.8	16.1
Women of reproductive age (15-49 yrs.)	2,535.5	2,600.9	2,583.4	2,546.4	2,347.5	2,230.3	1,874.5	1,616.6	1,370.1
of which are currently married	229.1	NA	NA	NA	NA	NA	NA	NA	NA
Fertility rate	1.9	1.6	1.4	1.4	1.4	1.3	1.3	1.3	1.3

Except as noted, values for vital statistics are in thousands; life expectancy is in years.

Forests and woodland: 19%

Other: 15% (1993 est.).

Health Personnel (3)

Total health expenditure as a percentage of GDP, 1990-1997[a]

Public sector 4.5

Private sector 2.0

Total[b] 6.5

Health expenditure per capita in U.S. dollars, 1990-1997[a]

Purchasing power parity 459

Total 291

Availability of health care facilities per 100,000 people

Hospital beds 1990-1997[a] 900

Doctors 1993[c] 337

Nurses 1993[c] . . . . .NA

Health Indicators (4)

Life expectancy at birth

1980 70

1997 71

Daily per capita supply of calories (1996) 3,402

Total fertility rate births per woman (1997) 1.4

Maternal mortality ratio per 100,000 live births (1990-97) . . . . .14[b]

Safe water % of population with access (1995) . . . .

Sanitation % of population with access (1995) . . . .

Consumption of iodized salt % of households (1992-98)[a] . . . .

Smoking prevalence

Male % of adults (1985-95)[a] 40

Female % of adults (1985-95)[a] 27

Tuberculosis incidence per 100,000 people (1997) 47

Adult HIV prevalence % of population ages 15-49 (1997) 0.04

Infants and Malnutrition (5)

Under-5 mortality rate (1997) 11

% of infants with low birthweight (1990-97) 9

Births attended by skilled health staff % of total[a] . . .96

% fully immunized (1995-97)

TB 100

DPT 100

Polio 100

Measles 100

Prevalence of child malnutrition under age 5 (1992-97)[b] . . . . .NA

Ethnic Division (6)

Hungarian 89.9%

Gypsy 4%

German 2.6%

Serb 2%

Slovak 0.8%

Romanian 0.7%

Religions (7)

Roman Catholic 67.5%

Calvinist 20%

Lutheran 5%

Atheist and other 7.5%

Languages (8)

Hungarian 98.2%, other 1.8%.

EDUCATION

Public Education Expenditures (9)

Public expenditure on education (% of GNP)

1980 . . . . .4.7

1996 . . . . .4.7

Expenditure per student

Primary % of GNP per capita

1980 . . . . .14.1

1996 . . . . .20.6[1]

Secondary % of GNP per capita

1980 . . . .

1996 . . . . .20.3[1]

Tertiary % of GNP per capita

1980 . . . . .85.4

1996 . . . . .47.0

Expenditure on teaching materials

Primary % of total for level (1996) . . . .

Secondary % of total for level (1996) . . . .

Primary pupil-teacher ratio per teacher (1996) . . . . .11[1]

Duration of primary education years (1995) 4

Educational Attainment (10)

Age group (1990)[8] . . . . .25+

Total population 6,798,765

Highest level attained (%)

No schooling 1.3

First level

Not completed 24.3

Completed 33.6

Entered second level

S-1 . . . . .NA

S-2 . . . . .30.7

Postsecondary 10.1

Literacy Rates (11B)

Adult literacy rate

1980

Male 98x

Female 98x

1995

Male 99

Female 99

GOVERNMENT & LAW

Political Parties (12)

National Assembly	% of seats
Hungarian Socialist Party (MSzP)	.33.0
Alliance of Free Democrats (SzDSz)	.19.8
Hungarian Democratic Forum (MDF)	.11.7
Independent Smallholders (FKgP)	.8.9
Christian Democratic People's Party (KDNP)	.7.1
Hungarian Civic Party (FiDeSz)	.7.0
Hungarian Workers' Party (MMP)	.3.2
Hungarian Justice and Life Party (MIEP)	.1.6
Other	.7.7

Military Affairs (14B)

	1990	1991	1992	1993	1994	1995
Military expenditures						
Current dollars (mil.)	1,277[r]	1,261[r]	1,285	1,184	1,203	961
1995 constant dollars (mil.)	1,468[r]	1,393[r]	1,382	1,241	1,233	961
Armed forces (000)	94	87	78	NA	60	71
Gross national product (GNP)						
Current dollars (mil.)	62,590[e]	59,260[e]	59,310	61,040	63,510	65,660
1995 constant dollars (mil.)	71,940[e]	65,480[e]	63,800	63,990	65,100	65,660
Central government expenditures (CGE)						
1995 constant dollars (mil.)	35,990	27,500[e]	25,700	21,580	23,130	21,110
People (mil.)	10.4	10.3	10.3	10.2	10.1	10.1
Military expenditure as % of GNP	2.0	2.1	2.2	1.9	1.9	1.5
Military expenditure as % of CGE	4.1	5.1	5.4	5.8	5.3	4.6
Military expenditure per capita (1995 $)	142	135	135	122	122	95
Armed forces per 1,000 people (soldiers)	9.1	8.4	7.6	NA	5.9	7.0
GNP per capita (1995 $)	6,949	6,352	6,218	6,271	6,420	6,519
Arms imports[6]						
Current dollars (mil.)	0	0	0	925	10	30
1995 constant dollars (mil.)	0	0	0	970	10	30
Arms exports[6]						
Current dollars (mil.)	130	40	40	20	0	20
1995 constant dollars (mil.)	149	44	43	21	0	20
Total imports[7]						
Current dollars (mil.)	8,621	11,450	11,120	12,600	14,440	15,070
1995 constant dollars (mil.)	9,908	12,650	11,960	13,210	14,800	15,070
Total exports[7]						
Current dollars (mil.)	9,730	10,230	10,680	8,918	10,730	12,540
1995 constant dollars (mil.)	11,180	11,130	11,490	9,349	11,000	12,540
Arms as percent of total imports[8]	0	0	0	7.3	.1	.2
Arms as percent of total exports[8]	1.3	.4	.4	.2	0	.2

Government Budget (13A)

Year: 1997

Total Expenditures: 3,644.2 Billions of Forint

Expenditures as a percentage of the total by function:

General public services and public order 6.61

Defense 1.81

Education 2.45

Health 6.44

Social Security and Welfare 30.82

Housing and community amenities 97

Recreational, cultural, and religious affairs 1.15

Fuel and energy 04

Agriculture, forestry, fishing, and hunting 2.46

Mining, manufacturing, and construction 21

Transportation and communication 2.73

Other economic affairs and services 2.25

Crime (15)

Crime rate (for 1997)

Crimes reported 514,400

Total persons convicted 257,200

Crimes per 100,000 population 5,050

Persons responsible for offenses

Total number of suspects 130,700

Total number of female suspects 15,200

Total number of juvenile suspects 14,000

LABOR FORCE

Labor Force (16)

Total (million) 4.5

Services 65.0%

Industry 26.7%

Agriculture 8.3%

Data for 1996. Percent distribution for 1996.

Unemployment Rate (17)

9% (1997 est.)

PRODUCTION SECTOR

Electric Energy (18)

Capacity . . . . .6.979 million kW (1995)

Production . . . . .32.92 billion kWh (1995)

Consumption per capita . . . . .3,423 kWh (1995)

Transportation (19)

Highways:

total: 158,633 km

paved: 68,370 km (including 420 km of expressways)

unpaved: 90,263 km (1996 est.)

Waterways: 1,622 km (1988)

Pipelines: crude oil 1,204 km; natural gas 4,387 km (1991)

Merchant marine:

total: 8 cargo ships (1,000 GRT or over) totaling 35,522 GRT/47,792 DWT (1997 est.)

Airports: 25 (1997 est.)

Airports—with paved runways:

total: 15

over 3,047 m: 2

2,438 to 3,047 m: 8

1,524 to 2,437 m: 3

914 to 1,523 m: 1

under 914 m: 1 (1997 est.)

Airports—with unpaved runways:

total: 10

2,438 to 3,047 m: 3

1,524 to 2,437 m: 4

914 to 1,523 m: 3 (1997 est.)

Top Agricultural Products (20)

Wheat, corn, sunflower seed, potatoes, sugar beets; pigs, cattle, poultry, dairy products.

MANUFACTURING SECTOR

GDP & Manufacturing Summary (21)

Detailed value added figures are listed by both International Standard Industry Code (ISIC) and product title.

	1980	1985	1990	1994
GDP ($-1990 mil.)[1]	31,945	34,855	35,775	31,197
Per capita ($-1990)[1]	2,984	3,295	3,452	3,070
Manufacturing share (%) (current prices)[1]	26.4	26.2	22.5	20.2
Manufacturing				
Value added ($-1990 mil.)[1]	6,236	7,562	6,906	5,788
Industrial production index	100	112	104	80

	1980	1985	1990	1994
Value added ($ mil.)	5,907	5,356	7,805	7,523
Gross output ($ mil.)	24,898	21,690	25,081	23,110
Employment (000)	1,384	1,278	1,117	746
Profitability (% of gross output)				
Intermediate input (%)	76	75	69	67
Wages and salaries inc. supplements (%)	8	8	11	12
Gross operating surplus	16	16	20	21
Productivity ($)				
Gross output per worker	17,990	16,972	22,454	30,908
Value added per worker	4,268	4,191	6,988	10,087
Average wage (inc. supplements)	1,437	1,403	2,495	3,696
Value added ($ mil.)				
311/2 Food products	555	281	798	1,185
313 Beverages	83	107	171	299
314 Tobacco products	27	28	44	47
321 Textiles	353	325	322	242
322 Wearing apparel	194	158	233	270
323 Leather and fur products	48	39	40	30
324 Footwear	79	85	93	95
331 Wood and wood products	81	42	102	118
332 Furniture and fixtures	101	92	134	115
341 Paper and paper products	94	106	142	125
342 Printing and publishing	83	94	205	337
351 Industrial chemicals	417	320	443	241
352 Other chemical products	242	303	480	551
353 Petroleum refineries	153	193	591	1,103
354 Miscellaneous petroleum and coal products	2	2	6	8
355 Rubber products	55	71	92	34
356 Plastic products	61	80	166	187
361 Pottery, china and earthenware	57	46	59	59
362 Glass and glass products	70	71	90	84
369 Other non-metal mineral products	204	161	217	200
371 Iron and steel	370	200	413	149
372 Non-ferrous metals	215	54	276	80
381 Metal products	214	215	298	315
382 Non-electrical machinery	497	569	823	532
383 Electrical machinery	655	758	716	503
384 Transport equipment	486	507	422	408
385 Professional and scientific equipment	272	287	318	161
390 Other manufacturing industries	237	164	112	46

FINANCE, ECONOMICS, & TRADE

Balance of Payments (23)

	1992	1993	1994	1995	1996
Exports of goods (f.o.b.)	10,097	8,119	7,648	12,864	14,184
Imports of goods (f.o.b.)	−10,108	−12,140	−11,364	−15,297	−16,836
Trade balance	−11	−4,021	−3,716	−2,433	−2,652
Services - debits	−4,325	−4,275	−5,040	−6,231	−6,164
Services - credits	3,829	3,301	3,793	5,069	6,206
Private transfers (net)	15	21	13	13	−15
Government transfers (net)	843	711	896	1,047	937
Overall balance	352	−4,263	−4,054	−2,535	−1,689

Economic Indicators (22)

National product: GDP—purchasing power parity—$73.2 billion (1997 est.)

National product real growth rate: 4.4% (1997 est.)

National product per capita: $7,400 (1997 est.)

Inflation rate—consumer price index: 18% (1997 est.)

Exchange Rates (24)

Exchange rates:

Forints per US$1

January 1998	206.260
1997	186.789
1996	152.647
1995	125.681
1994	105.160
1993	91.933

Top Import Origins (25)

$18.6 billion (f.o.b., 1996) Data are for 1996.

Origins	%
European Union	59.8
Germany	23.6
Austria	9.5
Italy	8.1
FSU	14.9

Top Export Destinations (26)

$16 billion (f.o.b., 1996) Data are for 1994.

Destinations	%
Germany	22
Italy	21
Slovenia	18

Economic Aid (27)

$NA. NA stands for not available.

Import Export Commodities (28)

Import Commodities	Export Commodities
Machinery and equipment 36.5%	Machinery and equipment 36.6%
Other manufactures 43.7%	Other manufactures 40.6%
Fuels and electricity 11.8%	Agriculture and food products 15.1%
Agricultural and food products 4.4%	Raw materials 4.4%
Raw materials 3.6%	Fuels and electricity 3.3%

For Reference

Not to be taken from this room